The Official RFU Club Directory 1999-2000

First published in Great Britain in 1999 by
Queen Anne Press
a division of Lennard Associates Limited
Mackerye End, Harpenden
Hertfordshire AL5 5DR

A CIP catalogue record for this book
is available from the British Library

ISBN 1 85291 614 1

Compiled, typeset and designed by
Tony Williams Publications Ltd.
Helland, North Curry, Taunton TA3 6DU

Printed and bound in Great Britain by
WBC Book Manufacturers Limited

The Official RFU Club Directory 1999-2000

Editor: Stephen McCormack

Queen Anne Press

FOREWORD

by Francis Baron
Chief Executive, The Rugby Football Union

I am delighted to introduce readers to this official RFU Club Directory for the 1999/2000 season. This publication will now be the main reference handbook of English club rugby.

After 11 editions of the annual directory giving details of the 1,000 most senior clubs, the publication has been expanded to cover every single club affiliated to the RFU, from the grass roots of the game to Allied Dunbar Premiership One.

Aimed at players, officials and supporters at all levels of the sport, I hope that it will furnish you with the information you need, whether you want to find your way to an away game or arrange a fixture for your third XV.

This season of the Rugby World Cup and a new Millennium will prove an exciting one for everyone involved in playing, running or watching the game. I hope that you all enjoy your rugby over the coming months and congratulate everyone who continues to help keep the game alive in clubs and schools throughout the country.

A Welcome from Tetley's Bitter
"Official Beer of England Rugby"

by Ebbe Dinesen,
Chief Executive, Carlsberg-Tetley Brewing Ltd

The second year of the Tetley's Bitter Total Rugby sponsorship has proved again to be an outstanding success, and one which has helped Tetley's to build on its involvement with English rugby, from the grass roots through to national level, as the Official Beer of England Rugby.

In May this year, Twickenham played host to the finals of all four Tetley's competitions - the Tetley's Bitter Cup, the Tetley's Bitter County Championship, the Tetley's Bitter Under-21 Championship and the Tetley's Bitter Vase. These finals provided a fitting finale to the second season of the Tetley's Bitter Total Rugby Sponsorship, with fascinating encounters on each occasion.

Tetley's are proud of their association with English rugby and feel that the RFU club directory is an invaluable asset to all those involved in rugby union. It is a publication that provides the kind of detail that can not be found elsewhere and helps to feed the ever increasing interest in rugby.

May I take this opportunity to wish everyone involved in the sport a successful 1999/2000 season. Tetley's look forward to their continued association with English rugby into the next Millennium.

RFU CONTACTS

The Rugby Football Union,

Rugby House, Rugby Road, Twickenham, Middlesex TW1 1DS	Main Switchboard	0181 892 2000
	Fax	0181 892 9816
	Web:	http://www.rfu.com

Ticket Information (Recorded Message)	0181 744 3111
TW1 Twickenham Shop (Mail Order & General Enquiries)	0181 891 4141
The Museum of Rugby and Twickenham Experience Tour	0181 892 8877
Operations Department (All club enquiries)	0181 831 6503
	0181 831 6642
	0181 831 6501

National Centre for Schools & Youth

Castlecroft Stadium, Castlecroft Road, Wolverhampton WV3 8NA	Tel	01902 380302
	Fax	01902 380311

Referee Centre of Excellence

Castlecroft Stadium, Castlecroft Road, Wolverhampton WV3 8NA	Tel	01902 380302
	Fax	01902 765748

RFU Competition Sub Committee

Chairman: Jonathan Dance	Tel	0118 970 1246
Birch Cottage, Padworth Common, Reading, Berkshire RG7 4QG	Fax	0118 970 1237

National Clubs Association Executive

Chairman: Trevor Richmond	Tel	01924 472705
Inglenook, Carlinghow Hill, Batley, West Yorkshire WF17 0AG	Business	01274 480741
	Fax	01274 497437

Secretary: Colin Sewell	Tel	01705 421055
14 Edmund Road, Southsea, Hampshire PO4 0LL	Fax	01705 421055

Treasurer: Ivor Horscroft	Tel	01209 215941
Silver Fields, Chapel Street, Redruth TR15 2DT		

INDEX

Editorial & Acknowledgements	8
Tetley's Bitter Cup Index	12
Tetley's Bitter County Championship	28
Tetley's Bitter Vase	29
Allied Dunbar Premiership One Index	31
Allied Dunbar Premiership Two Index	127
Allied Dunbar Awards	227
Jewson National League One Index	229
Jewson National League Two North Index	329
Jewson National League Two South Index	401
Jewson Awards	469
Thwaites Northern Division Index	473
Midland Division Index	519
London & South East Division Index	567
South West Division Index	629
Other Affiliated Clubs	675
Student Rugby Football Union	693
Associate Members	700
International Section Index	705
World Cup Section	706
International Results 1998-99	718
Five Nations	727
General Fixtures' List	733

EDITORIAL & ACKNOWLEDGEMENTS

With the World Cup approaching the anticipation levels are rising quickly and the Tri Nations is whetting our appetites for the feast of rugby coming our way. The game has a global stage to help develop it for the future and to reach new parts of the world. Let's hope that it succeeds.

I would like to take this opportunity to wish Clive Woodward and the England boys the best of luck. They have had an ideal build up with the trip to Australia, which involved a training camp and a one-off Test against the Wallabies in which they were narrowly beaten. As we go into August, England are already having weekly training sessions and have build-up matches planned to get them match fit. Surely we will never have a better prepared squad to take on the world's best. If we cannot triumph this time we may never have a better opportunity.

This season we have incorporated all the club details previously published as part of the RFU Handbook and at the back of the Directory we have listed all the clubs who are affiliated to the RFU but are not in the league structure. I would like to thank the RFU for their commitment to the book and hope we can build on this relationship for the future.

I would also like to thank Tetley for their continued sponsorship of the Directory.This year we have increased our coverage of the Tetley's Bitter Cup and intend to increase it even further in the coming years.

As we go to press we are still awaiting the final fixtures for Allied Dunbar Premiership One. After all the trials and tribulations of the previous summers we were informed that the fixtures would be available by the end of May. But yet again the top clubs seem to have great difficulty in running the game on their own. We have had the merger/take over/whatever involving London Irish, Richmond and London Scottish. Rotherham decided to take out a high court injunction against ERP for breaking the Mayfair agreement. Worcester have been busy trying to a deal with various clubs in their efforts to break into the big time. Richmond and London Scottish have decided to reform and want a place in the Premiership. Where will it all end?

As I write this just one week before going to press we are still awaiting information from seven of the 12 clubs in Allied Dunbar Premiership One.

Isn't it strange that the amateur run clubs can manage to provide their information on time whilst these professional clubs have so much trouble. Surely there is a message there somewhere.

Stephen McCormack

We have changed the format of the double page spread so that all last season's matches run across the page. We have also put the scorers after the players name and any replacements used in brackets after that. We have put a guide on each page to help you get used to the new layout.

* after opponents name indicates a penalty try

Brackets after a player's name indicates he was replaced. eg (a) means he was replaced by replacement code `a` and so on.
/ after a player or replacement name is followed by any scores he made
eg /t, /c, /p, /dg or any combination of these.

It is time to thank those who have helped compile the Directory this year. Without their valuable help it would be impossible to put it together.
I would like to thank all those clubs who have looked after me on my travels around the country. Wherever I go I get a warm welcome and am fed and watered before settling down to enjoy the rugby. Again pride of place goes to Wharfedale where the hospitality is legendary. The company, the food, the setting and even the rugby was excellent last season on my visits there.
I would like to give a little mention to Whitchurch who were new to the Jewson leagues last season, I had a fine day out there on my first ever visit and was well received and superbly looked after.
In the Jewson leagues we run a little competition to find the most hospitable club in each of the three divisions. The winners were: -
Jewson National One: Wharfedale, although they were pushed all the way by Harrogate.
Jewson Two North: Walsall
Jewson Two South: Redruth

Well here we go with thanks to the following:

Bath - Helen Mercer
Bedford - Philip August
Bristol - John Harding
Gloucester - Geraldine Peake
Harlequins - Mark Anderson
Leicester - Stuart Farmer
London Irish - Paddy Lennon
Manchester Sale - Jean Swales
Newcastle - Alex Jackson
Saracens - Bill Edwards
Wasps - Emma Ward
Coventry - Paul Inglestone
Henley - Noel Armstead
Leeds Tykes - Mike Bidgood
London Welsh - Paul Bekan
Manchester - Russ Jenkins & Alex Keay
Orrell - Jeff Lightfoot
Rotherham - Allan Williams
Rugby Lions - Dennis Keen
Wakefield - Jim Coulson
Waterloo - Frank Spencer
West Hartlepool - Steve Smith
Worcester - Nicola Goodwin
Blackheath - Ron Bailey
Birmingham & Solihull - Dave Radburn
Bracknell - John Denman
Camberley - Gwynne Evans & Brian Divers
Fylde - Stuart Brown
Harrogate - Graham Siswick & Glyn Smith
Lydney - Gordon Sargant
Newbury - Sid Little
Nottingham - Andi Starr & Alan Royer
Otley - Marc Lawrence & John Finch
Preston - John Hetherington
Reading - Lorcan Mullaly
Rosslyn Park - Bernard Wiggins
Wharfedale - Keith Lewis
Aspatria - Melvyn Hanley
Hinckley - Trevor Williams
Kendal - John Hutton
Lichfield - David Lewis
Liverpool St Helens - Ged Garvey
Morley - Dennis Elam
New Brighton - Geoff Stone
Nuneaton - Dave Warden
Sandal - Philip Harrison & Len Bedford
Sedgley Park - John Lawrence
Sheffield - Andy Reichwald
Stourbridge - Vernon Davies
Walsall - Howard Clews
Whitchurch - Ginge Wills
Winnington Park - Bob Dean
Barking - Mike Hannon
Bridgwater - Tony Stickland
Cheltenham - Tom Parker
Clifton - Brian Jordan
Esher - Dave Page
Havant - Bill Sugden
Met Police - David Barham & Neil Sinclair
North Walsham - Tony Marcontonio
Norwich - Chris Gilham
Plymouth - Paddy Marsh
Redruth - Graham Still
Tabard - Geoff Bird
Weston super Mare - Clayton Hope.

Also, special thanks to Chris Burns at the RFU who helped enormously with the fixtures. There should be a special award for George Brown, our Production Editor, for his patience in the final few days as we awaited promised material that took an age to come through.
It is thanks to all the hard work and dedication of the above that it has been possible for the Directory to be with you in time for the start of the new season.

In a book of this size, and produced in such a short space of time, there is bound to be the odd mistake or two. If you come across any then I would be grateful if you would let me know at:
stephen.mccormack@btinternet.com.

TETLEY'S BITTER CUP SECTION

Tetley's Bitter Cup 1998-99 13

Tetley's Bitter Cup - The Individual Medallists 19

Tetley's Bitter Cup Final Facts 25
Results of every final since the start, with losing semi-finalists

Tetley's Bitter Cup - Trivia 26

Tetley's Bitter Cup - The Last Eight 27
The overall playing record of every team
who have reached the last eight of the competition

TETLEY'S BITTER COUNTY CHAMPIONSHIP 28

TETLEY'S BITTER VASE 29

Tetley's Bitter Cup 1998-99

First Round

(Saturday 19th September)

North

Aspatria 17 Bedford Ath 32
Banbury 15 Scunthorpe 17
Barkers Butts 17 Macclesfield 27
Bromsgrove 10 Sedgley Park 34
Cheshunt 33 Morpeth 26
Doncaster 30 Walsall 19
Hinckley 20 Nuneaton 24
Hull Ionians 59 Egremont 0
Kendal 13 Broadstreet 12
Malvern 14 Sandal 52
New Brighton 38 Lichfield 8
Preston 43 Kenilworth 6
Stourbridge 32 Sheffield 6
Tynedale 47 Winnington Park 10
Whitchurch 32 Aspull 10

In the Northern section Doncaster from Thwaites North One knocked out Walsall from Jewson Two North. Another Jewson Two North side to succumb to a side from lower down was Aspatria who despite home advantage lost to Midlands One side Bedford Athletic.

South

Clevendon 7 Barking 32
Clifton 3 Esher 60
Guildford & God 18 Bridgwater 28
Launceston 32 N Walsham 18
Met Police 34 Cheltenham 8
Norwich 15 Winchester 23
Penzance & N 32 Cambridge 13
Plymouth 32 Redruth 18
Ruislip 9 Old Colfeians 43
Spartans 10 Havant 24
Swanage & W 44 Abbey 7
Tabard 26 Wimbledon 23
Torquay Ath 15 Maidenhead 29
Westcombe Park 14 Bracknell 21
Weston-s-Mare 34 Ipswich 26

South West One side Launceston beat Jewson Two South side North Walsham to advance to the second round.

Winchester beat Jewson Two South side Norwich away from home as both the Norfolk sides went out in the first round.

Esher were the biggest scorers of the day as they thrashed Clifton 60-3 away from home.

Second Round

(Saturday 17th October)

Bridgwater 15 Rosslyn Park 49
Esher 41 Tabard 3
Henley 100 Havant 19
Hull Ionians 13 Macclesfield 3
Kendal 20 Liverpool St H 7
Lydney 44 Camberley 34 aet
Maidenhead 22 Launceston 21
Met Police 25 Winchester 14
New Brighton 25 Nuneaton 10
Newbury 37 Cheshunt 10
Nottingham 50 Preston 3
O Colfeians 23 Swanage & W 32
Otley 18 Morley 20
Plymouth 13 Barking 18
Reading 21 Penzance & N 5
Sandal 6 Doncaster 3
Scunthorpe 0 Harrogate 29
Sedgley Park 20 Manchester 17
Tynedale 22 Stourbridge 30
Weston-s-Mare 15 Bracknell 43
Wharfedale 27 Birmingham & Sol 5
Whitchurch 23 Bedford Ath 15

Preston Grasshoppers were flying high at the top of Jewson Two North but were brought down to earth by Nottingham, whom they will play if they win promotion. Nottingham were easy winners running up 50 points with Preston managing just a penalty in reply.

Sedgley Park continued to be Manchester's bogey side knocking they out at the first hurdle. Park built up a first half lead with the elements and defended well in the second half go into the hat for the next round.

Kendal put their poor league form behind them with victory over Liverpool St Helens from the division above.

Henley Hawks hit the 100 point mark as they thrashed Havant 100-19

Third round

(Saturday 14th November)

Blackheath 21 Sedgley Park 22
Bracknell 13 Met Police 6
Coventry 26 Worcester 36
Esher 42 Harrogate 17
Exeter 81 Whitchurch 11
Hull Ionians 7 Newbury 31
Lydney 44 Stourbridge 5
Morley 39 Maidenhead 25
Nottingham 27 Wharfedale 17
Reading 12 Orrell 23
Rosslyn Park 12 Henley 16
Rotherham 8 London Welsh 6
Swanage & W 6 Barking 36
Wakefield 8 Kendal 16
Waterloo 34 New Brighton 23
(Sunday 15th November)
Bristol 55 Sandal 0
Moseley 22 Fylde 15
Rugby 7 Leeds Tykes 68

It was a round of shocks with the minnows taking centre stage. Star billing went to Jewson Two North sides Kendal and Sedgley Park who both went to Allied Dunbar Premiership Two sides and came away with the win. Kendal went to Wakefield and winger Jason Balmer was the hero with two tries whilst fly half Casey Mee chipped in with two penalties. Sedgley Park went to Blackheath and came back from a 21-10 deficit late in the game thanks to tries from wing Paul Morris and No 8 Jon Duncan.

Jewson Two South side Esher beat Harrogate from Jewson National One thanks to a 22 point haul from former Richmond full back Jonathan Gregory.

Performance of the round by an individual was by Brisbane Broncos Wendall Sailor who turned out for Leeds Tykes at Rugby and ran in five tries, one short of the competition record.

Top scorers of the round were Exeter who ratted up 81 points against Jewson Two North side Whitchurch. They ran in 13 tries with Bryan Easson converting eight of them.

Fourth Round

(Saturday 9th January)

Gloucester 31 Worcester 17
Harlequins 46 Esher 10
Leicester 65 Barking 6
Moseley 24 Lydney 25
Newcastle 25 Bath 22
Nottingham 8 Exeter 24
Rotherham 24 Leeds 27
Sale 31 Northampton 47
Sedgley Park 3 Wasps 53
Waterloo 18 Orrell 11 aet
(Sunday 10th January)
Bedford 22 Henley 29
Bristol 19 London Irish 43
Kendal 20 London Scottish 25
Morley 8 Saracens 76
Richmond 46 Newbury 12
W Hartlepool 34 Bracknell 14

The 4th round saw the big boys from the Allied Dunbar Premiership joining the competition. One Premiership sides were beaten by a side from two divisions lower. Bedford were beaten at home by Henley Hawks who were pushing for promotion from Jewson National One at the time. Former Bristol winger gavin Sharp made a significant contribution with two tries.

The big match of the day was at Newcastle where Bath were the visitors. They got off to a great start and by half time had built up a n impressive 22-6 lead. In the second half Newcastle were the only side to get on the score sheet as they pegged back the Bath lead. Leading the comeback was England starlet Jonny Wilkinson who kicked all seven of his kicks at goal including the late penalty to snatch victory from Bath.

Kendal put up a brave performance at home to Premiership One side London Scottish but could not quite pull of a third successive giant killing act. They out scored the visitors 4 tries to 3 but fell down in the goal kicking.

Fifth Round

(Saturday 30th February)

Gloucester 31 Henley 9
Leicester 49 Leeds Tykes 0
London Scottish 33 Harlequins 37
Northampton 6 London Irish 21
W Hartlepool 21 Newcastle 32

(Sunday 31st January)

Lydney 0 Saracens 40
Richmond 37 Exeter 10
Wasps 27 Waterloo 10

London Irish win at Northampton for the second time in a month having earlier won there in the league. The hero then was winger Niall Woods and it was again this time. He scored an interception try just after half time and the Irish never looked back.
Henley, from Jewson National One, gave Allied Dunbar Premiership One side Gloucester plenty to think about on a muddy surface. After falling 12-0 behind in the opening 10 minutes they came back and with an hour gone they were 19-9 down. The home side scored two late tries to give the score line an unfair look.
At Welford Road Joel Stransky turned in an impeccable kicking display converting all 7 of the Leicester tries as they ran out convincing winners against Leeds Tykes.

Quarter Finals

Saturday 27th February

Gloucester 15 Harlequins 13

Richmond 15 Leicester 13

Sunday 28th February

Newcastle Falcons 15 Saracens 0

Wasps 19 London Irish 3

Last season's cup winners Saracens were beaten at Newcatle Falcons. They were shut out as Newcastle beat Premiership One opponents for the third round running.
Last season's runners up Wasps beat an in form London Irish at home in front on a club record 11,000 plus crowd.
Mark Mapletoft kicked Gloucester into the semi finals with five penalty goals against Harlequins.

Semi- Finals

Saturday 3rd April

Richmond 3 Newcastle 20

Attendance: 9,751
Referee: E Morrison (Bristol)

RICHMOND: M Pini: S Brown, M Dixon, J Wright, N Walne, E Va'a, A Pichot: D McFarland, B Williams, D Crompton, A Sheridan (rep:B Cusack 53), C Gillies, C Quinnell, R Hutton (rep: J Barfoot 9), B Clarke.
NEWCASTLE: S Legg: T Underwood, M Shaw, J Wilkinson, V Tuigamala (sin bin 72-80), R Andrew, G Armstrong: G Graham, R Nesdale, I Peel (rep: S Best 66), D Weir, G Archer, P Walton, R Arnold, R Beattie (rep: H Vyvyan 37-52)
Scoring sequence: (Richmond first) 0-7, 0-10, (half time), 3-10, 3-13, 3-20.
Scorers: Richmond: Penalty goal: Va'a (45).
Newcastle: Tries: Tuigamala 2 (23,56). Cons: Wilkinson, Andrew. Pen: Andrew (53). DG: Andrew(33)

Two tries from Va'aiga Tuigamala settled this match which was dominated by the defenses.
Tuigamala missed the final few minutes after being sent to the sin bin by referee Morrison.

Sunday 4th April

Wasps 35 Gloucester 21

Attendance: 10,064
Referee: G Hughes (Manchester)

WASPS: J Lewsey: P Sampson, F Waters, R Henderson, K Logan, A King, M Wood: D Molloy, T Leota, W Green, M Weedon, S Shaw (Reed 44-55, 69), L Dallaglio, P Volley, J Worsley.
GLOUCESTER: C Catling: M Mapletoft, T Fanolua (R Greenslade-Jones 44), R Tombs, P St Andre, S Mannix, I Sanders: T Woodman, N McCarthy (C Fortey 66), A Deacon (P Vickery 66), R Fidler, M Cornwell (D Sims 58), S Ojomoh, N Carter, E Pearce.
Scoring sequence: (Wasps first): 3-0, 3-3, 6-3, 9-3, 9-6, 9-9, 9-12, 16-12 (half time), 23-12, 23-15, 23-18, 28-18, 28-21, 35-21.
SCORERS: Wasps: Tries: Henderson (40), Sampson (51), Volley (70), Logan (80). Cons: Logan 3. Pens: Logan (10, 21, 25).
Gloucester: Pens: Mapletoft 6 (11,27, 38, 59, 61, 74). DG; Sanders (31).

Two controversial incidents settled this match either side of half time. Gloucester's Terry Fanolua should have been awarded a try, but the referee was in the wrong position whilst Wasps opening try of the second half was not grounded correctly. Both decisions went the way of Wasps and they were on their way to Twickenham looking for that elusive victory.

FINAL

Saturday 15th May

Newcastle 19 Wasps 29

Attendance: 48,000
Referee: S Lander (Liverpool)

NEWCASTLE: S Legg: J Naylor (T Underwood (rep 40), M Shaw, T May, V Tuigamala, J Wilkinson, G Armstrong: G Graham, R Nesdale, M Hurter (rep: I Peel 70), G Archer, D Weir, P Walton (rep: J Cartmell), R Arnold, R Beattie.
WASPS: G Rees: J Lewsey, F Waters, M Denney (rep: R Henderson 47), P Sampson (rep: K Logan 49), A King, A Gomersall (rep: M Friday): D Molloy, T Leota (rep: D Alexopoulos 32-40), W Green, M Weedon, S Shaw, L Dallaglio, J Worlsey, P Schrivener (P Volley 59-63).

Scoring sequence:
(Newcastle first): 3-0, 3-3, 3-6, 3-13, 3-16 (half time), 6-19, 9-19, 12-19, 12-22, 12-29, 19-29.

SCORERS:
Newcastle: Try: Tuigamala 81). Con: Wilkinson. Pens: Wilkinson 4 (5, 40, 48, 61).
Wasps: Tries: King (27), Lewsey (78). Cons: Rees 2. Pens: Rees 4 (17, 24, 32, 66). DG: King (43).

It was fifth time lucky for Wasps after four previous final defeats.

Wasps stand off Alex King out shone his opposite number Jonny Wilkinson, scoring an individual try and dropping a goal just after half time.

Josh Lewsey sealed the victory in the closing minutes after intercepting a pass as Newcastle looked to run the ball deep in their own half as they chased the game. Newcastle did not give up and Va'aiga Tuigamala scored an injury time try to close the gap to 10 points.

www.smoothlydoesit.co.uk

The Tetley's Bitter web site features everything that the fan of English Rugby could possibly want!

Everyone loves to relax with a pint of Tetley's Bitter after the match, so in our virtual clubhouse **"Over The Bar"**, the day's rugby news, both national and international, is updated throughout the day. You'll never be in the dark about what's happening in the game, and it's all available from Tetley's Bitter at the click of a mouse. Throughout the 1999 Rugby World Cup, www.smoothlydoesit.co.uk will be the best place to come for everything that's great about rugby. But the news and scores are just the start. We've got the best **rugby jokes** that you can email to your friends, and amazing **real-life tour stories** from stars of the past and present that you won't believe! Ever wondered what thebig boys get up to when they're away? Now you can find out.

If you've ever watched on TV as the pro's crumble under the pressure of a critical conversion, and thought "I could do better than that", you can test your nerve at that the big moment with our penalty-kicking game **"The Vital Kick"**.

Discuss the events of the game with other internet users over a perfect pint of Tetley's Bitter – now you can do it with a whole online community, courtesy of our **message boards**, where you can vent your spleen over the rugby issues of the day. Think it's a travesty that your winger has been overlooked for England again? Tell the world - and see what they have to say back!

The Tetley's Bitter web site is also the place to come to talk to the stars, as during the Rugby World Cup, you'll get the chance to pose your question for an England player with our exclusive **live online interview**. Thousands will be logging on to put the lucky man on the spot!

It's all at www.smoothlydoesit.co.uk – blood, sweat and beers

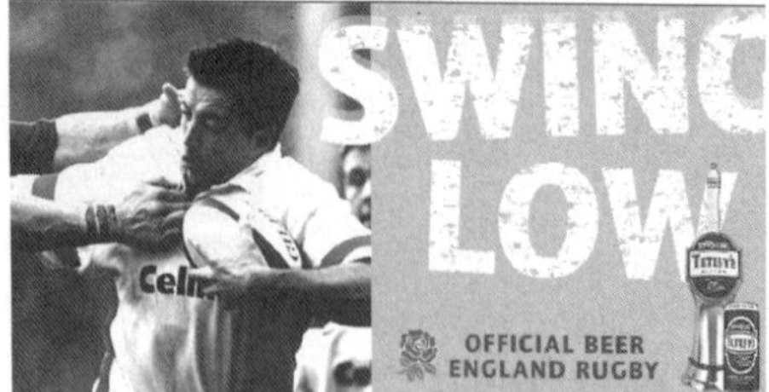

As if that wasn't enough, at www.smoothlydoesit.co.uk, you can also download the Official Beer of England Rugby **screensavers**, and support the boys even when you're away from your PC. Why are we bringing you all this? Because we're proud to be the Official Beer of England Rugby.

But the Tetley's Bitter web site isn't just about rugby. The Tetley's Bitter drinker is a smooth thinker, and won't let anything come between him and his pint of Tetley's. That's why at www.smoothlydoesit.co.uk, you can find out how smooth your thinking is with the Tetley's Bitter **"Smoothly Does It" Daily Teaser**. Every day there's a new brainteaser to stretch your mind to the limit. In fact there's a whole section devoted to the smoothest thinking. Try the **Smooth Solutions Lateral Thinkers**, if you think you can broaden your mind to solve some devilishly difficult problems which will need to be approached from a whole new angle. And once you've solved the problems, you can email them to your friends to let them have a go. There's also the **Smooth Solutions Competition**, where you can **win** a case of Tetley's Bitter if you come up with the smoothest solution to a very sticky situation.

Throughout the year we also give away tickets to the best rugby matches, signed England and Tetley's Bitter kit, and of course, loads and loads of smooth Tetley's Bitter. www.smoothlydoesit.co.uk is the place to win!

Want to see how other people do it? Visit the Smooth Thinker's Gallery, where we celebrate real-life examples of smooth thinking under pressure, as well as sharing examples of the exact opposite, where it's just gone very, very wrong!

As well as all this, there's everything you need to know about Tetley's Bitter – from our history, and involvement with rugby across the board, to details of how we're eduacting the world in the art of bitter drinking with Tetley's English Ale. We also show you what you really want to know – how you can avoid the queues and buy Tetley's on the web!

– It's easy to set Tetley's Bitter as your homepage –
just go to www.smoothlydoesit.co.uk now and click the button...

TETLEY'S BITTER CUP INDIVIDUAL MEDALLISTS

(* asterisk signifys an appearance as a substitute)

ACKERMAN, RA	Lon. Welsh	L - 85
ACKFORD, PJ	Harlequins	W - 88, 91 L - 92
ADCASTER, SD	Moseley	W - 82
ADEBAYO, AA	Bath	W - 90, 94, 95, 96
ADEY, GJ	Leicester	W - 79, 80, 81 L - 78
AKENHEAD, R	Moseley	L - 79
ALEXANDER, JR	Harlequins	L - 93
ALSTON, P	Northampton	L - 91
ANDERSON, TR	Gosforth	L - 81
ANDERSON, PG	Rosslyn Park	L - 75
ANDREW, CR	Wasps	L - 87, 95
ARCHER, G	Newcastle	L-99
ARCHER, JS	Gosforth	W - 77 L - 81
ARMSTRONG, G	Newcastle	L-99
ARNOLD, R	Newcastle	L-99
ASHURST, N	Sale	L - 97
ASTLEY, KJ	Moseley	L - 79
AYRE, B	Moseley	L - 79
BACK, NA	Leicester	W - 93, 97 L - 94, 96
BAILEY, MD	Wasps	L - 86, 87
BAILWARD, CJ	Bedford	W - 75
BAINBRIDGE, S	Gosforth	L - 81
BAKER, SJW	Gloucester	W - 82
BALCOMBE, P	Wasps	L - "86
BALDWIN, D	Sale	L - 97
BALDWIN, G	Northampton	L - 91
BALL, I	Waterloo	L - 77
BARKER, RG	Leicester	L - 78
BARKER, N	Bedford	W - 75
BARLOW, RL	Rosslyn Park	L - 75
BARNES, S	Bath	W - 86, 87, 89, 90, 92, 94
	BristoL	W - 83 L - 84
BARNWELL, RC	Coventry	W - 74
	Leicester	W - 79, 80, 81 L - 83
BARTON, J	Coventry	W - 73
BATES, SM	Wasps	L - 86, 87, 95
BATES, I	Leicester	W - 93 L - *83, 89
BAXENDALE, J	Sale	L - 97
BAYLISS, JA	Gloucester	W - 72
BAZALGETTE, MB	Rosslyn Park	L - 75
BEALE, JD	Moseley	L - 79
BEATTIE, R	Newcastle	L-99
BEIM, T	Sale	L - 97
BELL, JAH	Gosforth	L - 81
BELL, TP	Harlequins	W - 88
BELL, DE	Lon. Scot	L - 74
BENNETT, WN	Bedford	W - 75
BERINGER, GG	Lon. Irish	L - 80
BESS, G	Bath	W - 85, "87
BIGGAR, AG	Lon. Scot	L - 74
BIGGAR, MA	Lon. Scot	L - 74
BILLINGHAM, MF	Waterloo	L - 77
BLACK, A	Wasps	L-*98
BLACKHURST, F	Waterloo	L - 77
BLACKMORE, AG	Bristol	L - 88
BLAKEWAY, PJ	Gloucester	W - 82
BOGIRA, MK	Bristol	W - 83
BONNER, J	Wasps	L - 86, 87
BOOTH, MH	Gloucester	W - 72
BOWRING, K	Lon. Welsh	L - 85
BOYLE, LS	Leicester	L - 94
BOYLE, SB	Gloucester	W - 78 82
BRACKEN, K	Saracens	W-98
BRADLEY, B	Lon. Welsh	L - 85
BRAIN, J	Gloucester	L - 90
BRAY, KA	Harlequins	L - 93
BREAKEY, RW	Gosforth	W - 76, 77 L - 81
BREEZE, J	Gloucester	L - 90
BRINN, A	Gloucester	W - 72
BRITTEN, JK	Gosforth	W - 76, 77
BRODERICK, JM	Coventry	W - 73, 74
BULPITT, MA	Rosslyn Park	L - 76
BURTON, MA	Gloucester	W - 72, 78
BURWELL, T	Leicester	W - 79, 80
BUTLAND, R	Bath	W - 95
BUTLER, JL	Gosforth	L - 81
BUTLER, PE	Gloucester	W - 78
BYRNE, L	Rosslyn Park	L - *76
CALLARD, JEB	Bath	W - 90, 94, 95, 96
CARDUS, RM	Wasps	L - 86
CARDWELL, R	Coventry	W - 74
CARFOOT, DJ	Waterloo	L - 77
CARLING, WDC	Harlequins	W - 88, 91 L - 92, 93
CARR, JF	Bristol	W - 83 L - 84, 88
CARTMELL, J	Newcastle	L-*99
CASKIE, D	Gloucester	L - 90
CATT, MJ	Bath	W - 94, 96
CHADWICK, R	Bedford	W - 75
CHALLINOR, AP	Harlequins	L - 92, 93
CHIDGEY, DL	Bristol	L - 84
CHILCOTT, GJ	Bath	W - 84, 85, 86, 87, 89, 90, 92
CHILDS, G	Wasps	L - 95
CHRISTOPHERSON, SF	Waterloo	L - 77
CHUTER, G	Saracens	W-98
CLARKE, BB	Bath	W - 92, 94, 95
CLEWS, RJ	Gloucester	W - 72, 78
COCKERILL, R	Leicester	W - 93, 97 L - 94, 96
CODD, RA	Rosslyn Park	L - 75
COKER, T	Harlequins	W - 91
COLLINGS, P	Bristol	L - 88
COLLINS, J	Lon. Welsh	L - 85
CONDON, HC	Lon. Irish	L - 80
CONSTABLE, R	Saracens	W-98
CONNOR, L	Waterloo	L - 77
COOPER, MJ	Moseley	W - 82 L - 79
CORLESS, TF	Moseley	W - 82
CORLESS BJ	Coventry	W - 74
	Moseley	L - 79
CORSTORPHINE, AE	Lon. Scot	L - 74
COWLING, RJ	Leicester	W - 79, 80, 81
	Gloucester	W - 72
COWMAN, AR	Coventry	W - 73, 74
COX, GNJ	Moseley	W - 82 L - 79
CREED, RN	Coventry	W - 73
CRERAR, RD	Lon. Scot	L - 74
CRONIN, DF	Bath	W - 89, 90
CUE, PC	Bristol	L - 84
CUNNINGHAM, R	Gosforth	L - 81
	Bath	W - 84
CURTIS, PS	Harlequins	W - 88

CUSWORTH, L	Leicester	W - 79, 80, 81 L - 83, 89
CUTTER, AJ	Gosforth	W - 76, 77
DALLAGLIO, LBN	Wasps	W-99 L - 95, 98
DANDY, MJW	Bristol	L - 73
DANIEL, B	Saracens	W-98
DARNELL, IR	Coventry	W - 73, 74
DAVIDSON, JS	Moseley	W - 82
DAVIES, GH	Wasps	L - 87
DAVIS, EG	Harlequins	W - 88, 91 L - 92
DAWE, RGR	Bath	W - 86, 87, 89, 90, 92, 94, 95, 96
DEMMING, R	Bedford	W - 75
DENNEY, M	Wasps	W-99 L-98
DESBOROUGH, JE	Moseley	W - 82
DIAMOND, S	Sale	L - 97
DIPROSE, A	Saracens	W-98
DIX, J	Gloucester	W - 72
DIXON, PJ	Gosforth	W - 76, 77
DOBLE, SA	Moseley	L - 72
DOBSON, I	Leicester	L - 83
DODGE, PW	Leicester	W - 79, 80, 81 L - 78, 83, 89
DOUBLEDAY, RJ	Bristol	W - 83 L - 84, 88
DOUGLAS, MHJL	Lon. Welsh	L - 85
DUCKHAM, DJ	Coventry	W - 73, 74
DUGGAN, MJ	Leicester	L - 78
DUGGAN, IH	Bristol	W - 83 L - 88
DUN, AF	Bristol	L - 88
DUNN, KA	Wasps	L - 95
	Gloucester	L - 90
DUNSTON, I	Wasps	L - 95
EBSWORTH, M	Lon. Welsh	L - 85
EDWARDS, NGB	Harlequins	W - 88 L - 92
EDWARDS, EF	Bedford	W - 75
EGERTON, DW	Bath	W - 87, 89, 90
ELKINGTON, D	Northampton	L - 91
ERSKINE, D	Sale	L - 97
ETHERIDGE, J	Northampton	L - 91
EVANS, BJ	Leicester	L - 83, 89
EVANS, GW	Coventry	W - 73
FAIRBROTHER, KE	Coventry	W - 73, 74
FALLON, JA	Bath	W - 92
FIDLER, JH	Gloucester	W - 78
FIELD, R	Moseley	L - 79
FINLAN, JF	Moseley	L - 72
FISHER, RG	Rosslyn Park	L - 75
FISHER, CD	Waterloo	L - 77
FLETT, MA	Waterloo	L - 77
FLUSKEY, S	Rosslyn Park	L - 76
FORD, P	Gloucester	W - 82
FORFAR, DJ	Leicester	L - 78
FOUHY, D	Lon. Welsh	L - 85
Foulkes-ARNOLD, M	Leicester	L - 83, 89
FOULKS, D	Coventry	W - 74
FOWLIE, DG	Lon. Scot	L - 74
FRASER, G	Lon. Scot	L - 74
FRIDAY, M	Wasps	W-"99 L-98
FRIELL, AAS	Lon. Scot	L - 74
FRY, MJ	Bristol	L - 73
GADD, J	Gloucester	W - 82 L - 90
GALLAGHER, J	Coventry	W - 74
GARFORTH, DJ	Leicester	W - 93, 97 L - 94, 96
GAYMOND, N	Bath	W - 84, 85

GIFFORD, CJ	Moseley	L - 79
GILLINGHAM, NK	Leicester	W - 80 L - 83
GITTINGS, WJ	Coventry	W - 73, 74
DE GLANVILLE, PR	Bath	W - 92, 94, 95, 96
GLENISTER, RJ	Harlequins	W - 91 L - 93
GOMERSALL, A	Wasps	W-99 L-*98
GOODWIN, JM	Moseley	W - 82
GRAHAM, G	Newcastle	L-99
GRAU, R	Saracens	W-98
GRAY, JD	Coventry	W - 73
GREAVES, WH	Moseley	L - 79
GREEN, W	Wasps	W-99 L-98
GREENSTOCK, N	Wasps	L - 95
GREENWOOD, M	Wasps	L - 95
GREENWOOD, W	Leicester	W - 97
GREWCOCK, D	Saracens	W-98
GRIFFIN, SM	Gosforth	W - 76
GRIFFITHS, J	Moseley	L - 72
GUSCOTT, JC	Bath	W - *85, 87, 89, 90, 92, 95
GUSTARD, JS	Gosforth	W - 76, 77
HAAG, M	Bath	W - 92, 95, 96
HACKNEY, S	Leicester	L - 96
HADLEY, A	Sale	L - 97
HADLEY, N	Wasps	L - 95
HALL, C	Northampton	L - 91
HALL, BP	Leicester	L - 78
HALL, JP	Bath	W - 84, 85, 86, 87, 89, 94
HALLIDAY, SJ	Harlequins	W - 91 L - 92
	Bath	W - 85, 86, 87, 89, 90
HAMLIN, M	Gloucester	L - 90
HANCOCK, K	Waterloo	L - 77
HANNAFORD, M	Gloucester	L - 90
HANNAFORD, RC	Bristol	L - 73
HARDING, RM	Bristol	W - 83 L - 84, 88
HARE, WH	Leicester	W - 79, 80, 81 L - 78, 89
HARRIMAN, AT	Harlequins	W - 88, 91
HARRIS, JC	Leicester	W - 93 L - 94
HATTER, K	Moseley	L - 72
HAZLERIGG, AG	Leicester	W - 79 L - 78
HEALEY, A	Leicester	W - 97
HEDLEY, J	Gosforth	W - 77
HENDERSON, R	Wasps	W-"99 L-98
HESFORD, R	Bristol	W - 83
HILL, RJ	Bath	W - 84, 85, 86, 87, 89, 90, 92, 94
HILTON, DIW	Bath	W - 94, 96
HINTON, NP	Rosslyn Park	L - 75, 76
HOBLEY, MJ	Harlequins	L - 92
HOGG, ST	Bristol	W - 83 L - 84, 88
HOLLINS, AJ	Bedford	W - 75
HOLMES, G	Wasps	L - 86
HOLT, BC	Coventry	W - 73
HONE, W	Bristol	L - 88
HOOKER, C	Bedford	W - 75
HOPLEY, P	Wasps	L - 95
HOPLEY, DP	Wasps	L - 95
HORTON, JP	Bath	W - 84, 85
HORTON, NE	Moseley	L - 72
HOWARD, JM	Bedford	W - 75
HOWELL, PR	Gloucester	W - 78
HUGHES, J	Lon. Welsh	L - 85

HUNTER, I	Northampton	L - 91
HURTER, M	Newcastle	L-99
JACKSON, N	Leicester	W - 81
JACKSON, GT	Waterloo	L - 77
JARDINE, R	Gloucester	W - 78
JARRETT, JS	Gloucester	W - 72
JEAVONS, NC	Moseley	W - 82 L - 79
JOHNS, P	Saracens	W-98
JOHNSON, D	Gosforth	L - 81
JOHNSON, G	Saracens	W-98
JOHNSON, SR	Leicester	W - 79, 80, 81
		L - 78, 83
JOHNSON, MO	Leicester	W - 93, 97 L - 94, 96
JOINER, C	Leicester	W - 97
JONES, W	Lon. Irish	L - 80
JONES, TW	Lon. Welsh	L - 85
JONES, B	Leicester	L - 78
JONES, L	Gloucester	W - 82
JORDEN, AM	Bedford	W - 75
JOYCE, NJ	Leicester	W - 79, 80, 81 L - 78
KARDOONI, A	Leicester	W - 93,* 97
		L - 89, 94, 96
KEDDIE, RR	Lon. Scot	L - 74
KEEN, B	Bedford	W - 75
d'A KEITH-ROACH, P	Rosslyn Park	L - 75, 76
KENNEY, S	Leicester	W - 79, 80, 81 L - 78
KENT, CP	Rosslyn Park	L - 76
KERR, R	Moseley	L - 72
KILFORD, WA	Leicester	L - 94
KILLICK, N	Harlequins	L - 93
KING, A	Wasps	W-99 L-98
KING, S	Moseley	L - *79
KNIBBS, RA	Bristol	W - 83 L - 84, 88
KNIGHT, S	Bath	W - "90
KNIGHT, PM	Bristol	L - 73
LAIRD, R	Moseley	L - 79
LANE, DE	Moseley	L - 72
LANGHORN, RS	Harlequins	W - 88, 91 L - 93
LAWSON, RD	Moseley	W - 82
LEE, MR	Bath	W - 84, 85, 86, 89
LEGG, S	Newcastle	L-99
LEONARD, J	Harlequins	W - 91 L - 93
LEOPOLD, DA	Lon. Irish	L - 80
LEOTA, T	Wasps	W-99 L-"98
LEWIS, E	Lon. Welsh	L - 85
LEWIS, A	Bedford	W - 75
LEWSEY, J	Wasps	W-99
LIGHT, B	Lon. Welsh	L - 85
LILEY, J	Leicester	W - 93 L - 96
LINK, G	Rosslyn Park	L - 75
LLOYD, L	Leicester	W - 97
LLOYD-ROBERTS, G	Rosslyn Park	L - 76
LOGAN, K	Wasps	W-*99
LONGSTAFF, M	Gloucester	W - 82
LOVETT, MS	Lon. Scot	L - 74
LOZOWSKI, RAP	Wasps	L - 87
LUMSDEN, A	Bath	W - 96
LUNT, K	Waterloo	L - 77
LUXTON, TC	Harlequins	L - 92
LYNAGH, M	Sarecens	W-98
MacMILLAN, AJ	Gosforth	L - 81
MADDERSON, CS	Harlequins	L - 93
MADSEN, DF	Gosforth	W - 76, 77
MALLETT, J	Bath	W - *95, 96
MALLINDER, J	Sale	L - 97
MALONE, NG	Leicester	W - 97 L - 96
MANNIX, S	Sale	L - 97
MANTELL, ND	Rosslyn Park	L - 75, 76
MARTIN, CR	Bath	W - 84, 85, 86, 87
MAY, T	Newcastle	L-99
McDOWELL, NH	Gosforth	L - 81
McFADYAN, CW	Moseley	L - 72
McHARG, AF	Lon. Scot	L - 74
McKAY, DJ	Rosslyn Park	L - 75
McKENZIE, RA	Lon. Scot	L - 74
McKIBBIN, R	Lon. Irish	L - 80
McKIBBIN, AR	Lon. Irish	L - 80
MEANWELL, CA	Lon. Irish	L - 80
MILLER, E	Leicester	W - 97
MILLS, SGF	Gloucester	W - 78, 82
MITCHELL, J	Sale	L - 97
MITCHELL, S	Wasps	L-98
MOGG, RR	Gloucester	W - 78, 82 L - 90
MOLLOY, D	Wasps	W-99 L - 95, 98
MOON, RHQB	Harlequins	W - 88
MOORE, BC	Harlequins	W - 91 L - 92
MORDELL, R	Rosslyn Park	L - 76
MORGAN, D	Gloucester	L - 90
MORLEY, AJ	Bristol	W - 83 L - 73, 84
MORRELL, CC	Moseley	L - 72
MORRIS, D	Sale	L - 97
MORRIS, R	Gloucester	W - 72
MORRIS, R	Moseley	L - 72
MORRISON, JSC	Bath	W - 86, 87, 89
MOSS, P	Northampton	L - 91
MOYLES, JL	Rosslyn Park	L - 76
MULLINS, AR	Harlequins	W - 88, 91 L - 92, 93
MUNDEN, AC	Bristol	L - 73
MURPHY, BW	Lon. Irish	L - 80
NANCEKIVELL, R	Northampton	L - 91
NAYLOR, J	Newcastle	L-99
NEEDHAM, RJ	Leicester	L - 78
NESDALE, R	Newcastle	L-99
NEWBERRY, JA	Lon. Irish	L - 80
NEWTON, M	Leicester	W - 79
NICHOLLS, MJ	Gloucester	W - 72
NICHOLLS, AH	Bristol	L - 73
NICOL, AD	Bath	W - 96
NINNES, BF	Coventry	W - 73, 74
NUTT, DR	Moseley	W - 82 L - 79
O'DONNELL, P	Lon. Irish	L - 80
O'DRISCOLL, JB	Lon. Irish	L - 80
O'GRADY, D	Sale	L - 97
OJOMOH, SO	Bath	W - 92, *94, 95, 96
OLSEN, M	Saracens	W-*98
OLVER, A	Saracens	W-*98
OLVER, JC	Northampton	L - 91
	Harlequins	W - 88
ORLEDGE, RJ	Bristol	L - 73
ORWIN, J	Gloucester	W - 82
PACKMAN, F	Northampton	L - 91
PALMER, JA	Bath	W - 84, 85, 86, 87, 89
PALMER, T	Gloucester	W - 72
PALMER, DJ	Bristol	W - *83 L - 84, 88
PARSLOE, SG	Gloucester	W - 82
PASCALL, R	Gloucester	L - 90
PASK, P	Northampton	L - 91
PATRICK, B	Gosforth	W - 76, 77 L - 81

PATRICK, HE	Gosforth	W - 76, 77
PEARCE, GS	Northampton	L - 91
PEARN, AFA	Bristol	L - 73
PEARS, D	Harlequins	W - 91 L - 92
PEEL, I	Newcastle	L-*99
PEGLAR, DJ	Wasps	L - 86, 87
PELLOW, R	Wasps	L - 86
PERRY, MH	Moseley	W - 82
PETERS, EW	Bath	W - 96
PHILLIPS, CA	Bristol	L - 88
PICKERING, DA	Lon. Scot	L - 74
PIENNAAR, F	Saracens	W-98
PINNEGAR, MCF	Wasps	L - 86, 87
POLLEDRI, P	Bristol	W - 83 L - 84
POMPHREY, NJC	Bristol	W - 83 L - 84, 88
POOLE, MD	Leicester	W - 93, 97 L - 94, 96
POTTER, S	Leicester	W - 93, 97 L - 94, 96
POTTER, MJ	Gloucester	W - 72
PREECE, PS	Coventry	W - 73
PREEDY, M	Gloucester	W - 82 L - 90
PRESTON, AJ	Gosforth	W - 76
PRICE, C	Lon. Welsh	L - 85
PRINGLE, IN	Moseley	L - 72
PRITCHARD, P	Gloucester	W - 82
PROBYN, JA	Wasps	L - 86, 87
PULLIN, JV	Bristol	L - 73
RAFTER, M	Bristol	W - 83 L - 84
RALSTON, CS	Rosslyn Park	L - 76
RAVENSCROFT, S	Saracens	W-98
RECARDO, A	Moseley	W - 82
REDFERN, SP	Leicester	W - 79, 80, 81 L - 78, 83, 89
REDFERN, SB	Leicester	L - 83
REDMAN, NC	Bath	W - 84, 85, 86, 87, 90, 92, 94, 95, 96
REED, AI	Bath	W - 94
	Wasps	L-*98
REED, D	Waterloo	L - 77
REES, CWF	Lon. Welsh	L - 85
REES, D	Sale	L - 97
REES, GL	Wasps	W-99 L - 86, 98
REES, A	Bath	W - 84
RENDALL, PAG	Wasps	L - 87
RICHARDS, D	Leicester	W - 93, "97 L - 83, 89, 94, 96
RICHARDSON, WP	Leicester	L - 89
RIGBY, MA	Wasps	L - 86, 87
RIPLEY, AG	Rosslyn Park	L - 75, 76
ROBERTS, TC	Gosforth	W - 76, 77 L - 81
ROBINSON, D	Gosforth	W - 76, 77
ROBINSON, RP	Leicester	L - 96
ROBINSON, RA	Bath	W - 87, 89, 90, 92, 94, 95, 96
RODBER, T	Northampton	L - 91
RODGERS, AJ	Bristol	L - 73
RODGERS, AK	Rosslyn Park	L - 75, 76
ROGERS, DP	Bedford	W - 75
ROISER, S	Wasps	L-98
ROLINSON, LJ	Coventry	W - 74
ROLLITT, DM	Bristol	L - 73
ROSE, MA	Wasps	L - 86, 87
ROSSBOROUGH, PA	Coventry	W - 73, 74
ROWNTREE, GC	Leicester	W - 93, 97 L - 94, 96
RUSSELL, S	Lon. Welsh	L - 85

RUSSELL, MP	Harlequins	L - 92, 93
RYAN, D	Wasps	L - 95
SAGOE, FK	Bath	W - 89
SALMON, JLB	Harlequins	W - 88
SAMPSON	Wasps	W-99 L-*98
SANDERS, I	Bath	W - 95
SARGENT, GAF	Gloucester	W - 78, *82
SAVILLE, CD	Rosslyn Park	L - 75
SCRASE, L	Wasps	L-98
SCRIVENER, P	Wasps	W-99
SCRIVENS, N	Gloucester	L - 90
SELLA, P	Saracens	W-98
SHAW, M	Newcastle	L-99
SHAW, S	Wasps	W-99 L-98
SHEASBY, CMA	Harlequins	L - 92, 93
SHEEHAN, JM	Lon. Irish	L - 80
SHEPARD, A	Bristol	W - 83 L - 84
SHORROCK,, DW	Moseley	W - 82
SHORT, JJO	Gosforth	W - 76
SHORT, KS	Lon. Irish	L - 80
SHORT, KF	Waterloo	L - 77
SIMMONS, A	Wasps	L - 86, 87
SIMMS, KG	Wasps	L - 87
SIMONETT, JF	Gloucester	W - 78
SIMPSON, PD	Bath	W - 84, 85, 86, *89
SINGER, M	Saracens	W-*98
SKINNER, MG	Harlequins	W - 88, 91
SLEIGHTHOLME, JM	Bath	W - 96
SMITH, A	Sale	L - 97
SMITH, SM	Gosforth	L - 81
SMITH, ST	Wasps	L - 86, 87
SMITH, IR	Leicester	W - 79, 80, 81 L - 83, 89
SMITH, T	Leicester	L - 89
SMITH, R	Glouceste	W - 72
SMITH, T	Gloucester	L - 90
SMITH, I	Gloucester	L - 90
SMITH, TJ	Moseley	L - 72
SMYTHE, MJ	Lon. Irish	L - 80
SNOW, ACW	Harlequins	L - 93
SOLE, DMB	Bath	W - 87
SPAVEN, JN	Waterloo	L - 77
SPURRELL, RA	Bath	W - 84, 85, 86
STARLING, D	Rosslyn Park	L - 76
STEELE, J	Northampton	L - 91
STEPHENS,EJF	Gloucester	W - 72
STEVENSON, GB	Lon. Scot	L - 74
STIFF, PJ	Bristol	L - 84
STRANSKY, J	Leicester	W - 97
STRINGER, NC	Wasps	L - 86
STURNHAM, B	Saracens	W-98
SUTHERLAND, IS	Moseley	W - 82
SWAIN, MK	Moseley	L - 72, 79
SWATFIELD, RJ	Bristol	L - 73
SWIFT, AH	Bath	W - 86, 87, 89, 90, 92, 94, 95
TAYLOR, PA	Gloucester	W - 82
TEAGUE, MC	Gloucester	W - 82 L - 90
THACKER, T	Leicester	L - 89
THAME, J	Northampton	L - 91
THOMAS, DG	Bristol	L - 88
THOMAS, A	Moseley	L - 79
THOMPSON, AL	Harlequins	W - 88
THOMPSON, GJ	Harlequins	L - 93

THORBURN, CW	Lon. Scot	L - 74
THORNEYCROFT, H	Northampton	L - 91
THRESHER, SE	Harlequins	W - 88, 91
TICKLE, SG	Waterloo	L - 77
TRESEDER, PA	Rosslyn Park	L - 75, 76
TREVASKIS, B	Bath	W - 84, 85, 87
TRICK, DM	Bath	W - 84, 85, 86
TROUGHTON, AH	Bristol	W - 83
TUIGAMALA, V	Newcastle	L-99
UBOGU, VE	Bath	W - 90, 92, 94, 95
UFTON, J	Wasps	L - 95
UNDERWOOD, R	Leicester	W - 93 L - 89, 94, 96
	Newcastle	L-99
UNDERWOOD, T	Leicester	W - 93 L - 94
UTTLEY, RM	Gosforth	W - 77
VINE, BJ	Gloucester	W - 78
VOLLEY, P	Wasps	L-98
WALKER, R	Coventry	W - 74
WALLACE, P	Saracens	W-98
WALLACE, R	Saracens	W - *98
WALTON, P	Newcastle	L-99
WARD, B	Northampton	L - *91
WARDLOW, CS	Coventry	W - 73
WARREN, DG	Moseley	W - 82
WATERS, F	Wasps	W-99
WATKINS, M	Lon. Welsh	L - 85
WATKINS, JA	Gloucester	W - 72, 78
WATSON-JONES, A	Moseley	L - *79
WATT, DEJ	Bristol	L - 73
WEBB, JM	Bath	W - 92
	Bristol	L - 88
WEBSTER, JG	Moseley	L - 72
WEDDERBURN, MA	Harlequins	L - 92
WEEDON, M	Wasps	W-99 L-98
WEIR, D	Newcastle	L-99
WELLS, JM	Leicester	W - 93, 97
		L - 89, 94, 96
WESTON, LE	Rosslyn Park	L - 75, 76
WHEELER, PJ	Leicester	W - 79, 80, 81
		L - 78, 83
WHITE, C	Gosforth	W - 76, 77 L - 81
WHITE, L	Lon. Irish	L - 80
WHITE, M	Wasps	L - 95, *98
WHITE, JC	Moseley	L - 72
WILKINSON, J	Newcastle	L-99
WILKINSON, RM	Bedford	W - 75
WILLIAMS, K	Leicester	W - 81
WILLIAMS, CG	Gloucester	W - 78
WILLIAMS, CJ	Bristol	L - 73
WINSTANLEY, P	Sale	L - 97
WINTERBOTTOM, PJ	Harlequins	W - 91 L - 92, 93
WITHEY, K	Bath	W - 90
WOOD, P	Gloucester	W - *82
WOODWARD, C	Leicester	W - 80, 81 L - 83
WOOLEY, VJ	Gloucester	W - 78
WORSLEY, J	Wasps	W - 99 L-98
WYATT, D	Bedford	W - 75
YATES, K	Bath	W - 95
YOUNG, M	Gosforth	W - 76, 77 L - 81
YOUNGS, NC	Leicester	L - 83

Joel Stransky, a Tetley's Bitter Cup Winner in 1997, kicked all seven conversions in Leicester's 49-0 win over Leeds Tykes in this year's fifth Round match.

	Winners	Captain	Points Scored	Tries	Cons	Pens	DG	Runners-up	Captain	Points Scored	Tries	Cons	Pens	DG	Losing Semi-Finalists
1972	**Gloucester**	M Nicholls	**17**	2		1	2	**Moseley**	J Webster	**6**	1	1			Coventry, Wilmslow
1973	**Coventry**	D Duckham	**27**	4	1	4	1	**Bristol**	A Nicholls	**15**			5		Sale, London Welsh
1974	**Coventry**	D Duckham	**26**	4	2	2		**London Scottish**	M Biggar	**6**				2	Rosslyn Park, Orrell
1975	**Bedford**	D Rogers	**28**	5	4			**Rosslyn Park**	P Keith-Roach	**12**	3				Coventry, Morpeth
1976	**Gosforth**	M Young	**23**	4	2	2		**Rosslyn Park**	P Keith Roach	**14**	2		1	1	Sale, Wakefield
1977	**Gosforth**	R Uttley	**27**	5	2	1		**Waterloo**	C Fisher	**11**	2		1		London Welsh, Saracens
1978	**Gloucester**	J Watkins	**6**	1	1			**Leicester**	B Hall	**3**			1		Harlequins, Coventry
1979	**Leicester**	P Wheeler	**15**	1	1	2	1	**Moseley**	M Cooper	**12**	1	1	1	1	Wasps, Gosforth
1980	**Leicester**	P Wheeler	**21**			4	3	**London Irish**	J O'Driscoll	**9**	1	1	1		Rosslyn Park, Harlequins
1981	**Leicester**	P Wheeler	**22**	3	2	3		**Gosforth**	C White	**15**	1	1	3		London Scottish, Moseley
1982	**Gloucester**	S Mills	**12**			4		**Moseley**	D Nutt	**12**			3	1	Coventry, Leicester
1983	**Bristol**	M Rafter	**28**	4	3	1		**Leicester**	S Johnson	**22**	2	1	4		Coventry, London Scottish
1984	**Bath**	R Spurrell	**10**	1		1	1	**Bristol**	M Rafter	**9**	1	1	1		Nottingham, Harlequins
1985	**Bath**	R Spurrell	**24**	2	2	4		**London Welsh**	C Rees	**15**			5		Gloucester, Coventry
1986	**Bath**	J Palmer	**25**	4	3	1		**Wasps**	R Cardus	**17**	3	1	1		Leicester, London Scottish
1987	**Bath**	R Hill	**19**	3	2	1		**Wasps**	D Pegler	**12**	1	1	1	1	Orrell, Leicester
1988	**Harlequins**	J Olver	**28**	3	2	4		**Bristol**	N Pomphrey	**22**	2	1	3	1	Wasps, Moseley
1989	**Bath**	S Barnes	**10**	1		2		**Leicester**	P Dodge	**6**			2		Gloucester, Harlequins
1990	**Bath**	S Barnes	**48**	8	5	2		**Gloucester**	M Hamlin	**6**	1	1			Moseley, Northampton
1991	**Harlequins**	P Winterbottom	**25**	4	3	1		**Northampton**	G Pearce	**13**	1		3		Nottingham, Orrell
1992	**Bath**	A Robinson	**15**	1	1	2	1	**Harlequins**	P Winterbottom	**12**	1	1	3		Gloucester, Leicester
1993	**Leicester**	J Wells	**23**	2	2	2	1	**Harlequins**	P Winterbottom	**16**	1	1	3		Northampton, Wasps
1994	**Bath**	J Hall	**21**	2	1	3		**Leicester**	D Richards	**9**			3		Harlequins, Orrell
1995	**Bath**	P de Glanville	**36**	5	4	1		**Wasps**	D Ryan	**16**	2		2		Harlequins, Leicester
1996	**Bath**	P de Glanville	**16**	1	1	2	1	**Leicester**	D Richards	**15**	2	1	1		Gloucester, London Irish
1997	**Leicester**	M Johnson	**9**			3		**Sale**	J Mallinder	**3**			1		Gloucester, Harlequins
1998	**Saracens**	A Diprose	**48**	7	5		1	**Wasps**	L Dallaglio	**18**	2	1	2		Northampton, Sale
1999	**Wasps**	M Weedon	**27**	2	2	4	1	**Newcastle**	G Armstrong	**19**	1	1	4		Gloucester, Richmond

TETLEY'S BITTER CUP

MOST WINNERS MEDALS

9	Nigel Redman (Bath).
8	Richard Hill (Bath)
	Graham Dawe (Bath).
7	Stuart Barnes (Bristol 1, Bath 6)
	Andy Robinson (Bath)
	Tony Swift (Bath)
	Gareth Chilcott (Bath)
6	Jeremy Guscott (Bath-2 as Rep)
	John Hall (Bath)
	Simon Halliday (Bath 5, Harlequins 1)

MOST LOSERS MEDALS

4	Dean Richards (Leicester)
3	Steve Bates (Wasps)
	Paul Dodge (Leicester)
	Adel Kardooni (Leicester)
	Steve Redfern (Leicester)
	Rory Underwood (Leicester)
	John Wells (Leicester)

WINNERS MEDALS FOR TWO CLUBS

Stuart Barnes (Bristol, Bath)
Roger Barnwell (Coventry, Leicester)
RogerCowling (Gloucester, Leicester)

LOSERS MEDALS FOR TWO CLUBS

Kevin Dunn (Gloucester, Wasps)
Tony Underwood (Leicester, Newcastle)

PLAYERS APPEARING FOR TWO CLUBS

Stuart Barnes (Bristol, Bath); Roger Barnwell (Coventry, Leicester); Barrie Corless (Coventry, Moseley); Roger Cowling (Gloucester, Leicester); RobCunningham (Gosforth, Bath); Kevin Dunn (Gloucester, Wasps); Simon Halliday (Bath, Harlequins); John Olver (Harlequins, Northampton); Jonathan Webb (Bristol, Bath); Andy Reed (Bath, Wasps); Tony Underwood (Leicester, Newcastle).

PLAYERS SENT OFF

Player	Match	Year	Referee
Nigel Horton	Moseley v Gloucester	1972	Ron Lewis
Bob Mordell	Rosslyn Park v Gosforth	1976	Norman Sanson
John Gadd	Gloucester v Bath	1990	Fred Howard

TETLEY'S BITTER CUP

OVERALL PLAYING RECORD

OF TEAMS WHO HAVE REACHED THE LAST 8

	Winners	R-up	SF	QF	Years in competition	Played	Won	Drawn	Lost
Bath	10	0	10	13	27	77	60	-	17
Leicester	5	5	15	19	27	95	73	-	22
Gloucester	*3	1	10	16	27	82	57	1	24
Harlequins	2	2	11	18	26	80	56	-	24
Newcastle	2	2	5	11	28	73	47	-	26
Coventry	2	0	8	10	28	73	47	-	26
Bristol	1	3	4	11	27	69	43	-	26
Moseley	*1	2	6	12	28	74	46	1	27
Saracens	1	0	2	5	25	55	31	-	24
Bedford	1	0	1	3	27	50	24	-	26
Wasps	1	4	8	13	24	67	44	-	23
Rosslyn Park	-	2	4	7	27	63	36	-	27
London Welsh	-	1	3	8	26	66	40	-	26
London Scottish	-	1	4	6	27	59	32	-	27
Northampton	-	1	4	9	27	62	35	-	27
Sale	-	1	4	11	26	65	39	-	26
London Irish	-	1	2	5	25	52	27	-	25
Waterloo	-	1	1	5	22	45	23	-	22
Orrell	-	-	4	6	23	47	24	-	23
Nottingham	-	-	2	7	26	55	29	-	26
Wakefield	-	-	1	4	20	47	27	-	20
Wilmslow	-	-	1	2	5	11	6	-	5
Morpeth	-	-	1	1	3	6	3	-	3
Richmond	-	-	-	5	26	59	33	-	26
West Hartlepool	-	-	-	4	19	42	23	-	19
Penryn	-	-	-	2	4	9	5	-	4
Metropolitan Police	-	-	-	2	16	35	19	-	16
Exeter	-	-	-	2	21	52	31	-	21
Liverpool St Helens	-	-	-	2	23	40	17	-	23
Halifax	-	-	-	1	2	5	3	-	2
Roundhay	-	-	-	1	7	10	3	-	7
Fylde	-	-	-	1	18	40	22	-	18
Plymouth Albion	-	-	-	1	20	29	9	-	20
Total	29	27	112	224					

Tetley's Bitter County Championship 1998-99

NORTH & MIDLANDS LEAGUE ONE

Monday, 5th April 1999
Cumbria 16 Notts, Lincs, & Derbys 30 (Carlisle)
Saturday, 10th April 1999
Notts., Lincs, & Derbys 20 Warwickshire 13
Saturday, 24th April 1999
Warwickshire 31 Cumbria 38

TABLE	P	W	D	L	F	A	Pts
Notts., Lincs, & Derbys	2	2	0	0	50	29	4
Cumbria	2	1	0	1	54	61	2
Warwickshire	2	0	0	2	44	58	0

NORTH & MIDLANDS LEAGUE TWO

Saturday, 3rd April 1999
Northumberland 17 Durham 27 (Percy Park)
Monday, 5th April 1999
Cheshire 23 Lancashire 7 (New Brighton)
Saturday, 10th April 1999
Cheshire 23 Northumberland 18
Lancashire 23 Durham 21
Saturday, 24th April 1999
Durham 15 Cheshire 19
Northumberland 10 Lancashire 37

TABLE	P	W	D	L	F	A	Pts
Cheshire	3	3	0	0	65	40	6
Lancashire	3	2	0	1	67	54	4
Durham	3	1	0	2	63	59	2
Northumberland	3	0	0	3	45	87	0

NORTH & MIDLANDS LEAGUE THREE

Saturday, 3rd April 1999
Leicestershire 25 Staffordshire 31 (Syston)
North Midlands 8 Yorkshire 38 (Worcester)
Saturday, 10th April 1999
North Midlands 23 Leicestershire 23
Yorkshire 50 Staffordshire 0
Saturday, 24th April 1999
Leicestershire 17 Yorkshire 19
Staffordsshire 30 North Midlands 21

TABLE	P	W	D	L	F	A	Pts
Yorkshire	3	3	0	0	107	25	6
Staffordshire	3	2	0	1	61	96	4
Leicestershire	3	0	1	2	65	73	1
North Midlands	3	0	1	2	52	91	1

SOUTH LEAGUE ONE

Monday, 5th April 1999
Gloucestershire 34 Surrey 24 (Lydney)
Sunday, 11th April 1999
Surrey 18 Devon 16
Sunday, 25th April 1999
Devon 7 Gloucestershire 21 (Barnstaple)

TABLE	P	W	D	L	F	A	Pts
Gloucesters're	2	2	0	0	55	31	4
Surrey	2	1	0	1	42	50	2
Devon	2	0	0	2	23	39	0

SOUTH LEAGUE TWO

Sunday, 4th April 1999
Cornwall 18 Oxfordshire 6 (Camborne)
Monday, 5th April 1999
Berkshire 12 Sussex 24 (Bracknell)
Saturday, 10th April 1999
Cornwall 34 Berkshire 20
Oxfordshire 13 Sussex 17
Saturday, 24th April 1999
Saturday, 24th April 1999
Berkshire 36 Oxfordshire 19
Sussex 12 Cornwall 31

TABLE	P	W	D	L	F	A	Pts
Cornwall	3	3	0	0	83	38	6
Sussex	3	2	0	1	53	56	4
Berkshire	3	1	0	2	68	77	2
Oxfordshire	3	0	0	3	38	71	0

SOUTH LEAGUE THREE

Saturday, 3rd April 1999
Middlesex 36 Dorset & Wiltshire 12
Sunday, 4th April 1999
Hampshire 19 Kent 23
Saturday, 10th April 1999
Dorset & Wiltshire 22 Hampshire 22
Middlesex 21 Kent 22
Saturday, 24th April 1999
Hampshire 30 Middlesex 32
Kent 43 Dorset & Wiltshire 26

TABLE	P	W	D	L	F	A	Pts
Kent	3	3	0	0	88	66	6
Middlesex	3	2	0	1	89	64	4
Hampshire	3	0	1	2	61	67	1
Dorset & Wilts	3	0	1	2	60	101	1

SOUTH LEAGUE FOUR

Sunday, 4th April 1999
Eastern Counties 19 Hertfordshire 29 (Norwich)
Monday, 5th April 1999
Buckinghamshire 8 Somerset 44 (Slough)
Saturday, 10th April 1999
Eastern Counties 33 Buckinghamshire 23
Hertfordshire 18 Somerset 27
Saturday, 24th April 1999
Buckinghamshire 26 Hertfordshire 43
Somerset 67 Eastern Counties 9

TABLE	P	W	D	L	F	A	Pts
Somerset	3	3	0	0	138	35	6
Hertfordshire	3	2	0	1	90	72	4
East Counties	3	1	0	2	61	119	2
Buckinghams're	3	0	0	3	57	120	0

QUARTER-FINALS
(Saturday, 1st May 1999)

Cheshire 40 Yorkshire 13
(New Brighton)
Cornwall 30 Kent 24
(Redruth)
Gloucestershire 23 Somerset 18
(Cinderford)
Notts., Lincs., & Derbys 16 Lancashire 20
(Newark)

SEMI-FINALS
(Saturday, 8th May 1999)

Cornwall 35 Cheshire 16
(at Redruth)

Lancashire 20 Gloucestershire 23
(at Vale of Lune)
(after extra-time; 80 minutes score - 20-20)

FINAL

Saturday, 22nd May 1999. At Twickenham

CORNWALL 24
GLOUCESTERSHIRE 15

Half-time: 14-12
Referee: N Yates, Manchester
Attendance: 22,000

CORNWALL (Launceston unless stated): A Birkett; N Saumi (Penzance & Newlyn), J Tucker, C Laity (Exeter), S Larkins (Redruth); S Whitworth (Redruth), M Roderick (Penzance & Newlyn); P Risdon, N Grigg, J Thomas (Penzance & Newlyn), J Atkinson (Penzance & Newlyn), G Hutchings, K Moseley (Penzance & Newlyn), M Addinall (Penryn), D Shipton (captain).
Replacements: E Nancekivell for Larkins 39 minutes, S Rush for Thomas 63 minutes, L Mruk (Penzance & Newlyn) for Hutchings 82 minutes), P Gadsdon (Penzance & Newlyn) for Roderick 85 minutes.
SCORERS: Tries: Tucker (1), Whitworth (1). Pens: Larkins (3), Saumi (1). Con: Saumi.

GLOUCESTERSHIRE (Lydney unless stated): S Morgan (Gloucester); J Perrins (Stroud), L Osborne, D Edwards (Cinderford), C Dunlop; S Thompson (Stroud), J Davis; A Martin (Cinderford), N Nelmes (captain), A Powles (Gloucester), R York (Cheltenham), B Guy (Ashley Down & Bristol), A Adams (Clifton), A Tarples (Cheltenham), M Nicholls. Replacements: S Ward (Gloucester) for Thompson 61 minutes, J Roberts for Guy 61 minutes,
G Williams for Martin 69 minutes, P Knight (Sale) for Davis 71 minutes, R James (Matson) for Nicholls 77 minutes, N Matthews (Matson) for Nelmes 81 minutes.
SCORER: Pens: Osborne (5).

TETLEY'S BITTER VASE 1998-99

Sixth Round - Saturday, 23rd January 1999

North & Midlands
Heaton Moor 28 Leeds Corinthians 15
Scarborough 28 Old Hamptonians 10
Silhillians 13 Rushden & Higham 3
Wellingborough Old Grammarians 12 Knottingley 14

London South East & South West
Billericay 45 Millwall Albion 0
Hucclecote Old Boys 6 Old Tiffinians 7
Tetbury 3 St Just 23
Avon v Datchworth postponed
Avon beat Datchworth

QUARTER FINALS - Saturday, 13th February 1999

Billericay 12 St Just 8
Old Tiffinians 18 Avon 34
Scarborough 21 Knottingley 7
Silhillians 26 Heaton Moor 5

SEMI FINALS - Saturday, 13th March 1999

Billericay 18 Scarborough 6
Silhillians 22 Avon 10

FINAL

Saturday, 17th April 1999. At Twickenham.

BILLERICAY 19-3 SILHILLIANS

Half-time: 16-3.
Referee: J Burtenshaw, RFU.

BILLERICAY: J Stevens; M Coxford, R Schofield, N Glister, A Collings; K Harman, G Smith; G Pearmain, F Daly (capt.), A Bond, M Green, S Clow, R Holdgate, J Daley, J Hayter.
Replacements: W Hallett for Pearmain 33 mins., A Hudson for Glister 71 mins., J Hughes for Green 71 mins., A White for Hayter 75 mins., J Wicks for Stevens 78 mins., J Brown for Bond 78 mins.
Temporary replacement: White for Green 61-69 mins..
Scorers: Try: Bailey. Pens: Harman (4). Con: Harman.

SILHILLIANS: A Waight; S Liggins, G Atkinson, A Tapper, P Short; S Rutter, E Dawes; A Wiles, K Lane, G Webb, A Clutterbuck (capt.), I Hatley, R Lazenby, A Brown, D Stanley.
Replacements: N Savage for Lazenby 41 mins., A Durrant for Brown 54 mins., A Dent for Stanley 59 mins., J Brierley for Waite 71 mins., M Mallett for Wiles 75 mins., S Mair for Atkinson 77 mins..
Temporary replacement: Brierley for Dawes 37-40 mins.
Scorer: Pen: Rutter.

ALLIED DUNBAR

PREMIERSHIP ONE

1998-99 Season

Review & statistics 32-37

1999-200 Fixtures 38

CLUBS

Bath	39
Bedford	45
Bristol	51
Gloucester	57
Harlequins	63
Leicester	69
London Irish	75
Manchester Sale	81
Newcastle	87
Northampton	93
Saracens	99
Wasps	105

Match Facts & Records for
London Scottish 112-3; 116
& Richmond 114-5; 117

Division One Records
119 - 126

	P	W	D	L	F	A	PD	Pts	HOME W	HOME D	HOME L	HOME F	HOME A	HOME Tries For	HOME Pens For	HOME Tries Against	HOME Pens Against	AWAY W	AWAY D	AWAY L	AWAY F	AWAY A	AWAY Tries For	AWAY Pens For	AWAY Tries Against	AWAY Pens Against
Leicester	26	22	0	4	771	423	348	44	13	0	0	426	185	50	40	13	32	9	0	4	345	238	36	39	21	35
Northampton	26	19	0	7	754	556	198	38	10	0	3	389	243	41	42	30	19	9	0	4	365	313	44	27	34	28
Saracens	26	16	1	9	778	593	185	33	9	0	4	398	298	45	32	32	26	9	0	4	380	295	37	34	27	42
Harlequins	26	16	1	9	690	653	33	33	9	1	3	343	279	33	42	33	24	7	0	6	347	374	31	45	42	35
Wasps	26	15	1	10	717	506	211	31	9	1	3	431	248	46	47	22	31	6	0	7	286	258	34	25	23	34
Bath	26	15	0	11	698	574	124	30	10	0	3	405	214	47	36	24	23	5	0	8	293	360	34	25	44	28
London Irish	26	15	0	11	703	607	96	30	8	0	5	366	299	40	36	33	28	7	0	6	337	308	35	36	32	33
Newcastle	26	14	0	12	719	639	80	28	11	0	2	422	250	51	31	26	27	3	0	10	297	389	24	25	43	33
Richmond	26	11	2	13	720	715	5	*22	5	0	8	323	348	45	18	38	32	6	2	5	397	367	51	24	37	40
Gloucester	26	9	1	16	554	643	-111	19	8	1	4	358	284	35	45	29	30	1	0	12	196	359	23	19	38	38
Sale	26	9	1	16	604	731	-127	19	6	0	7	334	371	42	23	41	35	3	1	9	270	360	34	17	39	38
London Scottish	26	8	0	18	491	734	-243	16	5	0	8	241	331	21	35	37	32	0	0	13	149	339	19	36	48	32
Bedford	26	6	0	20	541	840	-399	12	4	0	9	266	428	31	20	52	30	2	0	11	275	412	32	20	49	37
West Hartlepool	26	3	1	22	501	1007	-506	7	2	1	10	252	489	23	33	61	29	1	0	12	249	518	27	24	73	21

Review of the season 1998-1999

Leicester Tigers were a cut above the rest and ended up winning the division by a comfortable six-point margin. First Joel Stransky and then Tim Stimpson were sound goal kickers taking most of their chances whilst Neil Back led the way in the try scoring with an impressive total of sixteen.

Northampton seemed to be making a serious attempt to catch Leicester but a mid season blip put paid to their hopes. They lost three out of four home matches with London Irish, Saracens and Leicester all winning at Franklin's Gardens. Pat Lam seemed to stiffen up their resolve and with Tim Rodber enjoying his new lease of life in the second row they got themselves in a great position to challenge Leicester before that bad run.

Two late wins pushed **Saracens** up to third place, a one-place drop on last season. They never really got going and failed to build on the platform from the previous season when they won the Tetley's Bitter Cup and were runners up in the Premiership pushing Newcastle all the way.

Harlequins came back well after a disastrous start to the season. New signing John Schuster proved an excellent acquisition and scored a new top division record of 331 points. He was instrumental in a number of their wins and was one of the most accurate kickers in the country.

Wasps despite no big name signings managed to compete with the best and qualified for Europe and then went on to win the Tetley's Bitter Cup. Kenny Logan did a superb job stepping into the goal kicking duties with Gareth Rees missing most of the season and ended the season on 261 points.

Bath had a mixed a season as you could possibly have. They had a bad run and a good run looked to have missed out on qualifying for Europe. But they thrashed London Scottish to move passed London Irish on points difference and put the pressure on Newcastle to get a big win at Saracens the week after the Cup Final. Newcastle could barely manage a win never mind pull back the big points difference, so Bath get the chance to defend the European Cup title a year late.

London Irish finished their league campaign in sixth place but were passed a week later after Bath won heavily at home to London Scottish and missed the last European Cup place. After such a promising season they will be terribly disappointed to lose the chance of playing in the European Cup.

After winning the Premiership title last season **Newcastle** fell from grace and dropped eight places, missed out on the European Cup qualification and lost in the Tetley's Bitter Cup final.

Richmond after a promising start to the season saw their season fall away with monetary problems off the field taking centre stage.

Manchester Sale were just above the relegation zone for most of the season but eventually their form improved and they moved up a couple of places. They were another club whose financial affairs were taking centre stage as they looked to off-load some of their big earners and re-negotiate certain players contracts in a bid to reduce the wage bill.

Gloucester had a miserable season with the Cheltenham & Gloucester Cup being their only consolation.

London Scottish were put up for sale at a very early stage and it says much for the professionalism of their players and staff that they lasted the season reasonably well and with dignity.

Bedford needed the play offs to survive in the Allied Dunbar Premiership One. Even then Rotherham took them to the wire before going through having scored more tries in the two play off matches. They need to seriously re think in the summer; with the league being reduced to twelve sides they are in danger of becoming the whipping boys if they are not careful.

West Hartlepool never recovered from a bad start and were relegated after just one season at the top level. They put up some spirited performances in the second half of the season, did not capitulate and went down with dignity.

ALLIED DUNBAR PREMIERSHIP ONE

1998-99 RECORD REVIEW (Individual Records)

The ALL-TIME RECORDS for MOST POINTS IN A MATCH, MOST POINTS IN A SEASON & MOST TRIES IN A MATCH can be found in the Records Section for this division.

MOST POINTS - IN A MATCH

The nearest anybody came to Niall Woods's record of 32 set last season was 30 by Steven Vile the West Hartlepool outside half.
Vile scored his 30 points in the home match against Richmond but could not stop his side going down 36-35. He scored a try, converted two and kicked 7 penalty goals as he recorded the highest score by someone finishing on the losing side in a top flight match. In the home match prior to this Vile scored 28 points as West Hartlepool beat Gloucester 33-32, not a bad two match haul 58 points.
Simon Mannix in his new start at Goucester set a new match record for the club with 28 points in the final match of the season against second placed Northampton. Mannix now holds the record of points in a match for two clubs. Whilst at Sale he set their record with 27 points again against Northampton.
The other player to score 28 points in a match during the season to move into joint fifth on the all time list for the division was John Schuster the Harlequins centre.

Most points in a match - 1998-99

30	Steven Vile	W Hartlepool v Richmond	02.01.99
28	Gavin Johnson	Saracens v London Scot	.98
28	John Schuster	Quins v Bath	.98
28	Steven Vile	W Hartlepool v Gloucester	.99
28	Simon Mannix	Gloucester v Northampton	17.05.99

EVOLUTION OF RECORD - Points in a match

21	Ian Aitchison	Waterloo v Sale	02.01.88
23	Jamie Salmon	Quins v Waterloo	27.02.88
24	Dusty Hare	Leicester v Rosslyn P.	19.11.88
26	John Liley	Leicester v Bedford	23.09.89
27	David Pears	Quins v Bedford	14.10.89
28	Martin Strett	Orrell v Rosslyn P.	21.03.92
31	John Liley	Leicester v Rosslyn P.	21.03.92
32	Niall Woods	Lon. Irish v Harlequins	25.04.98

MOST POINTS - IN A SEASON

John Schuster set a new record with 331 points beating the old record, set by Wasps' Gareth Rees during their championship season of 1996-97, by 40 points. He was one of four players who beat the old record. The others were:
318: Gavin Johnson - Saracens
306: Jonny Wilkinson - Newcastle
294: Mike Catt - Bath

In all 10 players passed the 200 point mark beating the record of eight from last season. Shane Howarth, Niall Woods and Joel Stransky both passed the mark for a second consecutive season. Gloucester's Mark Mapletoft missed out by two points on becoming the first player to score 200 points in three seasons in the top flight.

EVOLUTION OF RECORD - Points in a season

126	Dusty Hare	Leicester	1987-88
126	John Liley	Leicester	1989-90
126	Rob Andrew	Wasps	1990-91
202	Jez Harris	Leicester	1993-94
272	John Liley	Leicester	1996-97
291	Gareth Rees	Wasps	1996-97
331	John Schuster	Harlequins	1998-99

MOST TRIES - IN A MATCH

Kenny Logan's record of five set two seasons ago remained intact in a season which saw just 11 hat tricks scored.
The best haul of the season was four by two players. London Irish's wing Niall Woods became the first player to score four tries in an away match in the top division with his effort at high flying Northampton.
Jeremy Guscott became the first player to score four tries in a match twice in the division. He scored his four tries in the last match of the season at home to London Scottish.
Richmond's Brian Cusack became the first 2nd row forward to score a hat trick of tries in a division one match when he bagged three against Bedford in their final match of the season, or could it be their final match ever.

Bedford winger Darragh O'Mahony was the only player to score two hat tricks during the season.
Neil Back scored a hat trick in the last match of the season at home to West Hatlepool to become the 9th Tiger's player to achieve this feat in a league match.
Only Harlequins with 10 have had more players score hat tricks in league matches.

EVOLUTION OF RECORD - Tries in a match
(Only the first to reach the figure is shown)

3	Peter Shillingford	Moseley v Wasps	05.02.88
4	Gary Hartley	Nottingham v Bedford	18.11.89
5	Kenny Logan	Wasps v Orrell	22.03.97

MOST TRIES - IN A SEASON

Leicester's England flanker Neil Back failed by one to equal the division one record for tries in a season. Back scored a hat trick in the final match of the season at home to West Hartlepool

EVOLUTION OF RECORD - Tries in a season

11	Andrew Harriman	Harlequins	1987-88
11	Daren O'Leary	Harlequins	1993-94
14	Daren O'Leary	Harlequins	1995-96
16	Adedayo Adebayo	Bath	1996-97
17	Domonic Chapman	Richmond	1997-98

ALL-TIME RECORDS - Tries in a season

17	Domonic Chapman	Richmond	1997-98
16	Adedayo Adebayo	Bath	1996-97
16	Neil Back	Leicester	1998-99
15	Daren O'Leary	Harlequins	1996-97
14	Daren O'Leary	Harlequins	1995-96
14	Tom Beim	Sale	1997-98
13	Steven John	West Hartlepool	1996-97
13	Tom Beim	Sale	1996-97
13	Gary Armstrong	Newcastle	1997-98

ALL-TIME CAREER RECORDS

MOST POINTS

	Pts	T	C	P	DG	Apps	Pts/A
John Liley	1070	25	129	232	1	100	10.70
Jon Callard	1042	24	170	196	-	96	10.85
Rob Andrew*	1000	23	132	199	12	120	9.84
Mark Mapletoft	848	19	90	183	8	71	11.94
Paul Grayson	816	9	81	193	10	76	10.74
Mark Tainton	637	-	62	165	6	72	8.85
Tim Smith	593	10	57	142	2	94	6.31

* indicates more than one club.

All records are for Division/Premiership One matches only

MOST TRIES

	Tries	Apps	Strike rate
Jeremy Guscott	67	128	1.91
Daren O'Leary*	61	113	1.85
Rory Underwood*	56	115	2.05
Adedayo Adebayo	50	119	2.38
Tony Swift	43	90	2.09
Tony Underwood*	38	66	1.74
Tom Beim*	35	53	1.51

* indicates more than one club.

All records are for Division/Premiership One matches only

MOST CONVERSIONS - IN A MATCH

This was one of the oldest records in the book and was beaten in what could turn out to be Richmond's last ever match at this level. Rich Butland converted 13 of his sides 16 tries as they set a new points scoring record in the top division. Just like Barnes Butland got his conversions against Bedford.

EVOLUTION OF RECORD - Conversions in a match

10	Stuart Barnes	Bath v Bedford	13.01.90
13	Rich Butland	Richmond v Bedford	17.05.99

ALL-TIME RECORDS - Conversions in a match

13	Rich Butland	Richmond v Bedford	17.05.99
10	Stuart Barnes	Bath v Bedford	13.01.90
9	Paul Challinor	Quins v W. Hartlepool	23.03.96
8	Martin Strett	Orrell v Rosslyn P.	28.04.90
8	Will Carling	Quins v Orrell	05.10.96
8	Mike Catt	Bath v Sale	26.04.97
8	Niall Woods	Lon. Irish v Harlequins	25.04.98
8	Mike Catt	Bath v London Scottish	16.05.99

MOST CONVERSIONS - IN A SEASON

Johnson broke Jon Callard's record in his final match for the club with his four conversions taking him one past the old record of 51.

England starlet Jonny Wilkinson equalled the old record and Mike Catt moved into fourth place on the all time list with 50.

EVOLUTION OF RECORD - Conversions in a season

15	Dusty Hare	Leicester	1987-88
29	Stuart Barnes	Bath	1989-90
43	Jonathon Callard	Bath	1995-96
51	Jonathon Callard	Bath	1996-97
52	Gavin Johnson	Saracens	1998-99

ALL-TIME RECORDS - Conversions in a season

52	Gavin Johnson	Saracens	1998-99
51	Jonathon Callard	Bath	1996-97
51	Jonny Wilkinson	Newcastle	1998-99
50	Mike Catt	Bath	1998-99
45	Gareth Rees	Wasps	1996-97
44	Rob Andrew	Newcastle	1997-98
43	Jonathon Callard	Bath	1995-96
42	Shane Howarth	Sale	1998-99
39	Shane Howarth	Sale	1997-98
39	Joel Stransky	Leicester	1997-98
37	Michael Lynagh	Saracens	1997-98
36	John Schuster	Harlequins	1998-99

MOST PENALTIES - IN A MATCH

John Liley's record remained in tact but three players managed seven in a match. Two of the three, Joel Starnsky and Tim Stimpson, were Leicester players who both kicked seven out of seven and did not have the chance to equal the record.

EVOLUTION OF RECORD

6	Dusty Hare	Leicester v Rosslyn P.	19.11.88
7	David Pears	Quins v Rosslyn P.	07.12.91
8	John Liley	Leicester v Bristol	28.10.95

ALL-TIME RECORDS

8	John Liley	Leicester v Bristol	28.10.95
7	David Pears	Quins v Rosslyn P.	07.12.91
7	Jez Harris	Leicester v Bristol	11.12.93
7	Rob Andrew	Wasps v Orrell	11.12.93
7	Jez Harris	Leicester v Gloucester	29.01.94
7	Mark Tainton	Bristol v Leicester	05.1194
7	John Liley	Leicester v Bath	07.09.96
7	Simon Mannix	Sale v Northampton	08.03.97
7	Paul Grayson	N'hampton v Richmond	08.03.97
7	Shane Howarth	Sale v Wasps	18.04.98
7	Joel Stransky	Leicester v London Irish	
7	Steven Vile	W Hartlepool v Richmond	
7	Tim Stimpson	Leicester v Newcastle	

MOST PENALTIES - IN A SEASON

John Schuster in his record breaking season broke John Liley's record of 64 fairly easily and ended the season with a new total of 77. Saracen's South African full back, Gavin Johnson, moved into joint fourth on the all time list with 58.

EVOLUTION OF RECORD - Penalties in a season

31	Dusty Hare	Leicester	1987-88
31	Michael Corcoran	London Irish	1992-93
41	Jez Harris	Leicester	1993-94
56	Mark Tainton	Bristol	1994-95
64	John Liley	Leicester	1995-96
77	John Schuster	Harlequins	1998-99

ALL-TIME RECORDS - Penalties in a season

77	John Schuster	Harlequins	1998-99
64	John Liley	Leicester	1995-96
62	Gareth Rees	Wasps	1996-97
58	Mark Mapletoft	Gloucester	1996-97
58	Michael Lynagh	Saracens	1997-98
58	Mark Mapletoft	Gloucester	1997-98
58	Gavin Johnson	Saracens	1998-99
57	Gareth Rees	Wasps	1997-98
56	Mark Tainton	Bristol	1994-95

MOST DROP GOALS - IN A MATCH

This record was not challenged with nobody managing more than one drop goal in a match.

ALL-TIME RECORDS - Drop Goals in a match

3	John Steele	Northampton v Wasps	23.09.91
3	Jez Harris	Leicester v Wasps	23.11.91
3	Jez Harris	Leicester v Bath	15.04.95
3	Matthew McCarthy	Orrell v W. Hartlepool	07.12.96

1998-99

ALLIED DUNBAR PREMIERSHIP ONE

MOST POINTS

POINTS			T	C	P	DG
331	**John Schuster**	**Harlequins**	5	36	77	1
318	Gavin Johnson	Saracens	8	52	58	-
306	Jonny Wilkinson	Newcastle	9	51	53	-
294	Mike Catt	Bath	7	50	53	-
263	Kenny Logan	Wasps	8	35	51	-
246	Shane Howarth	Sale	9	42	37	-
240	Steven Vile	W Hartlepool	5	28	52	1
215	Niall Woods	London Irish	12	25	35	-
203	Earl Va'a	Richmond	8	32	33	-
202	Joel Stransky	Leicester	7	34	33	-
198	Mark Mapletoft	Gloucester	6	21	41	1
168	Jannie De Beer	London Scottish	1	17	37	6
161	Tim Stimpson	Leicester	2	14	41	-
156	Paul Grayson	Northampton	1	23	35	-
143	Jarrod Cunningham	London Irish	2	23	29	-
134	Sam Howard	Bedford	3	28	20	1
128	Ian McAusland	London Scottish	1	12	33	-
128	Alastair Hepher	Northampton	2	20	26	-

MOST PENALTIES

77	**John Schuster**	**Harlequins**
58	Gavin Johnson	Saracens
53	Mike Catt	Bath
53	Jonny Wilkinson	Newcastle
52	Steven Vile	W Hartlepool
51	Kenny Logan	Wasps
41	Mark Mapletoft	Gloucester
41	Tim Stimpson	Leicester
37	Shane Howarth	Sale
37	Jannie De Beer	London Scottish
35	Niall Woods	London Irish
35	Paul Grayson	Northampton
33	Ian McAusland	London Scottish
33	Joel Stransky	Leicester
33	Earl Va'a	Richmond

MOST TRIES

16	**Neil Back**	**Leicester Tigers**
14	Jeremy Guscott	Bath
14	Pat Lam	Northampton
13	Iain Balshaw	Bath
12	Gary Armstrong	Newcastle
12	Brandon Daniel	Saracens
12	Steve Hanley	Sale
12	Va'aiga Tuigamala	Newcastle
12	Rory Underwood	Bedford
12	Niall Woods	London Irish
11	Dan Luger	Harlequins
11	Darragh O'Mahony	Bedford
10	Matt Moore	Sale

MOST CONVERSIONS

52	**Gavin Johnson**	**Saracens**
51	Jonny Wilkinson	Newcastle
50	Mike Catt	Bath
42	Shane Howarth	Sale
36	John Schuster	Harlequins
35	Kenny Logan	Wasps
34	Joel Stransky	Leicester
32	Earl Va'a	Richmond
28	Sam Howard	Bedford
28	Steven Vile	W Hartlepool
25	Niall Woods	London Irish
23	Paul Grayson	Northampton
23	Jarrod Cunningham	London Irish
21	Mark Mapletoft	Gloucester
20	Alastair Hepher	Northampton

MOST DROP GOALS

6	**Jannie De Beer**	**London Scottish**
5	Tony Yapp	Bedford
4	Alain Penaud	Saracens
3	Alex King	Wasps
3	Thierry Lacroix	Harlequins
2	Shane Howarth	Sale
1	Steve Bachop	London Irish
1	Emmet Farrell	W Hartlepool
1	Sam Howard	Bedford
1	Mark Mapletoft	Gloucester
1	Conor O'Shea	London Irish
1	John Schuster	Harlequins
1	Steven Vile	W Hartlepool
1	Keith Wood	Harlequins

ALLIED DUNBAR PREMIERSHIP 1 FIXTURES 1999-2000

Away Teams

	HOME TEAMS	Bath	Bedford	Bristol	Gloucester	Harlequins	Leicester	London Irish etc	Newcastle	Northampton	Sale	saracens	Wasps	
1	BATH	X	12.02	25.03	9.10	29.04	26.12	30.10	13.11	25.09	18.04	6.05	22.01	1
2	BEDFORD	6.11	X	29.04	29.12	25.01	11.03	25.09	8.04	4.12	20.05	18.04	16.10	2
3	BRISTOL	16.10	11.09	X	4.12	11.03	8.04	6.05	22.04	6.11	25.01	26.12	2.10	3
4	GLOUCESTER	8.04	6.05	22.01	X	16.10	2.10	26.12	11.09	11.03	6.11	13.11	22.04	4
5	HARLEQUINS	11.09	13.11	30.10	25.03	X	6.05	12.02	22.01	18.04	9.10	25.09	26.12	5
6	LEICESTER	20.05	30.10	9.10	18.04	29.12	X	25.03	12.02	29.04	25.09	22.01	13.11	6
7	LONDON IRISH etc	11.03	22.04	29.12	20.05	6.11	16.10	X	2.10	25.01	4.12	29.04	8.04	7
8	NEWCASTLE	25.01	9.10	25.09	29.04	4.12	6.11	18.04	X	20.05	29.12	25.03	11.03	8
9	NORTHAMPTON	22.04	22.01	12.02	30.10	2.10	11.09	13.11	26.12	X	25.03	9.10	6.05	9
10	SALE	2.10	26.12	13.11	12.02	8.04	22.04	22.01	6.05	16.10	X	30.10	11.09	10
11	SARACENS	29.12	2.10	20.05	25.01	22.04	4.12	11.09	16.10	8.04	11.03	X	6.11	11
12	WASPS	4.12	25.03	18.04	25.09	20.05	25.01	9.10	30.10	29.12	29.04	12.02	X	12

1 2 3 4 5 6 7 8 9 10 11 12 13 14

BATH F.C.

Chief Executive	Andrew Brownsword
Coach	Andrew Robinson
Ticket Office Manager	Clare Matthews
Marketing Manager	Andrew Brown
PR Manager	Helen Mercer
Youth Developement Manager	Gareth Adams

Bath Rugby,
11 Argyle Street,
Bath BA2 4BQ
01225 325200 (Office)
01225 325201 (Fax)

Bath Rugby saw a season which began with high hopes of building on their Heineken Cup success of the previous campaign gradually become a desperate dogfight to qualify for the chance to defend that crown in 1999/2000.
New signings Kevin Maggs, Ben Sturnham and Jim Fallon were brought into the squad, while American Eagles skipper Dan Lyle sat out the first half of the season with a cruciate ligament injury.
The league campaign began in style with seven wins out of eight starts, their only blemish being a last minute defeat at the hands of Jonny Wilkinson and Newcastle - the player and team destined to knock Bath out of the Tetley's Bitter Cup in early January.
After topping Allied Dunbar Premiership One early on, defeat by London Scottish at a rain-lashed Stoop Memorial Ground began Bath's winter of discontent, where they suffered a record-breaking run of six straight defeats.
Once again coach Andy Robinson was dogged by injury woes, his latest new signing, former All Black Jon Preston, lasting less than 30 minutes of league rugby before rupturing his Achilles tendon, while England centre Phil de Glanville saw his season all but ended after dislocating his shoulder against South Africa.
Bath managed to turn the season around, notching up morale-boosting league wins over Sale, Newcastle and Bedford before the pendulum swung once again for a record 35-0 defeat by Wasps at Loftus Road.
Three more victories followed, however, including Saracens at Vicarage Road and the notable scalp of champions-to-be Leicester at the Rec.
Tension began to rise as the season came to a close, defeats by London Irish, Northampton and Harlequins leaving Bath on a knife-edge regarding qualification for Europe.
Sixth-place in the Premiership was all-but secured, however, with a crushing 76-13 win over the doomed London Scottish in the last match of the season and Saracens did the rest by beating Newcastle the following week.

BATH

Match No.	Date	H/A	Comp.	Opponents	Result & Score	Att.	15	14	13	12	11
1	05.09	H	AD1	Wasps	W36-27	8,000	Balshaw	Evans	deGlanville	Guscott/2t(l)	A Adebayo
2	12.09	A	AD1	Newcastle	L 17-19	3,452	Balshaw	Evans	deGlanville	Guscott	A Adebayo/t
3	19.09	H	AD1	Richmond	W36-14	7,600	Balshaw	Evans	Maggs(b)	Guscott/2t	A Adebayo/t
4	26.09	H	AD1	Gloucester	W21-16	8,200	Perry	Evans	Maggs	de Glanville	A Adebayo/t(A)
5	03.10	H	AD1	Bedford	W57-19	6,000	Perry/t	Fallon	Maggs	Guscott/2t(b)	Balshaw/t
6	10.10	H	AD1	London Irish	W23-20	7,000	Perry	Fallon(b)	Maggs	Guscott	Balshaw/t
7	17.10	A	AD1	W Hartlepool	W50-20	1,743	Balshaw/t	Evans	deGlanville	Guscott/2t	Maggs
8	24.10	H	AD1	Sale*	W 27-3	6,800	Perry	Evans	Maggs	Guscott	Balshaw
9	31.10	A	AD1	London Scot	L 11-13	3,267	Perry	Evans	deGlanville	Guscott	A Adebayo
10	07.11	A	AD1	Leicester	L 13-36	15,873	Perry	Balshaw	Maggs	Guscott/t	A Adebayo
11	21.11	A	AD1	Harlequins	L 31-43	6,875	Balshaw/t	Evans(r)	Tindall	deGlanville	A Adebayo
12	12.12	H	AD1	Northampton	L 9-15	8,200	Balshaw	Evans	Maggs	Guscott	A Adebayo
13	19.12	H	AD1	Saracens	L 11-19	8,200	Perry	Balshaw/t	Maggs	Guscott	A Adebayo
14	02.01	A	AD1	Gloucester	L 7-23	10,109	Callard/c	Balshaw	Maggs	Guscott	A Adebayo/t
15	05.01	A	AD1	Sale	W32-30	3,500	Perry/2p	Balshaw	Maggs	Guscott/t	A Adebayo/t
16	16.01	H	AD1	Newcastle	W 16-11	8,200	Perry	Balshaw	Maggs	Guscott	A Adebayo
17	23.01	A	AD1	Bedford*	W30-17	3,673	Perry	Balshaw/t	Maggs	Guscott	A Adebayo/t
18	07.02	A	AD1	Wasps	L 0-35	9,526	Perry	Balshaw	Tindall	Guscott	A Adebayo
19	13.03	A	AD1	Richmond	W30-23	10,096	Perry	Balshaw	Maggs	Guscott	A Adebayo/t
20	28.03	A	AD1	Saracens	W33-14	14,219	Perry	Balshaw/3t	Tindall	Maggs	A Adebayo
21	03.04	H	AD1	Leicester*	W24-16	8,500	Perry	Balshaw/t	Tindall	Maggs	A Adebayo
22	17.04	A	AD1	London Irish	L 22-47	6,600	Perry	Balshaw	Maggs	Tindall/t	A Adebayo
23	24.04	H	AD1	W Hartlepool	W56-24	6,500	Perry/2t	Balshaw/2t	Maggs/t	Tindall/t	T Adebayo
24	01.05	A	AD1	Northampton	L 17-40	8,843	Perry	Balshaw	Maggs	Tindall/t	A Adebayo
25	08.05	H	AD1	Harlequins	L 13-17	8,200	Balshaw	Tindall	Maggs	Guscott	A Adebayo
26	15.05	H	AD1	London Scot	W76-13	4,800	Perry/2t	Balshaw/t	Maggs	Guscott/4t	A Adebayo(b)
A	09.01	A	TB4	Newcastle	L 22-25		Perry(a)	Balshaw	Maggs	Guscott	A Adebayo

* after opponents name indicates a penalty try
Brackets after a player's name indicates he was replaced. eg (a) means he was replaced by replacement code "a" and so on.
/ after a player or replacement name is followed by any scores he made - eg /t, /c, /p, /dg or any combination of these

1998-99 HIGHLIGHTS

League debuts:
Ben Sturnham, Kevin Maggs, Jon Preston, Steve Borthwick, Gary Cooper, Tikumbo Adebayo.

Ever Presents: None
Most appearances Mike Catt 24.

Players used: 32 plus 3 as replacement only.

Most Points in a season:

Pts	Player	T	C	P	DG
294	M Catt	7	50	53	-
70	J Guscott	14	-	-	-
65	I Balshaw	13	-	-	-
44	M Perry	6	1	4	-
35	A Adebayo	7	-	-	-

MATCH FACTS

10	9	1	2	3	4	5	6	7	8	
Catt/3c5p	Hatley(n)	Hilton(m)	Regan(k)	Ubogu	Redman	Haag	Thomas	Sturnham	Peters/t	1
Catt/4p	Hatley(n)	Hilton(o)	Long	Ubogu	Redman	Haag	THomas	Sturnham(p)	Peters	2
Catt/2c4p	Hatley(n/t)	Hilton	Long	Ubogu(o)	Redman	Sturnham	Thomas	Webster(q)	Peters	3
Catt/c3p	Nicol	Hilton(m)	Long/t(f)	Mallett	Redman	Sturnham	Thomas	Webster(q)	Peters	4
Catt/5c4p	Hatley/t(n)	Yates	Long(f)	Mallett(s)	Haag	Sturnham	Thomas(q)	Webster/2t(t)	Peters	5
Catt/c2p	Hatley	Yates	Long	Mallett(g)	Haag	Sturnham/2t	Thomas	Webster(t)	Peters(q)	6
Catt/t6cp	Hatley/2t	Hilton	Long(f)	Ubogu(m)	Redman	Haag	Thomas	Webster	Sturnham(q/t)	7
Catt/3c2p	Hatley(n/t)	Hilton(m)	Long(f)	Ubogu	Redman	Sturnham	Thomas	Webster/t	Peters	8
Catt/2p	Hatley(n/t)	Yates(e)	Regan	Ubogu	Redman	Haag	Thomas	Webster	Peters	9
Catt/c2p	Hatley	Hilton	Long	Ubogu	Redman	Sturnham	Thomas(q)	Webster	Peters	10
Preston/p(u/2c3p)	Nicol/t	Yates(o)	Long(f/t)	Ubogu	Redman(t)	Haag	Earnshaw	Webster(v)	Sturnham	11
Catt/3p	Hatley(n)	Hilton	Regan(k)	Ubogu	Redman	Sturnham	Earnshaw	Webster(j)	Lyle	12
Catt/2p	Nicol(d)	Hilton(o)	Long	Ubogu	Borthwick(i)	Redman	Earnshaw(h)	Peters	Lyle	13
Catt	Nicol(w)	Hilton(m)	Regan	Ubogu	Borthwick	Redman(i)	Webster	Peters	Lyle	14
Catt/t3c(a)	Cooper	Hilton/t(m)	Regan	Ubogu	Haag	Borthwick	Webster(i)	Peters(q)	Lyle	15
Catt/tc3p(a)	Hatley	Hilton	Regan(k)	Ubogu	Haag	Borthwick	Earnshaw	Webster	Lyle	16
Catt/3c3p	Hatley(x)	Hilton	Regan	Ubogu	Haag	Borthwick	Earnshaw	Webster	Lyle	17
Catt	Cooper(x)	Yates	Regan	Ubogu(o)	Haag(i)	Borthwick	Earnshaw	Webster	Lyle	18
Catt/c6p	Cooper	Hilton	Regan	Ubogu(o)	Haag	Borthwick	Earnshaw	Bryan	Lyle	19
Catt/4c	Cooper/t	Hilton(o)	Regan(z)	Ubogu	Haag	Borthwick	Earnshaw	Peters/t	Lyle	20
Catt/c4p	Cooper	Hilton	Regan	Ubogu(m)	Haag	Borthwick	Earnshaw	Peters(v)	Lyle	21
Catt/t2cp	Cooper(n)	Hilton	Regan/t	Ubogu(m)	Haag(i)	Borthwick	Earnshaw(p)	Bryan	Lyle	22
Catt/5c2p	Cooper/t	Hilton	Regan/t	Ubogu(m)	Haag	Borthwick	Thomas	Webster	Lyle(i)	23
Catt/tc(y)	Cooper	Hilton(m)	Regan	Ubogu	Haag	Borthwick	Thomas	Webster(q/t)	Lyle	24
Perry/c2p	Cooper	Hilton(m)	Regan	Ubogu	Haag	Borthwick	Earnshaw/t	Thomas	Lyle	25
Catt/2t8c	Cooper/t(n)	Hilton/t(m)	Regan/t(k)	Ubogu	Haag	Borthwick	Earnshaw	Thomas	Sturnham	26
Catt/t2cp	Cooper	Hilton(m)	Regan	Ubogu	Haag	Borthwick	Earnshaw/t(i)	Webster/t	Lyle	A

REPLACEMENTS:
a - I Evans, b - P de Glanville, c - A Adebayo, d - S Hatley, e - D Hilton, f - M Regan, g - V Ubogu,
h - N Thomas, i - B Sturnham, j - E Peters, k - A Long, l - K Maggs, m - K Yates, n - A Nicol, o - J Mallett,
p - R Webster, q - R Earnshaw, r - J Fallon, s - C Horsman, t - D Jones, u - J Callard, v - R Bryan, w - G Cooper,
x - A Gomersall, y - T Adebayo, z - L Mears

Mike Catt broke Jonathan Callard's record of 236 points in a season set back in 1995-96. It also put him 4th on the all time list on points in a top flight season. Included in his total was a record breaking 53 conversions - 8 better than the previous record set in 1995-96 by Jon Callard.
Callard did manage to hold on to his record of 51 conversions in a season but only just, Catt finished one short on 50.
Jeremy Guscott equalled the club record of four tries in a match in the last game of the season and pipped Iain Balshaw as the leading try scorer, 14 to 13. It was the 3rd time that Guscott has topped the try scorers list at the Rec.
Guscott passed Phil De Glanville and is the leading back in the league appearance list with 128.
In the away win at Richmond Catt equalled Jon Callard's record of six penalties in a league match.

In the away match at London Irish Bath conceded a record seven tries in a league match. The previous record was six at Saracens last season.
Bath equalled their worst ever run with six straight defeats mid season.

BATH

LEAGUE STATISTICS
compiled by Stephen McCormack

SEASON	Division	P	W	D	L	F	A	Pts Diff	Lge Pts	Lge Pos	Most Points	Most Tries
89-90	1	11	8	0	3	258	104	154	16	2	103 Stuart Barnes	10 Tony Swift
90-91	1	12	11	0	1	280	104	176	22	1	98 Stuart Barnes	6 Tony Swift
91-92	1	12	10	1	1	277	126	151	21	1	95 Stuart Barnes	8 Tony Swift
92-93	1	12	11	0	1	355	97	258	22	1	122 Jon Webb	7 Stuart Barnes
93-94	1	18	17	0	1	431	181	250	34	1	178 Jon Callard	5 Mike Catt & Ben Clarke
94-95	1	18	12	3	3	373	245	128	27	2	150 Jon Callard	5 Adedayo Adebayo
95-96	1	18	15	1	2	575	276	299	31	1	236 Jon Callard	9 Jeremy Guscott
96-97	1	22	15	1	6	863	411	452	31	2	224 Jon Callard	16 Adedayo Adebayo
97-98	1	22	13	0	9	575	455	120	26	3	183 Jon Callard	9 Andy Nicol
98-99	1	26	15	0	11	698	574	124	30	6	294 Mike Catt	14 Jeremy Guscott

BIGGEST MARGINS

Home Win	77pts - 84-7 v Sale 26.4.97
Away Win	43pts - 49-6 v Saracens 10.4.98
	- 56-13 v Orrell 31.8.96
Home Defeat	16pts - 13-29 v Saracens 10.4.98
Away Defeat	27pts - 23-50 v Saracens 14.12.97

MOST CONSECUTIVE

Appearances	50 Tony Swift 9.9.89-25.9.93
Matches scoring Tries	6 Andy Nicol, Adedayo Adebayo
Matches scoring points	15 Jon Callard
Victories	15
Defeats	6 (2)

MOST POINTS

Scored at Home	84 v Sale 26.4.97
Scored Away	56 v Orrell 31.8.96
	v Lon. Irsih 5.10.96
Conceded at Home	40 v Wasps 14.9.96
Conceded Away	50 v Saracens 14.12.97

MOST TRIES

Scored in a match	14 v Bedford 13.1.90
	v Sale 26.4.97
Conceded in a match	7 v London Irish 17.4.99

MOST APPEARANCES

by a forward	140 Nigel Redman
by a back	128 Jeremy Guscott

	MOST IN A SEASON	MOST IN A CAREER	MOST IN A MATCH	
Points	294 MikeCatt 98-99	1044 Jon Callard 89-99	26 Stuart Barnes	v W. Hartlepool 27.3.93 (A)
			Mike Catt	v Sale 26.4.97 (H)
				v London Scot 15.5.99 (H)
Tries	16 Adedayo Adebayo 96-97	67 Jeremy Guscott 85-99	4 Jeremy Guscott	v Bedford 13.1.90 (H)
			Jeremy Guscott	v London Scot 15.5.99 (H)
			Tony Swift	v Bedford 13.1.90 (H)
Conversions	51 Jon Callard 96-97	170 Jon Callard 89-98	10 Stuart Barnes	v Bedford 13.1.90 (H)
Penalties	53 Mike Catt 99-99	196 Jon Callard 89-98	6 Jon Callard	v Harlequins 6.4.96 (H)
			Mike Catt	v Richmond 13.3.99 (A)
Drop Goals	2 Stuart Barnes 87-88	9 Stuart Barnes 87-94	1 by seven players	incl. Stuart Barnes (x9)
	Mike Catt 96-97			

BATH PLAYING SQUAD

BACKS

	Ht.	Wt.	Birthdate	Birthplace	CLUB	League Apps	Tries	Pts
Matt Perry England .	5.10	13.07	27.01.77	Bath	Bath	44(6)	13	79
Adedayo Adebayo England , A.	5.9	14.07	30.11.70	Ibadan	Bath	119(1)	50	244
Jeremy Guscott England , British Lions 8.	6.1	13.10	07.07.65	Bath	Bath	128	67	333
Phil de Glanville England , A.	5.11	13.06	01.10.68	Loughborough	Bath	118(5)	24	11
Andy Nicol Scotland , A.	5.11	13.04	12.03.71	Dundee	Bath	46(9)	24	123
Mike Catt England , A.	5.10	13.00	17.09.71	Port Elizabeth	Bath	100	27	514
Ieuan Evans Wales .	5.9	13.10	21.03.64	Capel Dewi	Bath	26(2)	8	40
Kevin Maggs England A.	5.11	14.00	03.06.74	Bristol	Bath	21(2)	1	5
Jon Callard England .	5.10	12.07	01.06.66	Leicester	Bath	96(5)	24	1042
Iain Belshaw England U21 Colts.	6.1	13.02	14.04.79	Lancashire	Bath	27(6)	14	72
Matt Tindall	6.2	14.07	18.10.78		Bath	1(8)	3	15
Gary Cooper	5.7	12.00	07.05.79	Bridgend	Bath	10(1)	3	15
Stephen Hatley	6.1	14.06	16.08.72	South Africa	Bath	15(3)	3	15
Jon Preston New Zealand	5.10	12.12	15.11.67	Dunedin	Bath	1	-	3

FORWARDS

	Ht.	Wt.	Birthdate	Birthplace	CLUB	League Apps	Tries	Pts
Dave Hilton Scotland .	5.10	15.04	03.04.70	Bristol	Bath	68(9)	5	25
					Bristol	16	-	-
Kevin Yates England , A.	5.11	16.02	06.11.72	Medicene Hut	Bath	37(15)	4	20
John Mallett England .	6.1	17.10	28.05.70	Lincoln	Bath	44(19)	2	9
Victor Ubogu England , A.	5.9	17.00	08.09.64	Lagos	Bath	119(13)	13	61
Mark Regan England .	5.1	16.02	28.01.72	Bristol	Bath	27(11)	5	25
					Bristol	66	4	20
Andrew Long England1.	5.11	15.08	02.09.78	Poole	Bath	16(11)	1	5
Martin Haag England , A, B.	6.5	16.07	28.07.68	Chelmsford	Bath	126(2)	8	38
Nigel Redman England .	6.4	17.02	16.08.64	Cardiff	Bath	140	10	46
Steve Borthwick	6.6	15.12	12.10.79	Carlisle	Bath	15	-	-
Dan Lyle US Eagles	6.5	17.12	28.07.70	San Diego	Bath	32(1)	7	35
Nathan Thomas Wales .	6.3	15.07	22.01.76	Bridgend	Bath	34(5)	2	10
Eric Peters Scotland , A, England Students	6.5	16.04	28.01.69	Glasgow	Bath Saracens	51(7)	12	60
Russell Earnshaw	6.4	15.03	08.04.75	Billingham	Bath	28(10)	8	40
					W Hartlepool	9	3	15
Richard Webster Wales 13.Salford RL.	6.2	17.00	09.07.76	Morriston	Bath Swansea	39(2)	9	45
Richard Bryan	6.3	16.00	21.01.77	Bristol	Bath	12(5)	-	-

BATH

FACT FILE

Founded: 1865
Colours: Blue with black and white
Change colours: Black with white and blue
Website: www.bathrugby.co.uk

GROUND The Recreation Ground, Bath. BA2 6PW.
Telephone: 01225 325200 Fax: 01225 325201 e-mail: enquiries@bathrugby
Capacity:7,622 Seated: (covered) 2,044 (uncovered) 3,696 Standing: 1,868
+ 560 in corporate boxes (8,182)

Directions: Follow signs to Bath City Centre and then signs to the Recreation Ground.
Nearest Railway Station: Bath Spa (BR). From station walk up Manvers St. towards centre of town. Turn right into North Parade & left down steps.

Car Parking: None on ground, unlimited `Park & Ride'.

Admission Matchdays: Variable depending upon fixture
Season Tickets:
From £85 Junior to £385 covered seating

Club Shop: 1 Argyle Street, Bath BA2 4BA
Tel: 01225 311950.

Clubhouse: Matchdays 11-11
Snacks & bar meals are available.
Functions: Capacity 250-300
Contact Humphrey Sheppard 01225 469230

PROGRAMME Size: A5
Pages: 48 + cover
Price: £2.00
Editor: 01225 325200

ADVERTISING RATES
Colour
Page £1800
1/2 page £970
1/4 page £520

Former New Zealand International, Jon Preston, managed less than half a game before injury wrecked his season.

BEDFORD R.U.F.C.

Chief Executive	Doug Braddock	Bedford Rugby 33-35 St Peters St. Beford MK40 2PN Tel: 01234 347980 Fax: 01234 347511
General Manager	Kathy Leather	
Press Officer	Philip August	

Bedford retained their Allied Dunbar Premiership One status by the narrowest of margins, beating Rotherham by virtue of scoring more tries in the two leg play offs last May.
The season was difficult from the outset, with Frank Warren's Sports Network, the club's then owners, fighting an expensive court case with American boxing promoter Don King. The players were often paid late and key personnel such as Paul Turner and Geoff Cook left before Christmas.
South African Rudi Straeuli became director of rugby and he and captain Alistair Murdoch ensured that the players stayed focused in rugby. Straeuli's man management and motivational skills were awesome and he was highly respected by players and supporters alike.
Losses at home to West Hartlepool in the League and Henley in the Tetley's Bitter Cup during December and January were the two low points and, thanks to four loan signings financed by local businessmen, vital league wins and a second successive Cheltenham and Gloucester Cup Final bought some cheer.
Beating West Hartlepool away 39-0 on 2nd May guaranteed that Bedford would not be automatically relegated and had the opportunity to end the season, with new owners, by determining their own fate - they did, but just.

PHILIP AUGUST

Bedford prior to their C&G Cup Final v Gloucester, April 1999

Back Row: Richard Elliott. Joe Ewens, Roy Winters, Alex Codling, Andy Duke, Richard Candin, Jason Forster, Aaron Davis.
Middle: Junior Paramore, Dan Zaltman, Phil Elphick, Paul Hewitt, Ben Whetstone, Virgil Hartland, Adrian Olver, James Cockle, Scott Stewart, Gareth Davies, Nick Randall.
Front: Darragh O'Mahony, Sam Howard, Charlie Harrison, Tony Yapp, Alastair Murdoch (Captain), Rudi Straeuli (Dir. of Rugby), Altan Ozdemir, Jimmy Richards, Dan Harris, Tabo Huntley (Fitness Advisor)

BEDFORD

Match No.	Date	H/A	Comp.	Opponents	Result & Score	Att.	15	14	13	12	11
1	12.09	A	AD1	Sale	L 21-39	2,114	Howard/tc3p	Underwood	Murdoch	Ewens	O'Mahony/t
2	19.09	H	AD1	London Scot	W 24-16	2,347	Howard/c3p	Underwood/t	Murdoch	Ewens	O'Mahony
3	26.09	H	AD1	Leicester	L 23-32	4,165	Howard/2c3p	Underwood/t	Murdoch	Ewens	O'Mahony
4	03.10	A	AD1	Bath	L 19-57	6,000	Howard/t2c	Underwood/t	Murdoch	Ewens	O'Mahony/t
5	10.10	H	AD1	Harlequins	W 35-33	3,521	Howard/3c2p	Underwood	Murdoch	Ewens/2t	O'Mahony/2t
6	17.10	A	AD1	Northampton	L 29-34	6,739	Howard/3cp	Underwood/2t	Murdoch	Ewens/t	O'Mahony
7	21.10	A	AD1	Wasps	L 19-35	3,216	Howard/c3p	Underwood	Ewens	Whetstone	O'Mahony
8	24.10	H	AD1	Newcastle	L 22-29	3,902	Howard	Whetstone	Murdoch	Ewens	O'Mahony
9	31.10	A	AD1	Richmond	L 32-38	6,541	Howard/3c2p	Whetstone	Murdoch	Ewens	O'Mahony/3t
10	07.11	A	AD1	Gloucester	L 21-31	5,147	Howard/3c	Underwood	Murdoch	Ewens	O'Mahony(p)
11	14.11	H	AD1	Saracens	L 20-25	5,125	Howard/2c2p	Whetstone	Murdoch	Ewens(q)	Underwood/t
12	21.11	A	AD1	London Irish	L 19-30	2,200	Howard/2c	Whetstone/t	Murdoch	Ewens/t	Underwood/t
13	12.12	H	AD1	W Hartlepool	L 10-23	2,398	Howard/t(b)	Whetstone	Murdoch	Ewens/t	O'Mahony
14	26.12	A	AD1	Leicester	L 0-26	10,689	Whetstone	Underwood	Murdoch	Harris(c)	O'Mahony
15	02.01	A	AD1	Saracens	L 13-44	6,593	Whetstone	Underwood	Murdoch	Harris	O'Mahony
16	05.01	A	AD1	Newcastle	L 23-34	2,070	Whetstone	Underwood/2t	Murdoch	Harris	O'Mahony
17	23.01	H	AD1	Bath	L 17-30	3,673	Whetstone(a/c)	Underwood	Murdoch/t	Harris	O'Mahony
18	13.02	H	AD1	Wasps	W 25-23	3,440	Stewart/t	Underwood/t	Murdoch	Harris	O'Mahony
19	27.02	H	AD1	Sale	L 7-18	3,139	Stewart	Underwood	Murdoch	Harris(c)	O'Mahony
20	13.03	A	AD1	London Scot	W 24-15	1,273	Stewart	Whetstone	Murdoch(b/t)	Harris	O'Mahony
21	27.03	H	AD1	Gloucester	W 19-15	2,417	Stewart	Underwood	Murdoch	Harris	O'Mahony
22	17.04	A	AD1	Harlequins	L 16-29	3,828	Stewart	Underwood/t(p)	Murdoch	Harris	O'Mahony
23	24.04	H	AD1	Northampton	L 31-42	4,689	Stewart/c	Whetstone(b)	Murdoch/t	Harris	O'Mahony/t(c/t)
24	02.05	A	AD1	W Hartlepool	W 39-0	1,400	Stewart	Whetstone	Murdoch	Harris(c/t)	O'Mahony/3t
25	08.05	H	AD1	London Irish	L 21-36	3,572	Stewart	Whetstone	Ewens	Murdoch	O'Mahony(b/t)
26	16.05	H	AD1	Richmond	L12-106	1,308	Hinkins(z)	Wells	Abrahams(A)	Howard/c	Kirkby(C)
A	10.01	H	TB4	Henley	L 22-29	1,806	Whetstone/2t	Underwood	Ewens	Harris	O'Mahony
B	20.05	A	ADpo	Rotherham	L 11-19	3,500	Stewart	Whetstone	Murdoch	Harris	O'Mahony
C	23.05	H	ADpo	Rotherham	W 27-19	4,102	Stewart	Whetstone	Murdoch/t	Harris	O'Mahony/t

* after opponents name indicates a penalty try
Brackets after a player's name indicates he was replaced. eg (a) means he was replaced by replacement code "a" and so on.
/ after a player or replacement name is followed by any scores he made - eg /t, /c, /p, /dg or any combination of these

1998-99 HIGHLIGHTS

League debuts:
Darragh O'Mahony, Charlie Harrison, Andy Duke, Virgil Hartland, Danny Zaltman, Rob Ashforth, Dan Harris, Phil Elphick, Chris Cano, Joe Beardshaw, Richard Ward, Altan Ozdemir, Scott Stewart, Aaron Davis, Adrian Olver, Alex Codling, Matthew Cook, Richard Candlin, Mark Kirkby, Justin Abrahams, Jim Hinkins.

Ever Presents: None
Most appearances 25 Jimmy Richards.

Players used: 41 plus 5 as replacement only.

Most Points in a season:

Pts	Player	T	C	P	DG
134	S Howard	3	28	20	1
120	T Yapp	3	15	20	5
60	T Underwood	12	-	-	-
55	D O'Mahony	11	-	-	-
35	J Ewens	7	-	-	-

MATCH FACTS

10	9	1	2	3	4	5	6	7	8	
Yapp	Harrison	Hatley	Richards	Boyd	Duke	Murray	Winters(i)	Forster	Straeuli	1
Yapp/tdg	Harrison	Hatley	Richards	Boyd	Duke(j)	Murray	Winters(k)	Forster	Straeuli	2
Yapp	Harrison	Hatley	Richards	Boyd	Duke(j)	Murray	Winters(k)	Forster/t	Straeuli	3
Yapp	Crabbe(d)	Hatley	Richards	Boyd(i)	Zaltman	Murray	Deans(g)	Forster	Cockle	4
Yapp/dg	Harrison	Hatley	Richards	Boyd	Zaltman	Murray	Cockle	Forster	Paramore	5
Yapp	Harrison	Hatley	Richards	Boyd	Zaltman	Murray	Cockle/t	Forster	Paramore	6
Yapp/dg	Harrison	Hatley	Richards	Boyd(i)	Zaltman	Murray(f)	Paramore	Forster/t	Straeuli	7
Yapp/c5p	Harrison(o)	Hatley	Richards	Hartland(e)	Duke	Zaltman	Cockle(n)	Forster	Paramore/t	8
Yapp	Harrison	Hatley	Richards	Boyd	Zaltman	Murray	Cockle(n)	Forster	Paramore/t	9
Yapp/t	Harrison	Boyd	Richards	Hartland	Zaltman/t	Murray	Cockle	Forster/t	Winters	10
Yapp	Harrison	Boyd	Richards	Hartland	Zaltman	Winters	Cockle	Elphick	Paramore/t	11
Ashforth	Harrison(o)	Boyd	Richards	Hartland(s)	Ward	Beardshaw	Cockle(g)	Forster	Paramore	12
Yapp	Harrison	Ozdemir(s)	Richards	Hartland	Ward	Beardshaw	Winters(k)	Forster	Paramore	13
Yapp	Elliott	Ozdemir	Richards	Hartland(e)	Beardshaw(k)	Murray	Winters	Forster	Paramore	14
Yapp/c2p	Elliott	Ozdemir	Richards	Boyd	Zaltman(t)(i)	Murray	Cockle	Forster	Paramore/t	15
Yapp/cpdg(a)	Elliott	Boyd	Richards	Hartland	Zaltman(f)	Murray	Cockle	Forster/t	Winters	16
Yapp	Elliott/t	Boyd	Richards	Hartland(u)	Zaltman/t	Murray	Cockle	Forster	Paramore	17
Howard/2cpdg	Elliott	Boyd	Richards/t	Hartland(u)	Zaltman(g)	Murray	Cockle	Forster	Paramore	18
Howard/c	Elliott	Ozdemir(w)	Richards	Boyd	Codling(k)	Murray	Winters	Forster	Paramore/t	19
Yapp/c4p	Harrison	Olver	Richards	Boyd(u)	Codling	Murray	Winters	Forster/t	Paramore(k)	20
Yapp/c4p	Harrison	Ozdemir	Richards(v/t)	Olver	Zaltman	Murray(x)	Cockle	Forster	Paramore	21
Yapp/c3p	Harrison	Olver	Richards	Boyd	Duke	Murray	Elphick	Forster	Winters	22
Yapp/2c	Elliott(d)	Olver/t(i)	Richards(v)	Boyd	Zaltman	Codling(f)(y)	Cockle	Forster/t	Winters	23
Yapp/4cpdg	Elliott	Olver	Richards	Boyd	Zaltman/t	Murray	Cockle	Forster	Winters	24
Yapp/t3c	Elliott(d/t)	Boyd(u)	Richards(v)	Hartland	Zaltman	Murray(f)	Cockle	Forster(r)	Winters	25
Ashforth	Crabbe(D)	Ozdemir	Davis	Cano	Codling	Candlin(h)	Elphick(B)	Hewitt	Cook/2t	26
Yapp/c	Harrison(l)	Boyd	Richards	Hartland	Zaltman	Murray	Winters	Forster/2t	Straeuli(k)	A
Yapp/2p	Crabbe(d)	Olver	Richards	Boyd	Zaltman	Murray	Cockle	Forster/t	Winters	B
Yapp/3cpdg	Crabbe	Olver	Richards	Boyd	Zaltman	Murray	Cockle	Forster/t	Winters	C

REPLACEMENTS:						
a- S Howard	b- R Underwood	c-J Ewens	d-C Harrison	e-C Boyd	f-A Duke	g-R Winters
h-R Straeuli	i-V Hartland	j-D Zaltman	k-J Cockle	l-S Crabbe	m-R Ashforth	n-M Deans
o-R Elliott	p-B Whetstone	q-D Harris	r-P Elphick	s-C Cano	t-J Beardshaw	u-A Ozdemir
v-A Davis	w-A Olver	x-A Codling	y-P Hewitt	z-M Mainwaring	A-B Watts	B-L Gibbons
C-S Burton	D- T Wood					

Fly half Tony Yapp set a new club record for drop goals in a season. He kicked 5 which beat Andy Finnie's record of 4 which he achieved twice.

Winger/centre Ben Whetstone became the first Bedford back to reach 100 league appearances. He also added to his club record 47 tries with a try at London Irish.

In the last league match of the season Bedford put out a weakened side with the play off's looming. They gave five players league debuts and were thrashed 106-12 by Richmond. It was a record score in the top flight and the first time a side had scored 100 points in a match.

They conceded a record 16 tries and also lost by a record 94 points.

Their Premiership one status was taken to the wire by Rotherham and in the end it came down to tries scored as the tie ended level on points after the two legs. With Bedford scoring four tries to Rotherham's three they just sneaked it.

Sam Howard and Tony Yapp became the third and fourth players to score 100 points in a league season for Bedford.

BEDFORD

LEAGUE STATISTICS
compiled by Stephen McCormack

SEASON	Division	P	W	D	L	F	A	Pts Diff	Lge Pts	Lge Pos	Most Points	Most Tries
89-90	1	11	0	0	11	70	467	-397	0	12r	13 Richard Creed	3 Mark Howe
90-91	2	12	4	2	6	138	203	-65	10	8	78 Andy Finnie	3 Tim Young
91-92	2	12	4	0	8	168	204	-36	8	10	92 Andy Finnie	5 Mark Rennell
92-93	2	12	6	2	4	185	186	3	14	7r	75 Andy Finnie	3 Mark Rennell
93-94	3	18	12	0	6	332	260	72	24	3	172 Andy Finnie	8 Vince Turner
94-95	3	18	13	1	4	421	250	172	27	1p	228 Andy Finnie	6 Ben Whetstone
95-96	2	18	5	1	12	289	520	-231	11	10	85 Andy Finnie	8 Matt Oliver
96-97	2	22	15	0	7	720	482	238	30	4	238 Mike Rayer	13 Ben Whetstone
97-98	2	22	20	0	2	791	365	426	40	1p	289 Mike Rayer	17 Ben Whetstone
98-99	P1	26	6	0	20	541	840	-299	12	13	134 Sam Howard	12 Rory Underwood

BIGGEST MARGINS

Home Win	55pts - 64-9 v Moseley 2.11.96
Away Win	60pts - 67-7 v Fylde 27.12.97
Home Defeat	94pts - 106-12 v Richmond 16.5.99
Away Defeat	76 - 0-76 v Bath 13.1.90

MOST CONSECUTIVE

Appearances	46 Paul Alston 19.9.92-12.4.95
Matches scoring Tries	6 Ben Whetstone & Martin Offiah
Matches scoring points	36 Andy Finnie
Victories	18
Defeats	14

MOST POINTS

Scored at Home	72 v Blackheath 22.2.97 & 25.4.98
Scored Away	67 v Fylde 27.12.97
Conceded at Home	106 v Richmond 16.5.99
Conceded Away	76 v Bath 13.1.90

MOST TRIES

Scored in a match	11 v Blackheath 22.2.97
Conceded in a match	16 v Richmond 16.5.99 (H)

MOST APPEARANCES

by a forward	97 Mark Upex
by a back	106 Ben Whetstone

	MOST IN A SEASON	MOST IN A CAREER	MOST IN A MATCH	
Points	289 Mike Rayer 97-98	867 Andy Finnie 87-96	25 Andy Finnie	v Coventry 27.3.93 (H)
Tries	17 Ben Whetstone 96-97	48 Ben Whetstone 92-99	4 Jason Forster	v Fylde 17.1.98
Conversions	67 Mike Rayer 96-97	127 Mike rayer 96-98	8 Mike Rayer	v Coventry 8.11.97 (H)
Penalties	56 Andy Finnie 94-95	203 Andy Finnie 87-96	7 Andy Finnie	v Coventry 27.4.94 (H)
Drop Goals	5 Tony Yapp 98-99	22 Andy Finnie 87-96	2 Andy Finnie	v Coventry 27.3.94 (H) v Clifton 14.1.95 (A)

BEDFORD PLAYING SQUAD

BACKS

Name	Ht.	Wt.	Birthdate	Birthplace	CLUB	League Apps	Tries	Pts
Charlie Harrison	5.10	12.0	06.09.72	Chippenham	Bedford Bath	15(3) 8(5)	1 1	5 5
Ben Whetstone	5.11	14.7	29.06.70	Holbeach	Bedford	106(2)	48	243
Darragh O'Mahoney	5.9	11.0	18.08.72	Cork	Bedford Moseley	23 33	11 32	55 160
Rory Underwood	5.9	13.8	19.06.63	Middlesborough	Bedford Leicester	39(5) 97(3)	19 43	95 192
Tony Yapp	5.10	12.6	26.07.77	Ludlow	Bedford Worcester	34(3)	5	133
John Wells	5.7	13.0	06.09.76	Kent	Bedford	3	-	-
Alastair Murdoch	6.1	14.7	09.05.67	Sydney	Bedford	38(1)	10	50
Dan Harris	5.10	13.12	17.05.77	H Wycombe	Bedford Moseley	11(1) 33	- 7	- 35
Richard Elliott	5.8	12.01	05.01.74	Durham	Bedford	9(2)	1	5
Simon Crabb	5.9	13.5	04.03.70	Hamilton (NZ)	Bedford	6(2)	3	15
Scott Stewart Canada.	6.2	13.3	16.01.69	Vancouver	Bedford Harlequins	8 14(2)	1 1	7 5
Jim Hinkins	6.1	13.7	11.05.77		Bedford	1(1)	-	-
Ryan O'Neil	6.3	14.0	19.09.76	Hampstead	Bedford	2	1	5
Joe Eewns England u21, 18, 16.	6.0	13.0	16.12.77	Bristol	Bedford Bath	21(4) 1(1)	10 -	50 -
Sam Howard	6.0	13.7	31.07.74	Gravesend	Bedford Blackheath	16(3) 56	3 6	134 349

FORWARDS

Name	Ht.	Wt.	Birthdate	Birthplace	CLUB	League Apps	Tries	Pts
Clem Boyd	6.1	18.7	08.11.73	Belfast	Bedford	42(5)	2	10
Chris Cano	5.10	16.05	25.01.77		Bedford	1(2)	-	-
Neal Hatley	6.0	19.2	23.12.69	Chorley	Bedford	24(2)	2	10
Aaron Davis	5.11	15.0	10.11.78	Luton	Bedford	1(3)	1	5
Scot Murray	6.6	16.7	15.01.76	Musselburgh	Bedford	57	7	35
Danny Zaltman Other club: Saracens	6.6	17.6	26.12.76	Hendon	Bedford Coventry	16(3) 12	3 -	15 -
Jason Forster	6.0	15.4	25.02.71	Derby	Bedford	44(1)	20	100
Junior Paramore	6.3	17.0	18.11.68	Apia (WS)	Bedford	48	18	90
Andy Duke	6.7	17.2	28.01.74		Bedford Newbury	5(4) 41	- 5	- 25
Virgil Hartland Other club: W Hartlepool 8(1)/-/-	5.10	15.02	23.04.77	Cinderford	Bedford Coventry	10(5) 5(2)	- -	- -
Rudi Straeuli	6.3	17.4	20.08.63	Pretoria(SA)	Bedford	17(3)	1	5
Jimmy Richards	5.9	15.3	11.09.75	Pembroke	Bedford	32(1)	1	5
Roy Winters	6.4	16.0	13.12.75	Cuckfield	Bedford	47(9)	5	25
Matt Deans	6.3	18.0	27.05.71	Zimbabwe	Bedford	45(15)	8	40
James Cockle	6.3	16.6	29.10.76	Clifton	Bedford Moseley	16(5) 26(2)	1 2	5 10

BEDFORD

FACT FILE

Founded: 1886 **Colours**: Oxford and Cambridge blue hoops

Nickname: The Blues **Change colours:** Cambridge blue

GROUND

Address: Goldington Road, Bedford. MK40 3NF.

Tel: 01234 348086 e-mail: info@bedford.rugby.co.uk

Capacity: 7,500 Seated: 3,000 (covered) 1,500 (uncovered) Standing: 3,000

Directions: M1 Jnc 13, to Bedford, follow signs for Cambridge A428 (Not bypass),over River Bridge, left into The Embankment, 3rd right into Bushmead Avenue,continue to junction, ground opposite.
Nearest Railway Station: Bedford Station. - one mile from the ground.

Car Parking: Approx 100 at the ground. Charge £2.

Admission: Match-day admission
£18 seated, £12 standing - concessions available
Season Tickets
available for seats only, £225 + £25 membership.

Club Shop: 33-35 St Peters St. & at ground
9-5pm Monday to Friday, 9-12.30 Saturday.
Contact Midd Lisa Elliott 01234 347980.

Clubhouse: Open during normal licensing hours. Two bars.
Snacks are available.

Functions: Up to 150, contact Mrs Helen Lovell 01234 363177.

PROGRAMME

Size: B5 Pages: Varies Price: £2.00
Editor: Philip August

ADVERTISING RATES
Contact Kathy Leather

LEFT
Sam Howard, Bedford's leading points scorer in season 98-99

RIGHT
Darragh O'Mahony, scored for the Blues on his debut against Manchester Sale.

BRISTOL R.F.C.

Chairman	Malcolm Pearce
Chief Executive	Nick de Scossa
Directors	John Rushton, John Newman
Non-Executive Directors	Stuart Smith (Company Secretary), Jack Rowell, Geoff Dunford
Commercial Director	Mike Turner
Club Secretary	Katie Turner
Registered Office	Bristol Rugby Limited, James Street West, Green Park, Bath BA1 2BU. Tel: 01225 320 809, Fax: 01225 448 390. E-mail: lcoles@jnggroup.co.uk
Director of Rugby	Bob Dwyer, Memorial Stadium, Horfield, Bristol. BS7 0AQ. Tel: 0117 908 5500, Fax: 0117 907 4682.
Press & P.R.	Ian & Sandy Bell, Bristol Rugby Press Office, Summerfield, Bristol Rd., Chew Stoke, Somerset. BS40 8UB. Tel: 01275 333128 Mobile: 07050 107918 Fax: 01275. 332316, E-mail: tintinna@aol.com
Matchday Press Officer	John Harding

Relegation to Premiership Two after a play-off defeat at the hands of London Scottish was not the worst of Bristol's problems. Only an 11th hour rescue by Malcolm Pearce saved the club from potential oblivion.

Even then, Bob Dwyer, newly appointed as Director of Rugby, had just 22 days to prepare a squad for the opening game of the season at Exeter in which eight players made their debut. And victory that afternoon by 22-15 was the first of seven successive league wins in a row.

Bristol's first season outside the top flight brought with it a number of trips to clubs for the very first time. One such was Rotherham - a visit Bristol will want to forget, as they tasted their first defeat of the season by a 16-5 margin. But three more league victories were chalked up before the next defeat, going down 20 - 9 at Worcester in December, a game in which the Austrialian International David Knox was sent off for dissent in the 18th minute.

The signing of Luke Nabaro looked a shrewd move, as he scored five tries in a 50 -17 victory over Blackheath. He went on to score 13 tries in six games by the end of the season.

Two tries, from Nabaro and the newly recruited Cambridge Blue Centre, Mark Robinson, during six minutes of injury time on the first ever visit to Fylde meant Bristol snatched a crucial 43-39 victory to stay top of the table.

It helped set up a memorable last Saturday of the season when Rotherham went to the top of the table with a 27 - 0 victory at home to Moseley. They led by two points, but the points difference was astonishingly identical.

More than seven thousand fans packed the Memorial Stadium hoping for victory over Worcester. Tries from flanker Christian Evans and lock Chad Eagle, plus a conversion and three penalties from full back Michael Horak, secured a famous 22 -11 victory which brought with it the Championship and promotion back to Premiership One.

In the Tetley's Bitter Cup, Bristol ran in nine tries in their 55-nil demolition of Jewson Two North side Sandal in the third round, only to fall at the next hurdle 43 -19 to London Irish. In the Cheltenham & Gloucester Cup Bristol win 66 -17 at home to Wakefield and 35-24 at College Grove to progress to the second round only for a below strength side to lose 50-3 at home to Northampton.

Back Row : Adam Larkin, Justin Wring, Scott Morgan, Jim Brownrigg, Gavin Giles, Al Charron, Christian Evans, Scott Lines, Mark Gabey, David Knox. **Third Row:** Keith James (physio), Phil Adams (team manager), Donna Sanderson (physio), Stean Williams, Mike McCarrick, Mark Griffiths, Craig Short, Simon Emms, Thompson Tapsell, Dawson Tamati, Paul Whittaker, George Davis, Carlos Hassan, Dean Ryan (forwards coach), Darryl Jones (backs coach), Bob Dwyer (Director of Rugby), Mark Spivey (fitness coach). **Second Row:** Mark Evans, George Leaupepe, Kevin Dunn, Dean Dewdney, Paul Hull, Chad Eagle, Simon Martin, Jon Evans, Ben Breeze, Sean Marsden, Gareth Pughe.
Front Row: Pablo Lemoine, Jonathan Pritchard, James Averis, Michael Misson, Ross Blake, Tom Jenkins, Gareth Baber

BRISTOL

MATCH FACTS

Match No.	Date	H/A	Comp.	Opponents	Result & Score	Att.	15	14	13	12	11
1	05.09	A	AD2	Exeter	W22-15	1,690	Marsden	Higgs	Martin	Pritchard	Breeze/t
2	12.09	H	AD2	Fylde	W55-14	4,527	Marsden/3t	Larkin	Barnard	Pritchard	Breeze
3	19.09	A	AD2	Rugby Lions	W30-20	763	Marsden	Barlow	Barnard	Pritchard/t	Breeze
4	26.09	H	AD2	London Welsh	W 37-3	3,459	Barlow/t	Misson	Barnard	Pritchard	Breeze/t(n/t)
5	03.10	A	AD2	Blackheath	W 41-9	1,150	Barlow	Misson	Martin/t	Barnard(c)	Larkin/3t
6	10.10	H	AD2	Orrell	W29-19	3,477	Marsden/t(q)	Misson/t	Barnard	Pritchard	Larkin
7	17.10	A	AD2	Leeds Tykes	W16-13	700	Hull/c3p	Misson	Barnard	Pritchard	Larkin
8	24.10	A	AD2	Rotherham	L 5-16		Marsden	Misson	Martin/t	Pritchard	Breeze
9	30.10	H	AD2	Coventry	W14-12	4,683	Breeze	Misson	Martin(c)	Leaupepe	Larkin/t
10	07.11	A	AD2	Wakefield	W46-15	450	Breeze/2t	Misson/t	Martin(c)	Leaupepe	Larkin/2t
11	22.11	H	AD2	Moseley	W58-18	2,304	Breeze/t(a)	Misson/2t	Barnard/t(b)	Leaupepe	Larkin/tc
12	12.12	A	AD2	Worcester	L 9-20	3,900	Hull/3p	Misson	Hassan	Leaupepe	Larkin
13	19.12	H	AD2	Waterloo	W 36-8	2,397	Hull/t(c)	Breeze	Leaupepe	Hassan/t(q)	Larkin/2t
14	02.01	A	AD2	Moseley	W 43-6	961	Hull/3c(a/t)	Misson/2t	Leaupepe	Hassan	Larkin/2t
15	16.01	H	AD2	Wakefield*	W35-19	2,516	Larkin	Higgs	Martin	Pritchard	Breeze
16	06.02	H	AD2	Rotherham*	L 31-36	2,496	Hull	Misson	Larkin(b)	Pritchard/t	Breeze
17	13.02	H	AD2	Leeds Tykes	W 20-5	2,012	Hull/p	Misson	Martin	Pritchard	Breeze
18	21.02	A	AD2	Coventry*	L 19-22	1,500	Hull	Misson/t	Martin(z)	Pritchard	Breeze
19	27.02	A	AD2	Orrell	W34-32	1,000	Hull	Misson	Hassan	Pritchard	Breeze
20	13.03	H	AD2	Blackheath	W50-17	2,353	Hull/4c(a)	Misson(c)	Robinson	Hassan/tc	Nabarro/5t
21	27.03	A	AD2	London Welsh	W 25-6		Hull/2c2p	Misson(c)	Robinson/t	Whitaker	Nabarro/2t
22	03.04	H	AD2	Rugby Lions	W49-13	2,615	Hull/t3cp	Misson	Robinson	Whitaker	Nabarro/3t(i)
23	17.04	A	AD2	Fylde	W43-39	700	Hull/tc2p	Nabarro/2t	Robinson/2t	Leaupepe	Horak(s/t)
24	24.04	H	AD2	Exeter	W36-17	3,204	Hull/3c(k)	Larkin/t	Robinson/t	Leaupepe/t	Breeze
25	01.05	A	AD2	Waterloo	W44-13	900	Horak/4cp	Larkin	Robinson(a)	Pritchard	Nabarro/t
26	09.05	H	AD2	Worcester	W21-11	7,326	Horak/c3p	Nabarro	Leaupepe	Pritchard	Breeze
A	15.11	H	TBC	Sandal	W 55-0	1,869	Breeze	Larkin	Martin(C/t)	Pritchard(a/t)	Barlow/t
B	10.01	H	TBC	London Irish	L 19-43	6,200	Hull/2c	Misson	Leaupepe	Hassan	Larkin

* after opponents name indicates a penalty try
Brackets after a player's name indicates he was replaced. eg (a) means he was replaced by replacement code "a" and so on.
/ after a player or replacement name is followed by any scores he made - eg /t, /c, /p, /dg or any combination of these

1998-99 HIGHLIGHTS

League debuts:
Sean Marsden, Chris Higgs, Simon Emms, Jon Evans, Neil Watkins, Mark Bennett, Christian Evans, Andre Barnard, Tim Barlow, Michael Misson, Mark Gabey, R Blake, David Knox, Dawson Tamati, Pablo Lemoine, Gavin Giles, George Leaupepe, Carlos Hassan, S Lines, Jeff Probyn, Luke Nabaro, M Robinson, Michael Horak, P Whitaker

Ever Presents: One - Mark Bennett.

Players used: 39 plus 5 as a replacement only.

Most Points in a season:

Pts	Player	T	C	P	DG
164	P Hull	5	35	23	-
82	D Knox	-	20	13	1
67	A Larkin	13	1	-	-
65	L Nabaro	13	-	-	-
45	G Baber	9	-	-	-

MATCH FACTS

10	9	1	2	3	4	5	6	7	8	
Hull/2cp	Baber(k)	Emms	J Evans/t	Hinkins(l)	Eagle	Watkins(m)	Charron/t	Bennett	C Evans	1
Hull/t5c	Dewdney/t(d)	Emms	J Evans/t(o)	Hinkins(l)	Eagle	Watkins(p/t)	Charron/t(m/t)	Bennett	C Evans	2
Hull/2c2p	Dewdney/2t(r)	Emms	J Evans	Hinkins(l)	Eagle	Watkins	Charron	Bennett/t(m)	C Evans(o)	3
Hull/t4c3p	Dewdney	Wring(e)	J Evans	Hinkins	Eagle	Charron	Brownrigg(t)	Bennett	C Evans	4
Hull/4cp	Baber(k)	Emms	J Evans	Hinkins(l/t)	Eagle/t	Charron	Gabey(m)	Bennett	C Evans	5
Hull/2p(b/c2p)	Dewdney/t	Hinkins	J Evans(m)	Wring(u)	Charron	Eagle	Gabey	Bennett	C Evans	6
Martin	Dewdney(d)	Emms	J Evans	Hinkins(l)	Eagle	Watkins	Charron	Gabey/t	Bennett	7
Hull	Dewdney	Emms	J Evans(o)	Lemoine(g)	Eagle	Watkins(v)	Charron	Bennett	Gabey	8
Knox/3p	Baber	Emms	Dunn	Wring(g)	Giles	Eagle	Lines	Bennett(x)	C Evans	9
Knox/4cp	Blake	Emms	Dunn(f)	Wring/t	Giles	Eagle(x)	Lines(t)	C Evans/t	Bennett	10
Knox/4cp	Baber/t(k)	Emms	J Evans(w)	Wring(u)	Eagle	Giles/t	C Evans	Bennett(x/t)	Gabey/t	11
Knox	Baber	Emms	Tamati(A)	Wring(g)	Eagle	Giles	C Evans(b)	Bennett(x)	Gabey(m)	12
Martin/3c	Baber(k)	Emms	Tamati	Wring(u)	Eagle	Giles	Charron	Bennett/t	Gabey/t	13
Martin/tc	Baber/t(k)	Emms	Tamati(f)	Wring(u)	Charron	Giles	C Evans(m)	Bennett(x)	Gabey	14
Knox/3c3p	Baber/t	J Evans	Tamati	Lemoine/t	Charron	Giles	Brownrigg	Bennett(j)	Gabey/t	15
Knox/4cp	Baber/t	Emms	Tamati	Probyn	Eagle(j)	Giles(m)	Charron	Bennett	Gabey/t	16
Knox/3pdg	Baber	Emms	Tamati(f/t)	Lemoine	Charron	Eagle	Brownrigg	Bennett(j)	Gabey	17
Knox/2c	Baber	Wring	Tamati	Lemoine	Eagle	Charron	Brownrigg	Bennett	Gabey/t	18
Knox/3cp	Baber/t	Sharp	Tamati(f/t)	Lemoine/2t	Charron	Giles	Lines/t(h)	Bennett	Gabey	19
Pritchard	Baber	Sharp	Tamati/t(f)	Wring	Charron(h)	Giles	Bennett	Eves	Gabey/t	20
Pritchard	Baber	Sharp	Tamati(f)	Lemoine	Eagle	Charron	C Evans	Bennett	Gabey	21
Pritchard	Baber/2t	Sharp	Tamati(f)	Lemoine	Eagle	Charron/t	C Evans	Bennett(B)	Gabey/t	22
Pritchard	Baber	Sharp	Tamati(f)	Wring	Eagle	Lines(m)	C Evans/t	Bennett(B)	Gabey	23
Pritchard/t	Baber/t	Sharp	J Evans	Lemoine	Eagle/t(m)	Charron	C Evans	Bennett	Gabey	24
Hull/c2p(k)	Baber/t	Sharp	Tamati(f/t)	Wring	Eagle(m)	Charron	C Evans	Bennett/t(B)	Gabey/t	25
Baber	Dewdney	Sharp	J Evans	Lemoine	Eagle/t	Gabey	Brownrigg	Bennett(B)	C Evans/t	26
Hull/t5c	Blake(d)	Emms	J Evans/3t	Wring(u)	Charron/2t	Giles	Brownrigg(j)	Short	Gabey	A
Martin	Baber/t	Emms	Tamati	Wring	Eagle	Giles	Charron	Bennett	Gabey	B

REPLACEMENTS:

	a- S Marsden	b- S Martin	c - J Pritchard	d - G Baber	e - S Emms	f - J Evans	g - D Hinkins
h - C Eagle	i - D Yapp	j - C Evans	k - D Dewdney	l - J Wring	m - J Brownrigg	n - A Larkin	o - B McConnell
p - A Adams	q - T Barlow	r - R Blake	s - M Misson	t - M Gabey	u - D Lemoine	v - G Giles	w - K Dunn
x - C Short	y - S Lines	z - C Hassan	A - T Tapsell	B - D Eves	C - A Barnard		

Utilty back Paul Hull had his best season notching up 164 points. Included in that total was 35 conversions which was a new club record beating the previous record of 27 set by Paul Burke in the 1996-97 season.
In the try scoring department both Adam Larkin and Luke Nabaro scored 13 tries to beat the record of 10 in a season set by David Tiueti in 1996-97.
Nabaro also set a new record for tries in a match with five against Blackheath during March. This easily beat the previous record of three shared by Mike Lloyd and Derek Eves.
Bristol set a new club record with 8 consecutive league wins.
Luke Nabaro set a new record for scoring tries in consecutive matches with a run of four.
Bristol record record wins both home and away with a 55-14 win over Fylde at home and a 43-6 win at Moseley for 41 and 37 point wins respectively.
They also achieved their highest ever scores with a 58-14 home win and a 46-15 win away against Moseley and Wakefield respectively.

BRISTOL

LEAGUE STATISTICS
compiled by Stephen McCormack

SEASON	Division	P	W	D	L	F	A	Pts Diff	Lge Pts	Lge Pos	Most Points	Most Tries
89-90	1	11	4	0	7	136	144	-8	8	9	47 Jon Webb	2 Paul Hull & John Davis
90-91	1	12	4	1	7	135	219	-84	9	11	35 Simon Hogg	4 Julian Horrobin
91-92	1	12	4	0	8	192	174	18	8	10	29 Mark Tainton	5 Pete Stiff
92-93	1	12	6	0	6	148	169	-21	12	6	68 Mark Tainton	3 Derek Eves
93-94	1	18	10	0	8	331	276	55	20	4	161 Mark Tainton	8 A Saveriamutto
94-95	1	18	7	0	11	301	353	-52	14	6	196 Mark Tainton	6 Derek Eves
95-96	1	18	8	0	10	329	421	-92	16	6	120 Mark Tainton	4 Martin Corry
96-97	1	22	8	1	13	432	625	-193	17	9	178 Paul Burke	10 David Tiueti
97-98	P1	22	2	0	20	351	733	-382	4	12r	163 Paul Burke	7 David Tiueti
98-99	P2	26	22	0	4	848	418	430	44	1p	164 Paul Hull	13 A Larkin & L Nabaro

BIGGEST MARGINS

Home Win	41pts - -55-14 v Fylde 12.9.98
Away Win	37pts - 43-6 v Moseley 2.1.99
Home Defeat	42pts 8-50 v Newcastle 27.12.97
Away Defeat	76pts 0-76 v Sale 9.11.97

MOST CONSECUTIVE

Appearances	81 Derek Eves 11.3.88 - 4.3.95
Matches scoring Tries	4 Luke Nabaro
Matches scoring points	31 Mark Tainton
Victories	8
Defeats	12

MOST POINTS

Scored at Home	58 v Moseley 22.11.98
Scored Away	46 v Wakefield 7.11.98
Conceded at Home	50 v Newcastle 27.12.97
Conceded Away	76 v Bath 30.10.96 v Sale 9.11.97

MOST TRIES

Scored in a match	10 v Rugby 28.3.92
Conceded in a match	12 v Sale 9.11.97 (A)

MOST APPEARANCES

by a forward	107(1) Dave Hinkins
by a back	146 (4) Paul Hull

	MOST IN A SEASON	MOST IN A CAREER	MOST IN A MATCH
Points	196 Mark Tainton	637 Mark Tainton 87-97	26 Mark Tainton v Leicester 5.1..94 (H)
Tries	13 Adam Larkin 98-99 Luke Nabaro 98-99	28 Paul Hull 87-99	5 Luke Nabaro v Blackheath 13.3.99 (H)
Conversions	35 Paul Hull 98-99	62 Mark Tainton 87-97	5 Jon Webb v Sale 24.10.87 (H)
Penalties	56 Mark Tainton 94-95	165 Mark Tainton 87-97	7 Mark Tainton v Leicester 5.11.94 (H)
Drop Goals	3 Simon Hogg 88-89 Arwel Thomas 95-96	6 Mark Tainton 87-97	2 Simon Hogg v Leicester 9.3.91 (H)

BRISTOL PLAYING SQUAD

BACKS

BACKS	Ht.	Wt.	Birthdate	Birthplace	CLUB	League Apps	Tries	Pts
Luke Nabaro	6.0	14.02	24.04.76	Fiji	Bristol	6	13	65
George Leaupepe Western Samoa, Wellington, Counties.	5.11	14.02	27.05.75	W Samoa	Bristol	9	1	5
Carlos Hassan Counties-Manukau, New Zealand U-21	6.1	16.07	22.01.71	Bristol	Bristol Rotherham	5(1)	2	10
Ben Breeze England students, South West U-21.	5.10	13.00	08.04.74	Exeter	Bristol	49(3)	8	40
Dean Dewdney Zimbabwe	5.10	10.10	05.11.74	Zimbabwe	Bristol Clifton	7(7)	4	20
David Knox Ausralia, New South Wales, Randwick	6.2	13.02	08.08.63	Sydney	Bristol	9	-	82
Simon Martin England U-18, U-19.	5.10	13.07	24.01.75	Thornbury	Bristol	32(7)	6	44
Paul Hull England 4, B, Emerging, U21, Colts.	5.9	12.10	17.05.68	Lambeth	Bristol	146(4)	28	335
Darren Yapp Welsh Exiles colts.	6.0	15.00	19.02.75	Wolverhampton	Bristol	13(2)	3	15
Adam Larkin Takapuna, North Harbour, New Zealand U-21.	5.11	13.02	14.02.74	Sydney	Bristol	19(1)	16	82
Mark Robinson Taranaki, New Zealand Univ, Cambridge Blue	6.1	14.02	17.01.74	Stratford (NZ)	Bristol	6	4	20
Gareth Baber Wales U-21, Oxford and Swansea Univ.	5.10	12.02	23.05.72	Cardiff	Bristol	28(3)	11	55
Michael Misson Randwicks, Norths (Sydney)	5.10	12.10	07.05.73	Australia	Bristol	17(1)	8	40

FORWARDS

FORWARDS	Ht.	Wt.	Birthdate	Birthplace	CLUB	League Apps	Tries	Pts
Christian Evans Welsh students, Univs.	6.4	16.09	27.12.69	Bridgend	Bristol	17(4)	3	15
Jon Evans Welsh schools &youths. Cambridge Blue..	5.9	13.00	05.04.72	Swansea	Bristol	12(9)	6	30
Kevin Dunn England A, B. Other club: Gloucester 42(3)/4/16.	5.10	14.05	05.06.65	Gloucester	Bristol Wasps	11(4) 54(7)	- 2	- 10
Dawson Tamati Taranaki	5.11	16.09	06.04.71	Toturua (NZ)	Bristol	13	1	5
Pablo Lemoine Uruyuay	6.1	19.03	02.03.78	Uruguay	Bristol	8(5)	3	15
Chad Eagle Takapuna, Currie	6.5	18.00	24.08.71	New Zealand	Bristol	51(2)	4	20
Mark Gabey Queenslands Reds	6.5	17.05	27.07.73	Queensland	Bristol	20(2)	6	30
Alan Sharp Scotland, England A. Other clubs; Clifton, London Scottish	5.10	17.04	07.10.68	Bristol	Bristol Coventry	78 26	- -	- -
John Brownrigg England U-21.	6.6	15.00	04.06.77	Chicester	Bristol	18(17)	2	10
Derek Eves England A	5.10	15.05	07.01.66	Bristol	Bristol Coventry	87(4) 65	17 17	85 85
Justin Wring Ireland 25.	6.3	19.08	04.01.78	Bristol	Bristol	12(5)	2	10
Craig Short	6.1	14.02	26.06.75	Kingswood	Bristol	18(9)	2	10
Gavin Giles Counties-Manukau	6.7	16.02	25.09.71	New Zealand	Bristol	10(1)	1	5
Simon Emms Llandovery	5.10	16.02	27.01.75	Camarthen	Bristol London Welsh	14(2)	-	-
Mark Bennett Wales.	6.2	16.00	26.01.68	Neath	Bristol	26	3	15

BRISTOL

FACT FILE

Founded: 1888

Colours: Blue and white hoops
Change colours: Blue and yellow quarters

GROUND

Address: Memorial Ground, Filton Avenue, Horfield, Bristol. BS7 0AQ
Tel: 0117 908 5500 Fax: 0117 907 4682
Club Newsline: 0839 44 66 33 Website: www.bristolrugby.co.uk
Capacity: 12,000 Seated: 2,780 Standing: Enclosure 2,200, Ground 7,020

Directions: M4 to junction 19, M32 to junction 2, then join B4469 towards Horfield. Turn left at 2nd set of traffic lights after `Brunel Ford' and bus garage (on the right) into Filton Ave. Ground is on the left.

Nearest Railway Station: Bristol Parkway or Bristol Temple Meads.

Car Parking: Very limited at the ground. Plenty of street parking nearby

Admission:
Season tickets
Matchday

Club Shop: Monday - Friday 9.30-5.00, & matchdays from noon

Clubhouse: Snacks & bar meals available. Contact: Robert Laurence
Tel: 0117 909 6648. Mob:07831 463437 Fax: 0117 908 5530
Corprate Hospitality: Kate Moore,
0117 908 3423, Fax: 0171 908 3422

PROGRAMME Contact Mike Turner at Bristol Rugby Ltd.
Tel: 01225 320843 Fax: 01225 448390

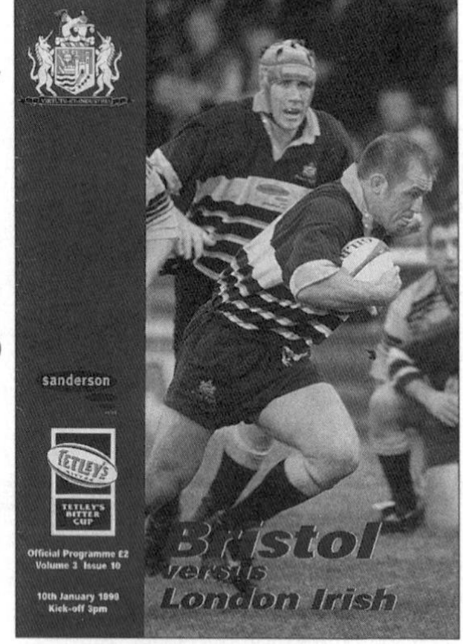

Right: Luke Nabaro

Left: Al Charron

GLOUCESTER R.F.C.

Chairman	David Foyle		c/o Gloucester RFC,
Company Secretary	A D Wadley		Kingsholm,
Director of Rugby	Philippe St. Andre		Gloucester GL1 3AX
Marketing Officer	Karen Ellis		Tel: 01452 381087
Press Officer	Andrew Harley		Fax: 01452 383321
Committe Chairman	Alan Brinn	01452 303722	

On this season:
We didn't start the season too badly. For example, we won our second game - away to Richmond; but we had a lot of injuries at the start of the season. One of the problems was that the guys who went on tour didn't have enough holiday, they came back quickly and came back tired. During the pre-season the lads worked hard but we didn't work hard enough for professional rugby. The game progresses each year and each year it's quicker and harder and it's faster.
So, we played well for the start of the season, but we had problems competing at this level after that. We were unlucky in a few games - games that we lost after seven minutes of injury time. But then sometimes you lose a game because you're unlucky, but, when you lose seven or eight games in a row, it's not because you're unlucky, but because you aren't clever enough or because you aren't good enough or not fit enough. Luck can effect one game, but it can't effect a whole season.
A consistent problem over the season was the make up of the squad; we had only two centres for example. So, when Terry Fanolua got injured and then later Richard Tombs was injured, we had big problems. It's not that the pre-season wasn't hard enough, but we need to make our preparation more scientific. Rugby isn't the same as it was five years ago. I've taken on a new fitness coach to work with Ed Archer. I think we need two fitness coaches because Ed is good with weights and with the rehabilitation of the players and perhaps for training the part-timers, but he needs someone to work with.
On taking over as Player-coach:
When I was captain of France, I took the training sessions. At Clermont-Ferrand I was captain but I was also backs coach, so to be coach here isn't too different from what I've done before. The big surprise for me is that I have to talk money with the players and I have to find a good balance for my team. I had a budget and I can't go over that. Sometimes it's hard because I have to say to a good player that he's earning too much for this level. If I was the coach of an amateur club, I would keep all the players and maybe call three or four more. But I can't do that.
I'm not trying to reduce the playing budget for the sake of reducing it. Some of the guys are earning too much for the level they're playing at. Some of the guys are unhappy about what I've been saying to them, because they think they've played well for England A. Me, I don't care about England A; the guys must play well for Gloucester. That attitude has to change.
For me, the perfect example is Leicester. They have six or seven full internationals. Those players play in five Nations games and then three days later play for their club and give it their all.
All the guys who accept this will be with me and the guys who don't accept this won't have a place at Gloucester. They must understand this because it's Gloucester who pays them. The guys must be hungry and must be hungry to play for Gloucester. After they have done that they can go on and play for England A and I will be very pleased for them. PHILIPPE SAINT-ANDRE

Gloucester RFC 98-99

L-R **Back Row:** Andy Deacon, Simon Mannix, Michael Worsley, Richard Tombs, Simon Deveraux, Nick Osman, Phil Vickery, Nathan Carter, Trevor Woodman, Laurie Beck. **Middle Row:** John Brain (Asst. Coach), Audley Lumsden, Brian Johnson, Chris Fortey, Ed Pearce, Richard Ward, Rob Fidler, Mark Cornwell, Pete Glanville, Tony Windo, Andrew Dawling, Richard Hill (Dir. of Rugby), John Fidler (Team Manager). **Front Row:** Phil Greening, Stve Ojomoh, Chris Catling, Mark Mapletoft, Dave Sims (Captain), Neil McCarthy, Scott Benton, Terry Fanolua, Philippe Saint-Andre.

GLOUCESTER

Match No.	Date	H/A	Comp.	Opponents	Result & Score	Att.	15	14	13	12	11
1	05.09	H	AD1	London Irish	W 29-22	5,267	Catling	Johnson	Fanolua	Tombs	St Andre
2	12.09	A	AD1	Richmond	W 25-22	7,054	Catling	Johnson	Tombs	Mannix	St Andre/t
3	20.09	H	AD1	W Hartlepool	W 36-3	5,576	Catling/t(s)	Jewell(w)	Tombs/2t	Mannix	St Andre/t
4	26.09	A	AD1	Bath	L 16-21	8,200	Catling	Jewell	Tombs	Mannix/t	St Andre/t
5	03.10	H	AD1	Wasps	L 12-13	5,232	Catling	Lumsden	Tombs	Mannix	St Andre
6	17.10	H	AD1	Newcastle	W 41-32	6,915	Catling/3t	Lumsden/t	Fanolua	Tombs	St Andre/t
7	20.10	A	AD1	Harlequins*	L 7-39	4,174	Catling(w)	Lumsden	Fanolua	Tombs	St Andre
8	25.10	H	AD1	London Scot	W 29-13	5,244	Lumsden	G'slade-Jones	Fanolua(a)	Tombs	St Andre/t(y)
9	31.10	A	AD1	Northampton	L 8-22	7,284	Catling	Lumsden/t	Fanolua	Tombs	Jewell
10	07.11	H	AD1	Bedford	W 31-21	5,147	Catling/t	Johnson	Fanolua	Tombs	Lumsden
11	21.11	H	AD1	Saracens	W 28-27	6,627	Lumsden	Johnson	Fanolua/t	Tombs/2t	St Andre
12	12.12	A	AD1	Sale	L 10-26	3,200	Lumsden	Johnson	Fanolua	Tombs	St Andre/t
13	19.12	H	AD1	Leicester	L 18-23	7,222	Catling	Johnson/t(c/tc2p	Fanolua	Tombs	St Andre
14	27.12	A	AD1	Wasps	L 9-23	5,362	Catling	Johnson	Fanolua/p	Tombs	St Andre(w)
15	02.01	H	AD1	Bath	W 23-7	10,109	Catling/2t	Johnson	Fanolua/t	Tombs	G'slade-Jones
16	05.01	A	AD1	London Scot	L 13-24	1,297	Catling	Johnson	Fanolua	Tombs	G'slade-Jones
17	16.01	H	AD1	Richmond*	D 24-24	4,811	Catling	Johnson	Fanolua	Tombs	St Andre
18	23.01	A	AD1	Leicester	L 16-23	11,394	Lumsden	Johnson	Fanolua	Tombs/t	St Andre
19	07.02	A	AD1	London Irish	L 20-42	5,020	Mapletoft/cp	Beim	Fanolua(s)	Tombs	St Andre/t(w)
20	13.02	H	AD1	Harlequins*	L 20-31	6,046	Lumsden	Beim/t	Mannix	Tombs	St Andre
21	14.03	A	AD1	W Hartlepool*	L 32-33	1,300	Catling	Johnson(b)	Mannix	Fanolua	Beim/t
22	27.03	A	AD1	Bedford	L 15-19	2,417	Catling	Beim	Fanolua	G'slade-Jones	St Andre/t(C)
23	24.04	A	AD1	Newcastle	L 15-39	3,748	Catling	Beim/t	Tombs	Davies/t	Jewell
24	01.05	H	AD1	Sale	L 24-34	4,528	Catling	Johnson	Tombs/t	G'slade-Jones	Beim
25	07.05	A	AD1	Saracens	L 10-26	5,261	Catling	Johnson(F)	Tombs	Ward/cp	G'slade-Jones
26	16.05	H	AD1	Northampton	W 43-31	4,935	Catling/t	Lumsden	Tombs/t	Davies	Jewell
A	09.01	H	TB4	Worcester	W 31-17	7,136	Catling/	Johnson	Fanolua	G'slade-Jones	St Andre/t
B	30.01	H	TB5	Henley	W 31-9	4,185	Lumsden(c)	Beim	Fanolua/2t	G'slade-Jones	St Andre
C	27.02	H	TBqf	Harlequins	W 15-13	6,755	Catling	Johnson	Mannix	Tombs(w)	St Andre
D	03.04	A	TBsf	Wasps	L 21-35	10,064	Catling	Mapletoft/6p	Fano;ua	Tombs	St Andre

* after opponents name indicates a penalty try
Brackets after a player's name indicates he was replaced. eg (a) means he was replaced by replacement code "a" and so on.
/ after a player or replacement name is followed by any scores he made - eg /t, /c, /p, /dg or any combination of these

1998-99 HIGHLIGHTS

League debuts:
Simon Mannix, Rory Greenslade-Jones, Andy Dawling, Kingsley Jones, Andy Hazell, Mike Davies, A Eustace.

Ever Presents: None
Most appearances Steve Ojomoh 25 (1)

Players used: 36 plus 5 as replacement only

Most Points in a season:

Pts	Player	T	C	P	DG
198	M Mapletoft	6	21	41	1
98	S Mannix	2	14	20	-
40	C Catling	8	-	-	-
40	P St Andre	8	-	-	-

MATCH FACTS

10	9	1	2	3	4	5	6	7	8	
Mapletoft/t2c5p	Benton	Woodman	McCarthy(m)	Vickery(n)	Fidler	Sims(o)	Ojomoh	Carter	Devereux	1
Mapletoft/2t2c2p	Benton	Woodman	McCarthy(m)	Deacon/(n)	Fidler	Sims	Ojomoh	Carter	Devereux	2
Mapletoft/4cp	Benton(v)	Windo(e)	Greening(m)	Deacon	Cornwell	Sims	Glanville(j/t)	Carter(u)	Devereux	3
Mapletoft/pdg	Benton	Windo(e)	Greening(m)	Deacon	Fidler	Sims(o)	Ojomoh	Carter	Devereux(t)	4
Mapletoft/4p	Benton	Windo	Greening(m)	Vickery	Fidler	Sims(o)	Ojomoh	Carter	Devereux	5
Mannix/2c4p	Sanders	Woodman	Fortey	Deacon	Cornwell	Sims	Pearce	Carter	Ojomoh	6
Mannix/c(y)	Sanders	Woodman(r)	Fortey(f)	Deacon	Cornwell(z)	Sims	Pearce	Carter	Ojomoh	7
Mannix/2c5p	Sanders	Windo	McCarthy	Deacon	Cornwell	Sims(h)	Pearce(l)	Dawling/t	Ojomoh	8
Mannix/p	Benton(x)	Windo(e)	Fortey(f)	Deacon	Cornwell	Fidler	Ojomoh	Carter	Devereux	9
Mapletoft/2c4p	Benton	Windo	Fortey/t	Deacon	Cornwell(i)	Fidler	Ojomoh/t	Carter	Devereux(u)	10
Mannix/2c3p	Sanders	Windo	Fortey(f)	Deacon	Cornwell(i)	Fidler	Pearce	Carter	Ojomoh	11
Mannix/cp	Sanders	Windo(e)	Fortey	Deacon	Cornwell	Fidler	Pearce	Carter(A)	Ojomoh	12
Mannix	Sanders	Windo	Fortey(f)	Deacon(B)	Cornwell(i)	Fidler	Jones	Carter	Ojomoh	13
Mapletoft/2p	Sanders(d)	Woodman	McCarthy	Deacon	Cornwell(i)	Fidler	Pearce	Jones(k)	Ojomoh	14
Mapletoft/tc2p	Benton	Woodman	McCarthy	Deacon(B)	Cornwell	Fidler(z)	Pearce	Carter	Ojomoh	15
Mapletoft/t2cp	Benton(D)	Woodman	McCarthy(m)	Deacon(B)	Fidler	Ward	Pearce(E)	Carter	Ojomoh	16
Mapletoft/c4p	Benton/t	Woodman	McCarthy(m)	Deacon	Fidler(i)	Cornwell	Pearce(E)	Carter	Ojomoh	17
Mapletoft/c3p	Benton	Woodman	McCarthy	Deacon	Sims	Cornwell	Pearce(E)	Carter	Ojomoh	18
Mannix	Benton/t	Woodman	McCarthy	Powles	Fidler	SIms	Pearce	Carter/t(E)	O)omoh	19
Mapletoft/2c2p	Benton	Woodman	McCarthy	Powles(G)	Fidler	Sims(o)	Pearce(E)	Carter	Ojomoh	20
Mapletoft/t2cp	Benton	Woodman(r)	McCarthy(m)	Deacon	Fidler	Sims(o)	Pearce(E)	Carter/t	Ojomoh/t	21
Mannix/cp(c)	Sanders	Windo	Fortey(f)	Woodman	Ward	Cornwell	Ojomoh	Eustace(B)	Pearce	22
Mannix/c(c/p)	Sanders	Windo	Fortey	Vickery	Ward(J)	Sims	Ojomoh	Carter(E)	Pearce	23
Mapletoft/c4p	Sanders	Woodman/t	McCarthy	Vickery	Ward	Sims(J)	Hazell	Carter(K)	Ojomoh	24
Kimber(p)	Sanders	Woodman	Fortey(f)	Vickery	Fidler	Ward	Eustace/t	Hazell(k)	Ojomoh	25
Mannix/t4c5p(y)	Sanders	Woodman(B)	McCarthy(m)	Vickery	Fidler	Ward	Eustace	Carter/t(E)	Ojomoh	26
Mapletoft/tc3p	Cane	Woodman	McCarthy(m/t)	Deacon(B)	Fidler	Cornwell	Pearce	Carter(E)	Ojomoh/t	A
Mannix/2t3c	Cane	Windo	McCarthy	Powles(G)	Fidler	Sims	Hazell	Pearce	Ojomoh(H)	B
Mapletoft/5p	Sanders	Woodman(r)	McCarthy(m)	Deacon	Fidler	Cornwell	Pearce(E)	Carter	Ojomoh	C
Mannix	Sanders/dg	Woodman	McCarthy(m)	Deacon(g)	Fidler	Cornwell(i)	Ojomoh	Carter	Pearce	D

REPLACEMENTS:
a - C Catling, b- P St Andre, c - M Mapletoft, d - S Benton, e - T Woodman, f - N McCarthy, g - P Vickery,
h - R Fidler, i - D Sims, j - S Ojomoh, k - N Carter, l - S Devereux, m - C Fortey, n - A Deacon, o - M Cornwell,
p - S Mannix, q - R Jewell, r - T Windo, s - A Lumsden, t - E Pearce, u - P Glanville, v - L Beck,
w - R Greenslade-Jones, x - I Sanders, y - M Kimber, z - R Ward, A - K Jones, B - A Powles, C - B Johnson, D - N Cane,
E - A Hazell, F - T Beim, G - D Hinkins, H - H Gay, J - A Eustace, K - I Stott

With the kicking duties split between Mark Mapletoft and Simon Mannix, Mapletoft failed to reach the 200 point mark for the first time in three seasons.
Mapletoft though scored six tries and is now the club's leading try scorer in league rugby with 19, 2 more than Paul Holford's previous record.
He did though lose a record with Simon Mannix taking his record for points in a match.

Mannix scored 28 points against Northampton in the last match of the season. Mannix scored a try, converted all four of his sides tries and kicked five penalties to beat the old mark by a point.

Full back Chris Catling became the third Gloucester player to score a hat tick of tries in a league match when he crossed the line three times in the home win against Newcastle.

Mark Mapletoft extended his record of scoring in consecutive league matches to 48.

Chris Catling and Phillipe St Andre finished the season on eight tries to equal the club record achieved previously by Paul Holford and Terry Fanolua.

GLOUCESTER

LEAGUE STATISTICS
compiled by Stephen McCormack

SEASON	Division	P	W	D	L	F	A	Pts Diff	Lge Pts	Lge Pos	Most Points	Most Tries
89-90	1	11	8	1	2	214	139	75	17	2	75 Tim Smith	6 Derek Morgan
90-91	1	12	6	0	6	207	163	44	12	6	75 Tim Smith	3 by 4 players
91-92	1	12	7	1	4	193	168	25	15	4	81 Tim Smith	5 Simon Morris
92-93	1	12	6	0	6	173	151	22	12	5	71 Tim Smith	3 Tim Smith & Derek Morgan
93-94	1	18	6	2	10	247	356	-109	14	8	82 Tim Smith	3 Paul Holford & Bruce Fenley
94-95	1	18	6	1	11	269	336	-67	13	7	85 Mark Mapletoft	8 Paul Holford
95-96	1	18	6	0	12	275	370	-95	12	8	79 Tim Smith	5 Paul Holford
96-97	1	22	11	1	10	476	589	-113	23	6	269 Mark Mapletoft	7 Mike Lloyd
97-98	1	22	11	1	10	512	528	-16	23	7	275 Mark Mapletoft	8 Terry Fanolua
98-99	1	26	9	1	16	554	643	-89	19	10	198 Mark Mapletoft	8 C Catling & P St Andre

BIGGEST MARGINS

Home Win	54pts - 61-7 v Sale 16.4.88
Away Win	46pts - 49-3 v Orrell 16.11.96
Home Defeat	16pts - 29-45 v Bath 21.9.96
Away Defeat	56pts - 19-75 v Harlequins 31.8.96

MOST CONSECUTIVE

Appearances	47 Dave Sims 11.4.92-25.3.95
Matches scoring Tries	4 Phillipe St Andre
Matches scoring points	48 Mark Mapletoft
Victories	7
Defeats	7

MOST POINTS

Scored at Home	61 v Sale 16.4.88
Scored Away	49 v Orrell 16.11.96
Conceded at Home	45 v Bath 21.9.96
Conceded Away	75 v Harlequins 31.8.96

MOST TRIES

Scored in a match	11 v Sale 16.4.88
Conceded in a match	11 v Harlequins 31.8.96 v Bath 30.4.97

MOST APPEARANCES

by a forward	130 Dave Sims
by a back	94 Tim Smith

	MOST IN A SEASON	MOST IN A CAREER	MOST IN A MATCH	
Points	275 Mark Mapletoft 97-98	848 Mark Mapletoft 94-99	28 Simon Mannix	v Northampton 16.5.99 (H)
Tries	8 Paul Holford 94-95 Terry Fanolua 97-98 Chris Catling 98-99 Phillipe St Andre 98-99	19 Mark Mapletoft 94-99	3 Derek Morgan Mike Lloyd Chris Catling	v Rosslyn P. 11.11.89 (H) v W. Harlepool 18.1.97 (H) v Newcastle 17.10.98 (H)
Conversions	35 Mark Mapletoft 97-98	90 Mark Mapletoft 94-99	6 Paul Mansell	v Sale 16.4.88 (H)
Penalties	58 Mark Mapletoft 96-97,97-98	183 Mark Mapletoft 94-99	6 Tim Smith Mark Mapletoft	v Harlequins 12.3.90 (H) v Wasps 6.10.96 (H) v Leicester 8.4.97 (H)
Drop Goals	6 Martyn Kimber 94-95,95-96	12 Martin Kimber 94-96	2 Martyn Kimber Mark Mapletoft	v Bath 4.3.95 (A) v Saracens 5.4.97 (H)

GLOUCESTER PLAYING SQUAD

BACKS

	Ht.	Wt.	Birthdate	Birthplace	CLUB	League Apps	Tries	Pts
Chris Catling	6.2	13.07	17.06.76	Surrey	Gloucester	60	12	63
Other club: Old Mid Whit 2/2/10					Exeter	6	1	5
Richard Tombs	5.11	14.02	01.04.68	New Zealand	Gloucester	44	11	57
Australia 5, U21, Schools.								
Terry Fanolua	6.0	14.08	03.07.74	Motoutua	Gloucester	37	9	48
Mike Davies					Gloucester	2	1	5
Mark Mapletoft	5.7	13.00	25.12.71	Mansfield	Gloucester	71(4)	19	848
England , A, U21, 18.					Rugby	41	6	201
Scott Benton	5.11	13.00	08.09.74	Bradford	Gloucester	55(3)	8	40
England , A.					Morley			
Audley Lumsden	6.0	13.07	06.06.67	London	Gloucester	31(4)	9	45
					Bath	44(1)	18	86
Ian Sanders	5.9	12.00	22.01.71	Penzance	Gloucester	12(2)	-	-
					Bath	30(4)	3	15
Brian Johnson	5.11	12.06	27.07.72	Wegberg	Gloucester	27(1)	6	30
England A. Army					Newbury	31	35	175
Martyn Kimber	6.0	13.10	20.09.68	Auckland	Gloucester	35(3)	1	60
Richard Jewell			11.10.78	Bromsgrove	Gloucester	6(4)	1	5
Andy Hazell					Gloucester	2(9)	-	-
Phillipe St Andre	5.11	13.08	19.04.67	Romans	Gloucester	30	14	70
France 64								
Tom Beim	5.11	13.09	01.12.75	Frimley	Gloucester	8(1)	4	20
					Sale	45(1)	31	155
Simon Mannix	5.8	13.09	10.08.71	Wellington	Gloucester	17(2)	2	98
					Sale	22	8	198

FORWARDS

	Ht.	Wt.	Birthdate	Birthplace	CLUB	League Apps	Tries	Pts
Tony Windo	6.0	16.00	30.04.69	Gloucester	Gloucester	86	11	55
England A.								
Phil Greening	5.11	17.00	03.10.75	Gloucester	Gloucester	363)	2	10
England								
Andy Deacon	6.2	17.00	21.02.65	Glouester	Gloucester	90(4)	5	25
Neil McCarthy	5.9	14.06	29.11.73	Slough	Gloucester	21(9)	1	5
England Colts					Bath			
Chris Fortey	6.0	16.07	25.08.75	Gloucester	Gloucester	21(12)	2	10
Phil Vickery	6.3	19.06	30.04.69	Gloucester	Gloucester	24(3)	1	5
England								
Dave Sims	6.7	18.00	22.11.69	Gloucester	Gloucester	130(8)	8	38
England , A,								
Rob Fidler	6.5	17.08	21.09.74	Gloucester	Gloucester	70(1)	5	25
England , A,								
Mark Cornwall	6.7	17.00	22.02.73	Gloucester	Gloucester			
England Colts.								
Steve Ojomoh	6.2	15.10	25.05.70	Benin City	Gloucester	32(7)	5	25
England , A, U21, Colts, Schools.					Bath	58(2)	4	20
Pete Glanville	6.3	16.03	10.06.71	Gloucester	Gloucester	67(2)	3	15
Nathan Carter	6.0	15.00	22.06.72	Gloucester	Gloucester	59(3)	5	25
Simon Devereux	6.3	16.10	20.10.68	Gloucester	Gloucester	60(4)	1	5
Adey Powles	5.11	17.00	14.03.67	Cowsford	Gloucester	15(10)	-	-
Ed Pearce	6.6	17.00	02.09.75	Bristol	Gloucester	26(3)	-	-
					Bath	2(1)	-	-

GLOUCESTER

FACT FILE

Founded: 1873
Nickname: Cherry & whites

Colours: Cherry & white.
Change colours: TBA

GROUND

Address: Kingsholm, Gloucester. GL1 3AX.
Tel: 01452 381087 Fax: 01452 383321
Capacity: 10,800 Seated:1,498 Standing: Covered 4,350 Uncovered 4,622

Directions: From M5 junction 11 or 11A follow signs for City Centre and then Kingsholm.
Nearest Railway Station: Gloucester. About a 5 minute walk from the ground. Follow signs

Car Parking: 250 spaces at ground, 1,000 at cattle market 5 mins walk

Admission: Season tickets Seated - Adults £235; OAPs £165; Youths £115
Standing - Adults £130; OAPs £80; Youths £65

Matchday Seated - Adults £22; OAPs & Youths no concessions
Standing - Adults £15; OAPs £8; Youths £8

Club Shop: 10-4 & matchdays. Contact Rachel Creed 01452 381087.

Clubhouse: Mon-Sat 6.30-11, Sat matchdays 11-11. Snacks & bar meals available
Function room: Available for hire, capacity 150.

Training Nights: Every day

PROGRAMME

Size: B5 **Pages:** 46 **Price:** £2
Programme Co-ordinator: Claudia Cox 01452 381082

ADVERTISING RATES
Colour Full page £1,900, Half £1,050, Qtr £560
Mono Full page £1,500 Contact SPP, 0117 977 9188

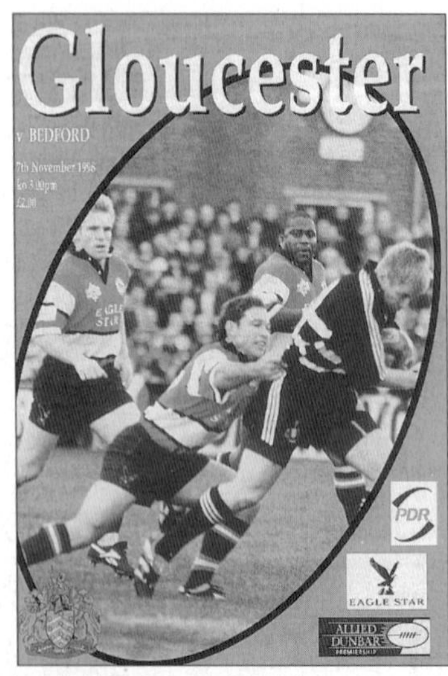

Steve Ojomoh voted Player of the Year 1998-99 by the Gloucester supporters

HARLEQUIN F.C.

Chairman	Malcom Wall
Chief Executive	Huw Morgan
General Manager	Ross Young
Director of Rugby	John Gallagher
Head of Sales	Abigal Findlay
Head of Marketing	Samantha Bird
Media Liason	Mark Anderson Mob: 07977 205984 e-mail:marka@quins.co.uk

c/o NEC Harlequins FC,
Stoop Memorial Ground,
Craneford Way,
Twickenham TW2 7SQ.
Tel: 0181 410 6000 Fax: 0181 410 6001

John Gallagher, Zinzan Brooke, Bernie McCahill and Adrian Skeggs were not given any help in settling into their new roles with the Player Management team at NEC Harlequins by a season that kicked off with three away fixtures on the trot. Not surprising them, in the circumstances, that `Quins' lost three out of three against Leicester, Northampton and Manchester Sale, and only managed one win, against tenants London Scottish, from five games.

The season and the fortunes of the club changed with the sixth match of the season against the unbeaten Saracens. The 41-28 point victory over the London rivals provided a platform for NEC Harlequins to record six straight league victories and put the form book on its head.

An indifferent start to the New Year saw consecutive defeats at home to Leicester, Northampton and London Irish, and put pay to any Premiership hopes. February was not much better with a frustrating loss to Gloucester at Kingsholm and the end of NEC Harlequin's run in the Tetley Bitter Cup in the Quarter Final stages. A highlight in March was the seventeen points scored by John Schuster in the game against Richmond giving him the Allied Dunbar Premiership record. Schuster finished the season with a staggering 331 points to his name.

Out of the Cup and looking unlikely to qualify for a top six spot and therefore qualification for Europe NEC Harlequins galvanised into action and produced some excellent performances, especially away from home. The reward came on the 8th May with the double against Bath, the first ever victory at Recreation Ground and a place in Europe with two league games remaining.

With a final victory over Tetley Bitter Cup winners Wasps at the end of the season NEC Harlequins secured a creditable fourth place.

HARLEQUINS

Match No.	Date	H/A	Comp.	Opponents	Result & Score	Att.	15	14	13	12	11
1	05.09	A	AD1	Leicester	L 15-49	13,130	Officer	O'Leary	Power	Mensah(l)	Luger
2	12.09	A	AD1	Northampton	L 6-25	5,870	Officer	Keyter	Power	Schuster/2p	Luger
3	26.09	A	AD1	Sale	L 34-44	2,794	O'Leary(c)	Keyter	Power(o)	Schuster/2c5p	Luger/2t
4	03.10	H	AD1	London Scot	W 22-20	3,609	O'Leary	Keyter	Schuster/c5p	Ngauamo	Luger/t
5	10.10	A	AD1	Bedford	L 33-35	3,521	O'Leary	Keyter	Schuster/t3c4p	Mensah	Luger/t
6	17.10	H	AD1	Saracens	W 41-28	6,396	Williams/t	O'Leary/t	Officer	Schuster/3c5p	Luger
7	20.10	H	AD1	Gloucester	W 39-7	4,174	Williams(l)	O'Leary/2t	Officer(c)	Schuster/2c5p	Luger/t
8	27.10	H	AD1	W Hartlepool	W 25-10	2,476	Williams	O'Leary	Schuster/2c2p	Ngauamo/t	Luger/t
9	01.11	A	AD1	Wasps	W 22-21	6,627	Williams	O'Leary	Schuster/c4pdg	Officer/t	Luger
10	07.11	H	AD1	Newcastle	W 25-20	5,974	Williams	O'Leary(m)(p)	Schuster/c6p	Officer	Luger/t
11	21.11	H	AD1	Bath	W 43-31	6,875	Stewart	O'Leary	Schuster/2t3c4p	Officer	Keyter/2t
12	19.12	A	AD1	London Irish	L 16-20	5,460	Williams	O'Leary(m)	Schuster/c3p	Officer	Luger
13	26.12	H	AD1	Sale	W 17-15	5,100	Williams/t	O'Leary	Schuster/4p	Officer(m)	Luger
14	02.01	A	AD1	London Scot	W 35-24	4,600	Williams	O'Leary	Schuster/c6p	Officer(m)	Luger
15	16.01	H	AD1	Northampton*	L 17-24	8,500	Williams	O'Leary	Keyter(c)	Schuster/t2c	Luger
16	23.01	H	AD1	London Irish	L 17-22	7,824	Williams(m)	O'Leary/t	Mensah/t	Schuster/2cp	Luger
17	06.02	H	AD1	Leicester	L 9-34	6,212	Williams	O'Leary	Mensah	Schuster/3p	Luger
18	13.02	A	AD1	Gloucester	W 31-20	6,046	O'Leary/t(l)	Keyter	Mensah	Schuster/2c4p	Officer
19	27.03	H	AD1	Richmond	D 32-32	5,217	O'Leary	Mensah(z)	Carling	Schuster/t3c2p	Luger
20	17.04	H	AD1	Bedford	W 29-16	3,828	Williams/t	O'Leary/t	Carling(c)	Schuster/c4p	Luger/t
21	21.04	A	AD1	W Hartlepool	W 47-37	1,365	Williams	O'Leary/t	Schuster/5c3p(a)	Mensah/t	Luger/t
22	25.04	A	AD1	Saracens	W 36-30	8,719	Williams	O'Leary/t(m)	Carling	Mensah	Luger/t
23	03.05	A	AD1	Richmond	W 30-23	3,300	Williams	Keyter/t	Carling	Mensah(a)	Luger
24	08.05	A	AD1	Bath	W 17-13	8,200	Williams/t	Keyter	Mensah/t	Schuster/c(a)	Luger/t
25	11.05	A	AD1	Newcastle	L 23-30	4,133	Williams/t	O'Leary	Mensah	Carling	Keyter/t
26	19.05	H	AD1	Wasps	W 27-20	5,232	Williams	Keyter(D)	Mensah	Carling	Luger
A	09.01	H	TB4	Esher	W 46-10	3,759	Williams/2t(w/t)	O'Leary/3t	Schuster/2cp(b)	Keyter	Luger
B	30.01	A	TB5	London Scot	W 37-33		WIlliams	O'Leary/t	Mensah/2t	Schuster/tcp	Luger
C	27.02	A	TBqf	Gloucester	L 13-15	6,755	O'Leary	Keyter	Mensah(C)	Schuster/c2p	Luger

* after opponents name indicates a penalty try
Brackets after a player's name indicates he was replaced. eg (a) means he was replaced by replacement code "a" and so on.
/ after a player or replacement name is followed by any scores he made - eg /t, /c, /p, /dg or any combination of these

1998-99 HIGHLIGHTS

League debuts:
David Officer, John Schuster, Gary Halpin, Garrick Morgan, Zinzan Brooke, Colin Ridgway, David Barnes, Tom Murphy.

Ever Presents: None - most appearances Daren O'Leary 23 (1) & Dan Luger 23.

Players used: 34 plus 1 as replacement only.

Most Points in a season:

Pts	Player	T	C	P	DG
331	J Schuster	5	36	77	1
68	T Lacroix	4	9	7	3
55	D Luger	11	-	-	-
40	D O'Leary	8	-	-	-

MATCH FACTS

10	9	1	2	3	4	5	6	7	8	
Schuster/5p	Harries	Leonard	Wood	Halpin	Morgan	Davison	Bibby	Jenkins	Brooke	1
Wright(c)	Harries(o)	Leonard	Wood(p)	Halpin(q)	Morgan	Davison	Leach	Jenkins(s)	Brooke	2
Wright(t)	Harries	Barnes	Ridgway/t(f)	Yates(g)	Morgan(v)	Davison	Leach	Jenkins	Brooke	3
Lacroix	Harries	Barnes	Ridgway(f)	Yates(x)	Llewellyn	Collier(h)	Davison	Leach	Sheasby	4
Lacroix	Walshe	Barnes	Wood	Halpin(x)	Llewellyn	Morgan	Davison	Jenkins/t	Leach	5
Lacroix	Walshe	Barnes	Wood/t	Halpin(e)	Llewellyn	Morgan	Davison	Jenkins/t	Leach	6
Lacroix	Wright/t	Leonard	Wood(p)	Yates(g)	Llewellyn(i)	Morgan	Leach	Jenkins	Brooke	7
Lacroix	Harries/t(n)	Leonard	Wood(A)	Halpin(x)	Llewellyn	Collier(i)	Brooke(r)	Jenkins	Sheasby	8
Lacroix(c)(m)	Walshe(n)	Leonard	Wood	Yates(u)	Llewellyn	Morgan	Brooke	Jenkins(r)	Sheasby	9
Lacroix	Harries(n)	Leonard(u)	Wood	Yates	Llewellyn(i)	Morgan	Brooke	Jenkins	Sheasby(r)	10
Lacroix	Harries(n)	Barnes	Ridgway(A)	Halpin(q)	Llewellyn(i)	Morgan/t	Brooke	Jenkins(r)	Sheasby	11
Lacroix	Harries(n)	Leonard	Wood/t	Halpin(u)	Llewellyn	Morgan	Leach	Jenkins	Sheasby	12
Lacroix	Harries(n)	Leonard	Murphy	Halpin(u)	Llewellyn	Morgan(i)	Brooke	Jenkins	Sheasby	13
Lacroix	Harries/t(o)	Leonard	Murphy(p)	Halpin/t	Llewellyn(i)	Morgan	Brooke/t(j)	Leach	Sheasby	14
Lacroix	Harries(o)	Leonard	Woods/dg	Halpin(u)	Llewellyn	Morgan	Brooke	Jenkins	Sheasby	15
Lacroix(a)	Harries(o)	Leonard	Wood	Halpin(u)	Llewellyn	Morgan(i)	Brooke(j)	Leach	Sheasby	16
Pears	Harries	Leonard	Murphy(p)	Halpin(q)	Llewellyn	Morgan	Jenkins	Leach	Sheasby(B)(i)	17
Lacroix(n/t)	Harries	Leonard	Woods	Halpin(q)	Llewellyn/t	Collier	Davison	Jenkins(y)	Leach	18
Lacroix/2t	Harries	Leonard	Woods	Halpin/t	Llewellyn	Collier	Sheasby	Jenkins(k)	Leach	19
Wright	Harries	Barnes	Ridgway(f)	Halpin(q)	Llewellyn	Morgan	Davison(k)	Jenkins	Leach	20
Lacroix/tp	Walshe(n)	Leonard	Woods	Nebbett(g)	Llewellyn	Morgan	Brooke	Jenkins/t	Sheasby	21
Liley/t2c2p(w/c2p)	Walshe(n)	Leonard	Murphy(p)	Nebbett(g)	Llewellyn	Morgan	Brooke	Jenkins(r)	Sheasby/t	22
Lacroix/t3c2pdg	Walshe	Leonard	Murphy(p)	Nebbett(g)	Llewellyn	Morgan/t	Jenkins	Leach	Sheasby	23
Lacroix	Harries	Leonard	Woods	Nebbett	Llewellyn	Morgan	Sheasby	Jenkins	Leach(r)	24
Lacroix/2c2pdg(a)	Harries(n)	Barnes	Murphy(p)	Halpin(e)	Llewellyn	Collier	Davison	W-Cooper(f)	Leach	25
Lacroix/t3cpdg	Harries/t(n)	Leonard	Murphy(p)	Nebbett(g)	Llewellyn	Morgan	Sheasby/t	Jenkins	Brooke(r)	26
Liley/2c	Walshe(d)	Barnes(x)	Murphy	Yates	Morgan(s)	Davison	Jenkins/t	Leach	Sheasby	A
Liley/t2cp	Harries	Leonard	Murphy(f)	Yates(x)	Llewellyn	Davison	Jenkins	Leach	Sheasby	B
Liley	Harries/t	Barnes	Wood	Halpin	Llewellyn	Davison(h)	Jenkins	Leach	Sheasby	C

REPLACEMENTS: a- D Officer, b-S Power, c-P Mensah, d-H Harries, e-J Leonard, f-K Wood, g-G Halpin, h-G Morgan, i-B Davison, j-R Jenkins, k-Z Brooke, l-V Going, m-J Keyter, n-C Wright, o-N Walshe, p-C Ridgway, q-A Yates, r-A Leach, s-G Llewellyn, t-S Stewart, u-D Barnes, v-T Collier, w-T Lacroix, x-R Tebbett, y-C Sheasby, z-J Williams, A-T Murphy, B-S White-Cooper, C-W Carling

John Schuster re-wrote Harlequins' scoring records during the 1998-99 season. His 331 points smashed the previous record of 176 set two seasons ago by Thierry Lacroix. It was also a new record for a season in the top flight breaking the record of 291 set by Gareth Rees two seasons ago.
His 36 conversions and 77 penalties were also seasonal records beating the 29, Thierry Lacroix, and 38, Kent Bray, respectively.
Schuster also set a new record for points in a match with 28 against Bath last November. It beat the previous record of 27 set by David Pears back in October 1989.

Harlequins equalled their record for consecutive wins with six during October and November before losing narrowly at London Irish.

Both Daren O'Leary and Will Carling passed the 100 league appearances mark with O'Leary ending the season just ahead on 103.

John Schuster also set a new record for scoring in consecutive matches, he scored in his first 21matches for the club before missing the trip to Saracens.

HARLEQUINS

LEAGUE STATISTICS
compiled by Stephen McCormack

SEASON	Division	P	W	D	L	F	A	Pts Diff	Lge Pts	Lge Pos	Most Points	Most Tries
89-90	1	11	6	0	5	218	180	38	12	7	114 David Pears	5 Craig Luxton
90-91	1	12	8	0	4	267	162	105	16	3	120 David Pears	9 Andrew Harriman
91-92	1	12	5	1	6	213	207	6	11	8	109 David Pears	4 David Pears
92-93	1	12	5	1	6	197	187	10	11	8	57 Sturat Thresher	3 by 4 players
93-94	1	18	8	0	10	333	287	46	16	6	143 Kent Bray	11 Daren O'Leary
94-95	1	18	6	1	11	275	348	-73	13	8	103 Paul Challinor	4 Peter Mensah
95-96	1	18	13	0	5	524	314	210	26	3	112 Paul Challinor	14 Daren O'Leary
96-97	1	22	15	0	7	745	416	329	30	3	176 Thierry Lacroix	15 Daren O'Leary
97-98	1	22	8	0	14	516	645	-129	16	10	109 Thierry Lacroix	9 Daren O'Leary
98-99	1	26	16	1	9	690	653	37	33	4	331 John Schuster	11 Dan Luger

BIGGEST MARGINS

Home Win	71pts - 89-18 v Orrell 5.10.96
Away Win	70pts - 91-21 v W. Hartlepool 23.3.96
Home Defeat	31pts - 26-57 v Wasps 17.9.94
Away Defeat	48 - 14-62 v Lon. Irish 25.4.98

MOST CONSECUTIVE

Appearances	42 Andy Mullins 16.11.91-30.4.94
Matches scoring Tries	5 Daren O'Leary
Matches scoring points	21 JohnSchuster
Victories	6 (twice)
Defeats	5

MOST POINTS

Scored at Home	89 v Orrell 5.10.96
Scored Away	91 v West Hartlepool 23.3.96
Conceded at Home	57 v Wasps 17.9.94
Conceded Away	62 v London Irish 25.4.98

MOST TRIES

Scored in a match	14 v W. Hartlepool 23.3.96
Conceded in a match	9 v Wasps 17.9.94

MOST APPEARANCES

by a forward	118 (2) Andy Mullins
by a back	103(2)1 Daren O'Leary

	MOST IN A SEASON	MOST IN A CAREER	MOST IN A MATCH	
Points	331 JohnSchuster 98-99	431 David Pears 89-96	28 JohnSchuster	v Bath 21.11.98 (H)
Tries	15 Daren O'Leary 96-97	58 Daren O'Leary 93-99	4 Daren O'Leary	v Gloucester 31.8.96 (H)
Conversions	36 JohnSchuster 98-99	57 David Pears 89-96	9 Paul Challinor	v W Hartlepool 23.3.96 (A)
Penalties	77 JohnSchuster 98-99	83 David Pears 89-96	7 David Pears	v Rosslyn Park 7.12.91 (A)
Drop Goals	7 David Pears 95-96	14 David Pears 89-96	3 David Pears	v Wasps 16.9.95 (H)

HARLEQUINS PLAYING SQUAD

BACKS

BACKS	Ht.	Wt.	Birthdate	Birthplace	CLUB	League Apps	Tries	Pts	
Jamie Williams	6.1	13.09	16.03.76	Marston(NZ)	Harlequins	324(1)	10	50	
Middlesex U21.									
David Officer	6.2	14.04	09.05.73	Aberdeen	Harlequins	11(5)	1	5	
Canada									
Daren O'Leary	6.0	13.00	27.06.73	Harold Wood	Harlequins	103	58	304	
England A, Emerging, U21.					Saracens	10	3	15	
Dan Luger	6.1	14.00	11.01.75	Chiswick	Harlequins	43	19	95	
John Schuster	6.0	14.03	17.01.64	W Samoa	Harlequins	22	5		331
					Blackheath	5	1		40
Peter Mensah	6.0	13.08	10.01.66	Ghana	Harlequins	60(8)	19	95	
England A, Emerging, London.									
Jason Keyter	5.11	13.02	20.12.73	Port Elizabeth	Harlequins	33(23)	15	75	
England A, U21, London.									
Johnny Ngauamo	6.1	15.03	20.07.70	Tonga	Harlequins	16(1)	4	20	
Auckland Blues, Tonga.									
Rob Liley	6.1	13.04	03.04.70	Wakefield	Harlequins	12(2)	4	95	
England A, U21. Other clubs:Wakefield 23/2/214, Sale 25/3/209					Leicester	11(2)	3	44	
Thierry Lacroix	6.0	13.05	02.03.67		Harlequins	46(2)	9	413	
France , Dax, Natal									
Nick Walshe	5.10	13.00	01.11.73	Chiswick	Harlequins	30(8)	7	39	
England Students					Rosslyn Park	23(-)	2	10	
Huw Harries	5.11	13.07	21.02.73	Cardiff	Harlequins	41(8)	13	65	
Wales A, Cardiff, Llanelli,									

FORWARDS

FORWARDS	Ht.	Wt.	Birthdate	Birthplace	CLUB	League Apps	Tries	Pts
Jason Leonard	5.10	17.02	14.08.68	Barking	Harlequins			
England , B, Colts, British Lions.					Saracens	19	1	4
Ricky Nebbitt	5.11	17.00	16.08.77	Kingston	Harlequins	11(6)	1	5
England U18.								
Alan Yates	6.0	18.00	05.02.63	Sale	Harlequins	14(7)	-	-
Wakefield 3/-/-					Sale	14(2)		
Keith Wood	6.0	16.10	27.01.72	Limerick	Harlequins	43(6)	9	48
Ireland , A, U21, British Lions, Garryowen , Munster.								
Garrick Morgan	6.7	18.02	25.01.70	Sydney	Harlequins	21(1)	2	10
.Australia, Queensland								
Gareth Llewellyn	6.6	18.00	27.02.69	Cardiff	Harlequins	58(4)	3	15
Wales , Youth, Llanharan, Neath.								
Zinzan Brooke	6.3	18.00	14.02.65	Waiuku	Harlequins	16(2)	1	5
US Eagles, Cincinatti Wolfhounds.								
Bill Davison	6.6	16.06	08.04.69	Zambia	Harlequins	30(9)	2	10
England A, Hawkes Bay.					Rosslyn Park	24	2	10
Rory Jenkins	6.2	16.05	29.06.70	Leicester	Harlequins	86(4)	6	30
England A, Emerging, Students.					London Irish	15	1	5
Chris Sheasby	6.3	16.00	30.11.66	Windsor	Harlequins	81(4)	5	25
England, A, 7s.					Wasps	22(5)	8	40
Adam Leach	6.2	15.06	24.11.71	Corowa(Aust)	Harlequins	28(9)	-	-
New South Wales, Eastwood.								
Steve White-Cooper	6.4	16.00	15.07.74	Cape Town	Harlequins	4(2)	-	-
Tim Collier	6.6	19.04	27.10.77	Farnborough	Harlequins	8(4)		

HARLEQUINS

FACT FILE

Founded: 1866
Nickname: Quins

Colours: Light blue, magenta, chocolate, french grey, light green & black
Change colours: None

GROUND Stoop Memorial Ground, Langhorn Drive, Twickenham. TW2 7SX
Tel: 0181 410 6000 Advance Ticket Line: 0181 410 6010 Fax: 0181 410 6001
Capacity: 8,000 Seated Covered: 4,600 Uncovered: 2,850

Directions: Langhorn Drive is off the westbound carriageway of theA316 Chertsey Road, 450 yards west of RFU roundabout. No entry for vehicles from Craneford Way
Nearest Railway Station: Twickenham (BR). 12 minutes walk, proceed towards RFUground, turn left into Court Way, then left into Craneford Way, ground at far end.

Car Parking: Limited amount available @ £5

Admission: (all seated & non-members)

Season	Adult £240/204/144	OAPs £240/144/120	Youth £240/120/60
Matchday	Adults £20/17/12	OAPs £20/12/10	Youth £20/10/5/3/1

Club Shop: Mon-Sat 10-5, contact Steve Rushworth 0181 410 6050
Mail order Mon-Fri 10-5 Freephone 07000 478467

Clubhouse: Matchdays 12-late, Evening games 18.30-23.00
Snacks & light meals available no restaurant.
Functions: 500-600 seated, 1000 buffet, 2000 bar.
Contact Catering Mgr 0181 410 6054, Fax 0181 410 6019

PROGRAMME

Size: A5
Pages: 40
Price: £2
Editor: Mark Anderson 0181 410 6049

ADVERTISING RATES
Contact - Simon Slater 0181 410 6000

Zinzan Brooke celebrates victory over Bath.
Photo: Joe McCabe

LEICESTER F.C.

Chief Executive	Peter Wheeler	Leicester Football Club plc, Aylestone Road, Leicester LE2 7TR Tel: 0116 254 1607 Fax: 0116 285 4766
Chairman	Peter Tom	
Operations Director	Bob Harrison	
Company Secretary	Adrian Jones	
First Team Manager	Dean Richards	
Press Officer	Stuart Farmer	2 Lundy Close, Hinckley, Leics. LE10 0SS 01455 631934 (B) 01455 447440 (Fax)

Leicester's 1998-99 Premiership campaign began with a seven try, 49-15, victory over Harlequins at Welford Road and, after disposing of London Scottish, Northampton and Bedford on the following three Saturdays, Leicester were riding high at the top of the table.

Team Manager Dean Richards already had potentially the best pack in the country and during the summer added top quality international backs to the equation, signing Wallaby Pat Howard, Tim Stimpson from Newcastle Falcons and burly Canadian wing Dave Lougheed. Richards also recruited rugby league maestro Phil Larder who worked tirelessly with the team, to produce one of the most miserly defences in the Premiership.

The title campaign stuttered in October with successive losses away to Saracens and London Irish, but by 1 November a 45-15 victory over West Hartlepool put Leicester back on the top of the table from where they were never caught. That was despite a third league loss at Wasps in November,

when short of eight players on England World Cup duty Leicester went down 45-17. They would go on to lose just once more in the Premiership - at Bath in April, and eventually finish the season with a six points clear of second placed local rivals Northampton. That was despite the team being dogged by injuries, Will Greenwood, Stuart Potter Joel Stransky and Pat Howard being the most notable absentees.

Involvement in the Tetley's Bitter Cup ended with the controversial 15-13 quarter final defeat at Reading's Madejski Stadium. An RFU disciplinary hearing later rescinded the white card Martin Johnson received from referee Steve Lander during the game, but the damage was already done, Richmond scoring 12 points whilst Johnson was off the field of play.

On the international front Tigers were well represented during the Five Nations championship and supplied a club record nine players, one quarter of Englands' squad to tour Australia this summer, Leon Lloyd earning a deserved call-up and Martin Johnson taking over the captaincy from Lawrence Dallaglio.

Stuart Farmer, Press Officer, Leicester Tigers

Leicester celebrate after receiving the Allied Dunbar Premiership Trophy at Welford Road

Photo courtesy of Neville Chadwick Photography

LEICESTER

Match No.	Date	H/A	Comp.	Opponents	Result & Score	Att.	15	14	13	12	11
1	05.09	H	AD1	Harlequins	W 49-15	13,130	Stimpson	Lloyd/2t	Potter	Howard	Ezulike/t(h)
2	12.09	A	AD1	London Scot	W 38-3	2,138	Stimpson/t	Lloyd	Potter	Howard	Ezulike/t
3	19.09	H	AD1	Northampton	W 35-25	13,292	Stimpson/t	Lloyd(l)	Potter	Howard	Ezulike/t
4	26.09	A	AD1	Bedford	W 32-23	4,165	Stimpson/cp	Lloyd	Potter/t	Howard	Ezulike/t
5	11.10	A	AD1	Saracens	L 10-22	17,346	Stimpson	Lloyd/t	Potter	Howard(p)	Ezulike
6	17.10	H	AD1	Sale	W 31-15	9,861	Stimpson(q)	Lloyd	Greenwood	Howard(r)	Ezulike
7	20.10	A	AD1	London Irish	L 23-24	2,950	Stimpson	Lloyd/t(q)	Greenwood	Howard	Ezulike
8	24.10	H	AD1	Richmond	W 27-0	8,443	Murphy	Lloyd(q)	Overend	Stuart	Ezulike
9	01.11	A	AD1	W Hartlepool	W 45-15	1,846	Murphy/2tp	Lloyd	Overend/2t	Stuart	Ezulike
10	07.11	H	AD1	Bath	W 36-13	15,873	Murphy	Lloyd	Greenwood/2t	Stuart/t	Ezulike
11	15.11	A	AD1	Wasps	L 17-45	6,027	Murphy/t	Lloyd	Overend	Stuart	Horak
12	12.12	H	AD1	Newcastle	W 31-18	11,226	Murphy/2c2p	Lougheed	Potter	Stuart/t	Lloyd
13	19.12	A	AD1	Gloucester	W 23-18	7,222	Stimpson/6p	Lloyd	Potter	Howard	Lougheed/t
14	26.12	H	AD1	Bedford	W 26-0	10,689	Stimpson/c3p	Lloyd(q)	Potter	Howard(r)	Lougheed/t
15	16.01	H	AD1	London Scot	W 24-12	9,985	Murphy/2p(a/p)	Lloyd/t	Potter	Howard(r)	Lougheed
16	23.01	H	AD1	Gloucester	W 23-16	11,394	Stimpson/c2p	Lloyd	Potter(l)	Howard	Lougheed/2t
17	26.01	A	AD1	Richmond	W 23-11	7,981	Stimpson/2p	Lloyd	Joiner	Howard	Lougheed/t
18	06.02	A	AD1	Harlequins	W 34-9	6,212	Stimpson	Lloyd/2t(q)	Joiner	Howard(r)	Lougheed
19	13.02	H	AD1	London Irish	W 31-10	15,132	Stimpson	Lloyd/t	Joiner	Howard	Lougheed/t
20	13.03	A	AD1	Northampton*	W 22-15	10,000	Stimpson/c2p	Lloyd(b)	Joiner/t	Stuart(t)	Lougheed
21	27.03	H	AD1	Wasps	W 16-6	12,449	Stimpson/c3p	Lloyd(b)	Joiner	Howard	Lougheed
22	03.04	A	AD1	Bath	L 16-24	8,500	Stimpson/3p	Ezulike(A)	Joiner	Howard/c	Lougheed
23	17.04	H	AD1	Saracens	W 25-18	14,823	Stimpson/c6p	Lloyd	Joiner	Stuart	Lougheed
24	24.04	A	AD1	Sale	W 41-17	4,800	Stimpson/2c4p	Lloyd	Joiner	Stuart	Lougheed/t
25	02.05	A	AD1	Newcastle	W 21-12	5,207	Stimpson/7p	Lloyd	Joiner(m)	Stuart	Lougheed
26	16.05	H	AD1	W Hartlepool	W 72-37	12,957	Stimpson/5c(t/2tc)	Lloyd	Joiner/t	Howard/t	Lougheed/t
A	09.01	H	TB4	Barking	W 65-6	4,884	Stimpson/t3c	Lloyd/4t	Potter(t)	Stuart/t	Lougheed/t
B	30.01	H	TB5	Leeds	W 49-0	5,930	Stimpson	Lloyd	Joiner	Howard(r)	Lougheed
C	27.02	A	TBqf	Richmond	L 13-15	7,088	Stimpson/p	Lloyd(b)	Joiner	Stuart	Lougheed

* after opponents name indicates a penalty try
Brackets after a player's name indicates he was replaced. eg (a) means he was replaced by replacement code "a" and so on.
/ after a player or replacement name is followed by any scores he made - eg /t, /c, /p, /dg or any combination of these

1998-99 HIGHLIGHTS

League debuts:
Tim Stimpson, Pat Howard, Dave Lougheed, H Toews, Jon Stuart,

Ever Presents: None - most appearances 25 Leon Lloyd and Darren Garforth

Players used: 31 plus 7 as replacement only.

Most Points in a season:

Pts	Player	T	C	P	DG
202	J Stransky	7	34	33	-
161	T Stimpson	2	14	41	-
80	N Back	16	-	-	-
46	G Murphy	5	3	5	-
40	D Lougheed	8	-	-	-
40	L Lloyd	8	-	-	-

MATCH FACTS

10	9	1	2	3	4	5	6	7	8	
Stransky/t4c2p	Healey/t	Jelley(i)	Cockeril/tl	Garforth	Johnson	v Heerden(j)	Gustard	Back/t	Corry	1
Stransky/t3c4p	Healey	Rowntree	Cockerill	Garforth	Johnson	V Heerden(j)	Gustard/t	Back(k)	Corry	2
Stransky/3c3p	Healey/t(m)	Rowntree(d)	Cockerill	Garforth	Johnson	V Heerden	Gustard	Back/t(k)	Corry	3
Stransky/2cp	Healey	Jelley(o)	Cockerill(n)	Garforth	Johnson	v Heerden	Gustard	Moody(g/t)	Corry	4
Stransky/cp	Healey	Jelley(i)	Cockerill(n)	Garforth	Johnson	v Heerden	Gustard	Back	Corry	5
Stransky/2c4p	Healey	Jelley(s)	West	Garforth	Johnson	V Heerden(j)	Gustard/t	Back/2t(k)	Corry	6
Stransky/2c3p	Healey/t	Jelley(s)	West	Garforth	Johnson	v Heerden(j)	Gustard(k)	Back	Corry	7
Stransky/t2c2p	Healey	Jelley(s)	Cockerill(n)	Garforth/t	Johnson	Fletcher	Gustard(w)	Back/t(k)	Corry	8
Stransky/t4c3p	Healey	Jelley(s)	Cockerill(n)	Garforth	Johnson	Fletcher	Moody	Back	Gustard(w)	9
Stransky/t4cp	Healey(m)	Jelley(i)	Cockerill(n)	Garforth	Johnson	Fletcher(y)	Gustard/t(k)	Back	Corry	10
Stransky/2cp	Hamilton	Jelley	West	Joews	Fletcher	Addison(x)	Wingham	Moody	Gustard/t	11
Howard(a/2p)	Healey	Jelley(i)	Cockerill(n)	Garforth	Johnson	v Heerden	Gustard	Back/2t	Corry	12
Murphy	Healey	Rowntree(d)	Cockerill	Garforth	Johnson	v Heerden	Gustard	Back	Corry	13
Murphy	Healey	Rowntree	Cockerill/t	Garforth(d)	Johnson	v Heerden(j)	Gustard	Back/t	Corry	14
Stransky	Healey(m)	Rowntree(d)	Cockerill(n)	Garforth	Corry	v Heerden/2t	Moody	Back	W Johnson	15
Stransky/t	Healey	Jelley	Cockerill(n)	Garforth	Johnson	v Heerden	W Johnson	Moody	Corry	16
Stransky/c	Healey	Rowntree(d/t)	Cockerill(n)	Garforth	Johnson/t	v Heerden	W Johnson	Moody	Corry	17
Stransky/t3cp	Healey	Rowntree(d)	Cockerill(n)	Garforth	Johnson	v Heerden	Moody/t(w)	Back/t	Corry	18
Stransky/7p	Healey	Rowntree(d)	Cockerill(n)	Garforth	Johnson	v Heerden	Moody(w)	Back	Corry	19
Howard	Hamilton	Jelley(i)	Cockerill(n)	Garforth	Johnson	v Heerden	Moody(w)	Back	Corry/t	20
Murphy	Hamilton	Rowntree(d)	Cockerill(n)	Garforth	Johnson	v Heerden	Moody	Back/t	Corry	21
Murphy	Hamilton	Rowntree(d)	Cockerill(n)	Garforth	Johnson	v Heerden	Moody(f)	Back/t	Corry(w)	22
Howard	Hamilton(c)	Rowntree(d)	Cockerill(n)	Garforth	Johnson	v Heerden	Moody	Back	Corry/t	23
Howard	Healey/t(m)	Rowntree(d)	Cockerill(n)	Garforth	Johnson	v Heerden	Moody(f)	Back/2t	Corry/t(w)	24
Howard(t)	Healey	Jelley(i)	Cockerill(n)	Garforth	Johnson	v Heerden	Moody	Back	Corry	25
Stransky(r)	Healey/2t	Rowntree(d)	Cockerill(n)	Garforth	Johnson	v Heerden	Moody(f/t)	Back/3t	Corry/t(z)	26
Stransky/2c	Hamilton/2t	Jelley	Freshwater/t	Rowntree	Corry	v Heerden(n)	Hurrell(z)	Moody/t	W Johnson	A
Stransky/7c	Healey/t(m)	Jelley/t	Cockerill(n)	Rowntree(e)	Johnson(j)	v Heerden	Moody	Back/2t(t)	Corry/t(w)	B
Howard	Hamilton	Rowntree(d)	Cockerill(n)	Garforth	Johnson	v Heerden	Moody(f)	Back/t	Corry/t	C

REPLACEMENTS: a- T Stimpson b- N Ezulike c - A Healey d - D Jelley e - D Garforth f - P Gustard g - N Back h - D Lougheed i - G Rowntree j - N Fletcher k - L Moody l - C Joiner m - J Hamilton n - D West o - H Joews p - W Greenwood q - M Horak r - J Stuart s - P Freshwater t - G Murphy u - A Goode v - G Beaconsall w - W Johnson x - B Smith y - M Poole z - A Balding A - J Ferris

Joel Stransky tops the 200 point mark for the second successive season which was shortened because of injury and only allowed him 17 starts.

England flanker Neil Back smashed the record for tries in a season with 16 which easily surpassed the previous record of 9. It was also the best ever haul by a forward in the top division and one short of Domonic Chapman's record set the season before. The previous best by a forward was 10 by Richmond No 8 Scott Quinnell.

On the last day of the season Leicester beat West Hartlepool 72-37 for their highest ever score in a league match. It beat the 66-5 win over fellow North East side Newcastle back in March 1994.
They also ran in a new recod of 12 tries beating the 11 they scored against Bedford back in September 1989.

Prop Darren Garforth extended his club record for league appearances to 142 with another 25 during the 98-99 campaign.

LEICESTER

LEAGUE STATISTICS
compiled by Stephen McCormack

SEASON	Division	P	W	D	L	F	A	Pts Diff	Lge Pts	Lge Pos	Most Points	Most Tries
89-90	1	11	6	0	5	248	184	64	12	5	126 John Liley	7 John Liley
90-91	1	12	8	0	4	244	140	104	16	4	110 John Liley	8 Rory Underwood
91-92	1	12	6	1	5	262	216	46	13	6	125 John Liley	9 Rory Underwood
92-93	1	12	9	0	3	220	116	104	18	3	106 John Liley	3 Rory Underwood Nigel Richardson
93-94	1	18	14	0	4	425	210	215	28	2	202 Jez Harris	8 Tony Underwood
94-95	1	18	15	1	2	400	239	161	31	1	181 Jez Harris	5 Steve Hackney
95-96	1	18	15	0	3	476	242	234	30	2	272 John Liley	8 Rory Underwood
96-97	1	22	14	1	7	600	395	205	29	4	195 John Liley	9 Penalty Tries
97-98	1	22	12	2	8	569	449	120	26	4	253 Joel Stransky	9 Will Greenwood
98-99	1	26	22	0	4	771	423	348	44	1	202 Joel Stransky	16 Neil Back

BIGGEST MARGINS

Home Win	61pts - 66-5 v Newcastle Gosforth 12.3.94
Away Win	39pts - 55-16 v London Irish 17.5.98
Home Defeat	10pts - 21-31 v Harlequins 26.11.89
Away Defeat	38pts - 9-47 v Bath 12.4.97

MOST CONSECUTIVE

Appearances	32 Darren Garforth 28.3.92-3.4.94
Matches scoring Tries	3 Rory Underwood/Joel Stransky
Matches scoring points	24 John Liley
Victories	9
Defeats	3

MOST POINTS

Scored at Home	72 v West Hartlepool 16.5.99
Scored Away	55 v London Irish 17.5.98
Conceded at Home	31 v Harlequins 26.11.89
Conceded Away	47 v Bath 12.4.97

MOST TRIES

Scored in a match	12 v W Hartlepool 16.5.99
Conceded in a match	7 v Bath 11.1.92

MOST APPEARANCES

by a forward	142 (2) Darren Garforth
by a back	100 (2) John Liley

	MOST IN A SEASON	MOST IN A CAREER	MOST IN A MATCH	
Points	272 John Liley 95-96	1070 John Liley 88-97	31 John Liley	v Rosslyn P. 21.3.92 (H)
Tries	16 Neil Back 98-99	43 Rory Underwood 87-97	4 Tony Underwood	v Newcastle G. 12.3.94 (H)
Conversions	39 Joel Stransky 97-98	129 John Liley 88-97	7 John Liley	v Rosslyn P. 21.3.92 (H)
Penalties	64 John Liley 95-96	232 John Liley 88-97	8 John Liley	v Bristol 28.10.95 (H)
Drop Goals	13 Jez Harris 94-95	37 Jez Harris 87-95	3 Jez Harris	v Wasps 23.11.91 (H) v Bath 15.4.95 (H)

LEICESTER PLAYING SQUAD

BACKS

	Ht.	Wt.	Birthdate	Birthplace	CLUB	League Apps	Tries	Pts
Tim Stimpson	6.3	15.13	10.09.73	Liverpool	Leicester	20(2)	2	161
England.Other clubs: W Hartlepool 23/7/203					Newcastle	23(2)	14	138
Leon Lloyd	6.4	14.00	22.09.77	Coventry	Leicester	48	12	60
England U21, Colts.								
Craig Joiner	5.10	14.00	21.04.74	Glasgow	Leicester	34(2)	11	55
Scotland , A, U21, Schools.								
Stuart Potter	5.11	14.07	11.11.67	Lichfield	Leicester	98	17	85
England , A, B.					Nottingham	30	5	20
Will Greenwood	6.4	15.00	20.10.72	Blackburn	Leicester	33(1)	16	80
England , A, Students, U21. Other clubs: Waterloo 4/1/5					Harlequins	24	6	47
Austin Healey	5.10	13.07	26.10.73	Wallasey	Leicester			
England , A, Students, U21. Other club:Waterloo 20/3/18					Orrell	32(1)	4	27
Joel Stransky	5.11	13.05	16.07.67	Johannesburg	Leicester	46(1)	14	556
South Africa 23, Barbarians.								
Dave Lougheed	6.2	14.09	11.04.68	Toronto	Leicester	15(1)	8	40
Fiji								
Pat Howard	5.10	13.09	14.11.73	Brisbane	Leicester	22	1	7
Australia.								
Jamie Hamilton	5.9	12.06	01.07.70	Guildford	Leicester	17(15)	3	15
					London Scottish	5(1)	1	5
James Overend	5.11	14.05	01.12.76	Leeds	Leicester	13(3)	3	15
Gordean Murphy	6.0	12.07	19.04.78	Dublin	Leicester	13(4)	5	46
Nnamdi Ezulike	6.0	13.06	16.02.71	Nigeria	Leicester	11(3)	4	20

FORWARDS

	Ht.	Wt.	Birthdate	Birthplace	CLUB	League Apps	Tries	Pts
Graham Rowntree	6.0	17.05	18.04.71	Stockton on Tees	Leicester	116(7)	2	10
England , A, U21, U18, Colts.								
Darren Garforth	5.10	18.00	09.04.66	Coventry	Leicester	142(2)	5	24
England .					Nuneaton		2	8
Richard Cockerill	5.10	15.10	16.12.70	Rugby	Leicester	113(3)	8	40
England .					Coventry	12	-	-
Dorian West	5.11	16.00	03.10.67	Wrexham	Leicester	15(26)	1	5
England , A.					Nottingham	41	6	30
Martin Johnson	6.7	18.04	09.03.70	Solihull	Leicester	130(1)	4	20
England , A, U21, Colts, U18, British Lions.								
Matt Poole	6.7	18.11	06.02.69	Leicester	Leicester	94(4)	5	25
England Emerging, U21, Colts, U18.								
Neil Fletcher	6.6	17.10	04.06.76	Walsall	Leicester			
Neil Back	5.10	14.04	16.01.69	Coventry	Leicester	123	40	199
England, A, B, U21, Colts, U18.				Nottingham				
Martin Corry	6.5	17.00	12.10.73	Birmingham	Leicester	37(3)	4	20
England , A, Emerging, U21, U18. Newcastle 24(1)/7/35					Bristol	29	8	40
Perry Freshwater	6.0	17.05	27.07.73	Wellington	Leicester	3(17)	-	-
Lewis Moody	6.4	15.11	12.06.78	Berkshire	Leicester	25(11)	2	10
Paul Gustard	6.4	17.03	02.02.76	Newcastle OT	Leicester	23(11)	9	45
Fritz van Heerdan	6.6	16.07	29.06.70	South Africa	Leicester	37	3	15
South Africa 13								
Will Johnson	6.4	17.04	18.03.74	Solihull	Leicester			

LEICESTER TIGERS

FACT FILE

Founded: 1880
Nickname: Tigers

Colours: Dark green with red and white hoops
Change colours: Navy with red band

GROUND Aylestone Road., Leicester. LE2 7TR
Tel: 0116 254 1607 Fax: 0116 285 4766
Capacity: 16,250 Seated: 12,000 Standing: 4,000
Web site: http://www.tigers.co.uk
e-mail: ltigers@compuserve.com

Directions: From M1, junction 21. Along the A5460 into Leicester. At the Post House Hotel traffic lights turn right onto B5418 (Braunstone Lane East). After 1 mile turn left at `T' junction traffic lights onto A426 (Aylestone Road). Ground 2 miles on right.

Nearest Railway Station: Leicester (London Road).
The ground is about 3/4 mile walk along Waterloo Way.
(Station Tel. No. 0116 248 1000)

Car Parking: None available at the ground.

Admission :

Season Standing Adults £95, Children £45, OAPs £65.
Seated Adults £120-220, Children £55-160, OAPs £70-170

Matchday Standing Adults £10, Children £5, OAPs £8.
Seated Adults £12-£20, Children £6-£15, OAPs £10-£16

Club Shop: Yes, manager Sarah Watson, 0116 254 0077

Clubhouse: 3 bars with snacks, barmeals & restaurant available.
Functions: Various rooms available.
For details contact Joanna Fairey, 0116 254 1607

PROGRAMME

Size: 170mm x 240mm Pages: 37 Price: £2.00
Editor: Stuart Farmer, Press Off. 01455 631934

ADVERTISING RATES - On application to Marketing Manager - Tracey Branson, c/o Leicester FC

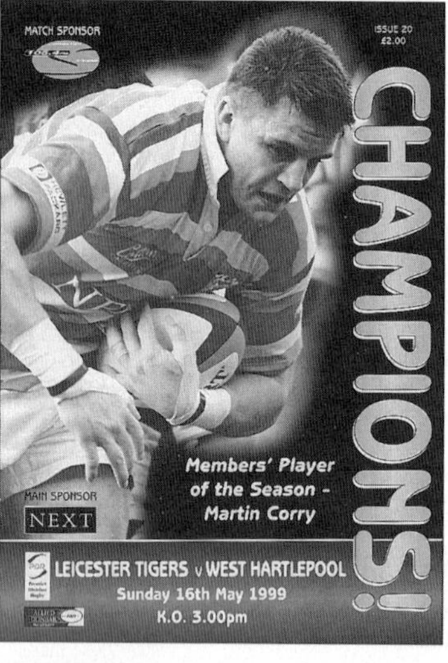

Martin Corry with his trophy as Tigers' Player of the Season.

Photo courtesy of Neville Chadwick Photography

LONDON IRISH R.F.C.

Media Liaison Officer Patrick Lennon
Tel: 01753 893050
Fax: 01753 893051
email: patrick@patricklennon.com

Chief Executive Geoff Huckstep

Director of Rugby Dick Best

Official Photographer Michael Peel
Tel: 0208 949 5082

Sunbury Administration

Tel: 01932 783034
Fax: 01932 784462
email: commercial@london-irish-rugby.com

London Irish celebrated its first hundred years with style both on and off the pitch last season.

The close season appointment of Dick Best as director of rugby, followed in early autumn by the arrival of Geoff Huckstep as chief executive, signalled the intentions of the Sunbury club to make an impact not just in the Premiership but also in Europe.

A hectic round of travel and negotiation saw Dick Best start the season with a much changed squad and coaching staff. The early season results were disappointing as the new look team struggled to adjust to playing with each other and to the demands of the Premiership.

By November results started going in the club's favour. A 20-16 home win over local rivals, NEC Harlequins, on 19th December sent the 5,460 crowd home in fine pre-Christmas spirits! This victory started a sequence of nine consecutive wins, which included Newcastle, Northampton (twice), NEC Harlequins and Gloucester. It took an away defeat to the eventual champions, Leicester to bring the sequence, the longest in the club's history in the Premiership to an end.

Not only were the victories enjoyable and a source of vital points, the players won universal praise from home and away fans for the attractive style of rugby that they played.

The final quarter of the season was marked by defeat by Wasps in the quarter final of the Tetley's Bitter Cup and by the first every home victory over Bath in the Premiership played in front of a 6,500 crowd.

London Irish finished the season in seventh place in the Premiership, exactly as forecast by Mr. Best in September 1998, in good shape to both progress in the league and European Conference.

The club's thriving amateur section continued to progress with the senior side winning the London Club's Cup and the Under 19s winning the National Club's Cup, the first national trophy won by Irish in its hundred years!

Off the field the Centenary was celebrated by the publication of a definitive history of the club, by a number of social events, the highlight of which was the centenary dinner in The London Hilton attended by over 1,000 guests. A fitting post-script to a memorable season, a charity CD `Sons from the Top Bar', that infamous venue much loved by visiting supporters at Sunbury, raised over £10,000 for the Cystic Fibrosis Society, thanks to all those wonderful fans who visited Sunbury and brought a copy.

L-R - **Back Row:** Neal Hatley, Robert Todd, Richard Kirke, Ryan Strudwick, Nick Harvey, Isaac Feaunati, Mike Howe, Adrian Flavin **Middle Row:** Matt Jones, Nick Burrows, Kevin Putt, Simon Berridge, Rob Gallacher, Jake Boer, Peter Richards, Brendan Venter, Matt Jarvis, Jarrod Cunningham, Rob Hardwick, Mike Worsley, Peter Rogers, Stephen Bachop (loan player), Simon Amor. **Front Row:** Kris Fullman, Kieran Campbell, Justin Bishop, Niall Woods, Conor O'Shea, Malcolm O'Kelly, Kevin Spicer, Kieron Dawson, James Brown

LONDON IRISH

Match No.	Date	H/A	Comp.	Opponents	Result & Score	Att.	15	14	13	12	11
1	05.09	A	AD1	Gloucester	L 22-29	5,267	O'Shea	Bishop	Venter	Burrows	Woods/c5p(j)
2	13.09	A	AD1	W Hartlepool	W 44-20	2,059	O'Shea/t	Bishop/t	Venter/t	Todd	Woods/t5c3p
3	19.09	H	AD1	Wasps	L 24-36	3,800	O'Shea/p	Bishop(j)(s)	Venter/t	Todd	Woods/tc3p
4	27.09	A	AD1	Newcastle	W 23-21	4,184	O'Shea/tc2p	Berridge	Todd	Venter	Woods/cp(z)
5	03.10	H	AD1	Richmond	L 29-33	3,900	O'Shea	Berridge(z)	Todd/t	Venter	Woods/2c5p
6	10.10	A	AD1	Bath	L 20-23	7,000	O'Shea/t	Bishop	Todd(z)	Venter	Woods/2tcp
7	20.10	H	AD1	Leicester	W 24-23	2,950	O'Shea/tdg	Bishop	Burrows	Venter	Woods/c3p
8	24.10	H	AD1	Northampton	L 10-26	2,560	O'Shea	Bishop	Burrows	Venter	Woods/tcp
9	08.11	H	AD1	Sale	L 25-31	2,300	O'Shea	Bishop	Burrows/2t	Venter	Woods/2c2p
10	15.11	A	AD1	London Scot	W 23-17	3,000	Cunningham/cp	Todd	Burrows	Venter	Woods/tc2p
11	21.11	H	AD1	Bedford	W 30-19	2,200	Cunningham/2c2p(n)	Berridge/t	Burrows/2t	Venter	Woods/cp
12	13.12	A	AD1	Saracens	L 26-40	10,373	O'Shea	Bishop(n)	Burrows	Venter	Cunningham/2c4p
13	19.12	H	AD1	Harlequins*	W 20-16	5,460	O'Shea	Bishop	Burrows(n)	Venter	Cunningham/2c2p(b)
14	26.12	A	AD1	Richmond	W 25-13	9,621	O'Shea	Bishop	Burrows	Venter	Cunningham/c6p
15	02.01	H	AD1	Newcastle	W 16-14	4,260	O'Shea	Bishop/t	Todd	Venter	Cunningham/c3p(b
16	05.01	A	AD1	Northampton	W 32-8	7,450	O'Shea	Berridge	Burrows/t	Venter	Woods/4t2cp
17	16.01	H	AD1	W Hartlepool	W 43-21	2,129	O'Shea	Bishop	Burrows/2t	Venter	Cunningham/4c(b)
18	23.01	A	AD1	Harlequins	W 22-17	7,824	O'Shea/2t	Bishop/t	Burrows	Venter	Woods/2cp
19	07.02	H	AD1	Gloucester	W 42-20	5,020	Cunningham/t2cp	Berridge/2t	Todd	Venter	Woods/tc
20	13.02	A	AD1	Leicester	L 10-31	15,132	O'Shea	Bishop	Todd	Venter/t	Woods/cp
21	14.03	A	AD1	Wasps	L 27-38	6,048	O'Shea	Bishop/t	Venter/t	Burrows/t	Woods/c2p(w/2c)
22	27.03	H	AD1	London Scot	W 35-12	4,400	O'Shea/c3p	Bishop	Venter	Burrows	Cunningham/c4p
23	03.04	A	AD1	Sale	L 27-30	3,515	O'Shea/t	Bishop	Venter	Burrows	Cunningham/3c2p
24	17.04	H	AD1	Bath	W 47-22	6,600	O'Shea/t3c2p	Berridge/t	Venter	Burrows/t	Todd/3t
25	01.05	H	AD1	Saracens	L 21-26	6,710	O'Shea	Bishop	Venter	Burrows	Woods/c3p
26	08.05	A	AD1	Bedford	W 36-21	3,572	O'Shea/t	Cunningham/t2c4p	Venter(a)	Burrows	Woods/t
A	10.01	A	TB4	Bristol	W 43-19		O'Shea/t	Bishop/t	Burrows	Venter/2t(n)	Woods/t4c
B	30.01	A	TB5	Northampton	W 21-6	7,110	O'Shea/t	Bishop	Burrows	Venter	Woods/tc3p
C	28.02	A	TBqf	Wasps	L 3-19	11,417	O'Shea	Bishop(w)	Venter	Burrows	Woods/p

* after opponents name indicates a penalty try
Brackets after a player's name indicates he was replaced. eg (a) means he was replaced by replacement code "a" and so on.
/ after a player or replacement name is followed by any scores he made - eg /t, /c, /p, /dg or any combination of these

1998-99 HIGHLIGHTS

League debuts: Matt Jones, Kieran Campbell, Peter Rogers, Richard Kirke, Rob Hardwick, Jake Boer, Simon Berridge, James Brown, Mike Howe, Kris Fulman, Robert Todd, Michael Worsley, Rob Gallagher, M Bird, Stephen Bachop, Kevin Putt, Neil Hatley, Jarod Cunningham.

Ever Presents: Brendan Venter.

Players used: 30 plus 1 as a repacement only.

Most Points in a season:

Pts	Player	T	C	P	DG
215	N Woods	12	25	35	-
143	J Cunningham	2	24	29	-
82	C O'Shea	9	5	8	1
45	N Burrows	9	-	-	-
25	R Kirke	5	-	-	-

MATCH FACTS

10	9	1	2	3	4	5	6	7	8	
Jones(k)	Campbell	Rogers/t	Kirke(l)	Hardwick(m)	Harvey	O'Kelly	Boer	Dawson	Spicer	1
Brown	Richards/t(d)	Rogers(p)	Kirke	Fulman	Harvey	O'Kelly		Dawson	Gallagher	2
Brown(c)	Richards(d)	Worsley	Kirke	Fulman(g)	Harvey	O'Kelly	Gallagher	Dawson	Spicer	3
Jones(k)	Campbell/t	Rogers(p)	Kirke(l)	Hardwick(m)	Harvey	O'Kelly	Spicer	Dawson	Gallagher	4
Brown	Campbell	Rogers(p)	Kirke(l)	Hardwick(m)	Harvey	O'Kelly/t	Spicer	Dawson	Gallagher	5
Jones(k)	Campbell	Worsley(l)	Kirke	Hardwick(m)	Harvey	O'Kelly	Spicer	Dawson	Gallagher	6
Jones(k)	Campbell(o)	Worsley	Kirke	Fulman	Harvey/t	O'Kelly	Boer	Dawson	Gallagher	7
Jones(k)	Campbell(o)	Worsley	Kirke	Fulman(g)	Harvey	O'Kelly	Boer	Dawson	Gallagher(i)	8
Bachop	Putt	Worsley(u)	Kirke	Fulman	Harvey/t	O'Kelly	Boer(o)(r)	Dawson	Feaunati	9
Bachop/t	Putt(o)	Hatley	Kirke	Hardwick	Strudwick	Bird(q)	Boer	Dawson	Feaunati	10
Bachop	Richards	Hatley	Kirke	Hardwick	Harvey	Strudwick	Boer(q)	Dawson	Feaunati	11
Bachop	Putt	Hatley	Kirke/t	Hardwick(m)	Strudwick	O'Kelly	Boer/t	Dawson	Feaunati(q)	12
Bachop/t	Putt	Hatley	Howe(f)	Fulman(g)	Strudwick	O'Kelly	Boer	Dawson	Gallagher(i)	13
Bachop	Putt(d)	Hatley	Howe(f)	Fulman	Spicer	O'Kelly	Boer	Dawson	Gallagher/t(v)	14
Bachop	Putt	Hatley	Howe(f)	Fulman	Spicer	O'Kelly	Boer	Dawson	Gallagher(v)	15
Bachop	Putt	Worsley(u)	Kirke	Hardwick(m)	Strudwick	O'Kelly	Boer	Dawson(i)	Feaunati(q)	16
Bachop/t	Richards	Hatley(e)	Kirke/3t(l)	Fulman(g)	Harvey	Strudwick	Boer/t	Dawson(t)	Gallagher	17
Bachop	Putt	Hatley	Kirke	Fulman(g)	Harvey	O'Kelly	Boer	Strudwick	Gallagher	18
Bacop/dg	Putt	Hatley/t	Kirke	Hardwick(m)	Strudwick	Bird(h)	Boer	Gallagher	Feaunati/t	19
Bachop	Putt	Hatley	Kirke	Hardwick	Strudwick	Harvey	Boer	Gallagher	Feaunati	20
Bachop	Putt	Hatley(e)	Howe	Fulman(g)	Strudwick	Harvey	Boer	Gallagher	Spicer	21
Bachop	Putt	Hatley(e)	Howe(f/t)	Hardwick(m)	Strudwick	Harvey	Boer	Gallagher/t	Spicer	22
Bachop	Putt	Worsley(u)	Howe(f)	Hardwick(m)	Strudwick	Harvey/t	Boer	Gallagher/t	Feaunati	23
Bachop	Richards	Rogers(u)	Kirke	Hardwick/t(m)	Bird	Harvey	Boer	Gallagher	Feaunati	24
Bachop	Richards	Rogers(u)	Kirke	Hardwick(m)	Strudwick	Harvey/t	Boer	Dawson/t	Gallagher(v)	25
Bachop/t	Richards	Hatley	Kirke	Hardwick(m)	Strudwick	Harvey	Boer	Dawson	Feaunati	26
Bachop	Putt	Hatley(p)	Kirke/t(l)	Fulman	Strudwick	O'Kelly	Boer/t	Gallagher	Spicer	A
Bachop	Putt	Hatley	Kirke	Hardwick(m)	Strudwick	O'Kelly(t)(l)	Boer	Gallagher	Feaunati	B
Bachop	Putt	Hatley	Kirke	Hardwick(m)	Strudwick	O'Kelly	Boer	Gallagher	Feaunati	C

REPLACEMENTS: a- J Bishop, b- N Woods, c-M Jones, d-Campbell, e-P Rogers, f-R Kirke, g-R Hardwick, h-N Harvey, i-K Spicer, j-S Berridge, k-J Brown, l-M Howe, m-K Fulman, n-R Todd, o-P Richards, p-M Worlsey, q-R Gallagher, r-R Strudwick, s-M Jarvis, t-M Bird, u-N Hatley, v-I Feaunati

Niall Woods tops the London Irish scoring list for the second consecutive season with over 200 points. He becomes the first man to score 200 points in a season twice for the Irish.

Woods also tops the try scorers list with a new record of 12 tries in a seaon beating the previous record of 10 set by Conor O'Shea. He also set a new record of four tries in a league match in the superb win at Northampton in January.

O'Shea though did set a new all time record for the Irish with a new total of 35. He also set a new record of appearances for a back for the Irish with 77 passing the previous record of 71 held by Michael Corcoran.

LONDON IRISH

LEAGUE STATISTICS
compiled by Stephen McCormack

SEASON	Division	P	W	D	L	F	A	Pts Diff	Lge Pts	Lge Pos	Most Points		Most Tries	
89-90	2	11	6	0	5	228	247	-19	12	5	111	Ian Aitchison	6	Shaun Brown
90-91	2	12	9	1	2	239	192	47	19	2p	117	Brian Mullen	6	Rob Saunders
91-92	1	12	3	3	6	147	237	-90	9	9	71	Michael Corcoran	5	Michael Corcoran
92-93	1	12	6	0	6	175	223	-48	12	7	111	Michael Corcoran	3	Simon Geoghegan
93-94	1	18	4	0	17	217	391	-174	8	9r	75	Michael Corcoran	5	Simon Geoghegan
94-95	2	18	9	0	9	363	381	-18	18	5	164	Michael Corcoran	6	Rob Henderson
95-96	2	18	15	0	3	583	405	178	30	2p	301	Michael Corcoran	10	Conor O'Shea
96-97	1	22	6	0	16	502	749	-247	12	10	189	David Humphreys	8	Conor O'Shea
97-98	1	22	6	0	16	457	673	-216	12	11	237	Niall Woods	8	Conor O'Shea Niall Woods
98-99	1	26	15	0	11	703	607	96	30	7	215	Niall Woods	12	Niall Woods

BIGGEST MARGINS

Home Win	48pts - 62-14 v Harlequins 25.4.98
Away Win	34pts - 50-16 v Waterloo 23.9.95
Home Defeat	39pts - 16-55 v Leicester 17.5.98
Away Defeat	59pts - 7-66 v Harlequins 14.9.96

MOST CONSECUTIVE

Appearances	29 Rob Henderson
Matches scoring Tries	4 Rob Saunders
Matches scoring points	24 Michael Corcoran
Victories	8
Defeats	7

MOST POINTS

Scored at Home	62 v Harlequins 25.4.98
Scored Away	50 v waterloo 23.9.95
Conceded at Home	65 v Northampton 9.9.95
Conceded Away	66 v Harlequins 14.9.96

MOST TRIES

Scored in a match	8 v Moseley 30.9.95 (H) v Harlequins 25.4.98 (H)
Conceded in a match	11 v Harlequins 14.9.96 (A)

MOST APPEARANCES

by a forward	96 (1) Gary Halpin
by a back	77 Conor O'Shea

	MOST IN A SEASON		MOST IN A CAREER		MOST IN A MATCH		
Points	301	Michael Corcoran	744	Michael Corcoran 89-98	32	Niall Woods	v Harlequins 25.4.98 (H)
Tries	12	Niall Woods 98-99	35	Conor O'Shea 95-99	4	Niall Woods	v Northampton 5.1.99 (A)
Conversions	36	Michael Corcoran 95-96	65	Michael Corcoran 89-98	8	Niall Woods	v Harlequins 25.4.98 (H)
Penalties	63	Michael Corcoran 95-96	169	Michael Corcoran 89-98	7	Michael Corcoran	v Lon. Scottish 13.1.96 (H)
Drop Goals	6	Paul Burke 92-93	10	Brian Mullen 88-92	2	Ralph Kuhn Brian Mullen Ian Aitchison Paul Burke	v Lon. Scottish 14.1.89 (A) v Richmond 8.4.89 (A) v Plymouth 13.1.90 (H) v Bristol 24.1.92 (H)

LONDON IRISH PLAYING SQUAD

BACKS

	Ht.	Wt.	Birthdate	Birthplace	CLUB	League Apps	Tries	Pts
Conor O'Shea Ireland , A, Leinster.	6.2	15.00	21.10.70	Limerick	London Irish	77	35	235
Justin Bishop Ireland, U21.	6.0	13.00	08.11.74	Crawley	London Irish	83(3)	17	85
Nick Burrows	6.1	13.12	19.05.73	Chester	London Irish	35(6)	11	55
Simon Berridge	6.1	15.04	29.07.65	Leicester	London Irish	6	4	20
Niall Woods Ireland .	6.0	13.00	21.05.71	Dublin	London Irish	57(3)	26	498
Kieran Campbell	5.8	11.08	06.07.69	Hillingdon	London Irish	6(5)	1	5
Stephen Bachop	5.10	13.09	02.04.66	New Zealand	London Irish	18	4	23
Peter Richards England A, U21.	5.10	12.00	10.03.78		London Irish	21(7)	5	25
Brendan Venter South Africa 14.	6.1	13.07	29.12.69	Johannesburg	London Irish	35	4	20
Robert Todd					London Irish	10(3)	4	20
Kevin Putt	5.10	12.04	28.07.65	Cambridge (NZ)	London Irish	13	-	-
Jarod Cunningham	5.11	14.05	07.09.68	New Zealand	London Irish	11(1)	2	143

FORWARDS

	Ht.	Wt.	Birthdate	Birthplace	CLUB	League Apps	Tries	Pts
Peter Rogers England Students.	5.11	18.06	20.01.69	Kent	London Irish	6(3)	1	5
Neil Hatley	6.0	18.07	23.12.69	Chorley	London Irish	13(5)	1	5
Richard Kirke	5.11	16.07	16.04.71	New Zealand	London Irish	20(5)	5	25
Kris Fulman	5.11	16.09	07.12.72	Gloucester	London Irish Bristol	11(14) 38(1)	-	-
Rob Hardwick England.	6.0	19.03	23.03.69	Kenilworth	London Irish Coventry	15(6) 88	1 8	5 39
Mike Howe	5.11	16.09	06.11.73	New Zealand	London Irish	6(5)	-	-
Malcolm O'Kelly Ireland , A, U21, Students.	6.7	16.07	19.07.74	Chelmsford	London Irish	41(3)	3	15
Ryan Strudwick Natal	6.5	16.09	03.08.73	Natal	London Irish	15	1	5
Rob Gallagher Australia U-21	6.3	16.06	10.04.69	Wigan	London Irish	19(4)	3	15
Nick Harvey	6.6	17.13	21.10.74	NSW	London Irish	30	4	20
Jake De Boer	6.2	16.6	01.11.75	Cape Town	London Irish	21	2	10
Kieran Dawson Ireland .	6.1	15.06	29.01.75	Bangor	London Irish	47(2)	3	15
Issac Feaunati	6.1	16.11	23.07.73	New Zealand	London Irish	20	6	30
Kevin Spicer	6.4	16.07	28.07.73	Dublin	London Irish	27(7)	1	5

LONDON IRISH

FACT FILE

Founded: 1898
Nickname: The Irish

Colours: Green/white/green
Change colours: Blue/white/blue

GROUND Stoop Memorial Ground, Langhorn Drive, Twickenham. TW2 7SX
Capacity: 8,000 Seated Covered: 4,600 Uncovered: 2,850

Directions: Langhorn Drive is off the westbound carriageway of theA316 Chertsey Road, 450 yards west of RFU roundabout. No entry for vehicles from Craneford Way
Nearest Railway Station: Twickenham (BR). 12 minutes walk, proceed towards RFUground, turn left into Court Way, then left into Craneford Way, ground at far end.

Car Parking: Limited amount available @ £5

Admission Matchdays Adults Standing £11, Seated £15. Children/OAPs £5
Season Tickets Adults Standing £100 Seated £150.

Sunbury Administration
Tel: 01932 783034 Fax: 01932 784462 email: commercial@london-irish-rugby.com

PROGRAMME
Size:B5 Price: £2.00
Pages: 72 + cover
Editor: Sian Isaac 01934 783034
ADVERTISING RATES
Colour - Page £2,000 Half £1,200
Spot Colour - Page 1,500 Half £850

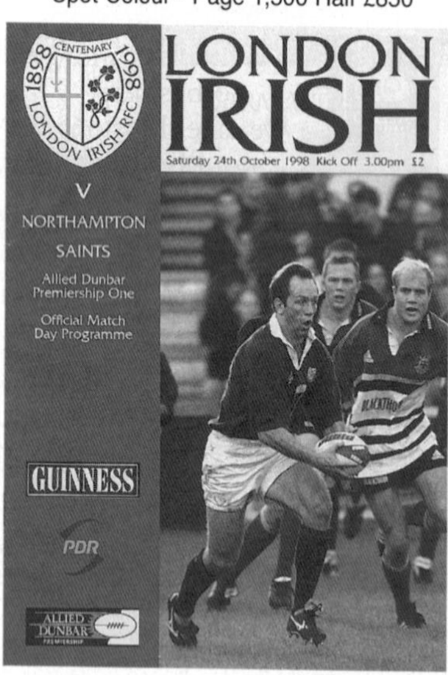

Niall Woods, London Irish leading try and points scorer, Centenary season 1998-99

MANCHESTER SALE F.C.

Chief Executive	Graham Walker	c/o Manchester Sale Rugby Club,
Director of Rugby	Adrian Hadley	Heywood Road,
Administration & Communications	Jean Swailes 0161 610 0405 (Direct line)	Sale M33 3WB Tel: 0161 283 1861 Fax: 0161 969 4124
Chairman	Patrick Austen	

Nobody at Heywood Road would dispute that last season was a difficult one for Sale. An inept start with weaknesses soon becoming obvious. In October they suffered four Allied Dunbar defeats including a record 39-10 home league mauling by Richmond in monsoon conditions; at half-time in the midst of that monsoon the Sale faithful were introduced to a genial figure almost hidden under an anorak. It was Phil Greening, who had completed his transfer from Gloucester that day.

October also saw them upstage the Welsh challenge punishing both Cardiff and Swansea. Cardiff had already gone down to Sale in a pre-season shock. Performances and results improved with Greening adding his experience and club captain Jim Mallinder rejoining the squad having missed the opening two months of the season following a serious rib-cage injury in the pre-season victory over Cardiff.

Late December saw the rollercoaster charging downhill again, almost coming off the rails - a record seven league defeats in a row. The brakes were applied by the arrival of experienced Springbok prop Dawie Theron. The front row began to take charge and good ball was delivered to arguably the best set of backs in the league.

The success story of the season was undoubtedly MEN Sale Sharks (sponsored by the Manchester Evening News). They topped the Mid-week Second XV league and just missed out in the championship play-off against second placed Leicester Extras. Their attacking style producing three outstanding young players in Joe Shaw, who captained England U19s and played for the U21 side, nineteen year old Alex Anderson who captained England U21s all season and Steve Hanley, just twenty, who made it to the very top scoring a debut try for England against the Welsh at Wembley.

A milestone was Jim Mallinder's 250th first-team appearance for Sale in early February. Jim's contribution over the years has been colossal - selected as a reserve British Lion before gaining his two England caps; the coming season will see him apply his teaching skills in a coaching role at the club.

For the second season Sale reached the C&G Cup semi-final. After massive wins over Orrell, London Scottish and Northampton they faltered to Gloucester at Kingsholm. Comfortably in the lead at half-time, playing against a strong wind, they gifted the game in injury time letting in two tries - courtesy of the Sale rollercoaster!

NORMAN TRAVIS

Dave Baldwin prepares to compete in a lineout against Gloucester - 1998-99 was his Testimonial Year after ten seasons at Heywood Road

MANCHESTER SALE

MATCH FACTS

Match No.	Date	H/A	Comp.	Opponents	Result & Score	Att.	15	14	13	12	11
1	05.09	A	AD1	London Scot	L 20-25		Howarth/cp	Moore/t	Davidson	Yates	O'Cuineagain
2	12.09	H	AD1	Bedford	W 39-21		Davidson	Moore/2t	Tetlow	Yates/t	Beim/t
3	20.09	A	AD1	Saracens	L 26-43		Davidson	Moore/t	Tetlow(t)	Yates	Beim/t
4	27.09	H	AD1	Harlequins	W 44-34		Davidson	Moore	Howarth3c6p	Yates/t(p)	Beim/t
5	03.10	A	AD1	Northampton	L 17-37		Davidson	Maher	Howarth/t2cp	Devereux(b)	Beim
6	17.10	A	AD1	Leicester	L 15-31		Howarth/tcp	Hanley	Maher	Devereux	Davidson
7	24.10	A	AD1	Bath	L 3-27		Howarth/p	Hanley	Maher(x)	Devereux	Beim
8	28.10	H	AD1	Richmond	L 10-39		Mallinder	Moore	Howarth/cp	Devereux	Beim
9	08.11	A	AD1	London Irish*	W 31-25		Mallinder	Moore(y)	Howarth/2c4p	Davidson	Beim/t
10	13.11	H	AD1	W Hartlepool*	W 42-26		Mallinder	Rees	Davidson/t4c3p	Yates	Moore
11	22.11	A	AD1	Wasps	L 19-32		Mallinder	Rees	Davidson/2t2c(t)	Yates/t	Moore(q)
12	12.12	H	AD1	Gloucester	W 26-10		Mallinder/t	Moore	Davidson(t)	Yates	Hanley/2t
13	20.12	A	AD1	Newcastle	L 15-30		Mallinder	Moore	Maher	Yates	Hanley/t
14	28.12	A	AD1	Harlequins	L 15-17		Mallinder	Moore	Maher	Yates/t	Hanley/t
15	02.01	H	AD1	Northampton	L 24-39		Mallinder	Moore/t	Maher	Yates	Hanley/2t
16	05.01	H	AD1	Bath	L 30-32		Mallinder(d)	Moore/2t	Maher	Yates	Hanley/t
17	23.01	H	AD1	Newcastle	L 20-28		Howarth/cp	Davidson/t	Maher	Yates(a)	Hanley/t
18	06.02	H	AD1	London Scot	L 7-23		Mallinder(y)	Yates	Davidson(A/c)	Maher/t	Hanley
19	14.02	A	AD1	Richmond	L 24-29		Mallinder	Rees	Baxendell	Maher/t(b)	Hanley/2t
20	27.02	A	AD1	Bedford	W 18-7		Mallinder	Rees	Baxendell	Yates	Hanley/2t
21	13.03	H	AD1	Saracens	W 32-24		Mallinder	Rees	Baxendell/t	Yates/t	Moore
22	28.03	A	AD1	W Hartlepool	D 33-33		Mallinder	Maher	Baxendell/t	Yates	Moore/t(w)
23	03.04	H	AD1	London Irish	W 30-27		Mallinder	Moore	Baxendell	Yates	Hanley
24	24.04	H	AD1	Leicester	L 17-41		Mallinder	Moore	Baxendell/t	Yates	Maher/t
25	01.05	A	AD1	Gloucester	W 34-24		Mallinder	Moore/t	Baxendell	Yates	Maher
26	08.05	H	AD1	Wasps	L 13-27		Mallinder	Maher/t	Baxendell	Yates	Moore/t
A	09.01	H	TBC	Northampton	L 31-47		Howarth/t3c	Moore	Maher	Yates/2t	Mallinder

* after opponents name indicates a penalty try
Brackets after a player's name indicates he was replaced. eg (a) means he was replaced by replacement code "a" and so on.
/ after a player or replacement name is followed by any scores he made - eg /t, /c, /p, /dg or any combination of these

1998-99 HIGHLIGHTS

League debuts:
Jan Machacek, Barry Jon Maher, Steven Hanley, Phil Greening, Dan Theron.

Ever Presents: None - most appearances 23 Shane Howarth and Duncan Bell.

Players used: 33 plus 2 as replacement only.

Most Points in a season:

Pts	Player	T	C	P	DG
242	S Howarth				
60	S Hanley	12	-	-	-
50	M Moore	10	-	-	-
41	S Davidson	4	6	3	-

MATCH FACTS

10	9	1	2	3	4	5	6	7	8	
Baxendell(p)	Smith/2t	P Smith(m)	Diamond(n)	Bell	Raiwalui	Murphy(o)	Anglesea	P Sanderson	Machacek	1
Howarth/4c2p	Smith(r)	Winstanley	Geraghty(s)	A Smith(g)	Baldwin	Murphy	Anglesea	P Sanderson	Machacek/t	2
Howarth/3c	Ellis(e/t)	Winstanley(g)	Dawe	Bell(u)	Baldwin	Murphy	Anglesea	P Sanderson	Machacek/t	3
Baxendell	Smith/t(r)	Winstanley/t	Geraghty(f)	Williamson	Baldwin	Murphy	Anglesea	P Snaderson	Machacek	4
Baxendell	Smith(r)	Winstanley(u)	Diamond	A Smith(g)	Raiwalui	Murphy	Anglesea	P Sanderson	Machacek/t	5
Baxendell	Smith/t	Bell	Diamond(n)	A Smith	Raiwalui	Murphy	Anglesea	P Sanderson(c)	Machacek	6
Baxendell	Smith(r)	Bell	Geraghty(f)	A Smith	Raiwalui	Murphy(o)	Anglesea	A Sanderson	O'Cuinneagain	7
Baxendell	Smith(r)	Bell	Geraghty(f)	A Smith	Raiwalui	Murphy	O'Cuinneagain	P Sanderson/t	Machacek	8
Baxendell	Ellis	Winstanley	Diamond(z)	Bell	Raiwalui	Baldwin(h)	O'Cuinneagain/t	P Sanderson	Machacek(i)	9
Baxendell	Ellis/2t(e)	Winstanley	Diamond(n)	Bell	Baldwin/t(h)	Raiwalui	A Sanderson	P Sanderson	Anglesea	10
Baxendell	Ellis(e)	Winstanley	Diamond	Bell	Raiwalui	Baldwin(h)	A Sanderson(	P Sanderson	Anglesea	11
Howarth/t3c	Smith(r)	Winstanley	Diamond(z)	Bell	Raiwalui	Baldwin(h)	Anglesea	P Sanderson(v)	O'Cuinneagain	12
Howarth/tcp	Smith(r)	Winstanley	Greening	Bell	Raiwalui	Baldwin	Anglesea	P Sanderson(v)	Machacek	13
Howarth/cp	Ellis	Winstanley(u)	Greening	Bell	Raiwalui	Baldwin	Anglesea(v)	P Sanderson	O'Cuinneagain	14
Howarth/2c	Smith	Winstanley(u)	Greening(f)	Bell	Baldwin(v)	Raiwalui	Raiwalui	P Sanderson	O'Cuinneagain	15
Howarth/2c2p	Smith	P Smith(u/t)	Diamond(z)	Bell	Raiwalui	Murphy	O'Cuinneagain	A Sanderson(i)	Machacek	16
Baxendell	Smith	Winstanley(u)	Greening	Bell	Raiwalui	Murphy	Anglesea	A Sanderson	O'Cuinneagain/	17
Baxendell	Smith(B)	Bell	Greening	Theron	Raiwalui(o)	Murphy	Anglesea	A Sanderson	Morris(j)	18
Howarth/t2c	Ellis(e)	Bell	Greening	Theron	Raiwalui	Murphy	Anglesea	A Sanderson	O'Cuinneagain	19
Howarth/c2p	Ellis	Bell	Greening	Theron	Raiwalui	Murphy(o)	Anglesea	A Sanderson	O'Cuinneagain	20
Howarth/c5p	Ellis(e)	Bell	Greening	Theron	Raiwalui/t	Murphy	P Sanderson	A Sanderson	O'Cuinneagain	21
Howarth/3c4p	Smith	Bell	Greening	Theron	Raiwalui	Murphy	Anglesea	A Sanderson	O'Cuinneagain/	22
Howarth/t3c2pdg	Ellis/t(e)	Bell	Greening/t	Theron	Raiwalui	Murphy(o)	Anglesea(C)	A Sanderson	O'Cuinneagain	23
Howarth/tc	Smith	Bell	Greening	Theron	Raiwalui(o)	Murphy	Anglesea	A Sanderson	O'Cuinneagain	24
Howarth/2t4cpdg	Smith/t	Bell	Greening	Theron	Baldwin	Murphy	Anglesea(c)	A Sanderson	Morris	25
Howarth/p	Smith	Bell	Diamond	Theron	Baldwin	Murphy	Anglesea	A Sanderson(j)	Morris(c)	26
Baxendell	Smit(r)h	P Smith(u)	Greening	Bell	Raiwalui/t	Murphy	Anglesea	A Sanderson/t(j)	Machacek(c)	A

REPLACEMENTS: a- M Moore, b- C Yates, c - D O'Cuinneagain, d - J Baxendell, e - R Smith, f - S Diamond, g - D Bell, h - C Murphy, i - P Anglesea, j - P Sanderson, k - J Machacek, l - A Smith, m - P Winstanley, n - D Geraghty, o - D Baldwin, p - J Devereux, q - T Beim, r - K Ellis, s - G Dawe, t - B-J Maher, u - D Williamson, v - A Sanderson, w - S Hanley, x - J Mallinder, y - D Rees, z - P Greening, A - J Shaw, B - P Knight, C - A Morris

Shane Howarth broke his own record for points in a season with 242, 15 more than the previous season.
That also took him past Paul Turner's career record of 305 points as Howarth ended the season on 473.
He also set a new record for scoring in consecutive matches with 18, one more than the previous record set by Rob Liley.

Manchester Sale suffered their heaviest ever home defeat when they lost by 29 points to Richmond at the end of October. They lost 39-10 which was a point more than the 46-17 defeat at the hands of Bath in April 1988.

Veteran full back Jim Mallinder managed to add just one try to his career record of 36 to leave him six clear of the now departed Tom Beim who moved back to Gloucester. Mallinder also extended his career appearance record for a back to 149 whilst Dave Baldwin extended his record for a forward to 142.

MANCHESTER SALE

LEAGUE STATISTICS
compiled by Stephen McCormack

SEASON	Division	P	W	D	L	F	A	Pts Diff	Lge Pts	Lge Pos	Most Points	Most Tries
89-90	2	11	4	0	7	153	182	-29	8	9	29 Graham Jenion	4 Phil Stansfield
90-91	2	12	5	1	6	224	156	68	11	7	82 Richard Booth	5 Jeff Powell
91-92	2	12	6	0	6	204	209	-5	12	8	79 Matthew Alexander	5 Jim Mallinder
92-93	2	12	7	1	4	237	102	35	15	5	63 Phil Jee	7 Mark Warr
93-94	2	18	13	2	3	438	160	278	28	1	144 Paul Turner	16 Simon Verbickas
94-95	1	18	7	2	9	327	343	+16	16	4	92 Paul Turner	5 Gareth Stocks & Jim Mallender
95-96	1	18	9	1	8	365	371	-6	19	5	167 Rob Liley	6 Jos Baxendall
96-97	1	22	13	2	7	603	525	78	28	5	150 Simon Mannix	13 Tim Beim
97-98	1	22	10	22	10	605	558	47	22	6	227 Shane Howarth	14 Tim Beim
98-99	1	26	9	1	16	604	731	-127	19	11	246 Shane Howarth	12 Steven Hanley

BIGGEST MARGINS

Home Win	79pts - 88-9 v Otley 12.2.94
Away Win	32pts - 40-8 v Orrell 18.1.97
Home Defeat	29pts - 17-46 v Bath 28.4.88
	10-39 v Richmond 28.10.98
Away Defeat	77pts - 7-84 v Bath 26.4.97

MOST CONSECUTIVE

Appearances	39 Phillip Stansfield 22.10.88-14.3.92
Matches scoring Tries	8 Simon Verbickas
Matches scoring points	18 Shane Howarth
Victories	7
Defeats	11

MOST POINTS

Scored at Home	88 v Otley 12.2.94
Scored Away	43 v West Hartlepool 5.4.97
Conceded at Home	46 v Bath 28.4.88
Conceded Away	84 v Bath 26.4.97

MOST TRIES

Scored in a match	14 v Otley 12.2.94 (H)
Conceded in a match	12 v Harlequins 23.4.88 (A)
	v Bath 24.4.97 (A)

MOST APPEARANCES

by a forward	142 (8) Dave Baldwin
by a back	149 (2) Jim Mallinder

	MOST IN A SEASON	MOST IN A CAREER	MOST IN A MATCH	
Points	246 Shane Howarth 97-98	473 Shane Howarth 97-99	27 Simon Mannix	v Northampton 9.3.97 (H)
Tries	16 Simon Verbickas 93-94	37 Jim Mallinder 88-99	5 Simon Verbickas	v Otley 12.2.94 (H)
Conversions	42 Shane Howarth 98-99	55 Paul Turner 92-96	9 Paul Turner	v Otley 12.2.94 (H)
Penalties	41 Shane Howarth 97-98	47 Paul Turner 92-96	7 Simon Mannix Shane Howarth	v Northampton 9.3.97 (H) v Wasps 18.4.98 (H)
Drop Goals	4 Paul Turner 95-96	13 Paul Turner 92-96	2 David Pears Paul Turner	v Bedford 22.2.89 (H) v Morley 3.10.92 (H) v Wakefield 9.4.94 (A) v Orrell 6.1.96 (H)

MANCHESTER SALE PLAYING SQUAD

BACKS

Name	Ht.	Wt.	Birthdate	Birthplace	CLUB	League Apps	Tries	Pts
Jim Mallinder England 2, A, North, Yorkshire.	6.3	16.00	16.03.66	Halifax	Sale Roundhay	149(2)	37	179
David Rees England 6 A, U21, Students,	5.9	13.10	15.10.74	London	Sale	41(3)	11	55
Stephen Hanley England 1,A, U21, 18.	6.3	16.00	11.06.79	Whitehaven	Sale Aspatria	12(1) 21	12 20	60 100
Matt Moore	5.11	13.00	02.04.76	Frimley	Sale	31(2)	16	80
Jos Baxendell England 2, A, North, U21.	6.0	14.04	03.12.71	Manchester	Sale Sheffield	97(1)	19	95
Chris Yates	6.1	16.00	13.05.71	Otahuhu	Sale	60(7)	19	101
Kevin Ellis Wales A. Rl: Great Brittain & Wales.	5.9	13.00	29.0565	Bridgend	Sale	24(8)	9	45
Richard Smith	5.10	12.12	06.06.73	Wales	Sale	24(8)	8	40
Shane Howarth New Zealand 4.	5.9	14.00	08.07.68	Auckland	Sale	41(2)	13	470
Steven Davidson North colts, Cumbria	6.2	16.00	28.04.76	Whitehaven	Sale Aspatria	12	4	41
John Devereux British Lions 86 & 89.	6.1	16.00	03.03.66	Pontycymmer	Sale	8(4)	-	-
Barrie Jon Maher England. England (RL), Great Britain (RL), WIgan, Castleford, Western Reds, Perth Reds.	6.6	16.04	15.01.73	Wigan	Sale	14(4)	4	20

FORWARDS

Name	Ht.	Wt.	Birthdate	Birthplace	CLUB	League Apps	Tries	Pts
Duncan Bell England U18.	6.2	18.00	01.10.74	Kings Lynn	Sale	37(5)	2	10
Phil Winstanley North, Lancashire.	5.11	16.10	16.09.68	Orrell	Sale Orrell	39(2) 36(2)	6 3	30 18
Phil Greening England	5.11	17.00	03.10.75	Gloucester	Sale Gloucester	13(3) 36	- 2	- 10
Steve Diamond England A, North, Lancashire.	5.10	14.07	03.02.68	Manchester	Sale	122(5)	4	20
Chris Murphy England A, U21.	6.8	17.10	02.02.76	Hull	Sale W Hartlepool	23(12) 36(1)	1 -	5 -
Dave Baldwin England A, Barbarians, Yorkshire, North.	6.6	19.04	03.09.65	Ilkley	Sale Wakefield	142(8) 11	14 -	69 -
Simon Raiwalui Fiji, Queensland.	6.6	17.00	08.09.74	Auckland	Sale	40	3	15
Dawie Theron South Africa 10, Super 12.	6.3	18.12	15.09.66	South Africa	Sale	9	-	-
Alex Sandrson England U16, U18	6.3	15.6	07.10.79	Chester	Sale	14(5)	1	5
Pat Sanderson England 3, A, U21, 18, 16.	6.4	16.00	06.09.77	Chester	Sale	31(5)	7	35
Dion O'Cuinneagin South Africa Schools, 7s.	6.4	16.00	02.05.72	Cape Town	Sale	27(7)	6	30
Paul Smith	6.1	17.00	28.03.69	Nantwich	Sale	52(1)	-	-
Andrew Smith	6.1	17.05	28.03.69	Nantwich	Sale	78(1)	1	5
Graham Dawe England 5.	5.11	14.00	04.09.59	Plymouth	Sale Bath	4(8) 118	- 4	- 23
Jan Machacek Czech Republic	6.3	16.04	15.02.72	Prague	Sale	10(2)	4	20

MANCHESTER SALE

FACT FILE

Founded: 1861

Colours: Blue with 4 white hoops
Change colours: Red with 4 blue hoops

GROUND

Address: Heywood Road, Sale, Cheshire M33 3WB
Tel: 0161 283 1861 Fax: 0161 969 4124
Capacity: 4,800 Seated: 2,254 Standing: 2,546

Directions: M6 J19, take A556/A56 for approx 8 miles. Turn right into Marsland Rd and Heywood Rd is on the right after 800m. M60 J6, take A6144. Old Hall Rd/Marsland Rd, Heywood Rd on left after 1.5 miles from J6.
Nearest Railway Station: Brooklands Metrolink, left out of station into Marsland Rd. Heywood Rd 200m on the right.

Car Parking: None on ground, 100 spaces nearby

Admission:

		Adults	Concessions	Family (2 A & 2 C)
Season	Seated (North Grandstand)	£143	£88	£360
	Standing	£ 99	£49.50	-
Matchday	Seated (North Grandstand)	£15	£10	£40
	Standing	£10	£ 5	-

Club Shop: 12-5 matchdays, 9-5 weekdays.
Contact Christine Capper 0161 283 1861 x 226

Clubhouse: Mon-Fri 7-11, Sat 11-11, Sun 12-3, Matchdays 12-11.
Snacks available
Functions: Up to 150
Contact Liz Burne 0161 283 1861 x 212

MATCHDAY MAGAZINE

Size: B5 Pages: 32 Price: £2
Co-ordinator: Norman Travis 0161 283 1861x215

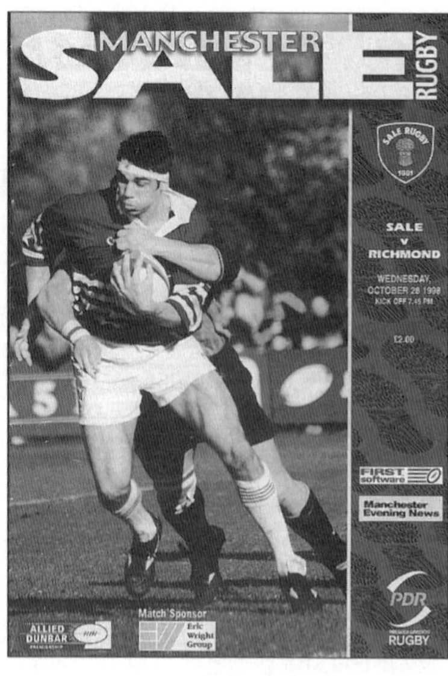

Jim Mallinder runs out for the 250th time in Sale colours, last February.

NEWCASTLE R.F.C.

President	Trevor Bennett
Chairman	Dave Thompson
Director	John Grey
Chief Executive	Paul Mackings
Director of Rugby	Rob Andrew
Commercial Director	John Oates Mobile - 07808 572986
Press Officer	Alex Jackson Mobile - 07808 572989
1st Team Coach	Steve Bates

c/o Newcastle R.F.C.
Kingston Park,
Brunton Road,
Kenton Bank Foot,
Newcastle upon Tyne NE13 8AF
Tel: 0191 214 5588
Fax: 0191 286 0824

Following the success last season, both on and off the pitch, when Newcastle Falcons took their bigger games to Gateshead Stadium, the increasing demand from supporters necessitated the move to a bigger capacity stadium offering top class facilities. So at the beginning of the season Newcastle Falcons decided to play all their home games at Gateshead.
However, in October 1998, Newcastle Falcons announced their decision to return to their home ground, Kingston Park, for the remainder of the Season. The move, which took place at the beginning of November last year, was a reluctant move from Gateshead which had evolved into an excellent rugby venue with great facilities, but due to disappointing support for the game, mirrored throughout the country, Newcastle made the hard business decision to return to Kingston Park.
The move was made back with a highly motivated team and committed squad, who were determined to achieve success again after becoming 1997/98 Allied Dunbar Champions. The support, once we had moved back to Kingston Park, grew again and was fantastic for the players.
In March 1999, Newcastle Falcons announced their new structure to the club, whereby the club was sold to new chairman Mr. Dave Thompson. All players and staff were highly delighted about the positive new takeover and look forward to the future of the club.
This season we have not been so successful on the pitch, but we did shake off our rivals to get to the final of the Tetley's Bitter Cup. This took us to Twickenham were we took on the London Wasps who sadly defeated us. Newcastle Falcons came eighth in the Allied Dunbar Premiership One, which meant unfortunately not making it into the European Cup next season. However, the Falcons are still looking forward to a highly successful year on and off the pitch for the 1999/2000 Millennium Season.

NEWCASTLE FALCONS

MATCH FACTS

Match No.	Date	H/A	Comp.	Opponents	Result & Score	Att.	15	14	13	12	11
1	05.09	A	AD1	Richmond	L 29-42	9,530	Legg	Naylor/t	Tuigamala/t	Andrew/2c	Underwood
2	12.09	H	AD1	Bath	W 19-17	3,452	Legg	Naylor	Tuigamala	Andrew	Underwood
3	26.09	H	AD1	London Irish*	L 21-23	4,184	Legg	Naylor	Shaw	Andrew	Underwood/t
4	03.10	A	AD1	W Hartlepool	W 24-19	2,702	Massey	Naylor	Tuigamala/t	Andrew	Underwood
5	11.10	H	AD1	Wasps	W 27-19	4,283	Legg(q)	Naylor	Tuigamala	Wilkinson/c5p	Underwood/t
6	17.10	A	AD1	Gloucester	L 32-41	6,915	Massey	Naylor/t	Tuigamala	Andrew	Underwood
7	24.10	A	AD1	Bedfoed	W 29-22	3,902	Massey	Tuigamala/t	Shaw	Andrew/2c	Underwood/t
8	31.10	H	AD1	Saracens	W 43-12	4,832	Legg	Tuigamala	Shaw/t	Andrew/c	Underwood/3t(b)
9	07.11	A	AD1	Harlequins	L 20-25	5,974	Legg	Tuigamala	Shaw	Andrew	Underwood/t(b/t)
10	14.11	H	AD1	Northampton	W 45-35	4,293	Legg	Naylor	Shaw	Andrew	Tuigamala/t
11	12.12	A	AD1	Leicester	L 18-31	11,226	Legg/t	Naylor	Shaw	Wilkinson/c2p	Tuigamala
12	18.12	H	AD1	Sale	W 30-15	3,020	Legg/2t	Naylor	Shaw/t	Wilkinson/cp	Tuigamala
13	27.12	H	AD1	W Hartlepool	W 29-13	3,403	Legg	Naylor	Tuigamala/t(j)	Andrew	Wood
14	02.01	A	AD1	London Irish	L 14-16	4,260	Legg	Naylor	Shaw	Andrew	Tuigamala/t
15	05.01	H	AD1	Bedford	W 34-23	2,070	Massey	Wood	Shaw/t	Andrew	Tuigamala/2t
16	16.01	A	AD1	Bath	L 11-16	8,200	Legg	Naylor/t(d)	Shaw	Andrew	Tuigamala
17	23.01	A	AD1	Sale	W 28-20	3,500	Massey	Naylor/t(d)(a)	Shaw	Andrew	Tuigamala
18	13.02	A	AD1	London Scot	L 17-27	2,101	Massey(a/t)	Underwood	Shaw/t	Andrew	Tuigamala
19	27.03	A	AD1	Northampton	L 16-57	6,540	Shaw	Naylor	Tuigamala	May	Wood
20	31.03	H	AD1	London Scot	W 43-20	2,506	Legg/t	Underwood	Shaw	Andrew	Tuigamala
21	13.04	A	AD1	Wasps	L 33-34	5,104	Legg	Tuigamala/2t	Shaw	Andrew	Underwood(b)
22	21.04	H	AD1	Richmond	W 47-14	2,728	Legg/6c	Tuigamala(j)	Naylor/t	Shaw	Wood
23	25.04	H	AD1	Gloucester	W 39-14	3,748	Legg/t	Naylor	Shaw	May	Wood/t
24	02.05	H	AD1	Leicester	L 12-21	5,207	Legg	Naylor	Shaw	Tuigamala	Wood
25	11.05	H	AD1	Harlequins	W 33-23	4,133	Legg	Tuigamala/2t	May	Shaw	Wood(d)
26	20.05	A	AD1	Saracens	L 26-40	6,982	Legg(j)	Naylor	Shaw/t	May	Underwood
A	09.01	H	TB4	Bath	W 25-22		Legg	Naylor	Shaw	Andrew	Tuigamala
B	31.01	A	TB5	W Hartlepool	W 33-21		Legg/t	Underwood	Shaw	Andrew/2cp	Tuigamala/t
C	28.02	H	TBqf	Saracens	W 15-0	3,496	Legg	Tuigamala/2t	Shaw	Andrew	Underwood
D	03.04	A	TBsf	Richmond	W 20-3	9,751	Legg	Underwood	Shaw	Andrew/cpdg	Tuigamala/2t
E	15.05	N	TBF	Wasps	L 19-29	48,000	Legg	Naylor(d)	Shaw	May	Tuigamala/t

* after opponents name indicates a penalty try
Brackets after a player's name indicates he was replaced. eg (a) means he was replaced by replacement code "a" and so on.
/ after a player or replacement name is followed by any scores he made - eg /t, /c, /p, /dg or any combination of these

1998-99 HIGHLIGHTS

League debuts:
Peter Massey, Ian Peel, Ross Beattie, Marius Hurter, Hugh Yvyvan, Mark Wood, Tom May, Huw Charlton, John Cartmell.

Ever Presents: None
Most appearances 25 Jonny Wilkinson.

Players used: 27 plus 4 as a replacement only.

Most Points in a season:

Pts	Player	T	C	P	DG
306	J Wilkinson	9	51	53	-
60	V Tuigamala	12	-	-	-
60	G Armstrong	12	-	-	-
40	T Underwood	8	-	-	-

MATCH FACTS

10	9	1	2	3	4	5	6	7	8	
Wilkinson/cp(j)	Armstrong	Popplewell	Nesdale	Graham	Archer	Weir/t	O'Neill	Arnold(i/t)	Ryan	1
Wilkinson/c4p	Armstrong	Popplewell	Nesdale	Graham	Archer	Weir	O'Neill(i)	Arnold	Ryan/t	2
Wilkinson/c3p	Armstrong	Popplewell	Nesdale	Graham(k)	Archer	Weir	Walton	O'Neill	Ryan	3
Wilkinson/3cp	Armstrong	Graham	Nesdale	Peel	Archer	Weir/t	Walton/t	Arnold	Ryan	4
Andrew	Armstrong/t	Popplewell(e)	Nesdale	Peel	Archer	Weir	Walton(g)	Arnold	Ryan(l)	5
Wilkinson/t3c2p	Armstrong	Popplewell(e)	Nesdale	Peel	Beattie(f)	Weir/t	Walton/t	Arnold(g)	Ryan	6
Wilkinson/cp(b/t)	Armstrong/t	Popplewell(e)	Nesdale	Peel	Archer	Weir	Walton	O'Neill	Ryan	7
Wilkinson/4cp(j)	Armstrong/t	Graham	Nesdale(m/t)	Peel	Archer	Weir	Walton(l)	Arnold	Ryan	8
Wilkinson/cp	Armstrong/t	Graham	Nesdale	Hurter	Archer(l)	Weir	Walton	Arnold	Ryan	9
Wilkinson/2t6cp	Armstrong/t(p)	Peel	Horton(o)	Hurter	Beattie	Weir	O'Neill	Arnold/t	Walton/t(n)	10
Andrew/t	Armstrong	Graham	Nesdale	Hurter	Archer	Weir	Walton	Arnold	Beattie	11
Andrew	Armstrong/t	Graham	Nesdale	Hurter	Archer/t	Weir	Walton	Cartmell(m)	Beattie	12
Wilkinson/t3cp	Charlton/t	Graham	Nesdale	Hurter	Archer	Weir	Walton	Arnold(r)	Beattie/t	13
Wilkinson/2c	Armstrong/t	Graham	Nesdale	Hurter	Archer	Weir	Walton	Arnold	Beattie	14
Wilkinson/t3cp	Armstrong	Peel(e)	Horton	Hurter	Archer	Weir	Arnold	Cartmell/t(i)	Beattie	15
Wilkinson/2p	Armstrong	Graham	Nesdale	Peel(s)	Archer	Weir	Arnold(i)	Cartmell(g)	Beattie	16
Wilkinson/2c3p	Armstrong	Graham/t	Nesdale	Hurter	Weir	Vyvyan/t	Arnold	Cartmell(i)	Beattie(k)	17
Wilkinson/2cp	Armstrong	Graham	Nesdale	Hurter	Vyvyan	Archer	O'Neill	Cartmell(h)	Beattie	18
Andrew/c3p	Charlton/t	Graham	Nesdale	Hurter(k)	Vyvyan	Archer	Walton(c)	Cartmell	Beattie	19
Wilkinson/t3c4p	Armstrong	Graham/t	Nesdale(m)	Peel(s)	Archer	Weir	Walton/t	O'Neill(r/t)	Beattie	20
Wilkinson/t3c4p	Armstrong	Graham	Nesdale	Hurter	Archer	Weir	Walton	Arnold	Beattie	21
Wilkinson/t	Armstrong/3t	Graham/t	Nesdale	Hurter	Archer	Weir	Walton	Arnold	Beattie/t	22
Wilkinson/4c2p	Armstrong/2t	Graham/t	Nesdale(m)	Hurter	Archer	Weir	O'Neill(i)	Arnold	Beattie	23
Wilkinson/4p	Armstrong	Graham	Nesdale	Hurter	Archer	Weir	Walton(n)	Arnold(r)	Beattie	24
Wilkinson/3c4p	Armstrong	Graham	Nesdale	Hurter	Archer	Weir	Walton	O'Neill(r/t)	Beattie	25
Wilkinson/t2c4p	Charlton(p)	Graham	Nesdale(m)	Hurter(k)	Archer	Weir	Walton	Arnold	Beattie(n)	26
Wilkinson/c6p	Armstrong	Graham	Nesdale	Hurter	Archer	Weir	Walton	Cartmell	Beattie/t	A
Wilkinson/cp(j)	Armstrong	Graham	Nesdale	Hurter	Weir	Vyvyan/t	Arnold(i)	Cartmell/t(g)	Beattie	B
Wilkinson/cp	Armstrong	Graham	Nesdale	Hurter	Archer	Vyvyan	Walton(g)	Arnold	Beattie	C
Wilkinson/c	Armstrong	Graham	Nesdale	Peel(s)	Archer	Weir	Walton	Arnold	Beattie(n)	D
Wilkinson/c4p	Armstrong	Graham	Nesdale	Hurter(k)	Archer	Weir	Walton(r)	Arnold	Beattie	E

REPLACEMENTS: a- S Legg b- J Naylor c-J Rule d-T Underwood e-G Graham f-G Archer g-S O'Neill h-R Arnold i-P Walton j-P Massey k-I Peel l-R Beattie m-R Horton n-H Vyvyan o-N Frankland p-A Chilten q-M Wood r-J Cartmell s-S Best

Jonny Wilkinson broke Rob Andrews record for most points in a season with his 21 point haul in the final match of the season at Saracens. He ended the season 9 points better than Andrew's effort from the 1996-97 season.
In that 306 points were a new club record 53 penalties which eclpsed Simon Mason' record of 45 from the 1994-95 season.

Scrum half Gary Armstrong topped the club's try scoring list for the third time in four season with 12, he shared the honour with Va'aiga Tuigamala.
That took his career record at Newcastle to a record 50 - well clear of his next rival.

With Wilkinson playing in 25 of Newcastle's league matches Rob Andrew did not get much chance of extending his club points record. He did manage 26 points and took his career total at Newcastle to 575.

NEWCASTLE

LEAGUE STATISTICS
compiled by Stephen McCormack

SEASON	Division	P	W	D	L	F	A	Pts Diff	Lge Pts	Lge Pos	Most Points		Most Tries	
89-90	2	11	1	1	9	108	266	-158	3	12	62	Graham Spearman	1	by eleven players
90-91	2	12	6	0	6	169	140	29	12	6	66	David Johnson	5	Steve Douglas
91-92	2	12	7	0	5	371	140	231	14	4	147	David Johnson	10	Peter Walton
92-93	2	12	10	0	2	241	106	135	20	1p	136	David Johnson	6	Ross Wilkinson
93-94	1	18	2	1	15	190	483	-293	5	10r	79	David Johnson	4	Ross Wilkinson
94-95	2	18	8	2	8	373	281	92	18	3	193	Simon Mason	8	Tony Penn
95-96	2	18	5	1	12	348	405	-57	11	8	73	Richard Cramb	4	Mike Brummitt & Gary Armstrong
96-97	2	22	19	1	2	1255	346	909	39	2p	297	Rob Andrew	23	John Bentley
97-98	1	22	19	0	3	645	387	258	38	1	226	Rob Andrew	13	Gary Armstrong
98-99	1	26	14	0	12	719	639	80	28	8	306	Jonny Wilkinson	12	Gary Armstrong

BIGGEST MARGINS

Home Win	151pts - 156-5 v Rugby 5.10.96
Away Win	66pts - 75-9 v Moseley 19.10.96
Home Defeat	43pts - 9-52 v Northampton 21.10.95
Away Defeat	61pts - 5-66 v Leicester 12.3.94

MOST CONSECUTIVE

Appearances	44 Neil Frankland 13.1.90-2.10.93
Matches scoring Tries	8 Gary Armstrong
Matches scoring points	22 Rob Andrew
Victories	6
Defeats	12

MOST POINTS

Scored at Home	156 v Rugby 5.10.96
Scored Away	75 v Moseley 19.10.96
Conceded at Home	52 v Northampton 21.10.95
Conceded Away	66 v Leicester 12.3.94

MOST TRIES

Scored in a match	24 v Rugby 5.10.96 (H)
Conceded in a match	10 v Leicester 12.3.94

MOST APPEARANCES

by a forward	113 (2)	Richard Arnold
by a back	105	Ross Wilkinson

	MOST IN A SEASON	MOST IN A CAREER	MOST IN A MATCH	
Points	306 Jonny Wilkinson 98-99	575 Rob Andrew 95-99	36 Rob Andrew	v Rugby 5.10.96 (H)
Tries	23 John Bentley 96-97	50 Gary Armstrong 95-98	5 Pat Lam	v Rotherham 4.5.97 (H)
Conversions	95 Rob Andrew 96-97	152 Rob Andrew 95-99	18 Rob Andrew	v Rugby 5.10.96 (H)
Penalties	53 Jonny Wilkinson 98-99	105 David Johnson 87-94	6 David johnson Rob Andrew	v Morlet 11.1.92 (H) v Richmond 26.10.97 (H)
Drop Goals	4 David Johnson 87-88	10 David Johnson 87-94	2 David Johnson	v Bedford 5.12.87 (A)

NEWCASTLE PLAYING SQUAD

BACKS

	Ht.	Wt.	Birthdate	Birthplace	CLUB	League Apps	Tries	Pts
Jim Naylor England A, U21.	5.11	14.00	06.02.74	Halifax	Newcastle Orrell	36(4) 60	13 16	65 80
Va'aiga Tuigamala New Zealand, Western Samoa. RL: Western Samoa	5.10	16.00	04.09.69	Faleasiu	Newcastle Wasps	48(2) 8	27 3	137 15
Jonny Wilkinson England , U21, Colts, Schools.	5.10	12.09	25.05.79	Surrey	Newcastle	34(3)	9	306
Tony Underwood England	5.9	12.10	17.02.69	Ipoh	Newcastle Leicester	44(3) 42	26 24	130 111
Allen Chilton					Newcastle	(2)		
Simon Legg	6.1	14.00	27.09.75	Solihull	Newcastle Birmingham Solihull	39(3) 2	12 2	74 10
Martin Shaw	5.11	14.00	02.09.75	B Auckland	Newcastle	20	5	20
Tim May					Newcastle	4	-	-
Rob Andrew England .	5.9	12.08	18.02.63	Richmond	Newcastle Wasps	68 77	14 16	575 748
Gary Armstrong Scotland	5.8	13.08	30.09.66	Edinburgh	Newcastle	68	50	250
Huw Charlton Scotland					Newcastle	3	2	10
Peter Massey Other club: Wakefield 22/7/35	5.11	13.07	03.04.75	Pontefract	Newcastle Moseley	6(6) 11(1)	- 3	- 15

FORWARDS

	Ht.	Wt.	Birthdate	Birthplace	CLUB	League Apps	Tries	Pts
Nick Popplewell Ireland .	5.10	17.03	06.04.64	Dublin	Newcastle Wasps	44(1) 13	15 -	75 -
Marius Hurter	6.2	17.13	08.10.70	South Africa	Newcastle	15	-	-
George Graham Scotland.	5.7	17.00	19.01.66	Stirling	Newcastle	44(12)	11	55
Ross Nesdale Ireland .	5.10	16.02	30.07.69	Auckland	Newcastle	66	11	55
Richie Horton	5.10	15.00	22.06.76	Middlesborough	Newcastle	3(6)	1	5
Dodie Weir Scotland , British Lions.	6.6	17.07	04.07.70	Edinburgh London Scottish	Newcastle 3	68(1) 1	8 4	40
Gareth Archer England	6.6	18.00	15.12.74	South Shields	Newcastle Bristol	79(2) 16	13 1	65 5
Ross Beattie	6.5	17.07	15.11.77		Newcastle	18(3)	2	10
Ian Peel					Newcastle	9(4)	-	-
Peter Walton Scotland .	6.3	18.00	03.06.69	Alnwick	Newcastle Northampton	50(17) 27	24 2	120 10
Jimmy Cartmell					Newcastle	6(4)	3	15
Richard Arnold	6.4	15.12	16.08.65	Taranaki	Newcastle	113(2)	15	69
Hugh Vyvyan					Newcastle	3(3)	1	5
Steve O'Neill Durham	6.1	16.07	10.10.72	Blaydon	Newcastle	21(10)	4	20

NEWCASTLE FALCONS

FACT FILE

Founded: 1877
Nickname: The Falcons

Colours: White with black hoops
Change colours: Green with white hoops

GROUND

Address: Brunton Road, Kingston Park, Kenton Bank Foot, Newcastle upon Tyne NE13 5HE
Tel: 0191 214 5588 Fax: 0191 286 0824
Capacity: 6,800 Seated: 2,525

Directions: Travelling from North or South on the City by-pass (A1 Western by-pass) take the Newcastle Airport sign and then follow signs for Kingston Park (Rugby Ground) - approx 1 mile.
Nearest Railway Station: Newcastle Central then Metro to Kingston Park (Green Line)

Car Parking: 600 spaces at ground

Admission: (Last Year's Prices)

Season	Standing, Adults £100, Children/OAPs £50.
	Seated, Adults £200,Children/OAPs £100
Matchday	Standing, Adults £10, Children/OAPs £5.
	Seated, Adults £20,Children/OAPs £10

Club Shop: Yes, at Kingston Park
Clubhouse: At Kingston Park, open normal licensing hours
4 inside bar facilities, including corporate facilities,
1 outside bar facility and snack bars.
Functions: Capacity 200 - contact Karen Errington 0191 214 2811

Training Nights: Tuesday & Thursday

PROGRAMME

Size: B2 Pages: 48 Price: £2
Editor: Alexandra Jackson 0191 214 2807
ADVERTISING RATES Negotiable
Contact Commercial Director John Oates 0191 214 2804

Richard Arnold, with 113 + 2 substitute, holds the record for most league appearances for Newcastle Falcons.

NORTHAMPTON SAINTS R.F.C.

Director of Rugby	John Steele	Trinity Pavilion, Abbey Street, St.James', Northampton. NN5 5LN. Tel: 01604 751543 (B), Fax: 01604 599100
Chief Executive	Keith Grainger	Sturtidge Pavilion, Franklin's Gardens, Weedon Road, St. James', Northampton. NN5 5BG Tel: 01604 751543 (B), Fax: 01604 599110
Rugby Administrator	Ros Hargreaves	Trinity Pavilion, as above

But for a sticky patch, both in form and literally at Franklin's Gardens, the Saints could have made Leicester sweat considerably more on the title run in.

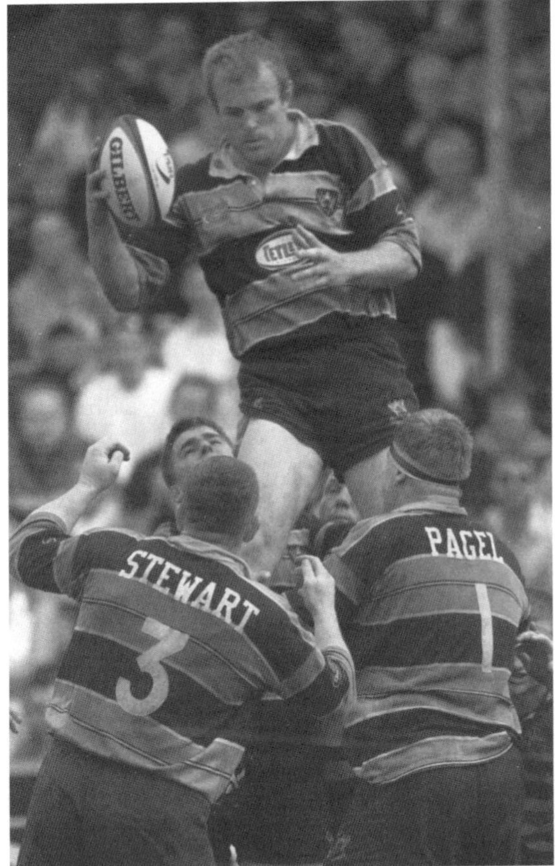

Tim Rodber, Saints' skipper last season, making a clean catch.

The arrival of top class internationals Pat Lam and Federico Mendez failed to have an immediate effect as the Saints were swept aside on the opening game of the season at home to Saracens.

Performances and results steadily improved to leave Northampton at the top of the table level on points with the Tigers at Christmas. The crucial game during last season proved to be the home fixture with London Irish in January when on a boggy Franklin's Gardens pitch the Saints were outplayed and suffered a 32-8 defeat.

Another defeat to Irish in the Tetley's Cup and a home defeat to Saracens looked ominous signs and the top of the table shoot out with Leicester in March was lost and so effectively was the title. As the weather dried up and the Northampton pitch improved so did results with the Saints saving their best rugby of the year for the final stretch to keep the Tigers honest in the final weeks of the season.

Superb victories over Newcastle Falcons, Wasps and Bath provide great encouragement for next season and secured second spot and a first European Cup place for the Saints. The summer departure of Ian McGeechan has seen the return of John Steele to the club as Director of Rugby and the arrival of two more internationals, Wales and British Lions centre Allan Bateman, and colossal Argentinian prop Martin Scelzo, further boost the club's squad and provide great optimism for the coming season.

NORTHAMPTON

Match No.	Date	H/A	Comp.	Opponents	Result & Score	Att.	15	14	13	12	11
1	05.09	A	AD1	Saracens	L 7-34	8,243	Beal	Moir	Dantiacq	Northey	Cohen
2	12.09	H	AD1	Harlequins	W 25-6	5,870	Beal	Moir	Dantiacq/t	Northey	Cohen
3	19.09	A	AD1	Leicester	L 25-35	13,292	Beal	Moir	Dantiacq	Northey(l)	Thorneycroft
4	03.10	H	AD1	Sale*	W37-17	6,464	Beal	Moir/t	Dantiacq/t	Allen/t	Cohen
5	10.10	A	AD1	London Scot	W33-22	1,963	Beal/(n/t)	Moir	Dantiacq	Allen/t	Sleightholme
6	17.10	H	AD1	Bedford	W34-29	6,739	Beal/t	Moir	Dantiacq(b)	Allen	Sleightholme/t
7	24.10	A	AD1	London Irish	W26-10	2,560	Beal	Moir	Dantiacq(b)	Allen	Sleightholme
8	31.10	H	AD1	Gloucester*	W 22-8	7,284	Beal	Moir	Dantiacq	Allen	Sleightholme
9	07.11	H	AD1	Wasps	W26-21	6,722	Beal/t	Moir	Dantiacq	Allen	Sleightholme
10	14.11	A	AD1	Newcastle	L 35-45	4,293	Blyth	Moir	Dantiacq	Allen	Sleightholme
11	21.11	H	AD1	Richmond*	W44-27	5,978	Dantiacq	Moir	Blyth/c	Allen/t	Sleightholme
12	12.12	A	AD1	Bath	W 15-9	8,200	Beal	Moir	Blyth	Allen	Sleightholme
13	20.12	A	AD1	W Hartlepool	W 33-9	1,613	Beal	Moir	Blyth	Allen	Sleightholme
14	02.01	A	AD1	Sale	W39-24	4,300	Beal	Moir	Blyth	Allen/t	Sleightholme
15	05.01	H	AD1	London Irish	L 8-32	7,450	Beal	Moir	Blyth/t	Allen	Sleightholme(a)
16	16.01	A	AD1	Harlequins	W24-17	8,500	Beal	Moir	Blyth	Allen	Cohen
17	23.01	H	AD1	W Hartlepool	W19-14	6,023	Beal	Moir	Blyth	Allen(a)	Cohen
18	06.02	H	AD1	Saracens	L 18-21	8,253	Beal	Cohen	Dantiacq	Blyth	Thorneycroft
19	13.02	H	AD1	Leicester	L 15-22	10,000	Beal	Moir	Northey	Allen	Cohen
20	27.03	H	AD1	Newcastle*	W57-16	6,540	Beal/t	Moir	Northey	Allen/t	Cohen/2t
21	13.04	A	AD1	Wasps	W24-15	3,126	Beal/t	Moir	Northey	Allen	Cohen
22	17.04	H	AD1	London Scot	W44-13	7,108	Beal/t	Moir/t	Northey(a)	Allen(q)	Cohen
23	24.04	A	AD1	Bedford*	W42-31	4,689	Beal(q)	Moir	Northey	Allen	Cohen/t
24	01.05	H	AD1	Bath	W40-17	8,843	Beal	Moir	Northey	Allen	Cohen
25	08.05	A	AD1	Richmond	W31-19	3,500	Beal	Moir	Northey(a)	Allen	Cohen
26	16.05	A	AD1	Gloucester	L 31-43	4,935	Beal	Moir/t	Dantiacq/t	Allen	Cohen(m)
A	09.01	A	TB4	Sale	W47-31	3,000	Beal/t	Moir/t	Blyth	Allen	Cohen
B	30.01	H	TB5	London Irish	L 6-21	7,110	Beal	Moir(b)	Blyth	Allen(a)	Cohen

* after opponents name indicates a penalty try
Brackets after a player's name indicates he was replaced. eg (a) means he was replaced by replacement code "a" and so on.
/ after a player or replacement name is followed by any scores he made - eg /t, /c, /p, /dg or any combination of these

1998-99 HIGHLIGHTS

League debuts:
David Dantiacq, Federico Mendez, Richard Metcalfe, Pat Lam, Domonic Malone, A Newman, Andy Blyth, Chris Allen, S Walter, Stephen Hepher.

Ever Presents: None
Most appearances 25 Craig Moir

Players used: 30 plus 3 as a replacement only.

Most Points in a season:

Pts	Player	T	C	P	DG
156	P Grayson	1	23	35	-
128	A Hepher	2	20	26	-
88	M Dawson	6	17	8	-
70	P Lam	14	-	-	-
45	B Pountney	9	-	-	-

MATCH FACTS

10	9	1	2	3	4	5	6	7	8	
Grayson/c(n)	Dawson/t	Pagel	Mendez(g)	Hynes	Phillips	Metcalfe	Lam	Pountney	Rodber	1
Grayson/cp	Dawson(h)	Pagel	Mendez	Hynes(j)	Chandler(e)	Metcalfe	Seely/2t	Pountney/t	Rodber	2
Grayson/6p(n/c)	Bramhall	Pagel	Johnson	Hynes(j)	Chandler(o)	Metcalfe	Seely(e)	Pountney/t	Rodber	3
Grayson/4c3p	Dawson	Pagel	Mendez(g)	Hynes(j)	Rodber(k)	Metcalfe	Mackinnon	Pountney	Lam	4
Grayson/2c3p	Dawson	Pagel	Mendez	Hynes(j)	Metcalfe(v)	Phillips	Mackinnon/t(k)	Pountney	Lam/t	5
Grayson/2p(n/c2p)	Dawson	Pagel/t	Mendez	Hynes(j)	Phillips	Newman	Mackinnon(k)	Pountney	Lam/t	6
Hepher/tc3p	Dawson	Pagel	Mendez	Hynes	Phillips	Metcalfe	Mackinnon(k)	Pountney/t	Lam/t	7
Hepher/c4p(c/p)	Dawson(p)	Pagel	Mendez	Hynes	Metcalfe	Rodber	Mackinnon(k)	Pountney	Lam	8
Grayson/2c4p	Dawson	Pagel	Johnson	Hynes	Metcalfe	Rodber	Mackinnon/t(k)	Pountney	Lam	9
Hepher/3c3p	Malone/t	Pagel/2t	Johnson	Hynes(j)	Phillips/t	Chandler	Mackinnon(r)	Lam	Seely	10
Hepher/3c4p	Malone	Pagel/t	Johnson	Volland(s)	Phillips	Chandler(f)	Lam	(t/t)	Seely/t	11
Grayson/cp	Dawson/t	Pagel	Mendez	Stewart	Metcalfe	Rodber	Seely	Pountney/t	Lam	12
Grayson/4c	Dawson/2t	Pagel	Mendez	Stewart	Metcalfe	Rodber	Seely(e)	Pountney/t	Lam/2t	13
Grayson/4c2p	Dawson(p/t)	Pagel	Mendez	Stewart(d)	Metcalfe	Rodber(e)	Seely	Pountney	Lam/3t	14
Grayson/p	Malone	Pagel	Mendez(g)	Stewart(d)	Metcalfe	Rodber(e)	Seely	Pountney	Lam	15
Grayson/t3cp	Dawson	Pagel/t	Mendez	Stewart(d)	Metcalfe	Phillips	Seely	Pountney	Lam/t	16
Grayson/c4p	Dawson	Pagel	Walter	Stewart(d)	Phillips	Rodber(q)	Seely	Pountney	Lam/t	17
Grayson/6p	Dawson	Pagel	Mendez	Hynes	Metcalfe(v)	Phillips	Seely(t)	Pountney	Lam	18
Hepher	Dawson/5p	Volland	Mendez	Stewart	Metcalfe	Rodber	Mackinnon(d)	Pountney	Lam	19
Hepher	Dawson/t6c	Volland	Mendez/2t(u)	Stewart	Metcalfe/t(e)	Rodber	Mackinnon(k)	Pountney	Lam	20
Hepher/c4p	Dawson	Volland	Mendez	Stewart	Phillips	Rodber	Mackinnon(k)	Pountney	Lam/t	21
Hepher/4c2p	Dawson/t	Volland	Mendez	Stewart	Phillips	Rodber(v)	Lam/t	Pountney/2t	Seely	22
Hepher/4c3p	Dawson	Pagel	Mendez	Hynes(j)	Phillips	Newman(v)	Lam/2t	Pountney	Seely/t	23
Hepher/2p	Dawson/4c2p	Pagel	Mendez/t(g)	Stewart(j)	Phillips	Rodber	Lam	Pountney/t	Seely/2t	24
Dawson/4cp	Malone/2t	Pagel	Johnson	Stewart(j)	Phillips/t	Rodber	Lam	Pountney	Seely/t(t)	25
Dawson/3c	Malone/t	Pagel	Johnson	Stewart	Phillips	Newman	Walter	Allen	Hepher/2t	26
Grayson/6c	Dawson	Pagel	Mendez/t	Stewart(d)	Metcalfe(i)	Phillips	Rodber(v)	Allen	Seely/3t	A
Grayson/2p	Dawson	Pagel	Mendez	Stewart	Metcalfe	Phillips	Mackinnon(t)	Lam	Seely	B

REPLACEMENTS: a- D Dantiacq b-A Northey. c-P Grayson. d-M Hynes. e-J Phillips. f-R Metcalfe. g-C Johnson h-J Bramhall. i-J Chandler. j-M Volland. k-G Seely. l-M Allen. m-H Thorneycroft. n-A Hepher. 0-D Mackinnon. p-D Malone. q-A Blyth. r-S Foale. s-M Stewart. t-C Allen. u-S Walter. v-S Hepher.

Due to injuries nobody was consistently kicking the goals and Grayson, Hepher and Dawson all had a go at various stages of the season.

Leading the way was Paul Grayson who topped the Northampton points scoring list for the sixth consecutive season.

In second place on 128 points was Alastair Hepher who became the forth player to top 100 points in a season for the Saints. The other two were John Steele and Matt Allen.

Matt Dawson became the second back after Harvey Thorneycroft to pass 100 league appearances and ended the season on 111. Nick Beal is next on the list just two short of his 100 on 98 appearances.

Pat Lam topped the try scorers list with 14 tries in his debut season for the club.

Matt Allen added five tries to his club record 32 tries and is eight clear of Matt Dawson who is second on 29.

NORTHAMPTON

LEAGUE STATISTICS
compiled by Stephen McCormack

SEASON	Division	P	W	D	L	F	A	Pts Diff	Lge Pts	Lge Pos	Most Points	Most Tries
89-90	2	11	9	1	1	192	135	57	19	1p	105 John Steele	4 Frank Packman & John Thame
90-91	1	12	5	1	6	149	254	-105	11	9	83 John Steele	3 Wayne Shelford
91-92	1	12	9	1	2	209	136	73	19	3	110 John Steele	5 Harvey Thorneycroft
92-93	1	12	8	0	4	215	150	65	16	4	52 John Steele	6 Harvey Thorneycroft
93-94	1	18	9		0	305	342	-37	18	5	132 Paul Grayson	2 by seven players
94-95	1	18	6	0	12	267	335	-68	12	10r	189 Paul Grayson	3 Grant Seely & Matt Dawson
95-96	2	18	18	0	0	867	203	664	36	1p	215 Paul Grayson	20 Matt Allen
96-97	1	22	10	0	12	515	477	38	20	8	129 Paul Grayson	7 Jonathon Bell
97-98	1	22	9	1	12	493	472	21	19	8	210 Paul Grayson	7 Matt Allen
98-99	1	26	19	0	7	754	556	198	38	2	156 Paul Grayson	14 Pat Lam

BIGGEST MARGINS

Home Win	64pts - 69-5 v Waterloo 13.4.95
Away Win	66pts - 69-3 v Waterloo 28.10.95
Home Defeat	47pts - 3-50 v Lon. Scottish 3.10.87
Away Defeat	60pts - 0-60 v Orrell 27.10.90

MOST CONSECUTIVE

Appearances	31 Frank Packman
Matches scoring Tries	4 Ian Hunter
Matches scoring points	18 Paul Grayson
Victories	20
Defeats	6

MOST POINTS

Scored at Home	69 v Waterloo 13.4.96
Scored Away	69 v Waterloo 28.10.95
Conceded at Home	50 v Lon. Scottish 3.10.87
Conceded Away	60 v Orrell 27.10.90

MOST TRIES

Scored in a match	11 v Blackheath 14.10.95 v Waterloo 28.10.95 & 13.4.96
Conceded in a match	11 v Orrell 27.10.90

MOST APPEARANCES

by a forward	117 (1) Tim Rodber
by a back	124 (7) Harvey Thorneycroft

	MOST IN A SEASON	MOST IN A CAREER	MOST IN A MATCH	
Points	215 Paul Grayson 95-96	1031 Paul Grayson 93-99	26 Paul Grayson	v Bristol 2.10.93 (A)
Tries	20 Matt Allen 95-96	37 Matt Allen 94-99	4 Craig Moir	v Waterloo 13.4.96 (H)
Conversions	76 Paul Grayson 95-96	157 Paul Grayson 93-99	7 Paul Grayson	v Lon. Irish 9.9.95 (H) v Lon. Scottish 4.11.95 (H) v Lon. Scottish 27.4.96 (A)
			Michael Dods	v Blackheath 14.10.95 (H)
Penalties	52 Paul Grayson 94-95	207 Paul Grayson 93-99	7 Paul Grayson	v Richmond 21.2.98 (H)
Drop Goals	4 Paul Grayson 96-97	13 Paul Grayson 93-98	3 John Steele	v Wasps 23.3.91 (A)

NORTHAMPTON PLAYING SQUAD

BACKS

	Ht.	Wt.	Birthdate	Birthplace	CLUB	League Apps	Tries	Pts
David Dantiacq					Northampton	13(4)	3	15
.								
Nick Beal	6.2	13.08	02.12.70	York	Northampton	98	22	171
England , A.					High Wycombe			
Craig Moir	5.10	14.10	25.10.73	Aberdeen	Northampton	58(5)	14	70
Wales U21, Schools.								
Matt Allen	6.2	15.02	28.02.74	Farnborough	Northampton	83(6)	37	185
England A, U21.								
Andy Northey	6.0	15.10	17.02.73	St Helens	Northampton	23(5)		
					Waterloo			
Harvey Thorneycroft	6.0	15.11	22.02.69	Northampton	Northampton	125(7)	31	148
England A, Students, U21,Colts.								
Jonathan Sleightholme	5.10	13.05	05.08.72	Malton	Northampton	24	2	10
England , A, Emerging, U21.Other club: Wakefield 38/27/127					Bath	39	22	110
Matt Dawson	5.11	12.10	31.10.72	Birkenhead	Northampton	111(1)	29	265
England , A,U21, U18, British Lions								
Paul Grayson	6.0	12.07	30.05.71	Chorley	Northampton	93(1)	12	1031
England , A, Emerging, U21.Other club: Preston ??/5/265					Waterloo	10	1	126
Ben Cohen	6.3	15.00	14.09.78	Northampton	Northampton	24(2)	4	20
Andy Blyth					Northampton	11(2)	1	7
					Ballymena			
Alastair Hepher	5.11	13.00	03.10.74	Yardley Gobian	Northampton	19(5)	4	224
Domonic Malone						7(2)	5	25
John Bramhall	5.11	12.06	20.05.78	Northampton	Northampton	6(3)	-	-

FORWARDS

	Ht.	Wt.	Birthdate	Birthplace	CLUB	League Apps	Tries	Pts
Martyn Hynes	5.9	16.00	23.08.68	Wigan	Northampton	51(9)	-	-
England A.					Orrell	65	1	4
Mattie Stewart	5.11	17.00	18.05.73	Dartford	Northampton	38(2)	-	-
Scotland .					Blackheath	41	2	10
Federico Mendez					Northampton	19	3	15
					Batn.			
Matt Volland	6.0	16.07	30.06.74	Peterborough	Northampton	49(15)	-	-
England U21.								
Chris Johnson	5.11	15.07	23.05.73	Oldham	Northampton	16(11)	2	10
England Students.					Leicester	7(1)	1	5
Jon Phillips	6.6	18.07	16.08.72	Peterborough	Northampton	102(9)	6	30
England U21, Colts.								
Jason Chandler	6.7	18.00	23.09.70	Wellington	Northampton	29	2	10
New Zealand XV, U21.								
Don Mackinnon	6.3	15.07	27.03.71	Australia	Northampton	27(2)	3	15
Budge Pountney	6.0	14.10	13.11.74	Southampton	Northampton	84(2)	22	110
Scotland A, England U21, Students.								
Tim Rodber	6.6	16.07	02.07.65	Richmond	Northampton	117(1)	17	82
England England ,A, B, U21.								
Grant Seely	6.4	18.04	17.01.73	Aylesbury	Northampton	60(15)	28	140
England U21, Students.								
Gary Pagel	6.1	18.04	17.09.66	South Africa	Northampton	37(1)	7	35
South Africa, Western Province								
Simon Foale	6.4	14.00	29.08.67	Northampton	Northampton	27(12)	2	10
Pat Lam	6.1	15.10	29.09.68	W Samoa	Northampton			
Western Samoa					Newcastle	31(2)	24	120
Richard Metcalfe	7.1	19.0	21.11.73	Leeds	Northampton	7(1)	2	10
					Newcastle	39(4)	2	10

NORTHAMPTON SAINTS

FACT FILE

Founded: 1880
Nickname: The Saints

Colours: Black, green, gold hoops
Change colours: Black

GROUND

Address: Franklin's Gardens, Weedon Road, Northampton NN5 5BG
Tel: 01604 751543 Fax: 01604 599110
Capacity: 9,800 Seated Covered: 5,300. Uncovered 1,200 Standing: 3,300

Directions: Take junction 16 from the M1, follow signs to StJames' and Town Centre, turn right into Abbey Street.
Nearest Railway Station: Northampton

Car Parking : 1000 spaces, £3.

Admission:

Season	Standing	Adults £150	Conc. £65	Jumior £65
	Seated	Adults £150-£280	Conc. £85-£280	Junior £65-£280
Family	1 adult + 1 junior £150-£195 2 adults + 2 juniors £300-£390			
Matchday	Standing	Adults £12	Conc. £8	Junior £5
	Seated	Adults £15-£20	Conc. £12-£20	Junior £8-20

Club Shop: Yes, Manager Jo Bage 01604 599111

Clubhouse: Matchday 12-11
Bar meals & restaurant available
Functions: Rooms for up to 200, contact Nicola Clarke 01604 751543

PROGRAMME

Size: A5
Pages: 64
Price: £2
Editor: Tom Sears 01604 751543

ADVERTISING RATES (Colour)
All prices subject to VAT
Full page £3,000
Half page £1,750
Qtr page £800

Federico Mendez,
Saints' Player of the Year 98-99

SARACENS F.C.

Managing Director	Tim Lawler
Marketing Director	Simon Hoskins
Commercial Manager	Tom Hill
Office Manager	Jon Salinger
Team Admin. Manager	Mike Scott
Finance Director	Mike Salinger
Brand & Media Director	Robin Bye

Vicarage Road Stadium
Vicarage Road
Watford
Herts. WD1 8ER

Tel: 01923 496200

There was a somewhat cyclical nature to the season, with Saracens finishing the calendar very much as they had begun it - well supported, bristling with promise, and amongst the favourites for impending campaigns.

The Premiership commenced with a clash against title rivals Northampton, and Saracens turned in a performance that fully justified their new signings, with newcomers Penaud, Coker and Thompson all scoring tries in the opening 25 minutes, and coming home convincing winners 34-7.

Indeed, Penaud seemed to embody the great start to the season, adorning magazine covers and winning the Allied Dunbar Premiership's Player of the Month title. Results against Sale, London Scottish and Swansea in the Anglo-Welsh friendly ensured that the momentum continued to the Clash of the Titans against Leicester at home on October 11th.

Victory at Vicarage Road saw Saracens emerge from the clash with the only remaining 100 percent record in the Premiership. Moreover, the 17,000 crowd saw them demonstrate an admirable ability to play a tight game, with good ball retention.

Having ascended to the top of the tree, they soon found other teams would raise themselves above their previous levels of performance when playing against them. So it was, as first a Lacroix-led Harlequins and then Wasps inflicted defeats. In between these two games, however, Francois Pienaar's first appearance of the season precipitated the 52-3 thrashing of West Hartlepool, and illustrated the erratic rollercoaster that pervaded the remainder of the season.

The defence of the Tetley's Bitter Cup was thwarted by Newcastle and the season seemed to have stalled, as they languished sixth in the league, without a competitive win for twenty weeks. Beset on all sides, the team showed tremendous character to turn the season around with successive victories in the last four fixtures, finishing third in the League, and qualifying for Europe as London's top club.

Saracens Squad 1998-99

Match No.	Date	H/A	Comp.	Opponents	Result & Score	Att.	15	14	13	12	11
1	05.09	H	AD1	Northampton	W 34-7	8,243	Johnson/t4c2p	Daniel	Thomson/t	Ravenscroft	Singer
2	19.09	H	AD1	Sale*	W 43-26	5,597	Johnson/3c4p	Daniel/2t	Constable/t	Thomson(d)	Singer/t
3	26.09	A	AD1	London Scot	W 58-20	2,414	Johnson/2t6c2p	Singer/t	Constable/t	Thomson(d)	Daniel/2t
4	11.10	H	AD1	Leicester	W 22-10	17,346	Johnson/c3p(y)	Singer	Constable/t	Thomson	Daniel
5	17.10	A	AD1	Harlequins	L 28-41	6,396	Singer	Daniel/t	Thomson	Sorrell(d/t)	Wallace
6	20.10	A	AD1	W Hartlepool*	W 52-3	1,877	Singer	Daniel	Thomson	Ravenscroft(y/t)	Wallace/t
7	25.10	H	AD1	Wasps	L 17-31	11,261	Johnson/t2cp	Singer	Thomson	Ravenscroft	Daneil/t(q)
8	31.10	A	AD1	Newcastle	L 12-43	4,832	Johnson/t	Constable	Thomson(z)	Ravenscroft	Wallace
9	08.11	H	AD1	Richmond	W 33-17	9,217	Singer	Taylor	Constable	Ravenscroft/2t	Wallace
10	14.11	A	AD1	Bedford	W 25-20	5,125	Johnson/2c2p	Taylor	Constable	Ravenscroft	Wallace/t
11	21.11	A	AD1	Gloucester	L 27-28	6,627	Johnson/3c2p	Taylor(b)	Sorrell/t	Ravenscroft/t	Wallace
12	13.12	H	AD1	London Irish	W 40-26	10,373	Johnson/4c4p	Daniel	Constable(y)	Ravenscroft	Wallace
13	19.12	A	AD1	Bath	W 19-11	8,200	Johnson/c3p	Daniel	Constable	Ravenscroft/t	Wallace
14	27.12	H	AD1	London Scot	L 7-24	10,257	Johnson/c	Daniel/t	Constable	Ravenscroft	Wallace
15	03.01	H	AD1	Bedford	W 44-13	6,593	Singer(w)	Daniel/t(x)	Constable	Ravenscroft	Wallace/t
16	06.01	A	AD1	Wasps	D 15-15	8,534	Johnson/5p	Daniel	Constable	Ravenscroft	Wallace
17	06.02	A	AD1	Northampton	W 21-18	8,253	Johnson/c3p	Daniel/t	Constable	Ravenscroft/t	Thirlby
18	14.02	H	AD1	W Hartlepool	W 48-27	5,872	Johnson/4cp	Thirlby/tc	Constable	Ravenscroft	Daniel
19	13.03	A	AD1	Sale	L 24-32	3,570	Thirlby/c3p(a)	Constable	Thomson	Sorrell	Daniel
20	28.03	H	AD1	Bath	L 14-33	14,219	Thirlby/2c	Constable	Thomson(d)	Sorrell	Johnston(e)
21	17.04	A	AD1	Leicester	L 18-25	14,823	Johnson/6p	Thirlby	Constable	Sorrell	Daniel(c)
22	25.04	H	AD1	Harlequins*	L 30-38	8,719	Johnson/3c3p(d)	Thirlby(c)	Constable	Sorrell	Daniel/2t
23	01.05	A	AD1	London Irish	W 26-21	6,710	Johnson/t2c3p	Thirlby	Thomson	Sorrell(d)	Constable
24	07.05	H	AD1	Gloucester	W 26-10	5,261	Johnson/c3p(r)	Constable	Thomson	Sorrell	Daniel/t
25	12.05	A	AD1	Richmond	W 25-18	2,613	Johnson/t2c2p	Constable	Thomson	Sorrell/t(d)	Daniel(r)
26	20.05	H	AD1	Newcastle	W 40-26	6,982	Johnson/4c3p	Constable/t	Thomson	Sorrell	Daniel
A	10.01	A	TB4	Morley	W 76-8	2,000	Johnson/t8c	Daniel/3t	Constable(D)(k)	Ravenscroft	Wallace(e/t)
B	31.01	A	TB5	Lydney	W 40-0	3,000	Johnson/4c(r/c)	Daniel/2t	Constable	Ravenscroft	Lea(e)
C	28.02	A	TBqf	Newcastle	L 0-15	3,495	Johnson	Thirlby	Constable(y)	Ravenscroft	Daniel

* after opponents name indicates a penalty try
Brackets after a player's name indicates he was replaced. eg (a) means he was replaced by replacement code "a" and so on.
/ after a player or replacement name is followed by any scores he made - eg /t, /c, /p, /dg or any combination of these

1998-99 HIGHLIGHTS

League debuts:
Jeremy Thomson, Alain Penaud, Troy Coker, Barry Cole, Rob Thirlby, David Flatman, Phil Ogilvie, B Taylor, Wayne de Jonge, Rob Johnston, Mike Powell.

Ever Presents: George Chuter

Players used: 33 plus 6 as a replacement only.

Most Points in a season:

Pts	Player	T	C	P	DG
318	G Johnson	8	52	58	-
66	A Penaud	5	7	5	4
60	B Daniel	12	-	-	-
30	T Diprose	6	-	-	-
30	S Ravenscroft	6	-	-	-

MATCH FACTS

10	9	1	2	3	4	5	6	7	8	
Penaud/t	Bracken	Grau	Chuter(l)	Wallace(m)	Yandell	Grewcock	Coker/t(n)	Hill	Diprose	1
Penaud	Bracken	Grau	Chuter(l)	Wallace(p)	Yandell	Grewcock	Coker	Hill	Diprose	2
Penaud	Bracken	Grau	Chuter/t	Wallace/t	Yandell	Grewcock	Coker(n)(p)	Hill	Diprose	3
Penaud/2p	Bracken	Grau	Chuter	Wallace	Johns	Grewcock	Coker(o)	Hill	Diprose	4
Penaud/t4c	Bracken	Grau	Chuter	Wallace/t	Johns	Grewcock	Coker(o)	Hill	Diprose	5
Penaud/3c3p(C/c)	Bracken/t(x)	Olver(f)	Chuter	Wallace	Johns	Grewcock	Coker	Pienaar/t(j/t)	Diprose/t	6
Penaud	Bracken	Grau	Chuter	Wallace	Johns(i)	Grewcock	Pienaar	Hill	Diprose	7
Penaud/c	Bracken	Olver	Chuter	deJonge(m)	Coker	Grewcock	Pienaar(v)	Hill/t	Diprose	8
Johnson/t3c4p	Bracken(x)	Reidy(p)	Chuter	Wallace	Johns	Grewcock	Coker(t)	Hill	Diprose	9
Penaud(e)	Free	Reidy	Chuter	Olver(A/t)	Chesney(B)	Yandell	Coker/t	Pienaar	Ogilvie	10
Penaud	Free	Reidy	Chuter	deJonge(p)	Chesney	Yandell	Ogilvie/t(n)	Pienaar	Diprose	11
Penaud(e)	Free/t(u)	Flatman/t	Chuter(l)	Wallace	Johns	Grewcock	Pienaar/2t	Hill(t)	Diprose	12
Penaud/dg	Bracken	Flatman(m)	Chuter	Wallace	Johns	Grewcock	Coker(t)	Pienaar	Diprose	13
Penaud	Bracken(x)	Flatman(m)	Chuter	Wallace	Johns	Grewcock	Coker	Pienaar	Diprose	14
Johnson/4c2p	Olsen/t	Flatman(p)	Chuter(l)	Wallace	Yandell(v/t)	Grewcock/2t	Coker(t)	Hill	Diprose	15
Penaud	Olsen	Flatman	Chuter	Wallace	Johns	Grewcock	Coker	Hill	Diprose	16
Penaud	Bracken	Flatman	Chuter	Reidy	Chesney	Grewcock	Pienaar	Hill(t)	Diprose	17
Penaud/t	Bracken/t	Flatman(m)	Chuter	Wallace	Johns	Grewcock/t	Pienaar	Hill(t)	Diprose/3t	18
Penaud/tdg	Bracken	Grau	Chuter	Wallace	Johns	Chesney	Hill/t	Pienaar	Diprose(t)	19
Penaud(G)	Powell	Grau/t(m)	Chuter	Wallace	Johns(q)	Yandell	Hill/t	Pienaar	Diprose	20
Penaud	Olsen(F)	Grau	Chuter	Reidy(g)	Chesney	Yandell	Hill	Pienaar(n)	Diprose	21
Penaud	Olsen	Grau	Chuter	Reidy	Johns	Chesney	Hill	Pienaar(n)	Diprose	22
Penaud/dg	Olsen(F)	Grau(s)	Chuter	Reidy	Johns	Chesney(h)	Cole(t)	Hill	Diprose/t	23
Penaud	Bracken/t	Grau(s)	Chuter(H)	Reidy	Johns	Yandell	Cole/t(t)	Hill	Diprose	24
Penaud/t	Bracken	Grau	Chuter(H)	Reidy	Johns	Grewcock(h)	Cole(t)	Hill	Diprose	25
Penaud/dg	Bracken/t	Grau	Chuter/t	Reidy(s)	Yandell(v)	Grewcock	Ogilvie(o)	Hill	Diprose/t	26
Penaud/t	Olsen2t(x/t)	Olver	Botterman		Chesney	Grewcock/t	Ogilvie	Hill(n/t)	Coker/t	A
Penaud	Bracken/t	Olver(f)	Chuter/t(l)	Reidy	Johns	Chesney	Pienaar(t)	Hill(n/t)	Diprose/t	B
Penaud	Bracken	Flatman(m)	Chuter	Wallace	Johns	Grewcock	Pienaar	Hill	Diprose	C

REPLACEMENTS: a- G Johnson, b- B Daniel, c-J Thomson, d-S Ravenscroft, e-M Singer, f-R Grau, g-P Wallace, h-C Yandell, i-T Coker, j-R Hill, k-T Diprose, l-G Botterman, m-B Reidy, n-B Cole, o-F Pienaar, p-A Olver, q-K Chesney, r-R Thirlby, s-D Flatman, t-P Ogilvie, u-M Olsen, v-P Johns, w-P Turner, x-B Free, y-K Sorrell, z-B Taylor, A-W de Jonge, B-A Rocque, C-A Lee, D-R Johnston, E-B Lea, F-M Powell, G-A Stanley, H-M Cairns

Gavin Johnson set 5 new points scoring records for Saracens in his final season before returning to South Africa.

He became the second player to top the 300 point mark in the top division after John Schuster and in the process beat Michael Lynagh's club record of 279 from last season. Included in that total were a record 52 conversions beating Michael Lynagh's record of 37 from last season. He equalled Lynagh's record of 58 penalties from last season.

Johnson scored a record 28 points in a match in the away win at London Scottish last September. Also in that match he kicked a new record of six conversions in a match, beating the previous record of 5 shared by Nick Holmes, Andy Kennedy and Michael Lynagh.
In the away defeat at Leicester he kicked a record equalling 6 penalties.

In the try scoring Brandon Daniel set a new record with 12 tries in a season whilst Tony Diprose became the third Saracens player to score a hat trick in a league match. Richard Wallace increased his club record to 20 tries.

SARACENS

LEAGUE STATISTICS
compiled by Stephen McCormack

SEASON	Division	P	W	D	L	F	A	Pts Diff	Lge Pts	Lge Pos	Most Points	Most Tries
89-90	1	11	7	1	3	168	167	1	15	4	50 Andy Kennedy	4 Ben Clarke
90-91	1	12	5	0	7	151	228	-77	10	10	36 Ben Rudling	4 Ben Clarke
91-92	1	12	7	1	4	176	165	11	15	5	91 Ben Rudling	4 Martin Gregory
92-93	1	12	3	0	9	137	180	-43	6	11	43 Ben Rudling	3 Daren O'Leary & Barry Crawley
93-94	2	18	11	1	6	299	238	61	23	3	149 Andy Tunningley	5 Richard Hill & Andy Tunningley
94-95	2	18	15	1	2	389	213	176	31	1	162 Andy Tunningley	7 John Green
95-96	1	18	5	0	13	284	451	-167	10	9	126 Andy Lee	4 Peter Harries
96-97	1	22	12	1	9	568	449	119	25	7	125 Michael Lynagh	9 Richard Wallace
97-98	1	22	18	1	3	584	484	100	37	2	279 Michael Lynagh	8 Richard Wallace
98-99	1	26	16	1	9	748	583	165	33	3	318 Gavin Johnson	12 Brandon Daniel

BIGGEST MARGINS

Home Win	45pts - 45-0 v Lon. Irish 30.4.97
Away Win	36pts - 48-12 v Blackheath 23.3.88
Home Defeat	43pts - 6-49 v Bath 27.4.91
Away Defeat	49pts - 3-52 v Sale 18.9.93

MOST CONSECUTIVE

Appearances	68 Brian Davies
Matches scoring Tries	6 Dave McLagen
Matches scoring points	20 Michael Lynagh
Victories	17
Defeats	7

MOST POINTS

Scored at Home	50 v Bedford 19.11.88
Scored Away	48 v Blackheath 23.3.88
Conceded at Home	49 v Bath 27.4.91
Conceded Away	52 v Sale 18.9.93

MOST TRIES

Scored in a match	9 v Gosforth 22.4.89
Conceded in a match	9 v Sale 18.9.93

MOST APPEARANCES

by a forward	124 Tony Diprose
by a back	106 John Buckton

	MOST IN A SEASON	MOST IN A CAREER	MOST IN A MATCH	
Points	318 Gavin Johnson 98-99	462 Andy Tunningley 90-97	28 Gavin Johnson	v W. Hartlepool 14.10.95 (H)
Tries	12 Brandon Daniel 98-99	20 Richard Wallace 98-99	3 Laurie Smith	v Gosforth 22.4.89 (A)
			Richard Wallace	v Lon. Irish 30.4.97 (H)
				v Bristol 14.2.98 (A)
			Tony Diprose	v W Hartlepool 14.2.99 (H)
Conversions	52 Gavin Johnson 98-99	53 Michael Lynagh 96-98	6 Gavin Johnson	v Lon Scot 26.9.98 (A)
Penalties	58 Michael Lynagh 97-98	92 Andy Tunningley 90-97	6 Andy Tunningley	v Fylde 15.10.94 (H)
	Gavin Johnson 98-99		Andy Lee	v W. Hartlepool 14.10.95 (H)
			Michael Lynagh	v Harlequins 11.1.98 (H)
				v Newcastle 25.3.98 (A)
			Gavin Johnson	v Leicester 17.4.99 (A)
Drop Goals	6 Andy Lee 94-95	16 Andy Lee 89-95	2 Andy Lee	v Wasps 22.2.92 (A)
				v Lon. Scottish 5.11.94 (H)
				v W. Hartlepool 14.10.95 (H)
			Ben Rudling	v Lon. Irish 11.4.92 (H)
			Gareth Hughes	v Bath 24.4.93 (H)

SARACENS PLAYING SQUAD

BACKS

	Ht.	Wt.	Birthdate	Birthplace	CLUB	League Apps	Tries	Pts
Matt Singer	6.1	13.05	07.11.72	Bristol	Saracens Neath	32(10)	7	42
Richard Wallace Ireland . British Lions	5.11	14.00	16.01.68	Cork	Saracens	43(1)	20	100
Brandon Daniel Bay of Plenty, New Zealand 7s squad.	6.1	14.04	19.07.77	New Zealand	Saracens	34(2)	16	80
Ryan Constable Australia 1, Queensland.	6.0	13.05	22.10.71	Durban (SA)	Saracens	41(2)	8	40
Phillipe Sella France 111	5.11	13.08	14.02.62	Cairac (Fra)	Saracens Agen	34	8	40
Steve Ravenscroft England , A, U21, Student.	5.11	14.02	02.11.70	Bradford	Saracens	103(7)	15	75
Gavin Johnson South Africa 7, Transvaal.	6.2	14.07	17.10.66	S Africa	Saracens	34(2)	10	363
Kyran Bracken England , U18, U16.	5.11	12.10	22.11.71	Dublin	Saracens Bristol	49(1) 47	7 7	35 35
Marcus Olsen England U21, Colts.	5.7	12.06	23.06.72	Salisbury	Saracens Bath	11(4)	2	10
Kevin Sorrell England U18.	6.0	12.08	06.03.77	Harold Wood	Saracens	14(3)	4	20
Jeremy Thomson	5.10	13.09	24.06.67	South Africa	Saracens	14(3)	1	5
Andy Lee England U21, Students.	5.9	13.07	10.11.68	Woodford	Saracens	57(7)	9	299
Brad Free Australian Barbarians	5.10	12.04	10.06.71	Australia	Saracens	8(4)	1	5
Alain Penaud France Other club: Brive.	5.11	14.00	19.07.69	Juillac	Saracens	24	5	66

FORWARDS

	Ht.	Wt.	Birthdate	Birthplace	CLUB	League Apps	Tries	Pts
Brendan Reidy Western Samoa.	6.1	17.00	13.09.68	Apia	Saracens	20(11)	1	5
Paul Wallace Ireland , British Lions 3.	6.0	16.00	30.12.71	Cork	Saracens	55(4)	8	40
Roberto Grau Argentina	5.9	17.03	16.07.70	Buenos Aires	Saracens	29(2)	1	5
Adrian Olver Eastern Counties	6.0	17.00	02.06.69		Saracens	16(19)	1	5
George Chuter England U19.	5.10	15.08	09.07.76	Greenwich	Saracens	41(5)	3	15
Paddy Johns Ireland , A, Students, Schools.	6.6	17.01	19.02.68	Portadown	Saracens	48(6)	3	15
Troy Coker .	6.6	18.00	30.05.63	Brisbane	Saracens Harlequins	13(1)	2	10
Danny Grewcock England , A, Students.	6.6	17.07	07.11.72	Coventry	Saracens Coventry	39 31	3 3	15 15
Francois Pienaar South Africa 29	6.4	17.01	02.01.67	Port Elizabeth	Saracens	43(4)	14	70
Richard Hill England, British Lions 2.	6.3	15.13	23.05.73	Dormansland	Saracens	87(1)	17	85
Tony Diprose England .	6.5	17.08	22.09.72	Orsett	Saracens	124(1)	22	110
David Flatman	6.0	17.07	20.01.80		Saracens	7(5)	1	5
Craig Yandell	6.7	17.00	16.08.73	Weston	Saracens	10(2)	-	-
Phil Ogilvie	5.11	17.02	12.03.75		Saracens	3(10)	1	5

Sports Minister, Tony Banks, presents the award for the Best Community Sports Programme to Tim Lawler (left) and Mike Atkins of Kenwood Electronics, the sponsor of Saracens' "Rugby in the Community" Programme, last October.

SARACENS

FACT FILE

Founded: 1876
Nickname: Sarries

Colours: Black, with red shoulders/black/red
Change colours: Black, red and white

GROUND

Address: Vicarage Road Stadium, Vicarage Road, Watford. WD1 8ER
Tel: 01923 496200 (Office), 496010 (Ticket Office), 496005 (Shop) Fax: 01923 496201
Web: www.saracens.com e-mail: general@saracens.net
Capacity: 22,000 - all covered seating

Directions: M1, junct. 6. Follow signs for Watford town centre, then signs for Watford Hospital next to ground
Nearest Railway Station: Watford Junction, 15-20 mins walk
Underground Watford Metropolitan station, 10-15 mins walk

Car Parking: No public parking available at the ground.
There are several multi-storey car parks nearby.

Admission: (all covered seating)

Season	Adults £154-395	Children/OAPs £25-£65
Matchday	Adults £10-25	Children/OAPs £5

Club Shop: Mon-Sat 9-5, Matchday 11-5.
Contact Julie Gingell 01923 496005

Clubhouse: Bramley Sports Ground, Chase Side, London N14 4AB
Snacks & restaurant available.

Functions: Contact Beeton Rumford Catering

PROGRAMME Size: B5 Pages: 64 Price: £2.00
Editor: Robin Bye
Advertising: Contact Commercial Department

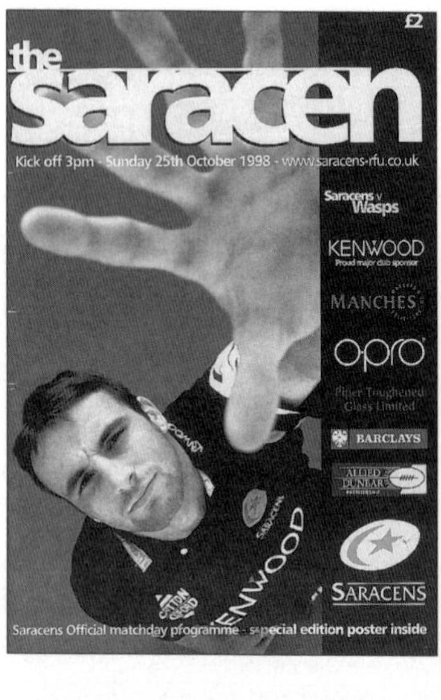

Sports Minister, Tony Banks, presents the award for the Best Community Sports Programme to Tim Lawler (left) and Mike Atkins of Kenwood Electronics, the sponsor of Saracens' "Rugby in the Community" Programme, last October.

LONDON WASPS R.F.C.

Group Chief Executive	Simon Crane	Loftus Road Stadium, South Africa Road, London W12 7PA. Tel: 020 8740 2523 Fax: 020 8740 2508
Director of Rugby	Nigel Melville	London Wasps Training Ground, Repton Ave., Sudbury, Middx HA0 3DW 0181 902 4200 (B), 0181 900 2659 (Fax)
Brand Manager (All Press Enquiries)	Emma Ward	Loftus Road Stadium, as above Tel: 020 8740 2513 Fax: 020 8740 2512
Commercial Manager	Mark Devlin	Loftus Road Stadium, as above Tel: 020 8740 2594 Fax: 020 8740 2508

After the grave disappointments of a non-existent title defence and a record Cup Final defeat in 1997/98, Wasps young side enjoyed a hugely improved campaign, qualifying for the European Cup and securing their first ever Tetley's Bitter Cup success.

Eschewing the free-spending policy of several Premiership opponents, Director of Rugby Nigel Melville has moulded a combative, organised unit based primarily on British stars, at relatively low cost. A youth structure which had already seen the emergence of Lawrence Dallaglio and Nick Greenstock amongst others, saw a new breed take centre stage in 1998/99. Paul Volley and Joe Worsley enjoyed superb seasons in the back row, whilst Josh Lewsey emerged as the man most likely to assume the full-back mantle of Wasps legend Gareth Rees. Elsewhere, experienced internationals such as Dallaglio and Scottish flyer Kenny Logan had magnificent campaigns and the side was of course led admirably by Kiwi lock Mark Weedon.

Wasps Premiership campaign produced some outstanding displays - the 71-14 mauling of West Hartlepool and the 35-0 defeat of Bath, their first ever shut out, were amongst the highlights. Glory, though, came in the Tetley's Bitter Cup. Sedgley Park and Waterloo were duly disposed of early on before the key match up saw Weedon's men overcome in-form London Irish 19-3 at a raucous Loftus Road quarter-final. Gloucester were swept away in the semis to set up a nostalgic final with Newcastle, led of course by former Wasps star, Rob Andrew. Nevertheless, injury prevented the former England fly-half from playing and his side were never in the game. Alex King and Josh Lewsey scored the tries in a 29-19 win to give Wasps their second major trophy in three seasons.

The task now is to build on such successes and enjoy a sustained challenge for the league title itself. Wasps often matched the endeavour and ability of the very best teams last season. Now they need to emulate their consistency - a task, which if completed successfully, could take them back to the top of the tree.

Phil Harris, London Wasps Programme Editor

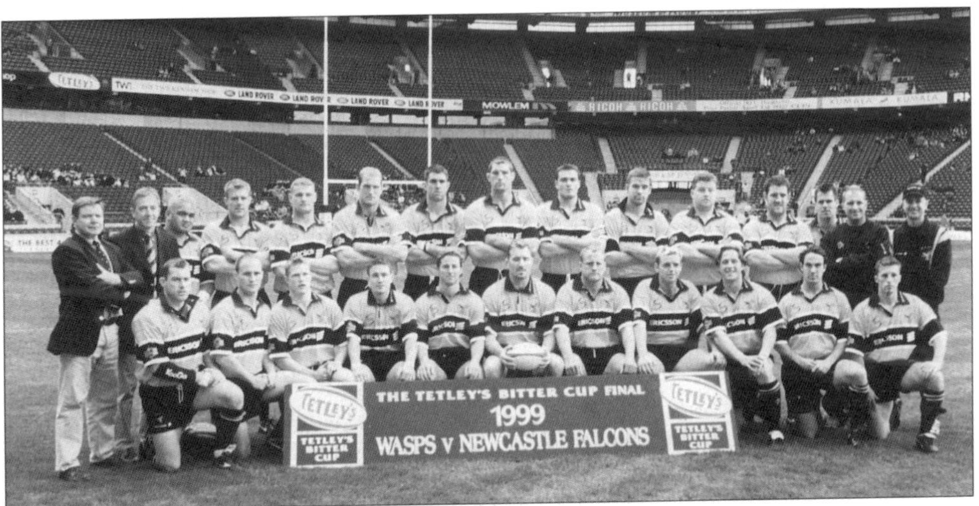

WASPS

MATCH FACTS

Match No.	Date	H/A	Comp.	Opponents	Result & Score	Att.	15	14	13	12	11
1	05.09	A	AD1	Bath	L 27-36	8,000	Lewsey	Roiser	Greenstock(k)	Henderson	Logan/t
2	19.09	A	AD1	London Irish	W 36-24	3,800	Ufton	Roiser/t	Scrase/t	Henderson	Logan/t2c4p
3	27.09	H	AD1	W Hartlepool	W 71-14	2,797	Ufton	Roiser/2t	Scrase(a/t)	Henderson	Logan/t6c3p
4	03.10	A	AD1	Gloucester	W 13-12	5,821	Ufton(q)	Roiser	Scrase	Henderson	Logan/c2p
5	11.10	A	AD1	Newcastle	L 19-27	4,283	Lewsey	Roiser/t	Scrase	Henderson	Logan/2c
6	18.10	H	AD1	Richmond	L 22-27	6,778	Lewsey	Roiser	Scrase	Greenstock	Logan/c5p
7	21.10	H	AD1	Bedford	W 35-19	3,216	Lewsey	Roiser	Scrase	Henderson	Logan/c6p
8	25.10	A	AD1	Saracens	W 31-17	11,261	Lewsey/t	Roiser	Scrase	Henderson/t	Logan/tc3p
9	01.11	H	AD1	Harlequins	L 21-22	6,627	Lewsey	Roiser	Scrase/t	Henderson	Logan/c3p(a/t)
10	07.11	A	AD1	Northampton	L 21-26	6,722	Ufton	Roiser	Scrase(a)	Henderson	Logan/tc3p
11	15.11	H	AD1	Leicester	W 45-17	6,027	Ufton	Roiser/t	Greenstock	Scrase	Logan/t3c3p
12	22.11	H	AD1	Sale	W 32-19	3,865	Lewsey	Roiser/t(t)	Greenstock	Henderson	Scrase
13	12.12	A	AD1	London Scot*	W 17-9	2,159	Lewsey/t	Roiser	Greenstock	Henderson(k)	Logan/2cp
14	27.12	H	AD1	Gloucester	W 23-9	5,362	Lewsey	Sampson/t	Scrase	Henderson	Logan/2c3p
15	03.01	A	AD1	W Hartlepool	L 12-21	2,133	Lewsey	Sampson	Scrase	Henderson(a/t)	Logan/c
16	06.01	H	AD1	Saracens	D 15-15	8,534	Rees	Roiser	Scrase	Henderson	Logan/5p
17	07.02	H	AD1	Bath	W 35-0	9,526	Lewsey	Roiser	Waters	Denney	Sampson
18	13.02	A	AD1	Bedford	L 23-25	3,440	Lewsey	Sampson	Waters	Denney(b)	Roiser
19	14.03	H	AD1	London Irish	W 38-27	6,048	Rees	Sampson/t	Waters	Denney	Logan/3c4p
20	27.03	A	AD1	Leicester	L 6-16	12,449	Rees	Sampson	Waters	Denney	Logan/p
21	18.04	H	AD1	Newcastle	W 34-33	5,104	Rees	Lewsey/t	Waters	Denney	Sampson
22	13.04	H	AD1	Northampton	L 15-24	3,126	Lewsey	Sampson	Waters	Denney(a)	Roiser
23	27.04	A	AD1	Richmond	W 29-5	3,594	Rees(n/t)	Sampson/t	Waters	Denney/t	Logan/t2c
24	02.05	H	AD1	London Scot*	W 45-22	4,419	Lewsey/t(t)	Sampson/t	Waters/t	Denney/t(b)	Logan/3c3p
25	08.05	A	AD1	Sale	W 27-13	4,495	Lewsey	Sampson/t	Waters	Denney(b)	Logan/t3c2p
26	19.05	A	AD1	Harlequins	L 20-27	5,236	Ufton	Greenstock	Waters	Henderson/t	Lewsey
A	09.01	A	TB4	Sedgley Park	W 53-3	3,000	Sampson/2t	Roiser	Greenstock	Scrase/t(s)	Logan/3t4c
B	31.01	H	TB5	Waterloo	W 27-10	1,963	Lewsey	Roiser(t)	Waters	Henderson	Logan/c
C	07.03	H	TBqf	London Irish	W 19-3	11,417	Lewsey(c/dg)	Sampson	Waters	Henderson	Logan/c3p
D	04.04	H	TBsf	Gloucester	W 35-21	10,064	Lewsey	Sampson/t	Waters	Henderson/t	Logan/t3c3p
E	15.05	N	TBF	Newcastle	W 29-19	48,000	Rees/2c4p	Lewsey/t	Waters	Denney(b)	Sampson(x)

* after opponents name indicates a penalty try
Brackets after a player's name indicates he was replaced. eg (a) means he was replaced by replacement code "a" and so on.
/ after a player or replacement name is followed by any scores he made - eg /t, /c, /p, /dg or any combination of these

1998-99 HIGHLIGHTS

League debuts: Josh Lewsey, Eben Rollitt, Fraser Waters, Dinos Alexopoulos, Florent Rossignaux, Alex Le Chavalier.

Ever Presents: None - most appearances 24 Mark Weedon.

Players used: 34 plus 1 as a replacement only.

Most Points in a season:

Pts	Player	T	C	P	DG
263	K Logan	8	35	51	-
87	A King	3	9	15	3
35	P Volley	7	-	-	-
30	T Leota	6	-	-	-

MATCH FACTS

10	9	1	2	3	4	5	6	7	8	
Rees/4p	Friday(m)	Molloy(l)	Leota/t	Green	Weedon	Reed	Rollitt	Volley	Worsley/t	1
Lewsey	Gomersall(d)	Molloy	Macer	Green	Weedon	Reed(p)	Dallaglio	Volley/t	Worsley(h)	2
Lewsey(q/t)	Gomersall	Molloy(r)	Macer	Green	Weedon	Reed(p/t)	Dallaglio/t	Volley/2t	Worsley/t	3
Lewsey	Gomersall(d)	Molloy	Macer(f)	Green/t	Weedon	Reed(p)	Dallaglio	Volley	Worsley	4
King	Gomersall(d)	Molloy	Macer(f/t)	Green	Weedon	Reed(p)	Dallaglio/t	Volley	Worsley(h)	5
King	Friday(m)	Molloy	Leota/t	Green	Weedon	Shaw	Dallaglio	Volley(y)	Worsley	6
King	Gomersall(d/t)	Molloy	Leota	Green	Weedon	Shaw(g)	Dallaglio/t	Rossignaux/t(h)	Worsley	7
King/t	Friday	Molloy	Leota	Green	Weedon	Shaw	Dallaglio	Rossignaux	Worsley	8
King(n)	Friday(m)	Molloy	Leota	Dunstan	Weedon	Shaw	Dallaglio	Rossignaux(h)	Worsley	9
Lewsey	Friday(m)	Molloy	Leota	Green	Weedon	Shaw	Dallaglio(h)	Volley/t	Worsley	10
King	Gomersall	Molloy(l)	Leota/2t(o)	Dunstan	Weedon	Shaw(g)	Rollitt	Volley/2t	Worsley	11
King/3cpdg	Gomersall(d)	Black(e)	Leota/t	Green	Weedon/t	Shaw	Rollitt/t	Volley	Worsley(y)	12
King	Friday(m)	Black	Leota	Green	Weedon	Shaw(g)	Dallaglio	Volley	Worsley(h)	13
King	Wood	Molloy	Leota(w)	Black(r/t)	Weedon	Reed(p)	Dallaglio	Volley	Worsley(v)	14
King	Wood(m)	LeChavalier	Macer(u/t)	Green	Weedon	Shaw(g)	Dallaglio	Volley	Scrivener/t(h)	15
King	Wood(d)	Molloy(r)	Mitchell	Green	Weedon	Reed(p)	Dallaglio	Volley	Rollitt(j)	16
King/2c2p	Wood/2t	Molloy	Leota	Green	Weedon/t	Reed(p)	Dallaglio	Volley(j)	Scrivener/2t	17
King/tc2p	Wood(d)	Molloy	Leota	Green	Weedon	Reed/t(p)	Dallaglio/t	Volley	Scrivener(j)	18
King	Wood(d)	Black	Leota(w)	Green	Weedon/t	Reed(p)	Dallaglio	Worsley	Scrivener/2t	19
King/dg	Wood	Molloy	Leota	Green	Weedon	Shaw	Dallaglio	Worsley	Scrivener	20
King/2c4pdg	Wood/t	Molloy/t	Leota	Green	Shaw	Reed(z)	Dallaglio	Volley	Worsley	21
King/5p	Friday	Molloy	Leota(w)	Green	Weedon	Shaw	Rollitt(A)	Volley	Worsley	22
King/cp	Wood	Molloy	Alexopoulos(w)	Green	Weedon	Shaw	Dallaglio	Volley	Worsley(v)	23
King	Gomersall	Molly(r)	Leota	Green	Weedon	Shaw	Dallaglio	Volley/t(j)	Scrivener	24
King	Gomersall(d)	Molloy	Leota	Green(l)	Weedon	Beardshaw	Dallaglio/t	Worsley	Scrivener(i)	25
Rees/t2c2p	Friday	Molloy(r)	Alexopoulos	Black	Weedon(g)	Beardshaw	Dallaglio	Volley(v)	Worsley	26
King	Friday	Molloy(r)	Alexopoulos	Green	Weedon	Shaw(g)	Rollitt	Rossignaux	Scrivener/2t	A
King	Wood(d/t)	Molloy/t	Alexopoulos	Green(l)	Weedon/t	Shaw	Dallaglio/t	Volley	Scrivener/t	B
King(A)	Wood	Black	Leota	Green	Weedon	Reed(p)	Dallaglio/t	Worsley	Scrivener(h)	C
King	Wood	Molloy	Leota	Green	Weedon	Shaw(g)	Dallaglio	Volley/t	Worsley	D
King/tdg	Gomersall(d)	Molloy	Leota	Green	Weedon	Shaw	Dallaglio	Worsley	Scrivener	E

REPLACEMENTS: a- N Greenstock, b- R Henderson, c-G Rees, d-M Friday, e-D Molloy, f-T Leota, g-A Reed, h-E Rollitt, i-P Volley, j-J Worsley, k-L Scrase, l-A Black, m-A Gomersall, n-J Ufton, o-D Macer, p-S Shaw, q-A King, r-A Le Chevalier, s-F Waters, t-P Sampson, u-D Alexopoulos, v-P Scrivener, w-S Mitchell, x-K Logan, y-F Rossignaux, z-J Beardshaw, A-J Ions

Kenny Logan in his first season kicking for Wasps moves into second place in the most points in a season list behind Gareth Rees. He also topped the try scorers list with 8 tries, three short of his club record set back in 1996-97.

That took his career total to 23 which moved him past Chris Oti into second on the club's all time list behind the new leader Shane Roiser, who now has 28 tries from his four seasons.

Logan beat his own record of 25 points in a match with 26 against West Hartlepool early in the season and he equalled the club record of 6 conversions in a match again against West Hartlepool.

That was also their highest score in a league match and equalled their biggest ever winning margin of 57 points.

Lawrence Dallaglio moved into second place on the club's appearance list as he became the second player to pass 100.

WASPS

LEAGUE STATISTICS
compiled by Stephen McCormack

SEASON	Division	P	W	D	L	F	A	Pts Diff	Lge Pts	Lge Pos	Most Points	Most Tries
89-90	1	11	9	0	2	250	106	144	18	1	90 Rob Andrew	7 Mark Bailey
90-91	1	12	9	1	2	252	151	101	19	2	126 Rob Andrew	7 Chris Oti
91-92	1	12	6	0	6	177	180	-3	12	7	101 Steve Pilgrim	5 Chris Oti
92-93	1	12	11	0	1	186	118	68	22	2	54 Alan Buzza	4 Phil Hopley & Chris Oti
93-94	1	18	10	1	7	362	340	22	21	3	159 Rob Andrew	5 Damian Hopley
94-95	1	18	13	0	5	470	313	157	26	3	135 Rob Andrew	7 Phil Hopley
95-96	1	18	11	0	7	439	322	117	22	4	91 Guy Gregory	8 Shane Roiser
96-97	1	22	18	1	3	685	406	279	37	1	291 Gareth Rees	11 Kenny Logan
97-98	1	22	8	1	13	490	609	17	-119	9	253 Gareth Rees	5 Mike Friday & Penalty Tries
98-99	1	26	15	1	10	717	506	31	211	5	263 Kenny Logan	8 Kenny Logan

BIGGEST MARGINS

Home Win	57pts - 62-5 v Orrell 22.3.97
Away Win	31pts - 57-26 v Harlequins 17.9.94
Home Defeat	31pts - 3-34 v Harlequins 9.3.96
Away Defeat	32pts - 6-38 v Leicester 12.10.93

MOST CONSECUTIVE

Appearances	36 Richard Kinsey 29.2.92-30.4.94
Matches scoring Tries	4 Kenny Logan
Matches scoring points	25 Gareth Rees
Victories	9
Defeats	4

MOST POINTS

Scored at Home	65 v Orrell 22.3.97
Scored Away	57 v Harlequins 17.9.94
Conceded at Home	34 v Harlequins 9.3.96
Conceded Away	42 v Orrell 30.4.94

MOST TRIES

Scored in a match 9
v Coventry 13.4.88 (H); v Bedford 12.3.90 (A);
v Liverpool St H 20.4.91 & v Orrell 2.3.97 (H)

Conceded in a match 6 v Orrell 30.4.94

MOST APPEARANCES

by a forward	116 Buster White
by a back	91 Steve Bates 87-96

	MOST IN A SEASON	MOST IN A CAREER	MOST IN A MATCH	
Points	291 Gareth Rees 96-97	748 Rob Andrew 87-96	26 Kenny Logan	v W Hartlepool 27.9.98 (H)
Tries	11 Kenny Logan 96-97	26 Shane Roiseri 95-99	5 Kenny Logan	v Orrell 22.3.97 (H)
Conversions	45 Gareth Rees 96-97	82 Rob Andrew 87-96	6 Rob Andrew	v Liverpool St H 20.4.91 (H)
				v Bristol 27.4.91 (H)
			Guy Gregory	v W Hartlepool 20.4.96 (H)
			Gareth Rees	v Orrell 22.3.97 (H)
			Kenny Logan	v W Hartlepool 27.9.98 (H)
Penalties	62 Gareth Rees 96-97	161 Rob Andrew 87-96	7 Rob Andrew	v Orrell 11.12.93 (H)
Drop Goals	6 Alex King 96-97	11 Rob Andrew 87-96	2 Jon Ufton	v Saracens 23.9.95 (H)
			Rob Andrew	v Sale 30.9.95 (A)
			Guy Gregory	v Leicester 6.4.96 (A)

WASPS PLAYING SQUAD

BACKS

Name	Ht.	Wt.	Birthdate	Birthplace	CLUB	League Apps	Tries	Pts
Paul Sampson England ,	5.10	12.09	12.07.77	Wakefield	Wasps Otley	29(3) 2	12 -	60 -
Gareth Rees	6.0	14.07	30.06.67	Duncan(BCol)	Wasps	47(2)	5	571
Jonathan Ufton England u21, Students, Colts.	6.1	13.10	31.01.74	Dulwich	Wasps Old Mid Whit	50(8) 8	8 1	78 75
Shane Roiser	6.0	12.07	10.09.72	Dubai	Wasps Rosslyn Park	77 42	26 19	130 95
Kenny Logan Scotland .	6.1	14.08	03.04.72	Stirling	Wasps	42(2)	23	340
Nick Greenstock England .	6.3	15.04	03.11.73	Dubai	Wasps	61(5)	20	100
Rob Henderson Ireland .	6.1	16.04	27.10.72	New Malden	Wasps London Irish	36(4) 56	5 22	25 110
Mike Friday England Students.	5.8	12.05	25.04.72	Chichester	Wasps Blackheath	16(14) 61(3)	6 19	30 95
Alex King England, A.	6.0	13.04	17.01.75	Brighton	Wasps Rosslyn Park	52(2) 7	8 2	137 70
Andy Gomersall England, A, u21, Students, u18.	5.10	14.00	24.07.74	Durham	Wasps Bath	54(9) (2)	12 -	60 -
Martyn Wood England A, u18.	5.9	13.07	25.04.77	Harrogate	Wasps	16(5)	5	25
Laurence Scrase	6.0	12.07	10.09.72	Dubai	Wasps	48(3)	9	45
Josh Lewsey England	5.10	12.07	30.11.76	Bromley	Wasps Bristol	21 22(3)	4 7	20 46

FORWARDS

Name	Ht.	Wt.	Birthdate	Birthplace	CLUB	League Apps	Tries	Pts
Darren Molloy	6.2	17.07	31.08.72	Middlesex	Wasps	85(5)	1	5
Will Green England .	5.11	17.02	25.10.73	Littlehampton	Waps	63	5	25
Trevor Leota	5.9	17.07	08.02.75	W Samoa	Wasps	25(13)	8	40
Simon Mitchell Other club: W Hartlepool 82(1)/7/32.	5.10	16.00	23.11.67	Saltburn	Wasps Harlequins	35(6) 13(1)	4 -	20 -
Ian Dunston	5.11	17.00	11.06.68	Essex	Wasps	53(6)	3	13
Mark Weedon Canterbury	6.5	18.09	31.07.68	Tauranga	Wasps	38(1)	5	25
Simon Shaw England , A, Students, Colts, U21, U18.	6.9	19.08	01.09.73	Nairobi	Wasps Bristol	28(13) 56	2 3	10 15
Damian Cronin Scotland . Other club: London Scottish 29/5/24.	6.6	17.10	17.04.63	Wegberg	Wasps Bath	21(7)	-	-
Andy Reed Scotland . Other clubs: Camborne 10(1)/2/8, Plymouth 10/2/8.	6.7	17.10	04.05.69	St Austell	Wasps Bath	36(12) 24	3 -	15 -
Mike White	6.1	15.08	30.06.66	Poole	Bath	116	14	66
Lawrence Dallaglio England , A, Emerging, U21, Colts.	6.4	16.04	10.08.72	Sheperd's Bush	Wasps	110(4)	18	90
Peter Schrivener England A, U21, U18, Schools.	6.6	17.12	27.10.73	Harold Wood	Wasps	42(9)	12	60
Joe Worsley England U21, Colts.	6.6	17.00	14.06.77	London	Wasps	28(10)	2	10
Paul Volley	6.1	15.06	02.11.71	Chinnor	Wasps	22(3)	7	35
Adam Black	6.1	17.00	24.03.75	Barking	Wasps	6(8)	-	-

LONDON WASPS

FACT FILE

Founded: 1867
Nickname: Wasps

Colours: Black and gold
Change colours: Gold and black

GROUND

Address: Loftus Road Stadium, South Africa Road, London W12 7PA
Tel: 020 8743 0262 Fax: 020 8740 2525 e-mail: waspspromos@loftusroadplc.co.uk
Capacity: 19,500 all seated 16,304 covered 3,196 uncovered

Directions: A40(M) Westway (London-Oxford). Turn south at White City (BBC) into Wood Lane. Turn right into South Africa Road, ground 200yards on right
London Transport: White City (Central Line). In Wood Lane, turn right, then left into South Africa Rd. Shepherds Bush (Hammersmith & City Line).
By Bus: 72, 95, 220 to White City Station.

Car Parking: Weekends only, £6 per match

Admission:
Season: Adults £107-215, Children/OAPs £30-£90
Matchday: Adults £11-£16, Children/OAPs £5-£8

Club Shop: Yes - Loftus Road Stadium 020 8740 6862

Clubhouse: Loftus Road Stadium
Bars & kiosks open on matchdays

PROGRAMME
Size: B5 Pages: 48 Price: £2
Editor: Phil Harris

ADVERTISING RATES
PIA Sport - contact Peter Tripp or Heidi Rackham
Tel: 01625 35546 Fax: 01635 845811

Wasps celebrate after their Tetley's Bitter Cup victory over Newcastle.

At the time of going to print the exact position regarding the future of both London Scottish and Richmond was unclear.

However, in order to complete our statistical records of last season, we have included here the match by match details for both clubs as, of course, they competed in Allied Dunbar Premiership One in 1998-99.

We have also updated their statistics pages and these follow the match by match details.

LONDON SCOTTISH
1998-99 MATCH FACTS 112

RICHMOND
1998-99 MATCH FACTS 114

LONDON SCOTTISH STATISTICS 116

RICHMOND STATISTICS 117

LONDON SCOTTISH

Match No.	Date	H/A	Comp.	Opponents	Result & Score	Att.	15	14	13	12	11
1	05.09	H	AD1	Sale	W25-20	1,200	McAusland/c6p	Milligan/t	Davies	Bonney(n)	Sharman
2	12.09	H	AD1	Leicester	L 3-38	2,950	Lee	McAusland/p	Davies	Eriksson	Sharman
3	19.09	A	AD1	Bedford	L 16-24	2,347	Lee(e)	Milligan	Davies	Eriksson(c)	Sharman/t
4	26.09	H	AD1	Saracens	L 20-58	2,414	McAusland/cp	Milligan/2t	Davies	Bonney/t	Sharman
5	03.10	A	AD1	Harlequins	L 20-22	3,609	McAusalnd/5p	Milligan	Davies	Bonney	Sharman
6	10.10	H	AD1	Northampton	L 22-33	1,963	McAusland/c5p	Milligan	Davies	Bonney(n)	Sharman
7	25.10	A	AD1	Gloucester	L 16-29	5,244	McAusalnd/c3p	Milligan	Davies	Hepi(n)	Goodwin
8	31.10	H	AD1	Bath	W13-11	3,267	McAusalnd/c2p	Milligan	Davies	Eriksson	Sharman/t(p)
9	14.11	H	AD1	London Irish	L 17-23	3,000	Smith	Sharman	Davies(c)	Eriksson	Forrest
10	22.11	A	AD1	W Hartlepool	W 37-7	1,981	Smith	Forrest/t	Bonney	Eriksson(e)	Sharman
11	12.12	H	AD1	Wasps	L 9-17	2,159	McAusalnd	Milligan	Bonney	Eriksson	Sharman(y)
12	19.12	H	AD1	Richmond	L 16-28	1,540	McAusland(x)	Milligan	Bonney	Eriksson	Forrest
13	27.12	A	AD1	Saracens	W 24-7	10,257	McAusalnd/3cp	Milligan/t	Bonney	Eriksson	Sharman(b)
14	02.01	H	AD1	Harlequins	L 24-35	4,600	McAusland/3p(y/cp)	Milligan/t	Bonney	Eriksson	Sharman
15	05.01	H	AD1	Gloucester	W24-13	1,297	Forrest	Milligan	Bonney	Eriksson(b)	Sharman
16	16.01	A	AD1	Leicester	L 12-24	9,985	McAusland(y)	Milligan	Lee	Eriksson	Sharman
17	23.01	A	AD1	Richmond	L 22-40	3,445	McAusland/c	Milligan	Lee	Eriksson(b)	Sharman
18	06.02	A	AD1	Sale	W 23-7	2,200	Binns	Milligan	Davies	Bonney	Forrest(z)
19	13.02	H	AD1	Newcastle	W27-17	2,101	Binns	Milligan	Bonney	Eriksson	Sharman(a)
20	13.03	H	AD1	Bedford	L 15-24	1,273	Binns	Milligan	Bonney/t	Davies(p)	Sharman
21	27.03	A	AD1	London Irish	L 12-35	4,400	Binns	Milligan	Bonney	Eriksson(b)	Sharman
22	31.03	A	AD1	Newcastle	L 20-43	2,506	Binns(p)	Milligan	Davies	Bonney	Sharman
23	17..04	A	AD1	Northampton	L 13-44	7,108	Binns(a/t)	Milligan	Bonney	Eriksson	Sharman(z)
24	02.05	A	AD1	Wasps	L 22-45	4,419	McAusland/c3p	Milligan	Bonney	Eriksson	Phillip(d/t)
25	08.05	H	AD1	W Hartlepool	W26-14	1,459	McAusland	Milligan	Bonney	Eriksson	Sharman/2t
26	15.05	A	AD1	Bath	L 13-76	4,800	McAusland/c	Milligan	Bonney	Erikson	Phillip(b)
A	10.01	A	TB4	Kendal	W25-20	3,000	Forrest/t	Milligan	Davies	Bonney(p)	Sharman
B	30.01	H	TB5	Harlequins	L 33-37		McAusland(y)	Milligan	Davies	Barnes	Sharman(e)

* after opponents name indicates a penalty try
Brackets after a player's name indicates he was replaced. eg (a) means he was replaced by replacement code "a" and so on.
/ after a player or replacement name is followed by any scores he made - eg /t, /c, /p, /dg or any combination of these

1998-99 HIGHLIGHTS

League debuts: Simon Binns, Guy Easterby, Damian Cummins, Mark McAtamney, Peter Robertson, G Manson-Bishop, D Rudham, R Smith, Simon Forrest, Jannie De Beer, Barry Irving, J Philip, Brad Hepi, L Goodwin, Charlie Mulraine, J Barnes.

Ever Presents: Paul Johnstone

Players used: 35 plus 4 as replacement only

Most Points in a season:

Pts	Player	T	C	P	DG
168	J de Beer	1	17	37	6
128	I McAusland	1	12	33	-
35	G Easterby	7	-	-	-

Jannie de Beeer topped the points scorers list in his first season for at the club. He scored in the last 12 maches of the season to equal the club record set by Nick Grecian.

MATCH FACTS

10	9	1	2	3	4	5	6	7	8	
Binns	Easterby	Johnstone	Cummins	Burnell	Jones	Watson(l)	Fenn	Holmes(o)	Hunter(m)	1
Binns	Easterby(q)	MacDonald(s)	Cummins	Burnell	M-Bishop(i)	Watson	Fenn	Davies(j)	Hunter(m)	2
McAusland/c3p	Easterby	Johnstone	Robertson(v)	Burnell	M-Bishop	Watson(l)	Fenn	Holmes	Hunter(m)	3
Cameron(e)	Easterby	Johnstone	Robertson(v)	Burnell	M-Bishop	Watson(i)	Hunter(o)(r)	Holmes	Tarbuck	4
Binns	Easterby	Johnstone	McLellan	Burnell	M-Bishop	McAtamey(i//t)	Fenn	Holmes	Tarbuck	5
Binns	Easterby	Johnstone(r)	McLellan(u)	Burnell	Jones/t	Watson(l)	Fenn(m)	Holmes	M-Bishop	6
Binns	Easterby	Johnstone	Rudham	Burnell	Jones(l)	Watson	Fenn	Holmes/t	Hunter	7
Binns	Easterby	Johnstone(r)	Rudham(u)	Burnell	Jones	Watson(l)	Fenn	Holmes	Hunter(t)	8
deBeer/2cp	Easterby/t	MacDonald	Rudham	Johnstone	Jones	Watson	Fenn(t)	Holmes/t	Hunter	9
deBeer/3c2p	Easterby/t	Johnstone	Rudham	MacDonald(h)	Jones	Watson(l)	Fenn/t	Holmes	Hunter/2t	10
deBeer/3p	Easterby	Johnstone	Rudham	Burnell	Jones	Watson(l)	Fenn	Holmes	Hunter(t)	11
deBeer/c3p	Easterby/t	Johnstone	Rudham(g)	Burnell	Jones(l)	Watson	Fenn	Holmes	Hunter(t)	12
Irving/t	Easterby	Johnstone	Rudham(g)	Burnell	Jones	Watson/t	Fenn	Holmes	Hunter	13
Irving	Easterby(q)	Johnstone	Cummins(w)	Burnell	Jones	Watson	Fenn	Holmes	Hunter/t	14
deBeer/c3pdg	Easterby/t	Johnstone/t	Cummins(w)	Burnell	M-Bishop	Watson	Fenn(o)	Holmes	Hunter	15
deBeer/3pdg	Easterby	Johnstone	Cummins(w)	Burnell	Jones	Watson	Fenn	Holmes	Hunter	16
deBeer/4pdg(y)	Easterby	Johnstone	Rudham(g)	Burnell	Jones	Watson(l)	Fenn(o)	Holmes	Hunter/t	17
deBeer/2c3p	Cook(f/t)	Johnstone	Rudham	MacDonald(A)	Jones	Watson	Fenn(k)	Davies/t	M-Bishop	18
deBeer/2cp	Easterby/t	Johnstone/t(r)	Rudham(g)	Burnell	Jones	Watson(l)	Fenn/t	Holmes/t	Hunter(o)	19
deBeer/cp	Easterby(q)	Johnstone	Rudham(g)	Burnell	Jones	Watson/t	Fenn	Holmes	Hunter	20
deBeer/3pdg	Easterby	Johnstone(A)	Rudham(g)	Burnell	Jones(t)	Watson	Fenn(o)	Holmes(a)	Hunter	21
deBeer/t2cpdg	Easterby/t	Johnstone	Rudham(g)	Burnell	Jones	Watson	Fenn	Holmes	Hunter	22
deBeer/c2p	Easterby	Johnstone	Rudham(g)	Burnell	Jones	Watson(t)	Fenn	Holmes	Hunter(o)	23
deBeer/pdg	Easterby	Johnstone	Cummins(w)	Burnell(A)	Jones	M-Bishop	Davies	Holmes(D)	Hunter	24
deBeer/2c4p	Mulraine	Johnstone	Cummins(w)	Burnell	Jones(t)	Watson	Fenn	Holmes(o)	Hunter	25
deBeer/2p(e)	Mulraine(E)	Johnstone(A)	Cummins(w)	Burnell	Jones(t)	Watson	Fenn	Homes/t(o)	Hunter	26
deBeer/2c2p	Cook(B)	MacDonald/t	Cummins(w)	Johnstone	M-Bishop/t	McAtamey	Davies	Holmes(C)	Hunter	A
deBeer/t3c4p	Easterby	Johnstone	Cummins(w)	Burnell	Jones	Watson	Fenn/t	Holmes/t	Hunter	B

REPLACEMENTS: a- I McAusland, b-R Davies, c-J Bonney, d-C Sharman, e-S Binns, f-G Easterby, g-D Cummins, h-Burnell, i-E Jones, j-S Holmes, k-R Hunter, l-M McAtamey, m-C Tarbuck, n-R Eriksson, o-T Davies, p-D Lee., q-S Cook., r-M MacDonald, s-R Bijl, t-G M-Bishop, u-P Robertson, v-J McLellan, w-D Rudham., x-R Smith, y-S Forrest., z-J Phillip., A-C Johnston., B-C Mulraine, C-B Pegna., D-D McFadyen, E-D Millard

De Beer's points total of 168 was the second highest in a season by a Scottish player.
He did break one record though the record for most drop goals in a season. He dropped 6 goals to break the record of 5 set by Murray Walker back in the 1993-94 season.

Their 37-7 win at West Hartlepool was a new record for biggest win away from home. The 30 point margin broke the record of 29 set when they won 45-16 at Rugby in 1997.

In their last match of the season at Bath they suffered their worst defeat in both terms of points and points difference against. They lost 76-13 to eclipse the 60 point thrashing at Coventry a couple of seasons ago and the 71 points they conceded against Newcastle in April 1997.
In the defeat at Bath they conceded a record 12 tries one more than the 11 they conceded at Newcastle in April 1997.

Full back Ian McAusland scored a record breaking six penalties in the early season win against Sale. It broke the previous record of 5 that McAusland shared with John Steele.

Veteran scrum half Dave Millard added just one replacement appearance to his record 97 +16 record for a back.

RICHMOND

Match No.	Date	H/A	Comp.	Opponents	Result & Score	Att.	15	14	13	12	11
1	05.09	H	AD1	Newcastle	W 41-29	9,530	Pini	Brown/t	Bateman/t	Deane	Chapman
2	12.09	H	AD1	Gloucester	L 22-25	7,054	Pini	Brown	Bateman/t	Deane	Chapman
3	19.09	A	AD1	Bath	L 14-36	7,600	Pini	Brown	Bateman	Deane/t	Chapman(k)
4	03.10	A	AD1	London Irish	W 33-29	3,900	Pini/p(b)	Walne	Bateman	Dixon	Brown/2t
5	10.10	H	AD1	W Hartlepool	W 41-23	4,357	Deane(t/2t)	Walne/t	Bateman(v)	Dixon	Chapman
6	18.10	A	AD1	Wasps	W 27-22	6,778	Pini/tp	Walne	Wright	Dixon	Brown/t
7	24.10	A	AD1	Leicester	L 0-27	8,443	Pini	Walne	Wright	Dixon	Brown
8	28.10	A	AD1	Sale	W 39-10	2,059	Pini	Walne/t	Bateman/t	Wright	Brown/t
9	31.10	H	AD1	Bedford	W 38-12	6,541	Pini	Walne	Wright	Deane	Brown
10	08.11	A	AD1	Saracens*	L 17-23	9,217	Va'a/t	Walne	Wright	Dixon	Brown
11	21.11	A	AD1	Northampton	L 27-44	5,978	Brown/t	Walne/2t	Wright	Dixon	Chapman
12	19.12	A	AD1	London Scot	W 28-16	1,540	Pini	Walne	Bateman	Dixon	Brown
13	26.12	H	AD1	London Irish	L 13-25	9,621	Pini/t	Walne	Bateman(o)	Wright	Brown
14	16.01	A	AD1	Gloucester	D 24-24	4,811	Pini	Walne	Bateman	Deane	Brown/t
15	23.01	H	AD1	London Scot	W 40-22	3,445	Pini/2c	Walne/t	Bateman/2t	Deane	Brown
16	26.01	H	AD1	Leicester	L 11-23	7,981	Pini	Walne/t	Bateman	Deane(o)	Brown
17	14.02	H	AD1	Sale	W 29-24	4,695	Best	Walne	Bateman(o)	Deane	Brown/t
18	13.03	H	AD1	Bath	L 23-30	10,096	Pini	Walne	Wright	Dixon(b)	Brown
19	27.03	A	AD1	Harlequins	D 32-32	5,217	Pini	Walne	Wright	Dixon/t	Brown
20	18.04	A	AD1	W Hartlepool	W 36-35	1,206	Best/t	Walne	Bateman	Wright/t	Brown
21	21.04	A	AD1	Newcastle	L 14-47	2,728	Pini	Walne	Bateman	Dixon	Brown(b)
22	25.04	H	AD1	Wasps	L 5-29	3,594	Pini(b)	Best	Wright	Dixon	Walne
23	03.05	H	AD1	Harlequins	L 23-30	3,300	Pini(p)	Walne/t	Bateman/2t	Deane	Best
24	08.05	H	AD1	Northampton	L 19-31	3,500	Pini	Walne	Bateman	Deane(p)	Best
25	12.05	H	AD1	Saracens	L 18-25	2,613	Va'a/tc2p	Wright/t	Bateman(y)	Deane	Walne
26	16.05	A	AD1	Bedford	W106-12	1,308	Pini(v/t)	Wright/2t	Bateman/t	Deane/3t	Walne/t
A	10.01	H	TB4	Newbury	W 46-12	2,859	Pini(c)	Walne/t	Bateman/t	Deane	Brown/3t
B	31.01	H	TB5	Exeter	W 37-10	1,259	Best	Walne/t(o)	Bateman	Deane	Brown/3t
C	27.02	H	TBqf	Leicester	W 15-13	7,088	Pini	Walne	Wright	Dixon	Brown
D	03.04	H	TBsf	Newcastle	L 3-20	9,751	Pini	Walne	Wright	Dixon	Brown

* after opponents name indicates a penalty try
Brackets after a player's name indicates he was replaced. eg (a) means he was replaced by replacement code "a" and so on.
/ after a player or replacement name is followed by any scores he made - eg /t, /c, /p, /dg or any combination of these

1998-99 HIGHLIGHTS

League debuts:
Laurant Cabannes, Nick Walne, Brian Cusack, Matt Dixon, M Swift, Jon Barfoot, Gary Powell, Lee Best, Rich Butland, Maurice Fitzgerald, A Sheridan, D Quinn.

Ever Presents: Craig Gillies

Players used: 34 plus 4 as a replacement only.

Most Points in a season:

Pts	Player	T	C	P	DG
203	E Va'a	8	32	33	-
42	R Butland	-	15	4	-
40	A Bateman	8	-	-	-
40	S Brown	8	-	-	-
40	A Vander	8	-	-	-
40	C Quinnell	8	-	-	-

10	9	1	2	3	4	5	6	7	8	
Davies/4cp(f)	Pichot/t	McFarland	Williams	Crompton(g)	C Quinnell(h)(i)	Gillies	Hutton/2t(j)	Vander	Clarke/t	1
Davies/2cp	Pichot	McFarland	Williams	Crompton(g)	C Quinnell/t	Gillies	Hutton(i/t)	Vander	Clarke(j)	2
Davies/2c	Moore	Crompton	Williams	Davies	C Quinnell	Gillies	Hutton(m)	Vander	Cabannes(n)	3
Davies/p(f/t2cp)	Pichot	McFarland	Williams	Crompton	C Quinnell	Gillies	Hutton	Vander	S Quinnell/t	4
Va'a/3c	Pichot/2t	McFarland	Williams(i)	Crompton	C Quinnell	Gillies	Clarke	Vander	S Quinnell/2t(e)	5
Va'a/t2c	Pichot	McFarland	Williams	Crompton	C Quinnell(n)	Gillies	Clarke/t	Vander(e)	S Quinnell	6
Va'a	Pichot	McFarland	Williams	Crompton	Cusack	Gillies	Clarke	Vander	S Quinnell	7
Va'a/3cp	Pichot/t(l)	McFarland	Williams(i)	Crompton(g)	C Quinnell/t	Cusack	Clarke/t(b)	Vander(e)	S Quinnell/t(h)	8
Va'a/t2c3p	Pichot	Davies	Williams/t	Crompton	C Quinnell/2t	Gillies	Hutton(j)	Vander/t	Clarke	9
Butland/2cp	Moore	McFarland	Williams	Crompton(g)	C Quinnell	Gillies	Hutton(j)	Vander	Clarke	10
Va'a/t2cp	Moore	McFarland	Cuthbert	Davies	Codling(m)	Gillies	Hutton(n)(u)	Vander	Cabannes	11
Va'a/t2c3p	Pichot	McFarland	Williams(i)	Davies	Cusack	Gillies	Hutton	Vander/2t	Cabannes	12
Va'a/p	Pichot/t	McFarland	Cuthbert	Davies	Cusack(h)	Gillies	Swift(r)	Hutton	Cabannes(s)	13
Va'a/c4p	Pichot	McFarland	Williams	Davies	C Quinnell	Gillies	Hutton	Vander	Clarke/t	14
Va'a/3c(t)	Pichot	McFarland	Williams	Davies(d)	C Quinnell/t(n)	Gillies	Hutton/t	Vander/t	Clarke(j)	15
Va'a/2p	Pichot	McFarland	Williams	Crompton	C Quinnell(n)	Gillies	Hutton	Vander(j)	Clarke	16
Va'a/c4p	Pichot/t	McFarland	Williams	Fitzgerald(s)(i)	Sheridan	Gillies	Clarke/t	Vander	Cabannes	17
Va'a/2c3p	Pichot	McFarland	Williams	Crompton	Sheridan	Gillies	Hutton/t	Vander/t	Clarke	18
Va'a/t3c2p	Pichot	McFarland	Cuthbert	Crompton	Sheridan	Gillies(n)	C Quinnell(r)	Hutton/t	Clarke/t	19
Va'a/3c5p	Moore	McFarland	Williams/t	Crompton	Cusack	Gillies	Quinn	Barfoot	Clarke	20
Butland/3p	Moore	McFarland	Williams/t	Crompton	Cusack	Gillies	Quinn(q)	Barfoot	Clarke	21
Butland	Pichot/t(l)	McFarland	Cuthbert	Crompton	Cusack	Gillies	Williams	Barfoot(v)	Swift(m)	22
Va'a/p	Moore	McFarland	Williams	Crompton	C Quinnell	Gillies(q)	Cusack	Vander	Clarke/t	23
Va'a/2c	Moore	Crompton	Williams(i)	Powell	C Quinnell/t	Gillies	Swift(x)	Vander/2t	Clarke	24
Butland(v)	Moore	Crompton	Williams(i)	Powell	Cusack(r)	Gillies	Swift(x)	Vander	Clarke	25
Butland/13c	Moore(y/t)	McFarland	Williams/t	Crompton	C Quinnell/2t(r)	Gillies	Cusack/3t	Vander/t	Clarke	26
Va'a/3c	Pichot/t(l)	McFarland	Cuthbert	Davies(w)	C Quinnell	Gillies	Hutton	Vander/t(j)	Clarke	A
Va'a/tcp(z/c)	Moore	McFarland	Williams(i)	Crompton	Sheridan/t	Gillies	Hutton	Vander(j)	Clarke	B
Va'a/cp	Pichot	McFarland	Williams/t	Crompton	C Quinnell	Gillies	Hutton	Vander	Clarke/t	C
Va'a/p	Pichot	McFarland	Williams	Crompton	Sheridan(n)	Gillies	C Quinnell	Hutton(r)	Clarke	D

REPLACEMENTS a- M Pini b- M Deane c-D Chapman d-D Crompton e-R Hutton f-E Va'a g-J Davies h-A Codling
i-A Cuthbert j-L Cabannes k-N Walne l-A Moore m-C Palmer n-B Cusack o-M Dixon p-J Wright q-M Swift
r-J Barfoot s-G Powell t-L Best u-J Hamilton-Smith v-T Whitford w-M Fitzgerald
x-A Sheridan y-B Shelbourne z-R Butland

Earl Va'a tops the scoring chart for the first time and becomes the second Richmond player to top 200 points in a league season.

Scott Quinnell took his tries for Richmond in league rugby to a new club record of 35, three more than Jim Fallon's old record.

In their final match of the season Richmond set a new points scoring record in the division as they became the first side to top 100 points in a match.

They also set a new record for biggest win, 94 points, and equalled the club record of 16 tries in a match.

Rich Butland set a new record for conversions with 13 successful attempts out of 16.

LONDON SCOTTISH

LEAGUE STATISTICS
compiled by Stephen McCormack

SEASON	Division	P	W	D	L	F	A	Pts Diff	Lge Pts	Lge Pos	Most Points		Most Tries	
89-90	3	11	11	0	0	258	92	166	22	1p	64	Gavin Hastings	4	Tim Exeter
90-91	2	12	7	0	5	240	178	62	14	5	89	Nick Grecian	9	Lindsey Renwick
91-92	2	12	11	0	1	304	130	174	22	1p	124	Nick Grecian	11	Nick Grecian
92-93	1	12	3	1	8	192	248	56	7	10r	40	Nick Grecian	4	Lindsey Renwick
93-94	2	18	6	0	12	232	325	-93	12	8	81	Murray Walker	3	Ronnie Eriksson
94-95	2	18	9	0	9	351	321	30	18	4	78	John Steele	4	Dave Millard & Fraser Harrold
95-96	2	18	10	2	6	361	389	-28	22	3	140	John Steele	5	Dave Millard
96-97	2	22	11	0	11	549	568	-19	22	5	256	John Steele	5	Chris Tarbuck
97-98	2	22	14	1	7	517	404	113	29	3	149	Derek Lee	14	Conan Sharman
98-99	1	26	8	0	18	491	734	-243	16	12	168	Jannie de Beer	7	Guy Easterby

BIGGEST MARGINS

Home Win	47pts - 50-3 v Northampton 3.10.87
Away Win	37pts -375-0 v W Hartlepool 22.11.98
Home Defeat	40pts - 19-59 v Northampton 27.4.96
Away Defeat	63pts - 13-76 v Bath 15.5.99

MOST CONSECUTIVE

Appearances	53 Nick Grecian 10.9.88-21.11.92
Matches scoring Tries	6 Nick Grecian
Matches scoring points	12 Nick Grecian/Jannie de Beer
Victories	12
Defeats	6 (2)

MOST POINTS

Scored at Home	50 v Northampton 3.10.87
Scored Away	45 v Rugby 31.10.91 & 29.3.97
Conceded at Home	59 v Northampton 27.4.96
Conceded Away	76 v Bath 15.5.99

MOST TRIES

Scored in a match	7 on three occasions
Conceded in a match	12 v Bath 15.5.99

MOST APPEARANCES

by a forward	148 Paul Burnell
by a back	97 (14) Dave Millard

	MOST IN A SEASON	MOST IN A CAREER	MOST IN A MATCH	
Points	256 John Steele 96-97	474 John Steele 94-97	30 John Steele	v Rugby 29.3.97 (A)
Tries	14 Conan Sharman 97-98	28 DaveMillard 89-99	3 Jerry Mackin Ronnie Eriksson Conan Sharman	v Northampton 3.10.87 (H) v Fylde 30.8.97 (H) v Bedford 20.9.97 (A)
Conversions	39John Steele 96-97	63 John Steele 94-97	5 Andy Mitchell Gavin Hastings Mark Appleson	v Northampton 3.10.87 (H) v Vale of Lune 23.9.89 (H) v Rugby 31.10.92 (A)
Penalties	47 John Steele 96-97	91 John Steele 94-97	6 Ian McAusland	v Sale 5.9.98 (H)
Drop Goals	6 Jannie de Beer 98-99	10 John Steele 94097	3 Murray Walker	v W Hartlepool 23.4.94 (H)

RICHMOND

LEAGUE STATISTICS
compiled by Stephen McCormack

SEASON	Division	P	W	D	L	F	A	Pts Diff	Lge Pts	Lge Pos		Most Points		Most Tries
89-90	2	11	7	1	3	282	135	147	15	3	120	Martin Livesey	7	Jim Fallon
90-91	2	13	3	1	8	134	245	-111	7	12r	38	Martin Livesey	6	Mike Hutton
91-92	3	12	10	1	1	296	124	172	21	1p	95	Martin Livesey	6	Phil Della-Savina
92-93	2	12	5	0	7	204	196	8	10	9r	95	Martin Livesey	3	David Sole
93-94	3	18	9	0	9	337	300	37	18	7	90	Martin Livesey	6	Paul Greenwood
94-95	3	18	6	1	11	319	290	29	13	8	136	John Gregory	4	Andy Cuthbert & Adrian Boyd
95-96	3	18	13	1	4	476	266	210	27	2p	196	John Gregory	11	Adrian Boyd
96-97	2	22	19	1	2	986	410	576	39	1p	324	Simon Mason	21	Scott Quinnell
97-98	1	22	12	0	10	607	499	108	24	5	150	Adrian Davies	17	Dominic Chapman
98-99	1	26	11	2	13	720	715	5	22	9	203	Earl Va'a	8	5 players

BIGGEST MARGINS

Home Win 78pts - 86-8 v Headingley 28.4.90

Away Win 94pts - 106-12 v Bedford 16.5.99

Home Defeat 25pts - 15-40 v Lon. Scottish 17.11.90

Away Defeat 41pts - 9-50 v Sale 10.9.88

MOST CONSECUTIVE

Appearances

Matches scoring Tries 5 Spencer Brown

Matches scoring points 19 Martin Livesey

Victories 13

Defeats 9

MOST POINTS

Scored at Home 86 v Headingley 28.4.90

Scored Away 106 v Bedford 16.5.99

Conceded at Home 40 v Lon. Scottish 17.11.90

Conceded Away 50 v Sale 10.9.88

MOST TRIES

Scored in a match 16 v Headingley 28.4.90

Conceded in a match 8 v Sale 10.9.88

MOST APPEARANCES

by a forward

by a back

	MOST IN A SEASON	MOST IN A CAREER	MOST IN A MATCH	
Points	324 Simon Mason 96-97	512 Martin Livesey 88-94	29 Simon Mason	v Rotherham 14.9.96 (H)
Tries	21 Scott Quinnell 96-97	35 Scott Quinnell 96-99	4 Scott Quinnell	v Waterloo 2.1.96 (H)
Conversions	83 Simon Mason 96-97	83 Simon Mason 96-97	13 Rich Butland	v Bedford 16.5.99 (A)
Penalties	36 Simon Mason 96-97	100 Martin Livesey 88-94	6 Nick Preston Martin Livesey Jon Clark Simon Mason	v Bedford 27.3.88 (H) v Lon. Irish 8.4.89 (H) v Lydney 14.3.92 (H) v Blackheath 26.10.96 (A)
Drop Goals	6 Simon Mason 91-92	14 Martin Livesey 88-94	3 Martin Livesey	v Northampton 19.11.88 (H)

HOW THE LEAGUES HAVE CHANGED OVER THE LAST 12 YEARS

	LEVEL 1	LEVEL 2	LEVEL 3	LEVEL 4		LEVEL 5
1987-88	Courage Division One 12 Teams - H or A	Courage Division Two 12 Teams - H or A	Courage Division Three 12 Teams - H or A	Courage Area League North 11 Teams - H or A	Courage Area League South 11 Teams - H or A	
1988-89	Courage Division One 12 Teams - H or A	Courage Division Two 12 Teams - H or A	Courage Division Three 12 Teams - H or A	Courage Area League North 11 Teams - H or A	Courage Area League South 11 Teams - H or A	
1998-90	Courage Division One 12 Teams - H or A	Courage Division Two 12 Teams - H or A	Courage Division Three 12 Teams - H or A	Courage Area League North 11 Teams - H or A	Courage Area League South 11 Teams - H or A	
1990-91	Courage Division One 13 Teams - H or A	Courage Division Two 13 Teams - H or A	Courage Division Three 13 Teams - H or A	Courage Division 4 North 13 Teams - H or A	Courage Division 4 South 13 Teams - H or A	
1991-92	Courage Division One 13 Teams - H or A	Courage Division Two 13 Teams - H or A	Courage Division Three 13 Teams - H or A	Courage Division 4 North 13 Teams - H or A	Courage Division 4 South 13 Teams - H or A	
1992-93	Courage Division One 13 Teams - H or A	Courage Division Two 13 Teams - H or A	Courage Division Three 12 Teams - H or A	Courage Division 4 North 13 Teams - H or A	Courage Division 4 South 13 Teams - H or A	
1993-94	Courage Division One 10 Teams - H & A	Courage Division Two 10 Teams - H & A	Courage Division Three 10 Teams - H & A	Courage Division Four 10 H & A	Courage Division 5 North 13 Teams - H or A	Courage Division 5 South 13 Teams - H or A
1994-95	Courage Division One 10 Teams - H & A	Courage Division Two 10 Teams - H & A	Courage Division Three 10 Teams - H & A	Courage Division Four 10 H & A	Courage Division 5 North 13 Teams - H or A	Courage Division 5 South 13 Teams - H or A
1995-96	Courage Division One 10 Teams - H & A	Courage Division Two 10 Teams - H & A	Courage Division Three 10 Teams - H & A	Courage Division Four 10 H & A	Courage Division 5 North 13 Teams - H or A	Courage Division 5 South 13 Teams - H or A
1996-97	Courage Division One 12 Teams - H & A	Courage Division Two 12 Teams - H & A	Courage Division Three 16 Teams - H & A	Courage Division 4 North 14 Teams - H or A	Courage Division 4 South 14 Teams - H or A	
1997-98	Allied Dunbar Premiership 1 12 teams H & A	Allied Dunbar Premiership 2 12 Teams - H & A	Jewson National 1 14 Teams - H & A	Jewson 2 North 14 Teams - H & A	Jewson 2 South 14 Teams - H & A	
1998-99	Allied Dunbar Premiership 1 14 teams H & A	Allied Dunbar Premiership 2 14 Teams - H & A	Jewson Jewson National 1 14 Teams - H & A	Jewson 2 North 14 Teams - H & A	Jewson 2 South 14 Teams - H & A	

DIVISION ONE
(CURRENTLY ALLIED DUNBAR PREMIERSHIP ONE

RECORDS SECTION

The Last Ten Years 120

A breakdown showing the champions, runners-up, those relegated, who scored most - points, tries, conversions, penalties & drop goals in each of the last ten seasons in this division (or its equivalent)

All Time Team & Individual Records 121

A list of the various records for this division (or its equivalent) since the start of the league system.

Most Points in a Season 122

The all-time list for this division

Most Points in a Match 123

The all-time list for this division

Most Tries in a Match 124

The all-time list for this division

Most Career Appearances 125

The all-time list for this division

Ten Year Record 126

A grid showing those clubs who have been part of this division (or its equivalent), and the league position they achieved for each of the last ten years

THE LAST TEN YEARS

1989-90	Champions	Runners-up	Relegated
	Wasps	Gloucester	Bedford

Most
Points: 126 John Liley (Leicester) — Tries: 10 Tony Swift (Bath)
Penalties: 24 David Pears (Harlequins) — Conversions: 29 Stuart Barnes (Bath) — D.Gs: 2 David Pears (Harlequins)

1990-91	Champions	Runners-up	Relegated
	Bath	Wasps	Moseley, Liverpool St. Helens

Most
Points: 126 Rob Andrew (Wasps) — Tries: 9 Andrew Harriman (Harlequins)
Penalties: 26 Rob Andrew (Wasps) — Conversions: 21 Martin Strett (Orrell) — D.Gs: 5 David Pears (Harlequins)

1991-92	Champions	Runners-up	Relegated
	Wasps	Gloucester	Bedford

Most
Points: 125 John Liley (Leicester) — Tries: 9 Rory Underwood (Leicester)
Penalties: 28 John Steele (Northampton) — Conversions: 19 John Liley (Leicester) — D.Gs: 2 Hugh Davies (Wasps)

1992-93	Champions	Runners-up	Relegated
	Bath	Wasps	Saracens, Lon. Scottish, West Hartlepool, Rugby

Most
Points: 122 Jon Webb (Bath) — Tries: 7 Stuart Barnes (Bath)
Penalties: 31 Michael Corcoran (L. Irish) — Conversions: 19 Jon Webb (Bath) — D.Gs: 6 Paul Burke (L. Irish)

1993-94	Champions	Runners-up	Relegated
	Bath	Leicester	London Irish, Newcastle Gosforth

Most
Points: 202 Jez Harris (Leicester) — Tries: 11 Daren O'Leary (Harlequins)
Penalties: 41 Jez Harris (Leicester) — Conversions: 25 Jonathon Callard (Bath) — D.Gs: 11 Jez Harris (Leicester)

1994-95	Champions	Runners-up	Relegated
	Leicester	Bath	Northampton

Most
Points: 196 Mark Tainton (Bristol) — Tries: 8 Paul Holford (Gloucester)
Penalties: 56 Mark Tainton (Bristol) — Conversions: 19 Rob Andrew (Wasps) — D.Gs: 13 Jez Harris (Leicester)

1995-96	Champions	Runners-up	Relegated
	Bath	Leicester	

Most
Points: 272 John Liley (Leicester) — Tries: 14 Daren O'Leary (Harlequins)
Penalties: 64 John Liley (Leicester) — Conversions: 43 Jonathon Callard (Bath) — D.Gs: 7 David Pears (Harlequins)

1996-97	Champions	Runners-up	Relegated
	Wasps	Bath	Orrell, West Hartlepool

Most
Points: 291 Gareth Rees (Wasps) — Tries: 16 Adedayo Adebayo (Bath)
Penalties: 62 Gareth Rees (Wasps) — Conversions: 51 Jonathon Callard (Bath) — D.Gs: 6 Alex King (Wasps)

1997-98	Champions	Runners-up	Relegated
	Newcastle	Saracens	Bristol (play-off)

Most
Points: 279 Michael Lynagh (Saracens) — Tries: 17 Dominic Chapman (Richmond)
Penalties: 58 Mark Mapletoft (Gloucester) — Conversions: 44 Rob Andrew (Newcastle) — D.Gs: 4 David Humphreys (L. Irish)

1998-99	Champions	Runners-up	Relegated
	Leicester	Northampton	West Hartlepool

Most
Points: 331 John Schuster (Harlequins) — Tries: 16 Neil Back (Leicester)
Penalties: 77 John Schuster (Harlequins) — Conversions: 52 Gavin Johnson (Saracens) — D.Gs: 6 Jannie de Beer (Lon. Scottish)

TEAM RECORDS

Highest score:	**106**	Bedford 12 Richmond 106. 16.5.99
Highest aggregate:	**118**	As above
Highest score by a losing side:	**41**	London Irish 52 W Hartlepool 41. 28.12.96
Highest scoring draw:	**38**	Bath 38 v Sale 38 27.4.96
Most consecutive wins:	**17**	Bath 1993-94 through 1994-95
Most consecutive defeats:	**18**	West Hartlepool 1995-96
Most points for in a season:	**863**	Bath 1996-97
Least points for in a season:	**70**	Bedford 1989-90
Most points against in a season:	**1007**	West Hartlepool 1998-99
Least points against in a season:	**95**	Orrell 1991-92
Most tries for in a season:	**116**	Bath 1996-97
Most tries against in a season:	**125**	Orrell 1996-97
Least tries for in a season:	**8**	Waterloo 1988-89
Least tries against in a season:	**6**	Bath 1988-89, Wasps 1992-93
Most conversions for in a season:	**77**	Bath 1996-97
Most conversions against in a season:	**69**	Orrell 1996-97
Least conversions for in a season:		
Least conversions against in a season:		
Most penalties for in a season:	**77**	Harlequins 1998-99
Most penalties against in a season:	**61**	Newcastle 1997-98
Least penalties for in a season:	**7**	Bedford 1989-90
Least penalties against in a season:	**11**	Harlequins 1987-88
Most drop goals for in a season:	**13**	Leicester 1994-95 & Harlequins 1995-96
Most drop goals against in a season:	**8**	Wasps 1993-94 & 1995-96

INDIVIDUAL RECORDS

Most points in a season:	**331**	John Schuster (Harlequins) 1998-99
Most tries in a season:	**17**	Dominic Chapman (Richmond) 1997-98
Most conversions in a season:	**52**	Gavin Johnson (Saracens) 1998-99
Most penalties in a season:	**77**	John Schuster (Harlequins) 1998-99
Most drop goals in a season:	**13**	Jez Harris (Leicester) 1994-95
Most points in a match:	**32**	Niall Woods, London Irish v Harlequins 25.4.98
Most tries in a match:	**5**	Kenny Logan, Wasps v Orrell 22.3.97
Most conversions in a match:	**13**	Rich Butland, Bedford v Richmond 16.5.99
Most penalties in a match:	**8**	John Liley, Leicester v Bristol 28.10.95
Most drop goals in a match:	**3**	John Steele, Northampton v Wasps 23.3.91
		Jez Harris, Leicester v Wasps 23.11.91
		David Pears, Harlequins v Wasps 16.9.95
		Matthew McCarthy, Orrell v W Hartlepool 7.12.96

ALL TIME RECORDS

MOST POINTS IN A SEASON

Points	Player	Club	Season	Tries	Cons.	Pens.	D.G.
331	John Schuster	Harlequins	1998-99	5	36	77	1
318	Gavin Johnson	Saracens	1998-99	8	52	58	-
306	Jonny Wilkinson	Newcastle	1998-99	9	51	53	-
294	Mike Catt	Bath	1998-99	7	50	53	-
291	Gareth Rees	Wasps	1996-97	3	45	62	-
279	Michael Lynagh	Saracens	1997-98	5	37	58	2
275	Mark Mapletoft	Gloucester	1997-98	5	35	58	2
272	John Liley	Leicester	1995-96	5	26	64	1
269	Mark Mapletoft	Gloucester	1996-97	6	25	58	5
263	Kenny Logan	Wasps	1998-99	8	35	51	-
253	Joel Stransky	Leicester	1997-98	5	39	47	3
253	Gareth Rees	Wasps	1997-98	1	34	57	3
246	Shane Howarth	Sale	1998-99	9	42	37	-
240	Steven Vile	W Hartlepool	1998-99	5	28	52	1
237	Niall Woods	London Irish	1997-98	8	34	43	-
236	Jonathan Callard	Bath	1995-96	3	43	45	-
226	Rob Andrew	Newcastle	1997-98	6	44	35	1
224	Jonathan Callard	Bath	1996-97	4	51	34	-
224	Shane Howarth	Sale	1997-98	4	39	41	1
215	Niall Woods	London Irish	1998-99	12	25	35	-
210	Paul Grayson	Northampton	1997-98	4	23	45	3
203	Earl Va'a	Richmond	1998-99	8	32	33	-
202	Jez Harris	Leicester	1993-94	2	18	41	11
202	Joel Stransky	Leicester	1998-99	7	34	33	-
198	Mark Mapletoft	Gloucester	1998-99	6	21	41	1
196	Mark Tainton	Bristol	1994-95	-	11	56	2
195	John Liley	Leicester	1996-97	3	24	44	-
189	Paul Grayson	Northampton	1994-95	1	11	52	2
189	David Humphreys	London Irish	1996-97	4	20	40	3
183	Jon Callard	Bath	1997-98	1	32	38	-
181	Jez Harris	Leicester	1994-95	-	11	40	13
178	Jonathan Callard	Bath	1993-94	4	25	36	-
178	Paul Burke	Bristol	1996-97	2	27	38	-
176	Thierry Lacroix	Harlequins	1996-97	2	29	33	3
169	Thierry Lacroix	Harlequins	1997-98	3	26	32	2
168	Jannie De Beer	London Scottish	1998-99	1	17	37	6
167	Rob Liley	Sale	1995-96	3	22	34	2
166	Simon Mason	Orrell	1995-96	4	16	38	-
161	Mark Tainton	Bristol	1993-94	-	19	40	1
161	Tim Stimpson	Leicester	1998-99	2	14	41	-
159	Rob Andrew	Wasps	1993-94	2	16	38	1
156	Paul Grayson	Northampton	1998-99	1	23	35	-
153	Paul Burke	Bristol	1997-98	2	22	31	2
150	Jonathan Callard	Bath	1994-95	1	14	39	-
150	Simon Mannix	Sale	1996-97	7	17	27	-
150	Adrian Davies	Richmond	1997-98	3	33	23	-
143	Kent Bray	Harlequins	1993-94	1	12	38	-
143	Jarrod Cunningham	London Irish	1998-99	2	23	29	-
135	Rob Andrew	Wasps	1994-95	2	19	26	3
134	Sam Howard	Bedford	1998-99	3	28	20	1
132	Paul Grayson	Northampton	1993-94	2	10	33	1
129	Paul Grayson	Northampton	1996-97	1	14	28	4

ALL TIME RECORDS

MOST POINTS IN A MATCH

Points	Player	Match	Date
32	Niall Woods	London Irish v Harlequins	25.04.98
31	John Liley	Leicester v Rosslyn Park	21.03.92
30	Steven Vile	West Hartlepool v Richmond	17.04.99
28	Martin Strett	Orrell v Rosslyn Park	28.04.90
	John Liley	Leicester v Bristol	28.10.95
	Gavin Johnson	Saracens v London Scottish	26.09.98
	John Schuster	Harlequins v Bath	21.11.98
	Steven Vile	West Hartlepool v Gloucester	14.03.99
	Simon Mannix	Gloucester v Northampton	16.05.99
27	David Pears	Harlequins v Bedford	14.10.89
	Mark Mapletoft	Gloucester v Leicester	01.02.98
	Niall Woods	London Irish v Northampton	05.01.99
26	John Liley	Leicester v Bedford	23.09.89
	Stuart Barnes	Bath v West Hartlepool	27.03.93
	Paul Grayson	Northampton v Bristol	02.10.93
	Mark Tainton	Bristol v Leicester	05.12.94
	Andy Lee	Saracens v West Hartlepool	14.10.95
	Paul Challinor	Harlequins v West Hartlepool	23.03.96
	Rob Liley	Leicester v London Irish	31.10.96
	John Stabler	West Hartlepool v London Irish	28.12.96
	Simon Mannix	Sale v Northampton	09.03.97
	Mike Catt	Bath v Sale	26.04.97
	Paul Grayson	Northampton v London Irish	13.12.97
	Thierry Lacroix	Harlequins v Wasps	13.12.97
	Kenny Logan	Wasps v London Irish	19.09.98
	Mike Catt	Bath v London Scottish	15.05.99
	Rich Butland	Richmond v Bedford	16.05.99
25	John Callard	Bath v Orrell	30.09.95
	John Liley	Leicester v Leicester v Bristol	13.04.96
	Kenny Logan	Wasps v Orrell	22.03.97
	Joel Stransky	Leicester v Wasps	17.01.98
	Jonny Wilkinson	Newcastle v Northampton	14.11.98
24	Dusty Hare	Leicester v Rosslyn Park	19.11.88
	Stuart Barnes	Bath v Bedford	13.01.90
	Rob Andrew	Wasps v Bristol	27.04.91
	Will Carling	Harlequins v Orrell	05.10.96
	Paul Grayson	Northampton v Richmond	21.12.97
	Mark Mapletoft	Gloucester v London Irish	05.09.98
	Niall Woods	London Irish v W Hartlepool	17.09.98
	Shane Howarth	Sale v Harlequins	27.09.98
	Shane Howarth	Sale v Gloucester	01.05.99

23 Jaime Salmon, Harlequins v Waterloo, 27.02.88
Rob Andrew, Wasps v Rosslyn Park, 22.10.88
David Pears, Harlequins v Saracens, 20.10.90
Rob Andrew, Wasps v Orrell, 11.12.93
Jez Harris, Leicester v Gloucester, 29.01.94
Arwel Thomas, Bristol v Orrell, 04.11.95
Simon Mason, Orrell v Saracens, 13.01.96
John Liley, Leicester v Orrell, 30.03.96
Andy Lee, Saracens v West Hartlepool, 30.03.96
John Callard, Bath v Orrell, 31.08.96
John Liley, Leicester v Bath, 07.09.96
Gareth Rees, Wasps v Saracens, 08.09.96John Liley, Leicester v Bristol, 18.01.97
Joel Stransky, Leicester v West Hartlepool, 08.03.97
Niall Woods, London Irish v Bristol, 20.02.98
Shane Howarth, Sale v Wasps, 18.04.98
Joel Stransky, Leicester v Lon. Scottish, 12.09.98
John Schuster, Harlequins v Bedford, 10.10.98
Gavin Johnson, Saracens v Richmond, 8.11.98
Jonny Wilkinson, Newcastle v L. Scottish, 31.03.99
Jonny Wilkinson, Newcastle v Wasps, 12.04.99

MOST TRIES IN A MATCH

5	Kenny Logan	Wasps v Orrel	22.03.97
4	Gary Hartley	Nottingham v Bedford	18.11.89
	Tony Swift	Bath v Bedford	13.01.90
	Jeremy Guscott	Bath v Bedford	13.01.90
	Paul Hamer	Orrell v Rugby	13.03.93
	Tony Underwood	Leicester v Newcastle Gosforth	12.03.94
	Daren O'Leary	Harlequins v Gloucester	31.08.96
	Tom Beim	Sale v Bristol	09.11.97
	Niall Woods	London Irish v Northampton	05.01.99

3

Peter Shillingford, Moseley v Wasps, 05.02.88
Mark Charles, Leicester v Sale, 26.03.88
Andrew Harriman, Harlequins v Nottingham, 01.04.88
Simon Smith, Wasps v Coventry, 13.04.88
Andrew Harriman, Harlequins v Sale , 23.04.88
Jeremy Guscott, Bath v Moseley, 12.11.88
Mark Bailey, Wasps v Moseley, 19.11.88
John Liley, Leicester v Bedford, 23.09.89
Mike Wedderburn, Harlequins v Bedford, 14.10.89
Mark Bailey, Wasps v Gloucester, 14.10.89
Derrick Morgan, Gloucester v Rosslyn Park, 11.11.89
Jonathan Callard, Bath v Bedford, 13.01.90
Chris Gerard, Leicester v Moseley, 13.01.90
Paul Manley, Orrell v Rosslyn Park, 31.03.90
Dewi Morris, Orrell v Liverpool StH, 13.10.90
Dewi Morris, Orrell v Northampton, 27.10.90
Rory Underwood, Leicester v Northampton, 21.01.91
Andrew Harriman, Harlequins v Bristol, 30.03.91
Will Carling, Harlequins v Bristol, 30.03.91
Graham Childs , Wasps v Liverpool StH, 20.04.91
Rob Andrew, Wasps v Bristol, 27.04.91
Rory Underwood, Leicester v Moseley, 27.04.91
Steve Hackney, Leicester v Lon. Irish, 04.01.92
Tony Swift, Bath v Leicester, 11.01.92
Rory Underwood, Leicester v Rosslyn Park, 21.03.92
Mike Lloyd, Bristol v Rugby, 28.03.92
Martin Pepper, Nottingham v Rosslyn Park, 04.04.92
Chris Oti, Wasps v Bristol, 25.04.92
Stuart Barnes, Bath v W. Hartlepool, 27.03.93
Derek Eves, Bristol v Rugby, 22.03.93
Ian Wynn, Orrell v Wasps, 30.04.94
Simon Morris, Gloucester v W. Hartlepool, 17.09.94
Damian Hopley, Wasps v Sale , 15.10.94
Jeremy Guscott, Bath v Bristol, 14.10.95
Graeme Smith, Orrell v Wasps, 28.10.95
Rob Kitchen, Harlequins v Bristol, 06.01.96
Graeme Smith, Orrell v Saracens, 13.01.96
Aadel Kardooni, Leicester v W. Hartlepool, 17.02.96
Spencer Bromley, Harlequins v Sale, 30.03.96
Aadel Kardooni, Leicester v Sale , 17.04.96
Michael Corcoran, Harlequins v Lon. Irish, 14.09.96
Adedayo Adebayo, Bath v Lon. Irish, 05.10.96
Huw Harries, Harlequins v Orrell, 05.10.96
Mike Lloyd, Gloucester v W. Hartlepool, 18.01.97
Jonathan Sleightholme, Bath v Northampton, 19.01.97
Jonathan Sleightholme, Bath v Lon. Irish, 08.03.97
Domonic Chapman, Harlequins v Orrell, 08.03.97
Nick Walshe, Harlequins v W. Hartlepool, 22.03.97
Tom Beim, Sale v W. Hartlepool, 05.04.97
Andy Nicol, Bath v Gloucester, 30.04.97
Richard Wallace, Saracens v Lon. Irish, 30.04.97
David Rees, Sale v Bristol, 09.11.97
Gary Armstrong, Newcastle v Bristol, 27.12.97
Jim Naylor, Newcastle v Lon. Irish, 11.01.98
Eric Peters, Bath v Gloucester, 11.02.98
Richard Wallace, Saracens v Bristol, 14.02.98
Harvey Thorneycroft, Northampton v Bristol, 14.03.98
Will Greenwood, Leicester v Richmond, 28.03.98
Domonic Chapman, Richmond v Bristol, 10.04.98
Justin Bishop, Lon. Irish v Harlequins, 25.04.98
Chris Catling, Gloucester v ????? 17.10.98
Darragh O'Mahoney, Bedford v Richmond, 31.10.98
Tony Underwood, Newcastle v Saracens, 31.10.98
Pat Lam, Northampton v Sale, 2.1.99
Tony Diprose, Saracens v W. Hartlepool, 13.2.99
Iain Balshaw, Bath v Saracens, 28.3.99
Richard Todd, London Irish v Bath 17.4.99
Gary Armstrong, Newcastle v Richmond, 21.4.99
Darragh O'Mahoney, Bedford v W. Hartlepool, 2.5.99
Brian Cusack, Richmond v Bedford, 16.5.99
Mel Deane, Richmond v Bedford, 16.5.99
Neil Back, Leicester v W. Hartlepool, 16.5.99

MOST APPEARANCES

164	Jim Mallinder	Roundhay, Sale	Full back
153	Dave Baldwin	Wakefield, Sale	2nd row
152	Derek Eves	Bristol, Coventry	Flanker
146	Ben Clarke	Saracens, Bath, Richmond	Flanker
	Paul Hull	Bristol	Utility back
145	Rob Andrew	Wasps, Newcastle	Stand off
142	Darrren Garforth	Leicester	Prop
140	Nigel Redman	Bath	2nd row
136	Rory Underwood	Leicester, Bedford	Winger
135	Dean Ryan	Saracens, Wasps, Newcastle	Back row
130	Simon Mitchell	W Hartlepool, Harlequins, Wasps	Hooker
	Martin Johnson	Leicester	2nd row
	Dave Sims	Gloucester	2nd row
128	Jeremy Guscott	Bath	Centre
	Stuart Potter	Nottingham, Leicester	Centre
126	Martin Haag	Bath	2nd row
125	Harvey Thorneycroft	Northampton	Winger
124	Tony Diprose	Saracens	No 8
123	Neil Back	Leicester	2nd row
122	Graham Dawe	Bath, Sale	Hooker

TEN YEAR RECORD

Club	SEASONS									
	89-90	90-91	91-92	92-93	93-94	94-95	95-96	96-97	97-98	98-99
Bath	3	1	1	1	1	2	1	2	3	6
Bedford	12	-	-	-	-	-	-	-	-	
Bristol	9	11	10	6	4	6	6	9	12	-
Gloucester	2	6	4	5	8	7	8	6	7	10
Harlequins	7	3	8	8	6	8	3	3	10	4
Leicester	5	4	6	3	2	1	2	4	4	1
Liverpool St Helens	-	13	-	-	-	-	-	-	-	-
London Irish	-	-	9	7	9	-	-	10	-	7
London Scottish	-	-	-	10	-	-	-	-	-	12
Moseley	11	12	-	-	-	-	-	-	-	-
Newcastle	-	-	-	-	10	-	-	-	1	8
Northampton	-	9	3	4	5	10	-	8	8	2
Nottingham	6	8	12	-	-	-	-	-	-	-
Orrell	8	5	2	9	7	5	7	12	-	-
Richmond	-	-	-	-	-	-	-	-	5	9
Rosslyn Park	10	7	13	-	-	-	-	-	-	-
Rugby	-	-	11	13	-	-	-	-	-	-
(Manchester) Sale	-	-	-	-	-	4	5	5	6	11
Saracens	4	10	5	11	-	-	9	7	2	3
Wasps	1	2	7	2	3	3	4	1	9	5
West Hartlepool	-	-	-	12	-	9	10	11	-	14

Review of the season 1998-1999

Bristol went straight back up to the Allied Dunbar Premiership One after a final day win against Worcester to clinch the title on points difference from Rotherham. Bristol with Bob Dwyer at the helm and a large turnover of players had enough ability to hold off a tremendous challenge from Rotherham. It could have all been so different, as late in the season they were trailing struggling Fylde when the match went into injury time but managed to pull it out of the bag and snatch victory and two vital points.

Rotherham, after losing four of their opening nine matches then went on a seventeen match winning streak with good wins at Bristol and Worcester against both of whom they did the double.

Worcester were hoping that the nucleus of the team that won Jewson National One the season before would be good enough to take them out of Allied Dunbar Premiership Two at the first attempt. They found the task to much and were finding it hard to keep pace with the top two, and in the end they were ten points adrift.

London Welsh acquitted themselves well in their first season back at this level and finished a highly creditable fourth. They had an excellent home record just losing to the three teams that finished above them. Andy Currier continues to go from strength to strength and finished the season with fifteen tries and after just two seasons is the club's leading try scorer ever in league rugby.

Exeter were a revelation and finished in their highest ever league position of fifth after fourteen wins. Bryan Easson made a big impact in his first season and proved the worth of having a consistent goal kicker with a valuable 241 points.

Leeds Tykes finished sixth after having four points deducted for playing Wendall Sailor before they had clearance from the RFU to do so. They will be disappointed with that after some heavy recruiting but they could never quite get a consistent run going.

Coventry finished seventh just as last season and after the upheaval of last summer they will be pleased with that and look to continue to build for the future. Summer signing Steve Gough made a huge impact in his first season topping 300 league points whilst winger Andy Smallwood scored an impressive fifteen league tries.

Eighth place went to **Orrell** who dropped down three places from the previous season. They relied heavily on Simon Verbickas, who for the second successive season finished top of both the points and try scoring lists for the club. Orrell had good home form including six successive wins to finish the season but away from home they managed just three wins.

Waterloo were ninth one place lower than last season. They again relied heavily on Lyndon Griffiths who scored nearly half their points. A good finisher is needed with Sean Woof finishing as leading try scorer with just five. They ended the season with four straight losses and suffered their last four at home as they lost direction. Their cause was not helped with Tony Russ announcing that he was to step down as Director of Rugby.

Moseley, another side to suffer financially last season, ended up in tenth place, which was a four-place drop on the previous season. They suffered from not having a settled goal kicker and through a big personnel change yet again.

Rugby Lions will be disappointed with eleventh place after nine league wins. Full back Martyn Davies was their main points scorer and scored nearly half their points in the league. Eddie Saunders continued to be the clubs best finisher and topped the try scorers list for the ninth time in twelve seasons.

Wakefield struggled all season and ended up twelfth and were just two points clear of the relegation zone. A 38-20 win at home to Moseley three weeks from the end of the season was the result that saw them home.

Blackheath, who were eighth last season, were bottom for most of the season, but with wins in their last two matches of the season they climbed above Fylde on the last day, but were still relegated after four years in the division.

Fylde finished bottom for the second season but this time there is no reorganisation to a save them. They went last on the penultimate weekend of the season when they lost to bottom side Blackheath at home in a close 27-26. So their two-year stay in the Premiership comes to an end.

ALLIED DUNBAR PREMIERSHIP TWO

1998-99 RECORD REVIEW (Individual Records)

The ALL-TIME RECORDS for MOST POINTS IN A MATCH, MOST POINTS IN A SEASON & MOST TRIES IN A MATCH can be found in the Records Section for this division.

MOST POINTS - IN A MATCH

The nearest anyone came to Jez Harris's record was when Coventry's Steve Gough scored 34 points against London Welsh from three tries, five conversions and three penalties. That put him third on the all time list also behind Rob Andrews 36 points.

EVOLUTION OF RECORD - Points in a match

26	Andy Mitchell	London Scot v North	03.10.87
28	David Johnson	New Gos v Morley	11.01.92
30	Michael Corcoran	L. Irish v Waterloo	23.09.95
42	Jez Harris	Coventry v Nott	05.10.96

MOST POINTS - IN A SEASON

Coventry's Steve Gough topped the points scorers list with 305 points, the third highest total ever in the division. Only Simon Mason,324, and Michael Corcoran, 310, have scored more.
Four players topped the 200 point mark which was the same as the previous record but one short of the record of five.

EVOLUTION OF RECORD - Points in a season

75	Andy Finnie	Bedford	1987-88
138	Andy Kennedy	Saracens	1988-89
147	David Johnson	Newcastle Gos	1991-92
172	Guy Gregory	Nottingham	1993-94
213	Mike Jackson	Wakefield	1994-95
310	Michael Corcoran	London Irish	1995-96
324	Simon Mason	Richmond	1996-97

Coventry's Steve Gough in action last season on his way to his 305 points.

Photo Derrick Warren, Coventry Evening Telegraph

MOST TRIES - IN A MATCH

Bristol wing Luke Nabaro equalled the divisions record with five tries in the home defeat of Blackheath in March. It was also his debut which was a record in itself for any of the top five divisions in English rugby.
Andy Currier, Luke Nabaro, Lennie Woodard and Dean Lax were the only four players to score two hat tricks during the season.
Nabaro scored five on his debut but both Lennie Woodard and Marden scored hat tricks on their debuts league for London Welsh.
Six players scored four tries in a match, only seven had achieved this in the first 11 seasons.

5	Luke Nabaro	Bristol v Blackheath	13.03.99
4	Dean Lax	Rotherham v Orrell	13.02.99
4	Lennie Woodard	London W v Blackheath	17.04.99
4	Andy Smallwood	Coventry v Wakefield	08.05.99
4	Ian Breheny	Wakefield v Moseley	24.04.99
4	John Fabian	Exeter v Waterloo	17.10.98
4	Jon Scales	Leeds v Exeter	07.02.99

EVOLUTION OF RECORD - Tries in a match
(Only the first to reach the figure is shown)

3	Peter Shillingford	Moseley v Wasps	05.02.88
3	Jerry Macklin	Lon Scot v Northampton	03.10.87
5	Simon Verbickas	Sale v Otley	12.02.94
5	Pat Lam	Newcastle v Rotherham	04.05.97
5	Luke Nabaro	Bristol v Blackheath	13.03.99

MOST TRIES - IN A SEASON

John Bentley's record of 23 was never in danger with the best effort being 17 by the Rotherham winger Dean Lax which just gets him into the all time top 10 for the division.

EVOLUTION OF RECORD

10	Dave McLagan	Saracens	1987-88
11	Nick Grecian	Lon. Scottish	1991-92
16	Simon Verbickas	Sale	1993-94
20	Matt Allen	Northampton	1996-97
23	John Bentley	Newcastle	1996-97

ALL-TIME RECORDS

23	John Bentley	Newcastle	1996-97
21	Gary Armstrong	Newcastle	1996-97
21	Scott Quinnell	Richmond	1996-97
20	Matt Allen	Northampton	1995-96
20	Jim Fallon	Richmond	1996-97
17	Andy Smallwood	Coventry	1996-97
17	Darragh O'Mahoney	Moseley	1997-98
17	Ben Whetstone	Bedford	1997-98
17	Dean Lax	Rotherham	1998-99

MOST CONVERSIONS - IN A MATCH

This record was never in danger and may never be beaten. The best efforts in 1998-99 were by Steve Gough and Craig Raymond with eight each. Gough kicked his eight as Coventry beat Fylde Welsh 64-9. Raymond kicked his eight in the clubs 71-22 win over Blackheath.

EVOLUTION OF RECORD

6	Chris Howard	Rugby v Gosforth	11.11.89
9	David Johnson	New Gos v Morley	11.01.92
9	Guy Gregory	Nott v Morley	24.10.92
9	Paul Turner	Sale v Otley	12.02.94
18	Rob Andrew	Newcastle v Rugby	05.10.96

ALL-TIME RECORDS

18	Rob Andrew	Newcastle v Rugby	05.10.96
13	Jez Harris	Coventry v Nottingham	05.10.96
9	David Johnson	New Gos v Morley	11.01.92
9	Guy Gregory	Nottingham v Morley	24.10.92
9	Paul Turner	Sale v Otley	12.02.94

MOST CONVERSIONS - IN A SEASON

Another Rob Andrew record that was not challenged. The best total for the season was the 48 by Coventry's Steve Gough which puts him joint 6th on the divisions all time list.

EVOLUTION OF RECORD

14	Andy Kennedy	Saracens	1988-89
24	Martin Livesey	Richmond	1989-90
31	David Johnson	Newcastle Gosforth	1991-92
76	Paul Grayson	Northampton	1995-96
95	Rob Andrew	Newcastle	1996-97

ALL-TIME RECORDS

95	Rob Andrew	Newcastle	1996-97
83	Simon Mason	Richmond	1996-97
76	Paul Grayson	Northampton	1995-96
67	Mike Rayer	Bedford	1996-97
65	Mike Rayer	Bedford	1997-98
48	Jez Harris	Coventry	1996-97
48	Steve Gough	Coventry	1998-99

MOST PENALTIES - IN A MATCH

Leeds, Tongan international full back, Sateki Tuipulotu got nearest to equalling the record of eight but never got the chance as he kicked seven out of seven.

EVOLUTION OF RECORD

7	Michael Corcoran	Lon Irish v Lon Scottish	13.01.96
8	Alastair Kerr	Moseley v Waterloo	17.02.96

ALL-TIME RECORDS

8	Alastair Kerr	Moseley v Water	17.02.96
7	Michael Corcoran	Lon Irish v Lon Scottish	13.01.96
7	Matt Inman	Rotherham v Richmond	14.09.96
7	Sateki Tuipulotu	Leeds v Coventry	03.01.99

MOST PENALTIES - IN A SEASON

Steve Gough and Sateki Tuipulotu topped the list for most penalties in the season with 53 to move into fourth place on the all time list and 12 short of the record of Lyndon Griffiths set two seasons ago.

EVOLUTION OF RECORD

30	Andy Kennedy	Saracens	1988-89
30	David Johnson	Newcastle	1992-93
43	Guy Gregory	Nottingham	1993-94
57	Mike Jackson	Wakefield	1994-95
63	MIchael Corcoran	London Irish	1995-96
65	Lyndon Griffiths	Waterloo	1997-98

ALL-TIME RECORDS

65	Lyndon Griffiths	Waterloo	1997-98
63	Michael Corcoran	London Irish	1995-96
57	Mike Jackson	Wakefield	1994-95
53	Steve Gough	Coventry	1998-99
53	Sateki Tuipulotu	Leeds Tykes	1998-99
51	Bryan Easson	Exeter	1998-99
48	Steve Swindells	Waterloo	1994-95
47	John Steele	London Scottish	1996-97
46	Lyndon Griffiths	Waterloo	1998-99
45	Simon Mason	Newcastle Gosforth	1994-95

MOST DROP GOALS - IN A MATCH

Nobody managed more than one in a match and the record was never challenged

ALL-TIME RECORDS

3	Martin Livesey	Richmond v Northampton	19.11.88
3	Murray Walker	London Scot v W Hartlepool	23.04.94

MOST DROP GOALS - IN A SEASON

The record was safe last season with only four players managing to score just three drop goals in the campaign.

EVOLUTION OF RECORD

4	Simon Smith	Bedford	1987-88
4	David Johnson	Gosforth	1987-88
8	Jon King	Blackheath	1988-89
9	Guy Gregory	Nottingham	1992-93

ALL-TIME RECORDS

9	Guy Gregory	Nottingham	1992-93
8	Jon King	Blackheath	1988-89
6	Andy Lee	Saracens	1994-95
5	Brian Mullen	London Irish	1990-91
5	Sam Howard	Blackheath	1995-96
5	Guy Gregory	Nottingham	1993-94
5	Murray Walker	London Scot	1993-94
5	Jez Harris	Coventry	1996-97
5	Matt Jones	Moseley	1997-98

1998-99

ALLIED DUNBAR PREMIERSHIP TWO

MOST POINTS

POINTS			T	C	P	DG
305	Steve Gough	Coventry	10	48	53	0
250	Sateki Tuipulotu	Leeds Tykes	3	38	53	-
241	Bryan Easson	Exeter	2	39	51	-
224	Simon Verbickas	Orrell	13	30	33	-
198	Lyndon Griffiths	Waterloo	2	25	46	-
189	Martyn Davies	Rugby Lions	4	23	41	-
164	Paul Hull	Bristol	5	35	23	-
162	Richard LeBas	Worcester	4	26	30	-
144	Doug Trivella	Rotherham	5	28	21	-
140	John Liley	Worcester	2	11	36	-
105	Jake Niarchos	Rotherham	1	26	16	-
102	Campbell Aitken	Blackheath	2	7	26	-
99	Andy Lee	London Welsh	1	26	14	-
90	Dean Lax	Rotherham	18	-	-	-
85	Andy Binns	Moseley	2	12	17	-
83	Simon Amor	Blackheath	-	16	16	1
82	Steffan Jones	Moseley	2	9	18	-
82	David Knox	Bristol	-	20	13	1

MOST PENALTIES

53	Steve Gough	Coventry
53	Sateki Tuipulotu	Leeds Tykes
51	Bryan Easson	Exeter
46	Lyndon Griffiths	Waterloo
41	Martyn Davies	Rugby
36	John Liley	Worcester
33	Simon Verbickas	Orrell
30	Richard LeBas	Worcester
26	Campbell Aitken	Blackheath
23	Paul Hull	Bristol
21	Doug Trivella	Rotherham
18	Steffan Jones	Moseley
18	Alun Peacock	Fylde
17	Andy Binns	Moseley
16	Simon Amor	Blackheath

MOST CONVERSIONS

48	Steve Gough	Coventry
39	Bryan Easson	Exeter
38	Sateki Tuipulotu	Leeds Tykes
35	Paul Hull	Bristol
30	Simon Verbickas	Orrell
28	Doug Trivella	Rotherham
26	Richard LeBas	Worcester
26	Andy Lee	London Welsh
26	Jake Niarchos	Rotherham
25	Lyndon Griffiths	Waterloo
23	Martyn Davies	Rugby Lions
20	David Knox	Bristol
16	Simon Amor	Blackheath
14	Craig Raymond	London Welsh
14	Phil Ure	Wakefield

MOST TRIES

18	Dean Lax	Rotherham
16	Ben Wade	Rotherham
15	Andy Currier	London Welsh
15	Andy Smallwood	Coventry
14	Lenny Woodard	London Welsh
13	Nick Baxter	Worcester
13	Luke Nabaro	Bristol
13	Simon Verbickas	Orrell
12	Jon Clarke	Blackheath
10	Greg Austin	Rotherham
10	Ian Breheny	Wakefield
10	Steve Gough	Coventry
10	Karl Johnson	Orrell
10	Simon Middleton	Leeds Tykes
10	Jon Scales	Leeds Tykes
9	Gareth Baber	Bristol
9	Marcus Cook	Moseley
9	Tim Fourie	Leeds Tykes
9	Mark Gabey	Bristol

MOST DROP GOALS

3	Luis Criscuolo	Coventry
3	Dean Morgan	Rugby Lions
3	Neil Ryan	Orrell
3	Jonathan Smart	Moseley
2	Tony Handley	Waterloo
1	Simon Amor	Blackheath
1	Andy Currier	London Welsh
1	David Knox	Bristol
1	Matt Tetlow	Fylde
1	Ian Wynn	Orrell

ALLIED DUNBAR PREMIERSHIP 2 FIXTURES 1999-2000

Away Teams

	HOME TEAMS	Coventry	Exeter	Henley	Leeds	London Welsh	Manchester	Moseley	Orrell	Rotherham	Rugby	Wakefield	Waterloo	West Hartlepool	Worcester	
1	COVENTRY	X	4.12	11.09	20.11	25.09	18.12	18.03	8.01	15.04	29.04	25.03	12.02	16.10	11.02	1
2	EXETER	15.01	X	23.10	22.04	27.11	9.10	25.03	18.09	22.01	26.02	25.09	7.09	6.05	11.12	2
3	HENLEY	22.04	12.02	X	11.03	7.09	8.01	20.11	16.10	6.05	4.12	11.12	2.10	8.04	18.09	3
4	LEEDS	22.01	11.09	9.10	X	23.10	25.09	15.04	29.04	26.02	25.03	6.05	11.12	15.01	27.11	4
5	LONDON WELSH	8.04	8.01	29.04	12.2	X	18.03	4.12	20.11	11.09	18.12	15.04	16.10	11.03	2.10	5
6	MANCHESTER	6.05	11.03	27.11	8.04	11.12	X	16.10	2.10	15.01	22.01	23.10	18.09	22.04	7.09	6
7	MOSELEY	11.12	2.10	22.01	18.09	15.01	26.02	X	8.04	27.11	23.10	9.10	22.04	7.09	6.05	7
8	ORRELL	27.11	15.04	26.02	1.09	22.01	25.03	25.09	X	23.10	9.10	11.09	6.05	11.12	15.01	8
9	ROTHERHAM	18.09	20.11	18.12	16.10	22.04	4.12	8.01	12.02	X	18.03	29.04	11.03	2.10	8.04	9
10	RUGBY	7.09	16.10	15.01	2.10	6.05	20.11	12.02	11.03	11.12	X	27.10	8.04	18.09	22.04	10
11	WAKEFIELD	2.10	8.04	18.03	18.12	18.09	12.02	11.03	22.04	7.09	8.01	X	4.12	20.11	16.10	11
12	WATERLOO	23.10	29.04	25.03	18.03	26.02	15.04	11.09	18.12	9.10	25.09	15.01	X	27.11	22.01	12
13	WEST HARTLEPOOL	26.02	18.12	25.09	4.12	9.10	11.09	29.04	18.03	25.03	15.04	22.01	8.01	X	23.10	13
14	WORCESTER	9.10	18.03	15.04	8.01	25.03	29.04	18.12	4.12	25.09	11.09	26.02	20.11	12.02	X	14
		1	2	3	4	5	6	7	8	9	10	11	12	13	14	

COVENTRY F.C.

President	Keith Fairbrother	Coventry F.C. Ltd., Barkers Butts lane, Coundon, Coventry CV6 1DU Tel: 01203 601174 Fax: 01203 601194	
Chairman	J Broderick	as above	
General Manager	Ian Carvell	as above	
Fixtures Secretary	Paul Ingleston	as above	Tel: 0247 6502587 (H) 07801 233 921 (M)
Commercial Manager	Vivien Robinson	as above	

From the debris of receivership, with no team two weeks before the season start, `Cov' have to see this as a successful season. The club, rescued by a consortium led by former England and Coventry prop Keith Fairbrother, had the modest aim of consolidation. The bulk of the playing staff stayed loyal to the club, with some new players such as Steve Gough from Fylde, and two former Moseley players, Kevin Whitley and Luis Criscuolo, Canadian and Argentina internationals respectively, joining the cause.

Lack of preparation was evident in a loss at Worcester, but Waterloo were beaten at home. A six point defeat at Exeter followed before high hopes were raised by a five match winning run. Fylde were demolished at home, a Criscuolo drop goal in injury time at rival Rugby Lions, London Welsh and thrashed at home, an away win at Blackheath, followed by a hard fought win at home to Orrell. The month of October ended with a narrow 12-14 loss at front runners Bristol.November started with a 22-12 home win over fancied Rotherham, before the unbeaten home record went in a thrilling Tetley's Bitter Cup clash with Worcester. A poor Sunday performance at Leeds Tykes was followed by a narrow 13-12 win over Bedford in a Cheltenham and Gloucester tie.

Back to league action brought a hard-fought win at Wakefield, followed by a big defeat in the return Cheltenham and Gloucester tie at Bedford. Moseley had an early Christmas present as they steamrollered Cov at Coundon Road.

The new year started with another home defeat in a crunching match against Leeds Tykes, followed by a one score defeat at Rotherham. February was a crunch time. A heavy defeat at Orrell, `nilled', hastened the departure of Derek Eves, replaced in his Director of rugby role by ex Harlequins and Gloucester coach, Keith Richardson. The change made an immediate impact. Already doomed Blackheath were crushed followed by a late, late Steve Gough try and conversion bringing victory over champions-elect Bristol. Away defeat at London Welsh and a surprise home defeat to Rugby Lions were followed by a shocking defeat and display at relegation haunted Fylde. It had been a sad March.

April brought better league results. Exeter were put to the sword on Easter Saturday, a one point win at Waterloo mid-month followed, then the big one. Worcester's dreams of promotion were finally buried in the best performance of the season, although this was followed by a last kick conversion at Moseley, Cov's rivals gaining a deserved double. The last match, Wakefield the visitors, brought its own reward, winger Andy Smallwood creating a club league record of four tries in a match.

For a club that was `dead', this was a season that had plenty of highlights with Steve Gough scoring 305 league points, AD 2's top points scorer, a happier feel at Coundon Road and, with a team working overtime to prevent a re-run of the previous summer, Coundon Road is `buzzing' again.

COVENTRY 98-99 - **Back Row:** Jason Soden, Mark Crane, Mark Fountaine, Kevin Whitley, Scott Edwards, Alan Sharp. **Middle**: Derek Eves, R. Lloyd (now Nottingham), Russ Morgan, Steve Gough, Jason Minshull, Lee Crofts, Dave Addleton, Luis Criscuolo. **Front**: Andy McAdam, Andy Smallwood, Martin Wallwork, Wayne Kilford, Julian Horrobin, Mick Curtis, Ricky Hyslop, Tigger Dawson, Richie Robinson. **Photo:** Tony Dickinson

COVENTRY

Match No.	Date	H/A	Comp.	Opponents	Result & Score	Att.	15	14	13	12	11
1	05.09	A	AD2	Worcester	L 7-22	2,500	Gallagher	McAdam	Robinson(k)	Curtis	Smallwood/t(l)
2	12.09	H	AD2	Waterloo	W21-15	1,950	Kilford	McAdam(a)	Curtis(c)	Criscuolo	Smallwood
3	19.09	A	AD2	Exeter	L 25-31	620	Kilford	Gallagher	Criscuolo(d)	Robinson	Smallwood
4	26.09	H	AD2	Fylde	W 64-9	1,200	Kilford/3t	Gallagher/t	Criscuolo	Curtis(c)	Hyslop(e/2t)
5	03.10	A	AD2	Rugby Lions	W20-17	1,500	Kilford	Gallagher	Criscuolo/dg	Curtis(c)	Smallwood
6	10.10	H	AD2	London Welsh	W63-19	1,360	Kilford/2t	Minshull	Criscuolo/t2c	Curtis/t	Smallwood(p)
7	17.10	A	AD2	Blackheath	W30-18	600	Kilford	Mimshull	Criscuolo	Robinson/2t	McAdam(d)
8	24.10	H	AD2	Orrell*	W26-14	1,200	Kilford	Minshull	Criscuolo	Curtis	Robinson/t
9	30.10	A	AD2	Bristol	L 12-14	4,683	Kilford	Minshull(e)	Criscuolo	Curtis	Robinson
10	07.11	H	AD2	Rotherham	W22-12	1,200	Gallagher/t	Minshull(b)	Robinson	Curtis	Smallwood/t
11	22.11	A	AD2	Leeds Tykes	L 12-36	760	Kilford	McAdam	Minshull	Robinson/t	Smallwood/t
12	12.12	A	AD2	Wakefield	W18-10	400	Gallagher	Minshull/t	Criscuolo	Curtis(c)	Smallwood
13	19.12	H	AD2	Moseley*	L 21-46	1,200	Gallagher(l)	McAdam(x)	Minshull	Robinson	Smallwood(y)
14	02.01	H	AD2	Leeds Tykes*	L 27-33	1,000	Kilford	Mafi/2t	Criscuolo	Curtis	Smallwood
15	16.01	A	AD2	Rotherham	L 12-19		Kilford	Minshull	Criscuolo(d)	Robinson	Smallwood
16	06.02	A	AD2	Orrell	L 0-31	600	Gallagher	Minshull(c)	Criscuolo	Curtis	McAdam
17	13.02	H	AD2	Blackheath	W 35-8	900	Gallagher/t3c2p	McAdam	Robinson	Curtis(l)	Smallwood/t
18	21.02	H	AD2	Bristol	W22-19	1,500	Kilford	Gough/t2cp	Robinson/t(v)	Curtis	Smallwood
19	27.02	A	AD2	London Welsh	L 34-42		Kilford(b)	Gough/2c4p	Minshull	Gallagher	Smallwood/t
20	13.03	H	AD2	Rugby Lions	L 19-21	1,100	Gallagher	Gough/tc4p	Minshull	Robinson	Smallwood
21	27.03	A	AD2	Fylde	L 22-27	350	Gallagher	Gought2cp	Minshull	Robinson	Smallwood/t
22	03.04	H	AD2	Exeter	W20-13	900	Gough/2c2p	Mafi	Minshull	Curtis/t	Smallwood
23	17.04	A	AD2	Waterloo	W25-24	450	Gough/t2c2p	Mafi	Minshull	Curtis	Smallwood/t
24	24.04	H	AD2	Worcester	W26-17	1,400	Gough/2c4p	Mafi	Minshull	Curtis	Smallwood/2t(c)
25	01.05	A	AD2	Moseley	L 29-30	1,064	Gough/3cp	Mafi	Minshull	Curtis	Robinson
26	08.05	H	AD2	Wakefield	W40-13	1,950	Gough/2c2p	Mafi/t	Minshull	Curtis	Smalwood/4t
A	14.11	H	TBC	Worcester	L 26-36	2,200	Kilford	McAdam	Robinson	Curtis/t	Smallwood/t

* after opponents name indicates a penalty try
Brackets after a player's name indicates he was replaced. eg (a) means he was replaced by replacement code "a" and so on.
/ after a player or replacement name is followed by any scores he made - eg /t, /c, /p, /dg or any combination of these

1998-99 HIGHLIGHTS

League debuts:
Steve Gough, Mark Fountaine, Kevin Whitley, Luis Criscuolo, Martin Wallwork, Scott Edwards, Ricky Hyslop, S Kerr, Neil Watkins, Carl Houston, M Mafi, B Dale, M Mika.

Ever Presents: None
Most appearances Steve Gough 25(1) and Kevin Whitley 25.

Players used: 31 plus 3 as a replacement only.

Most Points in a season:

Pts	Player	T	C	P	DG
305	S Gough	10	48	53	-
75	A Smallwood	15	-	-	-
27	M Gallagher	3	3	2	-
25	J Horrobin	5	-	-	-

MATCH FACTS

10	9	1	2	3	4	5	6	7	8	
Gough/c	Dawson(m)	Sharp	Addleton	Crane	Fountaine	Whitley	Crofts	Eves	Horrobin	1
Gough/c3p	Dawson	Sharp	Addleton	Crane	Fountaine/t	Whitley	Crofts	Eves/t	Horobon	2
Gough/t2c2p	Wallwork(f)	Sharp(h)	Soden(g)	Morgan	Crofts	Whitley/t(i)	Horrobin	Eves/t	Edwards	3
Gough/t8cp	Dawson(m)	Morgan	Addleton(n)	Crane/t(q)	Fountaine	Crofts/t	Horrobin	Eves	Edwards	4
Gough/4p	Dawson	Sharp	Addleton	Crane	Fountaine	Whitley(r)	Horrobin/t	Eves	Crofts	5
Gough/3t5c3p(b)	Dawson(m)	Sharp	Soden(g)	Crane(t)	Fountaine(r)	Whitley	Crofts/t	Eves	Horrobin	6
Gough/2c2p	Wallwork	Sharp	Addleton(n)	Crane(t)	Fountaine	Whitley	Crofts	Eves/t(r)	Horrobin/t	7
Gough/2c4p	Dawson	Sharp	Addleon	Crane(t)	Fountaine	Whitley	Crofts	Eves	Horrobin(r)	8
Gough/4p	Dawson	Sharp	Addleton	Crane(t)	Fountaine	Whitley	Crofts	Eves	Horrobin	9
Gough/t2cp	Dawson	Kerr	Soden(g)	Crane	Fountaine	Whitley	Crofts	Eves	Horrobin	10
Gough(k/c)	Wallwork	Sharp	Addleton	Kerr	Fountaine	Whitley	Crofts	Eves	Hottobin	11
Gough/c2p	Dawson	Sharp	Addleton	Crane(t)	Fountaine	Whitley	Crofts	Eves/t	Horrobin	12
Gough/3c	Dawson(s)	Sharp	Addleton	Crane(t)	Fountaine	Whitley	Crofts/t	Eves	Horrobin/t	13
Gough/3c2p	Hewlett	Sharp(o)(h)	Addleton	Kerr	Fountaine	Whitley	Crofts	Eves	Horrobin	14
Gough/4p	Dawson	Sharp	Addleton	Kerr(h)	Fountaine(y)	Whitley	Crofts	Eves	Salisbury	15
Gough	Dawson(s)	Sharp	Addleton	Crane	Fountaine	Whitley	Crofts	Eves	Salisbury	16
Criscuolo/dg	Hewlett	Sharp	Addleton	Kerr	Fountaine(u/t)	Whitley/t	Crofts	Houston(j)	Salisbury	17
Criscuolo	Dawson	Morgan(z)	Addleton	Kerr	Fountaine(u)	Whitley/t	Crofts	Houston(w)	Horrobin	18
Criscuolo/dg	Hewlett	Dale(z)	Addleton/t	Kerr	Watkins	Whitley	Crofts	Houston(w)	Horrobin/t	19
Criscuolo	Dawson(s)	Mika(h)	Addleton	Kerr	Fountaine(u)	Whitley	Crofts	Houston(w)	Horrobin	20
Criscuolo(b)	Hewlett(f)	Mika(h)	Addleton	Kerr/t	Watinns(i)	Whitley(w)	Crofts	Houston	Horrobin	21
Gallagher	Dawson	Mika	Addleton	Crane	Fountaine	Whitley	Crofts/t	Horrobin	Salisbury	22
Gallagher	Dawson/t	Mika	Addleton	Crane(z)	Watkins	Whitley	Houston	Horrobin	Salisbury	23
Gallagher	Dawson	Mika	Addleton	Crane	Watkins	Whitley	Crofts	Houston	Horrobin	24
Hewlett(a)	Dawson	Mika	Addleton	Crane/t	Watkins/t(i)	Whitley	Crofts	Houston	Horobin/t(w/t)	25
Gallagher(k)	Dawson(s)	Mika(z)	Addleton(n)	Crane(o)	Fountaine(w)	Watkins	Crofts	Houston/t	Horrobin	26
Gough/tc3p	Dawson	Sharp(h)	Addleton	Kerr	Fountaine	Whitley	Crofts	Eves	Horrobin	A

REPLACEMENTS: a- M Gallagher b- A McAdam c - R Robinson d - M Curtis e - A Smallwood f - T Dawson g - D Addleton h - M Crane i - M Fountaine j - D Eves k - L Criscuolo l - W Kilford m - M Wallwork n - J Soden o - R Morgan p - R Hyslop q - J Hadfield r - R Ayers s - J Hewlett t - S Kerr u - N Watkins v - J Minshull w - R Salisbury x - M Mafi y - B Dale z - A Kershaw

Steve Gough in his first season at Coventry having joined from Fylde re wrote the Coventry points scoring record. He started in all but one league game and ended the season on 305 points, the only player in the division to top the 300 point mark.
He beat Jez Harris's record old 236 points in a season and in the process set a new record for penalties ,53, which easily beat the old record. He also kicked 48 conversions to equal Jez Harris's from 1996-97.
Winger Andy Smallwood failed to beat his own record of 17 tries but did take the all time record from Julian Horrobin. Smallwood now has 36 tries in his three seasons at Coventry.
Smallwood also erased the record of most tries in a match which was three and shared by six players. He scored four in the home match against Wakefield in May as the season drew to a close.
He topped the try scoring list for the second time in his three years at the club.
Hooker Dave Addleton took his club record of league appearances to 139 with 23 starts during the 98-99 season.
Winger Smallwood also overtook Richard Angell and set a new record for league appearances by a back with 83.

COVENTRY

LEAGUE STATISTICS
compiled by Stephen McCormack

SEASON	Division	P	W	D	L	F	A	Pts Diff	Lge Pts	Lge Pos	Most Points		Most Tries	
89-90	2	11	6	1	4	206	185	21	13	4	79	Steve Thomas	6	Steve Thomas
90-91	2	12	8	0	4	172	129	43	16	4	37	Richard Angell	4	Richard Angell
91-92	2	12	7	0	5	187	196	-9	14	6	73	Steve Thomas	4	Kevin Hickey
92-93	2	12	3	0	9	192	236	-44	6	11r	53	Richard Angell	4	Barry Evans
93-94	3	18	14	0	4	406	259	197	28	1p	151	Richard Angell	9	Doug Woodman
94-95	2	18	2	0	16	213	436	-223	4	10r	90	Richard Angell	5	Mark Douglas
95-96	3	18	15	0	3	524	264	260	30	1p	84	Craig Quick	11	Julian Horrobin
96-97	2	22	16	1	5	738	394	344	33	3	236	Jez Harris	17	Andy Smallwood
97-98	P2	22	11	1	10	444	532	-88	23	7	133	Jez Harris	6	Julian Horrobin
98-99	P2	26	14	0	12	662	552	110	34	7	305	Steve Gough	15	Andy Smallwood

BIGGEST MARGINS

Home Win	80pts - 102-22 v Nottingham 5.10.96
Away Win	58pts - 61-3 v Rugby 14.9.96
Home Defeat	17pts - 16-33 v Saracens 29.10.94
Away Defeat	43pts - 6-49 v wasps 13.4.88

MOST CONSECUTIVE

Appearances	35 Richard Angell & Warwick Bullock
Matches scoring Tries	4 Andy Smallwood
Matches scoring points	11 Jez Harris
Victories	9
Defeats	13

MOST POINTS

Scored at Home	102 v Nottingham 5.10.96
Scored Away	61 v Rugby 14.9.96
Conceded at Home	33 v Saracens 29.10.94 Waterloo 7.3.98
Conceded Away	49 v Wasps 13.4.88 Newcastle 12.4.97

MOST TRIES

Scored in a match	14 v Nottingham 5.10.96
Conceded in a match	9 v Wasps 13.4.88

MOST APPEARANCES

by a forward	139 (3) Dave Addleton
by a back	83 (2) Andy Smallwood

	MOST IN A SEASON	MOST IN A CAREER	MOST IN A MATCH	
Points	305 SteveGough 98-99	396 Richard Angell 90-96	42 Jez Harris	v Nottingham 5.10.96 (H)
Tries	17 Andy Smallwood 96-97	36 Andy Smallwood 96-99	4 Andy Smallwood	v Wakefield 8.5.99 (H)
Conversions	48 Jez Harris 96-97 Steve Gough 98-99	53 Jez Harris 96-98	13 Jez Harris	v Nottingham 5.10.96 (H)
Penalties	53 Steve Gough 98-99	81 Richard Angell 90-96	6 Steve Thomas Jez Harris	v Sale 23.9.89 (A) v Fylde 13.9.97 (A) v Orrell 24.1.98 (H)
Drop Goals	5 Jez Harris 96-97	10 Mark Lakey 87-95	2 Mark Lakey Jez Harris	v Moseley 3.4.93 (H) v Lon. Irish 8.10.94 (H) v Wakefield 21.9.96 (H)

COVENTRY PLAYING SQUAD

BACKS

BACKS	Ht.	Wt.	Birthdate	Birthplace	CLUB	League Apps	Tries	Pts
Matt Gallagher	6.1	13.0	21.03.73	Solihull	Coventry	54(3)	10	95
					Nottingham	44	4	114
Jason Minshull	5.11	13.5	20.12.67	Leamington Spa	Coventry	69(2)	11	49
Andy Smallwood	5.10	13.11	13.06.72	Solihull	Coventry	83(2)	36	180
					Nottingham	47	12	60
Steve Gough	5.10	13.7	22.04.66	Leigh	Coventry	25(1)	10	305
					Fylde	118(3)	26	739
Luis Crisculo	5.10	14.02	10.09.70	Buenos Aires	Coventry	17(2)	1	20
					Moseley	6(1)	-	-
Andy McAdam	6.1	14.0	23.03.71	Coventry	Coventry	35(4)	15	75
					Leicester	6	-	-
Richie Robinson	6.1	14.0	05.07.67	Kendal	Coventry	45(8)	13	65
					Leicester	24	3	15
Wayne Kilford	5.11	13.0	17.04.69	Malvern	Coventry	46(4)	14	70
Mick Curtis	5.11	16.0	27.06.72	Coventry	Coventry	65(4)	9	45
Tigger Dawson	5.10	11.0	29.01.75	Crewe	Coventry	53(4)	10	50
Mateiki Mafi	6.0	15.10	19.09.72	Tonga	Coventry	6(1)	3	15
Martin Wallwork	5.11	12.0	30.03.78	Blackpool	Coventry	3(3)	-	-
					Fylde	6(3)	-	-
Jason Hewlett	5.8	12.10	30.05.74		Coventry	6(3)	1	5

FORWARDS

FORWARDS	Ht.	Wt.	Birthdate	Birthplace	CLUB	League Apps	Tries	Pts
Mark Fountaine	6.6	17.04	07.06.67	Leamington Spa	Coventry			
					Gloucester	-		
Dave Addleton	5.9	14.2	30.03.63	Coventry	Coventry	139(3)	5	25
Kevin Whitley	6.6	17.08	12.08.71	Brunei, Borneo	Coventry	24	2	10
Canada Other clubs: Stourbridge								
Alan Sharp	5.9	17.0	17.10.69	Bristol	Coventry	26	-	-
					Bristol	70	-	-
Mark Crane	6.3	20.0	10.10.71	Bristol	Coventry	18(5)	2	10
Other clubs: Clifton 11/5/25,					Worcester	5(9)	1	5
Michael Mika	6.1	18.00	24.07.68	Lower Hutt (NZ)	Coventry	7	-	-
Simon Kerr					Coventry	9(6)	1	5
Lee Crofts	6.4	17.7	07.09.68	Coventry	Coventry	83(7)	11	55
Ian Patten	6.5	16.0	31.08.70	Bristol	Coventry	45	10	50
					Bristol	35	3	15
Julian Horrobin	6.3	15.4	17.04.69	Lydney	Coventry	97(1)	28	140
					Bristol	10	4	16
Derek Eves	5.10	15.0	07.01.66	Bristol	Coventry	65(3)	17	85
					Bristol	86	17	80
Scott Edwards			11.01.76	Lydney	Coventry	2	-	-
Other clubs: Gloucester								
Carl Houston	6.0	14.06	28.04.75	Palmerston	Coventry	8(1)	1	5
Rob Salisbury	6.3	16.09	14.12.76	Birmingham	Coventry	7(8)	1	5
Jason Soden	5.11	16.7	17.04.71	Coventry	Coventry	6(4)	-	-

COVENTRY

FACT FILE

Founded: 1874
Nickname: Cov

Colours: Navy blue with white hoops
Change colours: Red & white

GROUND

Address: Barker Butts Lane, Coundon Road, Coventry. CV6 1DU.
Tel: 01203 601174 Fax: 01203 601194
Capacity: 9,900 Seated: 900 Standing - Covered: 4,000 Uncovered: 5,000

Directions: From ring road take the A414 to Birmingham, turn right at traffic lights and follow road across railway lights. Coming into Coventry on the A45pick up A414 turn left at Hollyhead P.H. right at traffic lights ground on right. Nearest Railway Station: Coventry

Car Parking: None

Admission: Standing/Seated
Season - £90/110 OAPs £55/65 u16 £25/30 17-20 £45/55
Matchday - To be announced

Club Shop: Open matchdays from 1 - 5.30pm. Manager TBA

Clubhouse: Open matchdays Noon - 11pm (except during match) & training eves, Mon & Wed.. Snacks available. Function facilities with a capacity of 200

Training Nights: Tuesday & Thursday

PROGRAMME

Size: A5 Pages: 32 Price: £1.50
Editor: Paul Ingleston

ADVERTISING RATES
Full page £1000 1/2 page £600 1/4 page £400

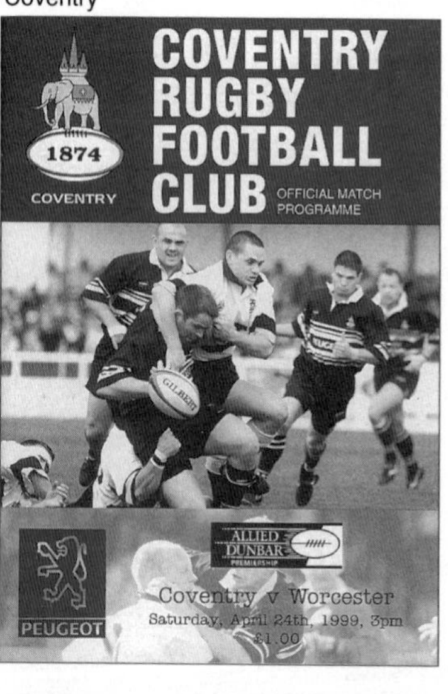

Left:
Steve Gough
Allied Dunbar Premiership 2
Leading Scorer

Right:
Andy Smallwood
Coventry's leading try scorer
for the 3rd successive season

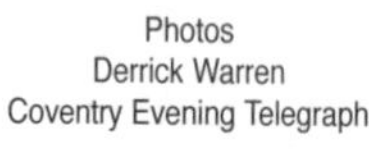

Photos
Derrick Warren
Coventry Evening Telegraph

EXETER F.C.

President	R Manley		c/o Exeter RFC,
Chairman	K Northcott		The County Ground,
Hon Secretary	Alan Griffiths		Church Road,
Rugby Manager	Ian Bremner	0410 901809	Exeter,
Press Officer	Neil Devons	01752 691386	Devon EX2 9BQ.
Treasurer	Steve Williams	01392 824777	Tel: 01392 278759
Match Secretary	R Huxtable	01392 277385(H & Fax)	Fax: 01392 427582

Despite avoiding relegation from the Premiership through restructuring at the end of the previous campaign, Exeter bounced back and ended last season with their best ever league position, finishing fifth.

The start of the season saw the arrival of new coach, Ian Bremner, who developed a very competitive squad through a combination of existing player development and new signings. Welsh International hooker Phil John and No 8 Andy Beattie from Richmond joined to strengthen an already formidable pack led by club captain, Rob Baxter. The reputation of the Devon forwards was further enhanced with huge contributions from existing local players including lock, Del Cross, and flankers Gary Willis and Richard Baxter, the younger of the Baxter brothers.

Brian Easson, a former Scotland `A' international, signed from Boroughmuir and left his particular mark on the season's performance by scoring a total of 296 points, while other notable newcomers included winger Chris Wall (UWIC), and Colin Laity from Neath, whose arrival mid-season considerably strengthened Exeter's back division. Winger Mark Woodman was the club's leading try scorer with thirteen in all competitions.

The season started with successive defeats against the eventual table-toppers, Bristol, and away to Rotherham, but results started to go Exeter's way and there were some notable victories including home and away wins against Orrell, Wakefield and Waterloo.

Exeter progressed through the early rounds of the Tetley's Bitter Cup with wins over Whitchurch and away to Nottingham, eventually losing at the Madjewski Stadium to Richmond in a very competitive match.

The close season will see more new signings as Exeter further strengthen their squad in a bid to progress and maintain their momentum. A new determination and optimism at the club has been accompanied by new marketing initiatives and a new image. The 1999/2000 season will see the Devon All-Blacks known as Exeter Chiefs

Jon Fabian trying to break away during the match against Rotherham. Photo: Nigel Chanter

EXETER

Match No.	Date	H/A	Comp.	Opponents	Result & Score	Att.	15	14	13	12	11
1	05.09	H	AD2	Bristol	L 15-22	1,690	Fabian	Doyle	Thomas	Turner	Wall
2	12.09	A	AD2	Rotherham	L 17-2		Fabian	Doyle	Thomas(g)	Turner/t	Wall
3	19.09	H	AD2	Coventry	W 31-25	620	Fabian	Woodman	Thomas	Turner	Wall
4	26.09	A	AD2	Wakefield	W 27-12	400	Fabian/t	Woodman	Thomas	Turner	Webber/t
5	03.10	H	AD2	Moseley	W 20-8	880	Fabian/t	Woodman/t(s)	Thomas/t	Turner	Webber
6	10.10	A	AD2	Worcester	L 15-40	2,122	Fabian	Woodman	Craig	Turner	Webber
7	17.10	H	AD2	Waterloo	W 41-14	800	Fabian/4t	Doyle	Craig	Turner	Wall/t
8	24.10	H	AD2	Leeds Tykes*	W 13-11	800	Fabian(c)	Doyle	Craig	Turner	Wall
9	31.10	A	AD2	Fylde	D 26-26	400	Fabian	Woodman	Craig	Turner	Wall
10	07.11	H	AD2	Rugby Lions	L 7-23	700	Fabian(x)	Webber	Thomas	Turner	Wall(j)
11	21.11	A	AD2	London Welsh	L 27-62	1,200	Doyle(u)	Woodman/t	Osman	Craig	Webber
12	12.12	H	AD2	Blackheath	W 26-7	700	Rose	Woodman	Webber(t)	Craig	Hargreaves/t
13	19.12	A	AD2	Orrell	W 23-21	1,000	Rose(t)	Woodman	Webber	Craig	Hargreaves
14	02.01	H	AD2	London Welsh	L 16-17	1,100	Rose	Woodman/t	Webber	Turner	Hargreaves(s)
15	23.01	H	AD2	Fylde*	W 42-10	700	Fabian	Woodman/t(b)	Webber	Laity/t	Rose
16	06.02	A	AD2	Leeds	L 7-44	800	Fabian	Woodman	Webber	Laity	Rose
17	13.02	A	AD2	Waterloo	W 13-11	400	Fabian(t)	Woodman(n)	Webber	Laity	Rose
18	27.02	H	AD2	Worcester	W 27-23	1,100	Fabian	Woodman	Webber/t	Laity	Rose
19	13.03	A	AD2	Moseley	W 15-12	609	Fabian(t)(s)	Woodman/t	Webber	Laity	Rose
20	20.03	A	AD2	Rugby Lions	L 9-13	400	Fabian(t)	Woodman	Webber	Laity	Rose
21	27.03	H	AD2	Wakefield	W 37-13	1,000	Rose(s)	Woodman/2t	Webber/t(a)	Laity	Greenaway
22	03.04	A	AD2	Coventry	L 13-20	900	Fabian	Woodman	Webber	Laity	Rose/t
23	10.04	A	AD2	Blackheath	W 41-26	500	Greenaway	Woodman/t	Webber/t	Laity	Rose/t(a)
24	17.04	H	AD2	Rotherham	L 24-35	2,000	Rose(a)	Woodman/t(t)	Webber	Laity	Wall
25	24.04	A	AD2	Bristol	L 17-36	3,204	Rose	Woodman	Webber	Laity(t)	Wall/2t
26	01.05	H	AD2	Orrell	W 42-32	1,200	Fabian	Woodman	Webber	Laity/t	Wall/t
A	14.11	H	TBC	Whitchurch	W 81-11		Doyle/t(u)	Woodman/3t	Osman/3t	Craig/2t	Webber/t
B	09.01	A	TBC	Nottingham	W 24-8	500	Fabian(s)	Woodman/t	Webber/t	Turner	Rose
C	31.01	A	TBC	Richmond	L 10-37	1,259	Fabian	Wall(t)	Webber	Laity	Rose

* after opponents name indicates a penalty try
Brackets after a player's name indicates he was replaced. eg (a) means he was replaced by replacement code "a" and so on.
/ after a player or replacement name is followed by any scores he made - eg /t, /c, /p, /dg or any combination of these

1998-99 HIGHLIGHTS

League debuts: Bryan Easson, Ricky Pellow, Steve Shortland, J Purnell, P Greenaway, Colin Laity, M Rose, A Beattie, J Sussex, Murray Craig, Nick Osman, S Ryan, P Hargreaves.

Ever Presents: One - Bryan Easson.

Players used: 33 plus 4 as a replcement only.

Most Points in a season:

Pts	Player	T	C	P	DG
241	B Easson	2	39	51	-
45	M Woodman	9	-	-	-
30	J Alvis	6	-	-	-
30	J Fabian	6	-	-	-
25	G Willis	5	-	-	-

MATCH FACTS

10	9	1	2	3	4	5	6	7	8	
Easson/5p	Pellow(j)	Gibbins	P John	Reed(k)	Rb Baxter	Shortland(l)	Rh Baxter(m)	Hutchinson	Armstrong	1
Easson/2cp	R John	Sluman(p)	P John	Reed(k/t)	Rb Baxter	Cross	Purnell(o)	Willis	Armstrong	2
Easson/t2c4p	R John(d)	Gibbins(n)	P John	Alvis/t	Rb Baxter	Cross/t	Armstrong(r)	Willis(g)	Barrow	3
Easson/4p	Pellow	Gibbins(n)	P John	Alvis(f)	Rb Baxter	Cross	Armstrong/t	Willis	Barrow	4
Easson/cp	Pellow	Gibbins	P John	Alvis	Rb Baxter	Cross(g)	Armstrong	Willis(h)	Barrow	5
Easson/cp	Pellow	Gibbins	P John/t	Alvis/t(f)	Rb Baxter	Cross	Armstrong	Hutchinson(r)	Barrow	6
Easson/3c	Pellow	Gibbins(w)	P John	Sluman(k)	Rb Baxter/t	Cross/t(l)	Willis	Hutchinson(r)	Armstrong	7
Easson/c2p	Pellow(j)	Gibbins	P John	Alvis	Rb Baxter	Cross(l)	Willis	Hutchinson	Armstrong(v)	8
Easson/2c4p	R John(d)	Gibbins	P John	Alvis/t	Rb Baxter	Cross(l)	Willis	Hutchinson/t	Beattie	9
Easson/c	Pellow	Gibbins(n)	P John	Alvis/t	Rb Baxter	Cross	Barrow	Willis	Armstrong	10
Easson/c	R John/t(d)	Sluman	Ryan	Reed/t(k)	Rb Baxter	Cross(v/t)	Willis/t(r)	Hutchinson	Armstrong	11
Easson/c3p	R John/t	Sluman/t	P John	Reed(k)	Rb Baxter(l)	Cross	Willis	Hutchinson	Armstrong	12
Easson/2c3p	R John	Sluman(l)	P John	Reed(k)	Rb Baxter	Cross	Rh Baxter	Willis/t	Armstrong/t	13
Easson/c3p	R John	Sluman	P John	Reed(k)	Rb Baxter	Cross	Willis(g)	Hutchinson(v)	Armstrong	14
Easson/3c2p(s)	Pellow	Sluman	P John	Alvis(f)	Rb Baxter	Cross	Rh Baxter/3t(h)	Willis	Armstrong(v)	15
Easson/c	R John(d)	Gibbins(y)	P John	Alvis(w)	Cross	Barrow/t(v)	Rh Baxter(h)	Willis	Armstrong	16
Easson/c2p	R John(d)	Sluman(w)	P John	Alvis	Rb Baxter/t(g)	Cross	Armstrong	Willis	Beattie/t	17
Easson/3c2p	R John	Sluman	P John	Alvis	Rb Baxter	Cross	Rh Baxter	Willis	Beattie/t(i/t)	18
Easson/cp	R John	Sluman(e)	P John(z)	Alvis/t(f)	Rb Baxter	Cross(l)	Rh Baxter	Willis	Armstrong(v)	19
Easson/3p	R John	Alvis	P John	Sluman	Rb Baxter	Cross(l)	Rh Baxter	Willis	Armstrong	20
Easson/3c2p	R John(d)	Sluman(e)	P John	Reed(k)	Rb Baxter	Cross(l)	Armstrong(g)	Willis/2t	Beattie	21
Easson/p	R John	Sluman(e)	P John	Reed(k)	Rb Baxter	Barrow	Rh Baxter(i)	Willis/t(h)	Beattie	22
Easson/t3c	R John/t	Sluman/t(e)	Wooltorton	Reed	Rb Baxter	Cross	Rh Baxter	Willis	Armstrong/t	23
Easson/c4p	R John(d)	Sluman	Wooltorton	Reed(e)	Rb Baxter/t	Cross	Rh Baxter(i)	Willis	Beattie	24
Easson/c	R John	Sluman(e)	Ryan	Reed	Rb Baxter	Barrow/t(q)	Rh Baxter(h)	Willis	Beattie	25
Easson/4c3p	R John(d)	Sluman(e)	Ryan	Reed/3t	Rb Baxter	Cross(h)	Armstrong(g)	Willis	Barrow	26
Easson/8c	R John(d)	Sluman(e)	P John(y)	Reed(k)	Rb Baxter/t	Cross	Willis(l)	Hutchinson/t	Armstrong/t	A
Easson/3cp	Pellow(j)	Sluman(e)	P John	Reed(k)	Rb Baxter	Cross	Rh Baxter	Beattie(m)	Armstrong/t(h)	B
Easson/cp	R John(d)	Sluman(e)	P John/t(y)	Reed(k)	Rb Baxter	Cross	Rh Baxter(v)	Willis	Armstrong(h)	C

REPLACEMENTS:					
	a- J Fabian	b- S Doyle	c - J Thomas	d - R Pellow	e - R Gibbins
f - W Reed	g - R ich Baxter	h - R Hutchinson	i - B Armstrong	j - R John	k - J Alvis
l - C Barrow	m - G Willis	n - P Sluman	o - L Inckledon	p - P Westcott	q - B Goss
r - N Southern	s - D Oxland	t - P Greenaway	u - M Rose	v - A Beattie	w - J Sussex
x - N Osman	y - S Ryan	z - M Wooltorton			

Bryan Easson in his first season at Exeter played in all 26 matches scoring 241 points, the second highest in a season for the club.
Easson scored in every match and needs to score in the first 7 of next season to pass the club record of scoring in 32 consecutive matches, currently held by Andy Green.
Easson broke Green's record of penalties in a season with 51, one more than Green kicked in the 1996-97 season.

Full back John Fabian equalled the club record for tries in a match. Fabian equlled Simon Dovall's record of 4 set in the 1996-97. Fabian scored his 4 in the home win over Waterloo.

Winger Mark Woodman topped the try scoring chart for the second time in his career at Exeter and in the process moved into second place on the clubs all time league try scoring list with 29 which leaves him 12 adrift of Andy Maunder.

EXETER

LEAGUE STATISTICS
compiled by Stephen McCormack

SEASON	Division	P	W	D	L	F	A	Pts Diff	Lge Pts	Lge Pos	Most Points	Most Tries
89-90	3	11	5	1	5	149	153	-4	11	6	99 Andy Green	2 Andy Green & Anndy Maunder
90-91	3	12	7	2	3	160	139	21	16	4	92 Andy Green	4 Jeff Tutchings
91-92	3	12	8	2	2	203	138	65	18	4	77 Andy Green	4 John Davies & Mark Chatterton
92-93	3	11	8	1	2	247	169	78	17	3	122 Andy Green	5 Andy Maunder
93-94	3	18	9	1	8	308	271	39	19	6	125 Andy reen	5 Andy Maunder
94-95	3	18	3	1	14	153	319	-166	7	10r	35 Ian Stewart	3 Mark Chatterton
95-96	4	18	14	0	4	448	230	218	28	1p	191 Andy Green	8 Andy Maunder
96-97	3	30	25	0	5	923	443	480	50	1p	300 Andy Green	15 Mark Woodman
97-98	P2	22	6	0	16	334	553	-219	12	11	174 John Fabian	6 James Alvis
98-99	P2	26	14	1	11	591	598	-7	29	5	241 Bryan Easson	9 Mark Woodman

BIGGEST MARGINS

Home Win	61pts - 71-10 v Clifton 9.11.96
Away Win	57pts - 60-3 v Clifton 22.3.97
Home Defeat	25pts - 8-33 v Rotherham 7.3.98
Away Defeat	35pts - 13-48 v Fylde 3.10.87

MOST CONSECUTIVE

Appearances	88 Andy Maunder 12.9.87- 17.9.94
Matches scoring Tries	3 Andy Maunder, John Davis, Ian Dixon & Bob Armstrong.
Matches scoring points	32 Andy Green
Victories	14
Defeats	8

MOST POINTS

Scored at Home	71 v Clifton 9.11.96
Scored Away	60 v Clifton 22.3.97
Conceded at Home	33 v Leeds 13.3.93 v Rotherham 7.3.98
Conceded Away	50 v Rotherham 25.4.98

MOST TRIES

Scored in a match	10 v Clifton 9.11.96 (H)
Conceded in a match	8 v Fylde 3.10.87 (A)

MOST APPEARANCES

by a forward	138 Richard Gibbins
by a back	142 (4) Andy Maunder

	MOST IN A SEASON	MOST IN A CAREER	MOST IN A MATCH	
Points	300 Andy Green 96-97	1085 Andy Green 87-97	24 Andy Green	v Wharfedale 7.9.96 (A)
Tries	15 Mark Woodman 96-97	41 Andy Maunder 87-98	4 Simon Dovell John Fabian	v Havant 21.12.96 (H) v Waterloo 17.10.98 (H)
Conversions	58 Andy Green 96-97	140 Andy Green 87-97	6 Andy Green	v Aspatria 23.3.96 (H) v Lydney 1.3.97 (H) v Clifton 22.3.97 (A)
Penalties	51 Bryan Easson 98-99	213 Andy Green 87-97	7 Andy Green	v Fylde 5.4.97 (H)
Drop Goals	6 Andy Green 95-96	22 Andy Green 87-97	2 Andy Green	v Sheffield 23.4.88 (H)

EXETER PLAYING SQUAD

BACKS

	Ht.	Wt.	Birthdate	Birthplace	CLUB	League Apps	Tries	Pts
John Fabian England Students, Universities.	6.3	14.7	18.09.76	Plymouth	Exeter	41(8)	9	241
Shaun Doyle Devon. South West u21.	6.0	14.10	21.08.74	Exeter	Exeter	76(4)	18	90
Andy Tuner South West u21. Devon u21.	6.1	14.0	27.11.70	Saddleworth	Exeter	103(5)	12	60
Jason Thomas	5.9	11.7	02.03.75	Aberdare	Exeter	71(3)	12	63
Mark Woodman Devon.	6.0	15.0	18.09.70	Exeter	Exeter	80	29	145
Chris Wall Devon, South West.					Exeter	10	4	20
Richard John South West, colts, u21.	5.10	13.0	30.05.74	Exeter	Exeter	44(4)	6	30
Bryan Easson	5.8	13.00	08.10.73		Exeter	26	2	241
Colin Laity	5.111	15.00	19.06.65		Exeter	12	2	10
Mark Rose					Exeter	14(1)	2	10
Ricky Pellow	5.8	11.07	19.02.78		Exeter	8(8)	-	-
Murrya Craig					Exeter	7	-	-

FORWARDS

	Ht.	Wt.	Birthdate	Birthplace	CLUB	League Apps	Tries	Pts
Richard Gibbins			06.08.67		Exeter	140(7)	5	25
Martin Wooltorton	5.10	14.0	03.03.67	Leeds	Exeter	40(4)	2	10
James Alvis	5.11	18.10	19.12.70		Exeter	32(10)	12	60
Paul John	5.9	14.00	05.02.62		Exeter	21	3	15
Rob Baxter England colts, Devon.	6.5	16.7	10.03.71	Tavistock	Exeter	131	9	45
Del Cross			05.08.71	Watford	Exeter	35	2	10
Nick Southern	5.11	14.0	30.09.67	Plymouth	Exeter	53(14)	6	30
Robert Armstrong Other club: Plymouth 23/4/19	6.4	18.0	17.08.67	Liverpool	Exeter Bristol	57(3) 38(2)	14 -	70 -
Roger Hutchinson	6.0	14.7	21.11.69	Singapore	Exeter	82(11)	10	50
Andy Beattie					Exeter	7(7)	2	10
Simon Ryan .					Exeter	3(1)	-	-
Wayne Reed	5.10	17.4	27.10.71	Tiverton	Exeter	35(8)	5	25
Phil Sluman Devon	6.0	17.0	15.03.67	Exeter	Exeter	85(10)	4	19
Gary Willis			02.10.65	Billingham	Exeter	24(1)	5	25

EXETER F.C.

FACT FILE

Founded: 1872
Nickname: The Chiefs

Colours: All black with Cambridge blue trim
Change colours: Cambridge blue/black

GROUND

Address: County Ground, Church Road, St. Thomas, Exeter. EX2 9BQ.
Tel: 01392 278759 Fax: 01392 427582
Capacity: 5,200 Seated: 700 Standing: Covered 500, Uncovered 4,000

Directions: M5 junction 31 follow A377 via A30 to city centre. Continueuntil you reach the turning for B3212 for Moreton Hampstead, turn into CowickStreet, pass under railway bridge. Turn left into Cecil Road at traffic lights, then right into Church Road and into ground
Nearest Railway Station: Exeter(St. Davids), then taxi to ground (appr 2miles)

Car Parking: None at ground.

Admission: (Children under 16 Free - accompanied by adult)
Season tickets **Standing** Adults £70, OAPs & Juveniles £50 **Seated** Adults £100, OAPs £75
Matchdays **Standing** Adults £8, Concessions £6 **Seated** £12

Club Shop: Open matchdays & training nights
Manager Mike May 01392 278759.

Clubhouse: Open matchdays 12-11. Training nights 6-11 Snacks and bar meals available
Functions: Capacity 160/60, contact Mrs K Chalmers 01392 411118

Training Nights: Tuesday and Thursday.

PROGRAMME Size: B6 Pages: 32 + cover + centrefold Editor: Neil Devons 01752 691386

ADVERTISING RATES
Prices on apllication. Contact - Mike Dalton, Commercial Manager 01392 278759

Paul Hargreaves on the move against Fylde. Photo: Nigel Chanter

HENLEY R.F.C.

President	Doug Ash	c/o Henley RFC, Dry Leas, Marlow Road, Henley-on-Thames Tel: 01491 574499 Fax: 01491 412335
Chairman	Graham Horner	c/o Henley RFC, as above
Director of Rugby	Tony MacArthur	c/o Henley RFC as above. 0118947 2392 (H).
Press Officer	Noel Armstead	8 Chiswick Lodge, Liston Rd, Marlow, Bucks SL7 1AG 01628 474398 (B & Fax).
Director of Coaching	Nigel Dudding	01491 576502 Mobile 0410 110654
Fixture & Match Secretary	Alan Richardson	01491 574664 (H) 01628 487755 (B)

Henley Hawks gained a promotion to Jewson One as runners-up in Jewson Two (South) in season 1997/98 courtesy of the re-organisation of the Allied Dunbar Leagues. They approached the challenge of Jewson One with confidence and Director of Rugby, Tony Macarthur, declared at the start of the season. "The Hawks team has been built to gain promotion. I do not believe in entering a competition unless the aim is to win it."

Despite some scorn from various quarters this confidence was not misplaced as the league was won by a margin of four points. Just three games were lost, two away at Manchester and Otley, and one the first game of the season, at home to Harrogate. Success was built on a first class defence, conceding just 32 tries in 26 league games and 299 points in total, the best record of any team from Jewson upwards.

The Hawks also had a record run in the Tetley's Bitter Cup reaching the fifth round for the first time by beating Premier One side Bedford at Goldington Road 29-22, before losing to Gloucester at Kingsholm. Here the Hawks had magnificent support with 1,000 supporters actually subduing the `shed' into silence at times.

The increased (and increasing) support was a feature of Henley's record season but above all the Hawks team spirit allowed them to win through when they were not able to produce their best form. Throughout they were true to their belief of playing entertaining rugby.

Three players were honoured by selection for the Barbarians during the course of the season, Trevor Walsh, Mark Venner and Pete Davies. Trevor Walsh (inside centre) was the Henley Players Player of the Year whilst Jerry Sampson (lock) was their Clubman of the Year - he played in all matches.

Nigel Dudding was Jewson One Coach of the Year having had the Jewson Two (South) award the previous season. He was assisted by Mike Poulson as backs coach from October onwards. Both have previously been captains of the Henley 1st XV.

Henley Hawks Squad 98-99 Photo: Adrian Lewington

HENLEY HAWKS

Match No.	Date	H/A	Comp.	Opponents	Result & Score	Att.	15	14	13	12	11
1	05.09	H	JN1	Harrogate	L 5-20	350	Stebbings	Davies	R Osman/t	Maudsley	Sharp(n)
2	12.09	A	JN1	Wharfedale	W 8-6	550	Stebbings/p	Davies	R Osman	Maudsley	Townsend
3	19.09	H	JN1	Manchester	W 39-20	450	Stebbings/4cp	Davies	R Osman/t	Walsh/t(t)	Maudsley(e)
4	26.09	A	JN1	Nottingham	W 35-6	400	Stebbings/cp(e)	Davies(v)	R Osman/t	Walsh	Maudsley/c
5	03.10	H	JN1	Camberley	W 22-7	600	Stebbings/t3p	Davies	R Osman	Walsh	Maudsley(e)
6	10.10	H	JN1	Newbury	W 44-10	600	Stebbings(n)	Maudsley/t3cp	R Osman/t	Walsh	Sharp/2t(b/t)
7	24.10	A	JN1	Morley*	W 13-10	600	Stebbings/c2p	Maudsley	R Osman	Walsh	Sharp
8	31.10	H	JN1	Lydney	W 23-11	350	Stebbings/2c3p	Davies	R Osman	Walsh	Sharp/t
9	07.11	A	JN1	Otley	L 8-19	400	Stebbings/p	Davies	R Osman	Walsh	Sharp(d/t)
10	21.11	H	JN1	Reading	W 25-9	550	Parton	Maudsley/2p	Roke/2c(e)	R Osman/t	Davies/2t
11	28.11	A	JN1	Rosslyn Park	W 10-7	250	Parton	Maudsley	R Osman	Walsh	Davies/t
12	05.12	H	JN1	Birmingham S*	W 26-13	300	Parton(a)	Maudsley/t3c	R Osman	Walsh	Sharp/2t
13	12.12	A	JN1	Liverpool StH*	W 67-12	150	Parton(a)	Maudsley/t7c	R Osman	Walsh(b/2t)	Sharp/3t
14	19.12	H	JN1	Rosslyn Park	W 18-15	500	Parton	Davies/t	R Osman/t	Maudsley/c2p	Sharp
15	28.12	A	JN1	Reading	W 36-6	850	Parton	Stebbings/t(z)	Maudsley/2c2p	R Osman	Davies
16	02.01	H	JN1	Otley	W 5-0	650	Parton	Davies	Maudsley(z)	ROsman	Sharp
17	23.01	H	JN1	Morley	W 24-13	450	Parton	Roke/t3cp	R Osman	Walsh	Sharp
18	06.02	A	JN1	Camberley	W 31-19	400	Parton(a)	Roke/2t2c4p	R Osman/t	Walsh	Sharp
19	13.02	H	JN1	Nottingham	W 43-24	450	Parton(a)	Roke/t4c	R Osman/t(d/t)	Walsh	Sharp(b)
20	20.02	A	JN1	Newbury	D 26-26	500	Parton	Davies/2t	Roke/tc3p	Walsh	Maudsley
21	27.02	A	JN1	Manchester	L 7-13	950	Parton	Davies	Roke/c	Walsh	Sharp/t
22	13.03	H	JN1	Wharfedale	W 30-0	650	Parton(a)	Davies/t	Roke/2p(d/2c)	R Osman	Sharp
23	20.03	A	JN1	Lydney	W 7-0	600	Parton	Davies	R Osman	Walsh	Sharp
24	27.03	A	JN1	Harrogate	W 31-17	400	Parton	Roke/3c	R Osman	Walsh/t	Davies/3t(q)
25	03.04	H	JN1	Liverpool St H	W 39-8	450	Stebbings(i)	Davies/t	Roke/t2c	Walsh	Sharp/t(p)
26	17.04	A	JN1	Birmingham S	W 22-8	300	Parton/t(d)	Roke/c5p	R Osman	Walsh	Davies
A	17.10	H	TBC	Havant	W 100-19		Stebbings/t3c(n)	Maudsley/t6c	R Osman/2t	Walsh/t	Sharp/t
B	14.11	A	TBC	Rosslyn Park	W 16-12	550	Parton	Davies/t	R Osman	Walsh	Maudsley/c2p
C	18.01	A	TBC	Bedford	W 29-22		Stebbings	Sharp/2t	R Osman	Walsh	Roke/3cp
D	30.01	A	TBC	Gloucester	L 9-31		Parton(q)	Maudsley/3p	R Osman(z)	Walsh	Sharp

* after opponents name indicates a penalty try
Brackets after a player's name indicates he was replaced. eg (a) means he was replaced by replacement code "a" and so on.
/ after a player or replacement name is followed by any scores he made - eg /t, /c, /p, /dg or any combination of these

1998-99 HIGHLIGHTS

League debuts:
Jon Stebbings, Peter Davies, Russell Osman, Ben Ayers, Janik Hendriksz, Steve Barnes, Dean Holder, Alastair Ramus, Duncan Roke, Darren Cassidy.

Ever Presents: Jerry Sampson

Players used: 29 plus 7 as a replacement only.

Most Points in a season:

Pts	Player	T	C	P	DG
115	D Roke	6	20	15	-
84	M Maudsley	5	19	7	-
70	P Davies	14	-	-	-
62	J Stebbings	2	8	12	-
50	G Sharp	10	-	-	-

Duncan Roke, a mid season signing from Leicester, topped the try scoring with a blast of scoring in the second half of the season.

MATCH FACTS

10	9	1	2	3	4	5	6	7	8	
P Osman	Ayers	G Walker(o)	Phillips	New	Sampson	Hendriksz	Barnes	Venner	Mortimer(p)	1
P Osman	Smye(r)	G Walker	Phillips	Penney	Sampson	Hendriksz	R Walker/t	Venner	Barnes(m)	2
P Osman/dg	Ayers/t(r)	G Walker	Phillips/t	Penney(j)	Sampson	Hendriksz(p)	R Walker	Venner	Mortimer(u)	3
P Osman/p	Ayers(r)	G Walker(j)	Phillips	Penney	Sampson/t	Hendriksz	R Walker/t	Venner/2t	Mortimer(l)	4
P Osman/dg	Ayers/t	G Walker(o)	Phillips	Penney	Sampson	Hendriksz	R Walker	Venner	Mortimer	5
P Osman	Ayers/2t(w)	G Walker	Phillips(x)	Penney(o)	Sampson	Hendriksz	R Walker	Venner	Mortimer(p)	6
Davies	Ayers	Heginbotham	Phillips	Penney	Sampson	Hendriksz	Barnes	Venner(s)	Mortimer(u)	7
P Osman	Ayers	Heginbotham(h)	Phillips	Penney	Sampson	Hendriksz(y)	Barnes	Venner/t	Mortimer(p)	8
P Osman	Davidson(g)	Heginbotham(h)	Phillips	Penney	Sampson(y)	Hendriksz	Barnes(p)	Venner	Mortimer	9
P Osman(q)	Ayers(w)	Fuller	Phillips	Penney(o)	Sampson	Hendriksz(p)	Barnes	R Walker	Mortimer	10
P Osman	Ayers	Fuller	Phillips/t	Penney	Sampson	Hendriksz(p)	Barnes	Venner	Mortimer	11
P Osman	Ayers	Fuller(h)	Phillips	Penney	Sampson	Berryman	Barnes(y)	Venner(s)	Mortimer	12
P Osman/tdg	Ayers(q)	Fuller/t	Phillips(A)	Penney(B)	Sampson	Berryman	R Walker	Venner/t(u)	Barnes	13
P Osman	Ayers	Fuller(C)	Phillips	Penney(j)	Sampson	Hendriksz	Berryman	Venner	Barnes	14
P Osman/2dg	Ayers(E)	Heginbotham	Phillips(A)	Lehner	Sampson(y)	Hendriksz/t	Berryman(m/t)	Venner/t	Barnes	15
P Osman	Ayers	Lehner	Phillips	Penney(o)	Sampson/t	Hendriksz	Barnes	Venner	Mortimer	16
P Osman/t(d)	Ayers(w)	Fuller(o)	Phillips	Lehner	Sampson/t	Hendriksz	Barnes(y)	Venner	Mortimer	17
P Osman(d)	Ayers	Fuller	Phillips	Lehner(o)	Sampson	Hendriksz	Barnes(s)	Venner	Mortimer	18
P Osman/t	Ayers/2t	Fuller(h)	Phillips(A)	Penney	Sampson	Hendriksz	R Walker	Venner/t	Mortimer	19
P Osman	Ayers	Fuller	Phillips	Lehner	Sampson	Hendriksz	Barnes(s)	Venner	Mortimer	20
P Osman	Ayers	Fuller	Phillips	Penney	Sampson	Hendriksz	Barnes	Venner	Mortimer(s)	21
P Osman/t	Ayers(D)	Fuller(h)	Phillips(A)	Penney	Sampson	Hendriksz/t	Banres	Venner/t	Mortimer(s)	22
Roke/c	Ayers(D)	Fuller	Phillips	Penney	Sampson	Hendriksz/t	Barnes	Venner	Mortimer(s)	23
P Osman(d)	Ayers(W)	Fuller	Phillips(o)	Penney	Sampson(y)	Hendriksz/t	Barnes(s)	Venner	Mortimer	24
P Osman(c/t)	Ayers/t(D)	Fuller	Cassidy	Heginbotham	Sampson/t	Ramus	Barnes(s)	Venner/t	Mortimer	25
P Osman(e)	Ayers(W)	Fuller	Phillips	Penney(o)	Sampson	Hendriksz(p)	Barnes	Venner	Mortimer(s)	26
P Davies/2t(p/tc)	Davidson(g)	G Walker	Bradbury	Penney(o)	Sampson	Hendriksz/2t(l)	R Walker	Venner/2t	Mortimer/t	A
P Osman	Ayers	G Walker	Phillips	Penney	Sampson	Ramus	R Walker	Berryman	Barnes	B
P Osman/t	Ayers	Fuller	Cassidy(i)	Lehner	Sampson	Berryman/t(k)	Barnes	Venner	Mortimore	C
P Osman	Ayers(D)	Fuller	Phillips	Lehner(o)	Sampson(y)	Hendriksz	Barnes	Venner(s)	Mortimore	D

REPLACEMENTS: a- J Stebbings, b- P Davies, c - R Osman, d - M Maudsley, e - G Sharp, f - P Osman, g - B Ayers, h - G Walker, i - W Phillipd, j - P New, k - J Hendriksz, l - S Barnes, m - A Mortimer, n - A Parton, o - R Heginbotham, p - S Berryman, q - L Smye, r - B Ryan, s - R Walker, t - M Swadling, u - D Holder, v - A Noyce, w - B Davidson, x - N Bradbury, y - A Ramus, z - D Roke, A - D Cassidy, B - J Grindrod, C - R Lehner, D - B Hobbs

As well as kicking he also chipped in with six tries playing both centre and wing.

It was their wingers Peter Davies and Gavin Sharp who led the way in the try scoring stakes with 14 and 10 each. Davies's 14 was one short of the Henley league record set last season by openside flanker Mark Venner.

Utility back Matt Muadsley extended his career record for tries to 34. Mark Venner took his total after just two seasons to 24 with another nine this time round.

Outside half Phil Osman set a number of new records in the drop goal department. He set a new record for a season with 5, extended his all time record to 8 and became the first Henley player to score two drop goals in a match. He dropped two in the away win at Reading in December.

Willie Phillips, switching to hooker from flanker for the season, extended his career appearance record to 97 with 25 starts during the season. The record for a back was extended by Matt Maudsley to 75 with 16 starts during the season.

HENLEY

LEAGUE STATISTICS
compiled by Stephen McCormack

SEASON	Division	P	W	D	L	F	A	Pts Diff	Lge Pts	Lge Pos		Most Points		Most Tries
89-90	SW2	10	4	0	6	132	189	-57	8	8		C Woodward		M Duffelen
90-91	SW2	10	3	1	6	124	156	-32	7	8		C Woodward		M Duffelen
91-92	SW2	10	8	1	1	283	103	180	17	1p		C Woodward		M Duffelen
92-93	SW1	12	9	0	3	312	143	169	18	2		C Woodward		
93-94	SW1	12	12	0	0	328	125	203	24	1p		C Woodward		
94-95	D5S	12	5	0	7	190	299	-109	10	9		C Woodward		R Heginbotham
												Most Points		**Most Tries**
95-96	D5S	12	8	0	4	349	192	157	16	3	176	Richard Perkins	10	Richard Perkins
96-97	D4S	26	20	2	4	768	456	312	42	2	140	Matt Maudsley	12	Gavin Sharp Matt Maudsley
97-98	N2S	26	22	0	4	772	384	388	44	2p	204	Nick Buoy	15	Mark Venner
98-99	JN1	26	22	1	3	644	299	345	45	1P	118	Duncan Roke	14	Peter Davies

BIGGEST MARGINS

Home Win 85pts - 93-8 v Met. Police 28.3.98
Away Win 35pts - 47-12 v Camberley 30.3.96
Home Defeat 28pts - 6-34 v Lon. Welsh 24.9.94
Away Defeat 46pts - 3-49 v High Wycombe 25.4.94

MOST CONSECUTIVE

Appearances -
Matches scoring Tries
Matches scoring points
Victories 11
Defeats 3

MOST POINTS

Scored at Home 93 v Met. Police 28.3.98
Scored Away 47 v Camberley 30.3.96
Conceded at Home 34 v Lon. Welsh 24.9.94
Conceded Away 49 v High Wycombe 25.4.94

MOST TRIES

Scored in a match 15 v Met. Police 28.3.98 (H)
Conceded in a match 7 v High Wycombe 25.4.94

MOST APPEARANCES

by a forward 97(1) Willie Phillips
by a back 59(1) Matt Maudsley

	MOST IN A SEASON	MOST IN A CAREER	MOST IN A MATCH
Points	204 Nick Buoy 97-98	389 Matt Maudsley 95-99	34 Chris Spencer v Charlton Park 12.4.97(H)
Tries	15 Mark Venner 97-98	34 Matt Maudsley 94-99	4 Chris Spencer v Charlton Park 12.4.97 (H)
Conversions	28 Matt Maudsley 96-97	57 Matt Maudsley 96-99	8 Phil Osman v Met. Police 28.03.98 (H)
Penalties	38 Nick Buoy 97-98	38 Nick Buoy 97-98	7 Nick Buoy v Met. Police 25.10.97 (A)
Drop Goals	5 Phil Osman 98-99	8 Phil Osman 97-99	2 Phil Osman v Reading (A)

BACKS

	Ht.	Wt.	Birthdate	Birthplace	CLUB	League Apps	Tries	Pts
Russell Osman	6.2	13.8	17.6.72	Southampton	Henley Newbury	23(1) 29(3)	9 11	45 55
Bill Davidson Oxfordshire	5.11	12.8	07.07.67	Writtle	Henley	69(12)	10	50
Ben Hobbs Somerset U21	5.5	15.0	11.04.75	Bath	Henley	3(9)	3	15
Matt Maudsley England Students, Oxfordshire	6.0	14.0	16.10.70	Morecambe	Henley	75(8)	37	389
Duncan Roke	6.2	13.0	5.07.74	Malta	Henley	12(1)	6	118
Phil Osman Hampshire	6.0	13.7	18.12.68	Exeter	Henley	38(2)	8	122
Gavin Sharp Combined Services, RAF, Oxfordshire	5.9	13.7	04.01.75	Scarboriugh	Henley Bristol	51(8) 20	33 25	165 5
Peter Davies Welsh u21, Univ, Schools.	5.8	12.0	1.12.75	Newport	Henley	20(3)	14	70
Ben Ayers Oxfordshire			7.05.74	Crickhowell	Henley	24(1)	7	35
Liam Smye South West U21	5.10	11.8	18.01.78	Oxford	Henley	20(10)	2	10
Trevor Walsh Queensland Univ, Australian Univ	6.0	14.0	18.01.72	Tombsvlle(Aust)	Henley	41	8	40
John Stebbings England students, Irish exiles.	5.11	13.6	28.10.76	Wokingham	Henley	11(7)	2	59
Andy Parton Previous clubs: Coventry, Harlequins, Rosslyn Park.	6.2	14.9	31.01.68	Coventry	Henley	46(4)	10	67

FORWARDS

	Ht.	Wt.	Birthdate	Birthplace	CLUB	League Apps	Pts	
Steve Berryman Combined Services, Army, Cornwall	6.3	16.0	05.06.68	Penzance	Henley	11(9)	1	5
Nick Bradbury Oxfordshire	5.9	14.00	28.12.68	Horsham	Henley	75(1)	3	15
Darren Cassidy	5.9	14.04	13.07.67	Gt Yarmouth	Henley	1(4)	-	-
Ali Mortimer	6.2	16.00	12.12.73	Oakhampton	Henley	48(2)	1	5
Dave Penney	6.0	17.10	04.06.70	Newfoundland	Henley	38(1)	1	5
Willie Phillips NZ Moaris, N Auckland	5.10	15.11	16.04.58	New Zealand	Henley	97(1)	20	100
Rowan Fuller Oxfordshire	5.10	16.07	1.11.72		Henley	15	1	5
Jerry Sampson Kent, Somerset, Oxon.	6.0	16.08	04.06.68	Weston S Mare	Henley	71(2)	6	30
Mark Venner Somerset	6.2	15.00	14.04.69	Weston S Mare	Henley	50	24	120
Giles Walker	6.0	16.12	07.07.71	Aylesbury	Henley	12(5)	3	15
Rob Walker	6.2	15.08	11.05.73	Aylesbury	Henley	26(16)	6	30
Janik Hendriksz Western Province B	6.4	18.02	29.01.70	Cape Town	Henley Clifton	23 21	4 9	20 45
Steve Barnes			29.10.71	Henley on T	Henley Northampton	21(1)	-	-

HENLEY

FACT FILE

Founded: 1930

Nickname: Hawks

Colours: Gold with navy & dark green hoops

Change colours: White

Training Nights: Tuesday/Thursday; Women Wednesday

HENLEY HAWKS

GROUND

Address: Dry Leas, Marlow Rd, Henley-on-Thames, Oxon RG9 2JA
Tel. Nos. 01491 574499 Fax: 01491 412335 Web: www.henleyrugbyclub.org.uk
Capacity: 3,000 Seated: Covered 120 Standing: Uncovered 2,880

Directions: Centre of Henley follow signs to Marlow, ground on left 100 yards past roundabout
Nearest Railway Station: Henley, follow signs from Town Centre to Marlow - ground 100yds left at start of Marlow Rd. **Car Parking:** 600 at ground

Admission:
(Children/OAPs half price)

Season: Standing Adult Members £40, Non-Members £80
Matchday: Standing Adults £7, Seated Adults £10

Clubhouse: Tues, Wed, Thurs eves. Matchdays incl Sundays. Snacks & bar meals available.
Functions: Capacity 200

Club Shop: Yes

PROGRAMME Size: A5 Pages: 32 Price: Included with admission Editor: Mick Dudding, 01491 572948
ADVERTISING RATES (Mono) Inside covers £1000 Full page £450 Half page £250

Trevor Walsh on the charge against Gloucester in the 5th Round of the Tetley's bitter Cup

LEEDS TYKES R.U.F.C.

Chief Executive	Gary Hetherington	c/o Leeds RUFC, The Pavilion, Headingley Stadium, St Michaels Lane, Leeds LS6 3BR 0113 278 6181 (B), 0113 275 4284 (Fax)
Director of Rugby	Phil Davies	c/o Leeds RUFC, Chandos Park, Chandos Avenue,Leeds LS8 1RX 0410 342050 (Mobile), 0113 266 1406 (B), 0113 266 1406 (Fax)
Club Secretary	Mike Bidgood	c/o Leeds RUFC, The Pavilion as above 01423 734953 (H) 0113 278 6181 X 242 (B), 0113 275 4284 (Fax) 0410 342054 (MOBILE) E-Mail: mike.bidgood @ leedsrugby.co.uk
Managing Director	David Howes	c/o Leeds RUFC, The Pavilion as above
Fixtures Secretary	Les Jackson	4 Gledhow Wood Avenue, Leeds. LS8 1NY 0113 266 5544 (H,B & Fax)

For the first time since the Tykes started playing at the Stadium the season ended without the team being involved in a promotion race right up to the last game.

Realistically two defeats in February ended the challenge and it is a credit to the squad that they competed strongly, only losing once in the final seven games. The victory against Worcester was particularly memorable and three 50+ scores in the last four games showed some good finishing all round.

Sateki Tuipulotu leaves after three successful seasons since joining from Leeds Rhinos and he has only missed five league games in three season. He has broken most of the scoring records in that period and played for Tonga in he World Cup qualifiers in April. The club's first full international was club captain Stuart Reid who played in Scotland's historic victory in Paris to secure the 5-Nations Championship.

Following the achievement of the Academy in 97/98 that won through to the inaugural National Colts Cup final, Tom Palmer, Jon Feeley and Tom Rhodes successfully graduated to the Tykes 1st XV this season. The class of 98/99 came through the initial stages of the year unbeaten and went on to win the Yorkshire Cup Final for the first time. They also successfully negotiated several difficult hurdles in the National trophy including a heroic defensive effort against Gloucester in the semis. This gave the side the opportunity to play London Irish in the final at Northampton. They took the lead but had a bad ten minutes, conceded four tries in that period, and left themselves too much to do in the second period. They could lay claim to be the best English side in the country and may yet provide players for this season's Tykes squad.

LEEDS TYKES

Match No.	Date	H/A	Comp.	Opponents	Result & Score	Att.	15	14	13	12	11
1	06.09	H	AD2	London Welsh	L 18-20	1,152	Tuipulotu/c2p	Middleton	Emmerson	Rhodes	Kirkby
2	12.09	A	AD2	Moseley	L 22-27	503	Tuipulotu/2cp	Middleton	Emmerson	Rhodes	Kirkby/t
3	20.09	H	AD2	Blackheath	W 60-6	617	James	Feeley/2t	Emmerson	Tuipulotu/t6cp	Kirkby/2t)q)
4	27.09	A	AD2	Worcester*	L 19-24	4,000	James	Feeley	Emmerson	Tuipulotu/c4p	Kirkby
5	03.10	A	AD2	Orrell	W 13-11	700	James	Feeley	Emmerson	Tuipulotu/cp	Kirkby
6	10.10	A	AD2	Waterloo	L 12-13	500	James	Feeley	Tuipulotu/4p	Edwards	Kirkby
7	17.10	H	AD2	Bristol	L 13-16	700	Tuipulotu/tc2p	Feeley	Edwards	Emmerson	Kirkby
8	24.10	A	AD2	Exeter	L 11-13	800	Tuipulotu/2p	Middleton	O'Hare	Edwards	Emmerson
9	10.11	H	AD2	Rotherham	W 15-10	2,682	Tuipulotu/5p	Sailor	O'Hare	Edwards	Middleton
10	07.11	A	AD2	Fylde	W 26-6	650	Tuipulotu/c3p	Sailor/t	O'Hare/t	Edwards	Middleton
11	22.11	H	AD2	Coventry	W 36-12	760	Tuipulotu/2c4p	Sailor/t	O'Hare	Edwards/t	Emmerson
12	13.12	A	AD2	Rugby Lions	W 18-9	600	Tuipulotu/c2p	Sailor/t	O'Hare	Edwards(d)	Emmerson
13	20.12	H	AD2	Wakefield	W 38-0	1,211	Tuipulotu/t4c	Sailor/t	O'Hare	Edwards	Emmerson(a/t)
14	03.01	A	AD2	Coventry	W 33-27	1,000	Tuipulotu/c7p	Middleton	O'Hare	Edwards	Emmerson(x/t)
15	17.01	H	AD2	Fylde	W 48-0	921	James/t4c	Sailor/3t	Hughes(u/t)	Edwards(d)	Emmerson(w/t)
16	23.01	A	AD2	Rotherham*	L 10-25		James/cp	Middleton(w)	O'Hare	Edwards	Emmerson
17	07.02	H	AD2	Exeter	W 44-7	800	Tuipulotu/2cp(o)	Emmerson/t	O'Hare	Edwards/t	Scales/4t
18	13.02	A	AD2	Bristol	L 5-20		James	Emmerson	O'Hare	Edwards	Scales
19	28.02	H	AD2	Waterloo	L 9-10	400	Tuipulotu3p	Scales(a)	O'Hare	Edwards	Emmerson
20	14.03	H	AD2	Orrell	W 20-7	620	Cawthorn	Middleton/2t	O'Hare	Edwards	Emmerson
21	28.03	H	AD2	Worcester	W 24-16	530	Cawthorn	Middleton/t	O'Hare	Edwards(o)	Emmerson
22	03.04	A	AD2	Blackheath	W 37-22	500	James/t	Middleton/t	O'Hare/t	Cawthorn	Emmerson(w/t)
23	16.04	H	AD2	Moseley	W 50-6	287	James(v)	Middleton/t(b)	O'Hare	Cawthorn	Scales/t
24	25.04	A	AD2	London Welsh	L 17-24	1,400	Cawthorn	Middleton/t	O'Hare	Edwards(o)	Scales
25	02.05	A	AD2	Wakefield	W 51-13	450	James/3c	Middleton/t(p/t)	O'Hare	Emmerson	Scales/2t
26	09.05	H	AD2	Rugby	W 64-21	550	Tuipulotu/5c	Middleton/2t(p/t)	O'Hare/t	Emmerson(o/2c)	Scales/t
A	15.11	A	TBC	Rugby Lions	W 68-7		Tuipulotu/2t5cp(o)	Sailor/5t	O'Hare	Edwards/t	Middleton/2t
B	09.01	A	TBC	Rotherham	W 27-24		Tuipulotu/cp(d/c)	Sailor	O'Hare	Edwards	Middleton/t
C	30.01	A	TBC	Leicester	L 0-49		James(a)	Scales	O'Hare	Edwards	Sailor(b)

* after opponents name indicates a penalty try
Brackets after a player's name indicates he was replaced. eg (a) means he was replaced by replacement code "a" and so on.
/ after a player or replacement name is followed by any scores he made - eg /t, /c, /p, /dg or any combination of these

1998-99 HIGHLIGHTS

League debuts:
Craig Emmerson, Tom Rhodes, Mark Kirkby, Rob Faulkner, Mike Beckham, Paul Jones, Stuart Reid, Tom Palmer, Andy James, Jonathan Feeley, Hefin O'Hare, Wendall Sailor, Adam Hughes, Simon Crabb.

Ever Presents: Mark Luffman, Scott Easterby.

Players used: 31 plus 2 as a replacement only.

Most Points in a season:

Pts	Player	T	C	P	DG
250	S Tuipulotu	3	38	53	-
50	S Middleton	10	-	-	-
50	J Scales	10	-	-	-
45	T Fourie	9	-	-	-

MATCH FACTS

10	9	1	2	3	4	5	6	7	8	
Stephens	Cawthorn/t	Faulkner(j)	Luffman	Beckham(k)	Raducanu	Jones(l)	Fourie	Easterby/t	Reid	1
Stephens(n)	Cawthorn	Thomas	Luffman	Shelley/t	Griffiths	Raducanu	Easterby	Lancaster/t	Reid(h)	2
Rhodes	Cawthorn/t(s/t)	Shelley	Luffman	Thomas(e)	Griffiths	Palmer	Fourie	Lancaster(i/t)	Easterby/t(r)	3
Stephens	Cawthorn	Shelley	Luffman	Thomas(e)	Griffiths	Palmer	Fourie(r)	Lancaster	Easterby(i)	4
Duncombe/dg	Saverimutto	Shelley	Luffman	Thomas(e)	Griffiths(f)	Palmer	Fourie/t	Easterby(m)	Reid	5
Rhodes	Saverimutto	Shelley	Luffman	Thomas	Griffiths	Palmer	Fourie	Easterby	Reid	6
Rhodes(c)	Saverimutto	Beckham	Luffman	Thomas	Griffiths	Palmer	Fourie(r)	Easterby	Reid	7
Rhodes/t(c)	Saverimutto(d)	Beckham(j)	Luffman	Thomas	Griffiths	Palmer	Fourie	Easterby(m)	Reid	8
Rhodes	Saverimutto	Shelley	Luffman	Thomas(e)	Griffiths	Palmer	Fourie(r)	Easterby	Reid	9
Rhodes	Saverimutto(d)	Shelley	Luffman	Thomas(e)	Griffiths(g)	Palmer	Fourie/t(f)	Easterby	Reid(m)	10
Rhodes	Saverimutto	Shelley	Luffman	Thomas	Griffiths	Palmer	Fourie/2t	Easterby	Reid	11
Rhodes	Saverimutto/t	Shelley	Luffman	Thomas	Griffiths	Palmer(g)	Fourie	Easterby	Reid	12
Rhodes/t	Saverimutto/t	Shelley	Luffman	Thomas	Griffiths	Palmer(g)	Fourie(r/t)	Easterby	Reid(m)	13
Rhodes	Saverimutto	Beckham	Luffman	Thomas	Griffiths	Jones(n)	Fourie(r)	Easterby	Reid	14
Rhodes	Saverimutto	Shelley/t	Luffman	Beckham	Griffiths	Jones	Fourie/t(r)	Easterby	Reid(n)	15
Rhodes	Saverimutto(d)	Shelley	Luffman	Beckham	Griffiths	Jones	Denham(h)	Easterby	Reid	16
Rhodes/c	Cawthorn(t)	Shelley	Luffman	Beckham(k)	Griffiths(n)	Jones	Fourie(r)	Lancaster	Easterby/t	17
Rhodes	Saverimutto	Shelley	Luffman	Thomas(e)	Palmer(l)	Jones	Fourie(r/t)	Easterby	Reid	18
Duncombe	Saverimutto(y)	Shelley	Luffman	Thomas(e)	Griffiths	Palmer	Easterby	Lancaster(r)	Reid	19
Tuipulotu/2c2p	Crabb(t)	Shelley	Luffman(z)	Thomas	Griffiths	Jones(n)	Fourie(r)	Easterby	Reid	20
Tuipulotu/c4p	Crabb(t)	Shelley/t	Luffman	Thomas(e)	Palmer	Jones	Fourie(r)	Easterby(m)	Reid	21
Tuipulotu/2cp	Saverimutto	Shelley(e)	Luffman(z)	Thomas	Palmer	Jones	Fourie/t(r)	Easterby/t(m)	Reid	22
Tuipulotu/5c	Saverimutto/2t	Shelley(e)	Luffman(z)	Thomas	Palmer	Jones(l)	Fourie/t(r/t)	Lancaster	Easterby/2t	23
Tuipulotu/4p	Saverimutto	Shelley	Luffman	Thomas	Palmer	Jones	Fourie	Easterby	Reid	24
Cawthorn	Saverimutto(y)	Shelley/t	Luffman(z)	Thomas(e)	Palmer(l))	Jones/t	Fourie/2t	Easterby/t	Reid(r)	25
Cawthorn/t	Saverimutto/t(y)	Shelley	Luffman(z)	Thomas(e)	Griffiths	Jones/t(n/t)	Denham	Easterby/t	Reid	26
Rhodes	Saverimutto(d)	Shelley(e)	Luffman	Thomas	Palmer	Griffiths	Fourie(r)	Easterby(m)	Reid/t	A
Rhodes	Saverimutto	Shelley	Luffman	Thomas(e)	Griffiths	Palmer	Fourie(r)	Easterby/2t	Reid/t	B
Rhodes	Saverimutto(d)	Shelley	Luffman	Beckham(k)	Griffiths(n)	Jones	Fourie(r)	Easterby	Reid	C

REPLACEMENTS:

	a- S Middleton	b- C Emmerson	c - C Stephens	d - M Cawthorn	e - M Beckham
f - C Raducanu	g - P Jones	h - T Fourie	i - S Reid	j - M Shelley	k - H Thomas
l - S Griffiths	m - S Lancaster	n - T Palmer	o - A James	p - J Feeley	q - M Duncombe
r - L Denham	s - J Swarbrigg	t - C Saverimutto	u - H O'Hare	v - D Edwards	w - J Scales
x - W Sailor	y - S Crabb				

Sateki Tuipulotu topped the Leeds Tykes scoring list for a second successive season and in the process broke or extended a number of scoring records.
He kicked 7 penalties at Coventry to set a new record for penalties in a match to erase the record of 6 held by Colin Stephens and Gerry Ainscough.
His 53 penalties beat the previous record for a season which was 49 and shared by Tuipulotu and Ainscough.
His three tries took him to 29 and so passed Christian Raducanu's league record of 28.
He also extended his record for consecutive league appearances to 65 and extended his record for scoring in consecutive matches to 46 along the way.

Wingers Simon Middleton and Jonathan Scales topped the try scorers list jointly from just 14(2) and 7(3) appearances respectively.

Hooker Mark Luffman was an ever present and became Leeds Tykes leading appearance maker in the forwards, passing the departed Christian Raducanu.

LEEDS

LEAGUE STATISTICS
compiled by Stephen McCormack

SEASON	Division	P	W	D	L	F	A	Pts Diff	Lge Pts	Lge Pos	Most Points	Most Tries
89-90												
90-91												
91-92												
92-93	3	11	7	0	4	228	220	8	14		45 Ben Lloyd	7 Chris Thornton
93-94	4	18	7	0	11	243	318	-75	14		97 David Breakwell	3 Penalty Tries
94-95	4	18	8	0	10	335	291	44	16		83 Ralph Bennett	6 Phil Griffin & Chris Thornton
95-96	4	18	9	1	8	312	347	-35	19		67 Colin Stephens	6 Chris Thornton
96-97	3	30	24	0	6	1209	432	777	48		307 Gerry Ainscough	16 Mark Appleson
97-98	JN1	26	21	1	4	858	407	451	43		322 Sateki Tuipulotu	7 Simon Middleton
98-99	P2	26	16	0	10	713	367	336	28*	6	250 Sateki Tuipulotu	10 Simon Middleton Jonathan Scales

BIGGEST MARGINS

Home Win	81pts - 84-3 v Walsall 1.3.97
Away Win	75pts - 84-9 v Clifton 12.4.97
Home Defeat	6pts - 20-26 v Liverpool St. Helens 25.3.94
Away Defeat	25pts - 10-35 v Liverpool St H. 15.10.93

MOST CONSECUTIVE

Appearances	65 Sateki Tuipulotu 7.9.96 - 3.1.99
Matches scoring Tries	7 Simon Middleton
Matches scoring points	46 Sateki Tuipulotu
Victories	11 (twice)
Defeats	5

MOST POINTS

Scored at Home	84 v Walsall 1.3.97
Scored Away	84 v Clifton 12.4.97
Conceded at Home	26 v Liverpool St. Helens 25.3.94
Conceded Away	35 v Liverpool St Helens 15.10.93

MOST TRIES

Scored in a match	14 v Redruth 9.1.96 (H) v Walsall 1.3.97 (H)
Conceded in a match	6 v Aspatria 13.4.96 (A)

MOST APPEARANCES

by a forward	72 Mark Luffman
by a back	76 (1) Sateki Tuipulotu

	MOST IN A SEASON	MOST IN A CAREER	MOST IN A MATCH	
Points	322 Sateki Tuipulotu 97-98	769 Sateki Tuipulotu 96-99	27 Gerry Ainscough	v Rosslyn Park 14.9.96(H) v Walsall 1.3.97 (H)
Tries	17 Simon Middleton 97-98	29 Sateki Tupulotu 96-99	5 Simon Middleton	v Otley 24.1.98 (H)
Conversions	60 Sateki Tuipulotu 97-98	135 Sateki Tuipulotu 96-98	9 Gerry Ainscough	v Clifton 7.12.96 (H)
Penalties	53 Sateki Tuipulotu 98-99	118 Sateki Tuipulotu 96-98	7 Sateki Tuipulotu	v Coventry 3.1.99 (A)
Drop Goals	5 Colin Stephens 96-97	13 Colin Stephens 95-98	2 Dan Eddie Colin Stephens	v Broughton Park 19.2.94 v Exeter 9.9.95 (H) v Lon. Welsh 19.10.96 (H)

BACKS

	Ht.	Wt.	Birthdate	Birthplace	CLUB	League Apps	Tries	Pts
Sateki Tuipulotu	6.0	13.13	03.07.71	Tonga	Leeds	76	26	772
Tonga								
Simon Middleton			02.03.66	Kellington	Leeds	31(2)	27	135
					Otley	8	2	10
Diccon Edwards	5.10	13.10	13.03.73	London	Leeds	47(3)	6	30
England u21, North, Wales(RL).Other club: Wakefield 23/2/10					Leicester	15	-	-
Colin Stephens	5.8	12.06	29.11.69	Swansea	Leeds	49(5)	17	231
Wales, Llanelli.								
Mike Cawthorne	5.9	13.03	15.05.72	Bridlington	Leeds	45(16)	15	75
Yorkshire					Wakefield	6	-	-
Tom Rhodes	6.2	14.00	29.11.78		Leeds	16	1	1
Andy James	5.10	13.00	02.03.76		Leeds	10(5)	2	33
Matt Duncombe	6.0	13.00	27.08.75		Leeds	2(91	-	3
Wendell Sailor	6.3	16.08	16.07.74	Brisbane	Leeds	6(1)	8	40
Christian Saverimutto	5.8	12.07	08.08.71	Wallasey	Leeds	37(7)	9	45
Ireland (). Other club: Waterloo					Sale	25	3	15
Hefin O'Hare	5.10	14.00	02.06.79		Leeds	18(1)	4	20
					New Brighton			
Jonathan Feeley	6.0	17.00	12.04.79		Leeds	5(2)	4	20
Jonathan Scales			28.07.74		Leeds	7(4)	10	50

FORWARDS

	Ht.	Wt.	Birthdate	Birthplace	CLUB	League Apps	Tries	Pts
Mike Beckham					Leeds	7(13)	-	-
Mark Luffman	5.10	14.12	17.08.71	Nottingham	Leeds	72(3)	3	15
					Otley	10	1	5
Mike Shelley	6.0	18.08	13.03.72	Leeds	Leeds	70(4)	12	60
North.					W Hartlepool	18	4	20
Christian Raducanu	6.5	16.11	02.10.67	Bucharest	Leeds	69(3)	27	135
Romania.					Sale	7	1	4
Huw Thomas	5.10	16.00	29.10.74	St Asaph	Leeds	38	-	-
					Otley			
Steve Griffiths	6.6	18.00	04.08.73	Morecambe	Leeds	30(7)	2	10
Tim Fourie	6.4	16.00	12.03.68		Leeds	46(4)	18	90
Tom Palmer	6.5	16.00	27.03.79		Leeds	8(5)	1	5
Lee Denham	6.1	16.02	05.03.74		Leeds	19(27)	9	45
Stuart Reid	6.3	16.03	31.07.70	Kendal	Leeds	22(2)	1	5
Stuart Lancaster	6.0	13.03	09.10.69	Penrith	Leeds	17(8)	-	-

LEEDS TYKES

FACT FILE

Founded: 1991
Nickname: Tykes
Web site: www.leedsrugby.com

Colours: Royal blue, black, gold & white
Change colours: White, royal blue, gold

GROUND
Address: Headingley Stadium, St Michaels Lane, Headingley, Leeds. LS6 3BR
Tel: 0113 278 6181 Fax: 0113 275 4284 e-mail: mike.bidgood@leedsrugby.co.uk
Capacity: 23,000 Seated: 9,000 Standing: Covered 11,000, Uncovered 3,000

Directions: From East: M62 Junction 29 (M1). Follow signs Leeds M1,junction 43 (A61), Junc 47 leave motorway & follow signs City Centre. From City Centre follow signs Otley, Skipton A660 to leave by Woodhouse Lane. In 2.3miles turn left and then left again into St Michaels Lane. Ground on right.
Nearest Railway Station: Headingley (1/2 mile), Leeds City (2.5 miles)

Car Parking: 450 at ground £1

Admission:
Season Adult £80, Children £20, OAPs £40
Matchday Adult £8, Children £2, OAPs £4

Club Shop: Open 9-5 Mon-Fri + Matchdays. Tel 0113 274 0460

Clubhouse: Open during normal licensing hours
Snacks, bar meals & restaurant available.
Functions: Capacity 1,200, contact Leeds RUFC

Training Nights: Monday, Tuesday, Thursday.

PROGRAMME Full colour Size: A5 Pages: 36 + cover
Price: £1.50 Editor: Phil Daly 0113 278 6181 x246 (B)
0113 230 7617 (F) 07775 946935 (Mobile)

ADVERTISING RATES
Page £500 1/2 page £300 1/4 page £150

LONDON WELSH R.F.C.

President	S J Dawes OBE
Chairman	David Hammond
Club Secretary	Tudor Roberts
General Manager	Ron Holley
Commercial Manager	David Banks
Coach	Clive Griffiths
Press Officer	Allan Price

c/o London Welsh RFC,
Old Deer Park,
Kew Road,
Richmond,
Surrey TW9 2AZ
Tel: 0181 940 2368
Fax: 0181 940 1106

Being a London Welsh supporter in recent seasons has not been a rewarding experience with the halcyon years of the 1960s and 1970s now an honoured part of history. Nowadays, good Welsh players living in the London area can either play for a top division English club or travel swiftly to South Wales on a match day and demonstrate their abilities in front of their homeland fans. So the club has been forced to survive with resident London talent - not all of it Welsh and some of it from very foreign climes.

Nevertheless, after some lean years `Welsh' have shown signs of a definite revival and are now in the second of the Premier Leagues. In the season just past there was seldom any likelihood that promotion would be achieved with only half of the first ten games won and heavy defeats at Bristol and Coventry being a blot on the landscape.

There was then a vast improvement in form with a dozen wins in the last sixteen matches, but by then Bristol, Rotherham and Worcester were way ahead of the field and a top half of the table finish was a most creditable final outcome.

The Tetley's Bitter Cup challenge was over long before Christmas, but a narrow 8-6 defeat at Rotherham was no disgrace.

The stars of the season were outside-half Andy Lee (from Saracens), whose 99 points made him the club's top scorer, but he would ave done better if he had come into the team earlier than the eleventh game.

The former rugby league star Andy Currier was superb and his fifteen tries (28 in two seasons) were a magnificent effort, while the veteran Rowland Phillips (from rugby league) set a fine example in terms of fitness and commitment as he led the side from No 8. Others to shine were the prop Ian Buckett, the lock Paul Carr and the flankers Mike White and Colin Alexander, but there appeared to be a sense of pride returning to the club with anyone appearing in a red shirt prepared to give 100 per cent.

For the future the continued fitness of Currier and Phillips must be a key factor, but at least it would seem that the Old Deer Park is again a place where a Saturday afternoon can be enjoyed, which is really the true spirit of the game.

Bill Mitchell

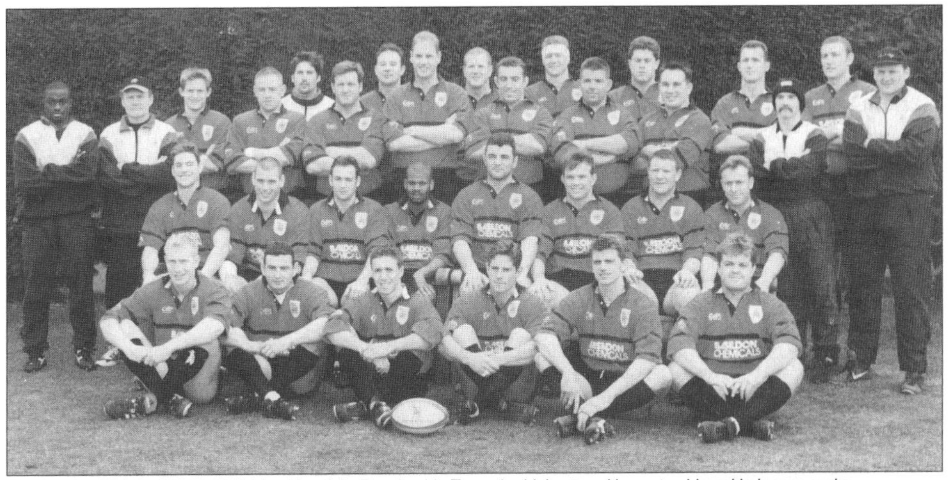

The London Welsh of 1998-99 finished fourth in Premiership Two - the highest position yet achieved in league rugby.
L-R - **Back Row:** Muna Embongalane, Clive Griffiths (coach), Adam Jones, Gary French, Scott Roskell, Ian Buckett, Luke Jones, Geoff Sage, Colin Alexander, Garry Holmes, Paul Carr, Richard Thomas, Matt Fitzgerald, Steve Pope, Andy Currier, Phil Chadwick (fitness coach), Colin Langley, Mark Langley. **Middle Row:** James Storey, Lennie Woodward, Darren Edwards, Martin Giraud, Rowland Phillips (captain), Charles Olney, Michael White, Andy Lee. **Front Row:** Tom Shanklin, Craig Raymond, Peter Shaw, Richard Lurie, Nick Mardon, Andy Millward.

LONDON WELSH

Match No.	Date	H/A	Comp.	Opponents	Result & Score	Att.	15	14	13	12	11
1	06.09	A	AD2	Leeds	W 20-18	1,152	Jones/t	Storey	Currier/t	Dawes	Giraud
2	13.09	A	AD2	Blackheath	W 20-16	1,300	Jones	Storey	Currier(n)	Dawes	Giraud
3	19.09	H	AD2	Orrell	W 24-17		Jones	Shaw/t	Currier/dg	Dawes	Giraud
4	26.09	A	AD2	Bristol	L 3-37	3,459	Jones	Shaw	Currier	Dawes	Giraud
5	03.10	H	AD2	Rotherham	L 13-27		Jones	Shaw/t	Currier	Pilgrim	Giraud
6	10.10	A	AD2	Coventry	L 19-63	1,360	Jones	Shaw/t	Currier	Pilgrim/c(y)	Giraud
7	17.10	H	AD2	Wakefield	W 45-21	1,300	Shaw	Storey/t(C)	Currier	Roskell	Giraud/t
8	24.10	A	AD2	Moseley*	W 31-16	631	Shaw/t	Storey/t	Currier	Roskell	Giraud
9	31.10	H	AD2	Worcester	L 14-22	1,400	Shaw	Storey	Currier	Roskell	Giraud
10	07.11	A	AD2	Waterloo	L 10-12	900	Shaw	Storey	Currier/t	Roskell	Giraud
11	21.11	H	AD2	Exeter	W 62-27	1,200	Shaw/t	Shanklin/2t	Currier/3t	Roskell	Giraud/2t
12	12.12	H	AD2	Fylde	W 36-15		Shaw	Storey	Currier/t	Dawes(w)	Woodard/3t
13	19.12	H	AD2	Rugby Lions	W 11-7		Shaw	Storey	Currier	Roskell	Woodard/t
14	02.01	A	AD2	Exeter	W 17-16	1,100	Jones	Roskell	Currier	Dawes(a/t)	Woodard/t
15	16.01	H	AD2	Waterloo	W 49-17		Jones/2t	Woodard/t	Currier	Storey/2t	Roskell(c)
16	23.01	A	AD2	Worcester	L 12-14	3,600	Jones	Roskell/t	Currier/t	Storey	Woodard
17	06.02	H	AD2	Moseley	W 26-14	650	Jones	Woodard	Currier/t	Storey(y)	Giraud/2t
18	13.02	A	AD2	Wakefield	W 30-16	410	Jones	Woodard	Currier/t	Storey	Giraud/t
19	27.02	H	AD2	Coventry	W 42-34		Jones	Woodard	Currier/3t	Storey	Giraud
20	13.03	A	AD2	Rotherham	L 8-28		Jones	Woodard	Currier/t	Storey	Giraud
21	27.03	H	AD2	Bristol	L 6-25		Jones	Woodard	Currier	Storey	Giraud
22	03.04	A	AD2	Orrell	L 15-18	1,000	Jones	Woodard	Currier	Shanklin/t	Giraud
23	17.04	H	AD2	Blackheath	W 71-22		Marden/3t	Woodard/4t	Currier/t	Shanklin	Storey/t
24	25.04	H	AD2	Leeds Tykes	W 24-17		Marden	Woodard/2t	Currier/t	Storey	Giraud
25	01.05	A	AD2	Rugby Lions*	W 33-12	720	Marden(n)	Woodard/2t	Currier	Storey/2t	Giraud
26	08.05	A	AD2	Fylde	W 21-11	500	Marden/t(n)	Woodard	Currier	Storey/t	Giraud
A	14.11	A	TBC	Rotherham	L 6-8	750	Shaw	Storey	Currier	Roskell	Giraud

* after opponents name indicates a penalty try
Brackets after a player's name indicates he was replaced. eg (a) means he was replaced by replacement code "a" and so on.
/ after a player or replacement name is followed by any scores he made - eg /t, /c, /p, /dg or any combination of these

1998-99 HIGHLIGHTS

League debuts: Matt Pearce, Ian Buckett, Colin Alexander, Gary French, Steve Pope, Paul Carr, Jason Hewlett, Matt Fitzgerald, Mike White, Lennie Woodard, Andy Lee, Richard Lorie, Tom Shanklin, Neil Marden.

Ever Presents: Andy Currier.

Players used: 34 plus 4 as a replacement only.

Most Points in a season:

Pts	Player	T	C	P	DG
99	A Lee	1	26	14	-
78	A Currier	15	-	-	1
75	M Pearce	2	13	13	-
70	L Woodard	14	-	-	-
45	J Storey	9	-	-	-

MATCH FACTS

10	9	1	2	3	4	5	6	7	8	
Pearce/cp	Edwards	Buckett	Olney(m)	Millward(l)	Sage	Whitaker/t	Alexander	Jones	Phillips	1
Pearce/t2c2p	Edwards	Holmes(p)	Olney(m)	Buckett/t	Sage(q)	Whitaker	Alexander	Jones	Phillips	2
Pearce/tcp(s/2p)	Edwards	Buckett(l)	French(g)	Millward	Carr(u)	Whitaker	Peacock(t)	Alexander	Phillips	3
Hewlett/p(d)	(e)	Buckett(l)	Olney(m)	Millward	Whitaker(i)	Langley	Fitzgerald	Alexander(v)	Phillips	4
Pearce/c2p(b)	Edwards	Buckett(l)	French(g)	Millward	Carr	Langley	Alexander	White	Phillips	5
Dawes(d/t)	Edwards(A)	Buckett(l)	French	Millward(g)	Langley(j/t)	Carr	Alexander	White/t	Phillips	6
Pearce/2c2p	Lorie(e)	Buckett(l)	French(g)	Millward	Langley	Carr	Alexander	White/3t(t)	Phillips/2t(j)	7
Pearce/4cp	Lorie	Holmes(p)	French(j)	Millward	Langley	Carr	Alexander	White	Phillips/t	8
Pearce/3p(z/t)	Lorie(e)	Holmes(f)	Olney	Millward(m)	Langley	Carr(j)	Alexander	White	Phillips(r)	9
Pearce/cp	Edwards(A)	Buckett(l)	Olney	Millward	Langley	Carr	White(D)	Griffiths	Alexander	10
Lee/6c	Edwards/t	Buckett	Olney(m)	Millward(l)	Langley(i)	Carr	Alexander	White(v)	Phillips/t	11
Lee/3c(d)	Edwards/t	Buckett	Olney	Millward(p)	Langley	Carr(E)	Alexander(t)	Griffiths	Phillips/t	12
Lee/2p	Lorie	Holmes(p)	French	Buckett	Langley(E)	Carr	Alexander(v)	White	Phillips	13
Lee/2cp	Edwards	Buckett(h)	Olney	Holmes(m)	Johansson	Carr(u)	Fitzgerald(v)	White	Phillips	14
Lee/3cp(D)	Edwards/t(A)	Millward	Olney	Buckett(p)	Langley(E)	Carr	White/2t	Jones(t)	Phillips	15
Lee/c(D)	Edwards	Millward(l)	Olney	Buckett	Langley(E)	Carr	Fitzgerald(v)	White	Phillips	16
Lee/c2p(B/p)	Edwards	Millward	Olney	Buckett	Langley	Carr	Alexander	White	Phillips	17
Lee/3c3p	Edwards/t(A)	Buckett(m)	Olney	Millward	Langley	Carr	White(t)	Alexander	Phillips	18
Lee/3c2p	Edwards/t	Buckett(l)	Olney	Millward	Langley	Carr	White/t(F)	Alexander/t	Phillips	19
Lee/p(B)	Edwards(A)	Buckett(m)	Olney	Millward(l)	Langley	Carr	White(t)	Alexander	Phillips	20
Lee/2p	Edwards(A)	Buckett	Olney	Millward(l)	Langley	Carr	White	Alexander(t)	Phillips	21
Lee(B)	Lorie/t	Buckett(p)	Olney	Millward(m)	Langley	Carr	Fitzgerald(i)	White	Phillips/t	22
Raymond/8c	Edwards(A)	Buckett(l)	Olney	Millward/t(m)	Langley(i)	Carr/t	White	Jones	Phillips	23
Raymond/3cp	Lorie	Buckett	Olney	Millward(k)	Sage	Langley	White	Jones	Phillips	24
Lee/4c	Edwards	Buckett(l)	Olney	Millward(m)	Langley(q)	Sage	Alexander(x)	Jones	Phillips	25
Raymond/t3c(z)	Lorie	Buckett(l)	French(g)	Millward	Langley	Carr	White	Jones(k)	Phillips	26
Lee/2p	Lorie	Buckett	Olney	Millward(p)	Langley(i)	Carr	Alexander	Griffiths	Phillips	A

REPLACEMENTS:		a- J Storey	b- M Dawes	c - M Giraud	d - M Pearce	e - D Edwards
f - I Buckett	g - C Olney	h - A Millward	i - G Sage	j - C Whitaker	k - C Alexander	l - G Holmes
m - G French	n - P Shaw	o - T Lewsey	p - S Pope	q - P Carr	r - G Peacock	s - J Hewlett
t - M Fitzgerald	u - C Langley	v - D Griffiths	w - S Pilgrim	x - M White	y - S Roskell	z - A Lee
A - R Lorie	B - C Raymond	C - T Shanklin	D - C Brown	E - A Johansson	F - T Moulton	

Former Saracens player Andy Lee topped the points scorers list with 99 points, the lowest total to top the list for 5 years.

All time leading points scorer Craig Raymond missed most of the season through injury and selection and added just 39 points to his total.

Andy Currier continued with his brilliant change from rugby league to rugby union with 15 tries and now heads the clubs all time try list for league matches. Currier now has 28 tries from his 46 starts over 2 seasons.
Currier equalled the club record of scoring in five consecutive league matches.

LONDON WELSH

LEAGUE STATISTICS
compiled by Stephen McCormack

SEASON	Division	P	W	D	L	F	A	Pts Diff	Lge Pts	Lge Pos	Most Points	Most Tries
89-90	3	11	3	0	8	141	179	-38	6		25 Lee Evans	3 Gareth Hughes, Mark Thomas & Jim Williams
90-91	D4S	12	7	0	5	235	165	70	14		30 Gareth Hughes	6 Mickey Bell
91-92	D4S	12	9	0	3	292	160	132	18		43 Graeme Peacock	7 Mark Douglas & Steve Thomas
92-93	D4S	12	10	0	2	353	170	183	20		111 Mike hamlin	6 Andy Tucker & Mickey Bell
93-94	D4S	12	5	3	4	216	140	76	13		41 David Shufflebotham	6 Peter Walters
94-95	D4S	12	10	2	0	409	126	283	22		109 Craig Raymond	7 Colin Charvis & David Lubliner
95-96	4	18	12	0	6	424	269	155	24		204 Craig Raymond	9 David Lubliner
96-97	3	30	12	0	18	634	777	-143	24		300 Craig Raymond	13 Tom Lewsey
97-98	N1	26	21	1	4	848	478	370	43		264 Craig Raymond	17 Scott Roskell
98-99	P2	26	17	0	9	662	552	110	34	4	99 Andy Lee	15 Andy Currier

BIGGEST MARGINS

Home Win	81pts - 88-7 v Sudbury 25.3.95
Away Win	43pts - 49-6 v Sidcup 16.11.91
Home Defeat	25pts - 3-28 v Lydney 18.11.90
Away Defeat	44pts - 19-63 vCoventry 10.10.98

MOST POINTS

Scored at Home	88 v Sudbury 25.3.95
Scored Away	49 v Sidcup 16.11.91
Conceded at Home	36 v Exeter 22.2.97
Conceded Away	63 v Coventry 10.10.98

MOST CONSECUTIVE

Appearances	33 Graeme Peacock
Matches scoring Tries	5 Mickey Bell (x2), Adam Jones & **Andy Currier**
Matches scoring points	23 Craig Raymond
Victories	10**Defeats** 6

MOST TRIES

Scored in a match	12 v Sudbury 25.3.95 (H)
Conceded in a match	8 v Wharfedale 15.2.97 (A) v Harrogate 1.3.97 (A) v Coventry 10.10.98 (A)

MOST APPEARANCES

by a forward	113 (5) Graeme Peacock
by a back	78 (4) Craig Raymond

	MOST IN A SEASON	MOST IN A CAREER	MOST IN A MATCH	
Points	300 Craig Raymond	916 Craig Raymond 94-99	28 Craig Raymond	v Clifton 28.12.96 (H)
Tries	17 Scott Roskell 97-98	28 Andy Currier 97-99	4 Mickey Bell David Lubliner Lennie Woodard	v N. Walsham 13.10.90 (H) v Sudbury 25.3.95 (H) v Blackheath 17.4.99 (H)
Conversions	64 Craig Raymond 97-98	160 Craig Raymond 94-98	8 Craig Raymond	v Wharfedale 21.3.98 (H) v Blackheath 17.4.99 (H)
Penalties	57 Craig Raymond 96-97	148 Craig Raymond 94-98	6 Craig Raymond	v Lydney 9.11.96 (H) v Clifton 28.12.96 (H) v Rosslyn Park 18.2.97 (H)
Drop Goals	7 Craig Raymond 96-97	14 Craig Raymond 94-98	2 Craig Raymond	v Exeter 27.4.96 (A) v Liverpool St H 31.8.96 (A)

LONDON WELSH PLAYING SQUAD

BACKS

Name	Ht.	Wt.	Birthdate	Birthplace	CLUB	League Apps	Tries	Pts
Andy Currier Great Britain (RL)	6.4	15.05	08.44.66	Widnes	London Welsh	46(1)	28	143
Michael Dawes Welsh Exiles, Middlesex	5.10	13.12	25.01.68	Walton	London Welsh	68(8)	22	154
Darren Edwards Welsh Univ, Wales (7s). Other clubs: Saracens 0(1)/-/-	5.8	12.06	25.03.71	Maesteg	London Welsh Bedford	44(4) 3(2)	10 3	50 15
Martin Giraud Wales u21, u19, Youth, Exiles.	5.11	12.11	16.11.77	Essex	London Welsh	57(2)	22	110
Craig Raymond London, Wales Development, Exiles.	5.11	13.7	10.01.69	Llanelli	London welsh	78(4)	22	916
Tom Lewsey English Univ. Welsh Exiles	5.11	13.09	03.05.75	Bromley	London Welsh	21(18)	14	70
Nick Mardon Scotland (RL).	6.1	13.10	24.09.71	Scotland	London Welsh	4(1)	4	20
Scott Roskell	6.2	15.00	25.04.70	Gold Coast	London Welsh	28(4)	18	90
Peter Shaw Wales (7s), Welsh Dev Squad, Exiles. English colts u19.	5.11	13.00	09.11.73	Hamersmith	London Welsh	48(7)	12	60
Richard White South Africans Students. Barbarians, Eastern Province.	5.10	13.00	25.09.70	Port Elizabeth	London Welsh	7(7)	1	5
Adam Jones Wales u21, Youth, Students, Exiles. Barbarians.	5.11	12.07	07.11.74	Basingstoke	London Welsh Richmond	20 2	10 -	50 -
Steve Pilgrim England B, u21 colts. Barbarians, London, Surrey.	5.10	14.0	26.10.67	Sidcup	London Welsh Harlequins	10(4) 2(1)	- -	17 3

FORWARDS

Name	Ht.	Wt.	Birthdate	Birthplace	CLUB	League Apps	Tries	Pts
Colin Alexander Eastern Province	6.5	15.10	31.08.72	Johannesburg	London Welsh Rugby	19(3) 17(2)	1 3	5 15
Colin Langley Wales U-21, Schools.	6.5	17.00	12.10.71	Cardiff	London Welsh	21(2)	-	-
Paul Carr Hampshire. Other clubs: Fylde 35/-/-	6.5	16.00	25.03.68	London	London Welsh Richmond	21(2) 65(1)	1 1	5 5
Garry Holmes England A/B, Colts, London, Middlesex.	5.11	17.00	07.07.65	Belsize Park	London Welsh Blackheath	21(25) 13(1)	- -	- -
Matt Fitzgerald English Univ	6.4	17.00	07.06.73	London	London Welsh Richmond	4(8) 46	- 6	- 30
Ian Buckett Wales. Wales A, U-21 Schools.	6.1	17.12	23.12.67	Holywell	London Welsh Swansea	24(1) 82(5)	1 1	5 5
Steve Pope England Schools, London U-21.	5.11	18.02	24.11.73	Harlow	London Welsh Blackheath	0(6) 30(5)	-	-
Geoff Sage Middlesex. Other clubs: Wasps 1/-/-	6.6	17.00	19.04.68	Hillingdon	London Welsh Richmond	7(6) 31	- -	- -
Rowland Phillips Wales (10),, Pembrokeshire. RL: Great Britain, Wales.	6.2	16.11	28.07.65	St David's	London Welsh Treorchy	51 7	13 1	65 5
Ashley Johansen NSW Scholls.	6.6	17.11	14.03.69	Sydney	London Welsh	9(6)	1	5
Luke Jones London u21.	6.3	15.07	06.11.70	Suffolk	London Welsh Richmond	33(1) 35(4)	4 6	20 30
Graeme Peacock North Harbour, Welsh Exiles, Middlesex.	6.5	15.00	15.04.66	Auckland	London Welsh	113(6)	12	96
Charles Olney	5.11	16.08	11.08.71	Somerset	London Welsh Saracens	24(8) 11(7)	1	5
Michael White London, Barbarians	6.1	15.07	30.03.66	Poole	London Welsh Wasps	20(1) 116	7 13	35 62
Andy Millward Welsh Univ, Students, Scholls.	5.10	17.00	01.12.71	Neath	London Welsh	35(1)	-	-

LONDON WELSH

FACT FILE

Founded: 1885
Nickname: The Welsh
Web site: www.london.welsh.co.uk

Colours: Scarlet & black hoops
Change colours: Black

GROUND **Address:** Old Deer Park, Kew Road, Richmond, Surrey TW9 2AZ
Tel: 0181 940 2368 **Fax:** 0181 940 1106 **e-mail:** rugby@lon/welsh.co.uk
Capacity: 4,000 Covered Seating: 1,000 Uncovered Standing: 6,000

Directions: Half mile north of Richmond BR station into Kew Road. Ground on left before Kew Gardens
Nearest Railway Station: Richmond (BR & Underground)

Car Parking: 200, public car park close by.

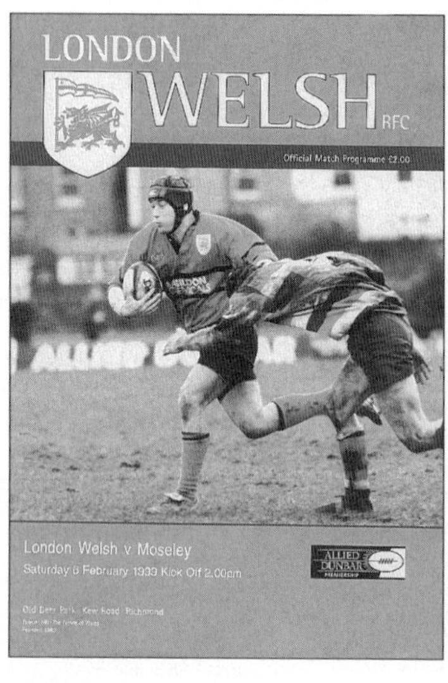

Admission: Season Tickets
Ground - Adult £70, OAPs £20,
Family £150 (2 adults & children u16)
Granstand - Adult £100, OAPs £60

Matchday Tickets £8 - concessions half-price

Club Shop: Yes open matchdays

Clubhouse: Three bars, open during normal licensing hours.
Snacks & bar meals available.
Functions: Capacity 300

Training Nights: Tuesday, Wednesday & Thursday

PROGRAMME Size: B5 Pages: 48 Price: £2
Editor: Paul Beken 0181 643 2456
Advertising - Contact David Banks, Commercial Manager at club

The 'Welsh' pack about to get to grips with the Rotherham pack, in this Tetley's Bitter Cup 3rd Round encounter at Rotherham.

Photo: Ken Barrington

MANCHESTER RUGBY CLUB

President	Alan Hanson	01625 261029 (H) 0161 236 4071 (B)
Chairman	Russ Jenkins	
Club Secretary	Norman R Thomas	94, Kitts Moss Lane, Bramhall, Stockport,Cheshire. SK7 2BQ. 0161 439 3385 (H), 0161 439 0518 (Fax).
Fixtures Secretary	Cliff Williams	
Press Officer	Alan Hanson	01625 261029 (H) 0161 236 4071 (B)
Director of Rugby	Alex Keay	

Correspondence: c/o Manchester Rugby Club, Grove Park, Grove Lane, Cheadle Hulme, Cheshire SK8 7NB
Tel: 0161 485 3733 Fax: 0161 485 3733

Another breath-taking season culminating in promotion to Allied Dunbar Premiership Two and a repeat success in the Lancashire Cup final 29-27 over local rivals Orrell.
Manchester held top place in the Jewson National League One from the end of September through to the end of March before being overhauled for top spot by Henley in the last month. Nevertheless, runners up position secured promotion for a record sixth time in nine years (three times in the last four seasons).
Again, the club finished top points scorers in their league, and Steve Swindells (captain) was the leading points scorer in the country. Two players were called up to the Barbarians, Dave Craddock who has come through the Clubs Mini and Junior ranks, and the ever consistent Tim Burgon. Phil Jee, Guy Parker and Nick Wheeler will go into semi retirement although continuing in a coaching capacity.
The club provided 21 players to county rugby for Cheshire, Lancashire and Cumbria. Newcomers this season included outstanding performances from James Batt, Matt Kirke, John Fowler, Richard Hughes, Simon Baker and Matt Dobson. But, stability, team spirit, fitness and a refreshing desire to play running rugby have been the bywords for Manchester success.
Many of the team have been together for the last four or five years and this has been reflected in the contributions made by Luke Hewson, Stewart Williams, Rod Ellis, Matt Ellis, Mike Blood, Tim Green and Lewis Gross.
The Lancashire Cup competition allowed many of the club's fringe and youth players to play good quality competitive rugby and the future of the club is extremely healthy with the likes of young locks Jim Sidwell and Richard Bradshaw, flanker Danny Collins, prop Rob Bieniasz, full back Marcus Barrow and fly half Gareth Gerrard.
The Premiership Leagues should hold no fears for Manchester and the availability of talent and the club's stability and spirit give high optimism in the challenge for further honours in 1999-2000

Manchester Rugby Club 1998-99

MANCHESTER

Match No.	Date	H/A	Comp.	Opponents	Result & Score	Att.	15	14	13	12	11
1	05.09	A	JN1	Nottingham	W29-13	400	Swindells/2c5p	Blood	Langhorn	M Ellis	Hoskin(k)
2	12.09	H	JN1	Camberley	W72-10	400	Swindells/8c2p	Blood(k/t)	M Ellis(l)	R Hughes	Hoskin/5t(q)
3	19.09	A	JN1	Henley	L 20-39	450	Swindells/c2p(l)	Blood/t	Hughes	M Ellis	Greenlees/t(u)
4	26.09	H	JN1	Morley	W 29-5	400	Swindells/2c5p	Blood(v)	Hughes	M Ellis	Gwilliam
5	03.10	A	JN1	Lydney	W16-12	750	Swindells/c3p	Blood	Hughes	M Ellis	Gwilliam
6	10.10	H	JN1	Otley	W36-26	500	Swindells/2c5p	Blood	Hughes	M Ellis	Gwilliam(u/t)
7	24.10	A	JN1	Reading	W28-14	300	Swindells/2c3p	Blood	Langhorn	M Ellis	Hughes
8	31.10	H	JN1	Rosslyn Park*	W26-25	550	Swindells/2c3p	Blood	Langhorn	M Ellis	Hughes
9	07.11	A	JN1	Birmingham S**	W30-27	200	Swindells/3c3p	Blood	Langhorn(y)	M Ellis	Hughes
10	21.11	H	JN1	Liverpool StH	W 50-5	400	Swindells/t6cp	Blood/t	Hughes/t(q)	M Ellis	Gross/t
11	28.11	A	JN1	Harrogate	W18-10	550	Swindells/6p	Blood	Hughes(q)	M Ellis	Gross
12	05.12	H	JN1	Wharfedale	W 15-3	500	Swindells/5p	Blood	Hughes(q)	M Ellis	Gross
13	12.12	A	JN1	Newbury	L 14-17	300	Swindells/3p	Blood/t	Langhorn	M Ellis(p)	Gross
14	19.12	H	JN1	Harrogate	W 27-0	500	Swindells/3c2p	Blood	Langhorn	Hughes	Gross/t
15	28.12	A	JN1	Liverpool StH	W40-15	300	Swindells/t4c4p	Blood(b)	Langhorn	Hughes	Gross/t
16	02.01	H	JN1	Birmingham S*	W 42-0	650	Swindells/4c3p	Crampton	Langhorn(l)	M Ellis(p)	Gross
17	16.01	A	JN1	Rosslyn Park	L 0-12	400	James	Blood	Langhorn(l)	M Ellis	Gross(p)
18	23.01	H	JN1	Reading*	W 41-0	475	Swindells/2t3c	Blood/t	Langhorn(p)	M Ellis	Crampton
19	30.01	A	JN1	Otley	L 6-20	500	Swindells/p	Blood	Hughes(q)	M Ellis	Crampton
20	06.02	H	JN1	Lydney**	W 67-0	600	Swindells/7cp	Blood/t	R Ellis/t	M Ellis	Crampton(q/t)
21	13.02	A	JN1	Morley	W23-17	700	Swindells/c2p(a)	Blood	R Ellis/cp	M Ellis	Crampton
22	27.02	H	JN1	Henley	W 13-7	950	Swindells/c2p	Blood	R Ellis	M Ellis	Gross
23	13.03	A	JN1	Camberley	W28-22	300	Swindells/2c2p	Hughes/t	R Ellis/dg	M Ellis	Gross/t
24	27.03	H	JN1	Nottingham	W32-17	460	Barrow(l/3c)	Blood(b)	Hughes	M Ellis/t	Griss/t
25	03.04	H	JN1	Newbury	L 26-31	350	Swindells/t2c4p	Greenlees	Hughes	M Ellis	Gross
26	17.04	A	JN1	Wharfedale	D 30-30	650	Swindells/2t3c3p	Hughes	R Ellis	M Ellis	Gross
A	17.10	A	TBC	Sedgley Park	L 17-20	400	Swindells/2cp	Blood/t	Hughes	M Ellis	Crampton

* after opponents name indicates a penalty try
Brackets after a player's name indicates he was replaced. eg (a) means he was replaced by replacement code "a" and so on.
/ after a player or replacement name is followed by any scores he made - eg /t, /c, /p, /dg or any combination of these

1998-99 HIGHLIGHTS

League debuts:
Matt Kirke, Matt Dobson, John Duggan, Simon Baker, James Batt, Richard Hughes, Marcus Barrow, Richard Bradshaw, Danny Collins, John Fowler.

Ever Prsents: Luke Hewson

Players used: 33 plus 5 as a replacement only

MATCH FACTS

10	9	1	2	3	4	5	6	7	8	
R Ellis(l)	Green/t(m)	Simpkins	Hewson	Wheeler(o)	D Craddock	Kirke	Dobson(n)	Burgon/t	Duggan	1
R Ellis	Baker/t	Simpkins	Hewson(r)	Wheeler(o)	D Craddock/t(n)	Kirke	Dobson/2t	Burgon	Duggan	2
R Ellis/c	Baker	Simpkins(t)	Hewson(s)	Wheeler	D Craddock	Kirke	Dobson	Burgon	Duggan(n)	3
Jee	Baker	Simpkins	Hewson	Batt	D Craddock	Kirke	Dobson(w)	Burgon/t	Duggan(n)	4
R Ellis	Baker	Simpkins	Hewson	Batt(f)	D Craddock	Kirke	Dobson(n)	Burgon/t	Duggan	5
R Ellis(l/t)	Baker	Simpkins(o)	Hewson(s)	Wheeler	D Craddock	Kirke	S Williams	Burgon/t	Duggan(n)	6
Jee/t	Baker(x)	Simpkins(o)	Hewson	Wheeler	D Craddock	Kirke	Duggan	Burgon/2t	Williams	7
Jee(c/tdg)	Jenn(m)	Batt(e)	Hewson(r)	Wheeler	D Craddock	Kirke	Duggan	Burgon	Williams(n)	8
R Ellis(l)	Jenn(m)	Batt	Hewson	Wheeler	D Craddock	Parker	Duggan	Burgon	Williams/t(h)	9
R Ellis	Baker(x)	Batt(e)	Hewson(r)	Wheeler	D Craddock	Kirke	Dobson/t	Burgon/2t	Williams(n)	10
R Ellis(l)	Baker	Simpkins	Hewson	Wheeler	D Craddock	Kirke	Dobson(n)	Burgon	Williams	11
R Ellis(l)	Baker	Simpkins(o)	Hewson	Wheeler	D Craddock	Bradshaw(n)	Dobson	Burgon	Kirke	12
R Ellis(l)	Baker(d)	Batt(e)	Hewson(s)	Wheeler	D Craddock	Kirke	Dobson	Burgon	Williams(n)	13
R Ellis	Baker(d)	Simpkins	Hewson	Wheeler(o)	D Craddock/t	Kirke/t	Dobson(n)	Burgon(z)	Williams	14
R Ellis/t(l)	Baker(d)	Palmer	Hewson	Simpkins	D Craddock(A)	Parker	Kirke	Collins	Williams/t	15
R Ellis/3t	Green(m)	Simpkins	Hewson	Wheeler(o)	Parker(g)	Fowler/t	Kirke	Dobson	Williams	16
R Ellis	Green(m)	Simpkins(o)	Hewson	Wheeler	D Craddock	Fowler	Kirke(i)	Dobson	Williams	17
R Ellis/t(l)	Green(m)	Simpkins/t	Hewson(s)	Wheeler(o)	D Craddock	Fowler	Kirke	Parker(z)	Williams	18
R Ellis/dg(l)	Green(m)	Batt(e)	Hewson	Wheeler	D Craddock(B)	Fowler	Kirke	Parker	Williams	19
Jee/t	Baker	Batt	Hewson	Wheeler(e)	D Craddock/t	Fowler/t	Kirke/t(n)	P Craddock/t	Williams(z)	20
Jee	Baker/t(x)	Batt(e)	Hewson	Wheeler	D Craddock	Fowler	Kirke	P Craddock(j/t)	Williams	21
Jee	Green	Batt	Hewson	Wheeler	D Craddock	Fowler	Kirke	Burgon/t	Williams	22
Jee(q)	Green(m)	Batt/t	Hewson	Simpkins(e)	D Craddock	Fowler	Kirke(n)	Burgon	Williams	23
R Ellis/2p	Baker(x)	Simpkins(f)	Hewson(s)	Batt	D Craddock	Kirke/t	Duggan(n)	Burgon/t	Williams	24
Jee(c)	Jenn(m)	Simpkins	Hewson	Wheeler(o)	D Craddock	Parker	Kirke(w/t)	Burgon	Williams	25
Jee (C)(D)	Green	Batt(e)	Hewson/t	Wheeler	D Craddock	Parker(E)	P Craddock	Burgon(z)	Duggan	26
Jee	Baker	Simpkins	Hewson	Wheeler	D Craddock/t	Parker	Dobson	Burgon	Williams(j)	A

REPLACEMENTS:

a- G Langhorn	b- M Ellis	c - R Ellis	d - T Green	e - D Simpkins
f - N Wheeler	g - D Craddock	h - M Dobson	i - T Burgon	j - J Duggan
k - J Greenleaves	l - P Jee	m - S Baker	n - G Parker	o - J Batt
p - R Hughes	q - P Jones	r - G Nuttall	s - N Bettridge	t - M Palmer
u - P Crampton	v - L Gross	w - S Williams	x - A Jenn	y - K Warhurst
z - D Collins	A - J Fowler	B - P Craddock	C - Gerrard	D - M Blood
E - R Bradshaw				

Most Points in a season:

Pts	Player	T	C	P	DG
365	S Swindells	7	60	70	-
55	T Burgon	11	-	-	-
57	R Ellis	7	2	3	3
35	Penalty tries	7	-	-	-

Full back and captain Steve Swindells had another huge season and finished the division's top points scorer with 365 points. That follows on from his 398 points the previous season.
He was also the most consistent kicker with a strike rate around 85% which was also one of the leading strike rates in all English senior rugby.

MANCHESTER

LEAGUE STATISTICS
compiled by Stephen McCormack

SEASON	Division	P	W	D	L	F	A	Pts Diff	Lge Pts	Lge Pos		Coach		Captain
89-90	N- NW1	10	8	1	1	212	62	150	17	1p		A Hanson		D Kelly
90-91	N- NW1	10	8	0	2	201	73	128	16	2		D Kelly		D Kelly
91-92	N- NW1	10	10	0	0	242	47	195	20	1p		D Kelly		D Kelly
92-93	N- N2	12	10	0	2	302	103	199	20	1p				
93-94	N- N1	12	8	0	4	208	159	49	16	4				
94-95	N- N1	12	7	3	2	217	166	51	17	3				
95-96	N- N1	12	10	1	1	362	124	238	21	1p				A Hanson
												Most Points		**Most Tries**
96-97	D4N	26	17	1	8	795	504	291	35	4	251	Steve Swindells	15	Tim Burgon Glen Pearson
97-98	N2N	26	21	2	3	1029	472	557	44	2p	398	Steve Swindells	21	Matt Hoskin
98-99	JN1	26	20	1	5	758	372	386	41	2	365	Steve Swindells	11	Tim Burgon

BIGGEST MARGINS

Home Win	89pts - 101-12 v Nuneaton 25.4.98
Away Win	37pts - 56-13 v Hinckley 22.11.97
Home Defeat	7pts - 16-23 v Winnington Park
Away Defeat	15pts - 31-46 v Winnington Park 15.3.97

MOST CONSECUTIVE

Appearances	
Matches scoring Tries	6 Tim Burgon
Matches scoring points	
Victories	9
Defeats	4

MOST POINTS

Scored at Home	101 v Nuneaton 25.04.98
Scored Away	62 v Aspatria 11.10.97
Conceded at Home	23 v Winnington Park
Conceded Away	46 v Winnington Park 15.3.97

MOST TRIES

Scored in a match	15 v Nuneaton 25.4.98
Conceded in a match	6 v Winnington Park 15.3.97

MOST APPEARANCES

by a forward	70 Dave Craddock
by a back	74 Steve Swindells

	MOST IN A SEASON		MOST IN A CAREER		MOST IN A MATCH	
Points	398	Steve Swindells 97-98	1014	Steve Swindells 96-99	28	Steve Swindells v Hereford 22.3.97 (H)
Tries	21	Matt Hoskin 97-98	40	Tim Burgon 96-99	5	Matt Hoskin v Camberley
Conversions	91	Steve Swindells 97-98	200	Steve Swindells 96-99	10	Steve Swindells v Nuneaton 25.4.98 (H)
Penalties	70	Steve Swindells 98-99	167	Steve Swindells 96-99	6	Steve Swindells v Sedgley Park 7.2.98 (A) v Sandal 6.12.97 (H) v Harrogate (A)
Drop Goals	3	Rod Ellis 98-99	3	Rod Ellis 96-99	1	Phil Gee v Winnington Park 15.3.97 Rod Ellis - 3 times

MANCHESTER PLAYING SQUAD

BACKS

	Ht.	Wt.	Birthdate	Birthplace	CLUB	League Apps	Tries	Pts
Steve Swindells Cheshire, England u21.	5.11	13.10	26.10.69	Manchester	Manchester Waterloo	74	22	1014
Matt Hoskins Cheshire, Barbarians.	6.0	15.13	25.12.68	London	Manchester	31	32	160
Lewis Gross	6.1	13.06	19.09.74	Manchester	Manchester	22(3)	12	60
Gary Langhorn Cheshire	6.2	15.00	27.09.70	Manchester	Manchester Stockport	53(10)	10	50
Andy Murison	5.10	14.10	20.03.69	Manchester	Manchester Stockport	36(2)	10	50
Rod Ellis Cheshire	6.1	14.00	06.06.68	Manchester	Manchester Rotherham	63(5)	27	157
Matt Ellis	6.0	15.00	22.06.71	Mirfield	Manchester West Park B	25(3)	-	-
Tim Green	5.9	12.09	002.08.69	Bradford	Manchester Winnington Park	24(3)	1	5
Mike Blood Cheshire	6.2	15.00	06.08.68	Manchester	Manchester Lymm	53(2)	24	120
Neil James	5.10	12.10	18.10.67	Manchester	Manchester Burnage	15(5)	2	78
Phil Jee Lancashire	5.10	14.02	24.07.62	Manchester	Manchester Sale	41(22)	10	92
Andy Jenn Lancashire	5.10	14.12	06.05.75	Stockton	Manchester Orrell	23(4)	1	5
Richard Hughes Cheshire	5.10	14.00	28.01.76	Liverpool	Manchester Sale	18(4)	3	15
Jamie Greenlees Cheshire	5.11	14.04	18.07.76	Manchester	Manchester	4(3)	2	10
Simon Baker Warwickshire	5.9	11.07	01.02.75	Rugby	Manchester Rugby	15(9) 12(17)	2 3	10 15

FORWARDS

	Ht.	Wt.	Birthdate	Birthplace	CLUB	League Apps	Tries	Pts
Nick Wheeler Cheshire	6.0	17.08	13.12.59	Liverpool	Manchester Sale	69(2)	1	5
Dave Simpkins	6.1	17.05	16.03.69	Mafeking(SA)	Manchester	48(11)	1	5
James Batt Lancashire	6.0	17.00	13.05.75	Barnet	Manchester Sale	13(10)	-	-
Mark Palmer	5.10	15.07	26.07.74	Leeds	Manchester	1(1)	-	-
Luke Hewson Cheshire	6.0	17.00	06.12.69	Salford	Manchester Sale	44 10(5)	4 1	20 5
Matt Kirke Cheshire	6.7	16.07	26.06.73	Fairlie (NZ)	Manchester Sale	24 1	3 -	15 -
Guy Parker Lancashire	6.6	16.00	28.01.63	Rochdale	Manchester Sale	49(15)	6	30
Dave Craddock Cheshire	6.6	15.10	06.11.69	Manchester	Manchester	70(1)	7	35
Pete Craddock	6.4	14.00	21.08.71	Manchester	Manchester	46(2)	12	60
Tim Burgon Cheshire	5.10	14.08	21.09.64	Manchester	Manchester Stockport	60(2)	40	200
John Duggan	6.5	16.00	16.03.74	Leicester	Manchester Fylde	12 22(3)	- 3	- 15
Stuart Williams	6.5	15.00	06.09.75	Wigan	Manchester Liverpool St Helens	6(4)	3	15
John Fowler England A	6.8 Richmond 9/4/1, Rosslyn Park 17/-/-, Newcastle 15/-/-, Sale 43/5/25	17.08	06.02.68	Kent	Manchester	8(1)	2	10
Danny Collins England Colts.	5.10	14.00	12.08.79	Manchester	Manchester	1(5)	-	-
Nick Betteridge	5.11	14.07	04.12.70	Bradford	Manchester Sale	(10)	-	-

MANCHESTER RUGBY CLUB FACT FILE

Founded: 1860

Colours: Red & white hoops/white/red & white
Change colours: Navy shirt with red & white pinstriped hoops

GROUND

Address: Grove Park, Grove Lane, Cheadle Hulme, Cheshire. SK8 7NB.
Tel: 0161 485 3733 Fax: 0161 485 3733 Clubcall: 09068 884508
e-mail: rugby@manchester-rugby.co.uk Website: www.manchester-rugby.co.uk
Capacity: 4,000 Seated: 250 Standing: 3,750

Directions: Exit Junct. 3 from M60 and head south on A34 (Wilmslow) for 2.5 miles to second roundabout. Exit left (B5095) and club is 400 metres on the right.
From South: M56, Manchester Airport to A34, Wilmslow to B5095, Bramhall, club is about a mile.
Nearest Railway Station: Cheadle Hulme.

Car Parking: 200 spaces available within the ground.

Admission: (inclusive of programme)
Match day Members & OAPs £5.00. Non Members £8
Children Free
Season Ticket £80 includes membership

Club Shop: Yes. Manager - Paula Johnson

Clubhouse: Has three bars and food is available.
Functions: up to 160 for a seated meal. 0161 485 1115

Training Nights: Tuesday and Thursday 7pm

PROGRAMME

Size: A5 Pages: 48
Price: with admission Editor: Barry Sheffiff

ADVERTISING RATES- Mono Special location - Page £250

Page £200 1/2 page £125 1/4 page £70

Manchester lock, Dave Craddock, makes sure of possession from this lineout.

MOSELEY F.C.

President	Tony Kenny	c/o Moseley FC
Managing Director	Simon Cooper	c/o Moseley FC
Director of Rugby	John White	c/o Moseley FC 0121 449 4848 (H)
Club Secretary	Mrs Jackie Thomas	c/o Moseley FC or 5 Mapperley Gardens, Moseley, Birmingham B13 8RN 0121 249 3293 (H)
Youth & Development Director	Tom Campbell	c/o Moseley FC
Commercial Manager	Brian McNamee	c/o Moseley FC

Moseley FC,
The Reddings,
Reddings Road,
Moseley,
Birmingham B13 8LW

Tel: 0121 449 2149
Fax: 0121 442 4147

Out of Administration on June 12th, 1998, director of rugby John White found he had inherited ten contract players including the Scottish international Ian Smith, who coached but was unable to play because of a long term injury. Three of the last season's all conquering Colts side who had had some 1st XV experience were available and two others became regulars in the squad during the season. Seventeen new players were engaged on part time contracts including Mark Chudleigh, the former Bristol scrum-half who returned to Moseley from Birmingham Solihull and was appointed captain.
All credit must go to John White, the players and the coaches for acquitting themselves so well. The club's league position was maintained and there were some notable performances. These included the adrenalin inspired win over Leeds in the second match of the season, the double over Coventry, the home win against Worcester, the splendid win away at Waterloo and the narrow defeat at London Welsh.
Canadian international lock Tony Healy won a cap against Argentina, flanker Peter Buxton won an England Under 21 cap against South Africa and lock Andy Hall only nineteen and a 1st XV regular represented Scotland Under 21. Moseley's 1st XV Player of the Year was Matt Long who missed only one league game, another prop Lee Fortey won the most improved player award and the supporters' awards went to Peter Buxton, the Player of the Year, and Marcus Cook, the Away Player of the Year voted by the travelling supporters. Mark Chudleigh won the Shakespeares Solicitors Player of the Year award. His form was at times inconsistent but in a difficult season his support as captain of the club was constant.
The Colts (U19) followed closely in the footsteps of last season's unbeaten side. They lost just one game against Gloucester in the National Clubs Colts Cup. They won the North Midlands Colts Cup, the Under 21s MEB Powerline Floodlit Cup and the Under 16s the North Midlands Under 16 Cup. The youth section with Alex Hadley (England Colts), Alistair Hall and Stephen Nutt (Scotland Under 18 Schools) and Adam Coniff (England Under 18 Clubs) winning international caps continues to thrive.
The club celebrated its 125th Anniversary, one of the highlights being a match against the Penguins International Rugby Football Club who won an exhilarating encounter 38-36.

Moseley Squad 1998-99

MOSELEY

Match No.	Date	H/A	Comp.	Opponents	Result & Score	Att.	15	14	13	12	11
1	05.09	H	AD2	Wakefield*	L 32-33	678	Cook	Simpson/t	Roberts(l)	Ayeb	Martin(n)
2	12.09	H	AD2	Leeds Tykes	W 27-22	503	Cook/t	Simpson	Eason/t	Ayeb(c)	Gregory/t
3	19.09	A	AD2	Worcester	L 8-23	3,500	Cook	Simpson/t	Eason	Ayeb	Gregory
4	26.09	H	AD2	Waterloo	L 13-15	616	Jones(y)	Simpson(c)	Roberts	Ayeb	Gregory/t
5	03.10	A	AD2	Exeter	L 8-20	880	Cook	Simpson(r)	Roberts	Martin/t	Gregory
6	10.10	H	AD2	Fylde	W 44-22	786	Cook(r)	Simpson/t	Martin/t(b/t)	Roberts	Gregory
7	17.10	A	AD2	Rugby Lions	L 8-20	650	Cook	Jones	Roberts	Martin(b)	Gregory
8	24.10	H	AD2	London Welsh	L 16-31	631	Cook	Simpson	Martin	Roberts	Gregory
9	31.10	A	AD2	Blackheath	W 18-14	550	Cook/t	Jones	Martin	Roberts	Gregory
10	07.11	H	AD2	Orrell	W 25-3	803	Cook/t	Simpson	Roberts	Ayeb	Jones/2tcp
11	22.11	A	AD2	Bristol	L 18-58	2,304	Binns	Simpson/t	Martin/t	Roberts	Gregory(b)
12	12.12	H	AD2	Rotherham	L 6-16	560	Binns	Simpson	Martin	Roberts	Jones/2p
13	19.12	A	AD2	Coventry	W 46-21	1,200	Jones/5c2p	Simpson	Martin(b/t)	Roberts	Gregory/t
14	02.01	H	AD2	Bristol	L 6-43	961	Cook	Simpson	Martin(b)	Roberts	Jones/2p
15	16.01	A	AD2	Orrell	L 14-20	800	Cook	Jones/3p	Martin	Roberts	Gregory(i)
16	23.01	H	AD2	Blackheath	W 22-16	641	Cook/t	Simpson/t	Ayeb	Binns	Gregory(c)
17	06.02	A	AD2	London Welsh	L 24-26		Cook/t	Simpson	Martin	Ayeb	Jones/4p(n)
18	13.02	H	AD2	Rugby Lions	W 35-20	677	Cook	Simpson/t	Martin/t	Ayeb(a)	Jones/3c3p
19	27.02	A	AD2	Fylde	L 8-17	500	Jones/p	Colvin	Roberts/t	Martin	Gregory
20	13.03	H	AD2	Exeter	L 12-15	609	Cook	Colvin	Roberts	Brading	Martin(r)
21	27.03	A	AD2	Waterloo	W 32-8	500	Cook/t	Gregory	Roberts/2t	Brading	Martin
22	03.04	H	AD2	Worcester	W 18-16	1,199	Cook	Gregory	Roberts	Brading/t	Martin/t
23	18.04	A	AD2	Leeds Tykes	L 8-50	287	Cook	Gregory	Roberts	Brading/t	Martin(b)
24	24.04	A	AD2	Wakefield	L 20-38	500	Cook/2tc	Gregory(b)	Martin	Brading	Coniffe
25	01.05	H	AD2	Coventry	W 30-29	1,064	Cook/t	Martin/t	Binns/t	Brading	Ayeb/t
26	08.05	A	AD2	Rotherham	L 0-27	3,000	Cook	Gregory	Binns	Brading	Martin
A	15.11	H	TB3	Fylde	W 22-15	491	Cook(n/t)	Simpson	Martin/t	Roberts	Jones/tp
B	09.01	H	TB4	Lydney	L 24-25	748	Cook	Jones/t(z)	Martin/t(a)	Ayeb	Gregory

* after opponents name indicates a penalty try
Brackets after a player's name indicates he was replaced. eg (a) means he was replaced by replacement code "a" and so on.
/ after a player or replacement name is followed by any scores he made - eg /t, /c, /p, /dg or any combination of these

1998-99 HIGHLIGHTS

League debuts: Marcus Cook, Nigel Simpson, Martin Roberts, Yazid Ayeb, Richard Protherough, Richard WHite, Ian Patten, Ben Eason, Tony Healy, Steffan Jones, Ian Cotton, Scot Bemand, Andy Hall, Simon Brading, C Colvin, A Coniff.

Ever Presents: none - most appearances Ian Patten 25.

Players used: 34 plus 2 as a replacement only.

Most Points in a season:

Pts	Player	T	C	P	DG
85	A Binns	2	12	17	-
82	S Jones	2	9	18	-
61	J Smart	1	10	9	3
47	M Cook	9	1	-	-

MATCH FACTS

10	9	1	2	3	4	5	6	7	8	1
Smart/t3c2p	Chudleigh/t	Long(k)	Protherough	Webber	White	Mitchell	Short(m)	D-Lee	Patten	2
Binns/2cp	Chudleigh/t	Mackinnon(e)	Hampton(f)	Webber	White	Mitchell	Buckton	D-Lee	Patten	3
Binns/p	Chudleigh	Mackinnon(e)(p)	Protherough	Webber	White(q)	Mitchell	Buckton	D-Lee	Patten	4
Binns/p	Chudleigh	Long	Hampton(f)	Webber	White/t	Healy	Buckton	D-Lee	Cotton	5
Binns/p	Chudleigh(t)	Long(s)	Protherough	Webber	White	Healy(h)	Buckton	D-Lee	Patten	6
Binns/5c3p	Chudleigh/t	Long(s)	Protherough	Webber	White(w)	Mitchell	Buckton/t	D-Lee	Patten	7
Binns/p	Chudleigh	Adams	Hampton	Webber	White	Mitchell	Buckton	D-Lee(m/t)	Patten	8
Smart/c3p	Chudleigh	Long	Protherough	Webber	Hall	Mitchell	Buckton/t	Mellors	Patten	9
Smart/cpdg	Chudleigh(t)	Long(u)	Protherough	Webber	Hall	Mitchell	Buckton	Mellors/t	Patten	10
Smart	Bemand(d)	Fortey(e)	Hampton	Adams	Hall	Mitchell	Buckton	Mellors/t	Patten	11
Smart/cpdg	Bemand	Fortey(e)	Hampton(f)	Adams	Mitchell	Healy(w)	Buckton	D-Lee(m)	Patten	12
Smart	Chudleigh	Long	Protherough	Webber	Mitchell	Healy	Buckton	D-Lee	Patten	13
Binns	Chudleigh(t)	Long	Protherough	Mackinnon/t	Mitchell/t	Healy/t	Buckton/t	D-Lee	Patten	14
Binns	Chudleigh(t)	Long(k)	Protherough(o)	Webber	Mitchell	Healy	Buckton	D-Lee	Patten	15
Binns	Chudleigh	Long	Protherough/t	Webber	Mitchell	Healy	Buckton	Mellors	Patten	16
Smart/2cp	Chudleigh(t)	Long	Protherough	Mackinnon(g)	Healy	Hall	Short	Buckton	Patten/t	17
Binns/c	Chudleigh	Fortey	Protherough	Long(v)	Healy	Mitchell/t	Short(j)	Buckton	Patten	18
Binns/t	Chudleigh	Fortey(v)	Protherough	Long	Healy	Mitchell(w)	Short(m/t)	Buckton	Patten	19
Binns	Chudleigh	Long	Protherough	Fortey(v)	Healy	Mitchell(w)	Short(j)	Buckton	Patten	20
Binns/4p	Bemand	Long	Protherough	Fortey	Healy	Hall	Short(h)	Buckton	Patten	21
Binns/2cp	Bemand(d)	Long	Protherough/t	Fortey(v)	Healy	Hall	Buckton(i)	D-Lee/t	Patten	22
Binns/c2p(b)	Bemand	Long	Protherough	Fortey(v)	Healy	Hall	Buckton(i)	D-Lee	Patten	23
Binns/p	Bemand(d)	Long	Hampton(A)	Fortey(k)	Healy	Hall	D-Lee	Buckton(x)	Short	24
Binns/p	Bemand(d)	Long	Hubbleby	Mackinnon	Healy	Hall	Buckton/t	D-Lee(i)	Patten	25
Smart/2cpdg	Chudleigh	Fortey	Hampton	Mackinnon	Hall	Mitchell	Buckton	Mellors	Patten	26
Smart	Chudleigh(t)	Fortey	Hampton	Mackinnon(e)	Hall	Healy(i)	Buckton(f)	Mellors	Patten	
										A
Binns/2c	Chudleigh(t)	Fortey(e)	Hampton(f)	Adams	Hall	Mitchell	Buxton	Mellors(j)	Patten	B
Smart/3p	Chudleigh	Long	Hampton	Webber	Healy	Mitchell	Buckton/t	D-Lee	Patten	

REPLACEMENTS:					
a- M Roberts	b- Y Ayeb	c - R Martin	d - M Chudleigh	e - M Long	f - R Protherough
g - N Webber	h - N Mitchell	i - P Short	j - B Drake-Lee	k - S Mackinnon	l - A Binns
m - J Mellors	n - G Gregory	o - R Hampton	p - R Sigley	q - A Healy	r - S Jones
s - H Adams	t - S Bemand	u - L Fortey	v - P Jones	w - A Hall	x - A Hubbleday
y - M Cook	z - N Simpson	A - R White			

With the kicking duties split between a number of players during the season none of the points scoring records were threatened.

Full back Marcus Cook in his first season at the club scored 9 tries to finish top of the list.

In the away win against Coventry they did achieve a record points total for an away match in league rugby with a 46-21 win. This beat the previous highest score away from home of 42 against Wakefield set in March 1997.

MOSELEY

LEAGUE STATISTICS
compiled by Stephen McCormack

SEASON	Division	P	W	D	L	F	A	Pts Diff	Lge Pts	Lge Pos	Most Points	Most Tries
89-90	1	11	2	0	9	138	258	-120	4		52 Carl Arntzen	6 Simon Robson
90-91	1	12	1	1	10	113	244	-131	3		68 Carl Arntzen	2 Carl Arntzen Graham Smith Laurence Boyle
91-92	2	12	6	0	6	215	196	19	12		62 Alastair Kerr	6 Dave Spiller
92-93	2	12	6	2	4	184	150	34	14		40 Bob Massey	3 Nick Parry & Bob Massey
93-94	2	18	9	1	8	266	220	46	19		83 Simon Hodgkinson	5 Mark Linett
94-95	2	18	8	1	9	299	303	-4	17		156 Simon Hodgkinson	2 by 6 players
95-96	2	18	7	0	11	327	447	-120	14		172 Alastair Kerr	7 Alastair Kerr
96-97	2	22	9	0	13	492	741	-249	18		177 Richard Le Bas	15 Darragh O'Mahoney
97-98	P2	22	11	1	10	478	421	57	23		178 Matt Jones	17 Darragh O'Mahoney
98-99	P2	26	10	0	16	498	633	-135	20	10	85 Andy Binns	9 Marcus Cook

BIGGEST MARGINS

Home Win	35pts - 44-9 v Fylde 25.4.98
Away Win	29pts - 42-13 v Wakefield 29.03.97
Home Defeat	72pts - 15-87 v Richmond 5.10.96
Away Defeat	69pts - 19-88 v Newcastle 22.3.97

MOST CONSECUTIVE

Appearances	32 Mark Linnett 3.11.92 - 1.10.94
Matches scoring Tries	5 Darragh O'Mahoney
Matches scoring points	11 Carl Arntzen
Victories	5
Defeats	8

MOST POINTS

Scored at Home	48 v Rotherham 26.4.97
Scored Away	46 v Coventry 19.12.98
Conceded at Home	87 v Richmond 5.10.96
Conceded Away	88 v Newcastle 22.3.97

MOST TRIES

Scored in a match	9 v Sale 4.4.92
Conceded in a match	14 v Richmond 5.10.96 (H) v Newcastle 22.3.97 (A)

MOST APPEARANCES

by a forward	84 Mark Linnett
by a back	63 Alastair Kerr

	MOST IN A SEASON	MOST IN A CAREER	MOST IN A MATCH	
Points	178 Matt Jones 97-98	364 Alastair Kerr 91-96	27 Simon Hodgkinson	v Lon. Irish 8.4.95 (H)
Tries	17 Darragh O'Mahoney 97-98	32 Darragh O'Mahoney 95-98	3 Peter Shillingford Dave Spiller Darragh O'Mahoney	v Wasps 5.2.88 (H) v Sale 4.4.92 (H) v Nottingham 2.2.97 (A) v Waterloo 14.2.98 (A) v Fylde 25.4.98 (H)
Conversions	27 Richard Le Bas 96-97	38 Alastair Kerr 91-96	6 Richard Le Bas	v Rotherham 26.4.97 (H)
Penalties	41 Simon Hodgkinson 94-95	61 Alastair Kerr 91-96	8 Alastair Kerr	v Waterloo 17.2.96 (H)
Drop Goals	5 Matt Jones 97-98	5 Alastair Kerr 91-96 Matt Jones 97-98	2 Alastair Kerr A Houston Matt Jones	v Plymouth 21.12.92 (H) v Blackheath 14.1.95 v Orrell 25.10.97 (H)

MOSELEY PLAYING SQUAD

BACKS	Ht.	Wt.	Birthdate	Birthplace	CLUB	League Apps	Tries	Pts
Marcus Cook	6.4	15.0	14.07.75	Cuckfield	Moseley	21(1)	9	45
Rod Martin	6.0	14.0	25.11.75	Southend	Moseley	47(4)	13	65
Martin Roberts	6.3	15.2	26.01.68	Gloucester	Moseley	18(1)	3	15
Andy Binns	5.10	13.0	29.06.76	Yorkshire	Moseley	36(2)	5	105
Simon Brading			03.07.79	Bedford	Moseley Bedford	7 3	2 1	10 5
Stefan Jones	6.2	14.00	09.02.74	Llanelli	Moseley Bristol	10	2	82
Scott Bemand			21.09.78	Hereford	Moseley	7(6)	-	-
Geoff Gregory			08.06.74	Wolverhampton	Moseley	17(3)	3	15
Mark Chudleigh			31.01.74	Launceston	Moseley	19(4)	3	15
Yazid Ayeb					Moseley	8(8)	3	15
Nigel Simpson					Moseley	15	6	30

FORWARDS	Ht.	Wt.	Birthdate	Birthplace	CLUB	League Apps	Tries	Pts
Lee Fortey			25.08.75	Gloucester	Moseley	13(5)	-	-
Nathan Webber	6.1	17.0	20.06.74	Stratford	Moseley	72(1)	-	-
Rich Protherough	5.9	14.00	09.11.76	Cheltenham	Moseley Worcester	17(5)	2	10
Jason Mellors			30.06.79	Birmingham	Moseley			
Tony Healy	6.6	17.12	17.07.69		Moseley	17(1)	1	5
Matthew Long	6.05	16.0	25.03.75	Gloucester	Moseley Newcastle	25(8) 31	- 1	- 5
Neil Mitchell British Police	6.6	17.5	22.06.66	Newcastle	Moseley	40(4)	5	25
Bill Drake-Lee	6.0	15.0	09.08.70	Kettering	Moseley Leicester	32(3) 20(6)	2 1	10 5
Richard White					Moseley Nottingham	7(1) 12	2 -	10 -
Andy Hall					Moseley	11(4)	-	-
Stuart Mackinnon	6.0	17.7	06.01.69	Kuala Lumpar	Moseley	27(9)	6	30
Peter Buckton	6.5	16.7	21.08.78	Cheltenham	Moseley	30(4)	4	20
Ian Patten Other clubs: Bristol 35/3/15	6.5	16.0	31.08.70	Bristol	Moseley Coventry	7 45	1 10	5 50

MOSELEY

FACT FILE

Founded: 1873
Nickname: Mose

Colours: Red with black hoops/black/red & black hoops
Change colours: Light grey & navy blue hoops

GROUND

Address: The Reddings, Reddings Road, Moseley, Birmingham. B13 8LW.
Tel: 0121 449 2149 Fax: 0121 442 4147 e-mail: moseleyfc@compuserve.com
Capacity: 5,000 Seating- Covered: 400 Uncovered: 200 Standing- Covered: 200 Uncovered : 4,000

Directions: A 38 South of Birmingham to Edgbaston Road, turn at traffic lights passing Edgbaston County Cricket ground on left, to traffic island, right into Russell Rd, left into Reddings Rd
Nearest Railway Station: Birmingham New Street,

Car Parking: 150 at ground, 400 nearby

Admission:

Season	Adult £100	Oap's £65	Students £26	Family £200
Matchday	Adult£9	Oap's £7	Students £3	

Club Shop: Yes; Manager Robin Shipway

Clubhouse: Normal Licensing hours, 3 bars with snacks avaiable
Functions: 2 rooms available for hire, capacity 80/200
Contact Club for details

Training Nights: Tuesday & Thursday

PROGRAMME

Size: B4 Pages: 20 Price: £2
Editor: Peter Woodrolfe
ADVERTISING RATES
Contact Brian McNamee c/o the club

Mark Chudleigh - Moseley Club Captain 98-99

Matt Long - Moseley Player of the Year 98-99

ORRELL R.U.F.C.

Chairman	Ron Pimblett	c/o Orrell RUFC, Edge Hall Road, Orrell, Nr Wigan WN58TL
Club Secretary	John Arrowsmith	1 Fisher Drive, Orrell, Wigan, Lancs. WN5 8QX 01942 216879 (H), 01695 632116 (Fax)
Office Manager	Miss Wendy Houghton	c/o Orrell RUFC, Club Office, Edgehall Rd, Orrell, Wigan WN5 8TL 01695 623193 (B), 01695 632116 (Fax)

President J Johnston | **Chairman of Rugby** D V Southern | **Chairman of Finance** J R Gaskell

Chairman of Colts & Juniors J Lloyd | **Chairman of Land & Property** N Lowe

Having lost almost a whole team at the beginning of the 1996/97 season, they were relegated for the first time in their history and, although still cushioned by First Division funding, they missed out on promotion to finish fifth in Allied Dunbar Two at the end of 1997/98.

Unable to return to the elite they suffered a severe reduction in income and, as the financial screws began to tighten, a drastic re-appraisal of the financial and rugby structure of the club was carried out. Refusing to mortgage their assets in an attempt to keep up with more wealthy competitors they attempted to cut their cloth accordingly. The whole squad moved to part time, a number of players departed including Director of Coaching Ged Glynn, who was replaced by `Sammy' Southern, and a coaching panel came in under former club captain Bill Lyon, assisted by Phil Moss and former British Lions and England wing Mike Slemen.

Before the season started Ian Wynn and Paul Manley returned and other players have since been recruited including David Slemen son of the former British Lion together with a number of others out of the local junior ranks.

Unfortunately with financial screws tightening and unable to satisfy creditors they were forced to go into administration leading to the departure of Manley and Stuart Turner to Worcester just before Christmas.

With the youngest squad ever to represent the club, all but four under the age of 25 including four still only 19, they finished a very creditable eighth in Allied Dunbar Two winning four our of the final five games of the season

Most of the squad have pledged themselves to the club for the coming season and, if they can recapture the form they showed at the close of the last campaign, they would expect to be very competitive this time round.

Geoff Lightfoot

Utility forward, Rob Rawlinson, getting to grips with the Coventry attack. Photo: Alison Goulding

ORRELL

Match No.	Date	H/A	Comp.	Opponents	Result & Score	Att.	15	14	13	12	11
1	05.09	A	AD2	Fylde	W 20-6	650	Lyon/t	Liptrot/t	Wright	Wynn	Verbickas/cp
2	12.09	H	AD2	Rugby Lions*	W 32-3	1,000	Lyon	Liptrot/t(i)	Wright(j)	Wynn/t	Verbickas/3c2p
3	19.09	A	AD2	London Welsh	L 17-24		Lyon	Liptrot/c	Wright	Wynn	Verbickas/cp(i)
4	26.09	H	AD2	Blackheath	W 60-3	1,000	Lyon/2t	Liptrot/2t	Oliver	Wynn	Hope
5	03.10	H	AD2	Leeds Tykes	L 11-13	700	Lyon	Hope	Wright(b/t)	Wynn	Oliver
6	10.10	A	AD2	Bristol	L 19-29	3,477	Lyon/t	Hope	Oliver(s)	Hamer/c(p/tc)	Smith
7	17.10	H	AD2	Rotherham	W 19-12	1,100	Lyon	Johnson	Sleman	Hope(p)	Verbickas/2p
8	24.10	A	AD2	Coventry	L 14-26	1,200	Lyon	Verbickas/3p	Sleman	Hope	Johnson/t
9	31.10	H	AD2	Wakefield	W 24-5	800	Lyon/t	Hamer	Hope	Wynn	Sleman/2t3p(s)
10	07.11	A	AD2	Moseley	L 3-25	803	Taberner	Sleman/p	Hope(p)	Wynn	Verbickas
11	21.11	H	AD2	Worcester	L 9-13	1,200	Lyon	Verbickas/2p	Hope(o)	Wynn	Sleman
12	12.12	A	AD2	Wakefield	W 17-10	500	Lyon	Johnson	Sleman	Wynn/t	Verbickas/3p
13	19.12	H	AD2	Exeter	L 21-23	1,000	Lyon	Johnson/2t(b)	Hope	Wynn	Verbickas/2p
14	02.01	A	AD2	Worcester	L 0-17	2,336	Lyon	Hope	Sleman	Wynn	Verbickas
15	16.01	H	AD2	Moseley	W 20-14	800	Lyon	Sleman/c	Hope	Wynn	Verbickas/tc2p
16	23.01	A	AD2	Wakefield	L 13-25	500	Lyon(p)	Hamer	Hope	Wynn	Verbickas/c2p
17	06.02	H	AD2	Coventry	W 31-0	600	Lyon	Hitchmough(o)	Hope/t	Wynn/t	Verbickas/t4cp
18	13.02	A	AD2	Rotherham	L 10-47		Lyon	Johnson/t	Hope/t	Wynn(j)	Verbickas(p)
19	27.02	H	AD2	Bristol	L 32-34	1,000	Hitchmough	Johnson/3t	Hope	Wynn	Verbickas/t3c2p
20	14.03	A	AD2	Leeds	L 7-20	620	Hitchmough	Johnson(a)	Hope	Wynn	Verbickas/tc
21	27.03	A	AD2	Blackheath	L 9-15	600	Lyon	Johnson	Hope	Wynn	Verbickas/3p
22	03.04	H	AD2	London Welsh	W 18-15	1,000	Lyon(v)	Johnson/t	Hope	Wynn	Verbickas/c2p
23	17.04	A	AD2	Rugby Lions	W 41-29	480	Lyon(v)	Johnson	Hope	Wynn/2t	Verbickas/2t3c
24	24.04	H	AD2	Fylde	W 28-18	600	Lyon	Johnson(v)	Hope(j)	Wynn/dg	Verbickas/2t2c2p
25	01.05	A	AD2	Exeter	L 32-42	1,200	Hitchmough	Johnson(x)	Wynn(i)(y/t)	Sleman	Verbickas/2t3c2p
26	08.05	H	AD2	Waterloo	W 59-15	800	Hitchmough/t(a)	Johnson/2t	Hope(y)	Wynn/t(j)	Verbickas/3t6c
A	14.11	A	TBC	Reading	W 23-12	400	Sleman/p	Hope	Wynn	D Wright	Verbickas/t
B	09.01	A	TBC	Waterloo	L 11-18	900	Lyon	Hope	Sleman	Wynn	Verbickas/2p

* after opponents name indicates a penalty try
Brackets after a player's name indicates he was replaced. eg (a) means he was replaced by replacement code "a" and so on.
/ after a player or replacement name is followed by any scores he made - eg /t, /c, /p, /dg or any combination of these

1998-99 HIGHLIGHTS

League debuts: Neil Liptrot, Gareth Russell, Matt Lacey, James Hayter, Andy Carroll, Kurt Johnson, David Sleman, Nick Wilkinson, Chris Bentley, David Bailey, Ian Grainey

Ever Presents: None - most appearances Paul Rees 25.

Players used: 36 plus 7 as a replacement only.

Most Points in a season:

Pts	Player	T	C	P	DG
224	S Verbickas	13	30	33	-
50	K Johnson	10	-	-	-
33	D Sleman	4	2	3	-
33	I Wynn	6	-	-	1
28	P Hamer	-	8	4	-

MATCH FACTS

10	9	1	2	3	4	5	6	7	8	
Oliver/t	Warr	Kelly	Moffatt	Turner	Rees	Cusani	Russell	Lacey(h)	Manley	1
Oliver/t	Warr	Kelly	Moffatt(k)	Turner(l)	Rees	Cusani	Lacey	Millerchip	Manley	2
Oliver/t	Newton	Cundick(d)	Moffatt	Turner	Rees	Cusani	Russell/t(g)	Millerchip	Manley	3
Hamer/7c2p	Newton(c)	Kelly/2t(l)	Moffatt/t(n)	Turner	Rees	Cusani	Russell	Millerchip	Manley/t	4
Hamer/2p	Newton(c)	Kelly	Moffatt(n)	Turner	Rees	Cusani	Russell	Millerchip(l)	Manley	5
Ryan	Warr	Cundick/t	Rawlinson	Turner	Rees	Cusani	Russell	Lacey	Manley	6
Ryan/dg	Warr/t	Cundick(q)	Rawlinson(e)	Turner	Rees	Cusani	Russell/t	Lacey	Manley(r)	7
Ryan	Warr	Kelly	Moffatt	Cundick	Rees	Cusani	Manley	Lacey	Bailey	8
Ryan	Warr	Cundick(d)	Rawlinson(e)	Turner	Rees	Cusani	Manley(g)	Gregory	Bailey	9
Ryan	Warr(t)	Cundick(q)	Moffatt	Turner	Rees	Cusani	Huxley	Lacey	Bailey(k)	10
Ryan/dg	Warr(m)	Kelly	Rawlinson	Turner	Rees	Glynn	Huxley(u)	Lacey	Bailey	11
Ryan/dg	Warr	Kelly	Moffatt	Cundick(q)	Rees	Cusani	Huxley	Lacey	Bailey	12
Ryan	Warr	Kelly/t	Rawlinson	Cundick(q)	Huxley	Cusani	Hayter(e)	Lacey	Grainey	13
Ryan	Newton(c)	Kelly	Rawlinson(e)	Cundick(q)	Rees	Cusani	Huxley	Lacey	Grainey	14
Ryan	Warr(m)	Kelly(q)	Hayter(e)	Cundick	Rees	Cusani	Huxley(n)	Lacey/t	Bailey	15
Sleman/t	Newton	Wilkinson(d)	Moffatt	Cundick	Rees	Bentley	Rawlinson	Lacey	Grainey	16
Sleman/t	Warr	Kelly	Moffatt	Cundick(q)	Rees	Bentley	Huxley	Lacey(k)	Rawlinson	17
Sleman	Warr(m)	Kelly(q)	Moffatt(k)	Cundick	Rees	Bentley(f)	Huxley	Lacey	Rawlinson	18
Ryan	Newton	Kelly	Hayter	Cundick	Rees	Cusani	Huxley(r)	Lacey	Rawlinson	19
Sleman	Newton	Kelly	Hayter	Cundick	Rees	Cusani	Huxley	Lacey	Bailey(u)	20
Sleman	Newton	Kelly	Moffatt	Cundick	Rees	Cusani	Grainey(j)	Lacey	Rawlinson	21
Sleman	Warr(m)	Kelly	Moffatt(k)	Cundick(q)	Rees	Bentley	Rawlinson	Lacey/t	Cusani	22
Sleman(j/t)	Warr/t(m/t)	Kelly(w)	Moffatt	Cundick(l)	Rees	Bentley	Grainey	Lacey(r)	Cusani	23
Sleman	Warr(m)	Kelly	Moffatt(k)	Cundick	Rees/t	Bentley	Grainey	Rawlinson	Cusani	24
Ryan	Newton/t(c)	Kelly	Hayter	Carroll	Rees	Bentley(s)	Grainey(r)	Rawlinson	Cusani	25
Sleman/c	Warr	Kelly/t	Hayter	Carroll(z)	Rees	Bentley(s)	Grainey/t(r)	Rawlinson	Cusani	26
Ryan/t	Warr	Kelly	Moffatt(n)	Turner(C)	Glynn(B)	Cusani/t	Huxley	Lacey	Bailey/t	A
Ryan	Warr/t	Kelly	Moffatt	Cundick(q)	Rees	Cusani(A)	Huxley	Lacey	Bailey(n)	B

REPLACEMENTS: a- D Lyon, b- N Liptrot, c - M Warr, d - S Kelly, e - A Moffatt, f - C Cusani, g - M Lacey, h - P Millerchi, i - G Hope, j - N Ryan, k - J Hayter, l - A Carroll, m - P Newton, n - R Rawlinson, o - K Johnson, p - G Bell, q - N Wilkinson, r - P Bailey, s - A Unsworth, t - G Povall, u - I Grainey, v - R Hitchmough, w - S Southern, x - P Engwell, y - M Brown, z - S Nichols, A - M Glynn, B - P Rees, C - J Cundick

Simon Verbikas topped the try and points scorers list for the second successive season. Both his totals, 13 tries and 224 points, were new league records for Orrell beating his own records of 12 and 165 from last season. He now holds the all time points scoring record for Orrell with 389 points in just 38(2) appearances.
He beat the previous record of 337 set by Gerry Ainscough.
Verbickas has now overtaken Dewi Morris as the clubs 2nd leading try scorer in league rugby after Nigel Heslop.
Verbickas passed Martin Street's career record of 46 conversions and ends the season with a new high of 54. In the process he set a new seasonal record with 30 easily beating the previous record of 21 also held by Street.

With Paul Manley going off to join Worcester mid season his record for most league appearances was passed in the last match of the season by Charles Cusani.

Steve Taberner extends his record for most appearances by a back by one to 96.

ORRELL

LEAGUE STATISTICS
compiled by Stephen McCormack

SEASON	Division	P	W	D	L	F	A	Pts Diff	Lge Pts	Lge Pos	Most Points	Most Tries
89-90	1	11	5	0	6	221	132	89	10		104 Martin Strett	5 Paul Manley
90-91	1	12	7	0	5	247	105	132	14		109 Martin Strett	7 Phil Halsall & Dewi Morris
91-92	1	12	10	0	2	204	95	109	20		104 Martin Strett	7 Dewi Morris
92-93	1	12	5	0	7	175	183	-8	10		63 Gerry Ainscough	6 Dewi Morris
93-94	1	18	8	0	10	327	302	25	16		84 Simon Langford	8 James Naylor
94-95	1	18	6	3	9	256	326	-70	15		81 Simon Langford	7 Ian Wynn
95-96	1	18	7	0	11	323	477	-154	14		166 Simon Mason	10 Graeme Smith
96-97	1	22	3	0	19	352	886	-534	6		116 Matthew McCarthy	5 Jim Naylor
97-98	P2	22	12	0	10	533	400	133	24		165 Simon Verbickas	12 Simon Verbickas
98-99	P2	26	12	0	14	566	483	83	24	8	224 SimonVerbickas	13 Simon Verbickas

MOST POINTS

Scored at Home	66 v Rugby 13.3.93
Scored Away	36 v Bristol 17.11.90
Conceded at Home	56 v Bath 31.8.96 v Harlequins 8.3.97
Conceded Away	89 v Harlequins 5.10.96

MOST CONSECUTIVE

Appearances	39 David Southern 26.9.87 - 17.11.90
Matches scoring Tries	3 Gerry Ainscough, Martin Strett & Phil Hassall
Matches scoring points	**17 Martin Strett**
Victories	5
Defeats	11

BIGGEST MARGINS

Home Win	66pts - 66-0 v Rugby 13.3.93
Away Win	33pts - 36-3 v Bristol 17.11.90
Home Defeat	43pts - 13-56 v Bath 31.8.96
Away Defeat	71pts - 18-89 v Harlequins 5.10.96

MOST TRIES

Scored in a match	11	v Rugby 13.3.93 (H) v Northampton 27.10.90 (H) v Rosslyn P. 28.4.90 (H)
Conceded in a match	14	v Harlequins 5.10.96 (A)

MOST APPEARANCES

by a forward	117 Charles Cusani
by a back	96 (5) Steve tavener

	MOST IN A SEASON	MOST IN A CAREER	MOST IN A MATCH	
Points	224 Simon Verbickas 98-99	389 Simon Verbickas 97-99	29 Simon Verbickas	v Wakefield 25.4.98 (H)
Tries	13 Simon Verbickas 98-99	26 Nigel Heslop 89-98	4 Paul Hamer	v Rugby 13.3.94 (H)
Conversions	30 Simon Verbickas 98-99	54 Simon Verbickas 97-99	8 Martin Strett	v Rosslyn P. 28.4.90 (H)
Penalties	38 Simon Mason 95-96	71 Gerry Ainscough 87-95	6 Martin Strett Matthew McCarthy	v Gloucester 28.3.92 (H) v Lon. Irish 22.2.97 (H)
Drop Goals	4 Matthew McCarthy 96-97	4 Martin Strett 88-93	3 Matthew McCarthy	v W. Hartlepool 7.12.97(H)

ORRELL PLAYING SQUAD

BACKS

	Ht.	Wt.	Birthdate	Birthplace	CLUB	League Apps	Tries	Pts
David Lyon	6.1	14.8	03.09.65	St Helens	Orrell	48(5)	13	65
Matt Oliver	6.1	13.7	30.11.76	Northampton	Orrell Bedford	18(1)	4	20
Simon Verbickas	6.1	13.7	22.04.75	Manchester	Orrell Sale	38(2) 23(3)	25 20	389 132
Neil Ryan	5.9	13.4	29.11.73	Wigan	Orrell Sale	31(8) 5(3)	8 4	58 20
Mark Warr	5.9	12.12	24.02.69	Birmingham	Orrell Sale	27(7) 38(4)	2 13	10 65
Darren Wright			17.01.68	Leigh	Orrell	16	4	20
Guy Hope England 10.			27.10.76	Beverley	Orrell	25(3)	3	15
Steve Taberner	5.10	13.0	15.09.62	Orrell	Orrell	96(5)	14	70
Paul Newton Ireland A			29.04.78	Penrith	Orrell	13(7)	2	10
David Sleman	6.2	13.09	12.09.78		Orrell	18	4	33
Kurl Johnson					Orrell	13(2)	10	50
Rob Hitchmough England U21.	5.10	12.07	17.12.75	St Helens	Orrell Wakefield	20(7) 13	5 2	33 10

FORWARDS

	Ht.	Wt.	Birthdate	Birthplace	CLUB	League Apps	Tries	Pts
Jason Cundick	6.0	17.0	09.09.73	Manchester	Orrell	58(4)	1	5
Stuart Turner			22.04.72	Southport	Orrell Waterloo	53(1) 38	1 -	5 -
Alex Moffatt	5.4	13.00	29.06.68	Workington	Orrell	41(14)	-	-
Rob Rawlinson	6.0	16.0	27.08.76	Littleborough	Orrell	23(12)	-	-
Steve Kelly			11.05.72	Manchester	Orrell	24(10)	4	20
Chas Cusani	6.6	17.0	22.10.65	Wigan	Orrell	119(2)	4	17
Paul Rees	6.6	17.0	10.04.73	Dagenham	Orrell	62(3)	2	10
Paul Manley England colts.	6.0	15.7	26.01.68	Stockport	Orrell Wakefield	116 19	14 3	64 15
Peter Millerchip			01.09.69	Bowden	Orrell	18(4)	1	5
Jeff Huxley	6.3	16.7	28.06.63	Billinge	Orrell	48(5)	2	10
Gareth Russell	6.0	15.5	30.07.72	Rochdale	Orrell Fylde	6	2	10
Ian Grainey					Orrell	8(2)	-	-
David Bailey			07.10.74	Whiston	Orrell	7(5)	-	-

ORRELL

FACT FILE

Founded: 1927

Colours: Amber & black
Change colours: Red

GROUND

Address: Edgehall Road, Orrell, Wigan, Lancs. WN5 8TL.
Tel: 01695 623193 Fax: 01695 632116
Capacity: 6,000 Seated: Covered 1,000 Standing: Covered 2,000, Uncovered 3,000

Directions: Ground is about 2 miles from M6 junct. 26. Left at traffic lights at end of slip road, then left at lights at the Stag Inn. After about 400 yds. left again at lights & after another 400 yds. left again at lights which take you into Edgehall Road.
Nearest Railway Station: Orrell

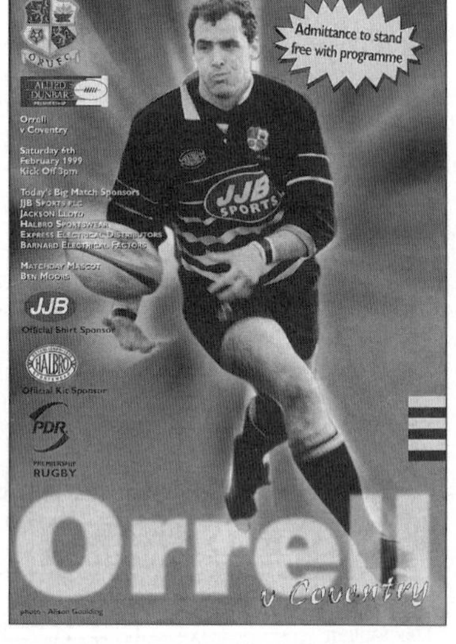

Car Parking: 250 spaces at the ground, 250 nearby

Admission:
Season Standing Adults £70, Children/OAPs £45
Matchday Standing Adults £6, (Seated £2 extra)
Children/OAPs £3. (Seated £1extra).

Club Shop: Yes, contact Office Manager 01695 623193

Clubhouse: Open normal licensing hours.
Snacks, bar meals & restaurant available
Functions: Capacity 250/300, contact Mr C Cusani House Manager

Training Nights: Tuesday and Thursday.

PROGRAMME (full colour)
Size: A5 Pages: 48 Price: £1.50
Editor: Geoff Lightfoot, c/o Club Office

ADVERTISING RATES - Contact - Club Office

Left:
Orrell full back, Rob Hitchmoore, sneaking thro' the Fylde defence.

Right:
Prop Steve Kelly shows his pace and strength against Liverpool St. Helens

Photos:
Alison E Goulding

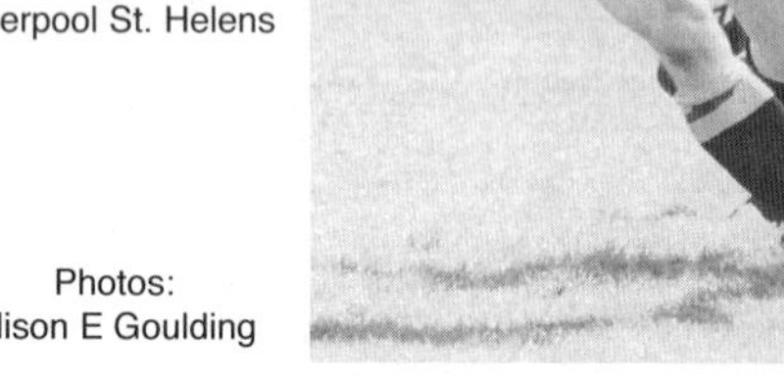

ROTHERHAM R.U.F.C.

Club Secretary	Allan Williams	116 Grange Road, Rotherham. S60 3LL. 01709 364190 (H & Fax)
Chairman	M Yarlett	High Beeches, Moorgate, Rotherham 01709 364306 (H), 01709 540982 (B), 01709 700648 (Fax)
Press Officer/Playing Mgr	S Cousins	c/o Yorkshire Window Co, Hellaby Ind Est., Hellaby, Rotherham 01246 413681 (H), 01709 540982 (B), 01709 700648 (Fax)
Coach		c/o Rotherham RUFC, Clifton Lane, Rotherham.S65 2AA
Commercial Manager	Wilf Duke	c/o Rotherham RUFC as above 0860 107973
Fixtures Secretary	Allan Williams	c/o Rotherham RUFC as above

Rotherham maintained their record of always improving their league position when they finished second in Allied Dunbar Division Two, level on points with Bristol, but losing the title by a ten point scoring margin.

This disappointment was compounded when they then drew with bottom but one in Allied Dunbar One Bedford over two legs in the play off and the First Division side survived.

The season started badly for Rotherham with a first game defeat at Waterloo as new players struggled to adapt to the style of new coach John Phillips. Victories, however, over Exeter, Rugby, London Welsh and Blackheath showed that they would once more be a threat. A defeat at Orrell slowed down the progress but league leaders Bristol went down at Clifton Lane before two Rotherham defeats at Leeds and Coventry left Bristol and Worcester clear. The rest of the season until the final game of the play offs was one of success. Seventeen consecutive league victories were recorded, and these included victories at both Bristol and Worcester, neither flukes as Rotherham dominated for long periods and the size of travelling support reached levels that would have not looked out of place at the top of the First Division.

The success of the season was once more based on the usual Rotherham ingredients of hard work throughout the team and a desire to win. Winger Dean Lax was the league's leading scorer with eighteen tries and Ben Wade in the back row notched sixteen for second place in the league list. The team scored over 100 league tries and once again improved their defence conceding just 30 tries.

Despite the disappointment at not gaining promotion Rotherham will once again be a force in 1999/2000 as they have now established themselves at the top end of the game and will be keen to retain their status, particularly as a club that values both its heritage and support.

L-R - **Back Row:** Neil Pattinson, Alan Buzza, Dean Lax, Martin Dawson, James Sinclair, Gerry Garnett, Scott Wilson, Matt Pinder, Lee Hall, Doug Trivella, Carlos Hassan. **Middle:** Jon Phillips, Richard Selkirk, Greg Austin, Craig West, Richard Bramley, John Dudley, Dan Cook, Gavin Webster, Howard Parr, Ben Wade, Ian Kearney, Jim Kilfoyle, Barry Forster. **Front:** Richard Wareham, Richard Hanson, Matt Walker, Darren McIntyre, Dave Scully, Mike Schmid, Neil Spence, Simon Bunting, Jon Harper, Jonathon Shepherd, Mike Umaga

ROTHERHAM

Match No.	Date	H/A	Comp.	Opponents	Result & Score	Att.	15	14	13	12	11
1	05.09	A	AD2	Waterloo	L 7-22	527	Umaga	Lax	Austin	Hassan	Harper
2	12.09	H	AD2	Exeter	W 28-17		Buzza/t	Lax	Austin/2t	Hassan	Harper(l)
3	26.09	H	AD2	Rugby Lions	W 44-0		Buzza	Lax	Austin/t	Hassan/t	Harper/t
4	03.10	A	AD2	London Welsh	W 27-13		Buzza	Lax	Austin/t	Hassan	Harper
5	10.10	H	AD2	Blackheath	W 46-3		Umaga	Lax/t	Austin(m)	Hassan	Harper
6	17.10	A	AD2	Orrell	L 12-19	1,100	Umaga	Lax/t	Austin	Hassan	Harper(i)
7	24.10	H	AD2	Bristol	W 16-5		Umaga	Harper	Austin	Hassan	Buzza
8	01.11	A	AD2	Leeds Tykes	L 10-15	2,682	Umaga	Harper	Austin	Hassan	Buzza
9	07.11	A	AD2	Coventry	L 12-22	1,200	Austin	Lax	Harper	Hassan	Buzza(l)
10	21.11	H	AD2	Wakefield*	W 34-7		Umaga/t	Harper	Austin	Hassan(p)	Walker
11	12.12	A	AD2	Moseley	W 16-6	560	Umaga	Buzza	Austin/t	Harper	Walker
12	19.12	H	AD2	Worcester	W 29-17	1,520	Umaga/t	Buzza	Austin/2t	Harper	Walker/t
13	02.01	A	AD2	Wakefield	W 40-13	800	Umaga	Lax	Austin/t(m)	Harper(p)	Walker/2t
14	16.01	H	AD2	Coventry	W 19-12		Umaga	Lax	Austin	Harper/t	Walker
15	23.01	H	AD2	Leeds Tykes	W 25-10		Umaga	Lax/t	Austin	Harper	Walker
16	06.02	A	AD2	Bristol	W 36-31	2,496	Umaga/t	Lax/t	Austin	Harper(m)	Walker
17	13.02	H	AD2	Orrell	W 47-10		Umaga	Lax/4t	Austin	Shepherd(p)	Walker
18	20.02	A	AD2	Fylde	W 34-5	600	Umaga	Lax/t	Sinclair	Shepherd	Walker
19	26.02	A	AD2	Blackheath	W 29-19	600	Umaga/t(b)	Lax/t	Sinclair	Shepherd/t	Walker/t
20	13.03	H	AD2	London Welsh	W 28-8		Trivella/4c	Lax	Sinclair	Shepherd	Walker
21	27.03	A	AD2	Rugby Lions	W 33-10	950	Umaga/t	Lax/2t	Austin	Shepherd	Walker/t
22	03.04	H	AD2	Fylde	W 43-16		Umaga	Lax/t	Austin	Shepherd/t(p/t)	Walker
23	17.04	A	AD2	Exeter	W 35-24	2,000	Umaga/t	Lax/t	Austin	Shepherd	Walker
24	24.04	H	AD2	Waterloo	W 44-3		Umaga	Lax/3t	Austin/t	Shepherd	Walker
25	01.05	A	AD2	Worcester	W 35-27	3,100	Umaga	Lax	Austin/t	Shepherd	Walker/3t
26	08.05	H	Ad2	Moseley	W 27-0	3,000	Umaga	Lax/t	Austin	Shepherd	Walker/t
A	14.11	H	TBC	London Welsh	W 8-6	750	Austin	Lax	Hassan	Harper	Walker
B	09.01	H	TBC	Leeds Tykes	L 24-27	2,000	Umaga	Lax/t	Austin	Harper	Sinclair
C	20.05	H	ADpo	Bedford	W 19-11	3,500	Umaga/t	Lax	Austin	Harper	Walker(m)
D	23.05	A	ADpo	Bedford	L 27-19	4,102	Umaga	Lax/t	Austin	Shepherd	Walker

* after opponents name indicates a penalty try
Brackets after a player's name indicates he was replaced. eg (a) means he was replaced by replacement code "a" and so on.
/ after a player or replacement name is followed by any scores he made - eg /t, /c, /p, /dg or any combination of these

1998-99 HIGHLIGHTS

League debuts:
Carlos Hassan, Doug Trivella, Dave Scully, Terry Garnett, Lee Hall, Howard Parr, Matt Walker, Richard Hanson, Jason Niarchos, Glen Kenworthy, Jim Thorp.

Ever Presents: Mark Schmid.

Players used: 31 plus one as replacement only.

Most Points in a season:

Pts	Player	T	C	P	DG
144	D Trivella	5	28	21	-
105	J Niarchos	1	26	16	-
90	D Lax	18	-	-	-
80	B Wade	16	-	-	-
50	G Austin	10	-	-	-

MATCH FACTS

10	9	1	2	3	4	5	6	7	8	
Trivella/c(i)	Scully	Pinder	Garnett	Hall	Webster	Dudley/t(j)	Parr	Spence(k)	Schmid	1
Trivella/2c3p(m)	Scully	Pinder	Garnett	Hall	Webster	Dudley(k)	Wade	Schmid	Parr	2
Trivella/t4c2p	Scully	Pinder	Garnett(n)	Hall	Webster	Cook	Wade/t	Spence	Schmid/t	3
Trivella/t2cp(m)	McIntyre	Pinder	Hall	Hanson	Cook	Dudley/t	Wade	Spence	Schmid/t	4
Trivella/t5c2p(i)	McIntyre(w)	Pinder(u)	Hall	Hanson	Dudley	Webster	Wade/2t	Spence(t)	Schmid/t	5
Trivella/c	McIntyre	Pinder	Hall	Hanson	Dudley(s)	Webster	Wade/t	Spence(t)	Schmid	6
Trivella/tc3p	Scully	Pinder	Hall	Wilson	Dudley	Webster	Wade	Spence(t)	Schmid	7
Trivella/cp	Scully	Pinder(n)	Hall(u/t)	Wilson(d)	Dudley(h)	Webster	Wade	Spence(t)	Schmid	8
Umaga	Scully/tc	Thorp	Garnett	Hanson	Webster	Bramley(g)	Wade/t	Parr	Schmid	9
Niarchos/2c	Scully/cp	Pinder	Garnett/t	Hall/t	Webster	Dudley(s)	Wade/t(u)(t)	Spence	Schmid	10
Niarchos/c3p	Scully	Bunting	Garnett	Hanson	Webster	Kenworthy	West	Spence	Schmid	11
Niarchos/3cp	Scully	Bunting	Garnett	Hanson	Dudley(f)	Kenworthy	Wade	Spence	Schmid	12
Niarchos/2c2p	Scully/t(o)	Bunting	Garnett	Hanson(c)	Webster	Kenworthy	Wade/t	Spence(h)	Schmid/t	13
Niarchos/c4p	Scully	Bunting	Garnett	Hanson	Webster(g)	Kenworthy	Wade	Spence(h)	Schmid	14
Niarchos	Scully	Bunting	Garnett	Hanson(c)	Dudley(f)	Kenworthy	Wade/3t(h/t)	Spence(t)	Schmid	15
Trivella/2c4p	Scully	Bunting	Garnett	Hanson	Dudley	Kenworthy	Wade/t	Spence/t	Schmid	16
Trivella/2c2p(q/c)	Scully/t	Bunting	Garnett(e)	Hanson(c)	Dudley/t(f)	Kenworthy/t	Wade	Spence(h)	Schmid	17
Niarchos/3cp	Scully/t	Bunting(u)	Garnett	Hanson	Dudley(f)	Kenworthy	Wade/t(h)	Spence	Schmid/2t	18
Niarchos/2c	Scully/t(o)	Bunting	Garnett	Hanson(v)	Dudley	Kenworthy	Wade	Spence(t)	Schmid	19
Niarchos/t	Scully(o/t)	Bunting	Garnett	Toews	Dudley/t	Kenworthy	Wade/t	Spence(h)	Schmid	20
Trivella/c2p(q)	McIntyre	Pinder	Garnett(e)	Toews	Dudley/t	Kenworthy	Wade	West(h)	Schmid	21
Niarchos/4c	Scully	Pinder	Garnett(e)	Toews	Dudley(f)	Kenworthy(k)	Wade/t(h/t)	West/t	Schmid/t	22
Trivella/t2c2p(q)	Scully	Bunting	Garnett(e)	Toews	Dudley(f)	Kenworthy	Wade/t	Parr/t	Schmid	23
Niarchos/3cp	Scully(w)	Bunting	Garnett(e/t)	Toews	Dudley/t(f)	Kenworthy(k)	Wade	Parr(t/t)	Schmid	24
Niarchos/3c3p(b)	Scully	Bunting(c)	Garnett	Toews	Dudley(f)	Kenworthy	Wade	Parr(e)	Schmid	25
Niarchos/cp(b/c)	Scully	Bunting	Garnett/t	Toews(c)	Dudley(f/t)	Kenworthy	Wade	West(h)	Schmid	26
Umaga/t	Scully	Hanson(e)	Garnett	Thorp	Dudley	Webster	Parr	Spence	Schmid	A
Niarchos/2c	Scully/t	Bunting	Garnett/t	Hanson(c)	Kenworthy/t(g)	Webster	Wade(e)	Spence	Schmid	B
Trivella(q/c4p)	Scully	Pinder	Garnett	Bunting	Webster	Kenworthy	Wade	Spence	Schmid	C
Niarchos/3p	Scully/t	Pinder(v)	Garnett(e)	Bunting	Webster(g)	Kenworthy(k)	Wade	Spence	Schmid	D

REPLACEMENTS: a- D Lax, b- D Trivella, c - M Pinder, d - T Garnett, e - L Hall, f - G Webster, g - J Dudley, h - H Parr, i - A Buzza, j - B Wade, k - D Cook, l - M Walker, m - J Shepherd, n - R Hanson, o - D McIntyre, p - J Sinclair, q - J Niarchos, r - S Wilson, s - R Bramley, t - C West, u - J Thorp, v - H Toews, w - N Pattinson

Winger Dean Lax broke Guy Easterby's record of 13 tries in a season with a new total of 18. He made a slow start to the season with just 2 tries in the opening 13 matches of the season. He then went on to score 16 tries in the last 12 matches of the season. He scored 4 at home to Orrell and a hat trick against Waterloo.

He also set a new record for scoring tries in consecutive league matches with a run of five, this beat the old record of four held by Grant Treece. Flanker Ben Wade also broke the old record with 16 tries.

2nd row forward John Dudley extended his club record for appearances to 157 with another 21 league appearances during the season.

Rotherham's 17 match winning run at the end of the season equalled the club record.

ROTHERHAM

LEAGUE STATISTICS
compiled by Stephen McCormack

SEASON	Division	P	W	D	L	F	A	Pts Diff	Lge Pts	Lge Pos	Most Points	Most Tries
89-90	North 2	10	9	0	1	214	134	80	18		98 Kevin Plant	6 Paul Scott
90-91	North 1	10	6	1	3	198	107	91	13		81 Kevin Plant	4 by 3 players
91-92	North 1	10	10	0	0	245	123	122	20	1p	60 Steve Worrall	7 Richard Selkirk
92-93	D4N	12	10	1	1	259	123	136	21		50 Steve Worrall	8 Andy Challinor
93-94	D5N	12	10	1	1	335	142	193	21		118 Kevin Plant	8 John Dudley
94-95	4	18	17	0	1	576	267	309	34		202 Kevin Plant	8 John Dudley & Paul Scott
95-96	3	18	12	0	6	384	368	16	24		155 Kevin Plant	5 Paul Scott, Richard Selkirk & Richard Heaselgrave
96-97	2	22	11	0	11	525	661	-136	22		92 Dean Lax	13 Guy Easterby
97-98	P2	22	14	0	8	566	386	180	28		244 Simon Binns	12 Greg Austin
98-99	P2	26	22	0	4	756	336	420	44	2	144 Doug Trivella	18 Dean Lax

BIGGEST MARGINS

Home Win	73pts - 76-3 v Durham 19.3.94
Away Win	40pts - 46-6 v Westoe 8.4.89
Home Defeat	37pts - 6-43 v Richmond 30.9.95
Away Defeat	48pts - 13-61 v Necastle 4.5.97

MOST CONSECUTIVE

Appearances	89 Richard Selkirk 12.9.87-1.4.94
Matches scoring Tries	4 Grant Treece
Matches scoring points	14 Kevin Plant (twice)
Victories	17
Defeats	6

MOST POINTS

Scored at Home	76 v Durham 19.3.94
Scored Away	46 v Westoe 8.4.89
Conceded at Home	45 v Newcastle 19.4.97
Conceded Away	61 v Newcastle 4.5.97

MOST TRIES

Scored in a match	11 v Durham 19.3.94
Conceded in a match	11 v Newcastle 4.5.97 (A)

MOST APPEARANCES

by a forward	157 (6) John Dudley
by a back	99 (1) Paul Scott

	MOST IN A SEASON	MOST IN A CAREER	MOST IN A MATCH	
Points	244 Simon Binns 97-98	922 Kevin Plant 87-96	24 Paul Scott	v Westloe 8.4.89 (A)
Tries	18 Dean Lax 98-99	42 Paul Scott 87-96	6 Paul Scott	v Westoe 8.4.89 (A)
Conversions	39 Simon Binns 97-98	141 Kevin Plant 87-96	9 Kevin Plant	v Durham 19.2.94 (H)
Penalties	41 Kevin Plant 90-91 Simon Binns 97-98	182 Kevin Plant 87-96	6 David Francis Dean Lax	v Keighley 8.4.89 (H) v Lon. Scottish 2.11.96 (H)
Drop Goals	5 Kevin Plant 95-96	17 Kevin Plant 87-96	2 Kevin Plant	v Coventry 28.10.95

ROTHERHAM PLAYING SQUAD

BACKS

	Ht.	Wt.	Birthdate	Birthplace	CLUB	League Apps	Tries	Pts
Jason Niarchos	6.0		30.10.78	Londobn	Rotherham	13(3)	1	105
Dean Lax	6.0	13.7	10.07.74	Rotherham	Rotherham Dinnington	25(2)	23	201
Greg Austin	5.10	13.0	14.06.65	Australia	Rotherham Leicester	40 1(3)	22 2	110 10
Matt Walker England schools.					Rotherham	17	9	45
Dave Scully	5.8	12.0	07.08.65	Doncaster	Rotherham Wakefield	22 160(1)	5 52	35 298
Jon Harper	6.0	13.7	09.09.74	London	Rotherham	73(1)	20	100
Alan Buzza England A, U21, Colts, Schools.	5.11	13.0	03.03.66	Beverley	Rotherham Wasps	35(6) 31	5 4	28 62
James Sinclair	6.0	13.7	14.09.74	Stowmarket	Rotherham	10(5)	2	10
Mike Umaga Western Samoa	6.0	14.2	19.02.66	Auckland	Rotherham	31	10	50
Doug Trevella	6.1	15.02	03.05.74	Harare	Rotherham	13(4)	2	13
Darren McIntyre	5.11	13.7		Hull	Rotherham	13(4)	2	13
Jonathan Shepherd	5.9	13.0	31.07.74	Dewsbury	Rotherham Morley	16(8) 63	5 18	25 90

FORWARDS

	Ht.	Wt.	Birthdate	Birthplace	CLUB	League Apps	Tries	Pts
Simon Bunting	6.0	16.0	17.09.70	Rotherham	Rotherham	80(2)	3	15
Terry Garnett	5.11	16.9	10.05.67	Hull	Rotherham Wakefield	21(1) 120(2)	2 6	10 30
Lee Hall					Rotherham	9(2)	2	10
Gavin Webster	6.3	16.7	11.05.73	Northampton	Rotherham	52(9)	4	20
Dan Cook	6.8	17.7	10.09.74	Hull	Rotherham	22(11)	-	-
Matt Pinder	6.0	16.07	18.12.70	Rotherham	Rotherham	23(12)	-	-
Ben Wade	6.3	15.0	11.09.74	Leeds	Rotherham Morley	44(3) 52(5)	23 23	115 115
Craig West	6.2	16.7	08.02.64	Rotherham	Rotherham	121(10)	25	118
John Dudley	6.4	18.0	16.07.66	Sheffield	Rotherham	157(6)	40	191
Richard Bramley	6.5	17.5	19.10.71	Doncaster	Rotherham Wakefield	6(2) 18(3)	1 1	5 5
Neil Spence	5.10	13.0	30.08.76	Hull	Rotherham	35(4)	2	10
Scott Wilson	5.11	16.0	14.01.72	Rotherham	Rotherham	31(10)	-	-
Mike Schmid Canadian international	6.3	16.11	28.11.69	Canada	Rotherham	34(2)	13	65
Richard Hanson Other club: Orrell 1			11.08.75	Whalley	Rotherham Fylde	13(2) 14(3)	- -	- -
Harry Toews	6.0	17.6	07.08.71	Canada	Rotherham Leicester	7(1) (1)	-	-

ROTHERHAM

FACT FILE

Founded: 1923
Nickname: Roth

Colours: Maroon, sky, navy & white 1" hoops
Change colours: Maroon

GROUND

Address: Clifton Lane Sports Ground, Badsley Moor Lane, Rotherham. S65 2AA.
Tel:
Fax:
Capacity: 4,000 Seated 1000 (300 covered) Standing: 3000 (1500 covered)

Directions: M1 Jnc 33. Follow Rotherway for half mile to r'about. Take 2nd exit signed Bawtry. Traffic lights straight on up hill to r'about. Exit 1st left, follow road into town centre. Ground approx 1 mile on right. M18 Jnc 1. follow signs Rotherham. After 2 miles at 2nd r'about (Brecks Hotel) fork right. At next r'about (Stag Inn) 2nd exit. Follow road into town centre. Ground approx 1 mile on right.
Nearest Railway Station: Rotherham

Car Parking: 20 on ground, 1,000 No Charge nearby.

Admission: Season - Adults £110
Matchday - Adult £10, OAPs £7, Children £2

Club Shop: Yes
Clubhouse: Normal Licensing Hours, snacks available
Functions: Capacity 100 Contact Michael Yarlett

Training Nights: Monday, Tuesday & Thursday

PROGRAMME

Size: A5 Pages: 38 Price: £1
Editor: A Williams 01709 364190

ADVERTISING RATES
Full page £200, 1/2 page £100, 1/4 page £ 50

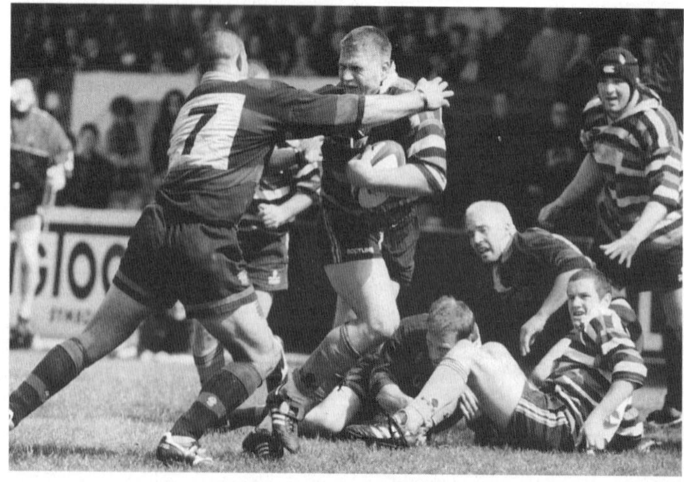

Ben Wade on the charge in the play-off match against Bedford

THE RUGBY FOOTBALL CLUB

President	Peter Galliford	c/o Rugby FC	
Chairman	David Owen	c/o Rugby FC	
Managing Director & Chief Executive	"Mal" Malik	c/o Rugby FC	01788 334884
Commercial Manager	Caroline Scott	c/o Rugby FC	01788 334882
Clubhouse Manager	Tracy Garrett	c/o Rugby FC	01788 334885
Director of Rugby	"Mal" Malik	c/o Rugby FC	01788 334881
Fixtures Secretary	Richard Stocking	c/o Rugby FC 01788 816598 (H)	01664 813925 (B) 01788 334888 (Fax)
Club Coach	Richard Kinsey	c/o Rugby FC	01788 334882

Rugby FC,
Webb Ellis Road,
Rugby,
Warwickshire CV22 7AU
Tel: 01788 334466
Fax: 01788 334888

The Rugby Football Club, back in the Allied Dunbar Premiership League Two, had high hopes for a successful season. With a plethora of Welsh players on full time contracts forming the backbone of the side, new recruits (but seasoned `pros') Kinsey and Tarbuck were added, together with Player of the Season, Alwyn Davies. There was little cheer on the filed however, as Rugby promised a lot on a number of occasions, but failed to deliver consistency. It turned out to be a disappointing campaign, with The Lions finishing eleventh in the League, winning nine of their league matches and falling heavily at the first hurdle of the Tetley Cup.
Following its flirtation with professional rugby, the Rugby Lions are adapting a more pragmatic approach for the coming season. Director, Mal Malik has taken over as Chief Executive with a brief to build up the rugby base of the club. Added to the Minis and Junior sides, ranging from Under 7's to Under 16's, The Lions are re-introducing two Colts Teams, and a Third and Second XV. The First XV, a semi professional side, will be at the apex of a `seamless club', where opportunities will be there for players to work their way up to a semi-professional status.
`Rugby in Schools Project', one of the highlights last season, will be further enhanced, with extra emphasis on development and coaching links with local schools. One of the Rugby Football Club's priorities is to establish a Rugby Academy in the very near future.

L-R - Back Row to Front Row: Matthew Davies, Jim Wingham, Fergie Gladstone, Trevor Revan, Rob Milner, Ben Harrison, Mike adnitt, Mick Tarrant, Paul Jackson, Paul Thompson, Chris Tarbuck, Richard Kinsey, Neil Underhill, Richard Robinson, Jim Withers, Rob Burdett, Dean watson, Neal Leeming, Geoff Davies, David Owen, Tom Harrison, Dai Rees, Paul Bale, Stephen Hopkins, Mark Ellis (Capt.), Martyn Davies, Dan Bailey, Rob Field, Alwyn Davies, Joe Czerpak, To'o Vaega, Dean Morgan, Steve Evans, Adrian Gilooly, Eddie Saunders, Andy Gallagher

RUGBY LIONS

Match No.	Date	H/A	Comp.	Opponents	Result & Score	Att.	15	14	13	12	11
1	05.09	H	AD2	Blackheath	W 18-12	500	Evans	Saunders	Vaega	Gillooly	Jasnikowski
2	12.09	A	AD2	Orrell	L 3-32	1,000	Evans/p	Saunders	Gillooly	Jasnikowski	T Harrison
3	19.09	H	AD2	Bristol	L 20-30	763	Davies/2c2p	Saunders/t	Gillooly	Jasnikowski	Bale
4	26.09	A	AD2	Rotherham	L 0-44		Davies	Saunders	Gillooly	Jasnikowski	Bale(a)
5	04.10	H	AD2	Coventry	L 17-20	1,500	Davies/3p(a)	Bale/t	Vaega	Gillooly	Jasnikowski
6	10.10	A	AD2	Wakefield	W 26-22	500	Davies/c2p	Jasnikowski(g)	Vaega	Gillooly/t	Bale/t(r)
7	17.10	H	AD2	Mosely	W 30-8	650	Davies/3c3p	Saunders	Vaega/t	Gillooly(b)	Bale/t
8	24.10	A	AD2	Worcester	L 6-29	1,763	Davies(g)	Saunders	Vaega	Gillooly	Bale
9	31.10	H	AD2	Waterloo*	W 20-9	400	Davies/2c2p	Saunders	Vaega	Gillooly	Bale/t(b)
10	07.11	A	AD2	Exeter	W 23-7	700	Davies/c2p	Saunders/t	Vaega	Gillooly	Bale
11	21.11	H	AD2	Fylde	W 30-16	650	Davies/2c2p	Saunders/t(r)	Vaega	Gillooly	Bale
12	12.12	H	AD2	Leeds Tykes	L 9-18	600	Davies/3p	Saunders	Vaega	Gillooly	Bale
13	19.12	A	AD2	London Welsh	L 7-11		Davies/c(b)	Saunders	Vaega	Gillooly	Bale
14	02.01	A	AD2	Fylde	W 14-6	800	Davies/3p	Saunders/t	Vaega	Gillooly	Bale
15	23.01	A	AD2	Waterloo	L 3-11	460	Davies/p	Saunders	Vaega	Jasnikowski	T Harrison
16	06.02	H	AD2	Worcester	L 2-36	1,200	Davies/t2c3p	Saunders/t	Vaega	Jasnikowski(g)	Blaise(a)
17	13.02	A	AD2	Moseley	L 20-35	677	Davies/p(a/c)	Saunders/2t	Vaega	Hopkin	T Harrison(p)
18	20.02	H	AD2	Wakefield	L 17-23	400	Davies/2cp	Saunders	Vaega	Hopkin	Bale
19	13.03	A	AD2	Coventry	W 21-19	1,100	Davies/c3p	Saunders	Vaega	Jasnikowski(g/t)	Bale(a)
20	20.03	H	AD2	Exeter	W 13-9	400	Davies/p	Saunders	Vaega/t	Jasnikowski(g)	T Harrison
21	27.03	H	AD2	Rotherham	L 10-33	950	Davies/tcp	Saunders	Vaega	B Harrison(g)	T Harrison
22	03.04	A	AD2	Bristol	L 13-49	2,615	Davies/c2p	Saunders(a)	Vaega	Hopkin	Bale/t
23	17.04	H	AD2	Orrell	L 29-41	480	Davies/t2c(a)	Saunders	Vaega/t(g)	Gillooly	Bale/t
24	24.04	A	AD2	Blackheath	L 20-43	600	Davies/t2c2p	Saunders	Gillooly(a)	B Harrison/t	Bale
25	01.05	H	AD2	London Welsh	L 12-33	720	Davies/4p	Saunders(p)	Vaega	Gillooly	Evans
26	09.05	A	AD2	Leeds Tykes	L 21-64	550	Evans/2c	T Harrison	Gillooly	Jasnikowski	B Harrison
A	15.11	H	TBC	Leeds Tykes	L 7-68		Evans/c	Czerpak	Gillooly	Jasnikowski	Morley(x)

* after opponents name indicates a penalty try
Brackets after a player's name indicates he was replaced. eg (a) means he was replaced by replacement code "a" and so on.
/ after a player or replacement name is followed by any scores he made - eg /t, /c, /p, /dg or any combination of these

1998-99 HIGHLIGHTS

League debuts:
Mark Jasnikowski, Jim Wingham, Richard Kinsey, Alwyn Davies, Steve Hopkin, Andy Gallagher, Colin Morley, Matt Davies, Ben Pain, Steve Evans, Fergie Gladstone, G Blaise, Chris Tarbuck, Robbie Harding, David Docherty.

Ever Presents: Rob Field.

Players used: 34 plus 4 as a replacement only.

Most Points in a season:

Pts	Player	T	C	P	DG
189	M Davies	4	23	41	-
35	E Saunders	7	-	-	-
30	P Bale	6	-	-	-
22	D Morgan	2	-	1	3

MATCH FACTS

10	9	1	2	3	4	5	6	7	8	
Morgan(g/c2p)	Bailey(h)	Rees/t	Burdett	Wingham(j)	Field	Kinsey	A Davies(i)	Thompson	Withers/t	1
Morgan(g)	Bailey(k)	Rees(l)	Burdett	Wingham(n)	Field	Kinsey	Withers(o)	Thompson	Pain	2
Hopkin	Morley(h)	Rees(n)	Burdett	Wingham/t(l)	Field	Kinsey	Gladstone(m)	Ellis	Thompson	3
Hopkin(c)	Morley(d)	Evans(j)	Burdett(l)	Wingham	Field	Kinsey	Thompson	Gladstone	Pain(f)	4
Morgan/dg	Bailey	Rees	Burdett	Wingham(j)	Field	Kinsey	A Davies	Ellis	Thompson	5
Morgan	Bailey	Rees	Burdett(l)	Revan	Field(f)	Kinsey	A Davies	Ellis	Thompson/t	6
Morgan(r)	Bailey	Rees	Milner	Revan	Thompson	Field	A Davies/t	Ellis	Pain(f)	7
Morgan/pdg	Bailey(h)	Rees	Milner(l)	Revan	Kinsey	Field	A Davies	Ellis(o)	Thompson(m)	8
Morgan	Gallagher	Rees	Milner	Revan	Kinsey	Field	A Davies	Ellis	Tarbuck	9
Morgan/2t	Gallagher	Rees	Milner	Revan	Kinsey	Field	A Davies	Ellis	Tarbuck	10
Morgan	Gallagher	Rees	Milner	Revan	Kinsey	Field/t(i)	A Davies	Ellis/t	Tarbuck/t	11
Morgan(g)	Gallagher	Rees	Milner	Revan(e)	Kinsey	Field	A Davies	Ellis	Tarbuck	12
Hopkin	Gallagher/t(d)	Rees	Milner	Wingham(j)	Kinsey	Field	A Davies	Ellis	Tarbuck	13
Morgan(g)	Gallagher	Rees	Milner	Wingham(j)	Field	Underhill	A Davies	Ellis	Tarbuck	14
Morgan(g)	Gallagher(d)	Rees	M Davies(s)	Wingham(j)	Kinsey	Field	A Davies	Ellis	Tarbuck	15
Morgan	Bailey	Evans(j)	Milner	Wingham	Kinsey(i)	Field	A Davies	Ellis	Tarbuck	16
Morgan	Bailey(h)	Evans	Milner	Wingham(j)	Kinsey(i)	Field(f)	A Davies	Ellis/t	Tarbuck	17
Morgan	Bishop	Evans(j)	Milner(s)	Wingham	Kinsey(f)	Field/t	A Davies	Ellis	Tarbuck/t	18
Morgan	Gallagher(d)	Revan	Milner	Wingham	Kinsey(f)	Field	A Davies	Ellis	Tarbuck/t	19
Morgan	Gallagher(d)	Revan(f)	Milner/t	WIngham	Kinsey	Field	A Davies	Ellis	Tarbuck	20
Morgan	Bishop(h)	Revan	Milner	Wingham	Kinsey(f)	Field	A Davies(u)	Ellis	Tarbuck	21
Morgan	Bishop(d)	Revan	Milner	Wingham	Kinsey(f)	Field	A Davies(m)	Ellis	Tarbuck	22
Morgan	Bailey(t)	Revan(n)	Milner(l)	Wingham	Kinsey(f/t)	Field(m)	A Davies	Ellis	Tarbuck/t	23
Hopkin	Bishop(d)	Revan	Milner	Wingham	Kinsey	Field(f)	A Davies	Ellis	Pain(v)	24
Morgan(g)	Gallagher(d)	Revan(n)	Milner(s)	Wingham	Withers(w)	Field	A Davies	Ellis	Tarbuck	25
Hopkin	Gallagher(d/t)	Revan	Harding	WIngham(n/t)	Withers	Field	Thompson(v/c)	Docherty/t	Tarbuck	26
Hopkin	Bailey	Evans	M Davies	Revan(e)	Underhill	Field	Pain	Ellis(w)	Tarbuck/t	A

REPLACEMENTS:

a- D Evans
b- M Jasnikowski
c - D Morgan
d - D Bailey
e - J Wingham
f - J Withers
g - S Hopkin
h - A Gallagher
i - N Underhill
j - T Revan
k - C Morley
l - Matt Davies
m - B Pain
n - S Evans
o - F Gladstone
p - B Harrison
q - C Tarbuck
r - J Czerpak
s - R Harding
t - D Bishop
u - R Robinson
v - M Bedden
w - P Thompson
w - T Harrison

Martyn Davies tops the points scorers list in his first full season and in the process sets a new record of 189 points. That beat the old record of Jim Quantrill which stood at 171.
Davies ended the season with a 17 match run of scoring and needs to score in his next two matches to equal Chris Howards record of scoring in 19 consecutive matches.

Veteran winger Eddie Saunders just keeps on going and topped the club's try scoring list for the 9th time in 12 seasons. He scored 7 last season and extended his record to 77.

Trevor Revan added 15 more appearances to his record of 133 and now has 148 which extends his record for a forward.

The record for a back and the overall club record was extended by Eddie Saunders from 140 to 163.

RUGBY

LEAGUE STATISTICS
compiled by Stephen McCormack

SEASON	Division	P	W	D	L	F	A	Pts Diff	Lge Pts	Lge Pos	Most Points	Most Tries
89-90	2	11	5	0	6	238	172	62	10		100 Chris Howard	7 Eddie Saunders
90-91	2	12	10	0	2	252	146	106	20		68 Stuart Vaudin	9 David Bishop
91-92	1	12	2	3	7	124	252	-128	7		60 Mark Mapletoft	2 Eddie Saunders & David Bishop
92-93	1	12	1	0	11	104	368	-264	2		26 Mark Mapletoft	3 Eddie Saunders
93-94	2	18	5	1	12	186	302	-116	11		115 Mark Mapletoft	5 Mark Mapletoft
94-95	3	18	11	0	7	355	271	84	22		131 Jim Quantrill	8 David Bishop
95-96	3	18	12	1	5	395	284	111	25		183 Jim Quantrill	8 Eddie Saunders
96-97	2	22	3	0	19	317	1060	-743	6		72 Jim Quantrill	8 Eddie Saunders
97-98	JN1	26	21	0	5	733	405	328	42		171 Jim Quantrill	11 Eddie Saunders
98-99	P2	26	9	0	17	425	660	-235	18	11	189 Martyn Davies	7 Eddie Saunders

BIGGEST MARGINS

Home Win	66pts - 69-3 v Morley 25.10.97
Away Win	34pts - 54-20 v Reading 28.3.98
Home Defeat	62pts - 8-70 v Newcastle 8.2.97
Away Defeat	151pts - 5-156 v Newcastle 5.10.96

MOST CONSECUTIVE

Appearances	42 Steve Smith 11.4.92-14.1.95
Matches scoring Tries	5 Eddie Saunders
Matches scoring points	19 Chris Howard
Victories	8
Defeats	12

MOST POINTS

Scored at Home	69 v Morley 25.10.97
Scored Away	54 v Reading 28.3.98
Conceded at Home	72 v Richmond 22.3.97
Conceded Away	156 v Newcastle 5.10.96

MOST TRIES

Scored in a match	11 v Morley 25.10.97 (H)
Conceded in a match	24 v Newcastle 5.10.96 (A)

MOST APPEARANCES

by a forward	148 (9)Trevor Revan
by a back	163 Eddie Saunders

	MOST IN A SEASON	MOST IN A CAREER	MOST IN A MATCH	
Points	189 Martyn Davies 98-99	559 Jim Quantrill 93-98	25 Chris Howard	v Gosforth 1.11.89 (H)
Tries	11 Eddie Saunders 97-98	77 Eddie Saunders 87-99	3 Chris Howard Eddie Saunders	v Vale of Lune 10.9.88 (H) v Bedford 12.4.95 (A) v Rotherham 23.9.95 (H) v Moseley 12.10.96 (H)
Conversions	33 Jim Quantrill 97-98	84 Jim Quantrill 93-98	6 Chris Howard	V Gosforth 11.11.89 (H)
Penalties	42 Jim Quantrill 95-96	109 Jim Quantrill 93-98	7 Denzil Evans	v Richmond 15.10.94 (H)
Drop Goals	4 Richard Pell 87-88	14 Richard Pell 87-95	1 by nine players Richard Pell (x14), Mark Mapletoft (x3) Dean Morgan (x4)	on 28 occasions incl. Stuart Vaudin (x3), & Jim McLeod (x3)

BACKS

	Ht.	Wt.	Birthdate	Birthplace	CLUB	League Apps	Tries	Pts
Adrian Gilooly	6.0	14.11	06.04.70	Rugby	Rugby	95(4)	8	40
Mark Jasnkowski	6.0	14.04	16.01.73	Kingston	Rugby Leicester	11(3) 1	- -	- -
Paul Bale	5.11	13.00	20.12.76	Rugby	Rugby Newbold	56(2)	20	100
Steve Hopkin			15.02.74		Rugby Gloucester	8(13)	1	3
David Bishop	5.10	13.08	05.01.65	Westminster	Rugby	143(7)	41	191
Andy Gallagher			15.05.73		Rugby	11(5)	1	5
Eddie Saunders	6.0	12.07	02.11.60	Birmingham	Rugby Coventry	159	77	355
Ben Harrison			08.09.78	Coventry	Rugby	6(2)	2	10
Martyn Davies			12.10.73	Ammanford	Rugby	33(2)	4	289
Joe Czerpak			25.08.75	Reading	Rugby	4(6)	1	19
To'o Vaega	5.11	14.02	17.08.65	W Samoa	Rugby	35(1)	9	45
Dan Bailey			28.03.75	Kettering	Rugby	15(10)	3	15
Tom Harrison			25.12.74	Rugby	Rugby	10(1)	2	10
Dean Morgan			01.12.74	Rugby	Rugby	45(2)	8	55

FORWARDS

	Ht.	Wt.	Birthdate	Birthplace	CLUB	League Apps	Tries	Pts
Rob Milner	5.11	14.09	05.06.68	Coventry	Rugby	60(4)	7	35
Alwyn Davies			14.10.75		Rugby	22	1	5
Rob Burdett	5.11	14.07	26.07.73	Rugby	Rugby	58(7)	-	-
Jim Wingham	6.0	16.07	01.06.70	Portsmouth	Rugby Leicester	19(1)	1	5
Neil Underhill	6.10	17.00	23.06.72	Lutterworth	Rugby	46(10)	6	30
Mark R Ellis	5.11	14.12	23.12.68	Kirby Muxloe	Rugby	118(1)	12	56
Paul Thompson	6.4	15.07	24.09.74	Warwick	Rugby	28(13)	5	25
Richard Kinsey	6.5	18.07	05.02.64	Barnett	Rugby Waspa	22 65(9)	- 4	- 20
Rob Field	6.7	18.00	22.06.71	Coventry	Rugby	36(11)	3	15
Chris Tarbuck Other clubs: Saracens 44/3/12, Leicester 16)2)/4/20	6.4	15.07	20.08.68	Harlow	Rugby London Scot	17(1) 42(6)	2 10	10 50
Ben Pain	6.4	16.6	11.05.76	Leicester	Rugby Nottingham	4(4) 25	- 5	- 25
Trevor Revan	6.0	19.00	05.12.63		Rugby Dijon	148(9)	8	36
David Rees			11.04.66	Merthyr Tydfil	Rugby	40	3	15
Jim Withers			15.03.73	Stratford	Rugby	8(18)	4	20

RUGBY

FACT FILE

Founded: 1873
Nickname: The Lions

Club Colours: White shirts, navy shorts
1st XV colours: Red shirts, navy shorts

GROUND

Address: Webb Ellis Road, Rugby. CV22 7AU.
Tel: 01788 334466 Fax: 01788 334888
Capacity: 3,396 Seated: 240 Standing: Covered 600; Uncovered 2,556

Directions: Second turn right, half mile south west of town centre on A4071,Bilton Road.
From NW: M6 Jnc 1 A426 Rugby A4071 From NE: M1 Jnc 20 A426 Rugby A4071:
From SE: M1 Jnc 17/M45/A4071 towards Rugby.
Nearest Railway Station: Rugby - recommend taxi 2 miles to ground

Car Parking: 100 on ground & £1, and on street nearby

Admission:
Season: Adult £85, OAPs £45, U/16 Free
Matchday: Adults standing £8, seated plus £1, OAPs £5, U/16 Free

Club Shop: Matchday PM & by appointment.
Manager Linda Dainty 01788 334880

Clubhouse: Matchdays 12-10.00 (or later) & training nights
Snacks & bar meals available
Functions: Capacity 120, contact Tracy Garrett c/o Club

Training Nights: Tuesday & Thursday

PROGRAMME

Size: A5 Pages: 20 + cover Price: £1
Editor: Dennis Keen 01788 334466

ADVERTISING RATES
Page £450 1/2 page £250 1/4 page £160

Rugby club chairman, David Owen, presenting stalwart winger, Eddie Saunders, with the "Clubman of the Year" award

WAKEFIELD R.F.C.

President	R P Hodson	c/o Wakefield RFC, College Grove, Eastmoor Rd., Wakefield WF1 3RR Tel: 01924 374801 Fax: 01924 290069
Chairman	D Beaumont	c/o Wakefield RFC, as above
Club Secretary	J B Coulson	39 Melbourne Road, St. Johns, Wakefield. WF1 2RL 01924 373586 (H)
Director of Rugby	S Townend	59 Gowthorpe, Selby, YO8 4HE

For a side which for many years had enjoyed the feeling of success, a season of being in the basement of Allied Dunbar Premier Two was a disappointment to say the least.

Aware that financial constraint for the 1998/99 season would still be the order of the day, problems were compounded by the pre-season loss of five senior players through either retirement or moving to another club.
The new season would revolve around the experience of Matt Greenwood and Neil Summers, supported by younger players and new recruits.
An away win at Moseley in the first League game of the season proved to be a false dawn as inconsistent form and loss of confidence led to a series of defeats, and an early exit from the Tetley's Bitter Cup.
There were periods in some games when they showed their true potential but a lack of concentration allowed possible victory to slip away into defeat.

Having secured their place in Division Two this term the feeling is that they have `bottomed out' and can face the new season with renewed optimism.

WAKEFIELD

Match No.	Date	H/A	Comp.	Opponents	Result & Score	Att.	15	14	13	12	11
1	05.09	A	AD2	Moseley	W33-32	678	Breheny	Hitchmough	Flint	Summers	McKenzie
2	12.09	H	AD2	Worcester	L 22-48	600	Breheny(k/t)	Hitchmough/t	Flint	Summers	McKenzie
3	19.09	A	AD2	Waterloo	L 25-36	400	Hitchmough	Flint/t	Summers	Maynard	McKenzie/t
4	26.09	H	AD2	Exeter	L 19-27	400	Breheny(o)	Hitchmough/t	Flint	Summers	McKenzie
5	03.10	A	AD2	Fylde	L 18-20	800	Summers	Hitchmough	Flint/t	Maynard	McKenzie/t
6	10.10	H	AD2	Rugby Lions	L 22-26	500	Hitchmough	Thompson	Flint	Maynard	McKenzie/t
7	17.10	A	AD2	London Welsh	L 21-45	1,300	Summers	Hitchmough	Flint/t	Dixon	McKenzie/t
8	24.10	H	AD2	Blackheath	W 19-9	400	Hitchmough	Edwards	Flint	Dixon/t	McKenzie/t
9	31.10	A	AD2	Orrell	L 5-24	800	Hitchmough(a)	Edwards(l)	Flint	Dixon	McKenzie
10	07.11	H	AD2	Bristol	L 15-46	450	Breheny	Thompson	Flint/t	Dixon	McKenzie
11	21.11	A	AD2	Rotherham	L 7-34		Hitchmough	White	Flint/t	Dixon	Breheny
12	12.12	H	AD2	Coventry	L 10-18	400	Hitchmough	White	Flint	Summers	McKenzie
13	20.12	A	AD2	Leeds Tykes	L 0-38	1,211	Hitchmough	Flint	Dixon(e)	Summers	Breheny
14	02.01	H	AD2	Rotherham	L 13-40	800	Hitchmough(b)	White/t(d)	Flint	Dixon/c2p	Breheny
15	16.01	A	AD2	Bristol	L 19-35	2,516	Breheny/t	White	Flint	Dixon/c4p	Shine
16	23.01	H	AD2	Orrell	W25-13	500	Breheny	White	Flint/t	Dixon/cp	Shine/2t
17	06.02	A	AD2	Blackheath	L 20-28	500	Breheny/t	White	Flint	Dixon/2c2p	Shine
18	13.02	H	AD2	London Welsh	L 16-30	410	Breheny	White	Flint	Dixon/2p	Shine(r)
19	27.02	A	AD2	Rugby Lions	W23-17	400	Breheny/t	Edwards	Summers/t	Dixon	Flint
20	13.03	H	AD2	Fylde	W27-11	800	Edwards/2t	White	Dixon	Summers	Flint/t
21	27.03	A	AD2	Exeter	L 13-37	750	Breheny	White(A)	Dixon/p	Summers/t	Shine
22	03.04	H	AD2	Waterloo	L 14-20	500	Edwards(q)	White	Dixon	Flint	Breheny/t
23	17.04	A	AD2	Worcester	L 19-67	2,600	Breheny	White	Flint(p/t)	Summers/t	Shine/t
24	24.04	H	AD2	Moseley	W38-20	450	Breheny/4t	White	Dixon/tc	Summers	Shine
25	02.05	H	AD2	Leeds	L 13-51	450	Breheny/t	Skurr/t	Dixon(c)	Summers	Shine
26	08.05	A	AD2	Coventry	L 13-40	1,000	Breheny/t	Skurr	Dixon/p	Summers	Shine
A	14.11	H	TBC	Kendal	L 8-16	400	Breheny	Hitchmough	Flint	Dixon/p	McKenzie

* after opponents name indicates a penalty try
Brackets after a player's name indicates he was replaced. eg (a) means he was replaced by replacement code "a" and so on.
/ after a player or replacement name is followed by any scores he made - eg /t, /c, /p, /dg or any combination of these

1998-99 HIGHLIGHTS

League debuts:
Rob Hitchmough, Leroy McKenzie, Phil Ure, Mark Burrow, Matt Morgan, Chris Simpson-Daniel, Ben Guildford, Andrew Hurdley, Stuart Dixon, Ben Shine, Owen Edwards, A Platt, Richard Hughes, Jonathan Skurr, Nick Lloyd, Matt Mills, Rob Ashforth.

Ever Presents: Glen Wilson.

Players used: 33 plus 3 as a replacement only.

Most Points in a season:

Pts	Player	T	C	P	DG
76	P Ure	-	14	16	-
66	S Dixon	3	6	13	-
52	R Ashforth	1	4	12	1
50	I Breheny	10	-	-	-
35	J Flint	7	-	-	-

MATCH FACTS

10	9	1	2	3	4	5	6	7	8	
Ure/3c4p	Birkby/2t	Hardcastle	Brooking	Latham(j)	Burrow	Greenwood	Wilson(i)	Yates	Elisara/t	1
Ure/2cp	Birkby(l/t)	Hardcastle	Brooking	Latham(j)	Burrow	Greenwood	Wilson	Yates	Elisara(i)	2
Ure/2c2p	Birkby(l)	Hardcastle(m)	Brooking	Latham	Burrow	Greenwood(n)	Wilson	Yates(i)	Elisara/t	3
Ure/3p	S-Daniel/t(k)	Latham	Brooking	Guildford(d)	Burrow(h)	Greenwood	Wilson	Sowerby	Elisara(n)	4
Ure/c2p	Birkby	Hardcastle	Brooking	Latham	Burrow	Greenwood	Wilson	Sowerby	Hurdley	5
Ure/2cp	Birkby/t	Morgan	Brooking	Guildford(p)	Burrow	Greenwood	Wilson/t	Sowerby	Hurdley	6
Ure/3c	Birkby(o)	Morgan(g)	Brooking(s)	Latham	Greenwood	Hurdley	Wilson	Sowerby	Elisara/t	7
Ure/3p	Summers	Morgan	Plevey	Latham	Burrow	Greenwood	Wilson	Hurdley	Elisara	8
Ure	Summers	Morgan(m)	Plevey/t	Latham	Burrow(u)	Greenwood	Wilson	Hurdley	Sowerby	9
Summers/t(c)	S-Daniel/t	Latham	Plevey(e)	Guildford(j)	Burrow(v)	Greenwood	Hughes	Sowerby	Wilson(w)	10
Ure/c(o)	Summers	Latham	Brooking(t)	Guildford	Burrow(x-u-w)	Greenwood	Wilson	Hurdley	Sowerby	11
Edwards/cp	Birkby	Latham(x)	Plevey	Guildford	Greenwood	Hurdley(y)	Wilson/t	Sowerby(h)	Elisara	12
Edwards	S-Daniel(o)	Latham(x)	Plevey(e)	Guildford	Greenwood	Hurdley(y)	Wilson	Sowerby(e)	Elisara	13
Edwards	Summers	Latham(d)	Plevey(e)	Guildford(x)	Greenwood	Hurdley(y)	Wilson	Yates	Sowerby(u)	14
Summers	S-Daniel	Lloyd(d)	Brooking	Latham	Greenwood	Hurdley	Wilson(u)	Sowerby(h)	Elisara	15
Summers	S-Daniel	Lloyd/t(d)	Brooking	Latham	Greenwood	Hurdley(y)	Wilson	Sowerby(h)	Elisara	16
Summers	S-Daniel/t	Lloyd(d)	Brooking	Latham	Greenwood	Hurdley	Wilson	Sowerby(h)	Elisara	17
Summers/t	S-Daniel	Platt	Brooking	Latham	Greenwood	Hurdley	Wilson	Sowerby	Elisara/t	18
Ashforth/c2p	S-Daniel	Lloyd(d)	Brooking	Latham	Greenwood	Hurdley(u)	Wilson	Yates/t	Elisara	19
Ashforth/4p	S-Daniel	Lloyd(d)	Brooking(t)	Latham	Greenwood	Mills	Hughes(i)	Yates	Wilson	20
Ashforth/cp	Birkby	Hardcastle(x)	Brooking(t)	Latham	Greenwood	Mills	Hughes(w)	Yates	Wilson	21
Ashforth/3p	Birkby	Hardcastle(x)	Brooking	Latham	Greenwood	Mills	Hurdley(i)	Yates	Wilson	22
Ashforth/2c	Birkby(u)	Lloyd(d)	Brooking(t)	Latham	Greenwood	Mills(i)	Wilson	Yates	Elisara	23
Ashforth/tpdg	S-Daniel	Lloyd	Brooking(t)	Latham	Greenwood	Hurdley(u)	Wilson(i)	Yates(y)	Elisara	24
Ashforth/p	Edwards	Lloyd	Brooking(t)	Latham(d)	Mills	Sowerby(z)	Wilson(y)	Yates	Elisara	25
Ashforth	Edwards/t	Hardcastle	Plevey	Latham(x)	Mills(v)	Sowerby	Wilson	Yates(z)	Elisara	26
Summers	S-Daniel/t	Latham	Plevy(e)	Guildford	Burrow	Greenwood	Hughes(B)	Hurdley	Sowerby(w)	A

REPLACEMENTS:	a- I Breheny	b- L McKenzie	c - P Ure	d - D Hardcastle	e - K Brooking
f - R Latham	g - M Burrow	h - K Yates	i - M Sowerby	j - M Morgan	k - P Maynard
l - C Simpson-Daniel	m - B Guildford	n - A Hurdley	o - R Thompson	p - S Dixon	q - B Shine
r - O Edwards	s - A Platt	t - S Plevey	u - R Hughes	v - R Wilson	w - J Skurr
x - N Lloyd	y - M Mills	z - N Dykes	A - E Smithies	B - G Wilson	

Phil Ure in his first season at the club tops the points scorers list with a lowly 76 points.

Winger/ful back Ian Breheny tops the try scoring list with 10 tries the first player to reach double figures since Jonathan Sleightholme back in 1993-94. Breheny also broke the club record for tries in a match with four against Moseley in April.

Rob Ashforth became the 8th player to drop a goal for Wakefield in a league match.

Winger Leroy McKenzie set a new club record of scoring tries in consecutive matches with a four match burst during October.

Wakefield were beaten both home and away by Worcester and each time it was a new record score against. At home they were beaten 48-22 and in the away match later in the season they lost 67-19.

Wakefield suffered their worst ever run when they lost eight straight league matches.

WAKEFIELD

LEAGUE STATISTICS
compiled by Stephen McCormack

SEASON	Division	P	W	D	L	F	A	Pts Diff	Lge Pts	Lge Pos	Most Points	Most Tries
89-90	3	11	7	1	3	210	126	84	15		31 Ray Adamson	7 Mike Harrison & Mike Murtagh
90-91	2	12	8	0	4	188	109	79	16		89 Andy Atkinson	4 Raz Brown & Dave Scully
91-92	2	12	7	0	5	187	194	-7	14		32 Rob Liley John Sleightholme	8 Jon Sleightholme
92-93	2	12	8	1	3	186	123	63	17		101 Rob Liley	7 Jon Sleightholme
93-94	2	18	8	3	7	347	240	107	19		90 Mike Jackson	12 Jon Sleightholme
94-95	2	18	12	1	5	354	261	93	25		213 Mike Jackson	7 Richard Thompson
95-96	2	18	8	0	10	328	331	-3	16		177 Mike Jackson	7 Dave Scully
96-97	2	22	11	0	11	504	557	-53	22		199 Mike jackson	9 Dave Scully
97-98	P2	22	6	0	16	382	556	-174	12		141 Greg Miller	6 Dave Scully
98-99	P2	26	6	0	20	469	812	-343	12		76 Phil Ure	10 Ian Breheny

BIGGEST MARGINS

Home Win	70pts - 70-0 v MetropolitanPolice 24.9.88
Away Win	47pts - 50-3 v Birmingham 31.10.87
Home Defeat	30pts - 17-47 v Newcastle 12.10.96
Away Defeat	48pts - 19-67 v Worcester 17.4.99

MOST CONSECUTIVE

Appearances	49 Dave Scully
Matches scoring Tries	4 Leroy McKenzie
Matches scoring points	21 Mike Jackson
Victories	10
Defeats	7

MOST POINTS

Scored at Home	70 v Metropolitan Police 24.9.88
Scored Away	50 v Birmingham 31.01.87
Conceded at Home	48 v Worcester 12.9.98
Conceded Away	67 v Worcester 17.4.99

MOST TRIES

Scored in a match	14 v Metropolitan Police 24.9.88
Conceded in a match	9 v Newcastle 8.3.97 v Richmond 19.4.97

MOST APPEARANCES

by a forward	130 Terry Garnett
by a back	160 (1) Dave Scully

	MOST IN A SEASON	MOST IN A CAREER	MOST IN A MATCH	
Points	213 Mike Jackson 94-95	707 Mike Jackson 93-98	23 Rob Liley	v Rugby 11.9.93 (H)
Tries	12 Jon Sleightholme 93-94	52 Dave Scully 87-98	4 Ian Breheny	v Moseley 24.4.99 (H)
Conversions	33 Mike Jackson 96-97	82 Mike jackson 93-98	7 Ray Adamson	v Birmingham31.10.87 (A)
Penalties	57 Mike Jackson 94-95	165 Mike Jackson 93-98	6 Ray Adamson Mike Jackson Greg Miller	v Vale of Lune 27.2.88 (H) v Nottingham 1.10.94 (A) v Lon. Irish 22.10.94 (H) v Blackheath 18.4.98 (H)
Drop Goals	3 Greg Miller 97-98	3 Greg Miller 97-98	1 by 7 players Greg Miller(x3) Rob Liley(x3) Steve Townend(x2)	on 13 occasions incl

WAKEFIELD PLAYING SQUAD

BACKS

BACKS	Ht.	Wt.	Birthdate	Birthplace	CLUB	League Apps	Tries	Pts
Paul White	5.10	12.07	03.12.69		Wakefield	67(6)	11	55
					Morley			
Phil Maynard	5.11	14.05	05.05.71	Wakefield	Wakefield	85(10)	13	62
Richard Thompson	6.0	13.07	03.12.69	Leeds	Wakefield	94(4)	25	123
England u18, u16. North. Yorkshire.					W Hartlepool	6	1	5
Stuart Dixon					Wakefield	18(1)	3	66
					Harrogate	37(3)	9	88
Ben Shine					Wakefield	9(1)	3	15
Jonathan Flint	6.2	13.08	06.06.71	Otley	Wakefield	31(1)	7	35
Ian Breheny			02.01.78		Wakefield	24(2)	10	50
Alex Birkby	5.9	12.05	21.07.77	Sheffield	Wakefield	17(3)	-	-
Chris Simpson-Daniel	5.9	13.07	15.07.78	York	Wakefield	10(3)	4	20
					Newcastle	1	-	-
Neil Summers			10.10.68	Leeds	Wakefield	39	8	40
Owen Edwards					Wakefield	10(1)	3	20
Leroy McKenzie			02.09.69	Birmingham	Wakefield	11(1)	5	25
					Mosley			

FORWARDS

FORWARDS	Ht.	Wt.	Birthdate	Birthplace	CLUB	League Apps	Tries	Pts
Nick Lloyd					Wakefield	8(7)	1	5
Keith Brooking	6.0	13.00	07.05.73	Tiverton	Wakefield	24(10)	-	-
					Exeter	34(2)	1	5
Rod Latham	6.1	18.04	01.08.69	Ghana	Wakefield	123(5)	-	-
North, Yorkshire.								
Glen Wilson	6.1	15.02	31.07.76	Wakefield	Wakefield	51(3)	5	25
Dean Hardcastle	5.10	16.2	26.01.76	Doncaster	Wakefield	12(17)	-	-
England u21, North u21, Yorkshire u21.								
Andrew Hurdley	6.6	16.09	09.10.62	Halifax	Wakefield	16(2)	12	59
North, Yorkshire.								
Alan Platt			26.11.69	Sheffield	Wakefield	1(1)	-	-
Matt Greenwood	6.5	17.00	25.09.64	Leeds	Wakefield	46	1	5
England A, u21.Other club: Nottingham 27/1/4					Wasps	77(1)	5	25
Scott Plevey	5.10	13.5	28.09.76	Doncaster	Wakefield	8(8)	1	5
Mark Sowerby	6.4	16.5	03.09.69		Wakefield	75(17)	1	5
Matt Mills	6.4	16.0	29.12.73	Selby	Wakefield	4(7)	-	-
					Rotherham	23(2)	1	5
Richard Hughes			12.06.76	Dewsbury	Wakefield	5(7)	1	5

WAKEFIELD

FACT FILE

Founded: 1901
Nickname: Field

Colours: Black & gold hoops/black/black
Change colours: Red shirts

GROUND

Address: College Grove, Eastmoor Road, Wakefield. WF1 3RR
Tel: 01924 374801 Fax: 01924 290069
Capacity: 2,450 Seated: 450 Standing: 2,000

Directions: From M1 Jnc 41, A650 into Wakefield City Centre, turn left at Queen Elizabeth Grammar School onto Westfield Road, ground in front 250 yards
From M62 Jnc 30, A642 into Wakefield, turn right at traffic lights immediately after Hospital onto Eastmoor Road, ground 300 yards on left
Nearest Railway Station: Wakefield Westgate

Car Parking: No parking in ground, 200 spaces nearby £1

Admission:

Season	Standing Adult £80, OAP £50, Children (12-17) £15 Family (2 adults & children) £150
Matchday	Seated Adults £8, OAP/Children £4.50 Standing Adult £7, OAP/Children £4

Club Shop: Yes; Manager Cath Brocklebby via club

Clubhouse: Normal Licensing Hours. Three bars with snacks & bar meals available
Functions: Contact John Scones via club.
Also Hospitality lounge seating 72

Training Nights: Seniors Tuesday & Thursday, Colts Wednesday

PROGRAMME

Size: B5 Pages: 30 Price: £1

ADVERTISING RATES

Colour:	Page £350	1/2 page £200	
Mono:	Page £300	1/2 page £175	1/4 page £100

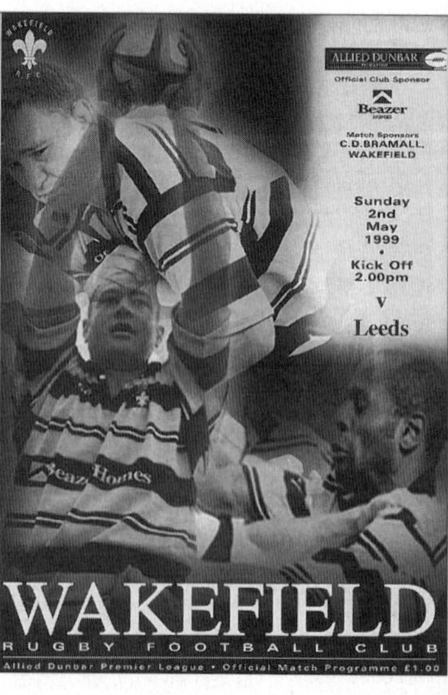

WATERLOO F.C.

President	J R H Greenwood	Maitland House, Maitland st., Preston PR1 5YP 01772 655223
Chairman	R H Wilson	Netherwood, Far Moss Road, Blundellsands, Liverpool L238TG 0151 924 1166 (H), 0151 928 9288 (B), 0151 928 4190 (Fax)
Club Secretary	Keith Alderson	66 St Michaels Road, Blundellsands, Liverpool.L23 7UW 0151 924 1168 (H)
Marketing	Paul Coyne	c/o Waterloo FC, St Anthonys Road, Blundellsands, Liverpool, L23 8TW 0973 779143 (H), 0151 924 4552 (B), 0151 924 0900 (Fax)
Director of Rugby	P Buckton	c/o Waterloo FC, as above
Fixtures Secretary	J Rimmer	01772 814277 (H) 01772 885000 (B)

The Waterloo season had its usual bright start, this time with a new name as the Drummers burst on to the scene with wins over Rotherham, Wakefield, Worcester and Leeds. A narrow defeat at Coventry and a close victory at Moseley put the Waterloo Drummers near the top of the table. There were hiccups at Exeter and Rugby but another home win against London Welsh, and it was looking very promising for a top four finish, which was their director of rugby,Tony Russ's, declared intention for this year.

December was the turning point for the Drummers as it marked the first home defeat against Orrell, later avenged in the Tetley's Bitter Cup, and the sacking of popular coach, Tosh Askew, for financial reasons. The players rallied for the next Tetley's Cup match and gave Wasps a real fright, but as the season progressed the results got worse. Tony Russ decided that the `financial uncertainties' of the game were too much and handed in his resignation. Although disheartened by the politics of the game the side managed a victory at Wakefield, but then slid to defeats by Coventry, Rotherham and Bristol, while the worst defeat of the season was saved for the last game against local rivals Orrell.

The new season starts without a new director of rugby but Tosh Askew has been reinstated and along with Peter Buckton is working to restore morale and to regenerate the team. Lee Stewart and Stephane La Rue have returned home and Ben Kay has moved to Leicester, but new players are expected shortly to replace them.

There are moves afoot to restore the second team that was disbanded by Tony Russ, to give more depth to the squad. Both coaches are confident that they will have a competitive team for September and with a little added depth will maintain the run after December.

WATERLOO

Match No.	Date	H/A	Comp.	Opponents	Result & Score	Att.	15	14	13	12	11
1	05.09	H	AD2	Rotherham	W 22-7	527	Handley(m)	Hackney	Mullins	Davies/t	Graham
2	12.09	A	AD2	Coventry	L 15-21	1,950	Graham	Hackney	Woof(a)	Davies	Mullins
3	19.09	H	AD2	Wakefield	W36-25	400	Handley	Mullins/t(r)	Woof/t	Davies(s)	Graham
4	26.09	A	AD2	Moseley	W15-13	616	Graham	Hackney	Woof	Davies	Mullins/t
5	03.10	H	AD2	Worcester	W31-26	550	Graham	Hackney(a)	Woof/t	Davies	Mullins
6	10.10	H	AD2	Leeds Tykes	W13-12	500	Graham	Hackney	Woof/t	Davies	Mullins
7	17.10	A	AD2	Exeter	L 14-41	800	Graham	Hackney(a)	Woof	Davies	Mullins/t
8	24.10	H	AD2	Fylde	W 27-6	500	Handley	Mullins	Woof(s)	Davies	Graham
9	31.10	A	AD2	Rugby Lions	L 9-20	400	Handley	Mullins	Woof(b)	Davies(s)	Graham
10	07.11	H	AD2	London Welsh	W12-10	910	Handley	Mullins	Woof	Davies	Graham
11	21.11	A	AD2	Blackheath	W24-18	550	Graham/t	Hackney/2t	Davies	Hill(m)	Mullins
12	12.12	H	AD2	Orrell	L 10-17	500	Graham	Hackney(a)	Woof	Davies	Smith(s)
13	19.12	A	AD2	Bristol	L 8-36	2,397	Handley	Hackney	Woof	Davies(s)	Graham
14	02.01	H	AD2	Blackheath	W31-25	400	Handley/dg(s)	Hackney	Woof/t	Davies	Graham
15	16.01	A	AD2	London Welsh	L 17-49		Handley/c	Hackney	Woof(s)	Davies	Graham/t(A)
16	23.01	H	AD2	Rugby Lions	W 11-3	400	Handley	Hackney/t	Davies	Graham(m)	Hill
17	06.02	A	AD2	Fylde	L 5-24	450	Handley	Hackney	Woof(A)	Hill	Graham
18	13.02	H	AD2	Exeter	L 11-13	400	Handley	Hackney	Woof	Hill	Graham/t
19	28.02	A	AD2	Leeds Tykes	W 10-9	400	Handley/dg	Hackney(A)	Woof	Hill	Graham
20	13.03	A	AD2	Worcester	L 15-41	2,600	Handley	Hackney(A/t)	Woof	Hill(l)	Graham/t
21	27.03	H	AD2	Moseley	L 8-32	450	Handley	Swetman/t	Woof(s)	Davies	Graham
22	03.04	A	AD2	Wakefield	W20-14	500	Handley	Woof	Davies	Hill	Graham
23	11.04	H	AD2	Coventry	L 24-25	450	Handley	Swetman	Woof	Hill	Graham
24	24.04	A	AD2	Rotherham	L 3-44		Handley	Swetman	Woof	Hill	Graham
25	01.05	H	AD2	Bristol	L 13-44	900	Graham	Edwards	Swetman/p	Hill(F)	Woof/t
26	08.05	A	AD2	Orrell	L 15-59	800	Handley	Edwards(a)	Woof	Hill	Graham
A	14.11	H	TBC	New Brighton	W34-23		Graham	Hackney/t	Woof	Hill	Mullins/t
B	09.01	H	TBC	Orrell	W16-11	900	Handley	Hackney	Woof	Davies(s)	Graham
C	31.01	A	TBC	Wasps	L 10-27		Handley/tdg	Hackney	Davies	Hill(m)	Graham

* after opponents name indicates a penalty try
Brackets after a player's name indicates he was replaced. eg (a) means he was replaced by replacement code "a" and so on.
/ after a player or replacement name is followed by any scores he made - eg /t, /c, /p, /dg or any combination of these

1998-99 HIGHLIGHTS

League debuts:
Andrew Charles, Gerraint Evans, Lee Stewart, Stephane LaRue, Louis McGowan, Steve Wands, Michael Swetman, James Edwards, L Smith.

Ever Presents: None
Most appearances Lyndon Griffiths 25(1)

Players used: 29 plus 7 as a replacement only.

Most Points in a season:

Pts	Player	T	C	P	DG
198	L Griffiths	2	25	46	-
25	S Woof	5	-	-	-
25	W Morris	5	-	-	-
20	J O'Reilly	4	-	-	-
20	P Graham	4	-	-	-
20	M Holt	4	-	-	-

MATCH FACTS

10	9	1	2	3	4	5	6	7	8	
Griffiths/c3p	Morris(n)	Charles	Holt	Beckett	White	Temman(o)	Kay	Larue(p)	Stewart	1
Griffiths/cp	O'Reilly/t	Charles	Holt	Beckett	White	Temman	Kay	Larue/t(q)	Stewart(p)	2
Griffiths/2c4p	O'Reilly/t	Charles(t)	Holt(u)	Beckett	White	Kay(v)	Blyth(o)	Larue/t	Stewart	3
Griffiths/cp	O'Reilly	Charles/t	Holt	Beckett	White	Temman	Blyth	Larue	Stewart(o)	4
Griffiths/2c4p	O'Reilly/t	Charles	Holt	Beckett	White	Temman	Blyth	Larue	Stewart/t	5
Griffiths/c2p	O'Reilly(z)	Charles(y)	Holt	Beckett	White	Temman	Blyth(o)	Larue	Stewart	6
Griffiths/2c	O'Reilly(s/t)	Charles	Holt(u)	Beckett(t)	White	Temman	Kay(o)	Larue(w)	Stewart	7
Griffiths/tc5p	O'Reilly(e)	Charles	Holt(u)	Evans	White	Temman	Kay	Larue/t(w)	Stewart	8
Griffiths/3p	O'Reilly(e)	Charles	Brittan(g)	Davies(h)	White	Temman(o)	Kay	Larue(w)	Stewart	9
Griffiths/4p	Morris	Charles	Holt	Beckett	White	Kay	Wolfenden(j)	Larue(w)	Stewart	10
Griffiths/3cp	O'Reilly(e)	Beckett	Britan(g)	Evans(f)	White	Temman	Kay	Wands	Larue(o)	11
Griffiths/cp	Morris	Charles	Holt	Beckett	White/t	Kay	Larue(p)	Wands(j)	Stewart	12
Griffiths/tp	O'Reilly(e)	Charles	Brittan(g)	Beckett	White(l)	Temman	Blyth(k)	Wands(o)	Kay	13
Griffiths/2c3p	Morris(n)	Charles	Holt/t	Beckett	Kay	Temman	Blyth	Wands/t	Stewart(k)	14
Griffiths	Morris(n/t)	Charles	Holt/t(t)	Beckett(u)	Kay	Temman(v)	Blyth	Wands	Larue(o)	15
Griffiths/2p	O'Reilly	Charles(t)	Holt	Beckett	White(j)	Kay	Wolfenden	Wands	Blyth	16
Griffiths	O'Reilly(e)	Beckett/t	Brittan(g)	Evans	Kay	Temman(v)	Stewart	Wands(B)	Blyth	17
Griffiths/2p	Morris	Charles	Holt	Beckett	Kay	McGowan	Wolfenden	Wands	Stewart	18
Griffiths/c	Morris/t	Charles	Holt	Beckett	Kay	Temman(i)	Wolfenden(l)	Wands	Blyth	19
Griffiths/cp	Morris(n)	Charles(t)	Holt(C)	Beckett	White	Kay	Wolfenden(j)	Wands(x)	Blyth	20
Griffiths/p(E)	O'Reilly(e)	Charles(D)	Holt(u)	Beckett	Kay	Temman(v)	Wolfenden(l)	Wands	Blyth	21
Griffiths/2c2p(E)	O'Reilly	Charles(D)	Holt/t	Beckett	Kay	Temman	Blyth	Wands	Stewart/t(o)	22
Griffiths/3cp	Morris/2t	Charles	Holt/t	Beckett	Kay	Temman	Blyth	Wands	Stewart	23
Griffiths/p	Morris(n)	Charles	Britan	Beckett	Kay	Temman	Wolfenden(l)	Wands(g)	Blyth	24
Handley(d)	Morris(n)	Charles	Brittan(g)	Beckett	Kay	Temman(v)	Wolfenden/t(l)	Wands	Blyth	25
Griffiths/cp	Morris/2t	Charles	Brittain(g)	Beckett(D)	Kay	Temman(v)	Wolfenden(l)	Wands	Blyth	26
Griffiths/2c	Morris(n/t)	Charles(y)	Holt/t(u)	Beckett/t	White	Kay/t	Larue	Wands(j)	Stewart(o)	A
Griffiths/p	O'Reilly(e)	Charles(t)	Holt/t	Beckett	Kay	Temman	Blyth/2t	Wands	Larue(o)	B
Griffiths/c	Morris	Charles(t)	Holt(u)	Beckett	Kay	Temman	Wolfenden(l)	Wands	Blyth	C

REPLACEMENTS:

	a- A Handley	b- S Hackney	d - L Griffiths	e - W Morris	f - A Charles
	g - M Holt	h - M Beckett	i - P White	j - K Temman	k - S Larue
	l - L Stewart	m - S Woof	n - J O'Reilly	o - C Wolfenden	p - D Blyth
q - A Towner	r - C Inkson	s - N Hill	t - G Evans	u - J Brittain	v - L McGowan
w - S Wands	x - Geraint Davies	y - S O'Keefe	z - R Saverimutto	A - M Swetman	B - D Tulley
C - B Thompson	D - M O'Keefe	E - J Edwards	F - S Johnson		

Lyndon Griffiths tops Waterloo's points scoring list for a 3rd successive season.
In the process he extends his all time scoring record to 588 in his three seasons at the club.
He also extended his record for conversions and penalties to 74 and 130 respectively.

Centre Sean Woof topped the clubs try scoring list for a second season.

Woof also extended his career record to 16 which is a new club record passing the 14 scored by Steve Bracegirdle.

Scrum half Wayne Morris twice scored a brace of tries to join the other 15 players who have scored a brace of tries for Waterloo in league games.

WATERLOO

LEAGUE STATISTICS
compiled by Stephen McCormack

SEASON	Division	P	W	D	L	F	A	Pts Diff	Lge Pts	Lge Pos	Most Points	Most Tries
89-90	2	11	3	0	8	147	193	-46	6		43 Richard Angell	5 Peter Cooley
90-91	2	12	4	0	8	154	206	-52	8		57 Ian Aitchison	8 Steve Bracegirdle
91-92	2	12	8	0	4	206	184	22	16		92 Ian Aitchison	4 Gary Meredith
92-93	2	12	10	0	2	228	138	90	20		126 Paul Grayson	3 Austin Healey
93-94	2	18	6	2	10	231	346	-115	14		137 Steve Swindells	2 Gary Meredith, Steve Swindells & John Ashcroft
94-95	2	18	8	0	10	287	331	-44	16		160 Steve Swindells	4 Neil Ryan & Steve Wright
95-96	2	18	7	2	9	309	482	-173	16		134 Martin Emmett	4 Peter McCaugheran
96-97	2	22	7	0	15	506	661	-155	14		99 Lyndon Griffiths	7 David Blyth
97-98	P2	22	11	0	11	510	525	-15	22		261 Lyndon Griffiths	7 Marcus Coates & Shaun Woof
98-99	P2	26	12	0	14	419	634	-215	24		198 Lyndon Griffiths	5 Shaun Woof

BIGGEST MARGINS

Home Win	35pts - 51-16 v Blackheath 27.9.97
Away Win	41pts - 56-15 v Rugby 16.11.96
Home Defeat	66pts - 3-69 v Northampton 28.10.96
Away Defeat	64pts - 5-69 v Northampton 13.4.96

MOST CONSECUTIVE

Appearances	39 Shaun Gallagher
Matches scoring Tries	4 Steve Bracegirdle
Matches scoring points	44 Lyndon Griffiths
Victories	7
Defeats	11

MOST POINTS

Scored at Home	51 v Blackheath 27.9.97
Scored Away	56 v Rugby 16.11.96
Conceded at Home	69 v Northampton 28.10.96
Conceded Away	69 v Northampton 13.4.96

MOST TRIES

Scored in a match	7 v Rugby 26.4.97
Conceded in a match	11 v Northampton 28.10.95

MOST APPEARANCES

by a forward	115 (1) Mark Beckett
by a back	99 (8) Tony Handley

	MOST IN A SEASON	MOST IN A CAREER	MOST IN A MATCH	
Points	261 Lyndon Griffiths 97-98	558 Lyndon Griffiths 96-99	23 Martin Emmett	v Bedford 13.1.96 (H)
Tries	8 Steve Bracegirdle 90-91	16 Shaun Woof 96-99	2 by 15 players incl Steve Bracegirdle twice	
Conversions	29 Lyndon Griffiths 97-98	74 Lyndon Griffiths 96-98	6 Lyndon Griffiths	v Blackheath 19.4.97 (A) v Blackheath 27.9.97 (H)
Penalties	66 Lyndon Griffiths 97-98	130 Lyndon Griffiths 96-99	6 Ian Aitchison Steve Swindells	v Blackheath 25.4.92 (A) v Otley 12.3.94 (A) v Newcastle G. 10.9.94 (H)
Drop Goals	6 Paul Grayson 92-93	9 Ian Aitchison 87-95	2 Ian Aitchison Ian Croper Paul Grayson Neil Ryan	v Gloucester 31.10.87 (H) v Sale 2.1.88 (H) v Sale 9.3.91 (H) v Sale 13.3.93 (H) v Lon. Irish 24.9.94 (H) v Newcastle G. 14.10.95 (A)

WATERLOO PLAYING SQUAD

BACKS

Name	Ht.	Wt.	Birthdate	Birthplace	CLUB	League Apps	Tries	Pts
Anthony Handley	5.11	13.7	12.11.73	Salford	Waterloo	99(8)	3	96
Steve Hackney	5.11	13.10	13.06.68	Stockton	Waterloo	21(2)	5	25
Other clubs: Nottingham 25/2/8, Leicester 25(3)/2/16					Moseley	6	1	5
Sean Woof	6.2	15.0	06.03.77	Liverpool	Waterloo	50(3)	16	80
Mike Mullins	6.0	13.6	29.10.70	Auckland	Waterloo	34	8	40
Phil Graham	5.10	13.7	02.12.76	Carlisle	Waterloo	47	8	40
					Liverpool StH	29(2)	8	40
Lyndon Griffiths	5.6	11.0	17.02.74	Bridgend	Waterloo	57(1)	4	558
Wayne Morris	6.0	12.8	06.12.72	Swansea	Waterloo	34(6)	13	65
Gareth Davies			02.08.73		Waterloo	18	1	5
John O'Reilly	5.10	13.8	07.01.76	Botswana	Waterloo	16(8)	4	20
England u21.					Sale	4(3)	-	-
	6.0	12.3	13.11.71	Widnes	Waterloo	25(4)	-	120
Nigel Hill	6.0	14.07	14.12.67	Amersham	Waterloo	81(11)	2	10
Michael Swetman					Waterloo	4(4)	2	13

FORWARDS

Name	Ht.	Wt.	Birthdate	Birthplace	CLUB	League Apps	Tries	Pts
Mark Beckett	6.2	19.7	16.10.65	Hartlepool	Waterloo	116(1)	6	29
Andrew Charles	6.0	15.0	04.07.73	Australia	Waterloo	24(1)	-	-
Matt Holt	6.0	16.0	30.10.71	Brisbane	Waterloo	43(11)	7	35
Louis McGowan	6.5	16.4	17.10.77	Liverpool	Waterloo	1(6)	-	-
Paul White	6.4	17.2	08.05.70	Worthing	Waterloo	85(3)	6	30
Karl Temmen	6.10	19.0	23.09.74	Salisbury	Waterloo	44(8)	1	5
					Preston G			
Ben Kay	6.6	17.0	14.12.75	Liverpool	Waterloo	68(1)	2	10
David Blyth	6.3	17.0	14.03.71	Glasgow	Waterloo	94(3)	12	60
					W Hartlepool	9	-	-
Steve Wands					Waterloo	16(4)	1	5
Carl Wolfenden	6.2	15.11	05.02.69	Waterloo	Waterloo	24(17)	6	30
Jason Brittain	5.10	15.5	24.10.73	Hawkes Bay	Waterloo	9(12)	-	-
Lee Stewart	6.3	15.06	26.03.71	South Africa	Waterloo	16(7)	2	10
Adam Towner	6.1	14.04	02.09.71	Toowoomba	Waterloo	(1)	-	-

WATERLOO

FACT FILE

Founded: 1882

Colours: Myrtle, scarlet & white hoops/green shorts
Change colours: White with myrtle,scarlet & white thin striped `V'

GROUND

Address: The Pavillion, St Anthony's Rd., Blundellsands, Liverpool. L23 8TW
Tel: 0151 924 4552
Capacity: 8,900 Seated: 900 Standing:8,000

Directions: From the end of the M57 follow signs for Crosby. Waterloo FC is then sign-posted to the ground. Nearest Railway Station: Crosby & Blundellsands, 1/2 mile down St Anthony's Road.

Car Parking: 100 spaces, Saturday only.

Admission
Matchdays Adults Standing £8, Seated £10. Children u16 £2

Club Shop: Open only on matchdays. Contact the club.

Clubhouse: Open during normal licensing hours. Three bars, with snacks and meals available on matchdays.
Functions: Capacity 150, contact Frank Spencer 0151 924 4552.

Training Nights: Monday, Tuesday and Thursday.

PROGRAMME

Size: A5 Pages: 34 Price: £1.50
Editor: F D Spencer 0151 924 4552

ADVERTISING RATES

Colour:	Page £500	Half £275
Mono:	Page £250	Half £125

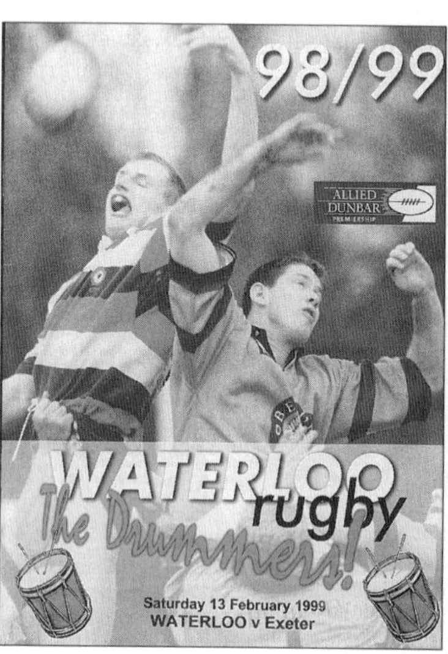

WEST HARTLEPOOL R.F.C.

President Ken Greig

Chairman Andy Hindle

Chairman of Rugby Les Smith

Club Secretary Steve Smith

c/o West Hartlepool RFC,
PO Box 132
Hartlepool,TS25 5YW
Tel: 01429 233642
Tel/Fax: 01429 272160

West Hartlepool's `yo-yo' existence continued, the inevitable result of financial problems which meant it was difficult for a simple members' club to compete with the elite in the country.

Mike Brewer recruited within his budget, and added mid season signings which arguably made his side the best seen in Hartlepool. At full strength West were most competitive in the second half of the campaign, their best win being against Wasps, while they fell narrowly short at Northampton and Newcastle. However, West were unable to fund a large enough squad to combat the inevitable injury list, particularly severe after the transfer deadline, and Bedford deservedly maintained the `play-off spot', which was West's only realistic aim after a poor start to the season.

Steve Vile maintained the fine form shown in the previous promotion season, while Duane Monkley, Shane McDonald, and the French US Eagle, Philippe Farner, were tireless workers in the pack. Pita Tangionoa, Mark Gaicheri and J.J. van der Esch made international appearances during the season, Farner at its close, while Mike Mullins was selected for the Irish Tour to Australia.

Support was poor and a question mark lies throughout the North of England as to the viability of a full time squad in soccer mad areas. West's future lies in consolidation and development of local talent, the policy that raised the club beyond mere County status in the first place twenty years ago.

Steve Smith

WEST HARTLEPOOL

MATCH FACTS

Match No.	Date	H/A	Comp.	Opponents	Result & Score	Att.	15	14	13	12	11
1	13.09	H	AD1	London Irish	L 20-44	2,059	Farrell	Bishop	Greaves	Connolly	John/2t
2	20.09	A	AD1	Gloucester	L 3-36	5,576	Benson(a)	Bishop	Greaves	Connolly	John
3	27.09	A	AD1	Wasps*	L 14-71	2,797	Farrell(o)	Bishop	Greaves	Connolly	John
4	04.10	H	AD1	Newcastle	L 19-24	2,702	Farrell/t	Benson/t	Tangonia	Connolly	John
5	10.10	A	AD1	Richmond	L 23-41	4,357	Farrell	Benson/t	Tangonia	Connolly	John/t
6	18.10	H	AD1	Bath*	L 20-50	1,743	Farrell/t	Benson(b)	Tangonia	Connolly	John
7	20.10	H	AD1	Saracens	L 3-52	1,877	Farrell	Lough	Tangonia	Connolly	John
8	24.10	A	AD1	Harlequins	L 10-25	2,476	Farrell	Lough	Tangonia	Connolly/t	John
9	01.11	H	AD1	Leicester*	L 15-45	1,846	Farrell	Lough	Tangonia	Connolly	John
10	13.11	A	AD1	Sale*	L 26-42	2,338	Farrell	Lough	Maclure	Connolly(u)	John/t
11	22.11	H	AD1	London Scot	L 7-37	1,981	Farrell	Lough/t	Tangonia(w)(o)	Connolly	John
12	12.12	A	AD1	Bedford	W 23-10	2,398	Farrell/t	Lough	Mullins	Connolly(u)	John
13	20.12	H	AD1	Northampton	L 9-33	1,613	Farrell	Tangonia	Mullins(w)	Greaves(o)	John
14	27.12	A	AD1	Newcastle	L 13-29	3,403	Farrell(c)	Benson	John/t	Tangonia	Maclure
15	03.01	H	AD1	Wasps	W 21-17	2,133	Farrell/dg	Benson/t	John	Tangonia	Handley/t
16	16.01	A	AD1	London Irish	L 21-43	2,129	Farrell	Benson	Connolly	Tangonia	John
17	23.01	A	AD1	Northampton	L 14-19	6,023	Farrell	Mullins	Connolly	Tangonia/t	John
18	14.02	A	AD1	Saracens	L 27-48	5,872	Farrell(p)	Benson	Connolly	Tangonia/t	John/t
19	14.03	H	AD1	Gloucester	W 33-32	1,300	Farrell	Benson(p)(w)	Mullins	Greaves	John
20	28.03	H	AD1	Sale	D 33-33	1,531	Farrell	Benson	Mullins/t	Greaves(d)	John
21	17.04	H	AD1	Richmond	L 35-36	1,206	Farrell	Handley(w)	Mullins/t	Connolly(c)	John
22	21.04	H	AD1	Harlequins	L 37-47	1,365	Farrell	Benson/t(p)	Mullins	Greaves	John
23	24.04	A	AD1	Bath	L 24-56	6,500	Farrell/t	Handley	Mullins	Greaves/t(w)	John
24	02.05	H	AD1	Bedford	L 0-39	1,400	Farrell	Handley	Mullins	John	Benson
25	08.05	A	AD1	London Scot	L 14-26	1,459	Farrell	Handley	Greaves/t	Mullins	Maclure
26	16.05	A	AD1	Leicester	L 37-72	12,957	Farrell/t	Maclure/2t	Greaves	Mullins(p)	John
A	10.01	H	TBC	Bracknell	W 34-14	600	Farrell/t	Benson	John	Tangonia(c)	Handley
B	31.01	H	TBC	Newcastle	L 21-32	2,600	Farrell	Benson	Tangonia(c)	Connolly	John

* after opponents name indicates a penalty try
Brackets after a player's name indicates he was replaced. eg (a) means he was replaced by replacement code "a" and so on.
/ after a player or replacement name is followed by any scores he made - eg /t, /c, /p, /dg or any combination of these

1998-99 HIGHLIGHTS

League debuts:
Phil Greaves, Bill Fuller, Richard Stone, Peter Tangonia, K Fourie, Shane McDonald, J van der Esch, M Bentley, Duane Monkley, Tim Collier, M Salter, Mike Mullins, Tim Lough, Mark Gilbert.

Ever Presents: None
Most appearances 25 Emmett Farrell.

Players used: 38 plus 1 as a replacement only.

Most Points in a season:

Pts	Player	T	C	P	DG
240	S Vile	5	28	52	1
41	J Benson	3	7	4	-
30	S John	6	-	-	-
28	E Farrell	5	-	-	1
20	Penalty Try	4	-	-	-

MATCH FACTS

10	9	1	2	3	4	5	6	7	8	
Vile/2p(l/2c)	Nu'ualitia	Sparks	Peacock(m)	Beal(n)	Fuller(B)	Schrader	Ponton	Cassidy	Brewer	1
Belgian/p	Nu'ualitia(p)	Sparks(n)	Herbert(f)	Beal(r)	Brewer()	Schrader(h)	Ponton	Cassidy	Hyde	2
Vile/t2c	Nu'ualitia(t)	Sparks	Herbert(f)	Beal(n)(r)	Webb(s)	Schrader	Ponton	Cassidy	Brewer	3
Vile/3p	Nu'ualitia	Sparks	Peacock(q)	Beal(r)	Fuller	Farner	Ponton	Hyde(j)	Brewer	4
Vile/2c3p	Nu'ualitia(t)	Sparks(x)	Peacock(m)	Beal(s)	Farner	Fuller	Ponton	Cassidy(s)	Brewer	5
Vile/2c2p	Stone	Sparks(n)	Peacock	Beal	Farner	Fuller	Ponton	Hyde	Brewer	6
Vile/p	Stone(p)	vd Esch	Cullinane(r)	Beal	Farner	Fuller	Ponton(m)	Cassidy	Hyde(k)	7
Vile/cp	Nu'ualitia	Sparks	Cullinane	Beal	Farner	Fuller	Ponton	Bentley(j)	Brewer	8
Benson/cp	Nu'ualitia/t	Sparks	Cullinane(f)	Beal	Farner	Fuller(A)	Ponton	Bentley(z)	Cassidy	9
Vile/c3p(o/cp)	Nu'ualitia(t)	Sparks	Cullinane	Beal	Farner(h)	Giacheri	Salter	Cassidy(j)	Brewer	10
Vile/c	Nu'ualitia	Seymour(e)	Cullinane(f)	Beal	Fuller	Giacheri	Salter(m)	Ponton	Cassidy	11
Vile/2c3p	Nu'ualitia(t)	Sparks	McDonald	Beal	Farner	Giacheri	Ponton	Monkley	Brewer/t	12
Vile/3p(p)	Stone	Sparks	McDonald	Beal	Farner	Giacheri(j)(m)	Ponton	Monkley	Brewer	13
Vile/p	Stone	vd Esch(e)	McDonald/t	Beal	Farner	Ponton	Bentley	Monkley	Brewer	14
Vile/c2p	Nu'ualitia	vd Esch(g)	McDonald	Sparks	Farner	Collier(z)	Ponton/t	Monkley	Brewer	15
Vile/3c	Nu'ualitia/2t	Sparks	McDonald/t	Fourie(g)	Farner	Collier	Ponton	Monkley	Brewer	16
Vile/t2c	Nu'ualitia	Sparks	McDonald	Fourie	Farner	Collier	Salter	Monkley	Ponton	17
Vile/c5p	Nu'ualitia	Sparks(x)	McDonald	Fourie(g)	Farner	Giacheri	Salter	Ponton	Brewer	18
Vile/tc6pdg	Nu'ualitia	Sparks	McDonald	Fourie	Farner	Giacheri	Salter	Monkley/t	Brewer	19
Vile/t2c3p	Nu'ualitia(t)	vd Esch(e)	McDonald	Fourie(r)	Farner/t	Giacheri	Ponton/t	Monkley	Brewer	20
Vile/t2c7p	Nu'ualitia	Sparks	McDonald	Beal(v)	Farner	Ponton	Hyde	Monkley	Brewer	21
Vile/4c3p	Nu'ualitia	vd Esch(e)	McDonald(m)	Fourie/2t	Farner	Ponton	Hyde/t	Monkley	Brewer	22
Vile/c4p	Nu'ualitia(t)	Sparks	McDonald(m)	Fourie(g)	Farner	Ponton	Hyde(j)	Monkley	Brewer	23
Vile(c)	Nu'ualitia(t)	Sparks	McDonald	Beal(v)(x)	Farner	Giacheri	Ponton	Monkley	Brewer	24
Benson/2c	Nu'ualitia	Sparks	McDonald(m)	Beal	Farner	Ponton	Cassidy(s/t)	Monkley	Brewer	25
Benson/3c2p	Nu'ualitia(t)	Sparks(x)	McDonald(m)	Beal/t	Gilbert	Ponton	Cassidy	Monkley	Brewer/t	26
Vile/3cp	Nu'ualitia	vd Esch	McDonald/t(m)	Fourie(g)	Farner	Collier/t	Salter/t	Ponton/t	Brewer	A
Vile/7p	Nu'ualitia	Sparks(x)	McDonald(m)	Fourie	Farner	Collier	Salter	Monkley	Ponton	B

REPLACEMENTS:						
a- E Farrell	b-H Bishop	c-P Greaves	d-J Connolly	e-S Sparks	f-A Peacock	g-P Beal
h-B Fuller	i-J Ponton	j-S Cassidy	k-M Brewer	l-P Belgian	m-S Whitehead	n-B Cullinane
o-J Benson	p-T Handley	r-P Seymour	s-D Hyde	t-R Stone	u-P Tangonia	v-K Fourie
w-G Maclure	x-J vd Esch	y-M Bentley	z-M Salter	A-M Giacheri	B-C Webb	

Outside half Steven Vile tops the 240 point mark for the second succesive season but finishes one point shy of his league record of 241 points set last season.
He did though kick a new record 52 penalties beating his own record of 42 from last season.
He also set new records for penalties in a match, 7, and points in a match 30.
He set both these record in the home match against Richmond in April.

Winger Steven John topped the try scorers list for a second time in three seasons. He extended his career total to 26 which puts him third on the clubs all time list.

West suffered their worst ever defeat when they lost 71-14 at Wasps to lose by a record 57 points. In their last match of the season at Leicester they conceded a record 72 points.

WEST HARTLEPOOL

LEAGUE STATISTICS
compiled by Stephen McCormack

SEASON	Division	P	W	D	L	F	A	Pts Diff	Lge Pts	Lge Pos		Most Points		Most Tries
89-90	3	11	5	2	4	175	120	55	12	3	65	Gary Armstrong	5	Dave Cooke
90-91	3	12	10	1	1	282	90	192	21	1p	87	John Stabler	9	John Wrigley
91-92	2	12	11	0	1	244	89	155	22	2p	118	John Stabler	7	John Wigley
92-93	1	12	3	0	9	149	236	-87	6	12r	89	John Stabler	3	Alan Brown
93-94	2	18	13	2	3	389	271	128	28	2p	103	John Stabler	7	John Wrigley
94-95	1	18	6	1	11	312	412	-100	13	9	93	Tim Stimpson	5	Paul Hodder
95-96	1	18	0	0	18	288	634	-346	0	10	110	Tim Stimpson	5	Tim Stimpson
96-97	1	22	3	0	19	382	795	-407	6	11r	126	Chris John	13	Steve John
97-98	2	22	15	1	6	617	431	148	31	2p	241	Steven Vile	10	Emmett Farrell
98-99	1	26	3	1	22	501	1007	-506	7	14	240	Steven Vile	6	Steve John

BIGGEST MARGINS

Home Win	54pts - 66-12 v Fylde 14.2.98
Away Win	45pts - 51-6 v Waterloo 11.4.98
Home Defeat	70pts - 21-91 v Harlequins 23.3.96
Away Defeat	57pts - 14-71 v Wasps 27.9.98

MOST CONSECUTIVE

Appearances	64 John Stabler 11.7.89-26.3.94
Matches scoring Tries	4 Owen Evans & Steve Cook
Matches scoring points	36 John Stabler
Victories	9
Defeats	19

MOST POINTS

Scored at Home	66 v Fylde 14.2.98
Scored Away	51 v Waterloo 11.4.98
Conceded at Home	91 v Harlequins 23.3.96
Conceded Away	72 v Leicester 16.5.99

MOST TRIES

Scored in a match	10 v Fylde 14.2.98 (H)
Conceded in a match	14 v Harlequins 23.3.96 (H)

MOST APPEARANCES

by a forward	101 Phil Lancaster
by a back	91 (3) John Stabler

	MOST IN A SEASON	MOST IN A CAREER	MOST IN A MATCH	
Points	241 Steven Vile 97-98	630 John Stabler 87-97	26 Steven Vile	v Richmond 17.4.99 (H)
Tries	13 Steven John 96-97	32 Owen Evans 87-96	3 Owen Evans	v Nuneaton 23.4.88 (H)
			Peter Robinson	v V. of Lune 2.3.91 (A)
			John Wrigley	v Moseley 14.1.291 (H)
Conversions	33 Steven Vile 97-98	83 John Stabler 87-97	8 Steven Vile	v Fylde 14.2.98 (H)
Penalties	52 Steven Vile 98-99	127 John Stabler 87-97	7 Steven Vile	v Richmond 17.4.99 (H)
Drop Goals	3 John Stabler 88-89	8 John Stabler 87-97	2 Kevin Oliphant	v V. of Lune 7.11.88 (A)
			John Stabler	v Sheffield 9.11.88 (H)

WEST HARTLEPOOL PLAYING SQUAD

BACKS

BACKS	Ht.	Wt.	Birthdate	Birthplace	CLUB	League Apps	Tries	Pts
Emmet Farrell Ireland u21.	5.10	13.7	06.03.77	Dublin	W Hartlepool	47(1)	15	84
Jamie Connolly	5.11	14.0	06.02.73	Wellington(NZ)	W Hartlepool	54(1)	7	35
Stephen John	5.10	13.0	11.10.73	Cardiff	W Hartlepool	67	26	133
Phil Greaves England u21,18.	6.0	14.08	16.02.78	Yorkshire	W Hartlepool	10(3)	2	10
Gareth Maclure	6.2	13.00	01.03.80	Bury	W Hartlepool	4(5)	2	10
Toby Handley	5.9	12.03	14.04.76	Catterick	W Hartlepool	5(8)	1	5
Jon Benson England u18. North u21.	5.11	11.10	11.01.76	Durham	W Hartlepool	22(12)	6	80
Steven Vile	5.11	13.01	16.07.70	Waratah	W Hartlepool	40	13	481
Tu Nu'ual'itia	5.7	13.06	22.02.66	W Samoa	W Hartlepool	42(1)	5	25
Paul Belgian	6.1	14.1	31.10.75	Gateshead	W Hartlepool Newcastle	9(3) 6	2 1	66 28
Hugo Bishop	6.0	13.6	17.06.76	Brighton	W Hartlepool	12(1)	2	10
Peter Tangonia	6.0	15.00	06.12.73	Vava'u	W Hartlepool	13(2)	2	10
Mike Mullins	5.10	14.02	29.10.70	Auckland	W Hartlepool Waterloo	11 34	2 8	10 40

FORWARDS

FORWARDS	Ht.	Wt.	Birthdate	Birthplace	CLUB	League Apps	Tries	Pts
Duane Monkley	6.1	15.02	31.10.66	New Zealand	W Hartlepool	14	1	5
Andrew Peacock	5.11	15.2	03.12.68	Newport	W Hartlepool	34(10)	1	5
Steve Whitehead	5.8		21.01.70	Edinburgh	W Hartlepool	6(15)	-	-
Paddy Seymour	6.0	17.07	18.07.78	Northallerton	W Hartlepool	3(7)	-	-
Steve Sparks	5.11	18.00	07.07.74	Blyth	W Hartlepool	41(5)	3	15
JJ van der Esch	6.3	17.07	07.06.69	Lower Hutt	W Hartlepool	5(4)	-	-
Phillipe Farner	6.7	16.09	09.01.70	Tanzania	W Hartlepool	40	3	15
Russell Schrader			02.05.74	New Zealand	W Hartlepool	14(1)	-	-
James Ponton	6.3	14.07	31.07.74	Hexham	W Hartlepool	42(3)	5	25
Shane McDonald	5.11	17.2	21.06.71	Stratford (NZ)	W Hartlepool	15	2	10
Shaun Cassidy England students. Other clubs: Wasps, Bedford			13.10.69	Middlesborough	W Hartlepool Newcastle	34(6) 31	1 1	5 5
Paul Beal	5.11	16.4	10.02.68	Redcar	W Hartlepool	46(4)	1	5
Mark Giacheri	6.8	17.11	01.02.69	Sydney	W Hartlepool	18(1)	2	10

WEST HARTLEPOOL

FACT FILE

Founded: 1881
Nickname: West

Colours: Green, red and white
Change colours: Blue, red and white

GROUND

Address: The Friarage, West View Road, Hartlepool TS24 0BP
Tel: 01429 233642 Fax: 01429 272160
Capacity: 4,900 Seated: 400 Standing - covered: 2,000 , uncovered: 2,500

Directions: Leave A19 at A179, 10 miles north of River Tees. Proceed down that road for approx. 4 miles aiming for the chimney seen in the distance.
Nearest Railway Station: Hartlepool.

Car Parking: Limited at ground, though nearby trading estate.

Admission : Season tickets £50
Match day £5 (both to be confirmed)

Club Shop: Yes

Clubhouse: Open matchdays 12noon - 11pm

Training Nights:

PROGRAMME Not applicable

WORCESTER R.F.C.

President	Richard Cumming	*	
Chairman	Derek Thompson	*	
Secretary	Adrian Harling	21 Cornmeadow Lane, Claines, Worcester	01562 822295 (B)
Operations Director	Michael Robins	* 01905 427973 (H), 01905 454183 (B), 01905 757222 (Fax)	
Registrations Secretary	Dick Cumming	* 01905 451618 (H)	01299 827250 (B)
Press Officer	Nicola Goodwin	* 01905 451396 (H)	01432 274413 ext 227 (B)

* c/o Worcester RFC, Sixways. Pershore Lane, Hindlip, Worcester WR3 8ZE
Tel: 01905 454183 Fax: 01905 757222

Worcester entered National Division Two full of confidence after gaining our fifth promotion in six seasons and winning Jewson Division One North in style.

Duncan Hall came on board as 1st XV coach to work alongside Les Cusworth and Phil Maynard and we welcomed new young editions Ben Harvey, James Lofthouse and Tom Robinson to Sixways. The season started with a bang with friendly victories over Swansea and Connacht and sixteen league wins from seventeen including memorable successes over Midland rivals Coventry and Moseley and near neighbours Bristol.

Injury hit the squad in November and, despite valiant efforts from a number of younger players, the club tumbled out of the Cheltenham and Gloucester Cup at the first round.

A thrilling victory over Coventry gained Worcester a fourth round tie against Gloucester in the Tetley's Bitter Cup, the first meeting between the sides, and 3,000 Worcester fans saw their side put up a valiant fight.

Injury problems resurfaced once more in January as Worcester saw fifteen of their first team squad laid low over the next six weeks. Losses against Exeter, Leeds and Moseley soon followed and Worcester found they lacked the strength in depth needed to bounce back. After a fantastic start to the season it was hugely disappointing to end with five losses in six games and see any chance of promotion disappear, but the squad fought hard until the end with a thrilling final match against Bristol at the Memorial Ground.

The highlight of the year has been the fantastic support gained by Worcester RFC. The travelling support grew and grew and home gates reached a record high with three league games being sell-outs. Captain Bruce Fenley resigned after three highly successful years in charge and second row Chris Raymond, an every present in the first team squad, was named Player of the Year. The summer was a time of re-assessment with many faces coming and going from Sixways. The ground continued to grow with the completion of a new south stand containing 34 corporate boxes and 1400 seats.

Worcester Rugby Club has come a long, long way in a short time but, whatever the outcome of the forthcoming season, the club, as ever, refuses to sit still.

NICOLA GOODWIN

L-R - Back Row: Phil Maynard (Coach), Nell Porteus (Physio), Gary Clark, Mike Crisp, James Lofthouse, Peter Mitchell, Gordie Houston, Richard Hilton-Jones, Ed Ofree, Richard Denhardt, Steve Lloyd, Chris Raymond, Jim Jenner, Neil Lyman, Richard Le Bas, Stuart Turner, Paul Manley, Carl Douglas (Dev. Off.) Ron Coward (Manager). Middle: Les Cusworth (Dir. of Rugby), Alistair McLaughlin, John Liley, Dean Ball, Mike Robins (Operations Dir.), Nick Baxter, Roger Murray (President), Bruce Fenley (Club Captain), Cecil Duckworth (Chairman), Duncan Hughes, Paul Holford, Ben Harvey, Simon Morris, Duncan Hall (1st XV Coach).
Front: Richard Tomlinson, Rob Myler, Nigel Richardson, Tim Smith.

WORCESTER

MATCH FACTS

Match No.	Date	H/A	Comp.	Opponents	Result & Score	Att.	15	14	13	12	11
1	05.09	H	AD2	Coventry	W 22-7	2,500	Smith	Holford(m)	Hughes	Tomlinson/t	Baxter/t
2	12.09	A	AD2	Wakefield	W 48-22	600	Smith/t	Myler/3t	Hughes/2t	Tomlinson(q)	Morris
3	19.09	H	AD2	Moseley*	W 23-8	3,500	Smith	Myler(r)	Hughes	Tomlinson	Baxter
4	26.09	H	AD2	Leeds Tykes	W 24-19	4,000	Smith(w)	Morris	Hughes/t	Tomlinson	Baxter/t
5	03.10	A	AD2	Waterloo	L 26-31	550	Smith(w)	Feurer	Hughes	Tomlinson	Baxter
6	10.10	H	AD2	Exeter	W 40-15	2,122	Liley	Holford	Hughes/t	Tomlinson	Baxter/t
7	17.10	A	AD2	Fylde	W 17-8	650	Liley/2cp	Holford	Hughes	Tomlinson	Baxter
8	24.10	H	AD2	Rugby Lions	W 29-6	1,763	Liley/2c5p	Holford/t	Hughes/t	Tomlinson	Baxter(m)
9	31.10	A	AD2	London Welsh	W 22-14	1,400	Liley/4p	Holford	Myler/2t	Hughes	Baxter
10	07.11	H	AD2	Blackheath	W 21-9	2,032	Liley/c3p	Holford/t	Myler	Hughes	Baxter/t
11	21.11	A	AD2	Orrell*	W 13-9	1,200	Liley/c2p	Morris	Hughes	Myler	Baxter(d)
12	13.12	H	AD2	Bristol	W 20-9	3,900	Liley/5p	Morris	Hughes	McLaughlin	Baxter
13	19.12	A	AD2	Rotherham	L 19-29	1,520	Liley/c4p	Morris	Hughes	McLaughlin/t	Myler(E)
14	02.01	H	AD2	Orrell	W 17-0	2,336	Liley/4p	Holford(a)	Hughes	McLaughlin/t(F)	Morris
15	16.01	A	AD2	Blackheath	W 51-3	600	Liley/t2cp(z/t2c)	Myler/t	Hughes	Devereux/2t	Morris/t
16	23.01	H	AD2	London Welsh	W 14-12	3,600	Liley/3p	Myler/t	Hughes	Devereux	Morris
17	06.02	A	AD2	Rugby Lions	W 36-23	1,200	LeBas/2c4p	Myler/t(w)	Hughes	Deveruex(b)	Moris
18	13.02	H	AD2	Fylde*	W 56-0	2,316	LeBas/t4c2p(w)	Holford/t	Hughes	McLaughlin/t	Morris/2t
19	27.02	A	AD2	Exeter*	L 23-27	1,200	LeBas/t2c3p	Holford	Hughes	McLaughlin	Morris(q)
20	13.03	H	AD2	Waterloo	W 41-15	2,600	Lofthouse/3c	Holford/t(c/2t)	Hughes	McLaughlin	Morris/t
21	27.03	A	AD2	Leeds	L 16-24	530	Lofthouse/p(w/c2p)	Holford	Hughes	Devereux	Morris
22	03.04	A	AD2	Moseley	L 16-18	1,199	Liley/c3p	Holford	Hughes	Devereux	Myler(k/t)
23	17.04	H	AD2	Wakefield	W 67-19	2,600	Crisp/t(w/t)	Goodwin/t(m)	Hughes	McLaughlin/2t	Baxter/3t
24	24.04	A	AD2	Coventry	L 17-26	1,400	LeBas	Myler(B)	Hughes(H)	McLaughlin	Baxter/t
25	01.05	H	AD2	Rotherham	L 27-35	3,100	LeBas/3c2p	Holford	Hughes(H)(w)	McLaughlin	Baxter/2t
26	09.05	A	AD2	Bristol	L 11-21	7,326	LeBas/2p	Holford	Hughes	McLaughlin	Baxter/t
A	14.11	A	TBC	Coventry	W 36-26	2,200	Liley/4cp	Morris/t	Hughes	Myler/2t	Baxter
B	09.01	A	TBC	Gloucester	L 17-31	7,136	Liley/2cp	Morris	Hughes	Myler	Baxter(z)

* after opponents name indicates a penalty try
Brackets after a player's name indicates he was replaced. eg (a) means he was replaced by replacement code "a" and so on.
/ after a player or replacement name is followed by any scores he made - eg /t, /c, /p, /dg or any combination of these

1998-99 HIGHLIGHTS

League debuts:
Richard Denhardt, James Lofthouse, Lee Feurer, Niall Malone, Steve Hobson, Ben Harvey, Stuart Turner, John Devereux, Paul Manley, Mike Crisp.

Ever Presents: Duncan Hughes

Players used: 35 plus 7 as a replacement.

Most Points in a season:

Pts	Player	T	C	P	DG
162	R LeBas	4	26	30	-
140	J Liley	2	11	36	-
65	N Baxter	13	-	-	-
40	R Myler	8	-	-	-

MATCH FACTS

10	9	1	2	3	4	5	6	7	8	
LeBas/c	Fenley/t	Linnett	Ball	Lyman(n)	Denhardt/t	Raymond(o)	Clark(p)	Scott	Jenner	1
LeBas/5cp	Fenley(s)	Linnett/t	Ball	Mitchell	Denhardt	Raymond	Clark(u)	Scott(t)	H-Jones	2
LeBas/c2p	Fenley	Linnett	Ball(v)	Lyman(n)	Denhardt/2t	Lloyd(j)	Clark	Richardson	H-Jones(l)	3
LeBas/c4p	Fenley(s)	Linnett(h)	Ball	Mitchell	Denhardt	Raymond	Clark(t)	H-Jones	Jenner	4
LeBas/2c4p	Fenley	Linnett/t	Ball	Mitchell	Lloyd	Raymond(i)	Orgee(k)	H-Jones	Jenner/t	5
LeBas/t4c4p	Fenley	Linnett	Ball(v)	Lyman	Denhardt(j)	Lloyd	Clark	Hobson	H-Jones/t	6
LeBas/t	Fenley/t	Linnett	Houston	Lyman	Denhardt	Lloyd	Clark	Hobson	Jenner	7
LeBas	Fenley(B)	Linnett	Ball(C)	Lyman	Denhardt	Raymond(o)	Clark	Richardson	Jenner	8
LeBas	Fenley	Linnett(n)	Ball	Lyman	Raymond(i)	Lloyd	Clark(l)	Richardson	Orgee	9
LeBas	Fenley	Linnett	Ball	Lyman	Denhardt	Raymond	H-Jones	Richardson	Orgee	10
Malone	Fenley(a)	Linnett	Ball	Lyman	Raymond(i)	Lloyd	Orgee	Richardson	Jenner	11
LeBas	Fenley	Linnett	Ball	Mitchell(D)	Raymond	Lloyd	H-Jones	Richardson	Jenner/t	12
LeBas(z)	Fenley	Linnett	Ball	Mitchell	Raymond	Lloyd(x)	H-Jones	Richardson	Jenner	13
Malone	Fenley	Linnett	Ball(v)	Turner(n)	Denhardt(G)	Raymond	H-Jones(x)	Richardson	Jenner	14
LeBas	Fenley/t	Mitchell	Ball(v)	Turner	Denhardt	Raymond	Clark(x)	Richardson	Jenner/t	15
LeBas	Fenley	Linnett	Ball(v)	Mitchell	Denhardt	Raymond	Clark	Richardson(p)	Jenner	16
Malone	Fenley	Lyman/t	Ball	Mitchell	Denhardt	Raymond	H-Jones/t	Richardson	Jenner/t	17
Malone/c	Fenley(a/t)	Linnett	Ball(u)	Mitchell	Raymond	Lloyd	H-Jones(x)	Richardson(i)	Jenner/t	18
Malone(w)	Fenley	Lyman	Ball	Mitchell(f)	Denhardt	Raymond	H-Jones	Richardson(x)	Jenner(k)	19
LeBas/cp(z)	Fenley/t(B)	Linnett/t	Ball(v)	Mitchell(h)	Raymond	Lloyd(i)	Clark	Richardson(l)	H-Jones	20
LeBas	Fenley(B/t)	Linnett	Ball	Mitchell(D)	Denhardt	Raymond	Clark	Richardson	H-Jones	21
Malone(y)	Harvey	Linnett	Ball(v)	Lyman(D)	Denhardt	Raymond	H-Jones	Manley(t)	Jenner	22
Lofthouse/6c	Harvey/t(e)	Lyman	Houston	Turner/t(f)	Raymond	Lloyd/t	Orgee	Manley(l)	H-Jones	23
Lofthouse/4p	Fenley	Lyman	Houston(g)	Mitchell(f)	Raymond	Lloyd	Orgee	Scott(l)	H-Jones	24
Lofthouse	Harvey(e)	Lyman	Houston(g)	Turner(f)	Raymond	Lloyd	Orgee(J)	H-Jones/t	Jenner	25
Lofthouse(w)	Harvey(e)	Lyman	Houston(g)	Mitchell(f)	Raymond	Lloyd(i)	Orgee	H-Jones(J)	Jenner	26
Malone	Fenley	Linnett/t	Ball(C)	Lyman	Denhardt/t(n)	Lloyd	H-Jones	Richardson	Orgee(l)	A
LeBas	Fenley(A)	Linnett	Ball(v)	Mitchell	Denhardt(G)	Raymond	Clark	Richardson/t	Jenner/t	B

REPLACEMENTS	a- T Smith	b- P Holford	c - N Baxter	d - R LeBas	e - B Fenley
f - M Linnett	g - D Ball	h - N Lyman	i - R Denhardt	j - C Raymond	k - G Clark
l - J Jenner	m - R Myler	n - P Mitchell	o - S Lloyd	p - R H-Jones	q - J Lofthouse
r - S Morris	s - A Martin	t - N Richardson	u - T Robinson	v - G Houston	w - J Liley
x - E Orgee	y - A McLaughlin	z - N Malone			
A - S Powell	B - B Harvey	C - T Beddow	D - S Turner	E - P Hanson	F - L Hinton
G - M Gilbert	H - J Devereux	J - P Manley	K - J Goodwin		

33 J Lofthouse - 9 5 -

Richard LeBas finished top of the Worcester points scorers list for the second successive season. In the process he also set a new league record for Worcester with 378 points which passed the 369 points scored by Tim Smith.
He equalled Tim Smith's career record of 80 conversions and seasonal reocord of 30 penalties.

Winger Nick Baxter finished top of the try scorers list at the club for a third consecutive season with 13 tries. Baxter extended his career record for Worcester to 65.

Prop Mark Linnett played 19 matches during the season and extended his record or league appearances to 77. Amongst the backs Duncan Hughes was ever present and passed Bruce Fenley as the back with the most

WORCESTER

LEAGUE STATISTICS

compiled by Stephen McCormack

SEASON	Division	P	W	D	L	F	A	Pts Diff	Lge Pts	Lge Pos	Coach	Captain
89-90	N Mid	10	8	0	2	237	72	165	16	1p	P John	R Everton
90-91	Mid 2W	10	5	0	5	146	131	15	10	5	P John	R Everton
91-92	Mid 2W	10	7	0	3	175	131	44	14	3		R Everton
92-93	Mid. 2	11	9	0	2	188	89	99	18	2p		
93-94	Mid. 1	12	8	0	4	234	104	130	16	2		
94-95	Mid. 1	12	11	1	0	278	82	196	23	1p	P Maynard	N Stoodley
											Most Points	**Most Tries**
95-96	D5N	12	9	0	3	317	187	130	18	2	50 Spencer Bradley	10 Spencer Bradley
96-97	D4N	26	23	3	0	830	375	455	49	1p	242 Tim Smith	18 Nick Baxter
97-98	JN1	26	24	0	2	1001	331	670	48	1p	221 Richard Le Bas	29 Nick Baxter
98-99	P2	26	18	0	8	716	409	307	34*	3	162 Richard Le Bas	13 Nick Baxter

BIGGEST MARGINS

Home Win	56pts - 78-22 v Liverpool St H 21.3.98
Away Win	61pts - 68-7 v Otley 21.12.98
Home Defeat	15pts - 13-28 v Lon. Welsh 25.10.97
Away Defeat	8pts - 15-23 v Birmingham Sol. 14.10.95 29-37 v Sandal 10.2.96

MOST CONSECUTIVE

Appearances	24 Duncan Hughes
Matches scoring Tries	9 Nick Baxter
Matches scoring points	17 Tim Smith
Victories	18
Defeats	1

MOST POINTS

Scored at Home	78 v Liverpool St Helens 21.3.98
Scored Away	68 v Otley 21.12.98
Conceded at Home	28 v London Welsh 25.10.97
Conceded Away	37 v Sandal 10.2.96

MOST TRIES

Scored in a match	12 v Otley 21.12.98 (A)
Conceded in a match	5 v Sandal 10.2.96 (A)

MOST APPEARANCES

by a forward	77 Mark Linnett
by a back	71 DuncanHughes

	MOST IN A SEASON	MOST IN A CAREER	MOST IN A MATCH
Points	242 Tim Smith 96-97	378 Richard Le Bas 97-98	30 Nick Baxter v Otley 21.2.98 (A)
Tries	29 Nick Baxter 97-98	65 Nick Baxter 95-99	6 Nick Baxter v Otley 21.2.98 (A)
Conversions	61 Tim Smith 96-97	86 Richard Le Bas 97-99	9 Richard Le Bas v Liverpool St H 21.3.98 (H)
Penalties	30 Tim Smith 96-97 Richard Le Bas 98-99	48 Tim Smith 96-98	5 Tim Smith v Leeds 27.12.97 (A)
Drop Goals	2 Rich Wylde 95-96 Gareth Hughes 96-97	2 Rich Wylde 95-98 Gareth Hughes n96-97 Greg Harwood 95-98	1 Ulan Richards v Birmingham 14.10.95 (A) Rich Wylde v Kendal 23.9.95 (A) v Broughton Park 13.1.95 (A) Greg Harwood v Sandal 10.2.96 (A) v Kendal 28.9.96 (H) Gareth Hughes v Lichfield 1.3.97 (A) v Preston G. 8.3.97 (H) Richard Le Bas v Rugby 25.4.98 (A)

WORCESTER PLAYING SQUAD

BACKS

	Ht.	Wt.	Birthdate	Birthplace	CLUB	League Apps	Tries	Pts
Tim Smith	5.11	13.00	10.05.62	Gloucester	Worcester	47(5)	14	374
					Gloucester	94	10	593
Rich Tomlinson	5.10	13.09	25.11.71	Worcester	Worcester	49(1)	12	112
					Nottingham	16	3	28
Nick Baxter	6.0	14.07	13.04.73	Birmingham	Worcester	62(3)	63	315
					Kings Norton			
Bruce Fenley	5.8	12.00	07.09.68	Cheltenham	Worcester	70(5)	24	120
Other clubs: Moseley 35(3)/4/18.					Gloucester	41	4	20
Richard LeBas	5.10	14.00	26.07.71	Carterton (NZ)	Worcester	45(1)	13	378
					Moseley	14	3	177
Duncan Hughes	5.11	14.00	14.07.72	Derby	Worcester	71(1)	20	110
Wales u21.					Newport, Llanelli.			
John Liley	6.0	13.10	21.08.67	Wakefield	Worcester	12(9)	2	140
Other clubs:					Moseley	8(2)	2	47
Ben Harvey	5.9	13.00	26.06.74	Redruth	Worcester	4(4)	2	10
					Richmond	1(4)		
Steve Powell	5.10	14.04	12.04.75		Worcester			
James Lofthouse	5.11	13.04	01.10.78		Worcester	6(2)		33
.					Coventry			
Simom Morris	6.0	13.00	03.05.69	Gloucester	Worcester	18(6)	6	30
Other club: Lydney								
Paul Holford	5.11	12.12	02.12.69	Gloucester	Worcester	36(1)	16	80
					Gloucester	56	17	85
Rob Myler	6.0	15.00	04.03.70		Worcester	17(2)	11	55

FORWARDS

	Ht.	Wt.	Birthdate	Birthplace	CLUB	League Apps	Tries	Pts
Peter Mitchell	6.0	17.07	31.01.69	Cheltenham	Worcester	42(11)	3	15
					Orrell	14	-	-
Mark Linnett	5.11	17.00	17.02.63	Rugby	Worcester	77(7)	14	70
England B, u23, Colts.					Moseley	87	11	52
Neil Lyman	6.1	18.00	06.05.70	Bedford	Worcester	50(6)	6	30
					Moseley	13	-	-
Gordy Houston	6.1	14.09	22.03.67	Bangor(NI)	Worcester	40(11)	3	15
Scottish Students.					Instonians			
Richard Denhardt	6.5	18.00	13.09.67	Birmingham	Worcester	14(6)	3	15
New Zealand colts, Auckland						Moseley	59	2 10
Steve Lloyd	6.6	17.00	11.07.68	Montevideo	Worcester	53(4)	5	25
Other clubs: Harlequins 2/-/-					Moseley	63	1	5
Chris Scott	5.11	15.03	01.07.74		Worcester	11(4)	7	35
Gary Clark	6.3	17.00	03.05.65		Worcester	34(14)	4	20
					Saracens	9	2	10
Chris Raymond	6.5	17.00	01.03.68	Cheltenham	Worcester	64(3)	6	30
Other clubs: Moseley 42(2)/1/5.					Gloucester	20(1)	1	5
Dean Ball	5.7	14.10	24.07.71		Worcester	41(6)	3	15
					Moseley	59(2)	1	5
Nigel Richardson	6.3	15.04	01.02.71	Worcester	Worcester	27(6)	1	5
Jim Jenner	6.4	16.7	27.11.71	Reading	Worcester	29(11)	21	105
Richard Hilton Jones	6.4	17.00	10.10.69	New Zealand	Worcester	10	2	10
Stuart Turner			22.04.72	Southport	Worcester	5(3)	1	5
Other clubs: Waterloo38/-/-					Orrell	53	1	5
Steve Hobson					Worcester	2		

WORCESTER

FACT FILE

Founded: 1871
Nickname: Gold `n` Blues

Colours: Old gold and navy
Change colours: White, old gold and navy

GROUND

Address: Sixways, Pershore Lane, Hindlip, Worcester. WR3 8ZE
Tel: 01905 454183 Fax: 01905 757222
email: rugby@wrfc.co.uk Website: www.wrfc.co.uk
Capacity: 5,300 Seated: 4,000(covered) 1,000 (uncovered) Standing: 300

Directions: M5 junction 6 (Worcester North). take the `Droitwich` turn and the club is 300 metres on the left.
Nearest Railway Station: Worcester (Shrub Hill). Shuttle buses from the Bus station

Car Parking: Limited at the ground. For match parking follow the AA signs to the Shire Business Park.

Admission: (98-99 prices)
Season Standing Adults £70, Children £30
Seated Adults £120
Matchday Adults Standing £7, Seated £9, Children £3

Club Shop: Open 12-2 Mon-Fri. & matchdays. Manager Mrs Jane Fudger

Clubhouse: Open lunchtimes & training nights.
Functions: Extensive conference & banqueting facilities.

Training Nights: Tuesday & Thursday Sunday am (Mini/Junior)

PROGRAMME
Size: A5 Pages: TBC Price: £2
Editor: Nicola Goodwin c/o the club
01432 274413 X 227 (B) 01905 451396 (H)

ADVERTISING RATES
Colour Full page £500 half £350

Chris Raymond
Worcester Player of the Year 1998-99

Photo: Tom Bader

DIVISION TWO
(CURRENTLY ALLIED DUNBAR PREMIERSHIP TWO

RECORDS SECTION

The Last Ten Years 220

A breakdown showing the champions, runners-up, those relegated, who scored most - points, tries, conversions, penalties & drop goals in each of the last ten seasons in this division (or its equivalent)

All Time Team & Individual Records 221

A list of the various records for this division (or its equivalent) since the start of the league system.

Most Points in a Season 222

The all-time list for this division

Most Points in a Match 223

The all-time list for this division

Most Tries in a Match 224

The all-time list for this division

Most Career Appearances 225

The all-time list for this division

Ten Year Record 226

A grid showing those clubs who have been part of this division (or its equivalent), and the league position they achieved for each of the last ten years

THE LAST TEN YEARS

1989-90 | Champions **Northampton** | Runners-up Liverpool St. Helens | Relegated -

Most
Penalties: 24 Martin Livesey (Richmond)
Points: 107 Ian Aitchison (Lon. Irish)
Conversions: 22 Ian Aitchison (L. Irish), John Steele (Northampton)
Tries: 7 Jim Fallon (Richmond)
D.Gs: 4 Jon King (Blackheath)

1990-91 | Champions **Rugby** | Runners-up London Irish | Relegated Richmond, Headingley

Most
Penalties: 16 Nick Grecian (Lon. Scottish)
Points: 117 Brian Mullen (Lon. Irish)
Conversions: 22 Brian Mullen (Lon. Irish)
Tries: 9 Lindsay Renwick (Lon. Scottish)
D.Gs: 5 Brian Mullen (Lon. Irish)

1991-92 | Champions **London Scottish** | Runners-up West Hartlepool | Relegated Plymouth Albion, Liverpool St Helens

Most
Penalties: 31 David Johnson (Newc. Gos.)
Points: 147 David Johnson (Newc. Gos.)
Conversions: 26 David Johnson (Newc. Gos.), John Stabler (West Hartlepool)
Tries: 11 Nick Grecian (Lon. Scottish)
D.Gs: 3 Andy Finnie (Bedford)

1992-93 | Champions **Newcastle Gosforth** | Runners-up Waterloo | Relegated Bedford, Rosslyn Park, Richmond Blackheath, Coventry, Fylde & Morley.

Most
Penalties: 16 David Johnson (Newc. Gos.)
Points: 136 David Johnson (Newc. Gos.)
Conversions: 30 David Johnson (Newc. Gos.)
Tries: 7 Jon Sleightholme (Wakefield)
D.Gs: 9 Guy Gregory (Nottingham)

1993-94 | Champions **Sale** | Runners-up West Hartlepool | Relegated Rugby, Otley.

Most
Penalties: 29 Paul Turner (Sale)
Points: 172 Guy Gregory (Nottingham)
Conversions: 43 Guy Gregory (Nottingham)
Tries: 16 Simon Verbickas (Sale)
D.Gs: 5 Guy Gregory (Nottingham), Murray Walker (Lon. Scottish)

1994-95 | Champions **Saracens** | Runners-up Wakefield | Relegated Fylde, Coventry.

Most
Penalties: 21 Simon Mason (Newc. Gos.), Andy Tunningley (Saracens)
Points: 213 Mike Jackson (Wakefield)
Conversions: 57 Mike Jackson (Wakefield)
Tries: 8 Tony Penn (Newcastle Gosforth)
D.Gs: 6 Andy Lee (Saracens)

1995-96 | Champions **Northampton** | Runners-up London Irish | Relegated -

Most
Penalties: 76 Paul Grayson (Northampton)
Points: 301 Michael Corcoran (Lon. Irish)
Conversions: 63 Michael Corcoran (Lon. Irish)
Tries: 20 Matt Allen (Northampton)
D.Gs: 5 Sam Howard (Blackheath)

1996-97 | Champions **Richmond** | Runners-up Newcastle | Relegated Rugby, Nottingham.

Most
Penalties: 47 John Steele (Lon. Scottish)
Points: 334 Simon Mason (Richmond)
Conversions: 95 Rob Andrew (Newcastle)
Tries: 23 John Bentley (Newcastle)
D.Gs: 5 Jez Harris (Coventry)

1997-98 | Champions **Bedford** | Runners-up West Hartlepool | Relegated Bristol (play-off)

Most
Penalties: 66 Lyndon Griffiths (Waterloo)
Points: 289 Mike Rayer (Bedford)
Conversions: 65 Mike Rayer (Bedford)
Tries: 17 Darragh O'Mahoney (Moseley), Ben Whetstone (Bedford)
D.Gs: 5 Matt Jones (Moseley)

1998-99 | Champions **Bristol** | Runners-up Rotherham | Relegated Blackheath, Fylde

Most
Penalties:
Points:
Conversions:
Tries:
D.Gs:

TEAM RECORDS

Highest score:	**156**	Newcastle 156 Rugby 5. 5.10.96
Highest aggregate:	**161**	As above
Highest score by a losing side:	**36**	Moseley 36 Blackheath 51. 27.4.96
Highest scoring draw:	**24**	London Scottish v London Welsh 13.4.88 Nottingham v Newcastle Gosforth 13.1.96
Most consecutive wins:	**18**	Northampton 1995-96
Most consecutive defeats:	**13**	Coventry 1993-94
Most points for in a season:	**1255**	Newcastle 1996-97
Least points for in a season:	**81**	Northampton 1987-88
Most points against in a season:	**1060**	Rugby 1996-97
Least points against in a season:	**80**	Saracens 1989-90
Most tries for in a season:	**189**	Newcastle 1996-97
Most tries against in a season:	**150**	Rugby 1996-97
Least tries for in a season:	**7**	Morley 1992-93
Least tries against in a season:	**5**	Sale 1992-93
Most conversions for in a season:	**119**	Newcastle 1996-97
Most conversions against in a season:	**101**	Orrell 1996-97
Most penalties for in a season:	**66**	Waterloo 1997-98
Most penalties against in a season:	**54**	London Scottish 1996-97
Least penalties for in a season:	**6**	Gosforth 1987-88
Least penalties against in a season:	**8**	Saracens 1987-88, Sale 1990-91
Most drop goals for in a season:	**11**	London Scottish 1994-95
Most drop goals against in a season:	**12**	London Irish 1994-95

INDIVIDUAL RECORDS

Most points in a season:	**334**	Simon Mason (Richmond) 1996-97
Most tries in a season:	**23**	John Bentley (Newcastle) 1996-97
Most conversions in a season:	**95**	Rob Andrew (Newcastle) 1996-97
Most penalties in a season:	**66**	Lyndon Griffiths (Waterloo) 1997-98
Most drop goals in a season:	**8**	Guy Gregory (Nottingham) 1992-93
Most points in a match:	**42**	Jez Harris, Coventry v Nottingham 5.10.96
Most tries in a match:	**5**	Simon Verbickas, Sale v Otley 12.2.94 Pat Lam, Newcastle v Rotherham 4.5.97 Luke Nabaro, Bristol v Blackheath 13.3.99
Most conversions in a match:	**18**	Rob Andrew, Newcastle v Rugby 5.10.96
Most penalties in a match:	**8**	Alastair Kerr, Moseley v Waterloo 17.2.96
Most drop goals in a match:	**3**	Martin Livesey, Richmond v Northampton 19.11.88 Murray Walker, Lon. Scottish v W. Hartlepool 23.4.94

ALL TIME RECORDS

MOST POINTS IN A SEASON

Points	Player	Club	Season	Tries	Cons.	Pens.	D.G.
324	Simon Mason	Richmond	1996-97	10	83	36	
310	Michael Corcoran	London Irish	1995-96	8	36	63	
305	Steve Gough	Coventry	1998-99	10	48	53	0
297	Rob Andrew	Newcastle	1996-97	7	95	23	1
289	Mike Rayer	Bedford	1997-98	6	65	43	
261	Lyndon Griffiths	Waterloo	1997-98	1	29	66	
256	John Steele	Northampton	1996-97	5	39	47	4
250	Sateki Tuipulotu	Leeds Tykes	1998-99	3	38	53	-
244	Simon Binns	Rotherham	1997-98	8	39	41	1
241	Steven Vile	West Hartlepool	1997-98	8	33	43	2
241	Bryan Easson	Exeter	1998-99	2	39	51	-
238	Mike Rayer	Bedford	1996-97	7	67	23	
236	Jez Harris	Coventry	1996-97	4	48	35	5
224	Simon Verbickas	Orrell	1998-99	13	30	33	-
218	Paul Grayson	Northampton	1995-96	3	76	14	3
213	Mike Jackson	Wakefield	1994-95	2	16	57	
199	Mike Jackson	Wakefield	1996-97	5	33	35	1
198	Lyndon Griffiths	Waterloo	1998-99	2	25	46	-
193	Simon Mason	Newcastle	1994-95	1	21	45	2
189	Martyn Davies	Rugby Lions	1998-99	4	23	41	-
178	Matt Jones	Moseley	1997-98	3	26	32	5
177	Mike Jackson	Wakefield	1995-96	2	19	43	
177	Richard Le Bas	Moseley	1996-97	3	27	36	
174	Jon Fabian	Exeter	1997-98	2	16	44	
172	Alastair Kerr	Moseley	1995-96	7	13	36	2
171	Guy Gregory	Nottingham	1993-94	1	11	43	5
165	Simon Verbickas	Orrell	1997-98	12	24	19	
164	Michael Corcoran	London Irish	1994-95	3	16	38	1
164	Paul Hull	Bristol	1998-99	5	35	23	-
162	Andy Tunningley	Saracens	1994-95	3	21	35	
162	Richard LeBas	Worcester	1998-99	4	26	30	-
160	Steve Swindells	Waterloo	1994-95		8	48	
158	Simon Hodgkinson	Nottingham	1995-96	1	18	35	4
156	Simon Hodgkinson	Moseley	1994-95		12	41	3
153	Sam Howard	Blackheath	1995-96	2	19	30	5
149	Derrick Lee	London Scottish	1997-98	5	17	28	2
149	Andy Tunningley	Saracens	1993-94	5	14	31	1
147	David Johnson	Newcastle Gosforth	1991-92	1	31	26	3
144	Paul Turner	Sale	1993-94	1	29	24	3
144	Doug Trivella	Rotherham	1998-99	5	28	21	-
141	Greg Miller	Wakefield	1997-98	3	12	31	3
140	John Steele	London Scottish	1995-96	4	18	26	2
140	John Liley	Worcester	1998-99	2	11	36	-
138	Andy Kennedy	Saracens	1988-89	5	14	30	
137	Steve Swindells	Waterloo	1993-94	2	5	39	
137	Chris Braithwaite	Blackheath	1996-97	2	23	25	2
136	David Johnson	Newcastle Gosforth	1992-93	1	16	30	3
134	Martin Emmett	Waterloo	1995-96	1	12	35	
133	Jez Harris	Coventry	1997-98		5	39	2

ALL TIME RECORDS

MOST POINTS IN A MATCH

Points	Player	Match	Date
42	Jez Harris	Coventry v Nottingham	05.10.96
36	Rob Andrew	Newcastle v Rugby	05.10.96
34	Steve Gough	Coventry v London Welsh	10.10.98
30	Michael Corcoran	London Irish v Waterloo	23.09.95
	John Steele	London Scottish v Rugby	29.03.97
29	Simon Mason	Richmond v Rotherham	14.09.96
	Simon Verbickas	Orrell v Wakefield	25.04.98
28	David Johnson	Newcastle Gosforth v Morley	11.01.92
	David Johnson	Newcastle Gosforth v Liverpool StH	29.02.93
27	Simon Hodgkinson	Moseley v London Irish	08.04.95
	Simon Verbickas	Orrell v Waterloo	08.05.99
26	Andy Mitchell	London Scottish v Northampton	03.10.87
	Michael Corcoran	London Irish v Bedford	21.10.95
	Michael Corcoran	London Irish v Blackheath	28.10.95
	Steven Vile	West Hartlepool v Fylde	14.02.98
25	Chris Howard	Rugby v Newcastle Gosforth	11.11.89
	Andy Finnie	Bedford v Coventry	27.03.93
	Guy Gregory	Nottingham v Otley	11.09.93
	Simon Verbickas	Sale v Otley	12.02.94
	John Steele	London Scottish v Bedford	14.10.95
	Simon Mason	Richmond v Nottingham	16.11.96
	Pat Lam	Newcastle v Rotherham	04.05.97
	Richard Le Bas	Worcester v Exeter	10.10.98
24	Simon Irving	Headingley v London Scottish	12.11.88
	Andy Kennedy	Saracens v Nottingham	12.11.88
	Nick Grecian	London Scottish v Blackheath	16.11.91
	Alastair Kerr	Moseley v Waterloo	17.02.96
	Simon Mason	Richmond v London Scottish	12.10.96
	Jez Harris	Coventry v London Scottish	19.10.96
	Simon Mason	Richmond v Rugby	22.03.97
	Steve Gough	Coventry v Fylde	26.09.98
23	Simon Hodgkinson	Nottingham v Blackheath	26.09.92
	David Johnson	Newcastle Gosforth v Nottingham	10.10.92
	Guy Gregory	Nottingham v Morley	24.10.92
	Gary Abraham	Rosslyn Park v Morley	27.03.93
	Rob Liley	Wakefield v Rugby	11.09.93
	Paul Turner	Sale v Otley	12.02.94
	Martin Emmett	Waterloo v Bedford	13.01.96
	John Steele	London Scottish v Rugby	07.09.96
	Matt Inman	Rotherham v Richmond	14.09.96
	John Steele	London Scottish v Nottingham	18.01.97
	Sateki Tuipulotu	Leeds v Coventry	03.01.99

ALL TIME RECORDS

Tries	Player	Match	Date
5	Simon Verbickas	Sale v Otley	12.02.94
	Pat Lam	Newcastle v Rotherham	04.05.97
	Luke Nabaro	Bristol v Blackheath	13.03.99
4	Craig Moir	Northampton v Waterloo	13.04.96
	Gary Armstrong	Newcastle v Nottingham	14.09.96
	Scott Quinnell	Richmond v Waterloo	02.11.96
	John Bentley	Newcastle v Wakefield	08.03.97
	John Clarke	Blackheath v Fylde	20.09.97
	Jason Foster	Bedford v Fylde	17.01.98
	Ben Wade	Rotherham v Exeter	25.04.98
	John Fabian	Exeter v Waterloo	17.10.98
	Lennie Woodward	Lon. Welsh v Fylde	12.12.98
	Jonathon Scales	Leeds Tykes v Exeter	07.02.99
	Dean Lax	Rotherham v Orrell	13.02.99
	Ian Breheny	Wakefield v Moseley	24.04.99
	Andy Smallwood	Coventry v Wakefield	08.05.99

3

Player	Match	Date
Jerry Macklin	Lon. Scottish v Northampton	03.10.87
Orsen Blewitt	Northampton v Bedford	21.11.87
John Roberts	Headingley v Northampton	16.04.88
Pete Rowland	Coventry v Lon. Irish	10.09.88
Dave Kennell	Headingley v Gosforth	14.01.89
Laurie Smith	Saracens v Gosforth	22.04.89
Nigel Saunders	Plymouth v Blackheath	14.10.89
Graham Robbins	Coventry v Waterloo	13.01.90
Rob Saunders	Lon. Irish v Rugby	13.10.90
Jonathan Wrigley	W Hartlepool v Moseley	14.12.91
Peter Walton	Newcastle G. v Blackheath	14.12.91
Jon Sleightholme	Wakefield v Blackheath	04.01.92
Gary Clark	Newcastle G. v Liverpool StH	29.02.92
Richard Arnold	Newcastle G. v Liverpool StH	29.02.92
Dave Spiller	Moseley v Sale	04.04.92
Richard Gee	Coventry v Moseley	19.09.92
Malcolm Walker	Nottingham v Moseley	24.10.92
Mark Warr	Sale v Otley	12.02.94
Matt Allen	Northampton v Lon. Irish	09.09.95
Conor O'Shea	Lon. Irish v Moseley	30.09.95
Gregor Townsend	Northampton v Blackheath	14.10.95
Grant Seeley	Northampton v Blackheath	14.10.95
Matt Allen	Northampton v Newcastle G.	21.10.95
Matt Allen	Northampton v Waterloo	28.10.95
Gregor Townsend	Northampton v Lon. Scottish	04.11.95
Gregor Townsend	Northampton v Lon. Irish	11.11.95
Gary Armstrong	Newcastle G. v Waterloo	28.04.90
Alan Royer	Nottingham v Moseley	30.03.96
Matt Allen	Northampton v Lon. Scottish	27.04.96
Mitch Hoare	Blackheath v Rotherham	07.09.96
Scott Quinnell	Richmond v Rotherham	14.09.96
Andy McAdam	Coventry v Nottingham	05.10.96
Derek Eves	Coventry v Nottingham	05.10.96
Jim Fallon	Richmond v Moseley	05.10.96
Scott Quinnell	Richmond v Moseley	05.10.96
Gary Armstrong	Newcastle v Rugby	05.10.96
Ross Nesdale	Newcastle v Rugby	05.10.96
George Graham	Newcastle v Rugby	05.10.96
Dean Ryan	Newcastle v Rugby	05.10.96
Eddie Saunders	Rugby v Moseley	12.10.96
Jim Fallon	Richmond v Rugby	19.10.96
John Bentley	Newcastle v Moseley	19.10.96
Andy McAdam	Coventry v Lon. Irish	19.10.96
Steve Wichary	Lon. Scottish v Moseley	26.10.96
Craig Quinnell	Richmond v Waterloo	02.11.96
Tim Stimpson	Newcastle v Lon. Scottish	16.11.96
Darragh O'Mahoney	Moseley v Nottingham	02.02.97
John Bentley	Newcastle v Rugby	08.02.97
Julian Horrobin	Coventry v Blackheath	08.03.97
Steve Bates	Newcastle v Nottingham	16.03.97
John Bentley	Newcastle v Moseley	22.03.97
Va'aiga Tuigamala	Newcastle v Moseley	22.03.97
Scott Quinnell	Richmond v Rugby	22.03.97
Matt Griffiths	Blackheath v Waterloo	19.04.97
Jason Hall	Nottingham v Rugby	19.04.97
Jim Fallon	Richmond v Wakefield	19.04.97
Ronnie Eriksson	Lon. Scottish v Fylde	30.08.97
Cunan Sharman	Lon. Scottish v Bedford	20.09.97
Nigel Heslop	Orrell v Fylde	04.10.97
Ben Whetstone	Bedford v Coventry	08.11.97
Jason Forster	Bedford v Fylde	27.12.97
Simon Verbickas	Orrell v Coventry	24.01.98
Darragh O'Mahoney	Moseley v Waterloo	14.02.98
Jason Minshull	Coventry v Waterloo	07.03.98
Julian Horrobin	Coventry v West Hartlepool	28.03.98
Darragh O'Mahoney	Moseley v Fylde	25.04.98
Richard Stone	Bedford v Blackheath	25.04.98
Simon Verbickas	Orrell v Wakefield	25.04.98
Rob Myler	Worcester v Wakefield	12.09.98
Wayne Kilford	Coventry v Fylde	26.09.98
Adam Larkin	Bristol v Blackheath	03.10.98
Steve Gough	Coventry v L. Welsh	10.10.98
Mike White	Lon. Welsh v Wakefield	17.10.98
Andy Currier	Lon. Welsh v Exeter	21.11.98
Wendal Sailor	Leeds Tykes v Fylde	17.01.99
Ben Wade	Rotherham v Leeds Tykes	23.01.99
Richard baxter	Exeter v Fylde	23.01.99
Andy Currier	Lon. Welsh v Coventry	27.02.99
Karl Johnson	Orrell v Bristol	27.02.99
Luke Nabaro	Bristol v Rugby Lions	03.04.99
Neil Marden	Lon. Welsh v Blackheath	17.04.99
Lennie Woodward	Lon. Welsh v Blackheath	17.04.99
Nick Baxter	Worcester v Wakefield	17.04.99
Dean Lax	Rotherham v Waterloo	24.04.99
Matt Walker	Rotherham v Worcester	01.05.99
Wayne Reed	Exeter v Orrell	01.05.99
Simon Verbickas	Orrell v Waterloo	08.05.99

MOST APPEARANCES

182	Dave Scully	Wakefield, Rotherham	Scrum half
164	Mark Linnett	Moseley, Worcester	Prop
160	Matt Greenwood	Roundhay, Nottingham, Wasps, Wakefield	2nd row
159	Eddie Saunders	Rugby	Winger
157	John Dudley	Rotherham	2nd row
148	Trevor Revan	Rugby	Prop
143	Steve Gough	Fylde, Coventry	Utility back
141	Tim Smith	Gloucester, Worcester	Full back
	Terry Garnett	Wakefield, Rotherham	Hooker
140	Richard Gibbins	Exeter	Prop
139	Dave Addleton	Coventry	Hooker
137	Paul Manley	Orrell, Wakefield, Worcester	Flanker
136	Mike White	Wasps, London Irish	Flanker
130	Adam Smallwood	Nottingham, Coventry	Winger
123	Rod Latham	Wakefield	Prop
121	Craig West	Rotherham	Flanker
119	Charles Cusani	Orrell	2nd row
118	MR Ellis	Rugby	Flanker

TEN YEAR RECORD

Club	SEASONS									
	89-90	90-91	91-92	92-93	93-94	94-95	95-96	96-97	97-98	98-99
Bedford	-	8	10	7	-	-	10	4	1	-
Blackheath	10	10	11	10	-	-	7	10	9	13
Bristol	-	-	-	-	-	-	-	-	-	1
Coventry	4	4	6	11	-	10	-	3	7	7
Exeter	-	-	-	-	-	-	-	-	11	5
Fylde	-	-	-	12	-	9	-	-	12	14
Gosforth/Newcastle	12	6	4	1	-	3	8	2	-	-
Headingley	8	13	-	-	-	-	-	-	-	-
Leeds	-	-	-	-	-	-	-	-	-	6
Liverpool St. Helens	2	-	13	-	-	-	-	-	-	-
London Irish	5	2	-	-	-	5	2	-	-	-
London Scottish	-	5	1	-	8	4	3	5	3	-
London Welsh	-	-	-	-	-	-	-	-	-	4
Morley	-	-	9	13	-	-	-	-	-	-
Moseley	-	-	7	6	5	6	6	8	6	10
Northampton	1	-	-	-	-	-	1	-	-	-
Nottingham	-	-	-	4	6	7	9	12	-	-
Orrell	-	-	-	-	-	-	-	-	5	8
Otley	-	-	-	-	10	-	-	-	-	-
Plymouth Albion	7	11	12	-	-	-	-	-	-	-
Richmond	3	12	-	9	-	-	-	1	-	-
Rosslyn Park	-	-	-	8	-	-	-	-	-	-
Rotherham	-	-	-	-	-	-	-	7	4	2
Rugby	6	1	-	-	9	-	-	11	-	11
Sale	9	7	8	5	1	-	-	-	-	-
Saracens	-	-	-	-	3	1	-	-	-	-
Wakefield	-	3	5	3	4	2	4	6	10	12
Waterloo	11	9	3	2	7	8	5	9	8	9
West Hartlepool	-	-	2	-	2	-	-	-	2	-
Worcester	-	-	-	-	-	-	-	-	-	3

AWARDS

Player of the Season

Winner: **Martin Johnson** (Leicester Tigers)

Nominees
Scott Murray (Bedford) Va'aiga Tulgamala (Newcastle Falcons)

Young Player of the Season
Winner: **Jonny Wilkinson** (Newcastle Falcons)
Nominees: Iain Balshaw (Bath Rugby) Steve Hanley (Manchester Sale)

International Player of the Season
Winner: **Scott Murray** (Bedford)
Nominees: Keith Wood (NEC Harlequins) Shane Howarth (Manchester Sale)

Coach of the Season
Winner: **Ian McGeechan** (Northampton Saints)
Nominees: Dick Best (London Irish) John Wells (Leicester Tigers)

Fair Play Award
Winner: **Wakefield**

Premiership One Players' Player of the Season
Winner: **Conor O'Shea** (London Irish)
Nominees: Gary Armstrong (Newcastle Falcons) Neil Back (Leicester Tigers)

Premiership Two Players' Player of the Season
Winner: **John Dudley** (Rotherham)
Nominees: Andy Currier (London Welsh) Neil Spence (Rotherham)

Unsung Hero of the Season
Winner: **Chris McCarthy** - NEC Harlequins
Nominees:
Alan Blease - Manchester Sale
Nathan Carter - Gloucester
Robbie Dickson - Manchester Sale
Ray Grieve - Newcastle Falcons
Derek Limmage - Leicester Tigers
Kieran McCarthy - London Irish
Roy Saunders - Worcester
Don Shaw - Blackheath
Mrs. Jackie Thomas - Moseley

Conor O'Shea (London Irish) Martin Johnson (Leicester Tigers) Scott Murray (Bedford) Jonny Wilkinson (Newcastle Falcons)

JEWSON NATIONAL LEAGUE

DIVISION ONE

1998-99 Season

Review & statistics 230-235

1999-200 Fixtures 236

CLUBS

Birmingham & Solihull 237
Blackheath 243
Bracknell 249
Camberley 255
Fylde261
Harrogate 267
Lydney 273
Newbury 279
Nottingham 285
Otley 291
Preston Grasshoppers 297
Reading 303
Rosslyn Park 309
Wharfedale 315

Division Three Records
321-328

	P	W	D	L	F	A	PD	Pts	HOME W	D	L	F	A	Tries For	Pens For	Tries Against	Pens Against	AWAY W	D	L	F	A	Tries For	Pens For	Tries Against	Pens Against
Henley Hawks	26	22	1	3	644	299	345	45	12	0	1	343	150	48	15	16	15	10	1	2	301	149	38	20	16	15
Manchester	26	20	1	5	758	372	386	41	12	0	1	476	124	56	35	16	8	8	1	4	282	248	24	38	27	26
Rosslyn Park	26	17	1	8	588	371	217	35	11	0	2	332	163	46	19	22	12	6	1	6	256	208	33	18	21	23
Nottingham	26	16	0	10	590	467	123	32	9	0	4	316	208	32	36	24	21	7	0	6	274	259	30	29	34	15
Otley	26	15	1	10	508	416	-7	31	12	1	0	340	135	46	31	16	11	3	0	10	168	281	22	14	31	28
Newbury	26	14	1	11	552	476	348	29	9	1	3	317	183	46	16	20	21	5	0	8	235	293	32	15	34	31
Wharfedale	26	13	1	12	477	421	51	27	9	1	3	336	163	35	37	17	18	4	0	9	141	258	11	22	30	25
Lydney	26	11	2	13	438	482	-44	24	9	1	3	278	152	32	24	17	17	2	1	10	160	330	19	14	40	26
Camberley	26	10	1	15	529	661	-132	21	8	0	5	298	245	27	44	30	20	2	1	10	231	416	28	16	55	21
Reading	26	10	0	16	468	635	-167	20	4	0	9	273	325	31	28	39	26	6	0	7	195	310	22	18	38	26
Birmingham & Solihull	26	9	0	17	422	523	-101	18	7	0	6	273	196	33	22	21	23	2	0	11	149	327	17	14	35	33
Harrogate	26	8	2	16	309	461	-152	18	5	1	7	157	193	15	19	26	15	3	1	9	152	258	18	13	30	25
Morley	26	7	1	18	468	643	-175	15	5	1	7	265	243	34	21	30	17	2	0	11	203	400	30	8	52	28
Liverpool St Helens	26	4	0	22	335	859	-524	8	3	0	10	182	410	23	15	54	23	1	0	12	153	449	24	7	61	24

Review of the season 1998-1999

Henley, who sat quietly in second place for most of the season, came through to pass Manchester and take the title by four points. They got a shock on the first day of the season when they were beaten at home by Harrogate but after that they won their remaining 12 home matches at Dry Leas. They ended the season as the leading try scorers and just to prove they were the best all round side they also conceded the fewest tries. If they had had a goal kicker in the Swindells class they would have ended up as leading points scorers. They played an exciting brand of rugby blessed with pace in all areas.

Manchester led the Jewson National One for most of the season but their away form was their undoing. They lost matches at Newbury and Rosslyn Park that proved crucial. They did end the season as leading points scorers and had the accurate boot of Steve Swindells to thank for that. He contributed over 350 points for the second season running and was the divisions most consistent goal kicker by an amazing 14%. Both sides can be proud of their achievement in their first season at this level. How ironic that both these sides came up last season finishing second in their respective leagues. In normal seasons they would not have gained promotion - it was only with the league being increased in Allied Dunbar that they were.

Rosslyn Park finished third but can count themselves unlucky with eight matches lost by four points or more. If only they had had a Steve Swindells type kicker they could have seriously threatened the top two. They managed to improve their away form and had no problem scoring tries with Tim Herman and Kent Bray making a difference in their first full season coaching the side. They will be confident that if they can solve the kicking problem, that has dogged them for a number of years now, that they can challenge for promotion if not the championship next season.

Nottingham finished fourth after a great second half to the season. In the first few months of the season they languished at the wrong end of the table. Then they found some form and stormed up the league table gaining fourth place on the final day of the season. They had a good set of forwards, a reliable goal kicker in Chris Atkinson and a try scoring half-back pair of Alan Royer and Sam Jack. They will look to start next season as they finished this and make a serious challenge for the title.

Otley will be looking to find a way of improving their away form. They had the best home record with 12 wins and a draw but their away form was dreadful. At home they beat Henley, Manchester, Rosslyn Park and Nottingham with a draw against Harrogate the only blemish on their record. On the road they managed just three wins and were losing to sides they should have been beating. They had a tough pack and a mean back row and will need to solve the away conundrum if they are to figure realistically next season.

Newbury were another side to struggle early on during the season. When Keith Richardson left and Kevin Bowring came in they was an improvement and they finished the season strongly with excellent home wins against Manchester and Otley and a draw against the champions, Henley. In fairness they were ravaged by injuries early on and their improvement coincided with a settled side going out week after week. They also will be hoping to start next season as they finished this and push for a promotion place.

Wharfedale equalled their best ever finish in this division with seventh place. At two months of the season they would probable settled for twelfth.They refused to believe they were a bad side and were eventually rewarded when their fortunes turned round. The signing of David Pears was a major help and he guided them up the table. He stayed clear of injury and even made a cameo appearance in Allied Dunbar One for Harlequins when they were having an injury crisis. They were brilliant at home after a shaky start and won nine on the trot, before drawing with Manchester on the final Saturday of the season.

Lydney will be disappointed after making a good start to the season. They were confident of a good finish but let it drift away and should have done better. Nick Paisley was badly missed when he decided to take time out to travel round the world half way through the season. They had a good record at Regentsholme but on the road they were a different side.

Camberley have not had a good season and probably made two many changes from the side that won them promotion last season. They also suffered more than their fair share of injuries and used more players than most. They were another side that did not travel well and that seems to be a common trait in the division.

Reading will be glad the season ended and that they had plenty of points on the board before their form fell away and they tumbled down the table. The club had a few financial problems that did not help their cause and lost a couple of players mid season, but they kept on going and will re group in the summer in preparation for next season.

Birmingham & Solihull did not win as many matches at home as they would have liked and with poor away form they found themselves just above the relegation battle. Despite coming up as Champions, they did not adjust as quickly as Manchester, and looked a mid-table side till their form nose-dived as the season drew to an end.

Harrogate escaped after a late season flurry and finally gained safety when they had a rare away win at Camberley in the last but one match of the season. They did not concede many points and were difficult to beat at home their problem was scoring points. They were the lowest points scorers in the division.

Morley had a strange season they had no problem scoring tries and were better than most. Their problem was defensive as they leaked too many tries. The club though went down in an optimistic mood confident that if they can hold onto some of their promising players they can bounce back up.

Liverpool St Helens dropped three places on the previous season finishing well adrift of the next side. They had a good spell just after Christmas but it was not to be and they slipped further adrift at the bottom. This will be the lowest they have ever been in league rugby since it was introduced back in 1987-88. They had trouble finding a consistent goal kicker and filling the problematic No 10 jersey, which did not help their cause.

JEWSON NATIONAL LEAGUE ONE

1998-99 RECORD REVIEW (Individual Records)

The ALL-TIME RECORDS for MOST POINTS IN A MATCH, MOST POINTS IN A SEASON & MOST TRIES IN A MATCH can be found in the Records Section for this division.

MOST POINTS - IN A MATCH

Nobody got near Paul Bretts record of 39points in a match.
The best effort during the season was 26 points by Henley Hawk's mid-season signing Duncan Roke. He scored two tries, two conversions and four penalties in Henley's win at Camberley in February.
Manchester's Steve Swindells scored 20 points in a match six times during the season, nobody else managed it more than twice during the season.

EVOLUTION OF RECORD - Points in a match

28	Steve Burnage	Fylde v Birmingham	07.11.87
29	Paul Morris	Lydney v Otley	14.09.96
29	Rob Ashworth	Havant v Clifton	21.09.96
30	Paul Brett	Liverpool v Redruth	01.02.97
39	Paul Brett	Liverepool v Clifton	15.02.97

MOST POINTS - IN A SEASON

Steve Swindells scored 365 points for Manchester as they won promotion at the first attempt in the division. That puts him second on the all time division record behind Steve Gough's 404 points set two seasons ago. Chris Atkinson moved into 12th place on the all time list with his 272 points.

EVOLUTION OF RECORD - Points in a season

121	Steve Burnage	Fylde	1987-88
123	Chris Howard	Rugby	1988-89
172	Andy Finnie	Bedford	1993-94
228	Andy Finnie	Bedford	1994-95
404	Steve Gough	Fylde	1996-97

MOST TRIES - IN A MATCH

Manchester's Matt Hoskin got near to Nick Baxter record with five tries against Camberley early in the season. He had to leave the field with over ten minutes to go otherwise, the way Manchester were playing, he could well have equalled the record if not beaten it.
2 other players managed four tries, Nottingham scrum half Alan Royer and Otley's No 8 Lafaele Filipo.

EVOLUTION OF RECORD - Tries in a match
(Only the first to reach the figure is shown)

3	Kevin Norris	Plymouth v Sheffield	12.09.87
4	Brendan Hanavan	Fylde v Exeter	03.10.87
5	Mark Kirkby	Otley v Redruth	08.02.97
6	Nick Baxter	Worcester v Otley	21.02.98

MOST TRIES - IN A SEASON

This was not a vintage try scoring season with 15 topping the list, the lowest for three seasons. Leading the way was the Morley winger/full back Adam Standeven and Otley's hard tackling No 8 Lafaele Filipo.

EVOLUTION OF RECORD

10	Brendan Hanavan	Fylde	1987-88
12	Brendan Hanavan	Fylde	1993-94
12	Colin Phillips	Reading	1994-95
22	Mark Kirkby	Otley	1996-97
29	Nick Baxter	Worcester	1997-98

ALL-TIME RECORDS

29	Nick Baxter	Worcester	1997-98
22	Mark Kirkby	Otley	1996-97
21	Andrew Hodgson	Wharfedale	1996-97
20	Mark Preston	Fylde	1996-97
17	Ben Wade	Morley	1996-97
17	Simon Middleton	Leeds	1997-98
17	Scott Roskell	London Welsh	1997-98
16	Mark Appleson	Leeds	1996-97
16	Jim Jenner	Worcester	1997-98
16	Craig Davies	Newbury	1997-98

MOST PENALTIES - IN A MATCH

The record of nine was never seriously challenged with the best effort being 7 by Camberley's Guy Gregory which put him joint fourth on the all time list.with seven others.

EVOLUTION OF RECORD

6	John Stabler	W Hart v Met Police	06.01.88
7	Andy Finnie	Bedford v Coventry	23.04.94
9	Paul Morris	Lydney v Otley	14.09.96

ALL-TIME RECORDS

9	Paul Morris	Lydney v Otley	14.09.96
9	Rob Ashworth	Havant v Clifton	21.09.96
8	Richard Mills	Walsall v Leeds	12.10.96
7	Andy Finnie	Bedford v Coventry	23.04.94
7	Denzil Evans	Rugby v Richmond	15.10.94
7	Phil Belshaw	Reading v Morley	14.10.95
7	Jamie Grayshon	Morley v Rugby	21.10.95
7	Andy Green	Exeter v Fylde	05.04.97
7	Richard Mills	Walsall v Redruth	19.04.97
7	Nat Saumi	Redruth v Clifton	03.05.97
7	Guy Gregory	Camberley v Birm &Solihull	

MOST PENALTIES - IN A SEASON

Steve Swindells, the Manchester full back, kicked 70 penalties in the season and moved up to third on the all time list.

Nottingham's Chris Atkinson equalled his record of the previous season and now has two entries at number five on the all time list.

EVOLUTION OF RECORD

21	Ray Adamson	Wakefield	1987-88
22	Andy Higgin	Vale of Lune	1989-90
26	Mike Jackson	Fylde	1991-92
31	Andy Green	Exeter	1992-93
45	Andy Finnie	Bedford	1993-94
56	Andy Finnie	Bedford	1994-95
82	Steve Gough	Fylde	1996-97

ALL-TIME RECORDS

82	Steve Gough	Fylde	1996-97
81	Richard Mills	Walsall	1996-97
70	Steve Swindells	Manchester	1998-99
66	Paul Morris	Lydney	1996-97
64	Chris Atkinson	Nottingham	1997-98
64	Chris Atkinson	Nottingham	1998-99
57	Craig Raymond	London Welsh	1996-97
56	Andy Finnie	Bedford	1994-95

MOST CONVERSIONS - IN A MATCH

Two players kicked eight conversions during the season and moved into joint 7th on the all time list. Steve Swindells, Manchester's full back, kicked eight conversions as Manchester trounshed Camberley 72-5. The other player to kick eight conversions last season was Dan Clappison, the Otley full back, in his sides 66-10 win at home to Reading.

EVOLUTION OF RECORD

9	Steve Burnage	Fylde v Birmingham	07.11.87
9	Gerry Ainscough	Leeds v Clifton	07.12.96
12	Paul Brett	Liverpool v Clifton	15.02.96

ALL-TIME RECORDS

12	Paul Brett	Liverpool v Clifton	15.02.97
10	Jason Dance	Reading v Clifton	01.03.97
9	Steve Burnage	Fylde v Birmingham	07.11.87
9	Gerry Ainscough	Leeds v Clifton	07.12.96
9	Jason Dance	Reading v Redruth	15.02.97
9	Jamie Grayshon	Morley v Walsall	17.05.97

MOST CONVERSIONS - IN A SEASON

Manchester's Steve Swindells got within four of Craig Raymond's all time record for the division and moved into joint fourth on the all time list.

EVOLUTION OF RECORD

30	Steve Burnage	Fylde	1987-88
63	Ralph Zoing	Harrogate	1996-97
64	Craig Raymond	Lon. Welsh	1997-98

ALL-TIME RECORDS

64	Craig Raymond	London Welsh	1997-98
63	Ralph Zoing	Harrogate	1996-97
61	Jason Dance	Reading	1996-97
60	Sateki Tuipulotu	Leeds Tykes	1997-98
60	Richard LeBas	Worcester	1997-98
60	Steve Swindells	Manchester	1998-99
58	Andy Green	Exeter	1996-97

MOST DROP GOALS - IN A MATCH

Henley Hawk's Phil Osman was the only man to drop two goals in a match last season in the away win at near neighbours Reading.

ALL-TIME RECORD

4	Andy Rimmer	Broughton P v Sheffield	17.11.90

Preston Grasshoppers' captain Neil Ashton, being presented with the Jewson National Two North Trophy by Lindsay Poston of Jewson, at the Jewson Annual Awards.

1998-99

JEWSON NATIONAL ONE

MOST POINTS

POINTS			T	C	P	DG
365	Steve Swindells	Manchester	7	60	70	0
272	Chris Atkinson	Nottingham	2	35	64	-
235	David Pears	Wharfedale	5	24	50	4
221	Guy Gregory	Camberley	2	29	50	1
193	Jason Dance	Reading	1	28	49	-
170	Matt Birch	Birmingham & S	1	30	35	-
138	Dan Clappison	Otley	-	33	23	1
119	Tom Bamber	Morley	1	24	21	1
115	Duncan Roke	Henley	6	20	16	-
105	Nick Paisley	Lydney	5	11	19	-
99	Lee Osborne	Lydney	2	19	17	-
95	Adam Standeven	Morley	15	4	4	-
93	Andy Maddock	Rosslyn Park	5	13	14	-
84	Matt Maudsley	Henley	5	18	7	-
77	Adam Mounsey	Wharefdale	8	5	9	-
75	Lafaele Filipo	Otley	15	-	-	-
74	Toby Knowles	Rosslyn Park	2	14	11	1
72	Justin Poihippi	Newbury	1	14	13	-

MOST PENALTIES

70	Steve Swindells	Manchester
64	Chris Atkinson	Nottingham
50	David Pears	Wharfedale
50	Guy Gregory	Camberley
49	Jason Dance	Reading
35	Matt Birch	Birmingham & S
23	Dan Clappison	Otley
19	Nick Paisley	Lydney
17	Lee Osborne	Lydney
16	Duncan Roke	Henley
15	Ralph Zoing	Harrogate
14	Andy Maddock	Rosslyn Park
13	Justin Poihippi	Newbury
12	Jon Stebbings	Henley
11	Toby Knowles	Rosslyn Park

MOST TRIES

15	Lafaele Filipo	Otley
15	Adam Standeven	Morley
14	Peter Davies	Henley
13	Alan Royer	Nottingham
12	Dave Muckalt	Reading
12	Bruce Rowland	Reading
11	Tim Burgon	Manchester
10	Tyrone Howe	Newbury
10	Gavin Sharp	Henley
9	Mark Venner	Henley
9	Russell Osman	Henley
9	Tom Holloway	Newbury
9	Jeremy Griffiths	Newbury
8	Adam Mounsey	Wharfedale
8	Chris Hall	Morley

MOST CONVERSIONS

60	Steve Swindells	Manchester
35	Chris Atkinson	Nottingham
33	Dan Clappison	Henley
30	Matt Birch	Birmingham & S
29	Guy Gregory	Camberley
28	Jason Dance	Reading
24	Tom Bamber	Morley
24	David Pears	Wharfedale
20	Duncan Roke	Henley
19	Lee Osborne	Lydney
18	Matt Maudsley	Henley
14	Toby Knowles	Rosslyn Park
14	Justin Poihippi	Newbury
13	Andy Maddock	Rosslyn Park
11	Nick Paisley	Lydney

MOST DROP GOALS

5	Phil Osman	Henley
5	Sam Jack	Nottingham
4	David Pears	Wharfedale
3	Rod Ellis	Manchester
2	Ralph Zoing	Harrogate
1	GuyGregory	Camberley
1	Simon Slater	Camberley
1	Howard Graham	Newbury
1	Rob Mills	Lydney
1	Tom Bamber	Morley
1	Andrew Lewis	Reading
1	Tom Ashworth	Rosslyn Park

JEWSON NATIONAL ONE FIXTURES 1999-2000

Away Teams

	HOME TEAMS	Birmingham & S	Blackheath	Bracknell	Camberley	Fylde	Harrogate	Lydney	Newbury	Nottingham	Otley	Preston G.	Reading	Rosslyn Park	Wharfedale	
1	BIRMINGHAM S.	X	18.09	26.02	08.01	02.10	28.08	27.11	04.09	15.04	11.12	23.10	22.01	06.11	18.03	1
2	BLACKHEATH	11.03	X	22.01	11.12	23.10	11.09	08.04	02.10	25.03	15.04	06.11	08.01	27.11	25.09	2
3	BRACKNELL	25.09	09.10	X	27.11	08.01	11.03	25.03	23.10	11.09	28.08	11.12	07.11	15.04	12.02	3
4	CAMBERLEY	30.10	20.11	22.04	X	04.12	15.01	12.02	18.03	09.10	25.09	04.09	08.04	11.03	18.12	4
5	FYLDE	12.02	15.01	30.10	15.04	X	25.09	11.09	06.11	11.03	25.03	27.11	11.12	28.08	09.10	5
6	HARROGATE	08.04	18.03	18.09	23.10	26.02	X	11.12	15.04	27.11	06.11	22.01	02.10	08.01	04.09	6
7	LYDNEY	22.04	29.08	04.09	02.10	18.03	20.11	X	08.01	18.12	23.10	26.02	18.09	22.01	04.12	7
8	NEWBURY	25.03	12.02	15.01	11.09	18.12	04.12	30.10	X	20.11	09.10	28.08	22.04	25.09	11.03	8
9	NOTTINGHAM	04.12	04.09	18.03	22.01	18.09	22.04	06.11	11.12	X	08.01	02.10	26.02	23.10	08.04	9
10	OTLEY	20.11	04.12	08.04	26.02	04.09	18.12	15.01	22.01	30.10	X	18.09	18.03	02.10	27.11	10
11	PRESTON G.	15.01	18.12	20.11	25.03	22.04	09.10	25.09	08.04	12.02	11.03	X	04.12	11.09	30.10	11
12	READING	09.10	30.10	18.12	28.08	20.11	12.02	11.03	27.11	25.09	11.09	15.04	X	25.03	15.01	12
13	ROSSLYN PARK	18.12	22.04	04.12	18.09	08.04	30.10	09.10	26.02	15.01	12.02	18.03	04.09	X	20.11	13
14	WHARFEDALE	11.09	26.02	02.10	06.11	22.01	25.03	15.04	18.09	28.08	27.12	08.01	23.10	11.12	X	14
		1	2	3	4	5	6	7	8	9	10	11	12	13	14	

BIRMINGHAM & SOLIHULL R.F.C.

Chairman	Roger Murphy	Merrimans Hill Farm, Mill Lane, Danzey Green, Solihull, West Midlands B94 5BB 01564 742564 (H) 0121 328 2145 (B)
Club Secretary (Acting)	David Radburn	35 Yoxall Road, Shirley, Solihull, West Midlands B90 3SD 0121 694 4864 (H), 0121 733 7033 (B)
Rugby Administrator	Keith Jervis	Earlsmere House, Warings Green Road, Earlswood, Solihull, West Midlands B94 6BS. 01564 702502 (H) 0121 359 4455 (B)
Commercial Manager	David Radburn	35 Yoxall Road, Shirley, Solihull, West Midlands B90 3SD 0121 694 4864 (H), 0121 733 7033 (B)

Following promotion B&S experienced a hard but rewarding season, which resulted in us maintaining our position in Jewson National Division One. An active summer recruitment campaign resulted in the squad being considerably strengthened and new additions included Steve Smith and Jim Quantrill from Rugby Lions plus Paul Lydster and Warwick Bullock from Coventry. Following the retirement of Keith Jervis, who led the club to promotion, former Coventry skipper Julian Hyde became 1st XV captain.

With three defeats in the first four games B&S experienced a difficult start, but took heart from the resounding 26-0 defeat of Otley in the second game. We fought back to win the next three games at Newbury and Liverpool, both away, and Harrogate. We then lost three close games on the bounce to Wharfedale, Manchester and Nottingham. The next game against Camberley produced out best performance of the season and by half time we led by 36 points to nil. The second half was a lot closer and the final score was 43-5. The following week we travelled to Henley and lost 26-13 to a very good side but then bounced back to beat Morley at home 35-7.

A lack of consistency and on occasions confidence was proving to be our downfall and this was emphasised when, following our magnificent performance at home top Camberley, just thee weeks later we travelled to them and lost 28-14. This was followed by another defeat at home to Nottingham on Boxing Day and by the New Year we knew we had a battle on our hands to avoid the drop.

Four points from the next four games gave us some breathing space, but then four consecutive defeats saw us drop right down into the danger zone. The next home game against Lydney resulted in a 34-14 win and safety with just two games remaining.

Top try scorers for the season were Steve Chapman, Paul Lydster and Ben Shepherd, each with six, and the top points scorer was Matt Birch with 167.

Scrum half, Paul Lydster, in action during the match against Henley at Sharmans Cross.

BIRMINGHAM & SOLIHULL

Match No.	Date	H/A	Comp.	Opponents	Result & Score	Att.	15	14	13	12	11
1	05.09	A	JN1	Lydney	L 13-21	750	Quantrill	Shepherd	R Chapman	Wilkinson	Quick
2	12.09	H	JN1	Otley	W 26-0	250	Quantrill	Goodwin(h)	R Chapman	Wilkinson	Batey
3	19.09	A	JN1	Reading	L 10-29	200	Quantrill	Shepherd	R Chapman	Wilkinson	S Chapman
4	26.09	H	JN1	Rosslyn Park*	L 15-39	200	Quantrill	Shepherd	R Chapman	Wilkinson(m)	S Chapman
5	03.10	A	JN1	Newbury	W 12-7	400	Quantrill	Shepherd/t	R Chapman	S Chapman	Banford
6	10.10	A	JN1	Liverpool StH	W 25-8	200	Quantrill	Shepherd	S Chapman	R Chapman	Banford/t
7	24.10	H	JN1	Harrogate	W15-12	200	Quantrill	Shepherd	R Chapman	S Chapman/t	Banford
8	31.10	A	JN1	Wharfedale	L 12-22	500	Quantrill	Shepherd	R Chapman	S Chapman	Banford
9	07.11	H	JN1	Manchester	L 27-30	200	Quantrill	Shepherd/t	R Chapman/2t	S Chapman/t	Quick
10	21.11	A	JN1	Nottingham	L 21-26	400	Quantrill	Shepherd	R Chapman/t	S Chapman/t	Quick
11	28.11	H	JN1	Camberley	W 43-5	100	Quantrill/t	Shepherd/2t	R Chapman(d)	S Chapman/2t	Banford
12	05.12	A	JN1	Henley*	L 13-26	300	Quantrill/c	Shepherd	R Chapman	S Chapman(l)	Banford(d)
13	12.12	H	JN1	Morley	W 35-7	150	Quantrill/tc	Shepherd	R Chapman	Wilkinson/t	Stuart
14	19.12	A	JN1	Camberley*	L 14-28	250	Quantrill	Shepherd	R Chapman	Wilkinson	Stuart
15	26.12	H	JN1	Nottingham	L 6-13	200	Quick	Shepherd	S Chapman	R Chapman(u)	Wilkinson
16	02.01	A	JN1	Manchester	L 0-42	650	Quick	Shepherd	Wilkinson	Stuart	R Chapman
17	16.01	H	JN1	Wharfedale	W27-12	250	Quick/2t	Shepherd	R Chapman	Wilkinson	Banford
18	23.01	A	JN1	Harrogate	L 7-14	500	Quick	Batey	R Chapman	Wilkinson(z)	Banford
19	30.01	H	JN1	Liverpool StH	W12-10	150	Quantrill	Shepherd	R Chapman	S Chapman	Banford(h)
20	06.02	H	JN1	Newbury	L 10-16	200	Quantrill	Shepherd	R Chapman	S Chapman	Batey
21	13.02	A	JN1	Rosslyn Park	L 0-42	300	Quantrill	Shepherd	R Chapman(b)	S Chapman	Batey
22	27.02	H	JN1	Reading	L 15-16	200	Quantrill	Shepherd/t	Wilkinson	S Chapman(a/t)	Batey(y)
23	13.03	A	JN1	Otley	L 12-37	300	Quantrill	R Chapman	S Chapman	Smart/t	Wilkinson/t
24	27.03	H	JN1	Lydney	W34-14	300	Smart/tp	Shepherd/t	R Chapman	S Chapman	Wilkinson/t
25	03.04	A	JN1	Morley	L 10-25	400	Smart	Shepherd	R Chapman	S Chapman	Wilkinson
26	17.04	H	JN1	Henley	L 8-22	300	Smart	Shepherd	R Chapman	S Chapman	Wilkinson(h)
A	17.10	A	TBC	Wharfedale	L 5-27	600	Quick	Banford	Wilkinson	S Chapman	R Chapman

* after opponents name indicates a penalty try
Brackets after a player's name indicates he was replaced. eg (a) means he was replaced by replacement code "a" and so on.
/ after a player or replacement name is followed by any scores he made - eg /t, /c, /p, /dg or any combination of these

1998-99 HIGHLIGHTS

League debuts:
Warwick Bullock, Gareth Beese, Damian Evans, Gary Banford, Willem Veldhuizen, James Gosling, John Brennan, Rob Stuart, Pete Glackin, Matt Griffin, Ian Davies

Ever Presents: Julian Hyde

Players used: 34 plus 2 as a replacement only

Most Points in a season:

Pts	Player	T	C	P	DG
170	M Birch	1	30	35	-
30	S Chapman	6	-	-	-
30	P Lydster	6	-	-	-
30	B Shepherd	6	-	-	-

MATCH FACTS

10	9	1	2	3	4	5	6	7	8	
Birch/c2p	Lydster/t	Lewis	Cox	Bullock	Hyde	McCrainor	Bastock	Beese	Maclean	1
Birch/c3p	Lydster/t	Lewis	Cox	Bullock	Hyde	McCrainor	Bastock	Beese	Maclean	2
Birch	Lydster/t	Lewis	Cox	Bullock/t	Hyde	McCrainor	Bastock	Beese	Maclean(i)	3
Birch/tcp	Lydster	Lewis	Cox	Bullock(j)	Hyde	McCrainor	Bastock(n)	Hughes	Evans	4
Birch/c	Lydster	Lewis	Cox	Bullock	Hyde	McCrainor	Veldhuizen	Meadows	Evans	5
Birch/2c2p	Lydster/t	Lewis	Cox	Bullock	Hyde	McCrainor	Veldhuizen	Meadows(g)	Evans(f/t)	6
Birch/cp	Lydster/t	Lewis	Cox	Bullock	Hyde	McCrainor	Veldhuizen	Meadows	Bastock(g)	7
Birch/4p	Lydster	Lewis	Griffin	Bullock	Hyde	McCrainor(r)	Veldhuizen	Meadows(g)	Bastock	8
Birch/2cp	Lydster	Lewis(B)	Cox	Bullock	Hyde	McCrainor	Veldhuizen	Beese(A)	Smith	9
Birch/c2p	Lydster	Davies	Cox	Bullock	Hyde	McCrainor	Veldhuizen	Beese	Smith	10
Birch/5cp	Lydster/t	Davies	Cox(o)	Bullock	Hyde	McCrainor	Veldhuizen	Beese(t)	Smith	11
Birch/2p	Lydster	Davies(c)	Cox	Bullock	Hyde	McCrainor	Veldhuizen(g)(p)	Brennan	Smith	12
Birch/2c3p(v)	Lydster	Lewis	Cox	Bullock	Hyde/t	McCrainor	Veldhuizen	Beese(t)	Smith/t	13
Birch/2c	Lydster	Lewis	Griffin	Bullock	Hyde	McCrainor	Beese	Brennan	Smith/t	14
Birch/2p	Lydster	Lewis(j)	Cox	Bullock	Hyde	McCrainor	Beese	Brennan	Veldhuizen	15
Glackim	Lydster(s)	Lewis	Griffin(d)	Davies(w)	Hyde	McCrainor	Veldhuizen	Beese(t)	Smith	16
Birch/3c2p	Cole	Lewis(j)	Cox	Mee/t	Hyde	McCrainor	Veldhuizen	Maclean	Smith	17
Birch/c	Gosling/t(v)	Lewis	Griffin	Mee(j)	Hyde	McCrainor	Veldhuizen	Maclean(t)	Smith	18
Birch/4p	Cole	Lewis	Griffin	Bullock	Hyde	McCrainor	Veldhuizen	Brennan	Smith	19
Birch/cp	Cole	Lewis	Griffin(j)	Bullock	Hyde	McCrainor	Maclean	Brennan(g)	Smith	20
Glackin	Cole	Lewis(w)	Davies	Bullock	Hyde	McCarinor(C)	Veldhuizen	Beese(t)	Smith	21
Birch/cp	Gosling	Lewis	Davies(x)	Bullock	Hyde	Smith	Veldhuizen	Brennan(g)	Maclean	22
Birch/c	Lydster	Lewis	Allen	Davies(A)	Hyde	Smith	Veldhuizen	Beese	Maclean	23
Birch/3c	Lydster	Lewis/t	Allen	Bullock	Hyde/t	Smith	Veldhuizen	Brennan	Maclean(e)	24
Birch/cp	Gosling	Lewis	Allen/t	Mee	Hyde	Smith	Veldhuizen	Brennan(g)	Maclean	25
Birch/p(v)	Lydster	Lewis	Allen/t(o)	Bullock	Hyde	Smith(e)	Veldhuizen	Brennan(g)	Maclean	26
Birch	Cole	Lewis	Griffin	Davies	McCrainor/t	Veldhuizen	Bastock	Beese	Maclean	A

REPLACEMENTS: a- R Chapman b- D Wilkinson c - N Lewis d - D Cox e - R McCrainor f - R Bastock g - G Beese h - G Batey i - D Evans j - I Davies l - B Cole m - G Banford n - W Veldhuizen o - M Griffin p - H Valarkis r - S Smith s - J Gosling t - J Brennan u - R Stuart v - P Glackin w - R Mee x - W Allen y - J Smart z - S Chapman A - P Meadows B - G Petitt C - R Maclean

Outside half Matt Birch topped the points scoring list for the second consecutive season.
His 170 points also take him past Jonathan Smart's career record of 363 with a new total of 466 in just two seasons.
He also sets new records for career conversions and penalties with 88 and 90 respectively.

Jonathan Smart came back and played on loan from Moseley and dropped three goals for a new record for a season and extend his career record to 5.

Winger Ben Shepherd finished joint leading try scorer and in the process passed Bob Robinson as Birmingham & Solihull's leading all time try scorer in league rugby with 22.

BIRMINGHAM & SOLIHULL

LEAGUE STATISTICS
compiled by Stephen McCormack

SEASON	Division	P	W	D	L	F	A	Pts Diff	Lge Pts	Lge Pos		Coach		Captain
89-90	Mid1	10	8	0	2	140	85	55	16	2p		R Smith		J Holliton
90-91	D4N	12	1	1	10	116	265	-149	3	13r		R Smith		R Richardson
91-92	Mid1	10	3	1	6	126	151	-25	7	9		R Richardson		T Ryan
92-93	Mid1	13	11	1	1	250	107	143	23	1p				
93-94	D5N	12	5	0	7	128	162	-34	10	9		M Swan		G Smith
94-95	D5N	12	5	0	7	167	226	-59	10	10		N Hurton		S Taylor
												Most Points		**Most Tries**
95-96	D5N	12	8	1	3	202	160	42	17	3	92	Jonathon Smart	3	Richard Packer
96-97	D4N	26	19	0	7	746	391	355	38	2	271	Jonathon Smart	10	David Cox
97-98	N2N	26	23	0	3	805	334	471	46	1p	296	Matt Birch	16	Ben Shepherd
98-99	JN1	26	9	0	17	422	523	101	18	11	170	Matt Birch	6	3 players

BIGGEST MARGINS

Home Win	46pts - 54-8 v Winnington Park 25.10.97
Away Win	62pts - 72-10 v Aspatria 30.8.97
Home Defeat	47pts - 3-50 v Wakefield 31.10.87
Away Defeat	79pts - 0-79 v Roundhay 26.11.88

MOST CONSECUTIVE

Appearances	
Matches scoring Tries	
Matches scoring points	
Victories	9
Defeats	13

MOST POINTS

Scored at Home	55 v Stoke on Trent 21.9.96
Scored Away	72 v Aspatria 30.8.97
Conceded at Home	50 v Wakefield 31.10.87
Conceded Away	79 v Roundhay 26.11.88

MOST TRIES

Scored in a match	11 v Aspatria 30.8.97
Conceded in a match	? v Roundhay 26.11.88

MOST APPEARANCES

by a forward	66 (2) Richard McCrainor
by a back	58 (1) Richard Chapman

	MOST IN A SEASON	MOST IN A CAREER	MOST IN A MATCH
Points	296 Matt Birch 97-98	466 Matt Birch 97-99	22 Jonathon Smart v Nuneaton 1.2.97 v Lichfield 15.3.97 Matt Birch v Stourbridge 18.10.97
Tries	16 Ben Shepherd 97-98	22 Ben Shepherd 97-99	4 Steve Chapman v Hinckley 31.1.98
Conversions	58 Matt Birch 97-98	88 Matt Birch 97-99	7 Matt Birch v Aspatria 30.8.97
Penalties	55 Matt Birch 97-98	90 Matt Birch 97-99	6 Matt Birch v Hinckley 8.11.97
Drop Goals	1 Jonathon Smart 95-96,96-97	2 Jonathon Smart 95-97	1 Jonathon Smart v Preston G. 24.2.96 v Aspatria 26.04.97

BIRMINGHAM& SOL PLAYING SQUAD

BACKS

BACKS	Ht.	Wt.	Birthdate	Birthplace	CLUB	League Apps	Tries	Pts
Gary Banford					Birmingham S	9(1)	1	5
Matt Birch	5.11	13.03	28.11.72	Stourbridge	Birmingham S Moseley	50	4	466
Dave Wilkinson	5.11	15.00	30.05.69	Ipswich	Birmingham S Moseley	35(4)	9	45
Richard Chapman	6.0	14.04	12.02.74	Solihull	Birmingham S Rugby	58(2)	19	95
Steve Chapman	6.1	13.10		Coventry	Birmingham S Coventry	32(2)	11	55
Ben Shepherd	6.0	14.10	12.02.74	Coventry	Birmingham S Coventry	48	22	110
Gavin Batey	6.4	17.07	04.10.72	Birmingham	Birmingham S Moseley	16(5)	8	40
Craig Quick	6.1	13.03	15.12.75	Coventry	Birmingham S Coventry	20(2)	8	42
James Gosling				I	Birmingham S	3(1)	1	5
Paul Lydster	6.1	14.00	28.05.70	Coventry	Birmingham S Coventry	19	6	30
Jim Quantrill	6.2	15.00	30.05.69	Poole	Birmingham S Rugby	19 102(3)	2 13	14 559
Pete Glackin					Birmingham S	2(3)	-	-

FORWARDS

FORWARDS	Ht.	Wt.	Birthdate	Birthplace	CLUB	League Apps	Tries	Pts
John Brennan	5.11	14.00	20.12.71	Birmingham	Birmingham S Nottingham	9(5) 41	- 3	- 15
Warwick Bullock Other club: Gloucester.	6.0	17.12	09.02.70	Stourbridge	Birmingham S Coventry	21	1	5
Ian Davies Other club: Moseley	5.10	16.02	13.06.75	Abergavenny	Birmingham S London Welsh	7(8)	-	-
Mark Griffin	5.9	14.02	06.04.75	Oakham	Birmingham S	6(2)		
Dave Cox	6.1	16.00	29.03.72	Birmimgham	Birmingham S Worcester	39(1)	9	45
Richard McCrainor	6.4	17.07	25.01.71	Solihull	Birmingham S	66(3)	3	15
Julian Hyde	6.5	18.00	22.05.68	Coventry	Birmingham S Coventry	52	3	15
Paul Meadows					Birmingham S	7(4)		
Steve Smith Other club: Coventry	6.6	17.03	20.06.68	Solihull	Birmingham S Rugby	17(1) 111(5)	2 5	10 25
Bob Robinson	5.11	15.10	16.06.69	Birmingham	Birmingham S Moseley	43	19	95
Rory MacLean	6.2	15.00	26.06.72	Birmingham	Birmingham S Moseley			
Rob Bastock	6.4	16.00	21.09.72	Solihull	Birmingham S			
Will Allen					Birmingham S	12(3)	2	10
Gareth Beese	5.11	14.10	14.11.72	Newport	Birmingham S Nottingham	13(9)	-	-

BIRMINGHAM & SOLIHULL

FACT FILE

Founded: 1989
(Birmingham RFC & Solihull RUFC merged)
Nickname: The Bees

Colours: Black with broad red & narrow amber hoops
Change colours: Red, black, amber & white quarters

GROUND

Address: Sharmans Cross Road, Solihull.
Tel: 0121 705 7995
Capacity: 3,000 Seated: None Standing: 3,000

Directions: From Solihull centre take Streetsbrook Road, through the traffic llights, over hump-back bridge. Second left into Sharmans Cross Road and the ground is 300 yards on the left.
Nearest Railway Station: Solihull

Car Parking: 500 spaces are available at the ground.

Admission

Season tickets Adults £55, OAPs £36, Children u'16 Free
Matchday Adults £5, Children u'16 Free.

Clubhouse: Open Sat. 12-2, Sun 10-3, Tue & Thur 7-11.30.
Snacks and bar meals are available.
Functions: Capacity 150, contact David Radson 0121 733 7033

Club Shop: Yes, manager Dave Radburn.

Training Nights: Tuesday and Thursday.

PROGRAMME

Size: A5 Pages: 88 + cover
Price: Included with entry
Editor: David Radburn 0121 733 7033

ADVERTISING RATES
Mono only Full Page £250 Half Page Not available

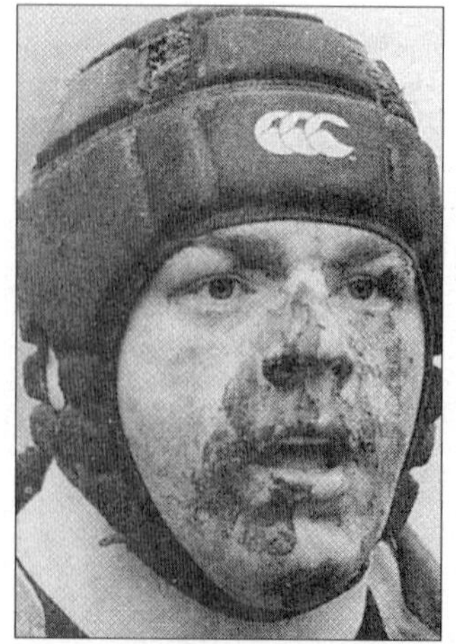

Julian Hyde, Birmingham & Solihull Captain

BLACKHEATH

President	Sir Hal Miller	Moorcroft Farm, Sinton Green, Worcester WR2 6NW 01322 555906
Chairman	Frank McCarthy	Easter Hill, Romford Road, Pembury, Nr Tunbridge Wells, Kent 01892 822149 (H)
Club Secretary	Barry Shaw	86 Crown Woods Way, Eltham, London. SE9 2NN. 0181 850 7976 (H), 0171 494 1454 (B), 0181 850 7421 (Fax)
Fixtures Secretary	J Collett	8 Vanbrugh Fields, Blackheath, London. SE3 7TZ. 0181 858 7571 (H), 0181 539 3348 (B)
Rugby Administrator	Bob Evans	01689 853002 (H), 0171 489 0291 (B)
Press Officer	Phil Ubee	0181 293 0853 (B), 0181 305 1702 (H)
Head Coach	Danny Vaughan	0181 293 0853 (B)
General Manager	Ron Bailey	01732 762428 (H), 0181 293 0853 (B), 0181 293 0854 (Fax)

The team endured a season which must have been one of the worst on record for our distinguished club. The main emotion that comes to mind is bitter disappointment and unfulfilled potential. Missed opportunities, much bad luck and, it must be said, a fair number of indifferent performances both individually and collectively were also partly the reason for the poor showing.

The summer was spent trying to build a new squad almost from scratch. This created one fatal problem, namely that the task of gathering the squad together took so long that our pre season preparations were very much disturbed. The building of team spirit as well as the foundation of lasting fitness was the major cause of our problems.

The season opened with narrow defeats at Rugby and at home to London Welsh and although we showed some promising signs a lack of killer instinct proved decisive.

There followed four heavy defeats in which 208 points were conceded and only seven penalties scored. Following some harsh words from the coaching staff and senior players there followed six much improved performances especially giving Worcester a run for their money at their superbly appointed ground. However, we still lacked a cutting edge as shown against Moseley when we completely dominated but still managed to lose.

Some familiar names were brought back to the club, but even these additions failed to halt the urge to drag defeat from the jaws of victory as against Sedgeley Park. At last a win was secured against fellow strugglers Fylde, but unfortunately, this did not signal a sequence of victories. For example we were only 31-22 down at half time against Waterloo and playing into a gale, however in the second half we managed only one penalty. Lady luck still refused to smile on us. We were winning at Moseley well into injury time, when we lost the ball on their line, and we lost the match. A series of injuries to key players didn't help either.

This was not an ideal preparation for the final six matches. However, pleasingly, the team showed that they had acquired some resilience and retained some pride through all our trials and tribulations and won three of them including a heart warming and almost heart stopping 27-26 win at Fylde.

BOB EVANS

1998-99 Squad - L-R: **Back Row:** Russell Ticehurst, Mark Hanslip, Greg Ellis, Johan Vanvuuren, Tiger Carrol, Matt Griffiths, Tony Redmond, Dwayne Bishop, Aadel Kardooni. **MiddleRow:** Mike Mein, Danny Vaughan (head coach), Jim Roques, Rob McCorduck, Dave Merlin, Paul Jennings, Steve Johnson, Dave Mayhew, Maru Ririnui, Campbell Aitken, Chris Braithwaite, Rob Evans (manager), Phil Ubee (coach). **Front Row:** Nick McGrath (physio), Marcus Briggs, Aaron James, Josh Taylor, Bobby Howe, Chris Wilkins (capt.), Craig Sangster, Chris Pawson, Phil Delaney, Laurence Boyle, Ron Bailey (general manager)

BLACKHEATH

Match No.	Date	H/A	Comp.	Opponents	Result & Score	Att.	15	14	13	12	11
1	05.09	A	AD2	Rugby Lions	L 12-18	500	Briggs	Aitken/4p	Delaney	James	Pawson
2	12.09	H	AD2	London Welsh	L 16-20	1,300	Sangster	Aitken/c3p	Delaney	James	Briggs
3	20.09	A	AD2	Leeds Tykes	L 6-60	617	Sangster	Aitken/2p(s)	Delaney	Tassle(r)	Briggs
4	26.09	A	AD2	Orrell	L 3-60	1,000	Sangster	Aitken/p	Delaney	Boyle	Briggs(u)
5	03.10	H	AD2	Bristol	L 9-41	1,150	Sangster	Aitken/3p	Delaney	James	Hoare
6	10.10	A	AD2	Rotherham	L 3-46		Aitken/p	Sangster	Boyle	James	Griffiths
7	17.10	H	AD2	Coventry	L 18-30	500	Aitken/c2p	Sangster	Delaney	James	Griffiths/t
8	24.10	A	AD2	Wakefield	L 9-19	400	Aitken/3p	Sangster	Delaney	James	Griffiths(B)
9	31.10	H	AD2	Moseley	L 14-18	550	Aitken/2c	Sangster	Delaney	James	Griffiths
10	07.11	A	AD2	Worcester	L 9-21	2,032	Aitken/3p	Sangster	Delaney	James	Griffiths
11	21.11	H	AD2	Waterloo	L 18-24	550	Aitken/c2p	Razak/t	Fitzgerald	James	Griffiths
12	12.12	A	AD2	Exeter	L 7-26	700	Coates	Sangster	Fitzgerald	James	Razak
13	19.12	H	AD2	Fylde	W 24-17	500	Coates	Sangster	Fitzgerald(b)	James	Razak/t
14	02.01	A	AD2	Waterloo	L 25-31	400	Ratcliffe	Sangster/t	Fitzgerald/t	James	Griffiths
15	16.01	H	AD2	Worcester	L 3-51	600	Coates	Sangster	Fitzgerald	James	Griffiths
16	23.01	A	AD2	Moseley	L 16-22	641	Coates	Sangster	Fitzgerald/t	Pawson	Razak
17	06.02	H	AD2	Wakefield	W 28-20	500	Sangster/t	Griffiths/t	Fitzgerald	Pawson	Razak
18	13.02	A	AD2	Coventry	L 8-35	800	Sangster	Griffiths(f)	Fitzgerald	Pawson/t	Razak
19	27.02	H	AD2	Rotherham	L 19-29	600	Ratcliffe(d)	Sangster/t	Fitzgerald	James	Razak(a)
20	13.03	A	AD2	Bristol	L 17-50	2,353	Aitken/c	Sangster(s)	Fitzgerald(d/t)	James	Razak
21	27.03	H	AD2	Orrell	W 15-9	600	Aitken/tp(v/c)	Sangster	Fitzgerald(c)	Pawson	Razak
22	03.04	H	AD2	Leeds Tykes	L 22-37	500	Aitken/tcp(o)	Sangster(p)	Fitzgerald	James	Griffiths
23	10.04	H	AD2	Exeter	L 26-41	500	Braithwaite	Griffiths	Fitzgerald/t	James	Razak/t(n/t)
24	17.04	A	AD2	London Welsh	L 22-71	1,300	Braithwaite	Sangster(w)	Fitzgerald	James	Griffiths(p)
25	24.04	H	AD2	Rugby Lions	W 43-20	600	Braithwaite	Griffiths(w)	Fitzgerald/t	James/t	Razak/t(n)
26	01.05	A	AD2	Fylde	W 27-26	300	Braithwaite/t	Sangster/t(a)	Fitzgerald	James	Griffiths(w)
A	14.11	H	TBC	Sedgley Park	L 21-22	800	Aitken/2p	Razak/2t	Delaney	James	Griffiths

1998-99 HIGHLIGHTS

League debuts:
Marcus Briggs, Campbell Aitken, Phil Delaney, Aaron James, Aadel Kardooni, Liam Mooney, Tony Redmond, Rob Salisbury, Dave Merlin, Maru Ririnui, Bernard Carroll, Craig Sangster, Paul Jennings, Aymun Razak, Matt Plowman, Dwayne Bishop, Simon Amor, Matt Jarvis, Tom Smith, John Ratcliffe, Derek Coates, Christian Martin, Jim Rocques, Greg Ellis.

Ever Presents: One - Chris Wilkins.

Players used: 42 plus 2 as a replacement only.

Most Points in a season:

Pts	Player	T	C	P	DG
102	C Autken	2	7	26	-
83	S Amor	-	16	16	1
60	J Clarke	12	-	-	-
29	C Braithwaite	2	5	3	-

MATCH FACTS

10	9	1	2	3	4	5	6	7	8	
Braithwaite	Kardooni	Mooney	Redmond	Taylor(l)	Mayhew	Ticehurst	Salisbury	Wilkins	Merlin(m)	1
Braithwaite	Kardooni/t	Mooney	Redmond	Taylor	Mayhew	Jennings	McCorduck	Wilkins	Merlin	2
Braithwaite	Percival	Mooney	Redmond(t)	Taylor	Mayhew	Jennings	McCorduck(m)	Wilkins	Merlin(q)	3
Braithwaite	Sharples	Mooney	Redmond(x)	Plowman(w)	Mayhew(i)	Jennings	Merlin(j)	Bishop	Wilkins	4
Braithwaite	Sharples	Mooney	Howe	Taylor	Mayhew(i)	Jennings(m)	Merlin	Wilkins	Bishop(j)	5
Braithwaite(u)	Sharples	Taylor(C)	Howe(g)	Ririnui	Mayhew	Jennings	Salisbury	Smith(m)	Wilkins	6
Braithwaite	Kardooni	Taylor	Howe/t	Ririnui	Mayhew	Jennings	Salisbury	Bishop(A)	Wilkins	7
Braithwaite	Kardooni	Mooney	Redmond	Ririnui(h)	Ticehurst	Jennings	Merlin	Bishop	Wilkins	8
Braithwaite	Kardooni	Mooney	Howe	Ririnui(C)	Mayhew	Jennings	Smith	Wilkins/t	Merlin/t	9
Ratcliffe	Kardooni	Mooney	Howe	Ririnui	Mayhew	Jennings	Walton	Wilkins	Merlin	10
Braithwaite	Percival	Mooney	Howe	Ririnui	Mayhew	Jennings/t	Smith	Wilkins	Walton	11
Braithwaite/c	Clarke/t(o)	Mooney	Howe(g)	Ririnui	Mayhew	Jennings	Jarvis	Wilkins	Smith	12
Braithwaite/3cp	Clarke/2t	Mooney	Howe(g)	Ririnui	Mayhew	Jennings	Jarvis	Wilkins	Merlin(A)	13
Braithwaite/tcp	Kardooni(o)	Mooney	Redmond(x)	Ririnui	Mayhew	Jennings	Smith/t	Wilkins	Merlin	14
Braithwaite/p	Clarke	Mooney	Redmond	Ririnui(D)	Mayhew	Jennings	Smith(E)	Wilkins	Merlin	15
Amor/c3p	Clarke	Mooney	Redmond	Ririnui	Mayhew	Jennings	Jarvis	Wilkins	Merlin	16
Amor/c2p	Clarke/2t	Mooney	Redmond(x)	Ririnui	Mayhew	Jennings(z)	Walton	Wilkins	Merlin	17
Amor/p	Clarke	Mooney	Howe	Ririnui	Mayhew	Jennings	Walton	Wilkins	Merlin	18
Amor/c4p	Kardooni	Mooney	Howe	Ririnui(F)	Merlin	Jennings	Walton	Jarvis	Wilkins	19
Amor/cp(e)	Clarke/t(f)	Mooney	Howe	Ririnui(F)	Merlin	Jennings	Walton	Jarvis	Wilkins	20
Braithwaite	Clarke/t	Mooney(F)	Howe	Ririnui(D)	Mayhew	Jennings	Walton	Jarvis	Wilkins	21
Braithwaite(v/c)	Clarke/t	Mooney	Howe	Ririnui(F)	Mayhew	Jennings(k)	Jarvis	Booth/t	Wilkins	22
Amor/3c	Clarke/t	Rocques(C)	Redmond(x)	Ririnui	Mayhew	Jennings(D)	Merlin	Jarvis	Wilkins	23
Amor/2cp	Percival/t	Scrivens	Howe(g)	Ririnui(q)	Merlin/t	Jennings	Ellis(y/t)	Booth	Wilkins	24
Amor/3c3pdg	Percival(y/t)	Scrivens	Howe	Ririnui(m)	Mayhew	Jennings(z)	Merlin	Booth	Wilkins/t	25
Amor/2cp	Percival(y/t)	Scrivens	Howe	Ririnui/t(g)	Mayhew	Jennings	Carroll	Ellis	Wilkins	26
Ratcliffe	Gaylord	Mooney	Howe	Ririnui	Mayhew	Jennings	Walton/t	Wilkins	Merlin	A

REPLACEMENTS:	a- C Aitken	b- P Delaney	c - A James	d - C Pawson	e - C Braithwaite	f - A Kardooni	g - T Redmond
h - J Taylor	i - R Ticehurst	j - R Salisbury	k - D Merlin	l - M Ririnui	m - B Carroll	n - C Sangster	o - M Percival
p - Razak	q - M Plowman	r - L Boyle	s - M Griffiths	t - R Sharples	u - J van Vanouran		v - S Amor
w - M Hoare	x - B Howe	y - J Clarke	z - M Jarvis				
A - T Smith	B - J Ratcliffe	C - W Scrivens	D - T Booth	E - C Martin	F - J Rocques		

Campbell Aitken in his first season at the club topped the points scorers list with 102 points from 14 starts, the third player to top the 100 point mark for the club in a season.

Aitken also equalled the club record of points in 11 consecutive matches, he now shares the record with Sam Howard.

John Clarke topped the try scoring list for a second successive season with 12 to add to his 13 from the season before. That took him to 25 career tries in the league for Blackheath to surpass the club record of 19 set by former scrum half Mike Friday. Clarke's tries came from just 9 starts and three more as a replacement.

BLACKHEATH

LEAGUE STATISTICS
compiled by Stephen McCormack

SEASON	Division	P	W	D	L	F	A	Pts Diff	Lge Pts	Lge Pos	Most Points	Most Tries
89-90	2	11	3	2	6	141	205	-64	8	10	57 Colin Parker	3 Jon King
90-91	2	12	4	0	8	134	169	-35	8	10	48 Colin Parker	3 Pat Jones
91-92	2	12	4	0	8	140	266	-126	8	11	61 Neil Munn	2 Andy Mercer
92-93	2	12	4	2	6	142	231	-89	10	10r	97 Grant Eagle	5 Joe McIntyre
93-94	3	18	11	0	7	305	222	83	22	4	78 Stuart Burns	9 Mike Friday
94-95	3	18	12	2	4	299	190	109	26	2p	147 Sam Howard	5 Matt Griffiths
95-96	2	18	6	1	11	341	469	-128	13	7	153 Sam Howard	5 Mike Hanslip
96-97	2	22	7	0	15	412	641	-229	14	10	137 Chris Braithwaite	8 Mike Hanslip
97-98	P2	22	8	0	14	474	621	-147	16	9	84 Chris Braithwaite	13 John Clarke
98-99	P2	26	5	0	21	419	842	-423	10	13r	102 Campbell Aitken	12 John Clarke

BIGGEST MARGINS

Home Win	39pts - 44-5 v Rotherham 7.9.96
Away Win	28pts - 28-0 v Exeter 29.4.95
Home Defeat	62pts - 10-72 v Newcastle 16.4.97
Away Defeat	64pts - 10-74 v Coventry 8.3.97

MOST CONSECUTIVE

Appearances	46 Mike Friday 1993-96
Matches scoring Tries	5 John Clarke
Matches scoring points	11 Sam Howard Campbell Aitken
Victories	4
Defeats	9

MOST POINTS

Scored at Home	50 v Fylde 20.9.97
Scored Away	32 v Rugby 12.4.97
Conceded at Home	72 v Newcastle 16.4.97
Conceded Away	74 v Coventry 8.3.97

MOST TRIES

Scored in a match	8 v Fylde 20.9.97 (H)
Conceded in a match	12 v Coventry 8.3.97(A) v Newcastle16.4.97 (H)

MOST APPEARANCES

by a forward	98 (1) Mike Harris
by a back	85 (2) Richard Smith

	MOST IN A SEASON	MOST IN A CAREER	MOST IN A MATCH	
Points	153 Sam Howard 95-96	349 Sam Howard 93-97	20 Grant Eagle John Clarke John Schuster	v Moseley 28.3.92 (H) v Fylde 20.9.97 (H) v Coventry 4.10.97 (H)
Tries	13 John Clarke 97-98	25 John Clarke 97-99	4 John Clarke	v Fylde 20.9.97 (H)
Conversions	23 Chris Braithwaite 96-97	32 Sam Howard 93-97	5 Sam Howard	v Moseley 27.4.96 (A)
Penalties	38 Sam Howard 94-95	76 Sam Howard 93-97	6 Grant Eagle Sam Howard John Schuster	v Moseley 28.3.92 (H) v Rosslyn Park 9.1.93 (H) v Morley 7.1.95 (H) v Coventry 4.10.97
Drop Goals	8 John King 88-89	16 John King 87-91	2 Jon King Chris Braithwaite	v Coventry 19.11.88 (A) v Lon. Irish 22.4.89 (A) v Lon. Irish 28.4.90 (H) v Nottingham 22.3.97 (H)

BLACKHEATH PLAYING SQUAD

BACKS	Ht.	Wt.	Birthdate	Birthplace	CLUB	League Apps	Tries	Pts
Campbell Aitken	6.2	14.05	31.03.75	Musselburgh	Blackheath	14(2)	2	102
Dave Fitzgerald England U21.	5.10	14.0	12.06.74	Farnborough	Blackheath	52	11	55
Mike Griffiths	5.8	13.4	30.03.72	London	Blackheath Wasps	85(2) 1	19 -	94 -
Chris Braithwaite	5.11	12.10	26.12.71	Amersham	Blackheath Wasps	47(2) 9(1)	5 6	250 76
Aymon Razak					Blackheath LondonIrish	11(2)	4	20
John Clarke	6.0	14.6	30.05.75	W Samoa	Blackheath	24(3)	25	125
John Ratcliffe	6.0	14.7	25.09.71	Auckland	Blackheath	3(1)	-	-
Phil Delaney	6.0	13.07	17.10.74	Wellsbourne	Blackheath Leicester	9(1)	-	-
Chris Pawson England U21, Colts, Schools.	5.11	13.5	21.09.76	Bromley	Blackheath	15(2)	7	35
Mark Percival England Colts.	5.7	12.8	20.04.76	London	Blackheath	12(4)	3	15
Richard Sharples	5.9	12.0	24.05.77	T Wells	Blackheath	4(6)	-	-
Craig Sangster	6.0	14.7	02.03.75	Galashiels	Blackheath	21(2)	5	25
Simon Amor England schools & colts.			24.04.79	Kingston-o-T	Blackheath	9(2)	-	81

FORWARDS	Ht.	Wt.	Birthdate	Birthplace	CLUB	League Apps	Tries	Pts
Liam Mooney Ireland U-21, students	6.0	17.10	18.05.73	Dublin	Blackheath London Irish	20 31(4)	- -	- -
Tony Redmond England Univ, Irish Exiles. Other club: Orrell	5.10	15.00	14.01.71	Wigan	Blackheath London Irish	10(6) 15(8)	- 1	- 5
Maru Ririnui	6.3	18.5	11.09.70	Invercargil	Blackheath	21(1)	-	-
John Taylor	6.2	18.0	06.01.70	London	Blackheath	43(12)	2	10
David Mayhew	6.6	17.6	07.02.69	Matamata(NZ)	Blackheath	40(1)		
David Merlin	6.4	16.05	22.05.72		Blackheath Northampton	19(1) 12(4)	2 5	10 25
Matt Jarvis			18.10.78	London	Blackheath London Irish	8(2) (2)	- -	- -
Rob McCorduck	6.4	16.0	09.01.72	Galway	Blackheath	33(1)	1	5
Chris Wilkins	6.3	16.2	03.07.71	London	Blackheath Wasps	67 17	9 2	45 10
Paul Jennings	6.6	17.10	07.02.74	Lanark	Blackheath	25(1)	-	-
Toby Booth	5.11	15.6	06.02.70	Folkstone	Blackheath	64(4)	5	25
Bobby Howe	5.8	14.0	12.04.63	Beckenham	Blackheath	44(6)	3	13
Tony Rocques	6.0	16.4	24.06.74	Bromley	Blackheath Sidcup	1(4)	-	-

BLACKHEATH

FACT FILE

Founded: 1858
Nickname: The Club

Colours: Red & black hoops, blue trim/black.
Change colours: Blue with red & black hoops/black.

GROUND

Address: The Rectory Field, Charlton Road, Blackheath. SE3 8SR.
Tel: 0181 858 1578 Fax: 0181 293 0854
Capacity: 6,000 Seated: 572 Standing: 5,428

Directions: The entrance to the Rectory Field is approx 800 yards from the start of Charlton Road B210 at its junction with Stratheden Road/Westcombe Hill which is a turning off Shooters Hill Road A2.
Nearest Railway Station: Blackheath (BR) or Westcombe Park (BR)

Car Parking: 250 spaces available on ground

Admission:
Season Adults £89 U17 Free
Matchday £10 includes programme

Club Shop: Yes. Manageress Mandy Allen 0181 293 5980

Clubhouse: Normal Licensing hours, snacks available.
Functions: Yes; capacity 100

Training Nights: Tuesday & Thursday

PROGRAMME

Size: A5 Pages: 36 + cover
Price: With admission
Editor Serge Orlov, 0181 293 0853

ADVERTISING RATES
Colour Full page £995, Half page £695

BRACKNELL R.F.C.

Chairman	S J Ward	13 Arden Close, Bracknell, Berks. RG12 2SG Tel: 01344 420236 (H) 0374 821190 (Mobile)
Club Secretary	P J (John) Denman	57 Lingwood, Bracknell, Berks RG12 7PZ Tel: 01344 455400 (H), 01344 306234 (Fax), 0411 197331 (Mobile)
Fixtures Secretary	S D Stevens	18 Abbey Close, Harnaswater, Bracknell, Berks RG12 9NX. Tel: 01344 422586 (H) 01344 789888 (B)

Following promotion three years running, Bracknell faced the start of the 1998/99 season in an apprehensive frame of mind. There had been some additions to the squad, notably Matt Dangerfield from Newbury, Nick Robinson, Andy Furley and Jim Kelly from London Scottish and Richard Parker from Camberley. However, Bracknell's worst fears were confirmed when after three matches, they had lost two, to North Walsham and Esher (both away), although they had also had a good and slightly unexpected win against Barking. Bracknell were not to know that the three sides they played in the first three games would be respectively third, fourth and second in the table at the end of the season.

Although Bracknell's debut in the National Leagues was inauspicious, alarm bells were not yet ringing but certainly concern was being expressed at the strength of the league that Bracknell had recently joined and it was realised that if the club were to challenge for honours, the season would have to be `turned around' immediately. The club then embarked on a string of league wins slowly climbing the table, obtaining their first away win in National Leagues against Bridgwater with one of their best pre-Christmas displays, it was noteworthy that the club, whilst winning were very often down at half-time and certainly were fortunate to win away at Cheltenham.

The second half of the season saw the side increasing in confidence and although table topping Esher were consistently winning their matches by large margins it became apparent that Bracknell were heading for a top four place. The side continued to win home and away, but only moved into first place in the table when Esher (having lost unexpectedly to Weston-Super-Mare earlier in the season) lost at home in a tightly contested confrontation with North Walsham who were the form team at the time.

The season was set up for a grand finale with Esher, Barking and North Walsham to be played in the five remaining matches. The possibility of promotion now became realistic and nine points from those matches would win the league. The contest against Esher was one of great commitment by both sides, but having established a lead, Bracknell had to defend fiercely for the last quarter to run out winners. Although taking a weakened side to Barking, and after a poor performance, a draw was salvaged. This meant that winning the title now really rested on one match, at home to North Walsham who at that stage had beaten every other side in the league. After an entertaining match Bracknell ran out comfortable winners. This win also set a record of 50 home league matches unbeaten, which was extended to 51 in the final match. The second last game at Plymouth saw the side record a score of 64 points, their highest score of the season. The final match against Cheltenham was not a foregone conclusion, but in the end went to form and the club were promoted as champions to Jewson One.

In the Tetley's Bitter Cup, the club recorded wins against Westcombe Park, Weston-Super-Mare and Metropolitan Police (yet again) to reach the 4th Round and a trip to Premier One side West Hartlepool. The club's first taste of Premier One opposition saw the side travel to the North East for a Sunday match and acquit themselves with much honour.

L-R **Back Row**, Standing: J Denman (sec.), J Turner (Coach), M Dangerfield, A Dix, M Draper, A Furley, J Kelly, A Orugboh, H Lamb, A Leishman, R Turner, S Newman, L Price, J Hart, P Hopley, G Spencer, M Kenworthy, J Maunder, J Payne, C Russell, E Strong, S Ward (Chairman), A Goble (Chair of Playing), J Lucas (Comm. Manager). **Front Row:** S Shaw, N Robinson (Physio), Dr J Thing, E Day, P Rendall (Dir. of Coaching), A Yates, G Mosses (Capt.), S Edwards, J Clarke, D Jackson, C Morley.

BRACKNELL

Match No.	Date	H/A	Comp.	Opponents	Result & Score	Att.	15	14	13	12	11
1	05.09	A	J2S	N Walsham	L 3-17		Dangerfield	Hopley	Hall	Nowak(l)	Clarke
2	12.12	H	J2S	Barking	W 23-8		Robinson/t	Hopley(c)	Hall	Furley	Clarke
3	26.12	A	J2S	Esher	L 6-27		Robinson	Hopley	Hall	Furley	Clarke
4	03.10	H	J2S	Clifton	W 22-12		Dangerfield/2t	Hopley	Hall	Furley	Priest
5	10.10	A	J2S	Bridgwater	W 42-25		Dangerfield	Hopley/t	Hall	Nowak/2t	Spencer
6	24.10	H	J2S	M Police	W 11-5		Dangerfield	Hopley	Hall	Clarke	Spencer(l)
7	31.10	A	J2S	Tabard	W 18-6		Dangerfield	Clarke	Hall	Furley	Spencer
8	07.11	H	J2S	Norwich	W 16-6		Hopley	Clarke	Nowak/cp	Furley	Spencer/t
9	21.11	A	J2S	Redruth	W 34-25		Nowak/2t	Clarke/t	Payne	Furley/t	Fellows
10	28.11	H	J2S	Weston	W 24-6		Robinson	Dangerfield	Payne	Furley	Clarke/2t
11	05.12	A	J2S	Havant	W 30-17		Robinson/t	Dangerfield	Payne	Furley	Clarke/t
12	12.12	A	J2S	Cheltenham	W 15-11		Robinson	Dangerfield/t	Payne	Nowak	Fellows(a)
13	19.12	H	J2S	Plymouth	W 24-13		Robinson	Hopley	Payne(b)	Furley	Dangerfield
14	28.12	H	J2S	Havant	W 39-13		Robinson	Hopley/2t	Hall	Priest	Spencer/t
15	02.01	A	J2S	Weston	W 20-10		Robinson	Dangerfield	Furley/t	Priest/t	Hopley
16	16.01	A	J2S	Norwich	W 19-15		Robinson	Dangerfield	Priest(u)	Furley	Hopley/t
17	23.01	H	J2S	Tabard	W 15-12		Robinson	Hopley	Payne	Furley	Spencer/t
18	31.01	A	J2S	M Police	W 18-6		Robinson	Hopley/t	Payne	Furley(b)	Spencer
19	06.02	H	J2S	Bridgwater	W 38-0		Robinson	Hopley/t	Payne	Priest/t	Spencer/t
20	13.02	A	J2S	Clifton	W 34-20		Robinson/t	Dangerfield	Payne	Nowak/c	Spencer
21	20.02	H	J2S	Redruth*	W 37-10		Robinson	Dangerfield	Payne	Furley	Spencer/2t
22	27.02	H	J2S	Esher	W 16-11		Robinson	Clarke	Payne	Furley	Spencer
23	13.03	A	J2S	Barking	D 13-13		Robinson/t	Spencer	Payne	Nowak/c2p(b)	Hopley
24	27.03	H	J2S	N Walsham	W 31-14		Robinson/t	Clarke	Payne	Priest	Spencer
25	03.04	A	J2S	Plymouth	W 64-12		Robinson	Clarke/3t(a/2t)	Payne	Priest/t	Spencer/t
26	17.04	H	J2S	Cheltenham	W 19-3		Robinson	Clarke	Payne	Kenworthy	Spencer
A	19.09	A	TB1	Westcombe P	W 21-14		Robinson/t	Hopley	Hall	Furley	Clarke
B	17.10	A	TB2	Weston	W 43-15		Dangerfield/t	Hopley	Hall/t	Clarke/2t	Spencer
C	14.11	H	TB3	M Police	W 13-6		Dangerfield	Clarke	Payne	Nowak/dg	Spencer
D	10.01	A	TB4	W Hartlepool	L 14-34		Robinson	Hopley	Priest(u)	Furley	Dangerfield

* after opponents name indicates a penalty try
Brackets after a player's name indicates he was replaced. eg (a) means he was replaced by replacement code "a" and so on.
/ after a player or replacement name is followed by any scores he made - eg /t, /c, /p, /dg or any combination of these

1998-99 HIGHLIGHTS

Ever Presents: None

Most appearances

23 Carson Russel.
22 Howard Lamb, Glyn Mosses, Alan Leishman

Players used: 34 plus 1 as a replacement only

Most Points in a season:

Pts	Player	T	C	P	DG
216	C Russell	-	39	45	1
63	B Nowak	4	4	11	-
40	H Lamb	8	-	-	-
40	P Hopley	8	-	-	-
35	D Jackson	7	-	-	-
35	G Spencer	7	-	-	-

MATCH FACTS

10	9	1	2	3	4	5	6	7	8	
Russell/p	Shaw	Kelly	Turner	Mosses(j)	Leishman	Orugbuh(k)	Chamberlain	Price	Lamb	1
Russell/2c3p	Shaw	Kelly(j)	Turner	Mosses	Leishman	Newman	Jackson/t	Price	Lamb	2
Russell/2p	Shaw	Kelly	Turner(q)(p)	Mosses	Leishman	Newman(h)	Parker(o)	Price	Lamb	3
Russell/2cp	Shaw	Strong	Turner	Kelly	Leishman	Newman	Jackson	Price	Lamb/t	4
Russell/4c3p(l)	Shaw	Kelly/t(r)	Sheddon	Mosses	Leishman	Newman	Parker	Jackson	Lamb/t(o)	5
Nowak/2p	Shaw	Kelly	Turner	Mosses	Leishman	Newman	Jackson	Parker(i)	Lamb/t	6
Nowak/6p	Shaw	Kelly	Turner	Mosses	Leishman	Newman	Jackson	Price(t)	Lamb	7
Russell/2p	Shaw	Kelly	Turner	Mosses	Leishman	Newman	Jackson	Draper(q)	Lamb	8
Russell/3cp	Dix(d)	Kelly	Turner	Edwards(g)	Leishman	Orugbuh	Jackson	Draper	Lamb/t	9
Russell/3cp(c)	Shaw	Kelly(p)	Turner	Edwards	Leishman	Orugbuh	Draper(v)	Jackson/t	Lamb(k)	10
Russell/2c2p	Dix	Kelly	Turner/2t	Mosses	Leishman	Orugbuh	Parker	Jackson	Draper	11
Russell/cp	Dix	Kelly	Yates(f)	Mosses	Leishman	Orugbuh	Jackson	Draper	Lamb/t	12
Russell/3p	Shaw/t(s)	Edwards	Yates	Mosses/t	Orugbuh	Newman/t	Draper	Parker(m)	Nowak	13
Russell/3cp	Shaw/t	Edwards(e)	Sheddon/t(f)	Mosses	Orugbuh	Newman	Draper	Nowak/t	Lamb	14
Russell/2cpdg	Shaw	Kelly	Sheddon	Mosses	Orugbuh	Newman	Draper	Nowak	Lamb	15
Russell/c4p	Shaw	Edwards(e)	Yates	Mosses	Orugbuh	Newman	Draper	Jackson	Lamb	16
Russell/cp	Shaw	Kelly(j)	Turner(q)	Mosses	Leishman	Orugbuh	Hart	Jackson	Lamb/t	17
Russell/c2p	Shaw	Kelly	Turner	Mosses	Leishman	Orugbuh	Hart	Jackson/t	Lamb	18
Russell/3c(c/c)	Shaw(s)	Strong	Turner(q)	Mosses	Leishman	Orugbuh	Hart(n)	Jackson/3t	Lamb(i)	19
Russell/3c2p(l)	Shaw(x)	Strong/t(e)	Turner(q)	Mosses/t	Leishman	Orugbuh	Hart/t	Price	Jackson(n)	20
Russell/c2p(y/2c	Morley(d)	Kelly/t(j)	Turner	Mosses	Leishman	Newman(h)	Hart(n)	Price/t	Jackson	21
Kenworthy/c2pdg	Shaw	Kelly/t	Turner	Mosses(j)	Leishman	Newman	Jackson	Price	Lamb	22
Russell	Shaw(s)	Kelly	Turner	Edwards	Leishman	Newman	Jackson	Price	Lamb	23
Russell/c8p	Shaw	Kelly(j)	Yates	Mosses	Leishman	Newman(h)	Jackson	Price	Lamb	24
Russell/5c(y/2c)	Morley/t	Edwards(p)	Yates(f)	Mosses	Leishman(h)	Newman	Jackson/t	Price(w)	Lamb/t	25
Russell/c4p	Morley	Edwards(e)	Yates(f)	Mosses	Leishman	Newman(h)	Jackson(w)	Price	Lamb/t	26
Nowak/c3p	Shaw/t	Kelly	Yates	Mosses	Leishman	Newman	Parker/t	Price	Lamb/t	A
Nowak/5cp	Shaw	Strong	Turner	Mosses	Leishman	Newman	Jackson	Parker	Lamb/2t	B
Russellc2p	Shawt	Kelly	Turner	Mosses	Leishman	Newman	Draper	Jackson	Lamb	C
Russell/2c	Shaw	Kelly(j)	Yates/t	Mosses	Orugbuh	Newman	Draper(o)	Jackson/t	Lamb	D

REPLACEMENTS:

	a- P Hopley	b- T Hall	c - B Nowak	d - S Shaw	e - J Kelly
f - R Turner	g - G Mosses	h - A Orugbuh	i - L Price	j - S Edwards	k - S Newman
l - A Furley	m - D Jackson	n - R Parker	o - S Nowak	p - E Strong	q - A Yates
r - P Rendall	s - A Dix	t - M Draper	u - J Payne	v - B Phillips	W - J Hart
x - C Morley	y - M Kenworthy				

Bracknell went through the season unbeaten at home with 13 straight wins.

Went 23 matches unbeaten after losing at Esher late in September.

Carson Russell topped the points scoring list with 216 points which put him third on the division's scoring chart.

Despite winning the title they were only yhe third highest points scorers behind Esher and Barking.

In the try scoring list they were fourth behind the above two and North Walsham

They secured the title on the last day of the season with a 19-3 home win against struggling Cheltenham.

BRACKNELL

LEAGUE STATISTICS
compiled by Stephen McCormack

SEASON	Division	P	W	D	L	F	A	Pts Diff	Lge Pts	Lge Pos	Most Points	Most Tries
89-90	SWSC	10	4	0	6	153	147	6	8	6		
90-91	SWSC	10	4	0	6	97	142	-45	8	8r		
91-92	BDW1	10	9	0	1	222	50	172	19	1p		
92-93	SWSC	12	8	1	3	198	95	103	17	4		
93-94	SWSC	12	10	0	2	294	90	204	20	2		
94-95	SWSC	12	10	0	2	365	80	285	20	2		
95-96	SWSC	12	11	0	1	409	76	333	22	2		
96-97	SWSC	22	22	0	0	868	201	667	44	1p		
97-98	SW1	22	18	2	2	786	271	515	38	1p	293 Carson Russell	20 Alex Poole
98-99	J2S	26	23	1	2	631	317	314	47	1p	216 Carson Russell	8 Howard Lamb & Phil Hopley

BIGGEST MARGINS

Home Win	38pts - 38-0 v Bridgwater 06.02.99
Away Win	54pts -64-12 v Plymouth 03.04.99
Home Defeat	NA -
Away Defeat	21pts - 27-6 v Esher 26.09.98

MOST CONSECUTIVE

Appearances	17 Nick Robinson
Matches scoring Tries	3 John Clarke
Matches scoring points	19 Carson Russell
Victories	19
Defeats	1

MOST POINTS

Scored at Home	39 v Havant 28.12.98
Scored Away	64 v Plymouth 03.04.99
Conceded at Home	14 v Havant 28.12.99
Conceded Away	27 v Esher 26.09.98

MOST TRIES

Scored in a match	10 v Plymouth 03.04.99
Conceded in a match	3 on three occasions

MOST APPEARANCES

by a forward	22 Three players
by a back	23 Carson Russell

	MOST IN A SEASON	MOST IN A CAREER	MOST IN A MATCH
Points	216 Carson Russell 98-99	216 Carson Russell 98-99	26 Carson Russell v N Walsham 27.03.99 (H)
Tries	8 Howard Lamb 98-99 Phil Hopley 98-99	8 Howard Lamb 98-99 Phil Hopley 98-99	3 David Jackson v Bridgwater 06.02.99 (H) Jon Clarke v Plymouth 03.04.99 (A)
Conversions	39 Carson Russell 98-99	39 Carson Russell 98-99	5 Carson Russell v Plymouth 03.04.99 (A)
Penalties	45 Carson Russell 98-99	45 Carson Russell 98-99	8 Carson Russell v N Walsham 27.03.99 (H)
Drop Goals	1 Michael Kenworthy 98-99 Carson Russell 98-99	1 Michael Kenworthy 98-99 Carson Russell 98-99	1 Michael Kenworthy v Esher 27.02.99 (H) Carson Russell v Weston s Mare 02.01.99 (A)

All records relate to National league rugby only.

BRACKNELL PLAYING SQUAD

BACKS

	Ht.	Wt.	Birthdate	Birthplace	CLUB	League Apps	Tries	Pts
Matt Dangerfield	6.0	14.06	09.02.68	Southampton	Bracknell	13	-	-
Phil Hopley	6.2	14.01	06.10.66	London	Bracknell	15(2)	8	40
Tom Hall	5.10	13.06	14.06.69	Reading	Bracknell	8(3)	-	-
Ben Nowak	6.3	15.07	29.11.77	Hillingdon	Bracknell	9(3)	4	63
Jon Clarke	6.0	14.00	06.03.73	Tonbridge	Bracknell	13	7	35
Carson Russell	6.3	14.00	26.10.69	Berkhampstead	Bracknell London Scottish	23	-	216
Simon Shaw	5.9	14.00	21.08.72	High Wycombe	Bracknell High Wycombe	19(3)	2	10
Andy Furley	5.10	14.06	28.03.68	Edinburgh	Bracknell London Scottish	15(4)	2	10
Nick Robinson	6.4	15.00	07.12.68	Manchester	Bracknell London Scottish	19	5	25
Gareth Priest	5.9	14.05	02.04.73	Hillingdon	Bracknell	7	3	15
Guy Spencer Other club: Bournemouth	6.3	14.07	22.06.67	RAF Halton	Bracknell Reading	15	7	35
Jason Payne	5.8	13.10	02.02.71	Christchurch	Bracknell	15(1)	-	-
Colin Morley	5.7	13.08	17.12.73	Slough	Bracknell	3(1)	1	5
Michael Kenworthy	6.0	14.06	30.05.67	Dunedin	Bracknell	2(2)	-	19

FORWARDS

	Ht.	Wt.	Birthdate	Birthplace	CLUB	League Apps	Tries	Pts
Jim Kelly	6.3	18.00	16.02.76	Aldershot	Bracknell London Scottish	19(4)	1	5
Richard Turner	5.11	15.00	26.04.72	Exeter	Bracknell	17(4)	-	-
Glyn Mosses	5.11	18.05	02.01.61	Birmingham	Bracknell	22(1)	2	10
Alan Leishman	6.5	16.00	19.04.75	Reading	Bracknell	22	-	-
Andy Orugboh	6.4	15.07	25.05.69	London	Bracknell	13(5)	-	-
Lyndon Price	6.0	14.07	09.05.66	Bracknell	Bracknell	12(2)	1	5
Howard Lamb	6.3	18.02	13.03.69	Pinner	Bracknell	22	8	40
Simon Edwards	6.0	17.07	13.06.64	Swindon	Bracknell	8(6)	-	-
Simon Newman	6.5	15.08	13.09.65	Chester	Bracknelll	17(2)	1	5
David Jackson	6.2	15.08	24.02.70	Scotland	Bracknell	21(1)	7	35
Richard Parker	6.0	15.00	03.10.71	Birmingham	Bracknell Camberley	5(3)	-	-
Andy Yates	5.9	15.06	09.01.68	Manchester	Bracknell Lymm	6(3)	-	-
Mark Draper	6.2	14.08	26.09.67	Melbourne	Bracknell	9(1)	-	-
Jason Hart	6.0	14.09	15.10.73	Auckland	Bracknell Havant	5(2)	1	5

BRACKNELL

FACT FILE

Founded: 1955

Colours: Green, gold & black hoops/black
Change colours: All black

GROUND

Address: Lily Hill Park, Lily Hill Drive, Bracknell, Berks RG12 2UG
Tel: 01344 424013 Fax: 01344 306234 (Sec.)
Capacity: all uncovered standing

Directions: M4, J10 - A329(M) Bracknell, B3408 Binfield, follow to A329 Bracknell. Through town towards Ascot, turn left at 'Running Horse' PH roundabout, ground at rear.
M£, J3 - A322 Bracknell - A332 Ascot to Heatherwood Hospital roundabout, A329 Bracknell to 'Running Horse' PH (on Right). Ground at rear.
Nearest Railway Station: Bracknell (approx 1.5 miles), frequent service London & Reading

Car Parking: 70 spaces only at ground, but secure off-site parking about 5 mins away.

Admission: Season ticket: £59
Matchday: Adults: £6, OAPs £4 - includes programme

Clubhouse: Lounge bar & Players bar.
Snacks & bar meals available.
Functions: Contact Graham Hughes (Bar Manager) on 01344 424013

Club Shop: Open on match days plus Tues, Wed & Thur evenings 7.30 - 9.30

Training Nights: Tuesday & Thursday (1st XV squad). Lower XVs & Juniors Wednesday

PROGRAMME

Size: A5
Pages: 36
Price: £1, included with admission
Editor: John Denman
Tel: 01344 455400; Fax: 01344 306234
ADVERTISING RATES
Full page £450, Half £250, Qtr £150.
Inside cover £650 Back cover £800
Full colour + 65%. Fly sheet £70/week,
Hoarding £300 per annum

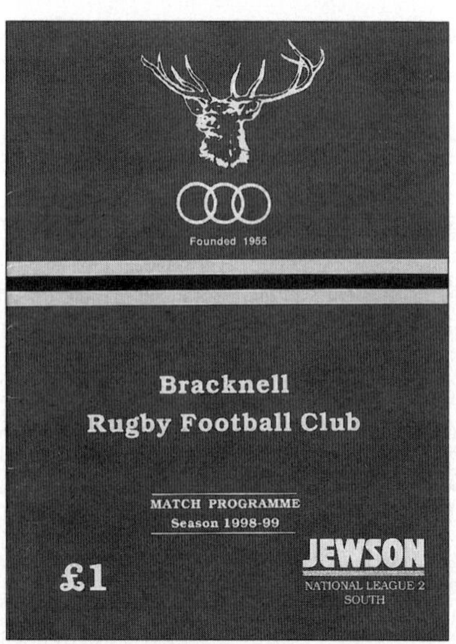

CAMBERLEY R.F.C.

President	Nick Carbury	9 Highgate Lane, Farnborough, Hants. GU14 8AF 01252 548261 (H)
Chairman	Peter Stevens	Wychwood, 17 Pine Avenue, Camberley, Surrey GU15 2LY. 01276 20839 (H) 01276 507335 (Fax).
Secretary	Gwynne Evans	Woodcroft, 4 Paddock Close, Camberley, Surrey. GU15 2BN 01276 65170 (H)
Director of Finance	Roger Chamberlain	'Harington', Kettlewell Hill, Horsell, Woking, Surrey GU21 4JJ 01483 723832 (H)
Director of Rugby	Phil Moyle	33 Sandy Lodge Way, Northwood, Middlesex. HA62AR. 01923 824739 (H).
Fixtures Secretary	Bill Fletcher	01344 777701 (H)

The 1999/99 season was the club's first season in National League One. In many ways it was a season of two halves with a good measure of success before Christmas and some disappointing performances thereafter. Nevertheless, the club achieved its highest league status ever. Having gained promotion, we managed to stay in the higher echelons of English rugby.

Life in Nation League One has not been without its difficulties for both players and administrators alike. On the playing side, performance was hampered by injuries to key players. The absence for sustained periods of Gary Hamer, Gareth Walker and Mark Russell gave captain Guy Gregory and coaches Phil Moyle and Martin Pepper particular problems. A post season review revealed that we had fielded over 50 different players including six different hookers! These factors undoubtedly placed a brake on hopes of a further promotion bid as well as having an unwelcome effect on the Second XV. On the administrative side, the club wrestled with the common problems of smaller gates and lack of income. It has been a steep learning curve but the lessons have been learned and the club looks forward to even better results in the new season. We remain an ambitious outfit always on the look out for quality players.

While the First XV is the flagship of every club, Camberley RFC remains a family club where financial and coaching resources continue to be devoted to the `junior' sides, Colts, Vets, Ladies and a very strong Mini/Junior section, where numerous players have won county honours with Surrey, Hampshire and Berkshire. These sides are the backbone of a club with over 650 members and will remain so.

We look forward to providing a warm welcome both on and off the field to our new found friends in Jewson National One and remain committed under our directory of rugby, Phil Moyle, to playing both entertaining and winning rugby at all levels led by a strong First XV squad.

CAMBERLEY

Match No.	Date	H/A	Comp.	Opponents	Result & Score	Att.	15	14	13	12	11
1	05.09	H	JN1	Wharfedale	W 24-11	350	Robinson/t(k)	Faulkner/t	Thompson	Burns	Slater
2	12.09	A	JN1	Manchester	L 5-72	400	Roinson	Faulkner	Thompson	Burns	Slater/t
3	19.09	H	JN1	Nottingham	W 25-18	450	Slater	Ebongalame(a)	Thompson/t	Burns/2t	Stafford
4	26.09	H	JN1	Newbury	W 23-18	500	Slater	Faulkner/t	Thompson	Burns	Stafford
5	03.10	A	JN1	Henley	L 7-22	600	Slater(s)	Faulkner(n)	Thompson(q)	Burns	Stafford
6	10.10	H	JN1	Morley	W 33-24	400	Malherbe/t(m)	Harbour/t	Thompson	Burns	Stafford/2c2p
7	24.10	A	JN1	Lydney	L 10-26	400	Robinson	Harbour(c/cp)	Thompson/t	Burns	Stafford
8	31.10	H	JN1	Otley	L 18-22	300	Slater	Harbour	Thompson	Burns	Stafford/t
9	07.11	A	JN1	Reading	W 36-28	350	Slater/t	Faulkner/t	Thompson/t	Burns	Allen
10	21.11	H	JN1	Rosslyn Park	L 18-25	400	Malherbe	Faulkner/t	Thompson	Burns	Slater
11	28.11	A	JN1	Birmingham S	L 5-43	100	Robinson(B)	Slater	Thompson	Burns	Stafford
12	05.12	H	JN1	Liverpool StH	W 42-7	250	Malherbe	Green/t	Thompson/t	Burns/2t	Stafford/2t
13	12.12	A	JN1	Harrogate	D 24-24	400	Malherbe	Green	Thompson/t	Burns	Stafford/t
14	19.12	H	JN1	Birmingham S	W 28-14	250	Malherbe	Green	Thompson	Burns	Stafford/t
15	28.12	A	JN1	Rosslyn Park	L 6-15	750	Slater	Green	Thompson	Burns	Stafford
16	02.01	H	JN1	Reading	W 26-18	300	Robinson	Green/2t	Thompson	Burns	Stafford
17	16.01	A	JN1	Otley*	L 18-22	400	Robinson	Green	Thompson/t	Burns	Stafford
18	23.01	H	JN1	Lydney	W 6-5	400	Robinson	Green	Thompson	Burns	Stafford
19	30.01	A	JN1	Morley	L 22-39	400	Slater/c	Green/t	Thompson	Burns	Stafford(a)
20	06.02	H	JN1	Henley	L 19-31	400	Robinson	Green	Thompson	Burns	Stafford
21	13.02	A	JN1	Newbury	L 5-41	300	Robinson	Green	Slater	Burns/t	Stafford
22	27.02	A	JN1	Nottingham	L 21-40	400	Gregory/2cp	Stafford	Thompson	Burns	Green/t
23	13.03	H	JN1	Manchester	L 22-28	300	Robinson	Green	Thompson	Burns	Stafford/tc5p
24	27.03	A	JN1	Wharfedale	L 16-27	450	Robinson	Green/t	Thompson	Burns	Stafford/c3p
25	03.04	H	JN1	Harrogate	L 14-24	300	Slater	Green/t	Thompson(a)	Burns	Stafford
26	17.04	A	JN1	Liverpool St H	W 50-17	150	Slater/2t(a)	Green	Thompson/t	Burns	Stafford/2t
A	17.10	A	JN1	Lydney	L 34-44	600	Robinson	Harbour	Thompson/t	Burns	Slater/2c5p

* after opponents name indicates a penalty try
Brackets after a player's name indicates he was replaced. eg (a) means he was replaced by replacement code "a" and so on.
/ after a player or replacement name is followed by any scores he made - eg /t, /c, /p, /dg or any combination of these

1998-99 HIGHLIGHTS

League debuts: Gavin Thompson, Sean Burns, Simon Slater, Nick Briers, Simon Orr, Phil Pye, James Winterbottom, Phil Joyce, Ross Evans, Huw Owen, Mark Russell, Duncan Hughes, Guillame Coetzee, Sam Gumbie, Gary Waters, Connie Malherbe, Tom Harbour, Liam Moore, Michael Hills, Alastair Allen, Matt Norman, Barry Green, Luke Welbelove, Domonic Little, Adrian Flavin, James McLleland, Jonathan Brookes

Ever Presents: Sean Burns and James Winterbottom

Players used: 44 plus 2 as a replacement only

Most Points in a season:

Pts	Player	T	C	P	DG
221	G Gregory	2	29	50	1
78	B Stafford	8	4	10	-
35	B Green	7	-	-	-
35	G Thompson	7	-	-	-

Guy Gregory tops the points scoring list for a second successive season.

MATCH FACTS

10	9	1	2	3	4	5	6	7	8	
Gregory/c4p	Briers	Orr(i)	Pye	Walker	Winterbottom	Hamer	Hughes	Scott(j)	Eke	1
Gregory	Briers	Orr	Pye	Walker	Winterbottom	Hamer	Evans	Scott	Eke(j)	2
Gregory/2c2p	Briers	Owen(i)	Pye(l)	Walker	Winterbottom	Hamer	Scott	Pepper	Russell(g)	3
Gregory/6p	Briers	Owen	Pye(l)	Walker	Winterbottom(s)	Gumbie	Kesley(h)	Pepper	Eke	4
Gregory/c	Briers	Owen(f)	Davies(i)	Walker	Winterbottom	Hamer	Scott(t)	Pepper	Eke/t	5
Slater/dg	Briers	Owen(e)	Pye(o)	Walker/t	Winterbottom	Butler	Kesley	Pepper/t(h)	Eke(t)	6
Slater	Briers(w)	Orr(H)	Pye(l)	Walker	Winterbottom	Butler	Kesley(g)	Scott(j)	Milne	7
Gregory/c2p	Briers	Orr	Davies/t	Walker(i)	Winterbottom	Butler	Milne(g)	Scott	Eke	8
Gregory3c4pdg	Moore	Walker	Davies(f)	Joyce(e)	Winterbottom	Butler	Smith	Hills(h)	Eke	9
Gregory/tc2p	Moore	Owen	Davies	Joyce(e)	Winterbottom	Butler(z)	Smith(j)	Hills	Eke	10
Gregory	Moore(m)	Fowers(i)	Davies/t(o)	Orr	Winterbottom(z)	Norman	Smith	Hills(j)	Eke	11
Gregory/3c2p	Moore(m)	Owen(e)	Coetzee(D)	Fowers	Winterbottom	Norman	Smith(y)	Pepper	Eke(C)	12
Gregory/t3cp	Moore	Owen	Pye	Fowers	Winterbottom	Butler	Smith(h)	Pepper	Eke	13
Gregory/c7p	Moore	Owen	Pye	Litle	Winterbottom	Butler	Scott	Pepper	Eke	14
Gregory/2p	Hughes(w)	Owen	Pye(E)	Little	Winterbottom	Butler	Scott	Pepper	Eke(t)	15
Gregory/c3p	Hughes	Owen	Flavin(f)	Litle	Winterbottom	Butler	Scott	Pepper	Smith/t	16
Gregory/c2p	Hughes	Owen	Flavin	Little	Winterbottom	Butler	Scott	Pepper	Smith	17
Gregory/2p	Hughes(d)	Owen	Flavin	Little(i)	Winterbottom	Butler	Scott(g)	Pepper	Smith	18
Gregory/cp(m/t)	Briers	Owen	Flavin	Little	Winterbottom/t	Butler(v)	Hughes	Welbelove(G)	Smith	19
Gregory/c4p	Briers	Owen/t	Flavin	Little(l)	Winterbottom	Butler	Smith	Pepper	Welbelove(K)	20
Gregory	Briers	Owen	Flavin	Little	Winterbottom	Butler	Smith	Pepper	Russell	21
Slater	Briers(w)	Owen/3t	McLelland	Waters(A)	Winterbottom	Butler(v)	Smith(g)	Pepper	Russell	22
Slater	Moore	Owen(A)	McLelland	Little	Winterbottom	Brookes(p)	Hughes	Pepper	Russell(v)	23
Slater(c)	Moore(d)	Fowers	McLelland	Joyce	Winterbottom	Brookes	Hughes	Pepper	Russell	24
Gregory/3p	Moore(d)	Joyce	McLelland(f)	Fowers(H)	Winterbottom	Brookes	Hughes	Pepper(v)	Russell	25
Gregory/6cp	Briers(w)	Owen(F)	McLelland(f)	Fowers	Winterbottom(p)	Brookes	Hughes/t(G)	Milne	Russell/t	26
Slater(c)	Briers	Owen	Pye(J)	Walker	Winterbottom	Butler	Smith(v)	Scott	Norman	A

REPLACEMENTS: a- T Robinson, b- S Slater, c - G Gregory, d - N Briers, e - S Orr, f - P Pye, g - B Hughes, h - D Scott, i - P Joyce, j - M Pepper, k - B Stafford, l - S Davies, m - D Hughes, n - J Wilkinson, o - G Coetzee, p - S Gumbie, q - R Kesley, r - G Waters, s - C Malherbie, t - C Smith, u - B Butler, v - W Milne, w - L Moore, y - M Hills, z - M Norman, A - J Fowers, B - B Green, C - L Welbelove, D- D Little, E - A Flavin, F - D Manthorpe, G - R Evans, H - H Owen, K - M Russell

His total of 221 is a new record for points in a season which he himself held at 144 from last season.
He set a new record for penalties in a season easily beating the 30 he kicked last season with 50 this time round.
He also sets a new career points record for league matches with 365 - beating the 150 set by Greg Way and Jason Hoad.
In the home win against Newbury early in the season Gregory equalled the club record of six penalties in a match but later in the season he actully beat the record - he kicked seven in the 28-14 win over Birmingham & Solihull.
In their first away match of the season, at Manchester, they suffered their worst ever defeat in terms of both points against and point difference when they were beaten 72-5.
They also conceded 10 tries for the first time erasing the nine they conceded at Newbury in April 97.

Winger Ben Stafford sets a new record for most appearances by a back, he plays 22 times to take his career total to 48, two more than Craig Grevelle's old record.

CAMBERLEY

LEAGUE STATISTICS
compiled by Stephen McCormack

SEASON	Division	P	W	D	L	F	A	Pts Diff	Lge Pts	Lge Pos		Coach		Captain
89-90	Lon2S	10	9	0	1	180	75	105	18	2		T Hart		C Gibson
90-91	Lon2S	10	5	1	4	148	109	39	11	5		T Hart		C Gibson
91-92	Lon2S	10	7	0	3	184	102	82	4	5		P Moyle		S Johnson
92-93	Lon2S	12	10	2	0	241	94	147	72	1p		P Moyle		
93-94	Lon1	12	9	0	3	242	137	105	18	3		P Moyle		
94-95	Lon1	12	12	0	0	375	122	253	24	1p		P Moyle		
												Most Points		**Most Tries**
95-96	D5S	12	5	1	6	151	212	-61	11	7	41	Dave Whitfield	3	D Adamson
96-97	D4S	26	15	2	9	688	515	173	32	4	138	Jason Hoad	13	Craig Grevelle
97-98	N2S	26	23	1	2	803	372	431	47	1p	144	Guy Gregory	14	Craig Grevelle
98-99	JN1	26	10	1	15	529	661	-132	21	9	206	Guy Gregory	7	Bruno Green

BIGGEST MARGINS

Home Win	84pts - 92-8 v Charlton Park 16.11.96
Away Win	45pts - 50-5 v Met. Police 20.12.97
Home Defeat	35pts - 12-47 v Henley 30.3.96
Away Defeat	62pts - 10-72 v Manchester 12.09.98

MOST POINTS

Scored at Home	95 v Askeans 16.11.97
Scored Away	56 v Bridgwater 27.9.97
Conceded at Home	47 v Henley 30.3.96
Conceded Away	72 v Manchester 12.09.98

MOST CONSECUTIVE

Appearances	
Matches scoring Tries	
Matches scoring points	
Victories	13
Defeats	4

MOST TRIES

Scored in a match	15 v Askeans 16.11.96
Conceded in a match	10 v Manchester

MOST APPEARANCES

by a forward	60(1) Gary Hamer
by a back	46(10 Craig Grevelle

	MOST IN A SEASON	MOST IN A CAREER	MOST IN A MATCH
Points	206 Guy Gregory 98-99	350 Guy Gregory 97-99	30 Jason Head v Askeans 16.11.96
Tries	14 Craig Grevelle 97-98	27 Craig Grevelle 96-98	4 Rory Jones v Askeans 16.11.96
Conversions	36 Jason Head 96-97	50 Guy Gregory 97-99	11 Jason Head v Charlton Park 15.3.97 (H)
Penalties	49 Guy Gregory 98-99	79 Gug Gregory 97-99	7 Guy Gregory v Birmingham & Sol (H)
Drop Goals	4 Jason Head 96-97	4 Jason Head 95-97	2 Jason Head v North Walsham 19.10.96

CAMBERLEY PLAYING SQUAD

BACKS	Ht.	Wt.	Birthdate	Birthplace	CLUB	League Apps	Tries	Pts
Guy Gregory					Camberley	33(2)	4	365
Tim Robinson					Camberley	16(4)	1	5
James Faulkner					Camberley	11	10	50
Simon Slater					Camberley	19(1)	3	25
Gavin Thompson					Camberley	25	7	35
John Wilkinson					Camberley	4(6)	-	-
Muna Ebongalame					Camberley	20	6	30
Sean Burns					Camberley	26	5	25
Ben Stafford					Camberley	48(1)	15	113
Duncan Hughes					Camberley	4(4)	1	5
Nick Briers					Camberley	13(3)	-	-
Bruno Green					Camberley	15(1)	7	35
Liam Moore					Camberley	9(4)	-	-

FORWARDS	Ht.	Wt.	Birthdate	Birthplace	CLUB	League Apps	Tries	Pts
Ben Butler					Camberley	15(1)	-	-
Stuart Davies					Camberley	23(11)	3	15
Gareth Walker					Camberley	33(4)	1	5
Gary Hamer					Camberley	53(1)	3	15
Dave Scott					Camberley	51(5)	13	65
Chris Eke					Camberley	32(3)	12	60
Martin Pepper					Camberley	36(7)	6	30
Jim Fowers					Camberley	20(2)	-	-
James Winterbottom					Camberley	26	1	5
Russell Kesley					Camberley	21(3)	5	25
Warren Milne					Camberley	11(12)	-	-
Chris Wood					Camberley	9(5)	-	-
Chris Smith					Camberley	23(8)	5	25
Huw Owen					Camberley	18(2)	4	20
Domonic Little					Camberley	9(1)	-	-

CAMBERLEY

FACT FILE

Founded: 1931

Colours: Black with amber collar.
Change colours: Yellow with black collar.

GROUND

Address: Watchetts Recreation Ground, Park Rd, Camberley, Surrey GU15 2SR
Tel: 01276 25395 Fax: 01276 25211
Capacity: 1,000 Seated: None Standing: 1000 (uncovered)

Directions: M3 Jnc 4, follow signs for Frimley/Guildford. At 1st roundabout turn left, signed Camberley, one & a half miles to mini roundabout turn right into Park Rd.
Nearest Railway Station: Camberley

Car Parking: 500 nearby

Admission: Matchday £6 with programme

Club Shop: Open matchdays 12 noon - 5pm.
Contact Alex Boyden 01276 26200

Clubhouse: Mon - Fri 6-11, Sat. 11-11, Sun. 11-7.
Snacks available.
Functions up to 90. Contact Lydia Rise 01276 25395.

Training Nights: Tuesday & Thursday

PROGRAMME Size: A5 Pages: 24 + cover
Price: Included with admission
Editor: Peter Stevens 01276 20839

ADVERTISING RATES	Colour
Page	£500
1/2 Page	£300
1/4 Page	£150

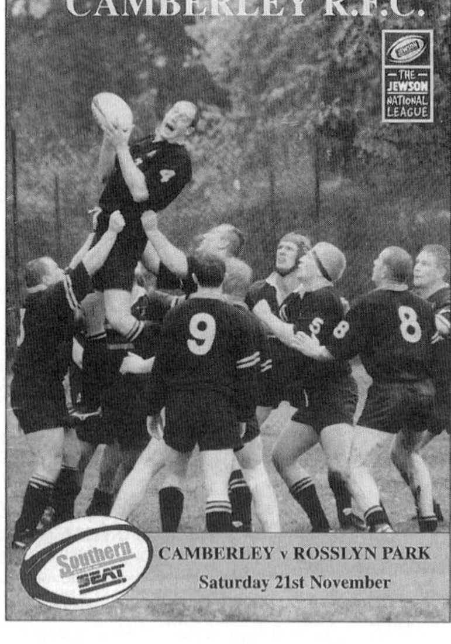

FYLDE R.U.F.C.

President	Peter Makin	Links Grange, Greenways, St. Annes, Lancs. FY8 3LY 01253 722713 (H) 01772 259625 (B) 01772 259628 (Fax)
Chairman	Arnie Halford	6 St Hildas Road, St. Annes, Lancs. FY8 2PT 01253 713765 (H) 01253 739137 (Fax)
Club Secretary	David Walsh	33 Kingsway, Lytham 01253 738452 (H) 01253 739137 (B) 01253 739137 (Fax)
Coach	Mark Nelson	c/o Fylde Rugby Club 0411 225693 (Mobile) 01253 734733 (B) 01253 739137 (Fax)
Chairman of Rugby	Tony Todd	c/o Fylde Rugby Club Tel/Fax: 01253 739137
Asst. Coach	Graham Smith	c/o Fylde Rugby Club Tel: as above (H) 01254 720270
	Mike Dixon	c/o Fylde Rugby Club Tel: as above
Press Officer	Stewart Brown	179 Hardhorn Road, Poulton-le-Fylde, Lancs. FY6 8ES 01253 883100 (H) 01253 739137 (Fax)

There can be no hiding our bitter disappointment at losing the last few games of the season and the resulting relegation.

Many people remarked, during the latter part of the season, how nice it would have been to have started the campaign with the present squad.

That was not to be. However, throughout the campaign, through thick and thin, players and coaches have stuck together despite injury lists, cost cutting exercises etc. No back biting, no bitterness, no recriminations. An attitude of being this together we should be proud of.

At the end of the season there were games there for the taking and we failed to take them and in the end relegation was avoidable but we did not take our chances. As the season went on the make up of the squad changed and by the time we found our best side it was too late. Sometimes losing becomes a habit and perhaps that was the case when we lost games we could have won. We did even get a run in the Tetley Bitter Cup losing away to Moseley at the first hurdle.

At this point we need to take a long hard look at the game and its future at Fylde. The game itself is in chaos, a financial minefield. It cannot continue. Look at all those great clubs going to the wall. Levels of payments need to be considered very carefully and realistically.

This season we are back in Jewson National One where we were two years previously and the club will be looking to re group and look to move forward again but this time with some prudent financial planning.

Sally Eaves (physio), Mark Nelson (coach), Dave Butcher, Nick Smith, Dave Whitehead, James Reid, Campbell Rae, Jonathon Taylor, Geoff Wappett, Gavin Moffatt, Ray Willoughby (youth coach), Graham Smith (asst. coach). Middle: Steve Rigby, Mark Croston, Julien Irving, Carl Lavin, Ian Barclay, Mark Evans, Dave Tanner, Dave Topping, Alun Peacock, Martin Scott. Front: Damian Lavin, Lee Seddon, Brendan Hanavan, Jonathon Webster, Matt Wilkes, Graeme Tasker, Greg Anderton. Photo courtesy of the West Lancashire Evening Gazette

Match No.	Date	H/A	Comp.	Opponents	Result & Score	Att.	15	14	13	12	11
1	05.09	H	AD2	Orrell	L 6-20	650	Evans	Irving	Peacock/2p	Tanner	Anderton
2	12.09	A	AD2	Bristol	L 14-55	4,527	Evans	Preston/t	McKeown	Tanner/c(o)	Anderton
3	26.09	A	AD2	Coventry	L 9-64	1,200	Evans	Preston	Peacock(n)	Tanner/3p	Anderton(a)
4	03.10	H	AD2	Wakefield	W 20-18	500	Evans	Preston	Leuila	Irving	Anderton
5	10.10	A	AD2	Moseley	L 22-44	786	Evans	Preston	Leuila	Tanner/t2cp	Irving(D)
6	17.10	H	AD2	Worcester	L 8-17	650	Evans	Anderton/t	Leuila	Irving	Preston
7	24.10	A	AD2	Waterloo	L 6-27	500	Evans	Anderton	Leuila	Irving(b)	Preston
8	31.10	H	AD2	Exeter	D 26-26	400	Evans/t	Anderton	Peacock/2c4p	Leuila	Preston/t
9	07.11	H	AD2	Leeds Tykes	L 6-26	650	Evans	Preston	Peacock/2p	Tanner(u)	Anderton
10	21.11	A	AD2	Rugby Lions	L 16-30	650	Evans	Leuila	Peacock/c2p	Tetlow/dg	Preston(a)
11	12.12	A	AD2	London Welsh	L 15-36		Evans	Irving(A)	Tetlow	Tanner/cp	Preston
12	19.12	A	AD2	Blackheath	L 17-24	500	Evans	Booth/t	Tetlow/t(s)	Peacock/2cp(b)	Preston
13	02.01	H	AD2	Rugby Lions	L 6-14	800	Evans(A)	Booth	Tetlow	Peacock/2p	Preston
14	17.01	A	AD2	Leeds Tykes	L 0-48	921	Peacock	Preston(E)	Tetlow	Tanner(v)	Booth
15	23.01	A	AD2	Exeter	L 10-42	700	Peacock/cp	Tanner	Tetlow	Connell	Preston
16	06.02	H	AD2	Waterloo	W 24-5	450	Peacock/2c	Evans/t	Tetlow	Tanner	Anderton/t(w)
17	13.02	A	AD2	Worcester	L 0-56	2,316	Peacock	Evans	Tetlow(v)	Tanner	Anderton
18	20.02	H	AD2	Rotherham	L 5-34	600	Evans	Tanner	Peacock(G)	Connell	Anderton
19	27.02	H	AD2	Moseley	W 17-8	500	Peacock/c	Loxton	Tetlow	Tanner	Evans/t
20	13.03	A	AD2	Wakefield	L 11-27	800	Loxton	Evans/t	Peacock/2p	Tetlow(b)	Anderton
21	27.03	H	AD2	Coventry	W 27-22	350	Evans(C)	Loxton/2cp	Barclay	Tetlow	Anderton/t
22	03.04	A	AD2	Rotherham	L 16-43		Evans(v)	Loxton/c3p	Tetlow(C)	Tanner	Anderton
23	17.04	H	AD2	Bristol	L 39-43	700	Peacock	Loxton/t4c2p	Barclay	Tetlow/t	Evans/2t
24	24.04	A	AD2	Orrell	L 18-28	600	Peacock(c)	Loxton/c2p	Barclay	Tetlow/t	Evans
25	01.05	H	AD2	Blackheath	L 26-27	300	Evans	Loxton/3c	Barclay	Tetlow(b)	Anderton/2t
26	08.05	H	AD2	London Welsh	L 11-21	500	Evans	Loxton/2p	Peacock	Tanner(u)	Anderton
A	15.11	A	TBC	Moseley	L 15-22	491	Evans	Leuila(a)	Peacock/cp	Tetlow	Preston/2t

* after opponents name indicates a penalty try
Brackets after a player's name indicates he was replaced. eg (a) means he was replaced by replacement code "a" and so on.
/ after a player or replacement name is followed by any scores he made - eg /t, /c, /p, /dg or any combination of these

1998-99 HIGHLIGHTS

League debuts: Geoff Wappett, Nick Smith, A McKeown, John Clarke, Dave Whitehead, Ali Leuila, Matt Tetlow, Morie Loxton, Dan Smaje, Dylan O'Grady, Sam Clarke, R Wareing, N Booth, Alan Hodkinson, Tim Barlow.

Ever Presents: None - most appearances 24 Mark Evans.

Players used: 36 plus 9 as a replcement only.

Most Points in a season:

Pts	Player	T	C	P	DG
72	A Peacock	-	9	18	-
57	M Loxton	1	11	10	-
30	M Evans	6	-	-	-
30	C Lavin	6	-	-	-
28	D Tanner	1	4	5	-

MATCH FACTS

10	9	1	2	3	4	5	6	7	8	
Barclay	Topping	Butcher(m)	Scott(k)	Webster	Rae	O'Neill	Tasker(l)	Lavin	Wappett	1
Barclay/c	Topping	Smith	J Clarke	Webster	O'Neill	Taylor	Rae	Ireland	Wappett/t(i)	2
Barclay	Topping	Butcher	J Clarke	Smith(q)	Taylor	O'Neill	Rae	Ireland(i)	Wappett(r)	3
Barclay/tcp	O'Toole	Butcher	J Clarke(e)	Smith(t)	Taylor	Whitehead	Rae/t	Lavin	Wappett/t	4
Barclay/t	O'Toole	Butcher(t)	J Clarke	Smith	Taylor(h)	Whitehead/t(l)	Rae	Lavin	Wappett/t(B)	5
Barclay	Smaje/p	Butcher	J Clarke	Smith	Whitehead	Taylor	Rae	Ireland	Wappett	6
Peacock/2p	Smaje(s)	Butcher	J Clarke	Smith	Whitehead(i)	O'Neill	Rae	Ireland	Wappett	7
Barclay	Smaje	Butcher	J Clarke	Webster(t)	Whitehead	Taylor	Rae	Ireland	Wappett(i)	8
Barclay	Smaje(s)	Butcher(t)	J Clarke(e)	Webster	Whitehead	Tayor	Rae	Ireland(y)	Wappett	9
Barclay/t	O'Toole(w)	S Clarke	J Clarke	Wareing	Whitehead	Taylor	Ireland	O'Grady	Rae	10
Barclay	Smaje/t(s)	S Clarke(t)	J Clarke(B)	Webster	Whitehead	Taylor	Ireland(j)(e)	Lavin/t	Rae	11
Barclay	Smaje	Butcher(t)	J Clarke	Webster	Whitehead	Taylor	Ireland(e)	Lavin	Rae(j)	12
Barclay	Smaje(s)	Webster	J Clarke	Rigby	Whitehead	Taylor	Ireland	Lavin	Wappett(g)	13
Barclay	O'Toole	Butcher	J Clarke(e)	S Clarke(t)	Whitehead	Taylor(h)	Ireland(j)	Lavin	Rae	14
Barclay	O'Toole/t(F)	Butcher(B)	J Clarke(e)	Webster(z)	Whitehead(j)	Taylor	Ireland	Lavin(x)	Rae	15
Barclay	O'Toole	Filipo(d)	Scott/t	Rigby/t	Whitehead	Taylor	Ireland	Lavin	Rae	16
Loxton	Smaje(s)	Filipo(f)	Scott	Rigby(d)	Whitehead	Rae	Stowe(h)	Lavin	Wappett	17
Barclay	O'Toole	Filipo	Scott(z)	Rigby(f)	Whitehead	Taylor(i)	Ireland(x)	Lavin(g)	O'Grady/t	18
Barclay	O'Toole	Filipo	Scott	Rigby	Whitehead	Taylor/t	Ireland(g)	Lavin/t	O'Grady	19
Barclay	O'Toole(w)	Filipo(d)	Scott	Rigby(f)	Whitehead	Taylor	Ireland	Lavin	O'Grady	20
Barlow	O'Toole	Filipo	Scott	Rigby	Whitehead	Taylor	Ireland/t(i)	Lavin/2t(x)	Rae	21
Barlow	O'Toole/t	Filipo	S Clarke(F)	Rigby(f)	Whitehead	Taylor	Ireland	Lavin	Rae(i)	22
Barlow	O'Toole	Filipo	Scott	Rigby(f)	Whitehead	Taylor	Ireland/t(x)	Lavin	Rae	23
Barlow	O'Toole	Filipo	Scott	Rigby(f)	Whitehead	Taylor	Ireland	Lavin/t	Rae	24
Barlow/t	O'Toole(w)	Filipo	Scott	Rigby(f)	Whitehead	Taylor	Ireland	Lavin/t	Rae	25
Barlow(v)	O'Toole	Filipo	Scott	Rigby(f)	Whitehead	Taylor	Ireland	Lavin	Rae/t	26
Barclay	Smaje(s)	Butcher(m)	J Clark(e)	Webster	Taylor(h)	Rae	Ireland	O'Grady	Wappett(B)	A

REPLACEMENTS:

a- J Irving	b- D Tanner	c - G Anderton	d - d Butcher	e - M Scott	
f - J Webster	g - C Rae	h - P O'Neill	i - G Tasker	j - G Wappett	k - S Williams
l - A Ireland	m - N Smith	n - A mcKeown	o - B Hanavan	p - J Clarke	q - M Wilkes
r - D Whitehead	s- C O'Toole	t - S Rigby	u - M Tetlow	v - S Connell	w - D Smaje
x - R Stowe	y - D O'Grady	z - S Clarke	A - R Woodfine	B - M Smithmeyer	C - N Booth
D - G Moffatt	E - I Tyson	F - C McIntyre	G - A Hodkinson		

Alun Peacock tops the Fylde points list with the lowest top for six years. During the season he topped 100 career points for the club he joined from Orrell a couple of seasons ago.

During a disappointing season they suffered a club record seven successive league defeats, 1 more than their previous worst run.

With 138, Ian Barclay moved past Steve Gough as the club's leadiing back in terms of league appearances. Barclay played 22 matches to move onto 138, 20 more than Gough's old record.

The 56-0 defeat at Worcester was their worst ever away defeat in terms of biggest defeat, 56 points, beating the 54 point loss at West Hartlepool last season.

The try scoring list was jointly topped by full back Mark Evans and Back row forward Craig Lavin with six.

FYLDE

LEAGUE STATISTICS
compiled by Stephen McCormack

SEASON	Division	P	W	D	L	F	A	Pts Diff	Lge Pts	Lge Pos		Most Points		Most Tries
89-90	3	11	5	0	6	169	222	-53	10	8	91	Steve Burnage	7	Brendan Hanavan
90-91	3	12	7	2	3	183	115	68	16	3	62	Mike Jackson	5	Brendan Hanavan
91-92	3	12	9	1	2	198	109	89	19	2p	106	Mike Jackson	4	Anthony Ireland
92-93	2	12	0	3	9	108	290	-182	0	12r	40	Mike Jackson	2	Steve Gough & John Nicholson
93-94	3	18	13	0	5	339	219	120	26	2p	109	Andy Parker	12	Brendan Hanavan
94-95	2	18	8	0	10	250	329	-79	16	9r	91	Andy Parker	5	Brendan Hanavan, Steve Gough & Greg Anderton
95-96	3	18	3	1	14	283	448	-165	7	10	138	Steve Gough	5	Greg Anderton
96-97	3	30	24	1	5	813	439	374	49	2p	404	Steve Gough	20	Mark Preston
97-98	P2	22	2	0	20	258	710	-452	4	12	98	Steve Gough	6	Mark Preston
98-99	P2	26	4	1	21	375	805	-430	9	14r	72	Alun Peacock	6	Mark Evans Carl Lavin

BIGGEST MARGINS

Home Win	61pts - 68-7 v Birmingham 7.11.87
Away Win	47pts - 60-13 v Havant 15.2.97
Home Defeat	60pts - 7-67 v Bedford 27.12.97
Away Defeat	56pts - 0-56 v Worcester 13.2.99

MOST CONSECUTIVE

Appearances	41 Andy Parker 12.3.94 to date
Matches scoring Tries	4 Greg Anderton
Matches scoring points	20 Steve Burnage
Victories	9
Defeats	7

MOST POINTS

Scored at Home	68 v Birmingham 7.11.87
Scored Away	60 v Havant 15.2.97
Conceded at Home	67 v Bedford 27.12.97
Conceded Away	66 v West Hartlepool 14.2.98

MOST TRIES

Scored in a match	10 v Birmingham 7.11.87 (H) v Redruth 9.4.94 (H)
Conceded in a match	10 v West Hartlepool 14.2.98

MOST APPEARANCES

by a forward	132 (9) John Taylor
by a back	138 Ian Barclay

	MOST IN A SEASON	MOST IN A CAREER	MOST IN A MATCH	
Points	404 Steve Gough 96-97	739 Steve Gough 92-98	28 Steve Burnage	v Birmingham 7.11.87 (H)
Tries	20 Mark Preston 96-97	41 Brendan Hanavan 87-96	4 Brendan Hanavan	v Exeter 3.10.87 (H) v Birmingham 7.11.87 (H) v Redruth 9.4.94 (H)
Conversions	57 Steve Gough 96-97	85 Steve Gough 92-98	9 Steve Burnage	v Birmingham 7.11.87 (H)
Penalties	82 Steve Gough 96-97	143 Steve Gough 92-98	6 Steve Gough	v Walsall 21.9.96 (H) v Morley 25.1.97 (A)
Drop Goals	5 Ian Barclay 94-95	7 Ian Barclay 87-95	2 Ian Barclay	v Waterloo 25.3.95 (A)

FYLDE PLAYING SQUAD

BACKS

BACKS	Ht.	Wt.	Birthdate	Birthplace	CLUB	League Apps	Tries	Pts
Nick Booth	5.10	13.2	28.10.76		Fylde	3(2)	-	-
Mark Preston England u21, B.	5.10	12.7	03.04.67	Lytham	Fylde	68	36	172
Ian Barclay Lancashire	5.11	14.0	29.07.69	Lytham	Fylde	138(4)	20	164
Dave Tanner Lancashire	6.1	15.7	29.09.65	Keighley	Fylde	41(8)	4	52
Stuart Connell Cumbria	5.11	14.0	17.04.67	Bolton	Fylde	54(6)	2	8
Julian Irving	6.0	14.3	13.02.71	Oldham	Fylde	23(5)	3	15
Mark Evans	5.11	13.0	21.02.75	Leeds	Fylde	47(4)	10	50
Gavin Moffatt	6.3	15.7	09.09.72	Lancaster	Fylde	15(6)	3	15
Alan Peacock England U21. Other club: Morley.			16.01.74	Billinge	Fylde Orrell	33(1) 8(2)	- -	137 10
Alan McKeown	6.0	14.2	06.05.75		Fylde Edinburgh Ac	1(1)	-	-
Chris O'Toole Lancashire.	5.10	14.10	08.02.66	St Helens	Fylde	96(8)	16	83
Greg Anderton Lancashire, North.	5.11	16.05	26.02.75		Fylde			

FORWARDS

FORWARDS	Ht.	Wt.	Birthdate	Birthplace	CLUB	League Apps	Tries	Pts
Craig Burns Lancashire.	6.0	15.0	01.08.64	Blackburn	Fylde	97(5)	4	19
Martin Scott Scotland 1, A, u21.	6.0	15.10	05.07.67	Falkirk	Fylde Orrell	33(6) 28	3 1	15 5
Matt Filipo			28.10.71	Otahuhu	Fylde	28(1)	-	-
Sam Clark England U-21, students.	5.11	15.11	05.06.77		Fylde	4(2)	-	-
Dave Whitehead					Fylde	23(1)	1	5
PaulSmith	6.1	17.5	28.03.69		Fylde Sale	-	-	-
Gareth Russell Lancashire.	5.11	15.0	30.07.72	Rochdale	Fylde	99	10	50
Paddy O'Neill	6.7	17.9	29.02.68	Chesterfield	Fylde Orrell	56(4) 6	- -	- -
Alastair Bell Cumbria.	6.3	16.7	15.04.74	Carlisle	Fylde	45(8)	4	20
Steve Rigby	5.10	17.6	05.06.59	Lytham	Fylde	49(10)	-	-
Anthony Ireland	6.0	15.0	05.03.66	Lancaster	Fylde	49(2)	6	26
John Taylor Lancashire	6.5	16.8	05.10.66	S Point (Aden)	Fylde	133(5)	8	40

FYLDE

FACT FILE

Founded: 1919

Colours: Claret, gold and white/white/claret
Change colours: Maroon

GROUND

Address: Woodlands Memorial Ground, Blackpool Road, Ansdell, Lytham St. Annes. FY8 4EL
Tel: 01253 734733
Capacity: 5,440 Seated: 440 Standing: 5,000

Directions: From the end of the M55 follow signs for Lytham St. Annes -B5230 then B5261 onto Queensway - ground is three miles on the left opposite Blossoms P.H. and R.C. Church.
Nearest Railway Station: Ansdell & Fairhaven. Left outside station, down the hill away from the sea, along Woodlands Rd to T junction (R.C. Church & Blossoms PH) - ground is opposite to the right.

Car Parking: 150 spaces available F.O.C. at the ground.

Admission: (Standing only)
Matchdays Non members £8, OAPs £4;
Members £6, OAPs £5.
Season tickets Members only £60 OAPs £35.

Club Shop: Open matchdays 1-6pm & Sundays 10-Noon.
Contact D Walsh 01253729253.

Clubhouse: Open matchdays Noon-11, Sun Noon-3,
Tue,Thur, Fri 7.30-11pm. 3 bars.
Snacks and bar meals available.
Functions: Approx 400
Contact D Walsh 01253 729253.

Training Nights: Tuesday and Thursday.

PROGRAMME
Size: B5 Pages: 40 Price: Free
Editor: Malcolm Jones, Commercial Manager 01253 739731
ADVERTISING RATES
Full page: Colour £650 Two Tone £450
1/2 page Colour £350 Two Tone £250
1/4 page: Two Tone £150
Back page (teams): Colour £650

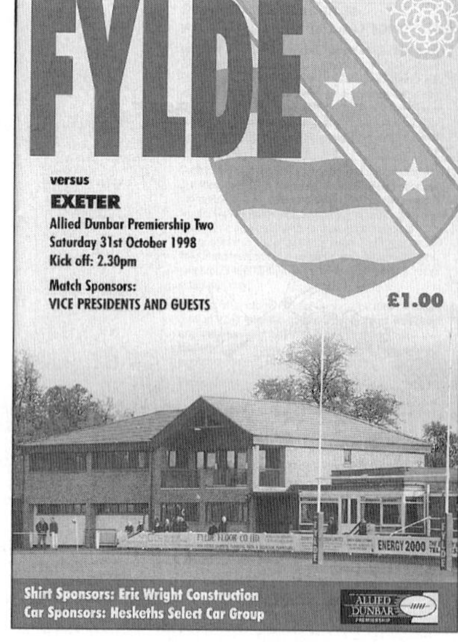

HARROGATE R.U.F.C.

President	Rodney Spragg	Pear Tree Cottage, Nidd, Harrogate, HG3 3BJ 01423 770126 (H), 01423 562634 (B), 01423 562776 (Fax)
Chairman	Alun Jones	3 Blenheim Court, Harrogate HG2 9DT 01423 565830 (H),01423 565830 (Fax)
Club Secretary	Roy Guy	4 Southway, Harrogate HG2 0EA 01423 503054 (H), 01423503054 (Fax).
Treasurer	Nic Davies	3 Hereford Road, Harrogate, N. Yorks. HG1 2NP 01423 522066 (H) 01423 863302 (B) 01423 867665 (F)
Fixtures Secretary	Graham Boyd	24 Melltonns Green, Pickhill, Thirsk, N. Yorks YO7 01845 567504 (H) 01765 603350 (B) 01765 603356 (F)
Administrator	Shirley Boyd	01423 566966

Another difficult and disappointing season saw Harrogate narrowly escaping relegation but improving on last season's bottom place. It started promisingly with a superb win at Henley, the only home defeat the eventual champions have suffered in two seasons. `Gate, however, were unable to sustain this early effort in a very competitive league as the loss of key players for varying periods and a lack of adequate replacements took its toll, especially in goal kicking. After Henley form fluctuated with defeats by Morley, Lydney and Reading balanced by nail biting wins over Otley and Rosslyn Park, a good win at Scunthorpe in the Tetley's Cup and finally a narrow home win over struggling Liverpool on October 31st. Gate did not win another match until 23rd January and during this time they were easily beaten in the Cup at Esher, possibly the low point of the season.

The January defeat of Birmingham heralded the fight back. Some inspirational selection behind the scrum and improvements in the back row brought a cutting edge to the attack and improved defence. A thrilling 12-12 draw at Otley (the only point they dropped at home) was followed by heart stopping victories over Lydney 5-0 and in the vital clash at Morley 21-19 Peter Taylor's last gasp penalty in this dramatic match effectively saved Harrogate and relegated the Maroons. A splendid win at Camberley clinched safety.

Player of the Year, flanker David Wheat, and lock Peter Taylor came back well from their serious injuries of last season. Taylor, Ronnie Kelly and Andy Caldwell played for Yorkshire, while Taylor became the first S.A.C. to captain the RAF in the I.S.C. Leigh Woodhouse played for the Army and `Gate's most improved player Mike Worden captained the North Students. Gareth Drane and Lee Cholewa played for Yorks U21.

Ronnie Kelly and Mark Ferrar appeared in all 26 league matches. Ralph Zoin was top scorer with 61 points, but the back injury which restricted him to thirteen appearances also enforced his retirement from playing. Ralph has since been appointed club coach following Simon Croft's resignation. Jeremy Hopkinson and ian Hassall have also retired from 1st XV rugby after each making over 120 league appearances and will assits Ralph on the coaching side.

Off the field Harrogate has not been exempt from the financial traumas which have affected many clubs since the advent of professionalism. Members have, however, rallied in support. The move to new pastures at Leeds Road awaits the decision of the public enquiry due in December. Meanwhile we look forward to another season in Jewson One with optimism but realising it will be as tough as ever.

GLYN SMITH

L-R - Back Row: M Peers (Rugby Ch.), R Guy (Hon Sec.), V Barrack (Physio), G Drane, I Salkeld, R Kelly, A Casey, A McClarron, S Brown, M Curtis, D Croft, S Carbutt, L Cholewa, T Kent-Jones (Comm Ch.), S Croft (Coach), A Jones (Chairman). Front: G Siswick (Man), K Morley, R Whyley, A Caldwell, I Hassall, R Morgan, D Wheat (capt), R Spragg (Pres), P Taylor, R Zoing, M Farrar, T Barley, C Reed. **Photo:** Peter Spragg

HARROGATE

Match No.	Date	H/A	Comp.	Opponents	Result & Score	Att.	15	14	13	12	11
1	05.09	A	JN1	Henley	W 20-5	350	Morgan	Morley	Reed/t	Caldwell	A McClarron
2	12.09	H	JN1	Morley	L 9-14	550	Morgan	Morley(k)	Reed	Caldwell	A McClarron
3	19.09	A	JN1	Lydney	L 8-25	700	Morgan	C McClarron	Reed(k)	Caldwell(m)	A McClarron
4	26.09	H	JN1	Otley	W 6-5	750	Hassall	C McClarron	Morgan	Caldwell	A McClarron
5	03.10	A	JN1	Reading	L 14-25	250	Hassall	C McClarron	Morgan	Caldwell	A McClarron
6	10.10	H	JN1	Rosslyn Park	W 6-3	350	Hassall	C McClarron	Morgan	Caldwell	A McClarron
7	24.10	A	JN1	Birmingham S	L 12-15	200	Hassall	C McClarron	Morgan	Mcgee	A McClarron
8	31.10	H	JN1	Liverpool StH*	W 24-17	450	Hassall(l)	Reed	Morgan	Caldwell	A McClarron
9	07.11	A	JN1	Newbury	L 10-27	400	Morgan	C McClarron	Reed	Caldwell/t	A McClarron
10	21.11	A	JN1	Wharfedale*	L 12-27	600	Hassall	C McClarron/t	Reed	Caldwell	A McClarron
11	28.11	H	JN1	Manchester	L 10-18	550	Hassall	C McClarron	Reed/t	Caldwell	A McClarron
12	05.12	A	JN1	Nottingham	L 5-22	400	Yates	Hassall	Reed	Caldwell/t	A McClarron
13	12.12	H	JN1	Camberley	D 24-24	400	Hassall(t)	Whiting	Reed	Caldwell/t	A McClarron
14	19.12	A	JN1	Manchester	L 0-27	500	Morgan	Whiting	Reed	Caldwell	A McClarron
15	26.12	H	JN1	Wharfedale	L 0-6	1,200	Hassall	Whiting	Morgan	Caldwell	A McClarron
16	02.01	H	JN1	Newbury	L 16-44	500	Hassall	Whiting	Morgan	Caldwell	Wray
17	16.01	A	JN1	Liverpool StH	L 5-11	200	Morgan	Whiting/t	Reed	Caldwell	A McClarron
18	23.01	H	JN1	Birmingham S	W 14-7	500	Morgan	Whiting	Reed	Caldwell	A McClarron(a)
19	30.01	A	JN1	Rosslyn Park	L 8-27	300	Morgan	Whiting	Reed	Caldwell(B)	Morley/t
20	06.02	H	JN1	Reading	L 9-13	250	Yates/3p	A McClarron	Reed	Caldwell(B)	Morley
21	13.02	A	JN1	Otley	D 12-12	500	Hassall	A McClarron	Reed/tc	Caldwell	Morley
22	27.02	H	JN1	Lydney	W 5-0	350	Hassall	Farrar	Morley/t	Caldwell	A McClarron
23	13.03	A	JN1	Morley	W 22-21	500	Barley	Farrar/t	Morley	Caldwell/t	A McClarron(c)
24	27.03	H	JN1	Henley	L 17-31	400	Cholewa/2cp	Farrar	Morley/t	Caldwell	A McClarron
25	03.04	A	JN1	Camberley	W 24-14	300	Cholewa/3cp	Farrar/t	Morley	Caldwell	A McClarron/2t
26	17.04	H	JN1	Nottingham	L 17-21	400	Cholewa(E)	Farrar/t	Morley	Caldwell	A McClarron
A	17.10	A	TBC	Scunthorpe	W 29-0		Hassall	C McClarron/t	Farnsworth	Caldwell	A McClarron/t
B	14.11	A	TBC	Esher	L 17-42		Hassall/t	C McClarron	Reed/t	Caldwell(x)	A McClarron(d/t)

* after opponents name indicates a penalty try
Brackets after a player's name indicates he was replaced. eg (a) means he was replaced by replacement code "a" and so on.
/ after a player or replacement name is followed by any scores he made - eg /t, /c, /p, /dg or any combination of these

1998-99 HIGHLIGHTS

League debuts:
Rhys Morgan, Mark Curtis, Ian Salkeld, Ronnie Kelly, Ben Quick, Stephen Blight, Matthew Haskayne, Dan Cook, Lee Cholewa.

Ever Presents: None - most appearances Andy Caldwell 25 and Ronnie Kelly 25(1)

Players used: 38 plus 4 as a replacement only.

Most Points in a season:

Pts	Player	T	C	P	DG
61	R Zoing	-	5	15	2
29	M Yates	-	4	7	-
25	M Farrar	5	-	-	-
22	C Reed	4	1	-	-
21	M Farnsworth	-	3	5	-

MATCH FACTS

10	9	1	2	3	4	5	6	7	8	
Zoing/2cpdg	Farrar/t	Curtis(j)	Salkeld	Field	Taylor	Brown	Yoeman	Wheat	Ramus	1
Zoing/3p	Farrar	Kelly	Salkeld	Field	Taylor	Brown	Yoeman	Wheat	Ramus	2
Zoing(l/tp)	Farrar	Kelly	Salkeld	Curtis(g)	Taylor	Brown	Yoeman(o)	Wheat	Ramus(n)	3
Zoing/2p	Farrar	Kelly	Salkeld	Field(m)	Taylor	Ramus	Yoeman(s)	Wheat	Hopkinson	4
Zoing/3p	Farrar	Kelly	Salkeld	Field(m)	Taylor	Ramus	Yoeman/t	Wheat(s)	Hopkinson(u)	5
Zoing/pdg	Farrar(v)	Kelly	Salkeld	Field(m)	Taylor	Ramus	Yoeman	Wheat	Hopkinson(w)	6
Zoing/4p	Farrar	Kelly	Salkeld	Field(m)	Taylor	Croft(h)	Baker	Yoeman	Hopkinson	7
Farnsworth/c4p(r)	Farrar	Kelly	Salkeld	Carbutt/t	Taylor	Brown	Yoeman(v)	Wheat	Baker	8
Farnsworth/cp	Drane(d)	Kelly	Salkeld	Curtis(m)	Taylor	Brown	Yoeman	Wheat	Baker(o)	9
Farnsworth/c	Farrar	Kelly	Salkeld(y)	Carbutt	Taylor	Croft(h)	Yoeman	Wheat	Hopkinson	10
Quick/cp(t)	Farrar	Kelly(e)	Salkeld(y)	Carbutt	Taylor(h)	Croft	Woodhouse	Wheat	Yoeman	11
Quick(t)	Farrar(v)	Kelly(e)	Whyley	Carbutt	Blight(h)	Croft	Woodhouse(r)	Wheat	Baker	12
Yates/3cp	Farrar/t(v)	Kelly	Whyley(f)	Carbutt	Croft	Brown	Yoeman(n)	Wheat(s)	Baker/t	13
Yates	Farrar	Kelly	Whyley	Carbutt(z)	Brown	Croft	Yoeman(s)	Wheat(n)	Baker	14
Yates	Farrar	Kelly	Salkeld(y)	Haskayne(e)	Taylor	Brown	Worden(s)	Wheat	Hopkinson	15
Yates/c3p	Farrar(v)	Kelly(e)	Salkeld(y)	Haskayne	Taylor	Brown	Worden(s)	Wheat/t	Hopkinson(A)	16
Yates	Farrar	Kelly	Whyley(f)	Carbutt	Taylor	Brown(u)	Baker	Wheat	Hopkinson(r)	17
Zoing/2c	Drane/t(d)	Kelly	Whyley(f)	Haskayne	Taylor/t	Brown	Worden	Wheat(s)	Baker	18
Zoing/p	Farrar	Kelly(e)	Salkeld(p)	Haskayne	Taylor	Cook	Worden	Woodhouse(i)	Baker	19
Zoing	Farrar	Kelly	Whyley(f)	Haskayne(m)	Taylor	Cook	Worden	Wheat	Hopkinson	20
Morgan	Farrar(C)	Kelly	Whyley/t(f)	Carbutt(z)	Taylor	Cook(h)	Worden(i)	Wheat	Baker(o)	21
Reed	Morgan	Kelly	Whyley	Carbutt	Taylor	Brown	Worden	Wheat(s)	Hopkinson(f)	22
Reed	Morgan	Kelly	Salkeld	Carbutt/t	Taylor/2cp	Brown	Worden	Wheat	Baker(z)	23
Reed(c)	Morgan	Kelly	Salkeld(y)	Carbutt(z)	Taylor	Brown	Worden/t	Wheat(A)	Baker	24
Reed	Drane	Kelly	Salkeld	Carbutt	Taylor	Brown	Worden	Wheat	Baker	25
Reed/t(c/c)	Drane	Kelly	Salkleld(y)	Carbutt(e)	Taylor	Brown	Casey(u)	Wheat	Baker/t	26
Zoing/c4p	Farrar	Kelly(D)	Salkeld(p)	Carbutt	Taylor	Croft	Woodhouse	Wheat	Hopkinson(w)	A
Farnsworth/c	Drane	Kelly(e)	Salkeld(p)	Carbutt	Talor	Brown(F)	Woodhouse	Wheat	Hopkinson(u)	B

REPLACEMENTS:						
a- K Morley	b- A McClarron	c - R Zoing	d - M Farrar	e - M Curtis	f - I Salkeld	g - J Field
h - S Brown	i - C Yoeman	j - R Kelly	k - I Hassall	l - B Quick	m - S Carbutt	n - J Finnegan
o - J Hopkinson	p - T Anderson	r - M Worden	s - L Woodhouse	t - M Farnsworth	u - D Croft	v - G Drane
w - S Baker	x - D McGee	y - R Whyley	z - M Haskayne			
A - A Casey	B - K Kerr	C - T Borley	D - A Simpson	E - T Barley	F - B Macdonald	G - M Yates

Ralph Zoing, back at the club after a season at Leeds Tykes, tops the scoring charts for the 10th time in 12 seasons. His 61 points was the lowest to top the charts since sinces Zoing's own 45 back in the 1991-92 season.

Mark Farrar with a total of five topped the Harrogate try scorers list, the lowest total to top the list since Steve Baker's 3 back in 1991-92.

All time leading try scorer, No 8 Jeremy Hopkinson, failed to add to his total despite 10 appearances and stays on 42.

With Harrogate finding points scoring difficult during the season none of the seasonal or match records were beaten.

In the all time records Ralph Zoing added to all he records. Zoing extended his points scoring record to 1086, his conversions record to 175, his penalties record to 209 and his drop goal record to 16.

Three wins and a draw in their last six matches saw Harrogate to safety after looking in trouble at one stage.

HARROGATE

LEAGUE STATISTICS
compiled by Stephen McCormack

SEASON	Division	P	W	D	L	F	A	Pts Diff	Lge Pts	Lge Pos	Most Points	Most Tries
89-90	North1	10	8	0	2	188	82	106	16	1	88 Ralph Zoing	4 Clive Walker
90-91	D4N	12	6	1	5	220	204	16	13	6	43 Ralph Zoing	9 Jeremy Hopkinson
91-92	D4N	12	6	0	6	170	175	-5	12	7	45 Ralph Zoing	3 Steve Baker
92-93	D4N	12	10	1	1	363	115	248	21	1	131 Ralph Zoing	9 Steve Baker Guy Easterby
93-94	4	18	14	2	2	479	219	260	30	2	105 Ralph Zoing	13 Jeremy Hopkinson
94-95	3	18	7	2	9	275	404	-129	16	7	110 Dan Clappison	7 Rob Bell
95-96	3	18	6	3	9	333	387	-54	15	6	215 Ralph Zoing	5 Richard Marcroft
96-97	3	30	18	0	12	832	595	237	36	5	305 Ralph Zoing	13 Rob Bell, Mike Farrar & Kerry Morley
97-98	JN1	26	4	1	21	463	707	-244	9	14	79 Neil James	10 Lee Feurer
98-99	JN1	26	8	2	16	309	461	-152	18	12	61 Ralph Zoing	5 Mark Farrar

BIGGEST MARGINS

Home Win	72pts - 79-7 v Clifton 5.4.97
Away Win	28pts - 41-13 v Clifton 16.11.96
Home Defeat	54pts - 12-66 v Leeds 21.3.98
Away Defeat	47pts - 3-50 v Worcester 31.1.98

MOST CONSECUTIVE

Appearances	49 Rob Bell 9.92 -9.9.95
Matches scoring Tries	6 Clive Ware
Matches scoring points	24 Ralph Zoing
Victories	5
Defeats	10

MOST POINTS

Scored at Home	79 v Clifton 5.4.97
Scored Away	41 v Clifton 16.11.96
Conceded at Home	66 v Leeds 21.3.98
Conceded Away	50 v Worcester 31.1.98

MOST TRIES

Scored in a match	14 v Aspatria 30.4.94
Conceded in a match	10 v Leeds 21.3.98 (H)

MOST APPEARANCES

by a forward	121 Peter Taylor
by a back	118 (8) Ian Hassell

	MOST IN A SEASON	MOST IN A CAREER	MOST IN A MATCH
Points	305 Ralph Zoing 96-97	1086 Ralph Zoing 87-99	27 Ralph Zoing v Fylde 14.10.95 (H)
Tries	13 Jeremy Hopkinson 91-92 Rob Bell, Mark Farrar & Kerry Morley - all 96-97	42 Jeremy Hopkinson 90-98	5 Steve Baker v Lichfield 14.11.92 (H)
Conversions	63 Ralph Zoing 96-97	175 Ralph Zoing 87-99	9 Ralph Zoing v Towcestrians 13.3.93 (H)
Penalties	51 Ralph Zoing 95-96	209 Ralph Zoing 87-99	7 Ralph Zoing v Halifax 18.11.90 (H)
Drop Goals	5 Ralph Zoing 96-97	16 Ralph Zoing 87-99	2 Ralph Zoing v Askeans 20.11.93 (H)

HARROGATE PLAYING SQUAD

BACKS

	Ht.	Wt.	Birthdate	Birthplace	CLUB	League Apps	Tries	Pts
Ian Hassell					Harrogate	118(8)	-	-
Kerry Morley					Harrogate Wakefield	61(2) 23	22 4	110 20
Craig Reed					Harrogate	113(1)	24	134
Rhys Morgan					Harrogate Leeds	19 35(9)	- 8	 40
Mark Farrar					Harrogate	71(2)	27	135
Ben Quick					Harrogate	2(2)	1	13
Gareth Drane					Harogate	6(9)	-	-
Rupert Whiting					Harrogate	9(6)	1	5
Ralph Zoing					Harrogate Leeds	106(3) 2(2)	13 1	1086 5
Mark Farnsworth					Harrogate	10(3)	1	26
Andy Caldwell					Harrogate Leeds	84 2(1)	12 -	56 -
Domonic McGee					Harrogate	15(1)	-	-
Chris McClarron					Harrogate	12(1)	2	10
Alastair McClarron					Harrogate	30(1)	5	25

FORWARDS

	Ht.	Wt.	Birthdate	Birthplace	CLUB	League Apps	Tries	Pts
Andy Simpson					Harrogate	101(9)	12	58
Richard Whyley					Harrogate	121	5	25
Jason Field					Harrogate	46(14)	-	-
Mark Curtis					Harrogate	3(5)	-	-
Ian Salkeld					Harrogate	18(6)	-	-
Dan Cook					Harrogate	3	-	-
Peter Taylor					Harrogate	124(1)	14	77
Simon Brown					Harrogate	83(6)	2	9
Ronie Kelly					Harrogate Leeds	25(1) 3(1)	-	-
Mike Worden					Harrogate	21(7)	1	5
Jeremy Hopkinson					Harrogate	114(13)	42	219
Lee Woodhouse					Harrogate	14(9)	-	-
Matthew Haskayne					Harrogate	5(4)	-	-
Tom Anderson					Harrogate	8(1)	-	-

HARROGATE

FACT FILE

Founded: 1871
Nickname: Gate

Colours: Red, amber & black shirts & socks, black shorts.
Change colours: Red.

GROUND

Address: County Ground, Claro Road, Harrogate. HG1 4AG.
Tel : 01423 566966 Fax: 01423 509073
Capacity: 5,000 Seated: 500 Standing: 4,500

Directions: Claro Road is on the north side of the A59 (York Skipton road), just off the Stray (open grassed area adjacent to the town centre).
Nearest Railway Station: Harrogate, exit to East Parade turn left, right onto Parkview continues into Kingsway & Walkers passage, cross Stray to Claro Rd (10mins).

Car Parking: 400 at the ground, unlimited nearby

Admission (Prices include parking subject to availability) **Season** Adult £66, OAPs £38.50, Children Free
Matchday: Standing Adult £6, OAPs £3, Children Free Seated Adult £7, OAPs £4, Children Free.

Club Shop: Matchdays only. Contact Peter Clarke 01423 561301.

Clubhouse: Mon-Fri 7-11, Sat 11-11, Sun 12-3, bar meals available.
Functions: Up to 120, contact John Sutton at club

Training Nights: Monday and Thursday; u19 Wednesday

PROGRAMME Size: A5 Pages: 32 Price: £1
Editor: Glynn Smith 01423 865763
ADVERTISING RATES Mono (Contact Club)
Full page £300, 1/2 page £160, 1/4 page £90

Peter Taylor
seen here winning the ball in the match against Nottingham.

Photo: Peter Spragg

LYDNEY R.F.C.

President	T C Bailey	Montrose, Highfield, Lydney, Gloucester 01594 842287 (H)
Chairman	Dr. P Catlin	Gwynne Cottage, Saunders Green, Whitecroft, Lydney, Glos. GL15 4PN
Secretary	A J Jones	5 Kimberley Close, Lydney, Glos. GL15 5AE 01594 842709 (H), 01594 844604 (Fax)
Treasurer	R A Jones	Sweetwater Cottage, Neds Top, Old Croft, Glos. GL15 4NK 01594 845073 (B), 01594 845915 (Fax)
Team Manager	TBA	
Match Secretary	David Nelmes	01549 562038

Looking back on last season, under the guidance of coach Rhodri Lewis, the club ended eighth in Jewson National League Division One, a major advance on the previous year when relegation was always a worry.

It meant that we finished as the 36th club in England, a remarkable position for a town with a population of fewer than 10,000. More consistency away from home was still in short supply, but the loyal supporters were treated to some stirring performances at home.

In particular, almost 40 percent of the inhabitants turned up to watch an epic encounter with Saracens in the Tetley's Bitter Cup, a day to be remembered for many and various reasons, not least for the financial benefit that it brought to the club.

Success on the field seemed to have a knock on effect on the junior teams, honours coming the way of all sides from the United XV down to the Colts. Lydney also provided the bulk of the side that reached the Tetley's Bitter County Cup Final at Twickenham.

Looking forward to the 1999/2000 season sees the club having to undertake a certain amount of rebuilding. The appointment of a new coach and the loss of several leading players means that there will be no shortage of new faces at Regentsholm next season. This will also give some of the younger players coming through from the Colts and the Development team a chance to make their mark.

Several improvements to the ground are in hand which will result in Lydney providing some of the best facilities in the Division for players and spectators alike. The club remains confident that our best days are still in front of us and that every one connected to the Severnsiders can look forward to another successful season.

DAVE DOLAN

Tetley's Bitter Cup Fifth Round action as Lydney take on Saracens at Regentsholm

LYDNEY

Match No.	Date	H/A	Comp.	Opponents	Result & Score	Att.	15	14	13	12	11
1	05.09	H	JN1	Birmingham S*	W 21-13	750	Paisley/t	Hill	Bennett	Mills	Brooks
2	12.09	A	JN1	Liverpool StH	L 18-33	250	Paisley	Hill/t(c)	Bennett	Morgan	Brooks(o)
3	19.09	H	JN1	Harrogate	W 25-8	700	Paisley(s)(t)	Smith/t	Bennett	Mills(n)	Dunlop
4	26.09	A	JN1	Wharfedale	W 33-29	520	Paisley	Smith/2t	Bennett	Mills(o)	Dunlop
5	03.10	H	JN1	Manchester	L 12-16	750	Paisley/3p	Smith	Bennett	Betridge	Dunlop
6	10.10	A	JN1	Nottingham	L 11-25	350	Paisley/p(A)	Smith	Meek(j)	Johnson(B)	Dunlop
7	24.10	H	JN1	Camberley	W 26-10	400	Bennett	Smith/t	Holford	Meek	Dunlop
8	31.10	A	JN1	Henley	L 11-23	350	Paisley/p	Smith	Holford	Meek	Dunlop
9	07.11	H	JN1	Morley	W 35-10	500	Paisley/3c3p	Smith	Holford	Meek(a)	Dunlop
10	21.11	H	JN1	Newbury	W 25-16	700	Paisley/t2c2p	Smith	Meek	Osborne	Dunlop
11	28.11	A	JN1	Otley	L 3-34	400	Paisley/p	Smith	Hill	Meek	Dunlop
12	05.12	H	JN1	Reading	W 33-17	600	Paisley/t3c4p	Smith/t	Holford	Osborne	Dunlop
13	12.12	A	JN1	Rosslyn Park	L 10-20	200	Paisley/tcp	Smith(E)	Holford	Meek(o)	Dunlop
14	19.12	H	JN1	Otley	W 10-3	700	Paisley/cp	Smith	Holford	Osborne	Dunlop
15	26.12	A	JN1	Newbury	L 5-11	500	Paisley/t	Smith	Bright	Osborne	Dunlop
16	02.01	A	JN1	Morley	D 13-13	400	Paisley/c2p	Smith(z)	Bright(d)	Osborne	Dunlop
17	23.01	A	JN1	Camberley	L 5-6	400	Paisley	Bennett	Meek(A)	Osborne	Dunlop
18	06.02	A	JN1	Manchester	L 0-67	600	Bennett(y)	Smith	Holford	Bettridge	Dunlop
19	13.02	H	JN1	Wharfedale	W 20-18	600	Bennett	Smith	Small	Davis	Dunlop
20	27.02	A	JN1	Harrogate	L 0-5	350	Pollock	Smith	Small	Bright	Dunlop
21	06.03	H	JN1	Nottingham	L 3-11	550	Pollock	Smith	Holford	Small	Dunlop
22	13.03	H	JN1	Liverpool StH	W 62-17	500	Pollock(b/2t)	Smith/2t	Holford/t(c)	Small/t	Dunlop
23	20.03	H	JN1	Henley	L 0-7	600	Bennett	Smith	Holford	Small(v)	Dunlop
24	27.03	A	JN1	Birmingham S	L 14-34	300	Bennett	Smith	Pollock(d)	Davis(n)	Dunlop/t
25	03.04	H	JN1	Rosslyn Park	D 6-6	500	Bennett	Smith	Holford	Davis(n)	Dunlop
26	17.04	A	JN1	Reading*	W 37-31	200	Bennett(J)	Smith	Holford(d)	Davis	Dunlop
A	17.10	H	TBC	Camberley	W 44-34	600	Johnson(B)	Smith/2t	Meek	Mills	Dunlop/t
B	14.11	H	TBC	Stourbridge	W 44-5	500	Paisley/t3cp(A)	Smith/2t	Holford	Meek(a)	Dunlop/2t
C	09.01	A	TBC	Moseley	W 25-24		Paisley/cp(v)	Bennett	Meek	Osborne	Smith
D	31.01	H	TBC	Saracens	L 0-40		Paisley(j)	Bennett(v)	Osborne(p)	Meek	Smith

* after opponents name indicates a penalty try
Brackets after a player's name indicates he was replaced. eg (a) means he was replaced by replacement code "a" and so on.
/ after a player or replacement name is followed by any scores he made - eg /t, /c, /p, /dg or any combination of these

1998-99 HIGHLIGHTS

League debuts:

Nick Paisley, Lee Osborne, Andrew Jarrett, Ian Morgan, Lee Smith, Dwayne Edwards, John Nicholls, Alex Holford, Richard Turner, Gavin Cocks, Scott Edwards, Paul Hudson, Steve Small, Scott Pollock, Paul Kiely.

Ever Presents: Lee Smith, Chris Dunlop & Julian Davis

Players used: 38 plus 5 as a replacement only

Most Points in a season:

Pts	Player	T	C	P	DG
104	N Paisley	5	11	19	-
99	L Osborne	2	19	17	-
35	L Smith	7	-	-	-
35	D Edwards	7	-	-	-

Full back Nick Paisley topped the points scorers in his first season at the club.

MATCH FACTS

10	9	1	2	3	4	5	6	7	8	
Osborne/c3p	Davis	Williams	Price	Jarrett(l)	Roberts	Bashford	Mutyzambezi	Wakeham(m)	Nicholls	1
Osborne/c2p	Davis	Williams/t	Price	Jarrett	Roberts	Bashford	Mutyzambezi	Wakeham(m)	Nicholls	2
Osborne/2c2p	Davis	Williams	Price/t	Jarrett	Roberts(m)	Bashford	Burnett(w)	D Edwards/t	Nicholls	3
Osborne/2c3p	Davis/t	Williams	Price	Jarrett	Roberts(m)	Bashford	Burnett/t	D Edwards	Nicholls	4
Osborne/p	Davis	Williams	Price	Jarrett(x)	Roberts(m)	Bashford	Burnett(w)	Mutyzambezi	Nicholls	5
Mills/dg	Davis	Williams	Price	Nicholls(g)	Kilby(h)	Bashford	Burnett	D Edwards	Nicholls/t	6
Merrett/3c	Turner	Williams	Nelmes	Jarrett(l)	Roberts	Bashford	Burnett/t	D Edwards/t(j)	Nicholls/t	7
Merrett/p	Turner/t	Price	Nelmes	Bartlett	Roberts	Bashford	Burnett	Mutyzambezi	Nicholls	8
Davis	Turner	Price	Nelmes	Bartlett	Roberts	Bashford	Kilby(w)	D Edwards/3t	Nicholls/t	9
Davis	Turner(a)	Price	Nelmes	Jarrett(l/t)	Roberts	Bashford/t	Burnett	D Edwards	Nicholls	10
Osborne(o)	Davis	Bartlett	Nelmes	Jarrett(e)	Roberts	Bashford	Burnett(w)	Price(D)	Kilby	11
Davis	Turner	Bartlett	Nelmes	Jarrett(e)	Roberts	Kilby	Burnett/t	Price	Cocks(w)	12
Osborne	Davis	Bartlett	Nelmes	Williams(g)	Roberts	Bashford	Burnett	Price	Nicholls	13
Davis	Turner	Bartlett/t(g)	Nelmres	Williams	Roberts	Bashford(m)	Burnett	Price	Nicholls(F)	14
Davis	Turner	Bartlett	Nelmes	Jarrett(G)	Kilby	Roberts	Burnett	Price	S Edwards	15
Davis(A)	Turner	Price/t	Nelmes	Williams	Roberts	Kilby	S Edwards(r)	Hudson	Nicholls	16
Davis	Turner	Price	Nelmes	Williams(g)	Roberts/t	Bashford	Burnett	D Edwards	Nicholls(F)	17
Merrett	Bendall(d)	Williams	Price	Jarrett(x)	Roberts	Kilby(i)(t)	Hudson(k)	D Edwards	S Edwards	18
Osborne/cp	Turner(J)	Price	Nelmes	Williams(g)	Cocks/t	Bashford	Hudson(k)	D Edwards/t	S Edwards/t	19
Osborne	Davis	Price	Nelmes	Williams	Cocks	Bashford	S Edwards	D Edwards	Nicholls	20
Merrett/p	Davis	Bartlett	Price	Jarrett	Cocks	Bashford	Burnett	D Edwards	S Edwards	21
Osborne/t7cp	Davis	Bartlett(e/t)	Nelmes(t)	Jarrett	Kilby	Bashford	Burnett	DEdwards/t(w)	S Edwards(k)	22
Osborne(C)	Davis	Bartlett	Nelmes	Jarrett(e)	Kilby(w)	Bashford	Nicholls	D Edwards	S Edwards	23
Osborne/2c	Turner	Bartlett	Nelmes(t)	Jarrett(u)	Kiely	Bashford	Cocks/t	D Edwards(D)	Nicholls(H)	24
Osborne/2p	Turner	Bartlett(x)	Nelmes	Jarrett	Cocks	Bashford	Burnett	D Edwards	S Edwards(k)	25
Osborne/t3c2p	Turner/t	Nicholls	Nelmes	Williams	S Edwards/2t	Bashford	Burnett	Cocks	Nicholls(h)	26
Merrett/c3pdg	Turner	Williams(x)	Nelmes/t	Jarrett	Roberts	Bashford	Burnett(m)	Mutyzambezi/t(w)	Nicholls	A
Davis	Turner/t	Price/t	Nelmes	Jarrett (e)	Roberts(m)	Bashford	Burnett(w)	D Edwards	Nicholls	B
Davis(A)	Turner	Bartlett(f)	Nelmes	Williams(g)	Roberts	Kilby	Burnett	D Edwards(G)	Nicholls	C
Davis(A)	Turner	Bartlett	Nelmes(f)	Williams(g)	Roberts	Kilby(i)	Burnett(G)	D Edwards	S Edwards	D

REPLACEMENTS: a- J Hill, b- A Bennett, c - R Mills, d - L Brooks, e - G Williams, f - P Price, g - A Jarrett, h - J Roberts, i - J Bashford, j - C Mutyzambezi, k - M Nicholls, l - N Bartlett, m - N Kilby, n - I Morgan, o - J Bettridge, p - L Smith, r -N Burnett, s - P Morris, t - M Gunther, u - J Harris, v - D Bendall, w - P Kiely, x - J Nicholls, y - M Johnson, z - L Meek, A - N Merrett, B - A Holford, C - R Turner, D - D Emery, E - P Bright, F - S Edwards, G - P Hudson, H - N Evans, J - S Pollock

Paisley became the fourth player to score 100 points in a league season for Lydney.

Lee Osborne nearly beacme the fifth but managed 99 and finished one short.

The leading try scoring honour was shared by two players. Winger, Lee Smith, and flanker, Dwayne Edwards, both scored seven tries.

Lydney set a new record for points in a match with 62 against Liverpool St Helens late in the season. That beat the previous record of 56 scored against Clifton in April 97.

In that win they also set a new record for tries in a match with nine which beat the previous record of eight set against Clifton and Sidcup.

Lee Osborne set a new record for conversions in a match with seven against Liverpool St Helens, that beat the previous record of five shared by Gerry Price and Paul Morris.

LYDNEY

LEAGUE STATISTICS
compiled by Stephen McCormack

SEASON	Division	P	W	D	L	F	A	Pts Diff	Lge Pts	Lge Pos	Most Points	Most Tries
89-90	3	11	3	0	8	153	166	-13	6	11	79 Mark Smith	3 Simon Morris & Adrian Knox
90-91	3	12	4	1	7	125	188	-63	8	11	58 Paul Morris	5 Mike Stubbs
91-92	3	12	2	0	10	91	261	-170	4	13	15 Andy Berry	3 Mark Fennell
92-93	D4S	12	8	0	4	187	170	17	16	3	102 Andy Halford	6 John Edwards
93-94	D5S	12	7	2	3	181	111	70	16	2	54 Andy halford	5 Mike Stubbs & John Edwards
94-95	D5S	12	10	1	1	263	131	132	21	2	70 Andy halford	7 Mike Stubbs
95-96	D5S	12	11	1	0	320	132	188	23	1	107 Robert Mills	6 Nick Nelmes & Julian Davis
96-97	D3	30	13	0	17	668	766	-98	26	10	275 Paul Morris	8 Mike Stubbs & Adrian Knox
97-98	JN1	26	5	0	21	361	575	-214	10	12	82 James Reid	7 Julian Davis
98-99	JN1	26	11	2	13	438	482	-44	24	8	104 Nick Paisley	7 L Smith/D Edwards

BIGGEST MARGINS

Home Win	47pts - 47-0 v Sidcup 25.4.98
Away Win	38pts - 41-3 v High Wycombe 16.9.95
Home Defeat	29pts 12-41 v Worcester 14.3.98
Away Defeat	74pts - 0-74 v Leeds 15.3.97

MOST CONSECUTIVE

Appearances	53 Nick Nelmes
Matches scoring Tries	5 Mike Stubbs
Matches scoring points	16 Paul Morris
Victories	9
Defeats	10 (1997-98)

MOST POINTS

Scored at Home	62 v Liverpool St Helens
Scored Away	41 v High Wycombe 16.9.95
Conceded at Home	41 v Worcester 14.3.98
Conceded Away	74 v Leeds 15.3.97

MOST TRIES

Scored in a match	9 v Liverpool St Helens
Conceded in a match	11 v Leeds 15.03.97 (A)

MOST APPEARANCES

by a forward	139 Nick Nelmes
by a back	111 (1) Robert Mills

	MOST IN A SEASON	MOST IN A CAREER	MOST IN A MATCH
Points	275 Paul Morris 96-97	374 Paul Morris 88-98	29 Paul Morris v Otley (H) 14.9.96
Tries	8 Mike Stubbs 96-97 Adrian Knox 96-97	30 Mike Stubbs 90-97	4 David Ellis v Cheltenham (H) 31.10.87
Conversions	31 Paul Morris 96-97	43 Paul Morris 88-98	7 Lee Osborne v Liverpool St H (H)
Penalties	66 Paul Morris 96-97	91 Paul Morris 88-98	9 Paul Morris 14.9.96 (H)
Drop Goals	6 Mark Smith 89-90	6 Mark Smith 88-90 Gerry Price 87-95	2 Mark Smith v Exeter 11.11.89 (H)

LYDNEY PLAYING SQUAD

BACKS

	Ht.	Wt.	Birthdate	Birthplace	CLUB	League Apps	Tries	Pts
Danny Bendall	5.11	11.12	23.04.75	Gloucester	Lydney	20(3)	3	15
Lee Osbourne				Gloucester	Lydney	20	2	99
Nick Paisley					Lydney	16	5	104
Robert Mills	5.8	10.07	10.09.68	Gloucester	Lydney	115(5)	5	254
Paul Morris	5.11	12.00	08.04.71	Gloucester	Lydney Gloucester	39(1)	3	374
Mark Johnson	5.11	12.04	18.12.76	Gloucester	Lydney	9(2)	2	28
Leon Meek	5.8	13.00	07.02.73	Gloucester	Lydney Drybrook	32(4)	5	25
Julian Davis South West, Gloucestershire.	5.8	12.07	01.10.68	Gloucester	Lydney Bristol	104 27(1)	24 10	120 40
Chris Dunlop	5.8	11.02	03.08.77	Birmingham	Lydney	48	7	35
Lee Smith					Lydney	23	7	38
Richard Turner					Lydney	13(1)	2	10
Steve Small					Lydney	5	-	-
Neil Merrett					Lydney	10(6)	-	53
Alex Bennett					Lydney	33(1)	2	10

FORWARDS

	Ht.	Wt.	Birthdate	Birthplace	CLUB	League Apps	Tries	Pts
Nick Nelmes	5.11	14.12	11.09.66	Lydney	Lydney	157	21	104
Nicky Bartlett Royal Navy	6.0	17.00	10.04.69	Gloucester	Lydney	51(10)	7	35
Paul Price	5.10	15.02	12.05.74	Gloucester	Lydney Gloucester	70(1)	6	30
Gareth Williams Gloucestershire	5.11	16.10	12.02.66	Gloucester	Lydney Gordon League	115(6)	6	30
Scott Edwards Gloucestershire					Lydney	10(2)	3	15
Jimmy Roberts	6.3	16.06	24.08.77	Gloucester	Lydney	48(8)	1	5
Noel Kilby	6.4	15.00	19.01.74	Gloucester	Lydney	54(6)	3	15
Simon Wakeham	6.2	13.02	20.09.68	Bristol	Lydney	88(4)	14	67
John Nicholls Gloucestershire					Lydney	2(3)	-	-
Andrew Jarrett					Lydney	16(6)	-	-
James Bashford					Lydney	40(2)	1	5
Mark Nicholls					Lydney	42(5)	8	40
Dwayne Edwards					Lydney	15	7	35
Paul Kiely					Lydney	10(2)	3	15

LYDNEY

FACT FILE

Founded: 1887
Nickname: Severnsiders

Colours: Black and white hoops
Change colours: Red

GROUND

Address: Regentsholm, Regent Street, Lydney, Glos GL15 5RN
Tel: 01594 842479
Capacity: 3,000 + Seated: 490 Standing: 2,500 +

Directions: Turn into Swan Road off the A48 in the centre of Lydney. Straight on to the entrance to the recreation grounds, turn left inside ground.
Nearest Railway Station: Lydney BR Appr 1 mile

Car Parking: Restricted on ground, spaces nearby

Admission:

Season	Adults £60	Children/OAPs £ 30
Matchday	Adults £6	Children/OAPs £3

Club Shop: Yes, Manageress Ann Sargent, 01594 562822

Clubhouse: open during normal licensing hours, and has snacks available.
Functions: Contact Mrs Diane Emery 01594 841008 (H).

Training Nights: Tuesdays & Thursdays

PROGRAMME

Size: A5 Pages: 36 Price: £1
Editor: Dr David Dolan 01594 529348

ADVERTISING RATES (Mono)

Page £100	1/2 page £75	1/4 page £40
Board £150	all plus VAT	

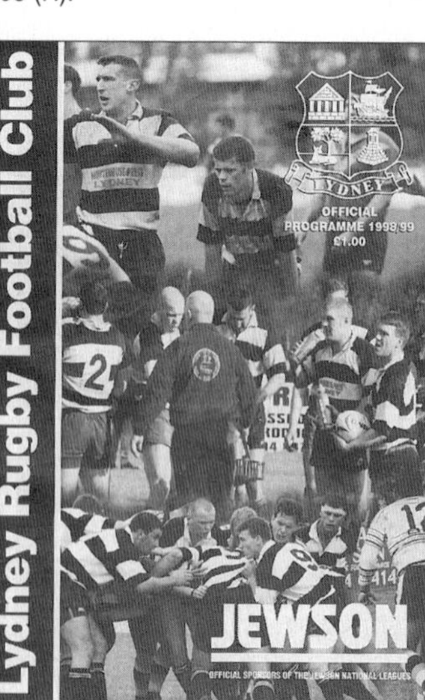

Chris Dunlop, Lydney's "Most Improved Young Player of the Year" sets off on another try scoring run.

NEWBURY R.F.C.

President	David G H Smith	c/o Drewweatt Neate, 35 London St., Andover, Hants SP10 2NV 01264 366616 (B), 01264 335515 (Fax)	
Chairman	Brian Count	c/o Newbury RFC	
Club Secretary	Ronan Cheffins-Barnard	2 Windmill Cottages, Little Bedwyn,Wilts SN8 3JF 01672 870960 (H), 01189 425544 (B), 01189 410051 (Fax)	
Comercial Manager	Adam Prickett	c/o Newbury RFC	
Chairman of Rugby	Pete Simmons	c/o Newbury RFC	Newbury RFC, Monks Lane, Newbury. 01635 40103 (B),01635 40533 (Fax)
Ist XV Coach	Kevin Bowring	c/o Newbury RFC	
Fixture Co-ordinator	John Mills	01635 200743	

In terms of results the 1998/99 season was a frustrating season. Highlights were certainly the double over promotion winning Manchester, the draw at home with league champions Henley and the quality of play particularly in the victories over Harrogate (away) and Camberley (home). The double over local rivals Reading was also very satisfying.
However, it was disappointing to lose a number of games that we should have won. Rosslyn Park (home), Birmingham (home), Camberley (away) and Morley (away) were all games in which we failed to turn pressure into points and failed to take our chances. And who can explain our dreadful performance at Liverpool?
Ending the season by finishing sixth, one position higher in the league than we did last year was an objective that was not achieved until we beat Otley in the last game of the season. As a club we have consolidated our position in Jewson League Division One and it may now be time to plan for promotion in order to achieve the Newbury RFC aim of Premiership status.
1998/99 was certainly not a season of peaks and troughs. When one looks back, we will kick ourselves for the lack of consistency in our play because we could have been challenging for promotion. However, considering the fact that the club had to cope with a change of coach and a change of captain during the season, then it did remarkably well.
The try of the season was a team effort finished by Jeremy Griffiths against Manchester at home which secured victory in the last few minutes. The `Most Improved Player of the Season' was Chris Hart, a back row forward who will be a force to be reckoned with next year. The 'Player of the Year' was Pete Curtis who was ever present and produced a consistently high level of performance.
The Tetley's Cup was a welcome relief from league action and the Blues gave a good account of themselves against Premiership opposition in the form of new neighbours, Richmond. The whole of Newbury was proud of the commitment and the manner in which we played the game that day and it was an enjoyable day for everyone.
We ended the season with three satisfying wins and can look forward to next season with the confidence of a settled coaching team and an improving squad.

NEWBURY

MATCH FACTS

Match No.	Date	H/A	Comp.	Opponents	Result & Score	Att.	15	14	13	12	11
1	05.09	H	JN1	Reading	W 28-14	600	Abernathy/c2p	Saltmarsh	Blake(m)	Reayer	Holloway/t
2	12.09	A	JN1	Nottingham	W 13-9	400	Bressington/c2p	Saltmarsh	Blake	Bellamy	Holloway(r)
3	19.09	H	JN1	Rosslyn Park	L 18-19	400	Abernathy	Bressington/c2p	Blake	Reayer(n)	Holloway
4	26.09	A	JN1	Camberley	L 18-23	500	Abernathy(o/t)	Saltmarsh	Blake	T Osman/c2p	Holloway(n)
5	03.10	H	JN1	Birmingham S	L 7-12	400	Blake	Saltmarsh/t	Jennings	T Osman/c	Howe
6	10.10	A	JN1	Henley	L 10-44	600	Bressington/cp	Saltmarsh	Jennings	T Osman	Howe
7	24.10	H	JN1	Liverpool StH	W 20-0	300	Hurst	Saltmarsh	Jennings/2c2p	Blake	Howe/t
8	31.10	A	JN1	Morley	L 8-13	500	Hurst(x)	Saltmarsh(o)	Jennings/p	Blake	Griffiths
9	07.11	H	JN1	Harrogate	W 27-10	400	Hurst(u)	Howe/t	Bellamy	Blake	Griffiths
10	21.11	A	JN1	Lydney	L 16-25	700	Smith	Haslam/t	T Osman	Reayer	Griffiths
11	28.11	H	JN1*	Wharfedale	W 18-10	250	Goddard	Griffiths	Blake	Reayer	Howe
12	05.12	A	JN1	Otley	L 11-20	300	Holloway	Griffiths	Blake	Reayer	Howe
13	12.12	H	JN1	Manchester	W 17-14	300	Holloway	Griffiths/t	Blake(z)	Reayer	Howe
14	19.12	A	JN1	Wharfedale	L 10-23	600	Holloway	Griffiths	Blake	Reayer	Howe/t
15	26.12	H	JN1	Lydney	W 11-5	400	Holloway	Haslam	Blake(m)	N Osman	Griffiths
16	02.01	A	JN1	Harrogate	W 44-16	500	Holloway/3t	Howe/t	Blake(b)	N Osman	Griffiths/4t
17	16.01	H	JN1	Morley	W 44-18	450	Holloway/t	Howe/3t	N Osman	Reayer	Griffiths/2t
18	23.01	A	JN1	Liverpool StH	L 14-31	200	Holloway	Howe	N Osman	Reayer	Griffiths/t
19	06.02	A	JN1	Birmingham S	W 16-10	200	Holloway(C)	Howe	Blake	Reayer	Griffiths
20	13.02	H	JN1	Camberley	W 41-5	300	Holloway/2t	McCormick/2t	Blake	Reayer	Griffiths
21	20.02	H	JN1	Henley**	D 26-26	500	Holloway	McCormick/t	Blake	Reayer	Griffiths
22	27.02	A	JN1	Rosslyn Park	L 24-35	400	Holloway/t	McCormick	Blake/t	Reayer	Griffiths
23	13.03	H	JN1	Nottingham	L 21-30	300	Holloway/t	Howe/2t	Blake(B)	Reayer	Griffiths
24	27.03	A	JN1	Reading	W 20-18	500	Holloway	McCormick/t	Graham/2c2p	Reayer	Griffiths/t
25	03.04	A	JN1	Manchester	W 31-26	500	Holloway	Howe/t(a/t)	Graham/3c	Reayer/t	Griffiths
26	17.04	H	JN1	Otley	W 39-20	450	Holloway	McCormick(a)	Graham/t3cp	Reayer	Griffiths
A	17.10	H	TBC	Chesent	W 37-13		Jennings/t2cp	Saltmarsh	Bellamy	Reayer/t	Howe/t
B	14.11	A	TBC	Hull	W 31-7		Smith	Saltmarsh/t	Howe	Blake	Haslam(o)
C	10.01	A	TBC	Richmond	L 12-46		Holloway/t	Howe	Blake	Reayer	Griffiths(m)

* after opponents name indicates a penalty try
Brackets after a player's name indicates he was replaced. eg (a) means he was replaced by replacement code "a" and so on.
/ after a player or replacement name is followed by any scores he made - eg /t, /c, /p, /dg or any combination of these

1998-99 HIGHLIGHTS

League debuts:
Ben Hyde, Simon Brown, Rob Kellam, Pete Curtis, Chris Hart, Bernie Williams, Paul Edwards, Alastair Bressington, Jon Bellamy, Simon Gully, John Farr, Giles Powell, Ed Jennings, Tyrone Howe, James Hurst, Toni Anticic, Dave Haslam, Dave Goddard, Justin Poihippi.

Ever Presents: Pete Curtis and Simon Miall

Players used: 41 plus 4 as a replacement only.

Most Points in a season:

Pts	Player	T	C	P	DG
72	J Poihippi	1	14	13	-
50	T Howe	10	-	-	-
45	T Holloway	9	-	-	-
45	J Griffiths	9	-	-	-
40	H Graham	1	10	4	1

Outside half Justin Poihippi topped the points scorers list after joining the club mid season.

MATCH FACTS

10	9	1	2	3	4	5	6	7	8	
Davis	Hyde(n)	Brown	Kellam(j)	Collins/t(k)	Curtis	Miall	Hart/t	Kingdon(l)	Davies/t	1
Davis	Hyde	Williams(q)	Kellam(j)	Collins	Curtis	Miall	Hart/t	Gully(l)	Davies	2
Davis(o)	Hyde	Williams(s)	Kellam(j)	Collins	Curtis	Miall(t)	Hart	Edwards(h)	Davies/t	3
Smith	Hyde	Williams	Kellam(j)	Collins/t	Curtis	Miall	Hart(v)	Kingdon	Davies	4
Smith	Hyde	D Davies	Brammer	Collins	Curtis	Miall	Hart	Kingdon	Davies	5
Smith	Philips(r)	Brown	Kellam	Collins(q)	Curtis	Miall	Hart/t	Kingdon(p)	Davies	6
A Hurst	Farr	Brown	Kellam/t(j)	Collins	Curtis	Anticic	Miall	Gully	Hart(h)	7
N Osman	Farr	Brown	Kellam(j)	Collins	Curtis	Anticic(g)	Miall	Gully	Davies/t	8
A Hurst/c	Farr/t	Brown(q)	Kellam/t(j)	Collins/2t	Curtis	Anticic(g)	Miall	Gully	Davies	9
A Hurst/2p(A)	Farr(n)	Brown	Kellam(j)	D Davies	Curtis(t)	Anticic	Miall	Gully/t	Davies	10
Poihippi/c2p	Wakfer(r)	Brown	Kellam	D Davies	Curtis(y)	Miall	Powell	Gully/t	Davies	11
Poihippi/2p	Wakfer(r)	Brown/t	Kellam(j)	Collins	Curtis(y)	Miall	Powell	Gully(h)	Davies	12
Poihippi/c	Wakfer(r)	Brown	Kellam(j)	Collins	Curtis	Miall	Powell	Gully/t(h)	Davies/t	13
Poihippi/cp	Wakfer(r)	D Davies	Kellam(j)	Collins	Curtis	Miall	Powell(h)	Gully	Davies	14
Poihippi/2p	Wakfer(r)	Brown/t(q)	Kellam(j)	Collins	Curtis	Miall	Powell(g)	Gully(h)	Davies	15
Poihippi/2c	Wakfer(r)	Brown	Kellam(j)	Collins(q)	Curtis	Miall	Hart(i)	Gully(h)	Powell	16
Poihippi/3p	Farr(n/t)	D Davies	Kellam	Brown	Curtis	Miall	Davies	Gully	Powell(g)	17
Poihippi/2c	Farr	Brown	Kellam	Collins/t	Curtis	Miall	Davies	Gully	Powell	18
Poihippi/2p	Farr(d)	Brown(q)	Brammer/t	Collins/t	Curtis	Miall	Hart	Kingdon(p)	Davies	19
Poihippi/t4cp	Farr(d)	Brown(q)	Brammer/t	Collins	Curtis	Miall	Hart(t)	Kingdon	Davies	20
Poihippi/3c	Farr(d)	Brown	Brammer(f)	Collins	Curtis	Miall	Hart(t)	Gully/t	Davies	21
Poihippi(F/2c)	Farr(d)	Brown(q)	Brammer/t(f)	Collins	Curtis	Miall	Davies(g/t)	Kingdon(p)	Powell	22
Graham/pdg	Farr(d)	Brown(q)	Brammer(f)	Collins	Curtis	Francis(t)	Miall	Gully(i)	Davies	23
Poihippi	Farr(d)	D Davies(e)	Brammer(f)	Collins	Curtis	Miall	Hart	Kingdon(p)	Powell(i)	24
Poihippi	Hyde/t	D Davies(e)	Kellam(j)	Collins	Curtis/t	Miall	Hart(t)	Kingdon(p)	Davies	25
Poihippi/t	Hyde(r/t)	D Davies(e)	Kellam(j)	Collins	Curtis	Miall	Hart/t	Kingdon(p)	Davies/2t	26
Smith	Farr	Brown/t	Kellam	D Davies	Curtis	Miall/t	Gully	Kingdon	Hart/t	A
Hurst/3c	Farr(n/t)	Brown(q)	Kellam(j)	Collins	Curtis(y)	Miall	Hart(t)	Gully	Davies/3t	B
Poihippi/c	Farr(n)	Brown	Kellam(j)	Collins	Curtis	Miall(y)	Davies	Gully/t(g)	Powell(h)	C

REPLACEMENTS:						
a- R Blake	b- G Reayer	c - M Knowles	d - B Hyde	e - S Brown	f - R Kellam	g - C Hart
h - J Kingdon	i - C Davies	j - J Brammer	k - B Williams	l - P Edwards	m - T Osman	n - B Wakfer
o - J Bellamy	p - S Gully	q - D Davies	r - J Farr	s - S Stewart	t - G Powell	u - K Smith
v - P Hennessy	w - J Hurst	x - A Hurst	y - T Anticic	z - N Osman	A - D Goddard	B - J Poihippi
C - M Knowles	D - M Baker	F - H Graham				

Also in his first season was Tyrone Howe who finished the seasonas leading try scorer with 10 just one ahead of Tom Holloway and Jeremy Griffiths.

Late season signing Howard Graham, who joined from nearby Reading, became the second Newbury player to drop a gaol in a league match with his effort against Nottingham.

Winger Jeremy Griffiths equalled Brian Johnson's record of four tries in a league match in the 44-16 win at Harrogate.

Tom Holloway is now Newbury's leading appearance maker in the backs with 62, Holloway had previously shared the with Nick Grecian.

In their 44-10 loss at Henley they conceded a record seven tries.

Newbury suffered their worst home defeat when they were beaten 30-21 by Nottingham, it was the most points they had conceded at home in the league and a record defeat.

NEWBURY

LEAGUE STATISTICS

compiled by Stephen McCormack

SEASON	Division	P	W	D	L	F	A	Pts Diff	Lge Pts	Lge Pos		Coach		Captain
89-90	SW2	10	3	0	7	124	149	-24	6	9		E Cripps		R King
90-91	SW2	10	7	1	2	137	100	37	15	2p		T Burwell		A Widdop
91-92	SW1	10	5	0	5	142	145	-3	10	6		T Burwell		W Phillips
92-93	SW1	12	8	1	3	251	158	93	17	3		T Burwell		W Phillips
93-94	SW1	12	8	1	3	173	165	8	17	3		T Burwell		J Booth
94-95	SW1	12	9	1	2	376	113	263	19	2		S Czerpak		J Brammer
95-96	SW1	12	11	0	1	364	169	195	22	1p		S Czerpak		J Brammer
96-97	D4S	25	25	0	0	1170	295	875	50	1p		S Czerpak		J Brammer
97-98	JN1	26	12	2	12	639	545	94	26	6		K Richardson		J Brammer
												Most Points		**Most Tries**
98-99	JN1	26	14	1	11	552	476	76	29	6	72	Justin Poihippi	10	Tyrone Howe

BIGGEST MARGINS

Home Win	87pts - 87-0 v Met. Police 22.2.97
Away Win	69pts - 74-5 v Askeans 19.4.87
Home Defeat	7pts - 21-28 v Worcester 13.9.97 - 13-20 v London Welsh 18.4.98
Away Defeat	23pts - 14-37 v Leeds 7.2.98

MOST CONSECUTIVE

Appearances	30 Colin Hall
Matches scoring Tries	5 Brian Johnson
Matches scoring points	24 Nick Grecian
Victories	26
Defeats	2

MOST POINTS

Scored at Home	91 v Tabard 28.3.97
Scored Away	74 v Askeans 19.4.97
Conceded at Home	28 v Worcester 13.9.97
Conceded Away	41 v Worcester 7.3.98

MOST TRIES

Scored in a match	15 v Tabard 28.3.97
Conceded in a match	6 v Worcester 7.3.98

MOST APPEARANCES

by a forward	48 Colin Hall
by a back	43 Nick Grecian & Tom Holloway

	MOST IN A SEASON	MOST IN A CAREER	MOST IN A MATCH
Points	391 Nick Grecian 96-97	563 Nick Grecian 96-98	32 Nick Grecian v Charlton Park 25.1.97 (H) v Met. Police 22.2.97 (H)
Tries	27 Brian Johnson 96-97	45 Craig Davies 96-99	4 Brian Johnson v Askeans 19.4.97 (A) v Plymouth 26.4.97 (H)
Conversions	100 Nick Grecian 96-97	135 Nick Grecian 96-98	11 Nick Grecian v Charlton Park 25.1.97 (H)
Penalties	42 Nick Grecian 96-97	71 Nick Grecian 96-98	5 Nick Grecian v Liverpool St. Helens 21.2.98 (H)
Drop Goals	1 Morgan Davis 97-98 Howard Graham 98-99	1 Morgan Davis 97-98 1 Howard Graham 98-99	1 Morgan Davis v London Welsh 22.11.97 (A) 1 Howard Graham v Nottingham 13.03.99 (H)

NEWBURY PLAYING SQUAD

BACKS

	Ht.	Wt.	Birthdate	Birthplace	CLUB	League Apps	Tries	Pts
Gareth Reayer	6.1	14.08	11.03.69	Wokingham	Newbury	19	2	10
					Coventry	12(1)	5	25
Tom Holloway	5.9	12.07	16.10.73		Newbury	62(1)	35	175
South West, Hampshire, England students					Wakefield	1(1)	2	10
Colin Phillips	5.7	12.00	15.09.69	Reading	Newbury	24(4)	12	60
Berkshire, The Army.					Reading	30	17	85
Kendal Smith	5.10	13.00	02.09.68	Edinburgh	Newbury	42(3)	11	61
Scotland u19, Anglo Scots u21.								
Tyrone Howe					Newbury	14	10	50
Tim Osman	6.3	15.00	17.04.76	Southampton	Newbury	36(3)	15	102
Richard Blake	6.1	13.07	30.06.70	London	Newbury	24(5)	2	10
Howard Graham	5.10	13.07	23.01.69	Whitehaven	Newbury	4(1)	1	40
Army, Combined Services, Berkshire. Other clubs: Morley					Reading			
Brett Wakfer	5.9	12.07	15.04.73	St Ives	Newbury	25(7)	2	10
RAF, Combined Services.					Clifton			
Morgan Davis	6.0	14.00	03.02.75	Ascot	Newbury	17(2)	3	15
England students					Wasps			
Rob Abernathy	6.1	14.00	13.04.68	India	Newbury	17	3	23
Army, Combined Services								
Rob Saltmarsh					Newbury	121)	-	-
Jeremy Griffiths	6.0	13.00	10.05.74	Camarthen	Newbury	19	9	45
Welsh Youth					Llandovery			
Kieron McCormick	6.1	14.00	11.03.76	Newbury	Newbury	5	4	20
Irish Exiles, Berkshire								

FORWARDS

	Ht.	Wt.	Birthdate	Birthplace	CLUB	League Apps	Tries	Pts
Julian Brammer	5.8	17.00	22.11.63	Whitehaven	Newbury	46	4	20
Army, Combined Services, Oxfordshire, Eastern Counties.								
Bernie Williams	6.0	15.07	01.06.68	Cardiff	Newbury	3(1)	-	-
RAF.					Coventry			
Lee Francis	6.5	18.00	15.11.74	Middlesborough	Newbury	1	-	-
Army, Combined Services.					York			
Neil Collins	6.0	18.00	30.04.69	Newbury	Newbury	65	11	55
Berkshire					Reading	8	-	-
Craig Davies	6.3	17.06	25.11.69	Swansea	Newbury	81(3)	51	255
Wales u21, Students.								
John Kingdon	6.1	14.07	24.06.67	Barnstaple	Newbury	57(9)	2	10
Devon								
Seb Stewart					Newbury	32(3)	-	-
Army, Combined Services.								
Giles Powell	6.2	15.07	07.04.69	Pontypool	Newbury	10(7)	-	-
Dan Davis	6.1	19.00	28.08.74	Eastbourne	Newbury	8(11)	-	-
Berkshire					Harlequins			
Simon Brown	5.9	18.07	13.10.72	Oxford	Newbury	18(3)	2	10
Other club: Harlequins. 20(1)/1/5						Bedford 16(3)		5 25
Simon Miall	6.5	16.00	13.03.76	Winchester	Newbury	324)	-	-
England students								
Simon Gully	5.10	16.00	12.08.75	Torquay	Newbury	15(6)	4	20
England colts, South West colts. Other clubs: Torquay, Bristol					Weston s Mare			
Rob Kellam	6.0	17.07	04.02.71	Southampton	Newbury	19(4)	3	15
England U-21, students					London Irish	75(5)	1	5
Chris Hart	6.4	17.00	20.12.74	Swindon	Newbury	14(4)	4	20
Dorset & Wiltshire.					Swindon			

NEWBURY

FACT FILE

Founded: 1928
Nickname: The Blues

Colours: Navy, sky & white irregular hoops
Change colours: Red

GROUND

Address: Monks Lane, Newbury, Berkshire RG14 7RW
Tel : 01635 40103
Capacity: 7,850 Seated: 350 Standing: 7,500

Directions: From M4 take A34 to Newbury, at 4th r'about on Newbury ring road(A34) turn right. Keep left at mini-r'about, ground is half mile on left. From south turn left at1st r'about on A34 ring road.
Nearest Railway Station: Newbury

Car Parking: 300 on ground, 1000 nearby @ £1.

Admission: Season — Adults Standing £90, Seated £150. No concessions
Matchday — Standing: Adults £7, Children £4, OAPs £3
Seated: Adults £8,Children £5, OAPs £4.

Club Shop: Open matchdays & evenings.
Manageress Caroline Luker 0163540103

Clubhouse: Normal licensing hours
Snacks, bar meals & restaurant.
Functions: Capacity 250
Contact Adam Prickett 01635 40103

Training Nights: Tuesday & Thursday

PROGRAMME

Size: A5 Pages: 40 + cover
Price: £1 included with entry
ADVERTISING RATES

Colour	Page £500	Half £300	Qtr. £150
Mono	Page £250	Half £150	Qtr £75

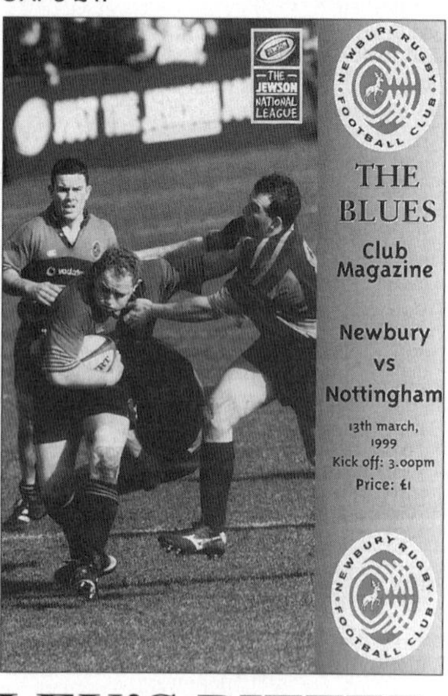

NOTTINGHAM R.F.C.

Chairman	Bryan Ford,	c/o Nottingham RFC
General Manager	Alan Royer	Ireland Avenue
Director of Coaching	Tony Rolt	Beeston
Club Secretary	Audrey Gill	Nottingham
Marketing	Adrian Bentley & George Holohan	NG9 1JD. Tel: 0115 925 4238 Fax: 0115 925 4255

Season 1998/99 started in the customary fashion of recent years at Nottingham with four losses in succession. This disastrous start ensured that Nottingham propped up the league for the early part of the season with a perilous position from which to climb. Two good home wins in the Tetley's Bitter Cup against Preston Grasshoppers and Wharfedale provided some impetus, though in our Fourth Round home tie against Exeter we were shown the ground that needed to be made up should we aspire to promotion.

At this particular time we were content merely to be above the bottom three and starting to string a few league wins together. The forwards were beginning to dominate for large proportions of our games and the midfield combination of Sam Jack (10), Rob Campbell (12) and Chris Atkinson (13) showed considerably more cohesion than in the early stages. The Christmas period saw the turning point in Nottingham's fortunes with a hard fought win in the mud at Birmingham/Solihull on Boxing Day and a solid victory against Rosslyn Park the following week. The only two blemishes on our results sheet from that point onwards were losses away at both Henley and Manchester.

In all, the final run in to the conclusion of the season saw fifteen wins from seventeen outings, a far cry from September and early October, ensuring a fourth place spot for the second year running. Cohesion and the resultant improvement lay much at the door of a side that more or less picked itself by the season's end.

The arrival of Richard Lloyd from Coventry was a bonus, as were the thirteen league tries contributed by scrum half Alan Royer and the 262 points provided by the boot of Chris Atkinson. The selection of Richard Byrom for the Barbarians game at Northampton was a fitting tribute to his services for Nottingham with 365 first team appearances (159 league) over his time at the club. Despite his departure, seasoned campaigners such as Mark Bradley and Martin Freer return for another term, as does Alan Royer.

The squad system at First Team level allowed us to blood several highly talented youngsters into the first team over the season - Adam Sturdy (21), Neil Foulkes (18), Tom Rolt (19), Gareth Taylor (19) and Ben Murphy (18) - and much is expected of them over the coming season. With a settled squad and these young players it augurs well for the forthcoming league campaign.

The Nottingham forwards at work down at Lydney.

NOTTINGHAM

Match No.	Date	H/A	Comp.	Opponents	Result & Score	Att.	15	14	13	12	11
1	05.09	H	JN1	Manchester	L 13-29	400	Atkinson/c2p	Bygrave	Carroll	Stuart	Reynolds
2	12.09	H	JN1	Newbury	L 9-13	400	Atkinson/3p	Bygrave	Redpath	Stuart	Reynolds
3	19.09	A	JN1	Camberley	L 18-25	450	Atkinson/6p	Bygrave	Redpath	Stuart	Reynolds(p)
4	26.09	H	JN1	Henley	L 6-35	400	Atkinson/2p	Bygrave	Redpath(o)	Stuart	Reynolds
5	03.10	A	JN1	Morley	W 19-17	600	Atkinson/2c	Bygrave	Redpath	Stuart	Spencer/t
6	10.10	H	JN1	Lydney	W 25-11	350	Atkinson/t2c2p	Byrom	Redpath	Stuart	Spencer/t
7	24.10	A	JN1	Otley	L 10-22	300	Atkinson/cp	Bygrave(o)	Redpath(v)	Stuart	Spencer
8	31.10	H	JN1	Reading	L 13-19	400	Atkinson/c2p	Bygrave(b)	Redpath	Stuart/t	Spencer(v)
9	07.11	A	JN1	Rosslyn Park	L 24-30	450	Byrom	Reynolds(q)	Redpath(v)	Beatham	Atkinson/3p
10	21.11	H	JN1	Birmingham S*	W 26-21	400	Byrom(b)	Bygrave	Redpath(v)	Beatham	Atkinson/2c3p
11	28.11	A	JN1	Liverpool StH	W 55-0	200	Byrom	Bygrave	Campbell	Beatham(b)	Atkinson/4c4p
12	05.12	H	JN1	Harrogate	W 22-5	400	Byrom	Bygrave	Redpath(b)	Beatham(v)	Atkinson/c4p
13	12.12	A	JN1	Wharfedale	L 5-25	500	Byrom	Bygrave	Redpath	Atinson(v)	Reynolds(q)
14	26.12	A	JN1	Birmingham S	W 13-6	200	Byrom	Spencer	Beatham	Atkinson/c2p	Bygrave
15	02.01	H	JN1	Rosslyn Park	W 21-9	450	Byrom	Bygrave	Campbell	Beatham	Atkinson/c2p(y)
16	16.01	A	JN1	Reading	W 27-18	200	Byrom	Clarke	Atkinson/c4p	Beatham	Bygrave/t
17	23.01	H	JN1	Otley	W 38-10	400	Atkinson/t3c3p	Spencer/t(b)	Beatham	Campbell	Bygrave/t
18	06.02	H	JN1	Morley	W 19-11	400	Atkinson/2p(y)	Spencer	Beatham	Campbell	Bygrave(b)
19	13.02	A	JN1	Henley*	L 24-43	450	Atkinson/3cp	Spencer	Beatham(o)	Campbel/t	Bygrave(b)
20	20.02	H	JN1	Liverpool StH	W 45-11	300	Byrom	Spencer/t	Atkinson/3c3p	Campbell(w)	Reynolds
21	27.02	H	JN1	Camberley	W 40-27	400	Byrom(w)	Spencer/3t	Atkinson/3c3p	Campbell	Reynolds(a)
22	06.03	A	JN1	Lydney	W 11-3	550	Byrom(w)	Spencer	Atkinson/2p	Campbell	Bygrave
23	13.03	A	JN1	Newbury	W 30-21	300	Byrom	Spencer/2t	Atkinson/3c3p	Campbell(w)	Bygrave/t
24	27.03	A	JN1	Manchester	L 17-32	460	Byrom(A)	Bygrave	Atkinson/2cp	Campbell(w)	Reynolds
25	03.04	H	JN1	Wahrfedale	W 39-7	500	Byrom(A)	Bygrave(w)	Atkinson/c4p	Campbell	Reynolds
26	17.04	A	JN1	Harrogate	W 21-17	400	Byrom(p)	Spencer/t	Atkinson/2p(w/t)	Campbell	Bygrave/t
A	17.01	H	TBC	Preston G*	W 50-3	350	Atkinson/t6cp	Bygrave/t(b)	Redpath	Stuart	Spencer(o/t)
B	14.11	H	TBC	Wharfedale	W 27-17	450	Byrom	Bygrave/t	Campbell	Beatham	Atkinson/2cp
C	09.01	H	TBC	Exeter	L 8-24	500	Byrom	Spencer	Atkinson/p	Beatham(y)	Bygrave

* after opponents name indicates a penalty try
Brackets after a player's name indicates he was replaced. eg (a) means he was replaced by replacement code "a" and so on.
/ after a player or replacement name is followed by any scores he made - eg /t, /c, /p, /dg or any combination of these

1998-99 HIGHLIGHTS

League debuts:
Rob Stuart, Sam Jack, Jon Adams, Andrew Knight, Nick Redpath, Richard Lloyd, Mark Lewis, Rob Campbell, Brandon Clarke, Matt Wright.

Ever Presents:
Chris Atkinson, Alan Royer, Sam Jack.

Players used: 27 plus 11 as replacement only.

Most Points in a season:

Pts	Player	T	C	P	DG
272	Chris Atkinson	2	35	64	-
65	Alan Royer	13	-	-	-
53	Sam Jack	7	-	1	5
50	Elloit Spencer	10	-	-	-

Utility back Chris Atkinson broke his own record for points in a season of 262 set last seaon. In his two seasons at Nottingham he has yet to miss a match and in 52 league matches he has scored 534 points.

MATCH FACTS

10	9	1	2	3	4	5	6	7	8	
Jack	Royer	Freer	Claydon(g/t)	Lewis	Delaney	Jones	Bradley	Adams(h)	Brookes	1
Jack	Royer	Freer	Knight(c)	Lewis	Delaney	Jones	Sussum(d)	Brennan(e)	Brookes	2
Jack	Royer	Freer	Knight(c)	Lewis	Delaney	Jones	Sussum(d)	Brennan(e)	Brookes	3
Jack	Royer(l)	Freer	Claydon(g)	Lewis	Delaney	Jones	Bradley	Adams(j)	Brookes(n)	4
Jack/2t	Royer	Freer	Claydon	Lewis	Delaney	Jones	Sussum	Lloyd	Bradley	5
Jack	Royer	Freer	Claydon/t(s)	Lewis	Delaney	Jones	Sussum(e)	Lloyd	Bradley	6
Jack	Royer/t(u)	Freer	Claydon	Lewis(s)	Sussum	Jones	M Wright(f)	Lloyd	Bradley	7
Jack	Royer	Freer	Claydon	Lewis	Sussum	Jones	M Wright(f)	Lloyd	Bradley	8
Jack/t	Royer	Freer	Knight(c)	Lewis	Delaney	Jones	Sussum(f)	Lloyd/t	Bradley/t	9
Jack/dg	Royer	Freer	Knight/t	Lewis	Delaney	Jones	Sussum(n)	Brookes	Bradley	10
Jack/2t	Royer/4t(u)	Freer	Knight	Lewis(k)	Delaney	Jones(x)	Sussum	Brookes/t	Bradley(n)	11
Jack/dg	Royer	Freer	Knight/t(x)	Lewis(m)	Delaney	Sussum	M Wright(r)	Brookes	Bradley	12
Jack	Royer/t(l)	Freer	Knight(x)	Lewis(m)	Delaney	Sussum	M Wright(r)	Brookes	Bradley	13
Jack	Royer	Sturdy	Knight	Lewis	Delaney	Jones/t	Brookes	Lloyd	Bradley(h)	14
Jack/p	Royer(l)	Freer(m)	Knight/t(c)	Lewis	Delaney	Jones	Brookes	Lloyd/t	Bradley(h)	15
Jack/dg	Royer/t	Sturdy	Knight	Lewis	Delaney	Jones	Brookes	Lloyd	Bradley	16
Jack/dg	Royer	Freer(m)	Knight/t	Lewis	Delaney	Jones	Brookes(h)	Lloyd	Bradley	17
Jack/dg	Royer/t(l)	Freer/t(m)	Knight(s)	Lewis	Delaney	Jones	Brookes	Lloyd	Bradley(h)	18
Jack	Royer/t	Freer(m)	Knight(s)	Lewis	Delaney	Jones	Brookes(h)	Lloyd	Bradley	19
Jack(a)	Royer/2t(l)	Freer/t(m)	Knight(s)	Lewis	Delaney/t	Jones	Brookes(h)	Lloyd	Bradley/t	20
Jack/t	Royer(z)	Freer(m)	Knight(x)	Lewis	Delaney/t	Jones	Brookes(h)	Lloyd	Bradley	21
Jack	Royer/t(l)	Freer	Knight	Lewis	Delaney	Jones	Brookes	Lloyd(e)	Bradley(h)	22
Jack	Royer	Freer	Knight	Lewis	Delaney	Jones	Brookes	Lloyd	Bradley(h)	23
Jack/t	Royer/t(l)	Freer	Knight	Lewis	Delaney	Jones(h)	Brookes	Lloyd	Bradley	24
Jack	Royer(l)	Freer/2t	Knight(x)	Sturdy(k)	Delaney/t	Jones(h)	Brookes	Lloyd/t	Bradley/t	25
Jack	Royer(z)	Freer(m)	Knight(x)	Lewis	Delaney	Jones	Brookes	Lloyd	Bradley(h)	26
Jack	Royer(u)	Freer	Claydon	Lewis(g)	Delaney/t	Jones	Sussum	Lloyd(i)	Bradley/t(m)	A
Jack	Royer	Freer	Knight	Lewis	Delaney	Jones	Sussum	Brookes	Bradley3t	B
Jack	Royer(l)	Sturdy/t	Knight(c)	Lewis	Delaney	Jones	Sussum(f)	Lloyd	Bradley	C

REPLACEMENTS: a- R Bygave b- T Reynolds c- C Claydon d- M Bradley e- J Adams f- M Brookes g- A Knight
h- R Sussum i- J Brennan j- D Wright k- D Holland l-T Roly m- A Sturdy n- M Wright o-R Byrom
p- M Holland q- E Spencer r- D Guy s- I Grantham t- G Howarth u- D Roberts v- R Campbell w- S Beatham
x- R Howarth y- B Clarke z- G Taylor A- B Murphy.

That's an average of 10.27 points per match.
He kicked a record 35 conversions, beating his own record from last season by one. His 64 penalties equalled his record of last season. He also passed Simon Hodgkinson's record of 54 career conversions and stands now on 65.
In the early season defeat at Camberley he equalled Guy Gregory's record of 6 penalties in a match.

Scrum half Alan Royer broke the club record for tries in a season with a new mark of 13. That easily beat the previous record of seven which Royer had achieved himself twice. That took his Nottingham career record to 32, 14 clear of Richard Byrom who failed to add to his total of 18.
Winger Elliot Spencer scored 10 and also beat the old record.
Chris Atkinson took his record for scoring in consecutive matches to a club record 38.
Ever present Alan Royer became the second Nottingham back to pass 100 league appearances.
Prop Martin Freer scored four tries in 24 appearnces, he had only managed four tries in his first 132 appearances, quite an improvement.

NOTTINGHAM

LEAGUE STATISTICS

compiled by Stephen McCormack

SEASON	Division	P	W	D	L	F	A	Pts Diff	Lge Pts	Lge Pos	Most Points	Most Tries
89-90	1	11	6	0	5	187	148	39	12	6	82 Simon Hodgkinson	5 Gary Hartley
90-91	1	12	6	0	6	138	194	-56	12	8	80 Simon Hodgkinson	3 Richrad Byrom
91-92	1	12	2	1	9	133	204	-71	5	12r	48 Guy Gregory	4 Martin Pepper
92-93	2	12	8	0	4	249	145	104	16	4	106 Guy Gregory	3 Richard Byrom
93-94	2	18	8	1	9	254	326	-62	17	6	171 Guy Gregory	5 Andy Smallwood
94-95	2	18	8	1	9	299	322	-23	17	7	97 Ian Stent	4 Andy Smallwood
95-96	2	18	5	1	12	333	433	-100	11	9	158 Simon Hodgkinson	7 Alan Royer
96-97	2	22	2	0	20	344	827	-483	4	12r	55 David Evans	5 Richard Bygrave
97-98	JN1	26	13	0	13	527	602	-75	26	7	262 Chris Atkinson	7 Alan Royer
98-99	JN1	26	16	0	10	590	467	123	32	4	272 Chris Atkinson	13 Alan Royer

BIGGEST MARGINS

Home Win 78pts - 78-0 v Morley 24.10.92

Away Win 55pts - 55-0 v Liverpool StH 28.11.98

Home Defeat 65pts - 5-70 v Richmond 16.11.96

Away Defeat 80pts - 22-102 v Coventry 5.10.96

MOST CONSECUTIVE

Appearances 41 Guy Gregory 23.11.91 - 30.4.94

Matches scoring Tries 4 Andy Smallwood

Matches scoring points 38 Chris Atkinson

Victories 5

Defeats 12

MOST POINTS

Scored at Home 78 v Morley 24.10.92

Scored Away 55 v Liverpool StH 28.11.98

Conceded at Home 74 v Newcastle 14.9.96

Conceded Away 102 v Coventry 5.10.96

MOST TRIES

Scored in a match 12 v Morley 24.10.92 (H)

Conceded in a match 14 v Coventry 5.10.96 (A)

MOST APPEARANCES

by a forward 156(1) Martin Freer

by a back 151 (1) Richard Byrom

	MOST IN A SEASON	MOST IN A CAREER	MOST IN A MATCH
Points	272 Chris Atkinson 98-99	597 Simon Hodgkinson 87-93 & 95-97	25 Guy Gregory v Otley 11.9.93 (H)
Tries	13 Alan Royer 98-99	31 Alan Royer 94-99	4 Gary Hartley v Morley 24.10.92 (H) Alan Royer v Liverpool St H 28.11.98 (A)
Conversions	35 Chris Atkinson 98-99	65 Chris Atkinson 97-99	9 Guy Gregory v Morley 24.10.92 (H)
Penalties	64 Chris Atkinson 97-98 & 98-99	142 Simon Hodgkinson 87-93 & 95-97	6 Guy Gregory v Saracens 12.3.94 Chris Atkinson v Camberley 19.09.98 (A)
Drop Goals	9 Guy Gregory 92-93	19 Guy Gregory 91-94	2 Andy Sutton v Harlequins 31.3.90 (A) Guy Gregory v Rosslyn Park 4.4.92 (H) v Rosslyn Park 21.1.92 (A) v Fylde 9.1.93 (H) v Bedford 13.2.93 (A) Simon Hodgkinson v L Irish 17.2.96 (A)

NOTTINGHAM PLAYING SQUAD

BACKS

	Ht.	Wt.	Birthdate	Birthplace	CLUB	League Apps	Tries	Pts
Richard Byrom	6.0	13.05	14.07.61	Kendal	Nottingham	167(3)	18	82
Richard Bygrave	5.9	13.07	02.05.71	Rotherham	Nottingham	86(3)	13	65
Alan Royer	6.0	12.07	01.12.70	Leicester	Nottingham Leicester	104(1)	32	160
Nick Carroll	5.11	12.07	09.01.70	Liverpool	Nottingham Moderns	17(1)	1	49
Mark Holland	5.8	12.10	10.09.72	Knutsford	Nottingham Wilmslow	17(6)	1	5
Brendan Clarke					Nottingham	1(2)	-	-
Chris Atkinson	5.11	14.00	19.05.79	S Africa	Nottingham	52	8	534
Nick Redpath					Nottingham	11	-	-
Elliott Spencer	0	13.00	05.02.71	Oakham	Nottingham Leicester	16(3)	10	50
Tom Rolt					Nottingham	(8)		
Simon Beatham	6.4	15.02	12.06.73	Lincoln	Nottingham	30	3	15
Sam Jack	6.0	14.00	06.02.76	Christchurch	Nottingham Linwood	26	7	53
Dave Roberts	5.8	13.00			Nottingham	3(2)		
Rob Campbell	5.11	15.00	03.02.73	Newport	Nottingham	12(6)	1	5

FORWARDS

	Ht.	Wt.	Birthdate	Birthplace	CLUB	League Apps	Tries	Pts
Martin Freer	5.11	15.07	15.10.63	Chatham	Nottingham	156(1)	8	39
Charlie Claydon	5.10	13.10	24.07.66		Nottingham	60(4)	3	15
Mark Bradley	6.3	15.07	21.12.69	Derby	Nottingham	109(4)	11	55
Lee Jones	6.4	17.00	16.06.71	Ilkeston	Nottingham	74	4	20
John Brennan	5.11	14.00	20.12.71	Birmingham	Nottingham	43	3	15
Andrew Knight					Nottingham	20(2)	5	25
Glen Delaney	6.6		16.11.73	New Zealand	Nottingham	50	7	35
Richard Lloyd					Nottingham Coventry	18 4(1)	3 1	15 5
Adam Sturdy					Nottingham	4(11)	-	-
Dave Wright	5.10	16.10			Nottingham Fylde	19(1)	-	-
Matt Wright					Nottingham	4(3)	-	-
Matt Lewis					Nottingham	25	-	-
Michael Brookes	6.1	15.04	20.11.74	Nottingham	Nottingham Moseley	26(10)	5	25
Jon Adams Other clubs: Wakefield	5.11	15.00	02.09.68	Wakefield	Nottingham Sandal	2(4)	-	-

NOTTINGHAM

FACT FILE

Founded: 1877
Nickname: Green & Whites

Colours: Green & white
Change colours: Yellow.

GROUND

Address: Ireland Avenue, Dovecote Lane, Beeston, Nottingham. NG9 1JD.
Tel: 0115 925 4238 Fax: 0115 925 4255
Capacity: 4,950 Seated: 450 Standing: 4,500

Directions: Off Queens Road, Beeston. Main Nottingham to Long Eaton Road
Nearest Railway Station: Beeston, left out of station to Main Queens Rd, left into Dovecote Lane, right into Ireland Ave, ground at end

Car Parking: 175 on ground

Admission:
Matchday Adults £7 OAPs/Children £3

Club Shop: Open matchdays. Club Marketing 0115 925 4238

Clubhouse: Matchday & training nights, snacks available.
Functions Yes

Training Nights: Tuesdays & Thursdays (Seniors)

PROGRAMME

Size: A5 Pages: 36 + cover Price: £1
Editor: George Holohan 0115 925 4238

ADVERTISING RATES
Colour Full page £500 Half page £250
Mono Full page £300 Half page £150

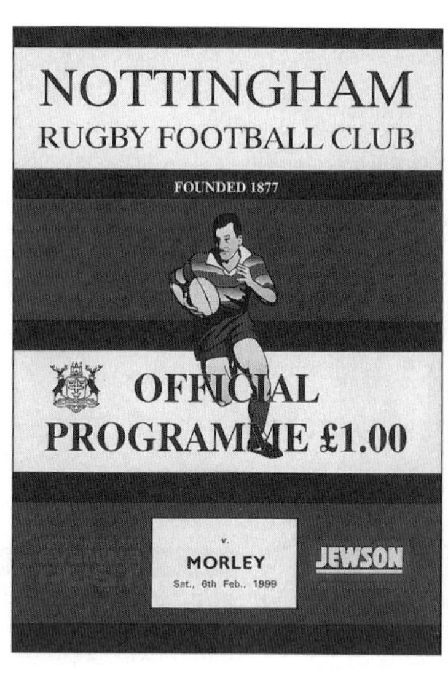

Richard Byrom, finally retiring after making his debut back in 1985.

He made 365 first team appearances (159 of those in league matches) over his time at the club.

He is seen here while representing the Barbarians last season.

OTLEY R.U.F.C.

President	Brian Agar	24 Park Row, Menston, Ilkley LS29 6EN 01943 872207 (H)
Chairman	Paul Jacques	Springsyde, Birdcage Walk, Otley. LS21 3HB 01943 462714 (H), 0113 258 1700 (B)
Club Secretary	Marc Lawrence	16 Bankfield Terrace, Baildon, Shipley BD17 7HZ 01274 593535 (H)
Director of Rugby	Mike Wright	Cherry Tree Cottage, Dacre, Harrogate HG3 4ES 01423 780216 (H)
Director of Coaching	Michael Barnett	28 Beech Road, Harrogate HG2 8AG
Press Officer	John C Finch	9 Glen Mount, Menston, Ilkley. LS29 6DJ 01943872491 (H)

Otley's season fell into a familiar pattern - an excellent home record, if you forgive the Tetley's Bitter Cup defeat at the hands of Morley plus the dropping of a point to neighbours Harrogate, and the continual dreadful run of away defeats.

They were successful only at Morley and Liverpool St. Helens and yet they relinquished big leads at both Manchester and Reading by relaxing too soon, whilst a single try gave Henley Hawks the edge.

A first match close victory over Rosslyn Park raised expectancy but a 26 nil drubbing by new boys Birmingham & Solihull the following week was a sobering experience as was the 5-6 defeat at Harrogate two weeks later after the game was played out in `Gate's" 22, but that proved to be an insight into what was to follow.

West Samoan Lafaele Filipo was a tower of strength in the back row, challenging for leading Division One try scorer until the final game and he will be present again although he has to recover from a broken shoulder bone first.

Two of last years recruits from Leeds, second row Paul Williams and No 6 Phil Griffin will be with us, Phil taking over as skipper from fellow back row Neil Hargreaves who, after three successful years at the helm had stated his intention to retire, but has had a change of heart and intends to compete for that No 7 spot he has graced so well over his years with Headingley, Wakefield, Leeds and Yorkshire before arriving at Cross Green.

Ex Harrogate coach, Peter Clegg, after a year assisting Mike Barnett is to assume full control of the First XV, Mike overseeing the whole aspect of coaching throughout the club with ex Great Britain RL scrum-half Ian Orum taking charge of the bundle of talent at colts level. Recruitment for the coming season has been good and is well within budget - it is the intention of chairman Paul Jacques that once again there is a profit on turnover at the end of the season.

Lafaele Filipo driving through against Wharfedale with Andy Brown in support.

OTLEY

Match No.	Date	H/A	Comp.	Opponents	Result & Score	Att.	15	14	13	12	11
1	05.09	H	JN1	Rosslyn Park	W23-20	450	Clappison/2c3p	Dardy(l)	Smith	Billington	Thornton
2	12.09	A	JN1	Birmingham S	L 0-26	250	Barlow	Duckett	Billington	Hartley	Thornton
3	19.09	H	JN1	Liverpool StH	W 13-7	400	Clappison/c2p	Duckett	Billington	Hartley/t	Thornton
4	26.09	A	JN1	Harrogate	L 5-6	750	Clappison	Duckett	Billington	Hartley	Thornton
5	03.10	H	JN1	Wharfedale	W25-11	550	Duckett	Smith/t	Billington	Hartley	Thornton
6	10.10	A	JN1	Manchester	L 26-36	500	Duckett	Smith/t	Billington	Hartley	Thornton
7	24.10	H	JN1	Nottingham	W22-10	300	Duckett	Smith	Billington	Hartley(x)	Gardner
8	31.10	A	JN1	Camberley	W22-18	300	Duckett	Smith(b)	Billington	Hartley	Gardner
9	07.11	H	JN1	Henley	W 19-8	400	Duckett/t	Gardner	Billington/t	Hartley	Thornton
10	21.11	A	JN1	Morley	W25-20	700	Duckett	Darby/t(y)	Billinton	Gardner	Thornton
11	28.11	H	JN1	Lydney	W 34-3	400	Duckett	Darby/t	Billington	Hartley	Thornton
12	05.12	H	JN1	Newbury	W20-11	300	Duckett	Darby/t	Billington	Hartley	Thornton
13	12.12	A	JN1	Reading	L 25-26	300	Duckett	Darby	Billington	Gardner	Thornton
14	19.12	A	JN1	Lydney	L 3-10	700	Duckett	Smith	Billington	Hartley	Thornton
15	26.12	H	JN1	Morley	W 21-7	700	Hawkin/2c	Smith	Gardner	Hartley/t	Thornton
16	02.01	A	JN1	Henley	L 0-5	650	Hawkin	Darby	Billington	Gardner	Smith
17	16.01	H	JN1	Camberley	W22-18	400	Duckett	Gardner	Whatmuff/t	Hartley	Thornton
18	23.01	A	JN1	Nottingham	L 10-28	400	Duckett	Gardner	Wahtmuff	Hartley/t	Thornton
19	30.01	H	JN1	Manchester	W 20-6	500	Duckett	Gardner	Whatmuff/t	Hartley	Smith
20	06.02	A	JN1	Wharfedale	L 3-21	1,000	Duckett	Gardner	Whatmuff	Hartley	Smith
21	13.02	H	JN1	Harrogate	D 12-12	500	Duckett	Gardner	Whatmuff	Hartley	Smith
22	27.02	A	JN1	Liverpool StH	W16-12	200	Hawkin	Gardner	Whatmuff	Hartley	Smith
23	13.03	H	JN1	Birmingham S	W37-12	300	Hawkin/p	Gardner/3t	Whatmuff	Hartley/t	Smith
24	27.03	A	JN1	Rosslyn Park	L 13-24	500	Hawkin	Gardner/t	Whatmuff	Hartley(n)	Smith
25	03.04	H	JN1	Reading	W66-10	450	Hawkin	Gardner	Whatmuff/t	Hartley	Smith(m)
26	17.04	A	JN1	Newbury	L 20-39	450	Hawkin(n/t)	Gardner	Whatmuff	Hartley/t	Smith/t
A	17.10	H	TBC	Morley	L 18-20	600	Duckett	Smith	Billington	Hartley/t(w)	Thornton

* after opponents name indicates a penalty try
Brackets after a player's name indicates he was replaced. eg (a) means he was replaced by replacement code "a" and so on.
/ after a player or replacement name is followed by any scores he made - eg /t, /c, /p, /dg or any combination of these

1998-99 HIGHLIGHTS

League debuts:
Dan Clappison, David Hall, Paul Williams, Phil Griffin, Ryan Duckett, Gary Cassidy.

Ever Presents: None - most appearances: 25 David Hall, 23(1) Dan Clappison.

Players used: 25 plus 7 as replacement only.
Did well using just 25 players in their starting line up, this was eight less than last season.

Most Points in a season:

Pts	Player	T	C	P	DG
138	D Clappison	-	33	23	1
75	L Filipo	15	-	-	-
35	S Hawkin	1	6	6	-
35	G Cassidy	7	-	-	-

Dan Clappison topped the points scoring list in his first season at the club having joined from Harrogate during the summer.

MATCH FACTS

10	9	1	2	3	4	5	6	7	8	
Hawkin	Brown/t	Rice	Kelley	Hall	Carroll	Williams	Henry(k)	Griffin	Burke	1
Clappison	Brown	Rice	Kelley	Hall	Williams	Henry(f)	Griffin(j)	Hargreaves	Filipo	2
Hawkin	Brown(s)	Halligan(r)	Sayers	Rice	Carroll(q)	Henry	Burke	Hargreavs	Filipo	3
Hawkin	Brown	Halligan(r)	Kelley	Hall	Williams	Henry(u)	Griffin	Hargreaves	Burke	4
Clappison/2cpdg	Brown	Hall	Kelley	Rice	Carroll	Henry	Griffin	Hargreaves	Burke	5
Clappison/2c4p	Brown	Hall	Kelley	Rice	Carroll	Henry	Griffin	Hargreaves	Filipo/t	6
Clappison/2c(c/p)	Cassidy/t(d)	Hall	Sayers	Rice	Carroll	Williams	Griffin/t(h)	Hargreaves	Filipo/t	7
Clappison/c	Cassidy/2t	Halligan	Sayers	Hall	Carroll	Williams	Henry	Hargreaves	Filipo	8
Clappison/2c	Cassidy/t	Halligan(e)	Sayers	Hall	Carroll	Williams(i)	Henry	Hargreaves	Filipo	9
Clappison/2c2p	Cassidy	Hall	Sayers	Rice	Carroll(i)	Williams	Henry(j)	Hargreaves	Filipo/2t	10
Clappison/2c2p(c/2c)	Cassidy/t	Halligan(r)	Sayers	Hall	Carroll/t	Williams/t	Griffin(h)	Hargreaves	Filipo	11
Hawkin/p(q)	Cassidy	Halligan	Sayers	Hall/t	Henry(f)	Williams	Griffin	Hargreaves	Filipo/t	12
Hawkin/t2c2p	Cassidy	Halligan(r)	Sayers	Hall	Carroll	Williams(h)	Griffin(j)	Hargreaves	Filpio/t	13
Hawkin/p	Cassidy	Halligan	Sayers	Hall	Carroll	Williams(j)	Griffin	Hargreaves	Filipo	14
Calppison/p(z)	Cassidy/t	Hall	Sayers	Rice	Carroll	Williams(h)	Griffin/t(j)	Hargreaves	Filipo/t	15
Clappison	Thornton	Rice	Sayers	Hall	Burke	Williams	Griffin	Hargreaves	Filipo	16
Clappison/2cp	Cassidy	Hall	Sayers	Rice	Carroll	Burke	Griffin	Hargreaves	Filipo/t	17
Clappison	Cassidy	Hall/t	Sayers	Rice	Carroll	Williams	Griffin	Hargreaves	Burke	18
Clappison/cp	Cassidy	Hall	Sayers	Rice	Carroll	Williams(h)	Griffin(j)	Hargreaves	Filipo	19
Clappison/p(b)	Cassidy(d)	Hall	Sayers	Rice	Carroll	Henry(g)	Burke	Hargreaves	Filipo	20
Hawkin	Cassidy/t(d)	Hall	Sayers	Rice	Carroll	Henry(g)	Burke(i)	Hargreaves	Filipo/t	21
Clappison/2p	Brown	Hall	Sayers	Rice	Carroll	Williams/t(h)	Burke	Griffin	Filipo/t	22
Clappison/3cp(x)	Cassidy(d)	Hall	Sayers(v)	Rice	Carroll	Williams	Burke	Griffin/t	Filipo	23
Clappison/p	Cassidy(d)	Hall	Sayers	Rice	Henry(o)	Williams	Burke/t	Griffin	Filipo	24
Clappison/8c	Cassidy(d/2t)	Hall	Sayers(v)	Rice	Carroll	Williams	Burke	Hargreaves	Filipo/4t	25
Clappison	Cassidy(d)	Hall	Sayers	Rice	Carroll	Williams	Burke(B)	Hargreaves	Filipo	26
Clappison/c2p	Brown	Hall(p)	Kelley(v)	Rice	Carroll	Williams	Griffin	Hargreaves/t(A)	Filiopo	A

REPLACEMENTS: a-D Clappison b-C Thornton c-S Hawkin d-A Brown e- S Rice f- I Carroll g- P Williams h- S Henry i- P Griffin j- J Burke k- L Filipo l- W Hartley m- R Barlow n- R Duckett o- N Hargreaves p- S Halligan q- R Smith r- C Baldwin s- G Cassidy t- R Moss u- S Hudson v- A Merkin w- S Gardner x- S Langley y- A Eastham z- R Whatmuff A-T Grieg

He was leading points scorer at Harrogate back in 94-95 with 110 points.

Otley achieved their biggest ever win and highest score when they beat struggling Reading 66-10 in their penultimate league match of the season. Their previous bests were both in the 61-6 win against Askeans back in the 1992-93 season.

The 10 tries scored against Reading equalled their record set against Hereford back in 1991 in Division Four North.

Dan Clappison converted eight of the tries, beating the club record of seven, held by Ian Colquhoun against Birmingham & Solihull in April 1991.

Otley went through the season unbeaten at home with the only blemish on their record a 12 all draw against fellow Yorkshire side Harrogate.

Where they fell down was their away form which was woeful. They managed just three wins and were beaten 10 times.

OTLEY

LEAGUE STATISTICS
compiled by Stephen McCormack

SEASON	Division	P	W	D	L	F	A	Pts Diff	Lge Pts	Lge Pos	Most Points	Most Tries
89-90	North 1	10	9	0	1	141	77	64	18		43 David Lester	3 John Walker & David Lester
90-91	D4N	12	11	0	1	426	89	337	22		77 David Lester	6 Adrian Scott
91-92	3	12	5	0	7	177	190	-13	10		62 Richard Petyt	4 Mark Farrar
92-93	3	11	8	1	2	274	118	156	17		121 Peter Rutledge	6 Glyn Melville & Mark Farrar
93-94	2	18	4	1	13	235	449	-214	9		119 Peter Rutledge	7 Sean Atkinson
94-95	3	18	9	0	9	278	258	20	18		167 Peter Rutledge	6 Peter Rutledge
95-96	3	18	6	1	11	278	441	-163	13		147 Peter Rutledge	3 John Hall & Jon Flint
96-97	3	30	13	0	17	720	766	-46	26		287 Peter Rutledge	22 Mark Kirby
97-98	JN1	26	10	1	15	447	679	-232	21		150 Peter Rutledge	7 Wayne Hartley Chris Thornton
98-99	JN1	26	15	1	10	508	416	92	31		138 Dan Clappison	15 Lafaele Filipo

BIGGEST MARGINS

Home Win	56pts - 66-10 v Reading 03.04.99
Away Win	30pts - 37-7 v Lichfield 13.10.90
Home Defeat	61pts - 7-68 v Worcester 21.2.98
Away Defeat	79pts - 9-88 v Sale 12.2.94

MOST CONSECUTIVE

Appearances	41 Richard Petyt 11.11.91 - 30.4.94
Matches scoring Tries	5 Glyn Melville
Matches scoring points	18 Peter Rutledge
Victories	9
Defeats	7

MOST POINTS

Scored at Home	66 v Reading 03.04.99
Scored Away	52 v Clifton 22.2.97
Conceded at Home	68 v Worcester 21.2.98
Conceded Away	88 v Sale 12.2.94

MOST TRIES

Scored in a match	10 v Hereford 1991, Reading 1999
Conceded in a match	14 v sale 12.2.94

MOST APPEARANCES

by a forward	157(2) Steve Rice
by a back	111 Peter Rutledge

	MOST IN A SEASON	MOST IN A CAREER	MOST IN A MATCH
Points	287 Peter Rutledge 96-97	991 Peter Rutledge 92-98	25 Mark Kirkby v Redruth 8.2.97
Tries	22 Mark Kirkby 96-97	41 Glyn Melville 87-96	5 Mark Kirkby v Redruth 8.2.97 (A)
Conversions	56 Peter Rutledge 96-97	125 Peter Rutledge 92-98	8 Dan Clappison v Reading 03.04.99 (H)
Penalties	45 Peter Rutledge 96-97	207 Peter Rutledge 92-98	6 Peter Rutledge v Harrogate 29.10.94 (A)
Drop Goals	7 Rihard Petyt 93-94	10 Richard Petyt 91-94	2 Richard Peyt v Nottingham 11.9.93 (A)

OTLEY PLAYING SQUAD

BACKS	Ht.	Wt.	Birthdate	Birthplace	CLUB	League Apps	Tries	Pts
Dan Clappison					Otley Harrogate	22(2)	-	138
Simon Smith					Otley	59(4)	15	75
Mark Billington	6.1	14.00	14.06.71	Huddersfield	Otley	82(4)	16	80
Simon Hawkin	5.7	13.00	31.03.75	Otley	Otley	68(9)	8	149
Anthony Cadman	5.8	11.08	12.07.76	Portsmouth	Otley	40(7)	4	34
Tony Grieg	6.0	14.00	01.09.71	Bebbington	Otley	10(2)	1	5
Sam Gardner					Otley	29(5)	9	45
Robert Whatmuff					Otley	23(7)	6	30
William Darby					Otley	12(2)	8	40
Andy Brown					Otley	56(7)	10	50
Ryan Duckett					Otley	18(3)	3	15
Wayne Hartley					Otley Leeds	47(2)	13	65
Chris Thornton					Otley Leeds	41(2) 62(1)	9 22	45 110
Gary Cassidy					Otley	18(1)	7	35
Richard Barlow					Otley	4(4	1	5

FORWARDS	Ht.	Wt.	Birthdate	Birthplace	CLUB	League Apps	Tries	Pts
Chris Baldwin	6.0	16.06	30.03.74	Sheffield	Otley	85(6)	1	5
Steve Rice	6.1	16.08	10.06.63	Otley	Otley	157(3)	2	9
Jonathan Burke	6.6	17.00	01.12.71	Bradford	Otley Rugby	83(6)	7	35
Neil Hargreaves Other clubs: Headingley 33/3/12, Leeds 8/1/5.	6.1	14.00	22.04.65	Leeds	Otley Wakefield	105(1) 9	5 -	25 -
Ian Judson					Otley	(1)	-	-
Andrew Merkin					Otley	(2)	-	-
Phil Griffin					Otley Leeds	18(4) 67(7)	5 13	25 65
Paul Williams					Otley Leeds	34(2) 3	7 -	35 -
Paul Kelley					Otley	43(1)	1	5
Simon Henry					Otley	36(8)	-	-
David Hall					Otley Harrogate	25(5) 74(2)	3 2	15 10
Lafaele Filipo					Otley	33(4)	16	80
Ian Carroll					Otley	29(5)	2	10
Duncan Sayers					Otley	256)	-	-
Sam Halligan					Otley	13(5)	1	5

OTLEY

FACT FILE

Founded: 1865

Colours : Black with irregular white hoops
Change colours: Red with irregualr white hoops

GROUND

Address: Cross Green, Otley. LS21 1HE
Tel: 01943 850142 Fax: 01943 461180
Capacity: 7,000 Seated: 499 Standing: 6,501

Directions: Left hand side of Pool Road, leading to Harrogate, 1/2 mile fromtown centre.
Nearest Railway Station: Leeds BR

Car Parking: 100 on ground

Admission: Season Adults Patrons £70, Members £60, Children/OAPs £30
Matchday Adults Standing £6, Children/OAPs £2;
Seated Adults £8,Children/OAPs £3

Club Shop: Yes, matchdays & Sunday lunchtime

Clubhouse: Normal licensing hours, three bars with snacks available
Functions: Capacity 130 seated Contact Peter Longstaffe 01943 - 461180 or 850142

Training Nights: Tuesdays & Thursdays

PROGRAMME

Size: A5 Price: £1
Pages: 28 + cover
Editor: Peter Thompson, 0113 284 2134

ADVERTISING RATES
Mono - Full page £200
Half page £120
Qtr page £60

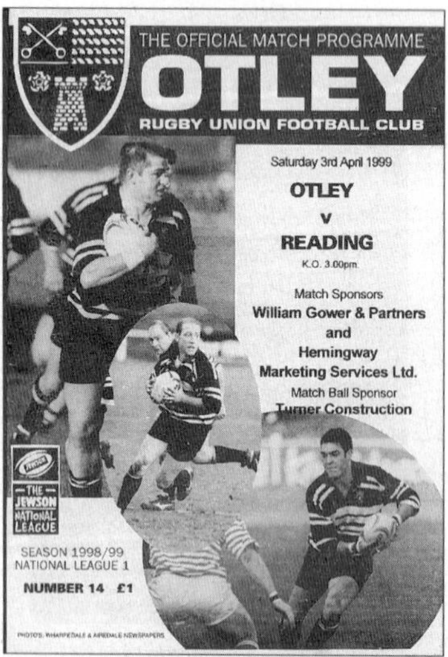

Neil Hargreaves, Otley captain for the past three season.

PRESTON GRASSHOPPERS R.F.C.

President	George Thompson		c/o Preston Grasshoppers RFC,
Chairman	David Taylorson		Lightfoot Green,Fulwood,
Club Secretary	Peter Ashcroft	01772744066 (H).	Preston, Lancs PR4 0AP Tel: 01772 863546
Admin Officer/ Commercial	Ken Moore	01772 720878 (H) .	Fax: 01772 861605
Fixtures Secretary	John Powell	121 Bare Lane, Bare, Morecambe, Lancs. LA4 4RD. 01524 424514 (H), 01772 863546 (B), 01772 861605 (Fax)	
Press Officer	John Hetherington	01772 712162 (H)	

After 130 years of trying, `Hoppers at last won their first senior trophy. Having come close on several occasions in recent seasons, the league championship finally found its way to Lightfoot Green.

At the end of January, `Hoppers looked odds-on for the title with seventeen wins from eighteen outings giving them a six point lead over Stourbridge. Away defeats at Sheffield and Kendal in February put a different complexion on things and four wins from the final four fixtures became the only certain route to promotion.

A victory over strugglers Lichfield proved straightforward but a first ever visit to Whitchurch was quite a different kettle of fish. Although `Hoppers had run in 50 points against the Jewson Two North newcomers on the opening day of the season, they quickly realised that their Midlands opponents had learned from their experience in the intervening months and a tense battle was joined. Not for the first time in the season, `Hoppers demonstrated that the game lasts at least 80 minutes as stand off Michael Lough ran in an injury time try to steal victory.

In the final home fixture, early Hinckley resistance was overcome and Hoppers passed the half century of points. The champagne was put on ice, however, as news came through that Stourbridge had claimed an injury time victory to put an end to a long unbeaten Kendal run. The last Saturday of the season saw a large following travel to Sandal knowing that defeat would almost certainly cost `Hoppers the title as Stourbridge were favourites for a big win at Lichfield. In fact, they ran in over 70 points, but it was all in vain as an Iain Bruce try midway through the first half set `Hoppers en route for victory. Thereafter they never looked back with a determined performance producing a deserved win.

Australian Michael Lough's first full season earned him the Jewson Two North player of the season award. The stand off's 27 tries included a number of match savers but when he passed the ball, wingers Iain Bruce and Gary Monaghan's finishing skills were also of the highest order with 25 and seventeen tries respectively.Skipper Neil Ashton's season was dogged by injury but his presence on the field proved inspirational. His brother Ian, who has now chosen to retire, had an outstanding season and, elsewhere in the pack, the fact that locks Josh Williams and Michael Bailey were ever present was a key factor.

Coaches John Morgan and Chris Dew produced a side whose style of rugby always entertain ed with an early season assessment that `Hoppers concede points but they inevitably score more than their opponents' holding true.

All smiles as the champagne flows following winning the Jewson National Two North Trophy

PRESTON GRASSHOPPERS

Match No.	Date	H/A	Comp.	Opponents	Result & Score	15	14	13	12	11
1	05.09	H	J2N	Whitchurch	W 50-7	Emmett/3c3p	Bruce/4t	Fields	Chesworth	Monaghan(l/t)
2	12.09	A	J2N	Lichfield	W 30-15	Emmett/t3c3p	Kirkpatrick	Fields	Chesworth	Swarbrick
3	26.09	H	J2N	Kendal	W 27-18	Emmett/3c2p	Bruce/t	Smith	Chesworth/t	Monaghan/t
4	03.10	A	J2N	Sedgley Park	W 27-19	Emmett/2cp	Bruce/2t	Smith	Chesworth	Monaghan
5	10.10	H	J2N	Sheffield	W 38-18	Emmett/2c3p	Bruce/t	Smith	Chesworth	Monaghan/t
6	24.10	A	J2N	Winnington P	W 50-20	Emmett/5c	Bruce/t	Smith/2t	Chesworth(b)	Monaghan
7	31.10	H	J2N	Aspatria	W 27-12	Emmett/3c2p	Bruce	Smith/t	Chesworth	Monaghan/t
8	07.11	A	J2N	Walsall	W 65-29	Emmett/7c2p	Bruce/t	Smith(b)	Chesworth	Monaghan/4t
9	21.11	H	J2N	Stourbridge	W 32-3	Emmett/3c2p	Bruce	Smith	Chesworth	Monaghan/2t
10	28.11	A	J2N	Nuneaton	W 31-8	Emmett/3c	Bruce/t	Smith	Chesworth	Monaghan/t
11	05.12	H	J2N	New Brighton	L 9-15	Emmett/3p	Bruce	Smith	Chesworth	Monaghan
12	12.12	H	J2N	Sandal	W 39-26	Emmett/2c	Bruce/3t	Smith	Chesworth	Monaghan/t
13	19.12	A	J2N	Hinckley	W 20-9	Emmett/cp	Bruce/t	Smith	Chesworth	Monaghan
14	27.12	A	J2N	New Brighton	W 15-13	Emmett/p	Bruce	Smith/c	Chesworth	Monaghan
15	02.01	H	J2N	Nuneaton	W 30-16	Emmett/t2c2p	Bruce	Smith/t	Chesworth	Monaghan/t
16	09.01	A	J2N	Stourbridge	W 25-10	Emmett/2cpdg	Bruce	Smith	Chesworth	Monaghan/t
17	16.01	H	J2N	Walsall	W 39-5	Smith/2c2p(a/t2c)	Bruce/t	Fields	Chesworth	Kirkpatrick/t
18	23.01	A	J2N	Aspatria	W 15-0	Smith/cp	Bruce/t	Fields	Chesworth	Monaghan
19	30.01	H	J2N	Winnington P	W 60-8	Smith/t5c	Bruce/5t	Fields	Chesworth/t	Monaghan
20	06.02	A	J2N	Sheffield	L 3-14	Emmett/p	Bruce	Smith	Fields	Monaghan
21	13.02	H	J2N	Sedgley Park	W 24-18	Emmett/2c	Mulholland	Smith	Chesworth	Monaghan
22	27.02	A	J2N	Kendal	L 7-15	Emmett/c	Bruce(b)	Smith	Chesworth	Monaghan
23	13.03	H	J2N	Lichfield	W 46-5	Smith/t2c	Kirkpatrick(a/c)	Fields	Chesworth/t	Monaghan/2t
24	27.03	A	J2N	Whitchurch	W 20-16	Emmett/cp	Bruce/t	Smith/t	Chesworth/t	Monaghan
25	03.04	H	J2N	Hinckley	W 57-11	Emmett/3c2p	Bruce/t(c)	Smith/t	Chesworth	Monaghan/2t
26	17.04	A	J2N	Sandal	W 36-11	Emmett/2c4p	Bruce/t	Smith/t	Chesworth	Monaghan
A	19.09	H	TB1	Kenilworth	W 43-6	Emmett/5cp	Bruce/2t	Fields	Chesworth	Smith
B	17.10	A	TB2	Notttingham	L 3-50	Emmett/p	Bruce	Smith	Chesworth	Monaghan

* after opponents name indicates a penalty try
Brackets after a player's name indicates he was replaced. eg (a) means he was replaced by replacement code "a" and so on.
/ after a player or replacement name is followed by any scores he made - eg /t, /c, /p, /dg or any combination of these

1998-99 HIGHLIGHTS

Ever Presents:
Michael Lough, Josh Williams, Mike Bailey
25 John Chesworth,
24 Gary Monaghan, John Bleasdale, Andy Roberts (1), Rob Smith
23 Iain Bruce

Players used: 28 plus three as a replacement only.

Most Points in a season:

Pts	Player	T	C	P	DG
226	M Emmett	3	53	35	-
135	M Lough	27	-	-	-
125	I Bruce	25	-	-	-
85	G Monaghan	17	-	-	-
76	R Smith	9	11	3	-
25	J Williams	5	-	-	-

MATCH FACTS

10	9	1	2	3	4	5	6	7	8	
Lough/2t	Bleasdale	D Chadwick	Evans(j)	Fenton(i)	Williams	Bailey	I Ashton(k)	Roberts	N Ashton(m)	1
Lough/t	Bleasdale(p)	Fenton	K Chadwick	D Chadwick(i)	Williams	Bailey	I Ashton/t	Roberts	N Ashton(q)	2
Lough	Bleasdale	D Chadwick	K Chadwick	Fenton	Williams	Bailey	I Ashton	Roberts	Sword	3
Lough/t	Bleasdale(u)	D Chadwick(i)	K Chadwick/t	Fenton	Williams	Bailey	I Ashton(k)	Roberts	Sword	4
Lough/t	Bleasdale	D Chadwick	K Chadwick	Fenton/t	Williams	Bailey	I Ashton(k)	Roberts/t(v)	Sword	5
Lough/t	Bleasdale/t(p)	D Chadwick	Porteous	Spicer	Williams/t	Bailey/t	I Ashton(k)	Roberts	Sword/t	6
Lough	Bleasdale	D Chadwick	Porteous	Fenton	Williams	Steel(r)	Edwards(g/t)	Roberts	Bailey	7
Lough/3t	Bleasdale(p)	D Chadwick(i)	Porteous(j)	Fenton	Williams	Bailey	Kay(q)	Roberts	N Ashton(h/t)	8
Lough/t	Bleaasdale	D Chadwick(i)	K Chadwick	Fenton	Williams	Bailey	N Ashton/t	Roberts	Sword	9
Lough/2t	Bleasdale	D Chadwick	K Chadwick	Fenton(i)	Williams	Bailey	N Ashtonr	Roberts(g)	Sword/t	10
Lough	Bleasdale	D Chadwick	K Chadwick	Fenton(i)	Williams	Bailey	N Ashton	I Ashton(h)	Sword	11
Lough	Bleasdale	D Chadwick	Porteous(j)	Spicer	Williams/t	Bailey	I Ashton(r)	Roberts/2t	N Ashton	12
Lough/t	Bleasdale	Fenton	K Chadwick	Spicer	Williams	Bailey(r)	I Ashton	Roberts	N Ashton/t	13
Lough/t	Bleasdale	Fenton	Evans	Spicer	Williams	Bailey	Sword	Roberts	N Ashton/t	14
Lough/t	Bleasdale	Fenton	Evans	Spicer	Williams	Bailey	Sword(g)	Roberts	N Ashton	15
Lough/2t	Bleasdale	Fenton	Evans	Spicer	Williams	Bailey	Sword(g)	Roberts	N Ashton	16
Lough/t	Lord	D Chadwick	K Chadwick/t	Spicer	Williams	Bailey	I Ashton(w)	Roberts	N Ashton(r)	17
Lough	Bleasdale/t	Fenton	Evans	Spicer	Williams	Bailey	Roberts	Dewhurst(g)	Sword(k)	18
Lough/t	Bleasdale	Fenton	Evans/t	Spicer	Williams/t	Bailey	I Ashton(k)	Roberts	Dewhurst	19
Lough	Lord	Fenton	Evans	Spicer	Williams	Bailey	Dewhurst	Roberts(g)	N Ashton	20
Lough/2t	Bleasdale	Fenton(d)	K Chadwick/t	Spicer	Williams/t	Bailey	Dewhurst(g)	Roberts	N Ashton	21
Lough	Bleasdale	Fenton	K Chadwick/t(e)	Spicer	Williams	Bailey	N Ashton	Roberts(w)	Sword(g)	22
Lough/2t	Bleasdale	Fenton(d)	K Chadwick(e)	Spicer	Williams/t	Bailey	I Ashton/t(t)	Edwards	Sword	23
Lough/t	Bleasdale	D Chadwick	K Chadwick	Spicer	Williams	Bailey	I Ashton	Roberts	Sword	24
Lough/3t	Bleasdale/t	D Chadwick	K Chadwick(e)	Spicer(f)	Williams	Bailey	I Ashton(q)	Roberts	N Ashton/t(r)	25
Lough	Bleasdale	Fenton/t	Evans(j)	Spicer	Williams	Bailey/t	I Ashton(w)	Roberts(r)	N Ashton	26
Lough/t	Bleasdale	D Chadwick	K Chadwick/t	Spicer	Williams	Battersby	Edwards/t	Roberts	Bailey/t	A
Lough	Bleasdal	D Chadwick(i)	K Chadwick(v)	Fenton(s)	Williams	Bailey	Edwards(q)	Roberts	Sword	B

REPLACEMENTS:					
	a- M Emmett	b- A Fields	c - P Bleadale	d - D Chadwick	e - C Evans
f - K Fenton	g - I Ashton	h - A Roberts	i - R Spicer	j - K Chadwick	k - P Edwards
l - J Swarbrick	m - N Battersby	n - J Kirkpatrick	p - M James	q - C Steel	r - M Sword
s - L Bell	t - J Kay	u - P Lord	v - J Porteous	w - G Dewhurst	

Former Waterloo player Martin Emmett topped the points scorers list for Champions Preston.

Australian Michael Lough was the leading try scorer with an incredible 27 tries in 26 matches from stand off.

Winger Iain Bruce also averaged over a try a match with 25 tries from 23 matches.

Preston had 3 ever presents which was the best by any side in the division.

Their only home defeat was in early December against New Brighton.

Did do the double over second placed Stourbridge beating them easily in both matches.

They clinched the Championship at Sandal to take the title by two points.

PRESTON GRASSHOPPERS

LEAGUE STATISTICS
compiled by Stephen McCormack

SEASON	Division	P	W	D	L	F	A	Pts Diff	Lge Pts	Lge Pos		Most Points		Most Tries
89-90	ALN	10	5	0	5	122	109	13	10	6	36	Ian Jackson	2	D Percy, SGreenhalgh
90-91	D4N	12	8	0	4	192	109	83	16	3	105	Paul Grayson	5	J Hindle, I Asgton
91-92	D4N	12	8	0	4	195	123	72	16	4	127	Paul Grayson	4	D Percy, P Grayson
92-93	D4N	12	8	0	4	144	140	4	16	3	27	Andy Taylorson	3	John Bleasdale
93-94	D5N	12	10	0	2	191	128	63	20	2	62	Mark Kirby	3	Joe Hindle
94-95	D5N	12	8	1	3	187	137	50	17	3	94	Willie Mould	2	Three players
95-96	D5N	12	5	1	6	167	209	-42	11	8	45	Nick Bell	3	Three players
96-97	D4N	26	17	2	7	568	394	174	36	3	317	Steve Kerry	7	Glyn Dewhurst
97-98	J2N	26	14	2	10	549	469	80	30	4	91	Rob Smith	15	Iain Bruce
98-99	J2N	26	23	0	3	822	341	481	46	1p	216	Martin Emmett	27	Michael Lough

BIGGEST MARGINS

Home Win	52pts - 60-8 v Winnington Park 30.01.99
Away Win	49pts -52-3 v Hereford 25.01.97
Home Defeat	17pts -13-30 v Broughton Park 26.11.88
Away Defeat	33pts -3-36 v Harrogate 09.01.93

MOST CONSECUTIVE

Appearances	
Matches scoring Tries	5 Michael Lough & Iain Bruce
Matches scoring points	26 Steve Kerry
Victories	10
Defeats	3

MOST POINTS

Scored at Home	60 v WinningtonPark 30.01.99
Scored Away	65 v Walsall 07.11.98
Conceded at Home	34 v Worcester 06.01.96
Conceded Away	36 v Harrogate 09.01.93

MOST TRIES

Scored in a match	10 v Winnington Park 30.01.99
Conceded in a match	6 v Worcester 06.01.96

MOST APPEARANCES

by a forward	128 Phil Crayston
by a back	130 John Chesworth

	MOST IN A SEASON	MOST IN A CAREER	MOST IN A MATCH
Points	317 Steve Kerry 96-97	489 Steve Kerry 87-89,96-97	25 Iain Bruce v Winnington Park .03.99 (H)
Tries	27 Michael Lough 98-99	40 Iain Bruce 97-99	5 Iain Bruce v Winnington Park
Conversions	53 Martin Emmett 98-99	55 Steve Kerry 87-89,96-97	7 Steve Kerry v Hereford25.01.97 Martin Emmett v Walsall 07.11.98
Penalties	64 Steve Kerry 96-97	99 Steve Kerry 87-89,96-97	6 Paul Grayson v Northern 28.03.92 (A) Steve Kerry v Hereford 31.08.96 Steve Kerry v Sandal 03.05.97
Drop Goals	9 Steve Kerry 96-97	14 Steve Kerry 87-89,96-97	4 Steve Kerry v Aspatria 07.09.96 (A)

PRESTON GRASSHOPPERS PLAYING SQUAD

BACKS

Name	Ht.	Wt.	Birthdate	Birthplace	CLUB	League Apps	Tries	Pts
Michael Lough	6.1	15.00	20.10.75	Port Lincoln	Preston	44	30	150
Australia 7s, South Australia, Lancashire. Other club: Burnside (S Aust)								
Iain Bruce	5.9	14.07	14.09.72	Preston	Preston	48	40	200
Scotland U-21, Exiles, Lancashire. Other club: Oreell					Waterloo	21	6	30
Gary Monaghan	5.10	12.07	22.06.71	Leigh	Preston	38	26	130
Lancashire, North. Other club: Leigh					Waterloo	9	-	-
Rob Smith					Preston			
John Chesworth	6.1	15.04	05.05.71	Preston	Preston	130	16	90
Lancashire								
John Bleasdale	5.8	12.00	19.12.69	Lancaster	Preston	117	13	74
Lancashire								
Martin Emmett	5.9	13.05	04.05.71	St Helens	Preston	30	3	280
Lancashire, England students					Waterloo	18	1	152
Peter Lord					Preston			
James Swarbrick	5.11	13.00	02.12.78	Preston	Preston	3	1	5
Simon Mulholland	5.10	13.00	23.05.73	Preston	Preston	8	-	3
Paul Bleadale	5.8	11.07	12.07.78	Preston	Preston	(1)	-	-
					Liverpool	6	-	-
John Kirkpatrick	6	13.00	03.01.79	Preston	Preston	8	1	5
Lancashire U-21								

FORWARDS

Name	Ht.	Wt.	Birthdate	Birthplace	CLUB	League Apps	Tries	Pts
Neil Ashton	6.3	16.00	08.02.70	Preston	Preston	96	17	85
Lancashire, British Police								
Michael Baiey	6.5	16.00	20.12.68	Preston	Preston	125	16	78
Lancashire								
David Chadwick	5.8	15.07	19.02.71	Burnley	Preston	49	1	5
					Calder Vale			
Kieron Chadwick	5.8	14.00	02.01.76	Burnley	Preston	19	4	20
Lancashire								
Glyn Dewhurst	6.0	15.07	20.04.74	Preston	Preston	43	11	55
Lancashire, South Australia								
Paul Edwards	5.10	14.00	28.04.68	Manchester	Preston	18	1	5
Chris Evans	5.8	13.07	18.11.76	Preston	Preston	25	2	10
Lancashire U-21					Waterloo	1	-	-
Karl Fenton	6.0	17.00	29.01.69	Londonderry	Preston	44	4	20
Lancashire, British students.Other clubs: Orrell 2					Waterloo	7	-	-
Josh Williams	6.4	19.00	28.08.70	Ormskirk	Preston	47	7	35
Lancashire, Army U-21, Combined Services U-21								
Mike Sword	6.4	17.00	28.11.68	Bury	Preston	78	5	23
Notts, Lincs & Derby U-21.								
Craig Steel	6.6	16.02	24.12.77	Preston	Preston	4	-	-
Richard Spicer	5.9	16.00	20.05.69	Potters Bar	Preston	79	-	-
Andy Roberts	6.2	14.00	18.08.71	Burnley	Preston	36	4	20
					Calder Vale			
James Porteous	5.10	14.00	07.07.77	Preston	Preston	5	-	-
Lancashire U-21								
Paul Shepherd	6.0	19.00	26.04.78	Preston	Preston	-	-	-

PRESTON GRASSHOPPERS FACT FILE

Founded: 1869
Nickname: Hoppers

Colours: Navy blue & white irregular hoops/navy blue/navy blue.
Change colours: Emerald green, red collar & cuffs.

GROUND

Address: Lightfoot Green, Fulwood, Preston, Lancs. PR4 0AP.
Web site: www.worldsites.net/prestongrasshoppers e-mail: preston.hoppers@virgin.net
Tel: 01772 863546 Fax: 01772 861605 Press Line: 01772 861605
Capacity: 4250 Seated: 250 Standing: 4000

Directions: Leave the M6 at Junct. 32 and head towards A6 Garstang. Turnleft at the end of the slip road towards Preston. Take first left and followsigns for Ingol. The ground is 1/2 mile on the right.
Nearest Railway Station: Preston (BR)

Car Parking: 400 spaces available adjacent to the ground.

Admission: Match days - Adults - Members £4, Others £6
OAPs £3 Under 14s Free

Clubhouse: Open Mon-Thurs 4.30-11.00, Fri 12-12, Sat 12-11, Sun 12-10.30,snacks, bar meals & restaurant available
Functions: Capacity 250, contact K Moore 01772 863546

Club Shop: Open daily contact K Moore 01772 863546

PROGRAMME

Size: A5 Price: With admission Pages: 32 + cover
Editor: John Hetherington 01772 863546

ADVERTISING RATES
Colour - Full page £300, half £175
Mono - Full page £250, half £140, qtr £85

Neil Ashton (left) with the Jewson Two North Trophy and Michael Lough with his Jewson Two North "Player of the Season" award

READING R.F.C.

President	Jeff Owen	66A Cressingham Road, Reading, Berks RG2 7GR 0118 954 7311 (H)
Chairman	Dave Wells	Chiltern View, Lower Road, Postcombe, Oxon OX9 7DU 01844 281234 (H), 0118 965 1611 (B)
Club Secretary	Phil Betts	7 Sherwood Road, Winnersh, Wokingham RG41 5NH 0118 978 7064 (H), 0118 976 3393 (B)
Rugby Manager	Phil Hall	173 Victoria road, Wargrave, Berks. RG10 8AH 0118 940 2313 (H) 0118 969 6592 (B) 0118 969 9593 (F)
Commercial Manager	Vic Hall	c/o Reading RFCHolme park, Sonning Lane, Reading RG4 6ST 0118 969 6592 (B) 0118 969 9593 (F)
Publicity Officer	Lorcan Mullally	0118 957 2357
Operations	Andrew Green	0118 969 7733 (H).
Chairman of Rugby	Andy Clark	0118 983 3883 (H)
Vice Chairman	Hugh Crabtree	0118 926 1236 (H) 0118 986 7252 (B)
Publicity	Dave Parish	0118 959 9061 (B) 0118 959 9062 (F) 0410 228154 (M)

Reading's performances never really came up to expectations and they eventually finished in tenth place in the Jewson National One League, winning ten and losing sixteen of their 26 games. They competed well in most of their matches, but basic errors and infringements at crucial stages meant that the team failed to convert good build-ups into points. Most of the players are young and with more experience will knit into a useful squad.

Reading had to use 41 players in competitive games during the season and injuries to skipper and front-row player, JJ Harris, meant that his leadership qualities were often missing, especially in the early months of the campaign. Reading also had a problem in that no player was able to stamp his authority on the fly-half position. full-back Jason dance took over the No 10 slot in the later games of the season and brought extra flair to that pivotal role.

Reading scored some outstanding tries including twelve each by wing Bruce Rowland and flanker Dave Muckalt which placed them fourth in the league's try-scoring table. Jason Dance was Reading's top points gatherer with 193 points, which included 35 penalties and 30 conversions. He finished fifth in the leading points scorers' table.

A big disappointment for Reading was that they only won four of their thirteen home league fixtures, albeit one of them was an impressive 26-25 victory over Otley as a result of a tremendous second-half come back. Reading's six away wins included gritty victories over Birmingham/Solihull, Harrogate, Liverpool and Wharfedale. They also won at Morley where another come back gave the Berkshire side the league points, and at Nottingham where two outstanding solo tries by left-wing Dave Underwood clinched the result. Reading scored home and away doubles over Birmingham/Solihull, Harrogate and Morley, whom they beat 55-9 at Holme Park.

Reading lost at home to Newbury when an injury time penalty kick swung the result for the visitors. In the last game of the season, also at home, against Lydney a penalty kick that had clearly gone wide was awarded to the visitors and that decision, as it turned out, had a profound effect on the result in the see-saw scoring game.

Lorcan Mullally

Dave Muckalt (in scum cap) sets up maul for Reading with next season's skipper, Simon Stevenson (No. 8 on his shorts) holding off the Nottingham players. Photo: Lorcan Mullally

READING

Match No.	Date	H/A	Comp.	Opponents	Result & Score	Att.	15	14	13	12	11
1	05.09	A	JN1	Newbury	L 14-28	600	Dance/2p(k)	Rowland/t	Barrett	Warren	Graham
2	12.09	A	JN1	Rosslyn Park	L 21-23	500	Dance/c3p	Rowland	Barrett	Warren/t(k)	Graham(o)
3	19.09	H	JN1	Birmingham S	W 29-10	200	Dance/2c5p	Rowland/t	Barrett	Kibe	Ellis
4	26.09	A	JN1	Liverpool StH	W 24-6	200	Dance/3cp	Rowland/2t	Barrett	Kibe	Ballard
5	03.10	H	JN1	Harrogate	W 25-14	250	Dance/2c2p	Rowland/t	Barrett	Kibe	Ballard
6	10.10	A	JN1	Wharfedale	W 17-11	400	Dance/2cp	Rowland	Barrett	Everts	Ballard(w)
7	24.10	H	JN1	Manchester	L 14-28	300	Dance/3p	Rowland	Barrett	Warren	Underwood
8	31.10	A	JN1	Nottingham	W 19-13	400	Dance/2c	Rowland/t	Barrett	Warren	Underwood/2t
9	07.11	H	JN1	Camberley	L 28-36	350	Dance/2c3p	Rowland	Barrett	Warren	Underwood//t
10	21.11	A	JN1	Henley	L 9-25	550	Dance/3p	Rowland	Barrett	Warren	Underwood
11	28.11	H	JN1	Morley	W 55-15	200	Dance/t5c	Rowland/t	Barrett/2t	Warren/t(v)	Underwood
12	05.12	A	JN1	Lydney	L 17-33	600	Dance/2cp	Rowland	Barrett	Everts	Underwood
13	12.12	H	JN1	Otley	W 26-25	300	Dance/2c4p	Rowland/t	Barrett	Everts	Underwood
14	19.12	A	JN1	Morley	W 17-14	500	Costoloe	Rowland	Barrettt	Everts/2cp	Underwood/t
15	28.12	H	JN1	Henley	L 6-36	850	Dance/2p	Rowland	Barrett	Everts	Costoloe
16	02.01	A	JN1	Camberley	L 18-26	300	Dance/p	Rowland	Barrett	Costoloe/t	Brooks
17	16.01	H	JN1	Nottingham	L 18-27	200	Dance/c2p	Rowland/t	Barrett	Kibe	Underwood/t
18	23.01	A	JN1	Manchester	L 0-42	475	Dance	Rowland	Barrett	Kibe	Ballard
19	30.01	H	JN1	Wharfedale	L 6-8	200	Dance/2p	Ellis(C)	Barrett	Kibe	Ballard
20	06.02	A	JN1	Harrogate	W 13-9	250	Dance/c2p	Rowland	Costoloe	Pitt/t	Ballard
21	13.02	H	JN1	Liverpool StH	L 10-31	200	Pitt	Rowland	Barrett	Costoloe	Ballard
22	27.02	A	JN1	Birmingham S	W 16-15	200	Ballard	Rowland/t	Barrett	Costoloe	Underwood
23	13.03	H	JN1	Rosslyn Park	L 7-34	250	Pitt(q)	Ballard/t	Barrett	Costoloe	Underwood
24	27.03	H	JN1	Newbury	L 18-20	500	Ballard	Rowland/t	Barrett	Costoloe	Underwood
25	03.04	A	JN1	Otley	L 10-66	450	Ballard	Rowland/t	Costoloe	Wyatt	Brooks
26	17.04	H	JN1	Lydney	L 31-37	200	Ballard/t	Rowland	Costoloe	Wyatt	Underwood/t
A	17.10	H	TB2	Penzance	W 21-5		Dance/3c	Rowland	Barrett	Kibe(q)	Underwood
B	14.11	H	TB3	Orrell	L 12-23		Dance/3p	Rowland	Barrett	Warren	Underwood

* after opponents name indicates a penalty try
Brackets after a player's name indicates he was replaced. eg (a) means he was replaced by replacement code "a" and so on.
/ after a player or replacement name is followed by any scores he made - eg /t, /c, /p, /dg or any combination of these

1998-99 HIGHLIGHTS

League debuts:
Steve Pearce, Chris De Ville, Steve Trethewey, Miles Hayman, Andy Ludiman, Dave Muckalt, Travis Barker, Eric Kibe, Andrew Grierson, Garron Everts, David Underwood, Andrew Lewis, Nick Brooks, Stuart Kerley, Richard Wyatt.

Ever Presents: None

Most appearances Bruce Rowland 25

Players used: 38 plus 2 as a replacement only

Most Points in a season:

Pts	Player	T	C	P	DG
193	J Dance	1	28	44	-
60	B Rowland	12	-	-	-
60	D Muckalt	12	-	-	-
30	D Underwood	6	-	-	-

Jason Dance tops the Reading scoring list for a third consecutive season, although his 193 was his lowest haul of the three.

This takes his career total at Reading to 719 and now he

MATCH FACTS

10	9	1	2	3	4	5	6	7	8	
Costoloe/p	Pearce	Rolfe(l)	DeVille	Trethewey(m)	Hayman	Ludiman	Muckalt	Barker	Hedberg(n)	1
Costoloe	Pearce	Rolfe(l)	DeVille(m)	Turnock	Hayman	Ludiman(p)	Muckalt	Barker	Hedberg(n)	2
Costoloe(a)	Pearce	Rolfe(l)	DeVille/t	Turnock(m)	Hayman	Ludiman(p)	Muckalt	Barker(r)	Sparks	3
Costoloe(a)	Pearce/t	Stevenson	DeVille(m)	Grierson(d)	Vatcher	Ludiman(f)	Muckalt	Barker(r)	Sparks	4
Graham	Pearce(o)	Stevenson	Harris(m)	Grierson(d)	Vatcher(f)	Ludiman	Muckalt/2t	Barker(r)	Sparks	5
Graham(b)	Ellis	Stevenson	Harris(e)	Grierson(m)	Hayman	Ludiman	Stewart(p)	Murley	Muckalt/2t	6
Graham(b)	Ellis	Stevenson	DeVille	Grierson	Vatcher	Hayman(g)	Muckalt/t	Murley	Sparks(u)	7
Graham(b)	Ellis	Stevenson	DeVille(m)	Grierson	Vatcher	Hayman	Muckalt	Murley	Sparks	8
Graham	Ellis	Stevenson	Perkin	Grierson(d)	Vatcher	Hayman	Muckalt/2t	Murley(u)	Sparks	9
Costoloe(a)	Ellis	Stevenson	Perkin	Grierson(d)	Vatcher	Till	Muckalt(x)	Murley(u)	Sparks	10
Lewis	Pearce	Stevenson/t	Harris(m/t)	Grierson(d)	Vatcher	Till(x)	Spencer(i)	Stewart/t	Sparks/t	11
Lewis	Pearce/t	Stevenson/t	Harris	Rolfe	Vatcher	Till(x)	Spencer	Stewart	Sparks	12
Lewis	Ellis	Stevenson	Harris	Rolfe	Vatcher	Till(j)	Muckalt/t	Barker(z)	Sparks	13
Lewis(b)	Ellis	Stevenson	Harris	Rolfe	Vatcher	Hedberg	Muckalt/t	Spencer(x)	Sparks	14
Costoloe(y)	Pearce(B)	Stevenson	Harris	Rolfe	Vatcher(x)	Hedberg	Muckalt	Spencer(A)	Sparks	15
Costoloe(y)	Kerley(c)	Stevenson	Harris	Anstead(s)	Vatcher(x)	Moors	Spencer(u)	Muckalt	Sparks/2t	16
Graham	Ellis	Stevenson(e)	Harris(m)	Anstead	Vatcher(f)	Moors	Saprks	Spencer	Muckalt(j)	17
Graham(y)	Ellis(c)	Rolfe(l)	DeVille	Anstead(s)	Vatcher	Moors	Sparks	Spencer	Hedberg(f)	18
Lewis	Pearce	Stevenson	Perkin	Anstead	Vatcher(f)	Moors	Sparks(z)	Muckalt	Hedberg	19
Lewis	Pearce	Stevenson	Perkin	Anstead	Vatcher(x)	Moors	Sparks	Spencer	Hedberg	20
Lewis	Pearce	Stevenson	Perkin(t)	Anstead(s)	Vatcher	Moors(f)	Sparks(z)	Muckalt/t	Hedberg/t	21
Dance/2p	Pearce	Stevenson	Harris	Grierson	Vatcher	Hayman	Sparks	Murley/t	Muckalt	22
Dance/c	Pearce(B)	Stevenson	Harris	Grierson	Vatcher(x)	Hayman	Sparks	Murley(u)	Muckalt	23
Dance/p	Pearce/t	Anstead	Harris	Grierson	Vatcher(A)	Hayman	Sparks	Murley	Muckalt/t	24
Lewis/cdg	Pearce(h)	Anstead	Stevenson	Grierson	Vatcher(A)	Hayman	Sparks	Murley(i)	Stewart	25
Dance/2c4p	Kerley	Anstead	Stevenson	Grierson(d)	Vatcher	Hayman(A)	Sparks(r)	Barker	Muckalt/t	26
Costoloe	Ellis	Stevenson	DeVille(m)	Grierson(d)	Vatcher(x)	Ludiman	Muckalt/t	Murley	Sparks(u)	A
Costoloe(y)	Ellis	Stevenson	Perkin	Grierson	Vatcher	Hayman(j)	Muckalt	Murley	Sparks	B

REPLACEMENTS:	a- H Graham	b- J Costoloe	c - S Pearce	d - A Rolfe	e - C De Ville	f - M Hayman	g - A Ludiman
h - P Belshaw	i - T Barker	j - J Hedberg	k - R Ballard	l - S Stevenson	m - S Perkin	n - G Sparks	o - T Ellis
p - M Vatcher	q - R Wyatt	r - J Murley	s - A Grierson	t - JJ Harris	u - R Stewart	v - G Everts	w - D Underwood
x - R Dow	y - A Lewis	z - P Spencer	A - E Moors	B - S Kerley	C - M Pitt		

has all time leader Phil Belshaw in his sights. Belshaw's record stands at 771 so if Dance stays with the club he will no doubt pass it this coming season.

Both Dave Muckalt and Bruce Rowland fail by one to equal Guy Spencer's record of 13 tries in a league season. Muckalt's 12 though is a record for a Reading forward in a season.

Winger Bruce Rowland misses just one match for the second consecutive season and has played 50 out of 52 matches since making his league debut at the start of the previous season.

Reading equalled their worst ever run in league matches when they suffered 5 straight defeats before breaking the run at Harrogate early in February.

When they lost 66-10 at Otley it was their worst defeat in terms of both biggest margin and most points. The previous records were: most points against 47 at Worcester last season, whilst the biggest losing margin was 36 when they were beaten by Gordon League in their South West One days.

READING

LEAGUE STATISTICS
compiled by Stephen McCormack

SEASON	Division	P	W	D	L	F	A	Pts Diff	Lge Pts	Lge Pos	Most Points	Most Tries
89-90	SW1	10	3	0	7	128	207	-79	6		45 Phil Belshaw	3 Gary Williams & Alan Spence
90-91	SW1	10	7	1	2	208	100	108	15		43 Phil Belshaw	6 Paul Roberts & Curtis Hutson
91-92	SW1	10	4	0	6	120	163	57	8		36 Martin Radford	4 John Dixon & Rodney Hutson
92-93	SW1	12	11	0	1	267	99	168	22	1	104 Phil Belshaw	6 Rodney Hutson & Mark Alexander
93-94	D5S	12	10	1	1	248	61	187	21	1	133 Phil Belshaw	5 Ian McGeevor
94-95	4	18	14	1	3	435	319	116	29	2	204 Phil Belshaw	6 Curtis Hutson
95-96	3	18	5	1	12	397	484	-87	11	8	103 Phil Belshaw	12 Colin Phillips
96-97	3	30	17	1	12	869	631	238	35	6	281 Jason Dance	13 Guy Spencer
97-98	JN1	26	11	1	14	617	697	-80	23	8	217 Jason Dance	11 Bruce Rowland
98-99	JN1	26	10	0	16	468	635	-167	20	10	193 Jason Dance	12 Bruce Rowland & Dave Muckalt

BIGGEST MARGINS

Home Win	68pts - 71-3 v Redruth 15.2.97
Away Win	36pts - 46-10 v Gordon League
Home Defeat	47pts - 15-62 v Worcester 22.11.97
Away Defeat	34pts - 10-44 v Harrogate 13.4.96

MOST CONSECUTIVE

Appearances	47 Ian Turnell
Matches scoring Tries	4 Colin Phillips
Matches scoring points	34 Phil Belshaw
Victories	18
Defeats	5

MOST POINTS

Scored at Home	75 v Clifton 1.3.97
Scored Away	46 v Gordon League
Conceded at Home	62 v Worcester 22.1.97
Conceded Away	47 v Worcester 13.12.97

MOST TRIES

Scored in a match	11 v Salisbury (H), v Clifton 1.3.97 (H)
Conceded in a match	10 v Worcester 22.1.97 (H)

MOST APPEARANCES

by a forward	Kevin Jones
by a back	Rodney Hutson

	MOST IN A SEASON	MOST IN A CAREER	MOST IN A MATCH
Points	281 Jason Dance 96-97	771 Phil Belshaw88-97	26 Greg Way v Harrogate 16.9.95 (H) Jason Dance v Liverpool St. H. 25.4.98 (H)
Tries	13 Guy Spencer 96-97	28 Curtis Hutson 87-97	3 Curtis Hutson v Torquay (H) Mark Alexander v Penryn (A) Colin Phillips v Otley 6.4.96 (H) Guy Spencer v Lydney 8.2.97 (A) Mark Scharrenberg v L. St. H. 22.3.97 (A)
Conversions	61 Jason Dance 96-97	115 Phil Belshaw 88-97	10 Jason Dance v Clifton 1.3.97 (H)
Penalties	49 Phil Belshaw 94-95	165 Phil Belshaw 88-97	7 Phil Belshaw v Morley 14.10.95 (H)
Drop Goals	3 Dave Hill 95-96	3 Simon Rogers 87-95 Dave Hill 95-96	1 on 13 occasions by 9 players including Simon Rogers (x3) & Dave Hill (x3)

READING PLAYING SQUAD

BACKS

	Ht.	Wt.	Birthdate	Birthplace	CLUB	League Apps	Tries	Pts
Andrew Lewis	5.9	11.07	30.06.74	Swansea	Reading	86	20	100
					London Welsh	3(1)	1	24
Jason Dance	5.8	12.10	08.11.70	Basingstoke	Reading	82	9	719
					Exeter	3	-	12
Tom Ellis	5.10	13.03	05.10.71	Kings Lynn	Reading	50(3)	10	53
					Saracens			
Jerry Costeloe	5.10	12.04	25.11.74	Weston SM	Reading	42(8)	13	85
Steve Pearce					Reading	15(2)	3	15
James Warren	5.10	14.10	20.11.72	Reading	Reading	24(1)	3	15
Danny Barrett England Univ.	5.8	13.00	27.11.74	Brentwood	Reading	65(1)	14	70
Phil Belshaw	6.0	13.06	15.12.69	Reading	Reading	89(3)		771
					Bracknell			
Eric Kibe					Reading	6	-	-
Richard Ballard	5.10	11.06	28.09.74	Reading	Reading	22(4)	3	18
Dave Underwood					Reading	13(1)	6	30
Howard Graham					Reading	32(5)	6	30
					Morley	27(1)	8	40
Bruce Rowland					Reading	49	23	115
					Morley			
Matthew Pitt					Reading	7(2)	1	43

FORWARDS

	Ht.	Wt.	Birthdate	Birthplace	CLUB	League Apps	Tries	Pts
Chris DeVille					Reading	8(2)	1	5
					Richmond			
Greg Anstead	5.11	17.00	06.03.75	Bridgetown(Bar)	Reading	50(3)	2	10
					Bracknell			
JJ Harris	5.9	15.00	22.10.72	Beaconsfield	Reading	67(4)	6	30
Scot Perkin England Colts, u18, u16.	5.7	14.00	19.03.74	Penzance	Reading	23(16)	3	15
Mark Vatcher	6.4	17.07	08.03.71	Carlshalton	Reading	84(9)	7	35
					Headingley			
Travis Barker				New Zealand	Reading	7(2)	-	-
Graham Sparks	6.2	16.00	16.07.74	Taplow	Reading	74(7)	8	40
					Maidenhead			
Rob Dow	6.4	17.10	12.10.70		Reading	24(14)	-	-
					Rosslyn Park			
John Murley				Penzance	Reading	42(4)	2	10
Eldon Moors Other club: Ebbw Vale 19/-/-	6.5	17.04	26.12.71	Auckland	Reading			
					London Welsh	36	-	-
Simon Stevenson	5.11	17.07	17.02.69	Oxford	Reading	42(12)	3	15
Adam Rolfe	5.08	16.00	06.11.75	Bath	Reading	10(8)	-	-
					Bath			
Andrew Grierson					Reading	13(3)	-	-
Ross Stewart					Reading	8(7)	1	5
Paul Spencer					Reading	8(5)	1	5

READING

FACT FILE

Founded: 1898
Nickname: Green Machine

Colours: Myrtle & white 'V'/myrtle.
Change colours: Yellow with myrtle 'V', collar & cuffs

GROUND

Address: Holme Park, Sonning Lane, Reading RG4 6ST
Tel: 0118 969 6592 Fax: 0118 969 6593
Capacity: 2,500 Seated: 200 Standing: 2,300

Directions: A4 Reading to Maidenhead Road, turn left 2.5 miles out of Reading, sign posted Sonning.
Nearest Railway Station: Reading Mainline, by short taxi journey (10 mins).

Car Parking: 250 at ground, 200 nearby

Admission:
Matchday Standing Adults £5, including programme

Club Shop: Open Sat 1-5 plus training times
Contact Andrew Green, c/o Club

Clubhouse: Open daily depending upon club activities
Snacks & bar meals available.
Functions: Capacity 150 - contact Tim Pratt 0118 969 6592

Training Nights: Tuesdays & Thursdays (Seniors)

PROGRAMME

Size: A5 Pages: 72 Price: with admission
Editor: Vic Hall

ADVERTISING RATES (Mono)
Contact Vic Hall

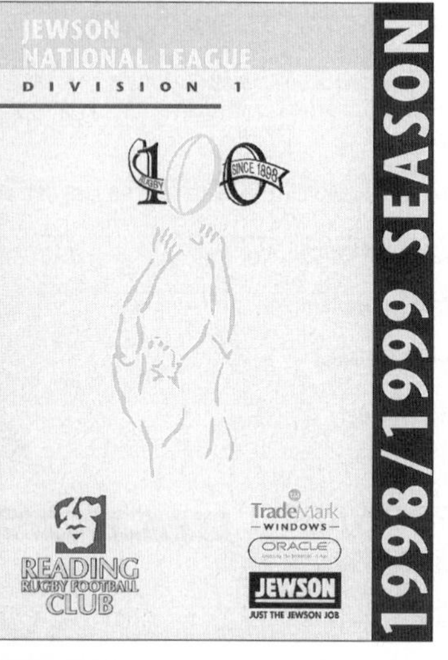

Lock, Mark Vatcher, gets the ball back from the line-out during the league match at Nottingham.
Photo: Lorcan Mullally

ROSSLYN PARK F.C.

President	David E Whittam FRCS	37 Queens Road, Kingston-on-Thames, Surrey KT2 7SL 0181 549 4209 (H), 0181 944 6594 (B), 0181 944 8059 (Fax)
Chairman	Geoff Bayles	Valley House, 6 Boyle Farm Rd.,Thames Ditton, Surrey KT7 0TS 0181 398 6656 (H), 0181 224 8607 (Fax)
Club Secretary	Peter Berryman	52 Crescent Road, kingston-upon-Thames, Surre. KT2 7RF 0181 546 1228 (H) 0181 547 1838 (Fax)
Press Officer	Bernard Wiggins	01403 711299 (H), 01273 323434 (B), 01273 202627(Fax)
Fixtures Secretary	David Booth	7 Catherine Road, Surbiton, Surre. KT6 4HA 0181 399 0955 (H) 0181 339 9300 (Fax)

Last season Park ended up as the top `amateur' club in the country, and hopes were high that the 998/99 season would be a promotion year for the club. The season turned on close matches in October and November, all of which were lost by less than a score, and by that time Henley and Manchester had taken a lead that they were never to relinquish.

An opening day reverse 23-20 at Otley showed how competitive the league was going to be, but then four straight wins put the show on the road, and confidence was high.

In view of what was to come, one of those victories at Newbury 19-18 with a last minute try and conversion under the posts by Andy Maddock, was the only game of the season where Park had snatched a crucial victory when all seemed lost. Indeed there was much merriment at the expense of the club Chairman Geoff Bayles, who had left five minutes before the end convinced that Park had lost and then spent a miserable weekend in the West Country only to discover the good news in Monday's Telegraph!

October and Novembr saw Park lose 6-3 away at Harrogate (the try that wasn't given), 5-6 at home to Wharfedale (D. Pears pen 85 mins), 26-25 at Manchester (86th min. drop goal in a half devoid of injuries) and 7-10 at Home to Henley. Bitter pills indeed to swallow, and from then on Park went into a metronomic win/lose sequence until the end of January, which included an 18-15 defeat at Henley, the eventual champions. A 12-0 shootout of Manchester was then followed by a 19-3 defeat at Wharfedale, in which David Pears gave a lesson in fly half play, but after that Park won eight out of the last nine with only a draw at Lydney (as good a win for most clubs).

The final match against Morley was marred by the death the previous week of Director of Rugby Robert `Windmill' Harding, so called because of his flamboyant hand movements whilst refereeing. One of the top ten referees of his time, Robert devoted a lot of time to the club, and will be missed by all those who were lucky enough to know him.

Rosslyn Park 1st XV Squad 1998-1999

ROSSLYN PARK

Match No.	Date	H/A	Comp.	Opponents	Result & Score	Att.	15	14	13	12	11
1	05.09	A	JN1	Otley	L 20-23	450	Dickinson/t	Casado/t	Wyatt(l)	Ashworth	Cook(i)
2	12.09	H	JN1	Reading	W 23-20	500	Maddock/p	Casado/2t	Fanning(p)	Ashworth	Futter/t
3	19.09	A	JN1	Newbury	W 19-18	400	Maddock/t	Casado	Fanning	Thyme	Cook/c4p
4	26.09	A	JN1	Birmingham S	W 39-15	200	Maddock/2c	Casado/3t	Fanning	Thyme	Futter
5	03.10	H	JN1	Liverpool StH	W 50-22	500	Burns/p(u/t)	Casado	Fanning	Thyme	Futter/t
6	10.10	A	JN1	Harrogate	L 3-6	350	Maddock/p	Casado	Wyatt	Fanning	Futter(w)
7	24.10	H	JN1	Wharfedale	L 5-6	400	Maddock	Casado	Wyatt	Brady	Henderson
8	31.10	A	JN1	Manchester*	L 25-26	550	Maddock/t	Cook/2cp	Brady	Thyme	Futter
9	07.11	H	JN1	Nottingham	W 30-24	450	Maddock	Casado	Brady	Thyme	Cook/2c2p
10	21.11	A	JN1	Camberley	W 25-18	400	Maddock/t	Cook/2c2p	Fanning	Brady	Futter
11	28.11	H	JN1	Henley Hawks	L 7-10	250	Maddock	Cook/c	Wyatt	Brady	Futter
12	12.12	H	JN1	Lydney	W 20-10	200	Maddock/2c2p	Futter	Wyatt	Brady/t(D/t)	Fanning
13	19.12	A	JN1	Henley Hawks	L 15-18	500	Maddock/cp	Futter/t	Wyatt/t	Marval	Fanning
14	28.12	H	JN1	Camberley	W 15-6	750	Maddock/cp	Futter	Wyatt	Marval	Fanning/t
15	02.01	A	JN1	Nottingham	L 9-21	450	Maddock/3p	Fanning	Ashworth	Wyatt	Futter
16	16.01	H	JN1	Manchester	W 12-0	400	Maddock/c	Futter/t	Wyatt	Marval	Fanning
17	23.01	A	JN1	Wharfedale	L 3-19	600	Maddock/p	Justice	Wyatt	Marval	Futter
18	30.01	H	JN1	Harrogate	W 27-8	300	Maddock/t2cp	Justice/t	Wyatt	Marval(a)	Adams/t
19	06.02	A	JN1	Liverpool StH*	W 22-7	200	Dowse/c	Justice(a)	Wyatt	Marval/t	Adams
20	13.02	H	JN1	Birmingham S	W 42-0	300	Maddock/t	Futter	Wyatt(j)	Marval/2t	Adams
21	20.02	A	JN1	Morley*	W 36-24	350	Maddock	Futter/t	Wyatt(j)	Marval	Wyatt
22	27.02	H	JN1	Newbury	W 35-24	400	Maddock(v)	Futter	Marval	Brady	Fanning(E/t)
23	13.03	A	JN1	Reading	W 34-7	250	Maddock	Justice/2t	Marval/2t	Brady	Fanning/t
24	27.03	H	JN1	Otley	W 24-13	500	Maddock	Drake	Brady(r)	Marval(E)	Fanning
25	03.04	A	JN1	Lydney	D 6-6	500	Maddock	Justice	Wyatt	Marval	Fanning
26	17.04	H	JN1	Morley	W 42-19	500	Maddock	Justice	Brady	Marval/t(a)	Fanning/t
A	17.10	A	TBC	Bridgwater	W 49-15		Maddock/t3cp	Casado/t	Wyatt/t	Brady	Henderson
B	14.11	H	TBC	Henley*	L 12-16		Dickinson	Futter	Thynne	Brady	Cook/c

* after opponents name indicates a penalty try
Brackets after a player's name indicates he was replaced. eg (a) means he was replaced by replacement code "a" and so on.
/ after a player or replacement name is followed by any scores he made - eg /t, /c, /p, /dg or any combination of these

1998-99 HIGHLIGHTS

League debuts:
James Wyatt, Jeremy Cook, James Pearce, Tim Jensen, Lee Fanning, Ben Thyme, Andy Craig, Simeon Adams, Peter Willis Dave Dahinton, Simon Young, Simon Pinder, James Justice, Johnson, Drake, Toby Knowles, Fay, Simon Kuiti, Hayes,

Ever Presents: None - most appearances Andy Maddock 25

Players used: 46 plus 9 as a replacement only

Most Points in a season:

Pts	Player	T	C	P	DG
93	A Maddock	5	13	14	-
74	T Knowles	2	14	11	1
43	J Cook	-	8	9	-

MATCH FACTS

10	9	1	2	3	4	5	6	7	8	
Maddock/cp	Smither	Fennell	Ritchie	Ford(j)	Gibson	Pearce(k)	Benson	Boardman/t	Smith	1
Jensen/cp	Smither	Fennell	Kearns(n)	Ford(j)	Milward(o)	Gibson	Rakison	Boardman	Smith	2
Jensen	Smither	Fennell	Kearns(e)	Ford(j)	Craig	Gibson	Milward	Boardman(o)	Smith(q)	3
Holder/cp(r)	Smither/t	Fennell	Ritchie	Cooke(f)	Milward/t	Gibson	Rakison(m)	Boardman(s/t)	McCormick(h)	4
Maddock/3c2p	Smither(r)	Fennell	Ritchie	Cooke(f)	Milward(g)	Gibson/t	Rakison/t	Boardman/t(s)	McCormick/2t	5
Jensen(u)	Thyme	Fennell	Ritchie	Ford(j)	Milward	Craig	McCormick	Jack(g)	Rakison(h)	6
Ashworth	Willis	Fennell(f)	Ritchie(n)	Cooke(f)	Craig	Pearce	Smith(s)	Rakison	McCormick(g/t)	7
Ashworth/dg	Willis(c)	Fennell	Ritchie	Yeldham(f)	Milward	Gibson/t	Benson	Rakison(h)	McCormick	8
Ashworth	Springhall	Fennell	Ritchie(t)	Yeldham	Milward	Gibson	Benson/t(z/2t)	Rakison(A)	McCormick/t	9
Ashworth	Young	Fennell/t	Kearns(e)	Yeldham	Milward	Gibson	Benson(s)	Smith(z)	McCormick/t	10
Jensen	Young	Fennell	Kearns	Yeldham	Gibson	Milward	Rakison/t	Boardman	McCormick	11
Holder	Young(y)	Fennell	Kearns	Yeldham	Milward	Gibson	Benson(s)	Boardman	McCormick	12
Holder(x)	Young(c)	Fennell	Kearns(e)	Yeldham	Milward	Gibson	Strong	Boardman	Rakison/t	13
Holder	Smither	Fennell	Kearns(e)	Yeldham	Milward	Pearce(q)(B)	Strong(g)	Boardman	Rakison/t	14
Holder(E)	Springhall(c)	Johnson(f)	Ritchie	Fay	Pearce(s)	Dahinton(l)	Benson	Boardman	Smith	15
Ashworth	Young	Fennell	Ritchie(m)	Yeldham	Pearce	Milward/t	Smith	Boardman	Rakison(s)	16
Brady	Young(c)	Cooke(d)	Kearns	Yeldham	Dahinton(F)	Milward	Smith	Boardman	Rakison	17
Brady	Young	Fennell	Kuiti(m)	Yeldham(j)	Pearce(H)	Milward	Benson(t)	Boardman	Rakison	18
Brady/t	Young(y)	Fennell	Kuiti(e)	Yeldham(j)	Milward/t	Hayes	Benson	Boardman(v)	Rakison(A)	19
Knowles/3c2p	Willis(B)	Fennell(j/t)	Ritchie(G)	Yeldham	Milward	Benson/2t	Hayes	Boardman(v)	Rakison(K)	20
Knowles/4cp	Willis(B/t)	Fennell	Ritchie(m)	Cooke/t	Benson	Gibson	Jack/t	Boardman	Hayes	21
Knowles/cp	Willis(C)	Fennell	Ritchie	Kearns	Milward/2t	Gibson(l)	Benson/t(q/t)	Boardman/t	Hayes	22
Knowles/t2c	Willis(C)	Fennell(j)	Kuiti(L)	Yeldham	Benson	Gibson	Hayes	Jack(K)	McCormick	23
Knowles/tc3pdg	Pinder	Fennell/t	Ritchie	Yeldham	Milward	Gibson	McCormick(H)	Boardman	Rakison	24
Knowles/2p	Young	Fennell	Ritchie(L)	Cooke(f)	Dahinton(q)	Gibson	Benson	Boardman	Hayes	25
Knowles/3c2p	Springhall(y)	Fennell	Ritchie/t(m)	Cooke/t(M)	Milward	Gibson	Benson/t(s)	Boardman	Rakison(H/t)	26
Ashworth	Willis/t(r)	Fennell	Ritchie	Cooke	Craig	Gibson	Smith	Jack	McCormick/2t	A
Maddock	Springhall/t	Fennel	Kearns(e)	Yeldham	Milward	Gibson	Benson(z)	Strong	McCormick	B

REPLACEMENTS:	a- E Dickinson	b- T Ashworth	c- T Smither	d- B Fennell	e- C Ritchie	f- J Ford	g- T Benson
h- S Smith	i- P Futter	j- J Cooke	k- Rakison	l- Holder	m- Kearns	n - H Smyth	o- A Snow
p- Thyme	q- L McCormick	r- Springhall	s- L Strong	t- R Harding	u- S Adams	v C Jack	w - T Colborne
x- P Brady	y- P Willis	z- A Walker	A- D Dahinton	B- S Young	C-S Pinder	D- N Marval	E- J Justice
F- Davis	G- S Kuiti	H- J Hayes	I-Goodbody	J- M Dowse	K- Cable	L- G Bibby	M- M Yeldham

Andy Maddock tops the Rosslyn Park points scoring list for a second consecutive season.

Rosslyn Park set a new record for points in a match when they beat Liverpool St Helens 50--22 at home in October, the first time they had reached the 50 point mark in a league match.

Park set a new record for most consecutive wins with a run of seven straight victories late in the season.

They were also nine unbeaten as the season ended with eight wins and a draw.

Outside half Andy Holder played five matches during the season and extended his appearances to 65 which was a new record for a back in league matches for Rosslyn Park. It beat the old record of 63 held by former player John Graves.

ROSSLYN PARK

LEAGUE STATISTICS

compiled by Stephen McCormack

SEASON	Division	P	W	D	L	F	A	Pts Diff	Lge Pts	Lge Pos	Most Points	Most Tries
89-90	1	11	4	0	7	164	243	-79	8	10	87 John Graves	4 Mark Jermyn
90-91	1	12	6	0	6	216	174	42	12	7	92 John Graves	3 Peter Taylor, Guy Leleu & Kelvin Wyles
91-92	1	12	0	1	11	111	258	-147	1	13r	53 John Graves	2 Mark Thomas & Kelvin Wyles
92-93	2	12	5	0	7	209	199	10	10	8r	61 John Graves & Gary Abraham	3 Paul Essenhigh
93-94	3	18	10	1	7	372	240	132	21	5	59 Paul Robin	9 Shane Roiser
94-95	3	18	10	0	8	313	280	33	20	4	54 Mike Griffin	5 Tim Smither & Adam Vander
95-96	3	18	3	2	13	290	426	-136	8	9	45 John Rowlands	5 Mike Griffin
96-97	3	30	17	0	13	630	620	10	34	8	121 Andy Holder	9 Toby Rakison
97-98	JN1	26	13	1	12	486	537	-51	27	5	178 Andy Maddock	11 Liam McCormick
98-99	JN1	26	17	1	8	588	371	217	35	3	93 Andy Maddock	7 Nick Marval

BIGGEST MARGINS

Home Win	48pts - 48-0 v Northampton 27.4.91
Away Win	22pts - 35-13 v Walsall 10.5.97
Home Defeat	31pts - 8-39 v Rugby 21.2.98
Away Defeat	50pts - 14-64 v Orrell 28.4.90

MOST CONSECUTIVE

Appearances	45 John Graves 19.9.87 - 27.4.91
Matches scoring Tries	4 Liam McCormick
Matches scoring points	25 John Graves
Victories	7
Defeats	8

MOST POINTS

Scored at Home	50 v Liverpool St H 3.10.98
Scored Away	50 v Harrogate 29.4.95
Conceded at Home	46 v Coventry 2.3.96
Conceded Away	64 v Orrell 28.4.90

MOST TRIES

Scored in a match	9 v Northampton 27.4.91 (H)
Conceded in a match	11 v Orrell 28.4.90 (A)

MOST APPEARANCES

by a forward	93 (2) Ian Campbell-Lamerton
by a back	65 Andy Maddock

	MOST IN A SEASON	MOST IN A CAREER	MOST IN A MATCH
Points	178 Andy Maddock 97-98	454 John Graves 87-93 & 96	22 John Graves 13.2.93 (H)
Tries	11 Liam McCormick 97-98	16 Tony Brooks 87-93 Liam McCormick 97-99	4 Toby Rakison v Otley 29.3.97 (H)
Conversions	28 Andy Maddock 97-98	44 John Graves 87-93 & 96	5 Alex King v Harrogate 29.4.95 (A)
Penalties	31 Andy Maddock 97-98	117 John Graves 87-93 & 96	7 Sean Burns v Leeds 10.1.98 (A)
Drop Goals	3 Andy Maddock 94-95 & 95-96 John Rowland 95-96	7 Andy Maddock 94-98	2 Paul Robin v Gloucester 4.1.92 (A) Andy Maddock v Rotherham 6.4.96 (A)

ROSSLYN PARK PLAYING SQUAD

BACKS

	Ht.	Wt.	Birthdate	Birthplace	CLUB	League Apps	Tries	Pts
Ed Dickinson Oxford Nuiv, England Univ.			18.11.70		Rosslyn Park Worcester	36(9)	4	20
Tim Springhall			13.05.68		Rosslyn Park Blackheath	35(7)	3	15
Crawford Henderson Scotland u21, Anglo Scots u21, Middlesex.	6.1	14.00	11.02.69		Rosslyn Park Harlequins	20(1) 6	7 1	35 5
James Wyatt					Rosslyn Park	15	1	15
Lee Fanning Yorkshire	5.10	13.00	08.07.72	Romford	Rosslyn Park Reading	16 86	3 20	15 100
Andy Holder			27.03.66		Rosslyn Park	65(1)	6	169
Jeremy Cook					Rosslyn Park Newbury	6 2	- 1	43 22
Simon Young					Rosslyn Park	9(2)	-	-
Tim Smither London u21, Surrey u21.			26.02.72		Rosslyn Park Harlequins	38(3)	8	40
Paul Futter London, Surrey.			16.04.71		Rosslyn Park Clifton	49(2) 20	11 2	55 14
Andy Maddock England u21, Students, u18, London			01.10.72		Rosslyn Park Wasps	97 8	12 1	346 16
James Justice					Rosslyn Park	7(3)	4	20
Nick Marval					Rosslyn Park	32(1)	11	55
Stuart Burns					Rosslyn Park	8(1)	1	45
Simon Pinder					Rosslyn Park	1(3)	-	-

FORWARDS

	Ht.	Wt.	Birthdate	Birthplace	CLUB	League Apps	Tries	Pts
Ben Fennell			16.08.71		Rosslyn Park	73(8)	11	55
Chris Ritchie London, Surrey, Welsh Univ.			03.11.70		Rosslyn Park	73(7)	4	20
Jason Ford England u21 squad, Hampshire.			11.08.71		Rosslyn Park Havant	45(8)	2	10
Alex Milward			23.10.68		Rosslyn Park	99(5)	8	40
James Pearce					Rosslyn Park	6	-	-
Toby Rakison			29.09.74		Rosslyn Park	47(1)	16	80
Simon Smith			06.08.72		Rosslyn Park Coventry	25(6) 14	3 2	15 10
Dave Dahinton					Rosslyn Park Liverpool St H	3(2)	-	-
Graham Boardman Surrey, Scottish Univ.			04.04.71		Rosslyn Park Watsonians	69	5	25
Lysander Strong East Midlands Colts.			13.08.74		Rosslyn Park Rugby	10(12)	2	10
Lee Gibson			12.08.72		Rosslyn Park	68(3)	2	10
Matt Yeldham	5.11	17.00	29.01.69		Rosslyn Park Richmond	27(7) 45(6)	- 2	- 8
Liam McCormick					Rosslyn Park	18(4)	16	80
Chris Jack					Rosslyn Park	8(3)	1	5
Richard Cable					Rosslyn Park	5(4)	-	-

ROSSLYN PARK

FACT FILE

Founded: 1879
Nickname: The Park
Training Nights: Tuesday & Thursday

Colours: Red and white hoops.
Change colours: Dark blue

GROUND Address: Priory Lane, Roehampton, London SW15 5JH
Tel: 0208 876 1879 (Clubhouse) 0208 876 6044 (Admin) Fax: 0208 878 7527
e-mail: rugby@rosslynparkfc.freeserve.co.uk
Capacity: 4,630 Seated: 630 Standing: 4,000

Directions: Ground situated at the junction of Upper Richmond Rd (Sth Circular) and Roehampton Lane
Nearest Railway Station: Barnes BR Southern from Waterloo. Leave station on downside, cross strip of common to Upper Richmond Rd traffic lights. Turn right entrance on Upper Richmond Rd.

Car Parking: 200 in the ground @ £1

Admission Season: Adult £58-£85 Matchday: Adults £5, Concessions forChildren/OAPs

Club Shop: Yes, open Tues/Thurs/Sat/Sun Contact Sarah Hughes 0181 876 6044

Clubhouse: 11-11 every day, except Wednesday. Snacks, barmeals & restaurant available.
Functions: Capacity 300, contact Doug Bradford 0181 876 1879

PROGRAMME
Size: A5 Pages: 32 + cover Price: £1
Editor: Sarah Hughes 0181 876 6044

ADVERTISING RATES

Colour	Page £400	Half £260
Mono	Page £300	Half £160

Andy Maddocks
Park's Top Points Scorer 1998-99

WHARFEDALE R.U.F.C.

President	John Spencer	High Pasture, Threshfield, Nr Skipton, N Yorks BD23 5NS 01756 752456 (H), 01756 753015 (B), 01756 753020 (Fax)
Club Secretary	Stuart Brown	7 Holme Croft, Threshfield, Skipton, N. Yorks.BD23 5HW 01756 752054 (H), 01756 753420 (Fax)
Director of Rugby/ Fixture Secretary	Michael Harrison	Old Hall Farm,Threshfield, Skipton, N. Yorks. BD23 5PL 01756 752777 (H & B & Fax)
Press Officer/ Administrator	Keith Lewis	Willow Bank, Bank Road, Cross Hills,Keighley, W. Yorks. BD20 8AA 01535 634318 (H, B & Fax)
Chairman	Frank House	Stocks House, Main St., Threshfield, Skipton, N Yorks BD23 5HD. 01756 753546 (H)

The main talking point of last season was probably the indifferent start which left Wharfedale adrift at the bottom of the table on 10th October with six defeats from the opening six games, after losing out twice by single scores. A mid-season revival then brought eleven wins from the next fourteen games to take the Greens up to an impressive fifth place before the gaps in the league programme at the end of the season resulted in an inconsistent run-in. The side finally settled into seventh place, equalling their previous best of 1996/97, but most people were still left thinking `if only'.

Former England and Harlequins fly half David Pears, who has family connections with Dales club, was an inspirational presence in his first season of league rugby for the Greens. His contribution of 235 points in 21 games was almost exactly half of the team's total and he fully deserved his award as `Jewson Player of the Season'.

The Wharfedale team performances of the season were undoubtedly the quartet of first-ever away wins - at Rosslyn Park, Reading, Harrogate and Liverpool St. Helens, and the string of nine consecutive home wins which concluded with an honourable 30-30 draw against Manchester in the last game of the season.

Most of the individual accolades go to the pack and the ever-present trio of Hedley Verity, David Lister and John Lawn who were later joined in the Yorkshire side by Russ Buckroyd and Neil Dickinson. Captain Charlie Vyvyan led by example in his first full season after returning from Sale and there were encouraging performances from newcomers richard Lancaster and Sam Allen while experienced former North Division back-row Paul Evans adapted to life in the second row with relish. Behind them, Pears was the play-maker supreme and full back Neil Heseltine had what many regarded as his best season for the club. Wharfedale's record point-scoring winger Adam Mounsey missed twelve games because of an appendix operation and gave up much of his kicking duties to Pears but still recorded 77 points and finished as the club's top try scorer with eight league touch downs in fourteen games.

Once again, the Greens hope to make a strong challenge in all competitions in 1999/2000 and extend a warm welcome to all the players, supporters, committee personnel and match officials who will visit Wharfeside Avenue in the coming season. The Greens look forward to renewing acquaintances with their old friends Preston Grasshoppers and Fylde and trust that newcomers to the league, Blackheath and Bracknell, will return home having enjoyed their first taste of Yorkshire Dales hospitality.

Back Row: Ben Whitfield, Sam Allen, Russ Buckroyd, Paul Evans, David Lister, Neil Dickinson. **Middle**: Michael Harrison (Dir. of Rugby), Rob Sugden, John Metcalfe, David Whitfield, Dennis Wood, Mick Harrison, Dan Harrison, John Lawn, Glen Harrison. **Front**: Steve McManus, Neil Heseltine, David Pears, Charlie Vyvyan (Capt.), Andy Hodgson, Richard Lancaster, Hedley Verity. **Photo:** Keith Lewis

WHARFEDALE

Match No.	Date	H/A	Comp.	Opponents	Result & Score	Att.	15	14	13	12	11
1	05.09	A	JN1	Camberley	L 11-29	350	Heseltine	Mounsey/t2p	G Harrison	Davies	McManus
2	12.09	H	JN1	Henley	L 6-8	550	Hodgson	Mounsey/2p	G Harrison	Davies	McManus
3	19.09	A	JN1	Morley	L 17-29	400	Hodgson	Mounsey/t2cp	G Harrison	M Harrison	Heseltine/t
4	26.09	H	JN1	Lydney	L 28-33	520	Hayes	Mounsey/t2c	Heseltine	Davies	B Whitfield
5	03.10	A	JN1	Otley	L 11-25	550	Hodgson	Mounsey	Davies	M Harrison	Heseltine
6	10.10	H	JN1	Reading	L 11-17	400	Hodgson	McManus	Davies	M Harrison	Heseltine
7	24.10	A	JN1	Rosslyn Park	W 6-5	400	Heseltine	McManus	G Harrison	Davies	Eccleston
8	31.10	H	JN1	Birmingham S*	W 22-12	500	Heseltine	McManus	Davies	M Harrison	Eccleston
9	07.11	A	JN1	Liverpool StH	W 32-20	250	Heseltine/t	McManus	G Harrison	M Harrison	Hodgson
10	21.11	H	JN1	Harrogate	W 27-12	600	Hodgson	McManus	G Harrison	M Harrison	Heseltine
11	28.11	A	JN1	Newbury	L 10-18	250	Hodgson	McManus	G Harrison	Davies	Heseltine
12	05.12	A	JN1	Manchester	L 3-15	500	Heseltine	McManus	Walker	Hodgson	B Whitfield
13	12.12	H	JN1	Nottingham	W 25-5	500	Heseltine/t	McManus/t	Hodgson	M Harrison	B Whitfield
14	19.12	H	JN1	Newbury*	W 23-10	600	Heseltine	McManus	Hodgson	M Harrison	B Whitfield
15	26.12	A	JN1	Harrogate	W 6-0	1,200	Heseltine	McManus	Hodgson	G Harrison	B Whitfield
16	02.01	H	JN1	Liverpool StH	W 59-0	700	Heseltine	McManus	Hodgson/t	G Harrison/t	B Whitfield
17	16.01	A	JN1	Birmingham S	L 12-27	250	Heseltine	McManus	G Harrison	M Harrison	B Whitfield
18	23.01	H	JN1	Rosslyn Park	W 19-3	600	Heseltine	Mounsey	Davies	M Harrison	B Whitfield
19	30.01	A	JN1	Reading	W 8-6	200	Heseltine	Mounsey/p	G Harrison	Davies	B Whitfield
20	06.02	H	JN1	Otley	W 21-3	1,000	Heseltine	Mounsey/c3p	Davies	G Harrison	B Whitfield
21	13.02	A	JN1	Lydney	L 18-20	600	Heseltine	Mounsey	Davies	G Harison	B Whitfield(c/t)
22	27.02	H	JN1	Morley	W 38-14	750	Heseltine	Mounsey/3t	Davies	G Harrison	B Whitfield
23	14.03	A	JN1	Henley	L 0-30	650	Heseltine	Mounsey	Davies	G Harrison	Gilbert
24	27.03	H	JN1	Camberley	W 27-16	450	Heseltine	Mounsey/t	Davies	G Harrison	B Whitfield
25	03.04	A	JN1	Nottingham	L 7-39	500	Heseltine	Mounsey/t	Davies	M Harrison	B Whitfield
26	17.04	H	JN1	Manchester	D 30-30	650	Heseltine	Mounsey	Davies	G Harrison/t	Gilbert
A	17.10	H	TBC	Birmingham S	W 27-5	600	Hodgson	McManus	Davies	M Harrison	Heseltine
B	14.11	A	TBC	Nottingham	L 17-27	450	Hodgson	McManus	Davies	Heseltine/t	Eccleston

* after opponents name indicates a penalty try
Brackets after a player's name indicates he was replaced. eg (a) means he was replaced by replacement code "a" and so on.
/ after a player or replacement name is followed by any scores he made - eg /t, /c, /p, /dg or any combination of these

1998-99 HIGHLIGHTS

League debuts:
Michael Hayes, Craig Ingram, Sam Allen, David Pears, Max Cummins, Ben Whitfield.

Ever Presents: David Lister and Hedley Verity

Players used: 32 plus 5 as a replacement only

Most Points in a season:

Pts	Player	T	C	P	DG
235	D Pears	5	24	50	4
77	A Mounsey	8	5	9	-
20	R Buckroyd	4	-	-	-
15	N Heseltine	3	-	-	-
15	J Lawn	3	-	-	-
15	C Vyvyan	3	-	-	-

Former England international David Pears made his debut for Wharfedale in their fourth match of the season

MATCH FACTS

10	9	1	2	3	4	5	6	7	8	
McCabe	D Harrison	Peel	Lawn	Lancaster	Lister	Dickinson	Evans	Verity	Vyvyan	1
McCabe	D Harrison	Metcalfe	Lawn	Lancaster	Lister	Dickinson	Evans	Verity	Vyvyan	2
Hayes	D Whitfield	Metcalfe	Lawn	Lancaster	Lister	Dickinson	Hartley	Verity	Evans	3
Pears/3p	Smith/t	Metcalfe	Lawn	Ingram	Lister/t	Wood	Hartley	Verity	Evans	4
Pears/t2p	Smith	Metcalfe	Lawn	Ingram	Lister	Wood	Allen	Verity	Evans	5
Pears/t2p	D Harrison	Metcalfe	Lawn	Dickinson	Lister	Wood	Evans	Verity	Vyvyan	6
Pears/pdg	D Harrison	Lancaster	Lawn	Dickinson	Lister	Wood	Allen	Verity	Buckroyd	7
Pears/c5p	D Harrison	Lancaster	Lawn	Dickinson	Lister	Vyvyan	Allen	Verity	Buckroyd	8
Pears/2c6p	Smith	Lancaster	Lawn	Dickinson	Lister	Wood	Buckroyd	Verity	Vyvyan/t	9
Pears/c5p	D Whitfield	Lancaster	Lawn	Dickinson	Lister	Wood	Buckroyd/t	Verity	Vyvyan/t	10
Pears/cp	D Whitfield	Lancaster	Lawn	Dickinson	Lister	Wood	Buckroyd/t	Verity	Vyvyan	11
Pears/p	D Whitfield	Lancaster	Lawn	Dickinson	Lister	Wood	Buckroyd	Verity	Vyvyan	12
Pears/t2cpdg	D Whitfield	Metcalfe	Lawn	Dickinson	Lister	Wood	Buckroyd	Verity	Vyvyan	13
Pears/t2c3p	D Harrison	Lancaster	Lawn	Dickinson	Lister	Evans	Buckroyd	Verity	Vyvyan	14
Pears/pdg	D Harrison	Metcalfe	Lawn	Dickinson	Lister	Evans	Buckroyd	Verity	Vyvyan	15
Pears/7c	D Harrison/t	Metcalfe/t(f/t)	Lawn/t	Dickinson	Lister	Evans	Buckroyd/t	Verity(r/t)	Vyvyan/t	16
Pears/4p	D Harrison	Lancaster	Lawn	Dickinson	Lister	Evans	Buckroyd	Verity	Vyvyan	17
Pears/c4p	D Harrison	Lancaster	Lawn/t	Dickinson	Lister	Wood	Allen	Verity	Vyvyan	18
D Harrison	D Whitfield	Lancaster/t	Lawn	Dickinson	Lister	Evans	Allen	Verity	Vyvyan	19
McCabe	D Harrison	Lancaster	Lawn	Dickinson	Lister/t	Evans/t	Allen	Verity	Vyvyan	20
Pears/c2p	D Harrison	Lancaster	Lawn	Dickinson	Lister	Evans/t	Allen	Verity	Vyvyan	21
Pears/tc2p	D Harrison	Lancaster	Lawn	Dickinson	Lister	Evans/t	Allen(x/t)	Verity	Vyvyan	22
Pears	Smith	Lancaster	Lawn	Metcalfe	Lister	Wood	Buckroyd	Verity	Vyvyan	23
Pears/c4pdg	D Whitfield	Metcalfe	Lawn	Lancaster	Lister	Evans	Allen	Verity/t	Buckroyd	24
Pears/c	Smith	Metcalfe	Lawn	Cummins	Lister	Wood	Evans	Verity	Buckroyd	25
Pears/3c3p	D HArrison	Metcalfe	Lawn/t	Dickinson	Lister	Evans	Allen	Verity/t	Buckroyd	26
Pears/c5p	Smith	Lancaster	Lawn	Dickinson	Cowley	Wood	Allen	Verity/t	Buckroyd/t	A
Pears/3p(m/p)		Lancaster	Lawn	Dickinson	Lister	Vyvyan	Allen	Verity	Buckroyd	B

REPLACEMENTS:

a- N Heseltine	b- J Davies	c - S McManus	d - D McCabe	e - D Harrison	f - R Lancaster
g - N Dickinson	h - P Evans	i - D Whitfield	j - A Hodgson	k - J Hartley	l - J Metcalfe
m - M Hayes	n - B Whitfield	o - G Smith	p - C Ingram	r - S Allen	s - D Wood
t - R Sugden	u - D Pears	v - S Gilbert	w - J Ogden	x - R Buckroyd	y - S Walker
z - R Cowley	A - M Cummins	B - P Hargreaves			

and went of to score 235 points for them, the second best total for the club in a league season.

Included in his total were 4 drop goals which set a new record for a season beating the previous record of three held by Russ Buckroyd.

Pears also equalled the club records of seven conversions and six penalties in a match in the games against Liverpool St Helens home and away respectively.

The home match against Liverpool St Helens saw Wharfedale achieve their biggest ever league win, 59 points, and their biggest ever score at home when they won 59-0.

Adam Mounsey scored 77 points and in the process passed Alex Howarth's club record of 486 league points, Mounsey ended the season on506 points.

Neil Heseltine and Hedley Verity extended their records for most appearances by backs and forwards to 111 and 139 respectively.

WHARFEDALE

LEAGUE STATISTICS
compiled by Stephen McCormack

SEASON	Division	P	W	D	L	F	A	Pts Diff	Lge Pts	Lge Pos	Most Points		Most Tries	
89-90	North 2	10	5	1	4	161	134	27	11	5	72	Mark Toseland	5	Les Ingham & Glen Harrison
90-91	North 2	10	5	0	5	129	104	25	10	5	63	Mark Toseland	3	Steve Howarth & David Swinglehurst
91-92	North 2	10	10	0	0	254	55	199	20	1p	111	Russ Buckroyd	11	Les Ingham
92-93	North 1	12	7	0	5	216	207	9	14	3	45	Mark Toseland	5	Glen Harrison
93-94	North 1	12	12	0	0	327	77	250	24	1p	127	Alex Howarth	8	Alex Howarth & Simon Slater
94-95	5N	12	6	1	5	209	198	11	13	4	94	Alex Howarth	5	Daniel Harrison
95-96	5N	12	12	0	0	331	146	185	24	1p	143	Alex Howarth	10	Neil Heseltine
96-97	3	30	17	0	13	710	635	75	34	7	182	Adam Mounsey	21	Andrew Hodgson
97-98	JN1	26	8	3	15	476	684	-208	19	10	247	Adam Mounsey	8	Jonathon Davies
98-99	JN1	26	13	1	12	477	421	51	27	7	235	David Pears	8	Adam Mounsey

BIGGEST MARGINS

Home Win	59pts - 59-0 v Liverpool St H 2.1.99
Away Win	34pts - 68-34 v Lichfield 30.3.96
Home Defeat	42pts - 8-50 v Walsall 25.3.95
Away Defeat	47pts - 24-71 v London Welsh 21.3.98

MOST CONSECUTIVE

Appearances	61 Denis Wood 13.4.91 - 14.9.96
Matches scoring Tries	5 Steve McManus & Adam Mounsey
Matches scoring points	50 Adam Mounsey
Victories	14 x 2
Defeats	8 (18.4.98 - 10.10.98)

MOST POINTS

Scored at Home	59 v Liverpool StH 2.1.99
Scored Away	68 v Lichfield 30.3.96
Conceded at Home	53 v Worcester
Conceded Away	71 v London Welsh 21.3.98

MOST TRIES

Scored in a match	12 v Sandbach 29.2.92
Conceded in a match	11 v London Welsh 21.3.98 (A)

MOST APPEARANCES

by a forward	139 Hedley Verity
by a back	111 Neil Heseltine

	MOST IN A SEASON	MOST IN A CAREER	MOST IN A MATCH
Points	247 Adam Mounsey 97-98	506 AdamMounsey 96-99	24 Les Ingham v Sandbach 29.2.92
Tries	21 Andrew Hodgson 96-97	32 Les Ingham 87-93	6 Les Ingham v Sandbach 29.2.92
Conversions	39 Adam Mounsey 96-97	75 Adam Mounsey 96-98	7 Mark Toseland v Huddersfield 12.11.88
Penalties	55 Adam Mounsey 97-98	95 Alex Howarth 93-97	6 Mark Toseland v Lymm 14.1.89 David Pears v Liverpool St H 7.11.98
Drop Goals	4 David Pears 98-99	8 Russ Buckroyd 87-97	1 on 19 occasions including 8 by Russ Buckroyd

WHAFEDALE PLAYING SQUAD

BACKS

	Ht.	Wt.	Birthdate	Birthplace	CLUB	League Apps	Tries	Pts
Jonathan Davies Wales Youth.	6.0	14.00	28.03.72	Bangor	Wharfedale Bangor(Wales)	60	11	69
Craig Eccleston North Colts	5.11	12.05	19.04.78	Keighley	Wharfedale N Ribblesdale	5	1	5
Sean Gilbert England Students(RL), Yorkshire Colts.	5.11	13.05	14.06.69	Norwich Leeds	Wharfedale	6	1	5
Dan Harrison Yorkshire	5.11	13.00	26.10.71	Skipton	Wharfedale	86	20	100
Mick Harrison Yorkshire u18.	5.11	14.05	31.01.68	Skipton	Wharfedale	92	6	33
Neil Heseltine Yorkshire	5.9	13.00	16.07.68	Skipton	Wharfedale Kelso	111	25	128
Andy Hodgson North u21.	5.11	13.00	09.02.76	Skipton	Wharfedale	55	27	135
Alex Howarth Yorkshire	6.0	14.00	30.11.68	Skipton	Wharfedale	58	15	496
David McCabe North Colts.	6.00	12.05	07.09.79	Manchester	Wharfedale Broughton Park	4	-	3
Steve McManus Yorkshire colts.	5.11	13.00	19.05.72	Keighley	Wharfedale W Hartlepool	65	13	65
Adam Mounsey Yorkshire u18.	5.10	13.05	18.09.72	Bradford	Wharfedale Morley	62	22	506
Ben Whitfield	5.11	13.00	20.10.75	Skipton	Wharfedale	14(3)	-	-
Craig Walker North Colts.	5.11	14.00	03.08.67	Keighley	Wharfedale Keighley	59	12	60
David Whitfield	6.0	13.03	08.08.72	Leeds	Wharfedale Selly Oak	17(5)	4	20
David Pears England. Other clubs: Aspatria, Sale, Camberley	5.10	13.00	06.12.67	Workington	Wharfedale Harlequins	21 40	5 7	235 431

FORWARDS

	Ht.	Wt.	Birthdate	Birthplace	CLUB	League Apps	Tries	Pts
Sam Allen North u21.	6.2	14.00	23.07.78	Skipton	Wharfedale	10(7)	1	5
Russ Buckroyd Yorkshire	6.0	14.05	31.01.67	Liverpool	Wharfedale	88(8)	14	188
Neil Dickinson	6.0	15.05	30.07.69	Otley	Wharfedale	56(3)	1	5
Paul Evans North, Yorkshire.	6.3	17.00	03.01.67	Bridlington	Wharfedale W Hartlepool	44(3) 55(3)	5 6	25 28
John Hartley Yorkshire u21.	6.1	14.07	17.08.75	Skipton	Wharfedale	5	1	5
John Lancaster	6.00	16.00	11.06.68	Skipton	Wharfedale	48(2)	-	-
John Lawn Yorkshire	5.7	14.00	07.08.70	Bradford	Wharfedale	125(1)	13	65
David Lister Yorkshire	6.5	16.00	19.10.73	Keighley	Keighley	77	10	50
John Metcalfe Yorkshire	6.00	16.00	27.04.68	Bournemouth	Wharfedale	96(7)	5	25
Philip Peel Yorkshire u21.	5.11	14.07	12.08.77	Harrogate	Wharfedale	3(2)	-	-
Hedley Verity Yorkshire	6.0	14.00	20.04.70	Harrogate	Wharfedale	139	25	118
Rob Sugden	5.10	13.00	19.12.74	Harrogate	Wharfedale Bradford & Bing	1(2)	-	
Charlie Vyvyan England Univ, North, Yorkshire. Other clubs: Richmond, Sale	6.6	17.00	01.09.65	Wimbledon	Wharfedale	63	13	65
Craig Ingrams England Univ.	5.11	16.00	04.07.74	Shrewsbury	Wharfedale Newport(Salop)	2(4)	-	-
Richard Lancaster Cumbria	6.1	17.00	12.03.73	Lancaster	Wharfedale Kirkby Lonsdale	18(2)	2	10

WHARFEDALE

FACT FILE

Founded: 1923
Nickname: Greens/Green Machine/Dalesmen

Colours: Emerald green/white/green
Change colours: Scarlet & white hoops/white/scarlet

GROUND

Address: Wharfeside Avenue, Threshfield, Skipton, N Yorks BD23 5ND

Tel : 01756 752547 Fax: 01535 634318 e-mail: keith@color55.freeserve.co.uk
web site: http://www.wharfedalerugby.co.uk

Capacity: 3,000 Seated: 120 Standing: Covered 180, Uncovered 2,700

Directions: Take B6256 from Skipton bypass, signed Grassington after 8 miles turn right after Old Hall Inn in Threshfield, left after 400 metres down 'The Avenue'
Nearest Station: Skipton, no bus service. Group transport can be arranged through club secretary

Car Parking: 120 adjacent, no charge

Admission:
Season Adults £100
Matchday Adults (incl. prog.) £5, u16 No Charge

Club Shop: Open 1 hour before & after 1st XV matches.
Manager Barbara Brown 01756 752054

Clubhouse: Normal licensing hours matchdays.
Snacks, bar meals & restaurant.
Functions Capacity 120, contact Chairman Frank House 01756 753546

Training Nights: Monday & Wednesday

PROGRAMME

Size: A5 Pages: 48 + cover
Price: Included with entry
Editor: Richard Toyn 01756 752484

ADVERTISING RATES
Colour Negotiable
Mono Full page £300 Half page £150

Delight for Wharfedale scrum half, Dan Harrison, as team-mate John Law touches down during the 30-30 draw at home to Manchester
Photo: Keith Lewis

DIVISION THREE
(CURRENTLY JEWSON NATIONAL LEAGUE ONE

RECORDS SECTION

The Last Ten Years 322

A breakdown showing the champions, runners-up, those relegated, who scored most - points, tries, conversions, penalties & drop goals in each of the last ten seasons in this division (or its equivalent)

All Time Team & Individual Records 323

A list of the various records for this division (or its equivalent) since the start of the league system.

Most Points in a Season 324

The all-time list for this division

Most Points in a Match 325

The all-time list for this division

Most Tries in a Match 326

The all-time list for this division

Most Career Appearances 327

The all-time list for this division

Ten Year Record 328

A grid showing those clubs who have been part of this division (or its equivalent), and the league position they achieved for each of the last ten years

THE LAST TEN YEARS

Season	Champions	Runners-up	Relegated
1989-90	**London Scottish**	Wakefield	-

Most

	Points: 102 Andy Higgin (Vale of Lune)	Tries: 7 Mike Harrison (Wakefield) Brendan Hanavan (Fylde)
Penalties: 13 Gavin Hastings (Lon. Scottish)	Conversions: 25 Andy Green (Exeter)	D.Gs: 4 Richard Cramb (Lon. Scottish)

Season	Champions	Runners-up	Relegated
1990-91	**West Hartlepool**	Morley	Metropolitan Police, Vale of Lune

Most

	Points: 108 Mark Rogers (Sheffield)	Tries: 9 Jonathon Wrigley (W. Hartlepool)
Penalties: 19 John Stabler (W. Hartlepool)	Conversions: 22 Andy Green (Exeter) Mark Rogers (Sheffield)	D.Gs: 2 by 5 players

Season	Champions	Runners-up	Relegated
1991-92	**Richmond**	Fylde	Lydney, Nuneaton

Most

	Points: Mike Jackson (Fylde)	Tries: 8 Matt Brain (Clifton)
Penalties: 16 Simon Hogg (Clifton)	Conversions: 26 Mike Jackson (Fylde)	D.Gs: 2 by 5 players

Season	Champions	Runners-up	Relegated
1992-93	**Otley**	Havant	Sheffield, Leeds, Clifton, Askeans, Liverpool St. H, Aspatria, Plymouth Albion, Broughton Park

Most

	Points: 122 Andy Green (Exeter)	Tries: 8 Martin Kelly (Broughton Park) Mark Sephton (Liverpool St. Helens)
Penalties: 14 Peter Rutledge (Otley)	Conversions: 31 Andy Green (Exeter)	D.Gs: 3 Andy Green (Exeter) Simon Hogg (Clifton)

Season	Champions	Runners-up	Relegated
1993-94	**Coventry**	Fylde	Havant, Redruth

Most

	Points: 172 Andy Finnie (Bedford)	Tries: 12 Bendan Hanavan (Fylde)
Penalties: 45 Andy Finnie (Bedford)	Conversions: 23 Richard Angell (Coventry)	D.Gs: 3 Jamie Grayshon (Morley)

Season	Champions	Runners-up	Relegated
1994-95	**Bedford**	Blackheath	Clifton, Exeter

Most

	Points: 228 Andy Finnie (Bedford)	Tries: 8 David Bishop (Rugby)
Penalties: 56 Andy Finnie (Bedford)	Conversions: 24 Andy Finnie (Bedford)	D.Gs: 5 Jamie Grayshon (Morley)

Season	Champions	Runners-up	Relegated
1995-96	**Coventry**	Richmond	-

Most

	Points: 215 Ralph Zoing (Harrogate))	Tries: 12 Colin Phillips (Reading)
Penalties: 53 Ralph Zoing (Harrogate)	Conversions: 28 John Gregory (Richmond)	D.Gs: 8 Jamie Grayshon (Morley)

Season	Champions	Runners-up	Relegated
1996-97	**Exeter**	Fylde	Walsall, Havant, Redruth, Clifton

Most

	Points: 404 Steve Gough (Fylde)	Tries: 22 Mark Kirkby (Otley)
Penalties: 82 Steve Gough (Fylde)	Conversions: 63 Ralph Zoing (Harrogate)	D.Gs: 7 Craig Raymond (Lon. Welsh)

Season	Champions	Runners-up	Relegated
1997-98	**Worcester**	Leeds	-

Most

	Points: 322 Sateki Tuipolotu (Leeds)	Tries: 29 Nick Baxter (Worcester)
Penalties: 64 Chris Atkinson (Nottingham)	Conversions: 64 Craig Raymond (Lon. Welsh)	D.Gs: 4 Colin Stephens (Leeds)

Season	Champions	Runners-up	Relegated
1998-99	**Henley**	Manchester	Morley, Liverpool St. Helens

Most

	Points: 365 Steve Swindells (Manchester)	Tries: 15 Lafaele Filipo (Otley) Adam Standeven (Morley)
Penalties: 70 Steve Swindellsd (Manchester)	Conversions: 60 Steve Swindells (Manchester)	D.Gs: 5 Phil Osman(Henley) & Sam Jack(Nottm)

TEAM RECORDS

Highest score:	**89**	Liverpool St Helens 89 Clifton 13. 15.2.97
Highest aggregate:	**103**	Clifton 19 Leeds 84. 12.4.97
Highest score by a losing side:	**42**	Walsall 42 Reading 44. 12.4.97
Highest scoring draw:	**34**	Reading v Rosslyn Park. 17.2.96
Most consecutive wins:	**14**	Exeter 1996-97
Most consecutive defeats:	**13**	Redruth 1996-97
Most points for in a season:	**1209**	Leeds 1996-97
Least points for in a season:	**46**	Birmingham Solihull 1987-88
Most points against in a season:	**1347**	Clifton 1996-97
Least points against in a season:	**89**	Plymouth 1988-89
Most tries for in a season:	**158**	Leeds 1996-97
Most tries against in a season:	**184**	Clifton 1996-97
Least tries for in a season:	**3**	Birmingham Solihull 1987-88
Least tries against in a season:	**5**	Plymouth 1988-89
Most conversions for in a season:	**94**	Leeds 1996-97
Most conversions against in a season:	**125**	Clifton 1996-97
Most penalties for in a season:	**85**	Fylde 1996-97
Most penalties against in a season:	**74**	Otley 1996-97
Least penalties for in a season:	**8**	Morley 1987-88
Least penalties against in a season:	**10**	West Hartlepool 1990-91
Most drop goals for in a season:	**8**	Morley 1994-95, London Welsh 1996-97
Most drop goals against in a season:	**8**	Rotherham 1995-96, Havant 1996-97

INDIVIDUAL RECORDS

Most points in a season:	**404**	Steve Gough (Fylde) 1996-97
Most tries in a season:	**29**	Nick Baxter (Worcester) 1997-98
Most conversions in a season:	**64**	Craig Raymond (London Welsh) 1997-98
Most penalties in a season:	**82**	Steve Gough (Fylde) 1996-97
Most drop goals in a season:	**8**	Jamie Grayson (Morley) 1995-96
Most points in a match:	**39**	Paul Brett, Liverpool St. Helens v Clifton 15.2.97
Most tries in a match:	**6**	Nick Baxter, Worcester v Otley 21.2.98
Most conversions in a match:	**12**	Paul Brett, Liverpool St. Helens v Clifton 15.2.97
Most penalties in a match:	**9**	Paul Morris, Lydney v Otley 14.9.96
		Rob Ashworth, Havant v Clifton 21.9.96
Most drop goals in a match:	**4**	Andy Rimmer, Broughton Park v Sheffield 17.11.90

ALL TIME RECORDS

MOST POINTS IN A SEASON

Points	Player	Club	Season	Tries	Cons.	Pens.	D.G.
404	Steve Gough	Fylde	1996-97	7	57	82	3
365	Steve Swindells	Manchester	1998-99	7	60	70	0
338	Richard Mills	Walsall	1996-97	1	42	81	2
322	Sateki Tuipulotu	Leeds	1997-98	11	60	49	-
307	Gerry Ainscough	Leeds	1996-97	14	45	49	
305	Ralph Zoing	Harrogate	1996-97	4	63	48	5
300	Andy Green	Exeter	1996-97	5	58	50	3
300	Craig Raymond	London Welsh	1996-97	6	39	57	7
287	Peter Rutledge	Otley	1996-97	8	56	45	
281	Jason Dance	Reading	1996-97	6	61	43	
275	Paul Morris	Lydney	1996-97	3	31	66	
272	Chris Atkinson	Nottingham	1998-99	2	35	64	-
264	Craig Raymond	London Welsh	1997-98	8	64	29	3
262	Chris Atkinson	Nottingham	1997-98	6	30	64	
247	Adam Mounsey	Wharfedale	1997-98	4	31	55	
246	Jason Dance	Reading	1997-98	4	35	52	
235	David Pears	Wharfedale	1998-99	5	24	50	4
228	Andy Finnie	Bedford	1994-95		24	56	4
221	Guy Gregory	Camberley	1998-99	2	29	50	1
216	Richard Lebas	Worcester	1997-98	9	60	16	1
215	Ralph Zoing	Harrogate	1995-96	3	19	51	3
210	Paul Brett	Liverpool St Helens	1996-97	14	40	20	
206	Jamie Grayshon	Morley	1995-96	2	20	44	8
197	Sateki Tuipulotu	Leeds	1996-97	15	37	16	
196	John Gregory	Richmond	1995-96	4	28	40	
195	Jamie Grayshon	Morley	1996-97	2	40	31	4
193	Jason Dance	Reading	1998-99	1	28	49	-
183	Jim Quantrill	Rugby	1995-96	3	21	42	
182	Adam Mounsey	Wharfdale	1996-97	10	39	18	
178	Andy Maddock	Rosslyn Park	1997-98	4	28	32	2
172	Andy Finnie	Bedford	1993-94		14	45	3
172	Nick Grecian	Newbury	1997-98	3	35	29	
171	Jim Quantrill	Rugby	1997-98	6	33	25	
170	Matt Birch	Birmingham & S	1998-99	1	30	35	-
167	Peter Rutledge	Otley	1994-95	6	13	37	
166	Jamie Grayshon	Morley	1994-95	2	12	39	5
155	Kevin Plant	Rotherham	1995-96		18	35	5
150	Peter Rutledge	Otley	1997-98	3	21	31	
147	Sam Howard	Blackheath	1994-95	1	11	38	2
147	Peter Rutledge	Otley	1995-96	1	11	40	
145	Nick Baxter	Worcester	1997-98	29			
138	Steve Gough	Fylde	1995-96	2	13	34	
138	Dan Clappison	Otley	1998-99	-	33	23	1
133	John Gregory	Richmond	1994-95	1	19	30	
131	Jim Quantrill	Rugby	1994-95	2	20	27	
128	Alan Peacock	Morley	1996-97	3	22	23	
127	Tim Smith	Worcester	1997-98	7	19	18	
125	Andy Green	Exeter	1993-94	3	16	24	2

MOST POINTS IN A MATCH

Points	Player	Match	Date
39	Paul Brett	Liverpool St Helens v Clifton	15.02.97
30	Paul Brett	Liverpool St Helens v Redruth	01.02.97
	Nick Baxter	Worcester v Otley	21.02.98
29	Paul Morris	Lydney v Otley	14.09.96
	Rob Ashworth	Havant v Clifton	21.09.96
28	Steve Burnage	Fylde v Birmingham	07.11.87
	Craig Raymond	London Welsh v Clifton	28.12.96
27	Ralph Zoing	Harrogate v Fylde	14.10.95
	Gerry Ainscough	Leeds v Rosslyn Park	14.09.96
	Craig Raymond	London Welsh v Lydney	09.11.96
	Gerry Ainscough	Leeds v Walsall	01.03.97
	Nat Saumi	Redruth v Clifton	03.05.97
	Adam Standeven	Morley v Newbury	25.04.98
26	Greg Way	Reading v Harrogate	16.09.95
	Andy Green	Exeter v Wharfedale	07.09.96
	Richard Mills	Walsall v Clifton	07.09.96
	Sateki Tuipulotu	Leeds v Nottingham	18.10.97
	Craig Raymond	London Welsh v Wharfedale	21.03.98
	Jason Dance	Reading v Liverpool St Helens	25.04.98
	Duncan Roke	Henley Hawks v Camberley	06.02.99
25	Domonic Cundy	Plymouth v Met Police	26.11.89
	Mark Rodgers	Sheffield v Askeans	13.03.93
	Richard Angell	Coventry v Redruth	30.04.94
	Steve Gough	Fylde v Rosslyn Park	26.10.96
	Mark Kirkby	Otley v Redruth	08.02.97
	Jason Dance	Reading v Clifton	01.03.97
	Richard Mills	Walsall v Redruth	19.04.97
	Simon Middleton	Leeds v Morley	14.02.98
	Matt Hoskin	Manchester v Camberley	12.09.98
	Steve Swindells	Manchester v Liverpool St. Helens	28.12.98
	Steve Swindells	Manchester v Wharfedale	17.04.99
24	Chris Howard	Rugby v Maidstone	26.11.88
	Richard Mills	Walsall v Leeds	12.10.96
	Jason Dance	Reading v Walsall	29.03.97
	Ralph Zoing	Harrogate v Clifton	05.04.97
	Steve Gough	Fylde v London Welsh	26.04.97
	Ralph Zoing	Harrogate v Liverpool StH	17.05.97
23	John Stabler	West Hartlepool v Broughton Park	09.03.91
	Ralph Zoing	Harrogate v Reading	16.09.95
	John Gregory	Richmond v Rotherham	30.09.95
	Phil Belshaw	Reading v Morley	14.10.95
	Peter Rutledge	Otley v Walsall	09.11.96
	Craig Raymond	London Welsh v Rosslyn Park	18.02.97
	Jamie Grayshon	Morley v London Welsh	12.04.97
	Murray Withington	Morley v Lydney	22.11.97
	Richard Le Bas	Worcester v Otley	07.02.98
	Nick Grecian	Newbury v Liverpool St Helens	21.02.98
	Morgan Davies	Newbury v Nottingham	11.04.98
	Nick Paisley	Lydney v Reading	05.12.98
	Guy Gregory	Camberley v Birmingham & Solihull	19.12.98

ALL TIME RECORDS

MOST TRIES IN A MATCH

Tries	Player	Match	Date
6	Nick Baxter	Worcester v Otley	21.02.98
5	Mark Kirkby	Otley v Redruth	08.02.97
	Simon Middleton	Leeds v Morley	14.02.98
	Matt Hoskin	Manchester v Camberley	12.09.98
4	Brendan Hanavan	Fylde v Exeter	03.10.87
	Steve Walklin	Plymouth v Birmingham	17.10.87
	Ian Russell	Plymouth v Fylde	31.10.87
	Brendan Hanavan	Fylde v Birmingham	07.11.87
	Dan Cottrell	Clifton v Askeans	04.01.92
	Mark Sephton	Liverpool St Helens v Aspatria	13.03.93
	Dean Crompton	Liverpool St Helens v Aspatria	13.03.93
	Mark Farrar	Otley v Askeans	27.03.93
	Brendan Hanavan	Fylde v Redruth	09.04.94
	Richard Matthias	Leeds v Clifton	07.12.96
	Simon Dovell	Exeter v Havant	21.12.96
	Ben Wade	Morley v Clifton	18.01.97
	Mark Sephton	Liverpool StH v Clifton	15.02.97
	Colin Stephens	Leeds v Lydney	15.03.97
	Toby Rakison	Rosslyn Park v Otley	29.03.97
	Steve Bartliffe	Leeds v Havant	26.04.97
	Nick Baxter	Worcester v Liverpol St Helens	21.03.98
	Alan Royer	Nottingham v Liverpool St. Helens	28.11.98
	Jeremy Griffiths	Newbury v Harrogate	02.01.99
	Lafaele Filipo	Otley v Reading	03.04.99

Tries	Player	Match	Date
3	Kevin Norris	Plymouth v Sheffield	12.09.87
	Mark Preston	Fylde v Morley	17.10.87
	Simon Cowling	Wakefield v Birmingham	31.10.87
	Simon Cowling	Wakefield v Nuneaton	05.12.87
	Andy Holloway	Wakefield v Morley	12.03.88
	Mike Cathery	Exeter v Birmingham	26.03.88
	Owen Evans	W Hartlepool v Nuneaton	23.04.88
	Chris Howard	Rugby v Vale of Lune	10.09.88
	Mike Harrison	Wakefield v Met Police	24.09.88
	Andy Atkinson	Wakefield v Met Police	24.09.88
	Simon Hughes	Plymouth v Fylde	19.11.88
	Paul Galvin	Met Police v Maidstone	14.01.89
	Mike Murtagh	Wakefield v Askeans	11.11.89
	Gareth Hughes	Lon. Welsh v Fylde	13.01.90
	Mike Harrison	Wakefield v Lon. Welsh	28.04.90
	Dan Cottrell	Clifton v Broughton Park	13.10.90
	Andy Green	Exeter v Met Police	10.11.90
	Mark Spearman	Clifton v Exeter	17.11.90
	Peter Robinson	W Hartlepool v Vale of Lune	02.03.91
	Gary Walker	Roundhay v Askeans	06.04.91
	Mark Chatterton	Exeter v Headingley	23.11.91
	Andy Ireland	Fylde v Askeans	14.12.91
	Phil Della-Savina	Richmond v Nuneaton	28.03.92
	Glyn Mellville	Otley v Aspatria	24.10.92
	Chris Thornton	Leeds v Exeter	13.03.93
	Harry Langley	Exeter v Broughton Park	24.04.93
	Martin Kelly	Broughton Park v Exeter	24.04.93
	Mike Friday	Blackheath v Morley	06.11.93
	Tony Brooks	Rosslyn Park v Havant	12.03.94
	Tony Clark	Morley v Bedford	25.02.92
	Eddie Saunders	Rugby v Bedford	12.04.92
	Eddie Saunders	Rugby v Rotherham	23.09.92
	Julian Horrobin	Coventry v Otley	30.03.96
	Andy Clarke	Richmond v Rosslyn Park	13.04.96
	Mark Preston	Fylde v Clifton	14.09.96
	Simon Dovell	Exeter v Harrogate	21.09.96
	Mark Kirkby	Otley v Clifton	05.10.96
	Brian Gabrial	Morley v Wharfedale	19.10.96
	Bob Armstrong	Exeter v Redruth	19.10.96
	Richard Matthias	Leeds v Redruth	09.11.96
	Andrew Hodgson	Wharfedale v Walsall	18.01.97
	Paul Brett	Liverpool StH v Redruth	01.02.97
	Guy Spencer	Reading v Lydney	08.02.97
	Andrew Hodgson	Wharfedale v Lon. Welsh	15.02.97
	Paul Brett	Liverpool StH v Clifton	15.02.97
	Julian Hill	Lydney v Lon. Welsh	22.02.97
	Brit Pearce	Havant v Walsall	22.02.97
	Mark Farrar	Harrogate v Lon. Welsh	01.03.97
	Gerry Ainscough	Leeds v Walsall	01.03.97
	Mark Scharrenberg	Reading v Liverpool StH	22.03.97
	Danny Jones	Liverpool StH v Exeter	29.03.97
	Mark Kirkby	Otley v Rosslyn Park	12.04.97
	Nick Green	Leeds v Clifton	12.04.97
	Mark Appleson	Leeds v Clifton	12.04.97
	Iain Dixon	Exeter v Otley	26.04.97
	Andrew Hodgson	Wharfedale v Rosslyn Park	03.05.97
	Kevin Hickey	Worcester v Wharfedale	11.10.97
	Jim Jenner	Worcester v Morley	08.11.97
	Brian Johnson	Newbury v Wharfedale	08.11.97
	Craig Davies	Newbury v Harrogate	15.11.97
	Chris Scott	Worcester v Reading	13.12.97
	Tom Holloway	Newbury v Harrogate	10.01.98
	Scott Roskell	London Welsh v Lydney	10.01.98
	Nick Baxter	Worcester v Harrogate	31.01.98
	Simon Middleton	Leeds v Nottingham	31.01.98
	Nick Baxter	Worcester v Wharfedale	07.02.98
	Craig Davies	Newbury v Liverpool St H.	21.02.98
	Mark Farrar	Harrogate v Nottingham	21.02.98
	Liam McCormick	Rosslyn Park v Nottingham	14.03.98
	Rob Myler	Worcester v Liverpool St. H.	21.03.98
	Liam McCormick	Rosslyn Park v Wharfedale	18.04.98
	Simon Middleton	Leeds v Nottingham	25.04.98
	David Casado	Rosslyn Park v Birmingham & S	26.09.98
	Dwayne Edwards	Lydney v Morley	07.11.98
	Gavin Sharp	Henley Hawks v Liverpool St. H.	12.12.98
	Tom Holloway	Newbury v Harrogate	02.01.99
	Tyrone Howe	Newbury v Morley	16.01.99
	Adam Mounsey	Wharfedale v Morley	27.02.99
	Hugh Owen	Camberley v Nottingham	27.02.99
	Elliott Spencer	Nottingham v Camberley	27.02.99
	Sam Gardner	Otley v Birmingham Solihull	13.03.99
	Peter Davies	Henley Hawks v Harrogate	27.03.99

ALL TIME RECORDS

MOST APPEARANCES

167	Richard Byrom	Roundhay, Sale	Full back
157	Steve Rice	Otley	Prop
	Nicky Nelmes	Lydney	Hooker
156	Martin Freer	Nottingham	Prop
155	Neil Hargreaves	Headingley, Leeds, Wakefield, Otley	Flanker
139	Hedley Verity	Wharfedale	Flanker
138	Ian Barclay	Fylde	Utility back
133	John Taylor	Fylde	2nd row
130	Jeremy Hopkinson	Wharfedale, Harrogate	No 8
128	Steve Smith	Rugby, Birmingham & Solihull	2nd row
125	John Lawn	Wharfedale	Hooker
	David Wheat	Harrogate	Flanker
124	Peter Taylor	Harrogate	2nd row
121	Jim Quantrill	Rugby, Birmingham & Solihull	Full back
	Richard Whyley	Harrogate	Prop
118	Ian Hassall	Harrogate	Full back
115	Richard Mills	Lydney	Utility back
	Gareth Williams	Lydney	Prop
113	Craig Reed	Harrogate	Centre
111	Neil Heseltine	Wharfedale	Utility back
109	Mark Bradley	Nottingham	Back row
108	Ralph Zoing	Harrogate, Leeds	Stand off
104	Alan Royer	Nottingham	Scrum half

TEN YEAR RECORD

Club	SEASONS									
	89-90	90-91	91-92	92-93	93-94	94-95	95-96	96-97	97-98	98-99
Askeans	5	6	7	10	-	-	-	-	-	-
Aspatria	-	-	-	9	-	-	-	-	-	-
Birmingham & Solihull	-	-	-	-	-	-	-	-	-	11
Broughton Park	-	8	6	11	-	-	-	-	-	-
Bedford	-	-	-	-	3	1	-	-	-	-
Blackheath	-	-	-	-	4	2	-	-	-	-
Camberley	-	-	-	-	-	-	-	-	-	9
Clifton	-	5	3	8	-	9	-	16	-	-
Coventry	-	-	-	-	1	-	1	-	-	-
Exeter	6	4	4	3	6	10	-	1	-	-
Fylde	8	3	2	-	2	-	10	2	-	-
Harrogate	-	-	-	-	-	7	6	5	14	12
Havant	-	-	-	2	9	-	-	14	-	-
Headingley	-	-	11	-	-	-	-	-	-	-
Henley	-	-	-	-	-	-	-	-	-	1
Leeds	-	-	-	6	-	-	-	3	2	-
Liverpool St Helens	-	-	-	7	-	-	-	12	11	14
London Scottish	1	-	-	-	-	-	-	-	-	-
London Welsh	12	-	-	-	-	-	-	11	3	-
Lydney	11	11	13	-	-	-	-	10	12	8
Manchester	-	-	-	-	-	-	-	-	-	2
Metropolitan Police	-	12	-	-	-	-	-	-	-	-
Morley	-	2	-	-	8	5	5	4	13	13
Newbury	-	-	-	-	-	-	-	-	6	6
Nottingham	-	-	-	-	-	-	-	-	7	4
Nuneaton	10	7	12	-	-	-	-	-	-	-
Otely	-	-	9	1	-	6	7	9	9	5
Plymouth Albion	-	-	-	12	-	-	-	-	-	-
Reading	-	-	-	-	-	-	8	6	8	10
Redruth	-	-	5	4	10	-	-	15	-	-
Richmond	-	-	1	-	7	8	2	-	-	-
Rosslyn Park	-	-	-	-	5	4	9	8	5	3
Rotherham	-	-	-	-	-	-	4	-	-	-
Roundhay	7	9	10	-	-	-	-	-	-	-
Rugby	-	-	-	-	-	3	3	-	4	-
Sheffield	4	10	8	5	-	-	-	-	-	-
Vale of Lune	9	13	-	-	-	-	-	-	-	-
Wakefield	2	-	-	-	-	-	-	-	-	-
Walsall	-	-	-	-	-	-	-	13	-	-
Wharfedale	-	-	-	-	-	-	-	7	10	7
West Hartlepool	3	1	-	-	-	-	-	-	-	-
Worcester	-	-	-	-	-	-	-	-	1	-

JEWSON NATIONAL LEAGUE

TWO NORTH

1998-99 Season

Review & statistics 330-333

1999-200 Fixtures 334

CLUBS

Aspatria	335
Bedford Athletic	339
Doncaster	343
Kendal	347
Liverpool St. Helens	351
Morley	355
New Brighton	359
Nuneaton	363
Sandal	367
Sedgley Park	371
Sheffield	375
Stourbridge	379
Walsall	383
Whitchurch	387

Match Facts 1998-99

Hinckley	392/3
Lichfield	394/5
Winnington Park	396/7

Division Four North Records

398-400

									HOME									AWAY								
	P	W	D	L	F	A	PD	Pts	W	D	L	F	A	Tries For	Pens For	Tries Against	Pens Against	W	D	L	F	A	Tries For	Pens For	Tries Against	Pens Against
Preston G'hoppers	26	23	0	3	822	341	481	46	12	0	1	478	162	69	21	22	12	11	0	2	344	179	47	16	20	18
Stourbridge	26	22	0	4	895	413	482	44	12	0	1	454	211	68	18	27	12	10	0	3	441	202	67	10	21	25
New Brighton	26	20	0	6	703	329	374	40	11	0	2	450	152	60	24	20	9	9	0	4	253	177	31	20	21	16
Kendal	26	18	0	8	635	347	288	36	11	0	2	337	137	46	19	16	13	7	0	6	298	210	41	18	25	19
Nuneaton	26	14	2	10	596	533	66	30	9	0	4	385	258	52	16	34	17	5	2	6	211	275	26	17	41	10
Sheffield	26	15	0	11	496	455	41	30	9	0	4	234	140	24	28	10	26	6	0	7	262	315	36	16	42	21
Sandal	26	13	0	13	697	611	86	26	9	0	4	385	238	55	12	33	10	4	0	9	312	373	38	24	47	22
Sedgley Park	26	12	1	13	710	553	157	25	8	1	4	455	253	61	24	36	13	4	0	9	255	300	36	14	41	17
Walsall	26	10	1	15	515	720	-205	21	6	1	6	315	306	43	18	42	18	4	0	9	200	414	25	15	56	26
Aspatria	26	10	0	16	578	675	-97	20	8	0	5	349	222	46	22	28	17	2	0	11	229	453	27	15	61	24
Whitchurch	26	9	1	16	450	599	-149	19	5	0	8	231	260	31	16	35	14	4	1	9	219	339	26	20	47	18
Hinckley	26	7	1	18	445	733	-288	15	5	1	7	268	264	33	23	35	17	2	0	11	177	469	20	19	67	14
Lichfield	26	3	0	23	371	949	-578	6	2	0	11	212	462	31	7	67	15	1	0	12	159	487	23	6	71	20
Winnington Park	26	3	0	23	310	965	-655	6	2	0	11	183	422	22	17	56	24	1	0	12	127	543	18	7	81	15

Review of the season 1998-1999

Preston Grasshoppers finally got out of the division after twelve seasons there.
They had to go to Sandal on the last day of the season but they clinched the title with a 36-11 win.
Their backs were prolific in the try scoring stakes and they had three in the top four try scorers in the division. Leading the way was their Australian outside half Michael Lough who scored 27 tries; he was closely followed by winger Iain Bruce with 25 and in joint third place was the other winger Gary Monaghan with 17. They actually beat second placed Stourbridge twice in convincing fashion and were deserved champions.

Stourbridge pushed Preston all the way with a great second half to the season. They were running in tries at will and ended up as leading try scorers in the division. They had six players in double figures in the try scorers list. As usual their front row lead the way with an amazing 28 tries. They won twelve matches at home with only Preston leaving with the points. With Lichfield being relegated Stourbridge are the only side still left in the division that started twelve years ago.

New Brighton finished third in their first campaign at this level and will be more than satisfied and looking forward to next season. They were exceptional at home with only champions Preston and fourth placed Kendal taking the points. They slipped up on the road and lost a couple of matches that they could well have won. They had a wily set of forwards and some exciting backs, who were perhaps not used as often as they should have been.

Kendal had a dreadful start to the season before finding first gear and climbing the table rapidly. In the second half of the campaign they were outstanding with only Stourbridge taking two points off them. They continued to play the game through their forwards who regularly appeared on the score sheet.

Nuneaton continue to search for some consistency; as the season drew to an end they seemed to have found it but they soon returned to normal with two defeats in the last week of the season to sides in the bottom four. New coach Harry Roberts will now be aware of the problem he has to overcome if he is to make them serious promotion candidates.

Sheffield made a superb start to the season playing some of the best rugby in the division in the opening few months. After that they became erratic and despite a good win over Champions Preston they finished the season on a downer. They had some of the most exciting backs in the division and centre Jamie Morley had an exceptional season whilst Andy Hulme, a latecomer, looked a great prospect in the last half dozen matches of the season he played.

Sandal had a disappointing start to the campaign but mid season hit top form and climbed the table with the some big wins. At home they were tough to beat but like a lot of teams in the division they struggled on the road. They scored plenty of tries but also conceded plenty as well.

Sedgley Park were one the biggest disappointments of the season. They have talented players in all positions but getting them to play together seems to be a problem. They scored tries all season but need to improve defensively to make an impact. Of the top four they only managed to win one of the eight matches, beating Kendal at home.

Walsall did enough to stay clear of relegation but were never going to finish any higher. Their best result was a 25-20 win against Kendal mid season. They did manage four away wins but they were all against the sides finishing in the bottom four.

Aspatria were as consistent as ever with good home form and poor away form. They did though lose to many home matches and with the division likely to be a lot stronger next season they will need to rectify that and look to improve their dreadful away form which saw them win just twice on their travels.

Whitchurch were looking to just stay up this season, their first at this level, and they achieved that aim. They had a superb set of forwards who were heavy try scorers, especially the front row. If they are to improve next season they will have to look at improving their back play.

Hinckley finished the season well but made a dreadful start when the side was ravaged by injury. This forced them to play a number of colts and it was probably a bit soon for them to play at this level and they suffered. When they were able to put their best XV on the pitch later in the season they started picking up the points but by then they were too far behind.

Lichfield and **Winnington Park** should have been relegated last season but with the Allied Dunbar increasing the size of its divisions they escaped. Their results this season have shown that this was a season too far for both sides.

1998-99 RECORD REVIEW (Individual Records)

MOST POINTS - IN A SEASON

Ian Shuttleworth topped the points scorers list for the first time with a total of 246 which puts him in ninth on the all time list. He also has an entry at 5th with 268 points set the previous season.

EVOLUTION OF RECORD

118	Steve Kerry	Preston G'hoppers	1987-88
127	Paul Grayson	Preston G'hoppers	1991-92
131	Ralph Zoing	Harrogate	1992-93
164	Richard Mills	Walsall	1994-95
317	Steve Kerry	Preston G'hoppers	1996-97
398	Steve Swindells	Manchester	1997-98

ALL-TIME LIST

398	Steve Swindells	Manchester	1997-98
317	Steve Kerry	Preston G.	1996-97
296	Matt Birch	Birmingham & Sol.	1997-98
271	Jonathon Smart	Birmingham & Sol.	1996-97
268	Ian Shuttleworth	Sandal	1997-98
251	Mike Scott	Aspatria	1996-97
251	Steve Swindells	Manchester	1996-97
248	Mark Hardcastle	Sandal	1996-97
243	Rob Pound	Sheffield	1997-98
242	Tim Smith	Worcester	1996-97

MOST PENALTIES - IN A SEASON

With so many tries being scored in the division last season and penalties not the vogue nobody got near the top all time leaders. Leading the way was Preston's Martin Emmett with 35.

EVOLUTION OF RECORD

21	Steve Kerry	Preston G'hoppers	1987-88
23	Jamie Grayshon	Morley	1988-89
28	Paul Grayson	Preston G'Hoppers	1990-91
31	Simon Pennington	Stourbridge	1992-93
31	Richard Mills	Walsall	1994-95
64	Steve Kerry	Preston G'hoppers	1996-97

ALL-TIME LIST

64	Steve Kerry	Preston G.	1996-97
62	Steve Swindells	Manchester	1997-98
55	Matt Birch	Birmingham & Sol.	1997-98
55	Ian Shuttleworth	Sandal	1997-98
53	Mark Hardcastle	Sandal	1996-97
48	Mike Scott	Aspatria	1996-97
43	Jonathan Smart	Birmingham & Sol	1996-97
43	Rob Pound	Sheffield	1997-98

MOST DROP GOALS - IN A SEASON

Martin Emmett, who was also leader in conversions and penalties, led the way with just three which was well short of the all time record of nine set by former Preston player Steve Kerry.

EVOLUTION OF RECORD

5	Steve Kerry	Preston G'hoppers	1987-88
6	Paul Grayson	Preston G'hoppers	1991-92
9	Steve Kerry	Preston G'hoppers	1996-97

ALL-TIME LIST

9	Steve Kerry	Preston G'hoppers	1996-97
6	Paul Grayson	Preston G'hoppers	1991-92
5	Steve Kerry	Preston G'hoppers	1987-88
4	Richard Mills	Walsall	1990-91
4	Ian Shuttleworth	Sandal	1997-98
4	Rob Pound	Sheffield	1997-98

MOST CONVERSIONS - IN A SEASON

Martin Emmett kicked 53 conversions in Preston's championship season. That puts him 4th on the all time list but well behind record holder Steve Swindells who kicked 91 the previous season.

EVOLUTION OF RECORD

12	Steve Kerry	Preston G'hoppers	1987-88
	Chris Howard	Rugby	1987-88
13	Gary Walker	Roundhay	1988-89
17	Jon Howarth	Otley	1990-91
28	Ralph Zoing	Harrogate	1992-93
29	Richard Mills	Walsall	1994-95
61	Tim Smith	Worcester	1996-97
91	Steve Swindells	Manchester	1997-98

ALL-TIME LIST

91	Steve Swindells	Manchester	1997-98
61	Tim Smith	Worcester	1996-97
58	Matt Birch	Birmingham & Solihull	1997-98
53	Martin Emmett	Preston	1998-99
50	Chris Mann	Stourbridge	1996-97
49	Steve Swindells	Manchester	1996-97
47	Jonathan Smart	Birmingham & Solihull	1996-97

MOST TRIES - IN A SEASON

League champions Preston had two players break the old record of 21 tries in a season set last season by Manchester's Matt Hoskin. Leading the way was outside half Michael Lough with 27 from 26 matches whilst just two behind was winger Iain Bruce with 25.

EVOLUTION OF RECORD

7	Eddie Saunders	Rugby	1987-88
10	Jim Mallinder	Roundhay	1988-89
16	Jon Walker	Otley	1990-91
18	Nick Baxter	Worcester	1996-97
21	Matt Hoskin	Manchester	1997-98
27	Michael Lough	Preston	1998-99

ALL-TIME LIST

27	Michael Lough	Preston	1998-99
25	Iain Bruce	Preston	1998-99
21	Matt Hoskin	Manchester	1997-98
19	Stephen Hanley	Aspatria	1997-98
18	Nick Baxter	Worcester	1996-97
17	Craig Marriott	Aspatria	1996-97
17	Richard Marsh	Walsall	1997-98
17	Ian Kennedy	New Brighton	1998-99
17	Gary Monaghan	Preston	1998-99
16	Jon Walker	Otley	1990-91
16	Ben Shepherd	Birmingham & Sol.	1997-98

1998-99

JEWSON TWO NORTH

MOST POINTS

POINTS			T	C	P	DG
246	Ian Shuttleworth	Sandal	12	45	29	3
226	Martin Emmett	Preston G'hoppers	3	52	35	1
200	Casey Mee	Kendal	6	37	31	1
186	Rob Pound	Sheffield	2	28	30	-
159	Murray King	New Brighton	1	32	30	-
151	Ian Kennedy	New Brighton	17	18	10	-
150	Rob Moon	Sedgley Park	12	27	12	-
149	Mike Scott	Aspatria	5	26	23	1
145	John Canney	Whitchurch	3	20	30	-
135	Michael Lough	Preston G'hoppers	27	-	-	-
135	Jez Harris	Nuneaton	1	32	22	-
124	Richard Mills	Walsall	-	26	24	-
125	Iain Bruce	Preston G'hoppers	25	-	-	-
124	Ben Barton	Winnington Park	6	14	22	-
105	Phil Curtis	Hinckley	-	12	27	-
105	Simon Bailey	Stourbridge	13	14	4	-
92	Marc Thomas	Nuneaton	5	17	10	1
87	Eddie Brittain	Hinckley	4	11	15	-

MOST PENALTIES

35	Martin Emmett	Preston
31	Casey Mee	Kendal
30	Rob Pound	Sheffield
30	Murray King	New Brighton
30	John Canney	Whitchurch
29	Ian Shuttleworth	Sandal
27	Phil Curtis	Hinckley
24	Richard Mills	Walsall
23	Mike Scott	Aspatria
22	Jez Harris	Nuneaton
22	Ben Barton	Winnington Park
15	Eddie Brittain	Hinckley
12	Rob Moon	Sedgley Park
10	Marc Thomas	Nuneaton
10	Ian Kennedy	New Brighton

MOST CONVERSIONS

52	Martin Emmett	Preston
45	Ian Shuttleworth	Sandal
37	Casey Mee	Kendal
32	Murray King	New Brighton
32	Jez Harris	Nuneaton
28	Rob Pound	Sheffield
27	Rob Moon	Sedgley Park
26	Mike Scott	Aspatria
26	Richard Mills	Walsall
25	Dan Lockley	Stourbridge
20	John Canney	Whitchurch
18	Ian Kennedy	New Brighton
17	Marc Thomas	Nuneaton
14	Ben Barton	Winnington Park
14	Simon Baylie	Stourbridge

MOST TRIES

27	Michael Lough	Preston
25	Iain Bruce	Preston
17	Ian Kennedy	New Brighton
17	Gary Monaghan	Preston
15	Jamie Morley	Sheffield
14	Mark Wolff	Sandal
13	Richard Trigg	Stourbridge
13	Steve Carter	Nuneaton
13	Simon Baylie	Stourbridge
12	Jon Duncan	Sedgley Park
12	Ian Shuttleworth	Sandal
12	Rob Merritt	Stourbridge
12	Rob Moon	Sedgley Park
12	Jason Balmer	Kendal
11	Jamie Richardson	Stourbridge
11	Alan Dickens	Stourbridge
11	Jacob John	Stourbridge
10	Mark Allatt	Sheffield
10	Chris Mould	Walsall
10	Matthew Woodcock	Aspatria
10	Jamie Bartle	Sheffield

MOST DROP GOALS

3	Ian Shuttleworth	Sandal
1	Martin Emmett	Preston
1	Casey Mee	Kendal
1	Mike Scott	Aspatria
1	Marc Thomas	Nuneaton
1	Steven Wood	Aspatria
1	Metcalfe	Sandal
1	Kevin Hussey	Sedgley Park
1	Richard Wynn	Whitchurch

JEWSON NATIONAL TWO NORTH FIXTURES 1999-2000

	HOME TEAMS / Away Teams	Aspatria	Bedford Athletic	Doncaster	Kendal	Liverpool St. Helens	Morley	New Brighton	Nuneaton	Sandal	Sedgley Park	Sheffield	Stourbridge	Walsall	Whitchurch	
1	Aspatria	X	22.01	11.12	22.04	08.01	11.03	25.03	11.09	23.10	28.08	27.11	12.02	02.10	06.11	1
2	Bedford Athletic	30.10	X	11.03	20.11	15.01	12.02	02.10	04.12	28.08	18.12	11.09	23.10	15.04	25.03	2
3	Doncaster	15.04	25.09	X	09.10	26.02	04.09	08.04	30.10	20.11	29.01	04.12	18.03	15.01	18.12	3
4	Kendal	04.12	08.01	12.02	X	27.11	22.01	23.10	28.08	11.09	15.04	02.10	06.11	25.03	11.03	4
5	Liverpool St Helens	20.11	06.11	02.10	18.12	X	23.10	12.02	15.04	25.03	04.12	11.03	22.01	28.08	11.09	5
6	Morley	25.09	09.10	25.03	30.10	29.01	X	11.09	20.11	04.12	15.01	28.08	26.02	18.12	15.04	6
7	New Brighton	04.09	26.02	28.08	29.01	09.10	18.03	X	15.01	18.12	30.10	15.04	25.09	20.11	04.12	7
8	Nuneaton	18.03	22.04	22.01	08.04	11.12	08.01	06.11	X	02.10	04.09	23.10	27.11	11.03	12.02	8
9	Sandal	29.01	08.04	08.01	18.03	04.09	22.04	27.11	26.02	X	25.09	06.11	11.12	09.10	22.01	9
10	Sedgley Park	08.04	27.11	23.10	11.12	22.04	06.11	22.01	25.03	11.03	X	12.02	08.01	11.09	02.10	10
11	Sheffield	18.12	18.03	22.04	26.02	25.09	08.04	11.12	29.01	15.01	09.10	X	04.09	30.10	20.11	11
12	Stourbridge	09.10	29.01	11.09	15.01	30.10	02.10	11.03	18.12	15.04	20.11	25.03	X	04.12	28.08	12
13	Walsall	26.02	11.12	06.11	04.09	08.04	27.11	08.01	25.09	12.02	18.03	22.01	22.04	X	23.10	13
14	Whitchurch	15.01	04.09	27.11	25.09	18.03	11.12	22.04	09.10	30.10	26.02	08.01	08.04	29.01	X	14
		1	2	3	4	5	6	7	8	9	10	11	12	13	14	

ASPATRIA R.U.F.C.

Secretary	Avril Quinn	1 Beacon Close, Aspatria, CA5 3HW 016973 21610 (H) 016973 31234 (B) 016973 32749 (Fax)
Director of Rugby	Melvyn Hanley	7 King Street, Aspatria, Cumbria, CA5 3AD. 016973 20328 (H), 01946 815111 (B), 01946 815082 (Fax)
Chairman	David Miller	The Annexe, Allerby Hall, Maryport. 01900 813118 (H)
President	Norman Lazonby	Croft House, Dubwath, Bass Lake, Cumbria 01768 776363
Treasurer	W Bell	Mawbray House, Mawbray, Maryport. 01900 881200 (H)
Fixture Secretary	P Gray	016973 21760
Team Secretary	M Ray	016973 21313
County Representative	J Hunter	016973 20207 (B)

We were pleased to see May 1999, as it heralded the end of another long season, which had started very well for us, for a change.

Success then tapered off in the league as we lost key players to Rugby League and through injury. I suppose our greatest loss was that of Steve Hanley, who went to Sale in late September. How do you replace last season's top try scorer with 22 league tries and numerous others in Cup matches? The answer is, with great difficulty! We were genuinely delighted that Steve progressed to full England colours, never more proud when he ran out on the pitch at Wembley versus Wales and then topped it off by scoring a try. This position has been hard to fill as have other key positions - Jason Spires with hamstring problems, Lee Chilton with ankle problems, Sean Cusack with a broken bone in his neck and Richard Hill, second row, who had to take over duties on the family farm, and the list goes on. Some players showed great commitment by playing in most games. Tom Wall, Guy Pattinson, Ashley Barton. Well done to these and the many others that have turned out this season.

We have been successful at local level winning both the Senior and Junior Cumbria Cups (we also won the Cumbria Cup in 1899). Of our senior squad, only one member had previously won a Cup medal, which shows how many changes our squad has had to endure over the previous two seasons. Our Eagles team, winners of the Junior Cup, used a pool of 59 players, some only playing one match to help out but three of them playing in 23 out of 24 matches, quite an achievement. Our Junior Reds go from strength to strength. Starting at nine we operate teams through to senior level now, supplying County players at every level, another achievement for a town of less than 3,000 people. It shows the dedication of players and coaches alike. Our U16 had a most successful season, finishing top of their league. We hope to bus these boys around the country with our 1st XV by getting them fixtures at the same venues. I don't know who will learn what from whom but it will be fun watching.

1st XV Squad 8th May 1999 - L-R Back Row: Peter Ritchie, Malcolm Brown (Coach), Liam Nicholls, Graeme Cook*, Nicky Crellin, Tom Wall*, Paul Brough, Guy Pattinson*, Keith Simpson, Derek Benson, Ben Brinicombe, Tom Borthwick (Coach). Front Row: David Bowyer, Stuart Bell, Andrew Little, Steven Wood*, Steven Irving* (Captain), Ashley Barton*, Julian Chapman, Mike Scott*, Lee Chilton, John McCune (* County Player)

Match No.	Date	H/A	Comp.	Opponents	Result & Score	Att.	15	14	13	12	11
1	05.09	H	J2N	Winnington P	W 57-7		Stoddart	Woodcock	Hanley/2t	Chilton/t	Cook/t
2	12.09	H	J2N	Sandal	W 18-15		Wood(b)	Marriott	Hetherington	Cook	Woodcock
3	26.09	A	J2N	Walsall	L 21-54		Wood	Woodcock	Nicholls	Chilton	Chapman/2t(v)
4	03.10	H	J2N	Stourbridge	L 21-42		Stoddart	Woodcock	Wood	Cook	Little/t
5	10.10	A	J2N	Nuneaton	L 20-42		Wood	Woodcock/t	Cook/t	Stoddart	Little
6	24.10	H	J2N	New Brighton	W 10-0		Cook	Woodcock/t	Chilton	Crellin	Little
7	31.10	A	J2N	Preston	L 12-27		Stoddart(m)	Woodcock	Chilton	Cook	Little
8	07.11	H	J2N	Hinckley	W 34-23		Stoddart/4c2p	Woodcock	Chilton/2t	Cook/t	Little
9	21.11	A	J2N	Whitchurch	W 20-8		Woodcock/t	Little	Chilton/t	Cook	Chapman
10	28.11	H	J2N	Lichfield	W 66-0		Woodcock/2t	Chapman/2t(a/c)	Chilton/t	Cook	Little/t
11	05.12	A	J2N	Kendal	L 23-30		Stoddart/2c3p	Woodcock	Chilton	Cook	Little/t(s)
12	12.12	H	J2N	Sedgley Park*	W 30-21		Stoddart/2c2p(m)	Woodcock	Crellin(v)	Cook	Chilton
13	19.12	A	J2N	Sheffield	L 13-16		Stoddart/c2p	Woodcock/t	Chilton	Cook	Little
14	26.12	H	J2N	Kendal	L 35-5		Stoddart	Woodcock/t	Chilton	Cook	Little
15	02.01	A	J2N	Lichfield	W 27-20		Wood	Woodcock/2t	Marriott(s)	Cook/t	Little
16	09.01	H	J2N	Whitchurch	W 24-15		Wood	Woodcock/t	Chilton	Cook	Little/t
17	16.01	H	J2N	Preston	L 0-20		Wood	Woodcock	Chilton	Cusack	Little
18	30.01	A	J2N	New Brighton	L 3-12		Stoddart	Woodcock	Chilton	Crellin	Little
19	06.02	H	J2N	Nuneaton	L 17-23		Stoddart/c	Woodcock	Chilton	Crellin(s)	Little(r)
20	13.02	A	J2N	Stourbridge	L 31-59		Woodcock/t	Chapman	Chilton(r)	Stoddart/4c	Little/t
21	27.02	H	J2N	Walsall	W 47-0		Stoddart/3t	Chapman/t	Nicholls	Scott/3c2p	Little
22	06.03	A	J2N	Hinckley	L 10-34		Wood	Chapman	Nicholls	Crellin/t	Little(t)
23	13.03	A	J2N	Sandal	L 7-51		Wood	Chapman	Chilton	Nicholls	Little
24	27.03	A	J2N	Winnington P	L 23-45		Wood	Chapman	Cook	Cusack	Little
25	03.04	H	J2N	Sheffield	L 20-22		Stoddart/t	Chapman/t	Chilton	Cook/t	Litle
26	17.04	A	J2N	Sedgley Park	L 19-55		Wood	Chapman	Crellin	Bell	Little
A	19.09	H	TB1	Bedford Ath	L 15-42		Wood(a)	Hanley	Chilton(p/t)	Hetherington	Woodcock

* after opponents name indicates a penalty try
Brackets after a player's name indicates he was replaced. eg (a) means he was replaced by replacement code "a" and so on.
/ after a player or replacement name is followed by any scores he made - eg /t, /c, /p, /dg or any combination of these

1998-99 HIGHLIGHTS

Ever Presents: None

Most appearances Guy Pattinson 25 (1)

24	Ashley Barton (1), Stephen Irving (1)
22	Andrew Little (2)
20	Matthew Woodcock, Jason Spires, Tom Wall(3)

Players used: 35 plus five as replacement only.

Most Points in a season:

Pts	Player	T	C	P	DG
149	M Scott	5	26	23	1
67	S Stoddart	4	10	9	-
50	M Woodcock	10	-	-	-
42	S Wood	-	12	5	1
30	D Benson	6	-	-	-
30	A Barton	6	-	-	-

MATCH FACTS

10	9	1	2	3	4	5	6	7	8	
Scott/t5c(m/c)	Spires/2t(p)	Wall/t	Barton(w)	McCune(n)	Hill	Pattinson(o)	Bowyer/t	Bowe	Benson(l)	1
Scott/5pdg	Spires	Irving	Barton	McCune(q)	Hill	Pattinson(o)	Bowyer	Bowe	Benson(l)	2
Scott/t3c	D Irving	Irving	Barton(w)	Miller	Hill	Thwaites(h)	Bowe	Bowyer	Benson(x)	3
Scott/c3p	Spires	Irving	Barton(w)	Wall	Pattinson	Thwaites(g)	Simpson(k)	Bowyer	Brough/t	4
Scott/2c2p	Spires	Irving	Barton	Miller	Hill	Pattinson(o)	Holmgren	Bowe(w)	Brough	5
Scott/cp	Spires	Irving	Barton	Wall	Hill	Pattinson	Holmgren(j)	Bowyer	Benson	6
Scott/tc	Spires	Irving(q)	Barton	Wall(f)	Thwaites(g)	Pattinson	Bowe(y)	Bowyer/t	Benson	7
Wood	Spires	Irving	Barton	Wall/t(f)	Hill	Pattinson(o)	Benson(A)	Bowyer	Brough	8
Wood/2c2p	Spires	Irving	Barton	Wall(q)	Pattinson	Holmgren	Benson	Bowe	Brough	9
Wood/4c2p(c)	Spires/t	Irving/t	Barton	Wall(q)	Pattinson	Thwaites	Benson/t(A)	Bowe(i)	Brough/t	10
Wood(c/t)	Spires	Irving	Barton	Wall	Pattinson	Hill	Benson	Brough(B)	Brough(q)	11
Scott/t	Spires	Irving	Barton	Wall	Thwaites	Hill	Bowe/t	Bowyer/t	Pattinson	12
Scott	Spires	Irving(f)	Barton	Miller(d)	Hill	Crellin(j)	Cusack	Bowyer/t	Pattinson	13
Scott	Spires	Irving(f(	Barton	Wall(q)	Hill	Pattinson	Cusack	Bowyer(j)	Crellin	14
Scott/2cp	Spires(u)	Irving/t	Barton	Wall(q)	Pattinson	Thwaites	Anlgren	Cusack	Benson(C)	15
Scott/c4p	Spires	Irving	Barton	Wall	Pattinson	Thwaites(k)	Bowyer	Bowe	Ahlgren	16
Scott	Spires	Irving	Barton	Wall	Pattinson	Crellin	Bowyer(i)	Bowe	Ahlgren	17
Wood/p	Spires	Irving	Barton	Wall	Bowe	Pattinson	Bowyer(k)	Cusack	Ahlgren	18
Wood	Spires	Irving	Barton/2t(f)	Wall	Pattinson	Bowe	Bowyer(k/t)	Cusack	Ahlgren	19
Wood/dg	Spires	Irving	Barton/2t	Wall	Pattinson	Thwaites(z)	Benson	Bowyer	Ahlgren	20
Wood	Spires(u)	Irving(f)	Barton/t(H)	Wall(q)	Pattinson	Bowe(z)	Benson/t	Bowyer	Ahlgren/t(B	21
Scott/cp	Stoddart	Irving	Barton	Wall	Miller(E)	Pattinson	Bowe	Bowyer	Benson(C)	22
Scott/c	D Irving	Wall	Barton	McCune(E)	Pattinson	Thwaites	Benson/t	Bowe	Crellin	23
Scott/2c3p	D Irving(D)	Irving	Barton	McCune(E)	Pattinson	Thwaites(G)	Benson/t	Bowyer/t	Crellin	24
Scott/cp	Bell	Irving	McCune(e)	Reay(d)	Pattinson	Crellin(o)	Simpson(C)	Cusack	Brough(k)	25
Scott/2c	D Irving	Wall	Barton/t	Irving(E)	Pattinson	Brinicombe(f)	Benson/t	M Brown/t(F)	Brough	26
Scott/tcp	Spires	Irving	Barton	Wall(f)	Hill	Pattinson	Benson	Bowe	Brough	A

REPLACEMENTS:

a- S Stoddart, b- L Chilton, c - M Scott, d - T Wall, e - A Barton, f - J McCune, g - Hill, h - Pattinson, i - D Bowyer, j - M Bowe, k - D Benson, l - K Simpson, m - S Wood, n - S Irving, o - R Thwaites, p - C Marriott, q - P Miller, r - L Nicholls, s - J Chapman, t - D Irving, u - J Miller, v - A Little, w - N Douglas, x - G Smith, y - P Brough, z - N Crellin, A - T Holmgren, B - S Cusack, C - M Brown, D - S Bell, E - A Reay, F - P Ritchie, G - A Ross, H - N Brown

Not surprisingly Mike Scott again topped the Aspatria scoring list with 149 points.

In the try scoring list Matthew Woodcock followed Steven Haley as the clubs leading try scorer with 10. Hanley did start the season with Aspatria playing in the opening league match scoring a brace of tries against Hinckley.

Aspatria had a good home record but on the road they managed just two wins at Lichfield and Whitchurch.

They had two players who played in the backs and the forwards. Sean Cusack played in the centre and on the flank. Nicky Crellin went one better playing in the centre, second row and back row.

ASPATRIA

LEAGUE STATISTICS

compiled by Stephen McCormack

SEASON	Division	P	W	D	L	F	A	Pts Diff	Lge Pts	Lge Pos	Most Points	Most Tries
89-90	N1	10	6	2	2	182	119	63	14		63 Jimmy Miller	5 Jimmy Miller
90-91	N1	10	8	0	2	178	93	85	16		59 Andrew Harrison	5 Jimmy Miller
91-92	D4N	12	11	0	1	253	100	153	22		55 Andrew Harrison	7 Jimmy Miller
92-93	3	11	3	1	7	170	308	-138	7		84 Andrew Harrison	2 by four players
93-94	4	18	8	0	10	303	372	-69	16		129 Mike Scott	7 Mark Richardson
94-95	4	18	7	1	10	265	378	-113	15		98 Mike Scott	7 Mark Richardson
95-96	4	18	5	1	12	356	497	-141	11		113 Mike Scott	7 Craig Marriott & Mark Richardson
96-97	4N	26	10	1	15	611	713	-102	21		251 Mike Scott	17 Craig Marriott
97-98	N2N	26	10	0	16	524	778	-254	20		95 Stephen Hanley	19 Stephen Hanley
98-99	N2N	26	10	0	16	578	675	-97	20	10	149 Mike Scott	10 Matthew Woodcock

FACT FILE

Founded: 1875
Nickname: Black/reds

Colours: Black & red hoops/black
Change colours: Black shirts/white

GROUND

Address: Bower Park, Station Road, Aspatria, Cumbria
Tel: 016973 20420
Capacity: 2,250 Seated: 250 Standing: 2,000

Directions: M6 Junc 41, B5305 to Wigton. Left in Wigton Town Centre - 2miles left onto by-pass. 7 miles to Aspatria - left in town centre towards station
Nearest Railway Station: Aspatria, right out of station, club 100yds on right

Car Parking: 200 at ground, 200 nearby

Admission: Season tickets £30
Matchdays - Adult £4, Children/OAPs £1

Clubhouse: Normal licensing hours.
Snacks & bar meals available match days only

Functions: Available up to 250, contact Club Steward

Club Shop: Yes, open 2-5 matchdays
Contact Mary Hanley 016973 20328

Training Nights: Tuesday & Thursday

PROGRAMME

Size: A5 Price: 50p
Pages: 56 Editor: Avril Quinn

ADVERTISING RATES
Mono only
Full page £100, Half page £50, Qtr £25

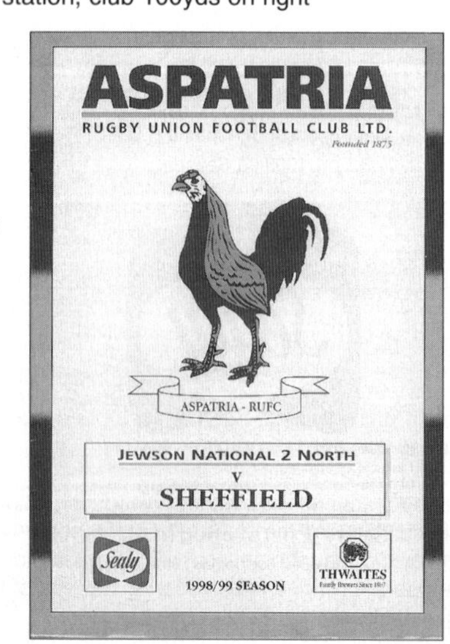

BEDFORD ATHLETIC R.U.F.C.

Chairman	Paul McGuckian	c/o Bedford Athletic RUFC, Putnoe Wood, Wentworth Drive, Bedford MK41 8QA 01234 350874
Secretary	John Donnelly	4 Donnelly Drive, Bedford MK41 9TU 01234 307909 (H)
Commercial Manager	Barry Enyon	c/o Bedford RUFC as above
Fixture Secretary	Mick Bowden	5 Cambridge Road, Bedford MK42 0LH 01234 401718 (H) 01234 768520 (B)

Bedford Athletic RUFC have just achieved their second promotion in two years. This means that they will be competing in the Jewson Two (North) League for the first time in the club's history. As well as achieving promotion, the `Ath' as they are known,also managed to win both the Bedfordshire and East Midlands Cups. Only one league game was lost last season, the same as unlucky Scunthorpe who lost out for a second time due to points difference.

Several new players were recruited to the cause last season with many of the youngsters growing in stature as the season progressed. The best known recruit was Justyn Cassell from Northampton whose performances in the big games helped foster a winning spirit. Ashley Tapper, captain and fly-half and a former Oxford blue, had an outstanding season becoming top points scorer with 263.

Joint top try scorers with sixteen apiece were lock Mike Curry and the flying Scottish wing Adam Lowles. Two Cup matches saw club records equalled with retiring No 8 Tom Gray scoring five tries in one match and Nick Gregory equalling Tapper's individual points record in one match, with a haul of 39 points, while also playing at fly-half. Chris Wright, the towering lock, appeared in every game last season and was a valuable source of possession throughout with his consistent line-out jumping.

The club is looking to recruit wisely this coming season to strengthen the squad and replace retiring players, but there will be many of the same faces again appearing in Ath colours. They have made a good start in winning the services of Paul Alston, the ex-Bedford back row who will be the main coach for the coming season. Due to other commitments, Neil Beytell, last season's coach, will be working more in a support role to Paul and, with fitness advisor Ian Kitchen also in support, the Ath will be well prepared for the challenges ahead.

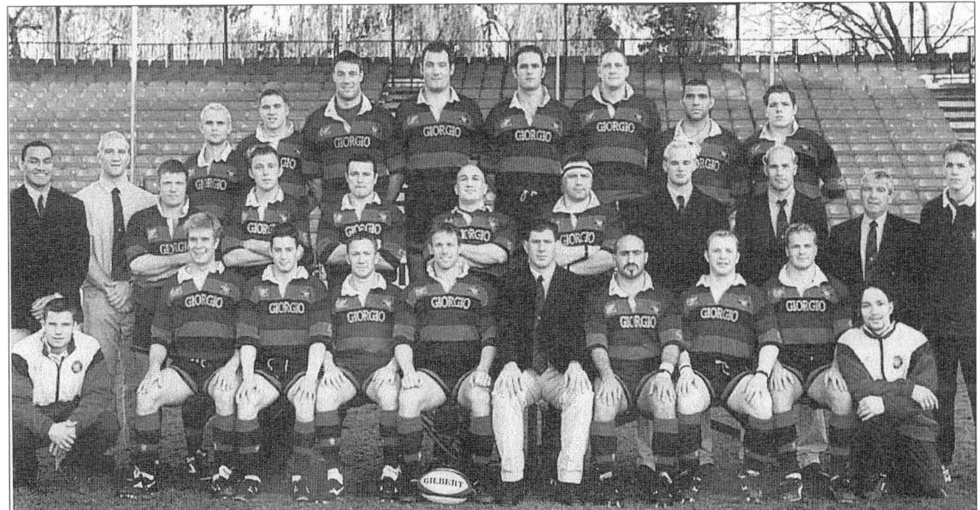

'Ath' after winning the East Midlands cup for the second successive year. Photo courtesy of the Times & Citizen

Date	Venue	Competition	Opponents	Result & Score	
12.09	A	Midlands1	Syston	W	13-5
26.09	H	Midlands1	Westleigh	W	85-16
03.10	A	Midlands1	Dudley K'ford	W	19-9
10.10	H	Midlands1	Wolverhampton	W	92-3
24.10	A	Midlands1	Barkers Butts	W	31-0
31.10	H	Midlands1	Belgrave	W	10-8
07.11	A	Midlands1	Broad Street	W	26-15
21.11	H	Midlands1	Burton	W	28-3
28.11	A	Midlands1	Camphill	W	39-3
12.12	A	Midlands1	Moderns	W	54-33
09.01	H	Midlands1	Banbury	L	13-23
30.01	H	Midlands1	Leighton Buzzard	W	55-3
06.02	A	Midlands1	Mansfield	W	38-7
27.02	H	Midlands1	Scunthorpe	W	22-13
13.03	A	Midlands1	Kenilworth	W	20-18
27.03	H	Midlands1	Stoke On Trent	W	64-15
17.04	A	Midlands1	Hereford	W	16-13
19.09	A	Tetley Bitter1	Aspatria	W	32-17
17.10	A	Tetley Bitter2	Whitchurch	L	15-23

A brief history of Bedford Athletic RUFC

The Club was founded in 1909 and has used many grounds in the town. The first was in Kimbolton Road opposite the Park Hotel. The second in Bedford Park By the lake, the third behind the Fox&Hounds PH in Goldington Road, 'where a pond encroached on the pitch in which stood the corner flag'. Many other grounds were used but the move in 1924 to Newnham Lane, now known as Newnham Avenue, was a significant one for we stayed there, apart from the war years, until 1970.

The Club has always been prepared to work hard to provide its facilities which we have then invited the public to share. In 1933, during the depression, the then Secretary, Captain E.H.G.Chambers raised funds and under his guidance, some unemployed, mainly ex-servicemen levelled the whole of the area which now contains municipal playing fields and Athletics Stadium.

It was because of these efforts that Bedford Corporation gave us priority over the use of these grounds. During the war the changing room at the north-east corner of the field suffered badly and, until Murketts garage (now Lex) was built, a redundant fire service hut at the corner of Barkers Lane became the HQ. We then moved the hut to where the fire station now stands.

The Council took pity on us when the County Fire Service took over the site and we were offered the lease on the land that we now occupy. This is green belt land adjacent to the town boundary. Our nearest neighbours lived in a pair of cottages opposite where the Bluebell pub now stands. Undeterred by the fact that it was over a half a mile down a track with no services, we set to and levelled, drained and seeded the pitches ourselves and like our 1930's members overcame all obstacles and eventually built the clubhouse you see today

POINTS SCORERS

1998-99

(Includes all league and cup matches)

	Appearances	Tries	Conversions	Penalties	Drop Goals	POINTS
Ashley Tapper	20	13	60	26	-	263
Nick Gregory	18	6	41	3	1	124
Mike Curry	20	16	-	-	-	80
Adam Lowles	14	16	-	-	-	80
Tom Gray	7	13	-	-	-	65
Ian Skingsley	16	10	-	-	-	50
James Lyle	18	7	-	-	-	35
Darren Stephenson	23	7	-	-	-	35
Leigh Mansell	22	5	-	-	-	25
Justyn Cassell	15	4	-	-	-	20
Jim Chandler	15	4	-	-	-	20
Cameron Glanville	13	4	-	-	-	20
Mick Norman	9	4	-	-	-	20
Giles Witheat	21	4	-	-	-	20
Alf Bartlett	18	3	-	-	-	15
Mark Burgess	5	3	-	-	-	15
Tommy Cassidy	10	3	-	-	-	15
John Egan	7	3	-	-	-	15
Ben Mason	9	3	-	-	-	15
Peter Smedley	10	3	-	-	-	15
Ross Thomson	10	3	-	-	-	15
Joe Thorp	9	3	-	-	-	15
Penalty try	-	3	-	-	-	15
Neil Beytell	6	2	-	-	-	10
Chris Eldridge	14	2	-	-	-	10
David P-Barnes	2	2	-	-	-	10
Paul Simmonds	8	2	-	-	-	10
Garry Wells	16	2	-	-	-	10
Lee Illott	2	1	-	-	-	5
Chris Mann	7	1	-	-	-	5
Neil Patterson	13	1	-	-	-	5
Robert Robinson	1	1	-	-	-	5
Jamie Steele	22	1	-	-	-	5

BEDFORD ATHLETIC

FACT FILE

Founded: 1908
Nickname: 'The Ath'

Colours: Black and white hoops/black/black
Change colours: Maroon

GROUND

Address: Putnoe Woods, Wentworth Drive, Bedford MK41 8QA
Tel: 01234 350874 e-mail: info@bedfordath.kbnet.co.uk
Web: www.bedfordath.kbnet.co.uk

Capacity: 400 all uncovered standing

Directions: Contact Mick Bowden or John Donnelly
Nearest Railway station: Bedford Midland Road (Thameslink or Midland mainline)
Car Parking: Spaces for approx. 50 cars at clubhouse.

Admission: £4 incl. programme Senior citizens £2
u16s Free

Clubhouse:

Club Shop: Selling general rugby kit & 'Ath' polo shirts & sweaters etc.

Training Nights: Tuesday & Thursday

PROGRAMME

Size: A5 Price: with admission
Pages: 24 + cover
Advertising: Contact Commercial Manager at clubhouse

DONCASTER R.F.C.

President	A De Mulder	c/o Doncaster RFC Ltd., Armthorpe Rd., Doncaster DN2 5QB 01302 832388 (Club)
Secretary	J Lowe	57 Wroot Road, Finningley, Doncaster DN9 3DR 01302 770275 (H)
Fixtures Secretary	H Potts	29 Nutwell Lane, Armthorpe, Doncaster DN3 3JH 01302 300319 (H) 01430 422471 (B)
Director of Playing	J Blount	7 Scaftworth Close, Bessacarr, Doncaster DN4 7RH 01302 537972 (H) 01302 320626 (B)
Coaching Co-ordinator	Paul Morris	25 Ravenswood Drive, Auckley, Doncaster DN9 3PA 01302 770890 (H)

After narrowly missing promotion to Jewson Two (North) to New Brighton on points difference last season, Doncaster were determined to make no mistake and won their first seven games including hard fought matches away at Wigton, Middlesbrough and Bridlington.

They then lost the next three (all away) in succession including, in the cases of Northern and Hull Ionians, scoring two tries to their opponents one. A further point was dropped away at Widnes three games later and all seemed lost, particularly as at that point the club had lost three fly-halves (and goal kickers) Dan Eddie, Richard Poskitt and Paul Matthews due to injury and work commitments. However, they stuck to the task and, with the arrival of goal kicking fly half Phil Ure on loan from Wakefield, won their remaining nine matches setting up the final fixture with previous promotion favourites Northern which they won convincingly by 33 points to 3 in front of a crowd of 2000.

Throughout the season the Doncaster pack has been outstanding completely dominating most of their opposition in the set pieces whilst the backs, mainly due to the uncertainty at fly half, stuttered through the first two thirds of the season. However, for the last six games the backs rediscovered their old form with the result that 220 points were scored.

Outstanding for Doncaster throughout the season were skipper and flanker Richard Senior, centre Matt Brain, prop Gavin Baldwin and lock Mike Bailey. Doncaster pride themselves on the development of home grown talent and, throughout the season, on average eleven of the fifteen had come up through their youth structure. Full back Jon Ellis and No 8 Mark Longworth both played for Yorkshire whilst hooker Mark Hyde played for Notts, Lincs and Derby. As well as winning Thwaites North Division One, Doncaster also won the Independent Agriculture Yorkshire Cup beating Sandal in the final.

For the coming season Doncaster have created a new coaching structure with former Leicester full back John Liley joining them as back's player-coach.

Doncaster 1st XV Squad Season 1998-99

Match No.	Date	H/A	Comp.	Opponents	Result & Score	Att.	15	14	13	12	11
1	12.09	H	N1	Tynedale	W 25-24		J Ellis	Whale	J Mortimore	Brain/t	Conway
2	26.09	A	N1	Wigton	W 28-19		J Ellis	DE Fairclough	J Mortimore	Brain	Conway/t
3	03.01	H	N1	Stockton	W 11-3		J Ellis	J Mortimore	Mell	Brain	Conway
4	10.10	A	N1	Middlesborough	W 9-3		J Ellis	J Mortimore	Mell	Brain	DE Fairclough
5	24.10	H	N1	Macclesfield	W 32-13		J Ellis/t	Poskitt/3c2p	DS Fairclough	Brain	Conway
6	31.10	A	N1	Bridlington	W 19-7		J Ellis	Poskitt/3p	DS Fairclough	J Mortimore	Conway/t
7	07.11	H	N1	Widnes*	W 42-15		J Ellis	Poskitt/t3cp(b/p)	DS Fairclough	Brain/2t	Conway/t
8	21.11	A	N1	Blaydon	L 8-20		J Ellis	J Mortimore	DS Fairclough	Brain	Poskitt/tp
9	28.11	A	N1	Northern	L 12-16		J Ellis	Poskitt/c	DS Fairclough	Brain	Conway
10	05.12	A	N1	Hull Ionians	L 12-16		J Ellis	Faulkner	Mell	Brain	DS Fairclough
11	12.12	H	N1	Broughton P	W 45-10		J Ellis	Faulkner	DS Fairclough/c3p	Mell/t	Conway/t
12	19.12	H	N1	Blaydon	W 22-3		J Ellis	Mell	DS Fairclough	Brain	Conway
13	09.01	A	N1	Widnes	D 10-10		J Ellis	J Mortimore	Mell	Brain	Conway
14	16.01	H	N1	Bridlington	W 17-0		J Ellis	J Mortimore	Mell	Brain/t	Conway
15	23.01	A	N1	Macclesfield	W 29-7		J Ellis	J Mortimore	Mell	Brain/t	Conway
16	30.01	H	N1	Middlesborough	W 9-3		J Ellis	J Mortimore	DS Fairclough	Brain	Conway
17	06.02	A	N1	Stockton	W 33-6		J Ellis	J Mortimore/t	DS Fairclough	Brain/t	Conway
18	13.02	H	N1	Wigton	W 79-0		J Ellis/3t	J Mortimore/t	DS Fairclough	Brain/t	Conway/t
19	27.02	A	N1	Tynedale	W 8-5		J Ellis	J Mortimore	DS Fairclough	Brain	Conway
20	13.03	H	N1	Hull Ionians	W 41-17		J Ellis	J Mortimore/t	Faulkner	Brain/t	Conway/t
21	27.03	A	N1	Broughton P	W 26-14		J Ellis	J Mortimore/t	DS Fairclough	Brain/2t	DE Fairclough
22	17.04	H	N1	Northern	W 33-3		J Ellis	J Mortimore	DS Fairclough	Brain/t	Conway/t
A	19.09	H	TB1	Walsall	W 30-19						
B	17.10	A	TB2	Sandal	L 3-6						

* after opponents name indicates a penalty try
Brackets after a player's name indicates he was replaced. eg (a) means he was replaced by replacement code "a" and so on.
/ after a player or replacement name is followed by any scores he made - eg /t, /c, /p, /dg or any combination of these

1998-99 HIGHLIGHTS

Ever Presents:
Jon Ellis & Richard Senior

Most appearances
21 Kevin Westgarth, Longworth
20 Matt Brain
19 Bailey

Players used: 29 plus eight as replacement only.

Most Points in a season:

Pts	Player	T	C	P	DG
75	R Senior	15	-	-	-
64	P Ure	-	17	10	-
60	M Brain	12	-	-	-
57	Poskitt	3	6	10	-
35	Conway	7	-	-	-

MATCH FACTS

10	9	1	2	3	4	5	6	7	8	
Eddie/cp	Greenslade	Waddington	Hyde	Page	Bailey/t	Westgarth	R Senior/2t	D Senior	Longworth	1
Poskitt/tcp(a/p)	Greenslade	Waddington	Hyde	Page	Hill	Westgarth	R Senior/t	D Senior/t	Longworth	2
Poskitt/p(a/dg)	Greenslade	Waddington	Hyde	Page	Bailey	Westgarth	R Senior	D Senior	Longworth/t	3
Poskitt/3p	Greenslade	Waddington	Hyde	Page	Bailey	Westgarth	R Senior	D Senior	Longworth	4
Matthews	Pascoe/t	Baldwin	Hyde	Page	Bailey	Westgarth	R Senior	D Senior/2t	Longworth	5
Matthews	Pascoe/t	Baldwin	Hyde	Page	Bailey	Westgarth	R Senior	D Senior	Longworth	6
Matthews	Pascoe	Baldwin	Hyde	Page	Bailey	Westgarth	R Senior/t	D Senior	Longworth	7
Matthews	Pascoe	Baldwin	Hyde	Page	Bailey	Westgarth	R Senior	Cox	Longworth	8
Matthews	Pascoe/2t	Baldwin	Hyde	Page	Bailey	Westgarth	R Senior	D Senior	Longworth	9
Poskitt/c	Pascoe	Baldwin	Hyde	Page	Hill	Westgarth	R Senior	D Senior	Goose/t	10
Matthews4c4p	Pascoe/t	Baldwin	Hyde	Waddington	Bailey/t	Westgarth	R Senior	D Senior/t	Longworth	11
Matthews/2p	Pascoe	Baldwin	Hyde	Waddington	Bailey	Westgarth	R Senior/t	D Senior	Longworth	12
DS Fairclough	Pascoe	Baldwin	Hyde	Waddington	Hill	Westgarth	R Senior/t	D Senior/t	Longworth	13
DS Fairclough/c	Pascoe	Baldwin	Hyde	Waddington	Bailey	Westgarth	R Senior/t	D Senior	Longworth/t	14
DSFairclough3cp	Greenslade	Baldwin	Hyde	Waddington	Bailey/t	Westgarth	R Senior/t	D Senior	Longworth/t	15
Ure/3p	Greenslade	Baldwin	C Mortimer	Waddington	Bailey	Westgarth	R Senior	D Senior	Longworth	16
Ure2c3p	Greenslade	Baldwin	Atkinson/t	Waddington	Bailey	Westgarth	R Senior/t	Cox	Longworth	17
Ure/7c	Greenslade/t	Baldwin	Atkinson	Waddington	Bailey/2t	Westgarth	R Senior/2t	Cox	Longworth/2t	18
Ure/p	Greenslade	Baldwin	Atkinson	Waddington	Bailey	Westgarth	R Senior/t	Cox	Longworth	19
Ure/c3p	Greenslade/t	Baldwin	Atkinson	Waddington	Bailey	Westgarth	R Senior/t	D Senior	Longworth/t	20
Ure3c	Greenslade	Baldwin/t	Atkinson	Waddington	Bailey	Hill	R Senior	D Senior	Longworth	21
Ure4c	Greenslade	Baldwin/t	Atkinson	Waddington	Bailey	Westgarth	R Senior/2t	D Senior	Longworth	22

REPLACEMENTS (who scored): a- D Eddie b- J Mortimore

Richard Senior led the way in the try scoring stakes. Richard scored 15 tries playing at blindside flanker

Leading the way in the goal kicking was Phil Ure a mid season signing from Wakefield who helped himself to 64 points from seven starts.

Doncaster had a 100% home record with only two losses and two draws since 1990.

The only matches in which they failed to score were the two games against arch-rivals Middlesborough where the score was 9-3 to Doncaster on both occasions.

This season's promotion to National Division Two North was their fifth promotion in eight seasons.

DONCASTER

LEAGUE STATISTICS

SEASON	Division	P	W	D	L	F	A	Pts Diff	Lge Pts	Lge Pos
89-90	Yorks 1	10	5	0	5	131	93	38	10	4
90-91	Yorks 1	10	5	0	5	129	109	20	10	6
91-92	Yorks 1	10	8	0	2	163	100	63	16	2p
92-93	North E 2	12	11	0	1	294	39	255	22	1p
93-94	North E1	12	11	0	1	232	70	162	22	1p
94-95	North 2	12	7	0	5	136	155	-19	14	6
95-96	North 2	12	4	2	6	183	168	15	10	9
96-97	North 2	22	22	0	0	690	259	431	44	1p
97-98	North 1	22	17	2	3	489	285	204	36	2
98-99	North 1	22	18	1	3	550	214	336	37	1p

FACT FILE

Founded: 1875

Colours: Navy blue with 2 thin red & white bands
Change colours:

GROUND
Address: Armthorpe Road, Doncaster DN2 5QB
Web Site: www.drfc.co.uk
Tel: 01302 831388 Fax: 01302 831496 e-mail: admin@drfc.co.uk
Capacity: 4.252 Seated: 252 Standing: 4,000

Directions: Leave M18 at junction 4 and follow signs to Doncaster. At 2nd roundabout turn left towards Armthorpe. At next roundabout turn right and the ground is 1.25 miles on the left.
Nearest Railway station: Doncaster

Car Parking: Spaces for 400 cars at the ground

Admission:
Season £45
Matchday Adults £4; Members £2; Children/OAPs £1

Clubhouse: Open every evening except Sunday
Functions: Yes - Contact club to book

Club Shop: Yes - contact Paul Turton at club.

Training Nights: Monday & Thursday, 7.15pm

PROGRAMME
Size: A5 Price: With admission
Pages: 36 + cover Editor: John Lowe

ADVERTISING RATES
Colour: Full Page £200
Mono: Full Page £150 Half £80

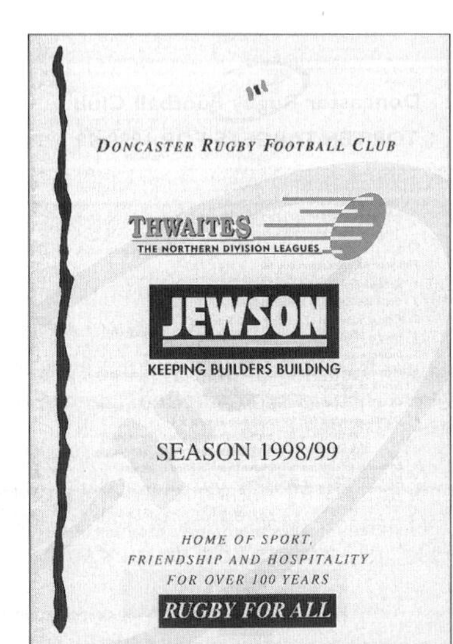

KENDAL R.U.F.C.

President	J D Healey	55 Calder Drive, Kendal LA9 6LR. 01539 723913 (H)
Chairman	Ian W Hutton	168 Vicarage Drive, Kendal, Cumbria, LA9 5BX 01539 733152 (H), 01539 733333 (B)
Hon/Match Secretary	Roger Wilson	31 Hills Wood Avenue, Kendal, Cumbria. 01539740449 (H)
Fixture Secretary	Andrew Quarry	14 Collinfield, Kendal, Cumbria LA9 5SD 01539 731640 (H) 01539 720391 (B) 01539 720645 (Fax)
Rugby Manager	Chris Hayton	106 Burneside Road, Kendal, Cumbria LA9 4RT. 01539 724600 (H), 01539 725822 (B), 01539 730613 (Fax)
Press Secretary	John Hutton	168 Vicarage Drive, Kendal LA9 5BX 01539 733152(H)

Kendal finished the season off in style winning all but three games in '99 and those losses included London Scottish and Orrell. Unfortunately Kendal got off to probably their poorest start for the season, losing four out of their first six Jewson League games. This was mainly due to a large change in the players making up the 1st XV squad, with no fewer than four new players making their debut in the Kendal first team in the first three weeks of the season.

The squad quickly gelled and victories soon followed with Kendal going on to win sixteen out of their remaining twenty league games including doing the double over six sides and recording nine straight victories between January and March to finish a very creditable fourth. Out of the squad five players gained the much coveted club badge for playing twenty games in a season.

Kendal's real success was the Tetley's Bitter Cup, a narrow home victory against Broadstreet set-up a second round tie against Jewson League One side Liverpool St. Helens. Kendal achieved an excellent 20-7 victory to progress to the next round. A third round away tie at Allied Dunbar Two side, Wakefield, saw the club produce probably their best away performance of the season coming away 16-8 victors. The fourth round draw presented the team with a home tie against Premiership side London Scottish. On a glorious January afternoon Kendal put in a tremendous performance which will linger for many, many years to come in the memories of the 3,000 strong crowd. Kendal ran Scottish close losing by just five points, 20-25, but out-scoring the Premiership side by four tries to three.

KENDAL RUFC

The 1st XV squad and coaches, pictured here before their final league game against Walsall at Mintbridge on 17.4.99

Photo: courtesy of Mr. P Hine

KENDAL

Match No.	Date	H/A	Comp.	Opponents	Result & Score	Att.	15	14	13	12	11
1	05.09	A	J2N	Nuneaton	L 22-25		Dodds	Balmer	S Healey/t	Voortman/2tc	Wood/cp(m)
2	12.09	H	J2N	New Brighton	L 12-17		Dodds	Balmer	S Healey	Voortman	Wood/c
3	26.09	A	J2N	Preston	L 18-27		Dodds	Balmer/t	S Healey	Voortman	Wood/p
4	03.10	H	J2N	Hinckley	W 36-0		Dodds	Balmer/t	S Healey	Voortman/t	Wood/2cp(c)
5	10.10	A	J2N	Whitchurch	L 11-13		Dodds/p	Seith	S Healey	Voortman	Wood/tp(c)
6	24.10	H	J2N	Lichfield	W 35-3		Dodds/cp	Balmer	S Healey	Voortman	Pearce/t
7	31.10	H	J2N	Sandal	W 15-8		Dodds	Balmer	S Healey	Voortman	Pearce
8	07.11	A	J2N	Sedgley Park	L 18-23		Dodds	Balmer	S Healey	Voortman	Pearce
9	21.11	H	J2N	Sheffield	W24-16		Dodds	Balmer/t	S Healey(c)	Voortman	Pearce(t)
10	28.11	A	J2N	Winnington P	W54-13		Dodds	Balmer/2t	S Healey	M Healey	Pearce
11	05.12	H	J2N	Aspatria	W30-23		Dodds	Balmer	S Healey/t	Voortman/t	Pearce(r)
12	12.12	A	J2N	Walsall	L 20-25		Dodds	Balmer/t	S Healey/t	Voortman	Pearce
13	19.12	H	J2N	Stourbridge	L 7-20		Dodds	Balmer/t	S Healey	Voortman	Seith
14	28.12	A	J2N	Aspatria	W 35-5		Dodds(u)	Balmer	S Healey	Voortman	Seith
15	02.01	H	J2N	Winnington P	W 37-3		Dodds/t	Balmer	S Healey/2t	Voortman	Seith(b)
16	16.01	H	J2N	Sedgley Park	W 20-7		Dodds/t	Balmer	S Healey	Voortman/t	Seith
17	23.01	A	J2N	Sandal	W 25-3		Dodds(c)	Balmer/2t	S Healey	Voortman	Seith(s)
18	30.01	A	J2N	Lichfield	W 17-5		Dodds	Balmer	S Healey/t(c)	Voortman	Pearce
19	06.02	H	J2N	Whitchurch	W26-10		Dodds(z)	Balmer/t	S Healey(q)	Voortman/t	Seith(c)
20	13.02	A	J2N	Hinckley*	W15-14		Dodds	Pearce	S Healey(y)	Voortman	Seith
21	20.02	A	J2N	Sheffield	W 23-3		Dodds	Balmer	M Healey(a)	Voortman	Seith(y)
22	27.02	H	J2N	Preston*	W 15-7		Dodds	Balmer	S Healey	Voortman	Seath
23	13.03	A	J2N	New Brighton	W35-31		Dodds	Balmer	S Healey	Voortman/t(y)	Seith
24	27.03	H	J2N	Nuneaton	W26-20		Dodds	Balmer	S Healey	Voortman/2t	Seith(t)
25	03.04	A	J2N	Stourbridge	L 15-18		Dodds	Balmer	S Healey/t	Voortman	Seith
26	17.04	H	J2N	Walsall	W 44-8		Dodds	Balmer/2t	S Healey/2t	Voortman	Bailey
A	19.09	H	TB1	Broadstreet	W13-12		Dodds/t	Balmer/t	S Healey	Voortman	Wood/p
B	17.10	H	TB2	Liverpool St H	W 20-7		Dodds	Balmer	S Healey	Voortman/t	Wood/p
C	14.11	A	TB3	Wakefield	W16-10		Dodds	Balmer/2t	S Healey	Voortman	Pearce
D	09.01	H	TB4	London Scot	L 20-25		Dodds	Balmer	S Healey	Voortman	Seith

* after opponents name indicates a penalty try
Brackets after a player's name indicates he was replaced. eg (a) means he was replaced by replacement code "a" and so on.
/ after a player or replacement name is followed by any scores he made - eg /t, /c, /p, /dg or any combination of these

1998-99 HIGHLIGHTS

Ever Presents:

	Paul Dodds & Billy Coxon
25	S Healey (1), Ian Voortman, Adrian Bateson
24	Jason Balmer, Casey Mee
23	Paul Thompson (2)

Players used: 26 plus eight as replacement only

Most Points in a season:

Pts	Player	T	C	P	DG
200	C Mee	6	37	31	1
60	J Balmer	12	-	-	-
50	R Harryman	10	-	-	-
47	I Voortman	9	1	-	-
45	S Whitehead	9	-	-	-
40	S Healey	8	-	-	-
40	C Wolstenholme	8	-	-	-

MATCH FACTS

10	9	1	2	3	4	5	6	7	8	
M Healey	Airey(j)	Coxon	Nicholson	Thompson(k)	Harryman/t	Madge(l)	Bateson	Wolstenholme	Robinson	1
M Healey	Thompson(d)	Pearson	Nicholson	Thompson	Harryman(n)	Robinson(i)	Bateson	Wolstenholme/t(l)	Coxon/t	2
Mee/t	Thompson/t(d)	Pearson(q)	Gowing	Thompson	Harryman(p)	Capstick	Bateson	Wolstenholme(l/t)	Coxon	3
Mee/2c	Thompson(d)	Pearson	Gowing	Thompson	Harryman(n)	Capstick/t	Bateson/t	Wolstenholme(l)	Coxon	4
Mee	Airey(j)	Pearson	Gowing	Thompson	Harryman	Capstick	Bateson	Wolstenholme(l)	Coxon	5
Mee/tcp	Thompson/2t	Coxon	Gowing/t	Pearson(f)	Harryman	Robinson	Wolstenholme(q)	Whitehead	Bateson	6
Mee/cp	Thompson	Coxon	Gowing/t	Pearson(f)	Robinson(g)	Capstick/t	Wolstenholme	Whitehead	Bateson	7
Mee/c2p	Thompson	Coxon/t	Gowing	Thompson(k)	Robinson	Capstick	Wolstenholme	Whitehead/t(g)	Bateson	8
Mee/3p	Thompson/t	Coxon	Gowing	Pearson(f)	Harryman	Robinson	Wolstenholme	Whitehead	Bateson/t	9
Mee/t4c2p	Thompson/t	Coxon	Gowing	Pearson/t	Harryman/2t	Robinson	Wolstenholme/t	Whitehead	Bateson	10
Mee/3c3p	Thompson	Coxon	Gowing(e)	Pearson/t(f)	Capstick	Robinson(g)	Wolstenholme	Whitehead	Bateson	11
Mee/cp(c)	Thompson	Coxon	Gowing	Pearson(f)	Capstick	Robinson	Wolstenholme	Whitehead/t	Bateson	12
Mee/c	Thompson	Coxon	Nicholson(o)	Thompson	Harryman(k)	Capstick	Wolstenholme	Whitehead(h)	Bateson	13
Mee/2c2p	Thompson	Coxon	Nicholson(o)	Thompson	Harryman/t	Capstick(h)	Wolstenholme/t	Whitehead/2t(q)	Bateson/t	14
Mee/t2cp	Thompson(c)	Coxon	Gowing/t(e)	Pearson(v)	Harryman/t	Robinson	Rigg	Wolstenholme(q)	Bateson	15
Mee/cp	Thompson	Coxon	Nicholson(o)	Pearson	Harryman	Capstick	Robinson(w)	Whitehead/t(q)	Bateson	16
Mee/2c2p	Thompson	Coxon	Nicholson(o)	Pearson	Harryman/t	Capstick	Robinson(w)	Whitehead	Bateson	17
Mee/c	Thompson	Coxon	Gowing(e)	Pearson	Harryman	Capstick	Robinson(w)	Whitehead/2t	Bateson	18
Mee/t3c	Thompson	Coxon	Nicholson(o)	Pearson	Harryman/t	Capstick	Bowman(h)	Whitehead	Bateson	19
Mee/cp	Thompson	Coxon	Nicholson(o)	Pearson	Harryman	Capstick	Whitehead/t	Bowman	Bateson	20
Mee/t2c3p	Thompson	Coxon	Nicholson	Pearson	Harryman/t	Capstick	Robinson(w)	Whitehead	Bateson	21
Mee/cp	Thompson	Coxon	Nicholson(o)	Pearson	Harryman/t	Capstick	Wolstenholme(w)	Robinson	Bateson	22
Mee/2cpdg	Thompson/2t	Coxon	Nicholson(o)	Pearson	Harryman	Capstick	Robinson	Wolstenholme/2t(w)	Bateson	23
Mee/c3p	Thompson(c)	Coxon	Nicholson	Pearson(v)	Harryman	Capstick	Robinson(l)	Wolstenholme/t	Bateson	24
Mee/cp	Thompson	Coxon	Nicholson	Pearson(f)	Harryman/t	Capstick(w)	Wolstenholme	Whitehead	Bateson	25
Mee/4c2p	Thompson(c)	Coxon	Nicholson	Harryman	Bowman(v)	Capstick	Wolstenholme/2t(k)	Whitehead	Bateson	26
Mee	Airey	Pearson	Nicholson(l)	Thompson	Harryman	S Capstick(w)	Bateson	Wolstenholme	Coxon	A
Mee	Thompson	Coxon	Gowing	Pearson	Harryman/t	Capstick	Wolstenholme	Whitehead	Bateson	B
Mee/2p	Thompson	Coxon	Gowing	Pearson	Robinson	Capstick(g)	Wolstenholme	Whitehead	Bateson	C
Mee/t	Thompson	Coxon	Nicholson(o)	Pearson(f)	Harryman	Capstick	Wolstenholme/2t	Whitehead/t(h)	Bateson	D

REPLACEMENTS:

a- S Healey, b- M Wood, c - M Healey, d - M Airey, e - J Nicholson, f - I Thompson, g - R Harryman, h - K Robinson, i - C Madge, j - P Thompson, k - N Pearson, l - S Whitehead, m - P Spivey, n - H Nicholson, o - I Gowing, p - S Captick, q - P Kremer, r - D Seith, s - D Pearce, t - A Dolan, u - D Stephens, v - J Bracken, w - S Bowman, x - M Airey, y - R Bailey, z - R Morris

South African fly half Casey Mee in his first season with the clubs tops the points scorers list with 200 points.

Winger Jason Balmer tops the try scoring list for a second successive season.

Kendal ended the season in style with just one defeat in their last 13 league matches, and that was a loss at second placed Stourbridge.

Lost just twice at home to New Brighton and Stourbridge.

Conceded fewer points at home than any other side in the division, just 137. That was three fewer than the next best by Sheffield.

Second row Richard Harryman averged a try every other game.

KENDAL

LEAGUE STATISTICS
compiled by Stephen McCormack

SEASON	Division	P	W	D	L	F	A	Pts Diff	Lge Pts	Lge Pos		Coach		Captain
89-90	ALN	10	6	0	4	130	136	-6	12	5		R Lee		D Sharpe
90-91	D4N	12	6	2	4	191	132	59	14	5		R Lee		S Hulme
91-92	D4N	12	8	1	3	157	123	34	17	3		R Lee		S Hulme
92-93	D4N	12	6	0	6	182	189	-7	12	6				
93-94	D5N	12	4	1	7	142	171	-29	9	10				
94-95	D5N	12	9	1	2	226	162	64	19	2		P Kremer		J Nicholson
												Most Points		**Most Tries**
95-96	D5N	12	5	0	7	215	227	-12	10	9	36	Paul Dodds	6	Paul Dodds
96-97	D4N	26	11	1	14	541	451	90	23	9	163	Jason Hudson	7	Paul Dodds
97-98	N2N	26	18	2	6	614	357	257	38	3	135	Jon Nicholson	15	Jason Balmer
98-99	N2N	26	18	0	8	635	347	288	36	4	200	Casey Mee	12	Jason Balmer

FACT FILE

Founded : 1905
Nickname : The Black & Ambers

Colours: Black and amber.
Change colours: Amber jerseys with black trim

GROUND
Address: Mint Bridge, Shap Road, Kendal. LA9 6DL.
Tel: 01539 734039
Capacity: 1300 Seated: 300 Standing: 1000

Directions: From the M6 junction 36 take A591. Then A6 (Kendal to Penrith). Keep left at the `Duke of Cumberland' and the ground is 400 metres onthe left.
Nearest Railway Station: Kendal (via Oxenholme)

Car Parking: Space for 100 cars on ground.

Admission: Season tickets - £30 for all.
Matchdays - Adults members £2.50
non-members £4; Children/OAPs £1

Clubhouse: Has two bars and has food available.
Functions: Capacity up to 200.

Club Shop: Shop manager - Ron Hayes Tel. 01539 734039

Training Nights: Tuesday and Thursday

PROGRAMME
Size: A5 Price: 50p extra to admission.
Pages: 24 + cover
Editor: John Kremer 01539 734039

ADVERTISING RATES
Full page £160; Half £80; Quarter £50

LIVERPOOL St. HELENS F.C.

President	Ian Clark	
Chairman	Alan Walker	
Club Secretary	John D Robertson	36 Beryl Road, Noctorum, Wirral. L43 9RT. 0151 677 5611 (H)
Fixtures Secretary	R Hall	21 Childwall Abbey Road, Liverpool. L16 0JL. 0151 722 3588 (H & Fax)
Chairman of Rugby	Dennis Brady	
Press Officer	Chris Brown	47 Cowley Hill Lane, St. Helens. WA10 2AR. 01744 759075 (H), 01744 23281 (B), 01744 451955 (Fax)

Despite suffering relegation from Jewson National One there were still encouraging signs of progress made during the season and the optimism continues as we prepare for competition in Jewson Two North this time round.

Last season, although not possessing the largest of packs, the forwards still managed to hold their own against much heavier opposition. The secret of the success was that although they used a total of 29 players in the pack six of them appeared in 20 games or more during the season. In the back division it was a different story although again 29 players were used, but only eight played in 10 matches or more. With the back division constantly chopping and changing they were never really allowed to gel into an effective unit. By December they had lost five of their most experienced backs. Simon Humphreys succumbed to long term injury, Paul Brett moved on to New Brighton, Mike Hitchen and Ian Callaghan switched codes and John Aby also moved on.

In a division where there was little to choose between the majority of the sides it was always likely that any weaknesses would be exploited and LSH's difficulty in turning possession into points was all too often cruelly exposed, a total of 335 points were scored. This was the second lowest figure in the division. A lack of cutting edge in the back division put far too much pressure on the defence which conceded 859 points, the highest in the division resulting in just four wins from 26 league matches.

With finances once again in a delicate situation it is heartening to learn that so many players have decided to keep faith with the club. We are hoping that the spirit within the club will see our fortunes change and look forward to giving as good as we get in Jewson Two North - if not a little bit more.

LIVERPOOL St HELENS

Match No.	Date	H/A	Comp.	Opponents	Result & Score	Att.	15	14	13	12	11
1	05.09	A	JN1	Morley	L 18-23	400	Humphreys(h)	Brett/p	Hitchen	Aby	Sephton/t
2	12.09	H	JN1	Lydney	W 33-18	250	Humphreys/t	Brett/2c3p	Hitchen	Aby/t	Sephton
3	19.09	A	JN1	Otley	L 7-13	400	Humphreys(m)	Brett/c	Hitchen/t	Aby	Sephton
4	26.09	H	JN1	Reading	L 6-24	200	Brett/2p	Brooks	Hitchen	Aby(o)	Sephton
5	03.10	A	JN1	Rosslyn Park	L 22-50	500	Brett/c	Brooks/t	Hitchen/2t	Aby	Sephton(a)
6	10.10	H	JN1	Birmingham S	L 8-25	200	Humphreys(b/t)	Brett/p	Hitchen	Aby	Brooks
7	24.10	A	JN1	Newbury	L 0-20	300	Humphreys	Brooks	Close(t)	Hitchen	Sephton
8	31.10	A	JN1	Harrogate	L 17-24	450	Humphreys/c	Brooks	Hitchen	Aby	Sephton/t
9	07.11	H	JN1	Wharfedale	L 20-32	250	Close/t	Brooks/t	Hitchen	Callaghan/cp	Sephton
10	21.11	A	JN1	Manchester	L 5-50	400	Nicholls	Brooks	Close(v)	Aby/t	Sephton(t)
11	28.11	H	JN1	Nottingham	L 0-55	200	Carter	Brooks	Nicholls	Walker	Murphy
12	05.12	A	JN1	Camberley	L 7-42	250	Carter/c	Brooks	Walker	Davies	Sephton/t
13	12.12	H	JN1	Henley	L 12-67	150	Pearson	Brooks(B)	Walker(v)	Davies	Sephton/2t
14	28.12	H	JN1	Manchester	L 15-40	350	Pearson	Brooks	Walker/t	Carter	Murphy
15	02.01	A	JN1	Wharfedale	L 0-59	700	Pearson	Brooks	Walker	Carter	Sephton
16	16.01	H	JN1	Harrogate	W 11-5	200	Glynn/2p	Brooks	Davies(o)	Carter	Sephton
17	23.01	H	JN1	Newbury	W 31-14	200	Glynn/t2c4p	Brooks	Davies/t(o)	Carter	Sephton(D)
18	30.01	A	JN1	Birmingham S	L 10-12	150	Glynn	Brooks/t	Davies	Carter	Sephton
19	06.02	H	JN1	Rosslyn Park	L 7-22	200	Glynn/c	Brooks(B)	Hatton	Walker	Sephton
20	13.02	A	JN1	Reading	W 31-10	200	Glynn/tc3p	Brooks/t	Hatton	Walker	Sephton
21	20.02	A	JN1	Nottingham	L 11-45	300	Glynn/2p	Brooks	Carter	Walker	Sephton
22	27.02	H	JN1	Otley	L 12-16	200	Glynn/c	Brooks	Davies(o)	Hatton	Sephton
23	13.03	A	JN1	Lydney	L 17-62	500	Glynn/c	Brooks	Walker	Carter(t)	Sephton/t
24	27.03	H	JN1	Morley	L 10-42	150	Pearson(C)	Brooks	Davies	Walker	Sephton
25	03.04	A	JN1	Henley	L 8-39	450	Pearson	Jones	Carter(H)	Hatton	Sephton
26	17.04	H	JN1	Camberley	L 17-50	150	Pearson	Jones	Carter	Hatton	Sephton/t
A	17.10	A	TBC	Kendal	l 7-20	500	Humphreys/c	Brooks	Hitchen	Aby	Sephton/t

* after opponents name indicates a penalty try
Brackets after a player's name indicates he was replaced. eg (a) means he was replaced by replacement code "a" and so on.
/ after a player or replacement name is followed by any scores he made - eg /t, /c, /p, /dg or any combination of these

1998-99 HIGHLIGHTS

League debuts:
Peter Dadswell, Paul Bleasdale, Ian Hamer, Alex Pruden, Domonic Carter, Liam Nicholls, Bruce Thompson, Scott Pearson, Matt Murphy, Simon Worsley, Will Pilkington, Chris Glynn, Dave Topping, Domonic Brown, Anthony Hatton, Njike Tchakoute, Simon O'Keefe, Martin Gaskell

Ever Presents: None - most appearances 25 Mike Nugent

Players used: 44 plus 7 as a replacement only

Most Points in a season:

Pts	Player	T	C	P	DG
55	C Glynn	2	6	11	-
45	M Sephton	9	-	-	-
30	J Hitchen	6	-	-	-
29	P Brett	-	4	7	-
20	N Brooks	4	-	-	-

10	9	1	2	3	4	5	6	7	8	
Callaghan	Liddle	Lever(g)	Hitchen	Jackson	Nugent	Bailey	Gaskell	Wood/t	Lupton	1
Callaghan	Liddle	Lever	Hitchen	Jackson/t	Nugent	Bailey	Jones	Wood	Lupton	2
Callaghan	Liddle(i)	Lever	Hitchen	Jackson(g)	Nugent	Boyd	Gaskell(j)	Wood	Lupton	3
Callaghan	Eldoy	Lever	Hitchen(n)	Jackson	Nugent(d)	Boyd	Gaskell	Wood	Lupton	4
Callaghan/t	Bleasdale	Lever(g)	Dadswell	Jackson	Boyd	Bailey	Gaskell	Wood	Lupton	5
Callaghan(t)	Eldoy(p)	Lever(g)	Hitchen	Jackson	Nugent	Bailey(u)	Boyd	Wood	Lupton	6
Callaghan	Liddle	Waite	Hitchen(k)	Lever	Nugent	Bailey(s)	Gaskell	Wood	Lupton	7
Callaghan	Liddle/t	Lever/t	Hitchen	Jackson	Nugent	Bailey	Gaskell	Wood	Lupton	8
Wellens	Liddle	Lever	Hitchen	Jackson(w)	Nugent/t	Bailey(l)	Gaskell	Wood	Lupton	9
Callaghan	Liddle	Wales	Hitchen	Jackson	Nugent	Lupton	Gaskell	Wood	Jones	10
Wellens(C)(A)	Liddle	Wales(g)	Thompson(n)	Jackson	Nugent	Pruden	Jones(d)(x)	Wood	Lupton	11
Humphreys(A)	Liddle	Waite	Hitchen	Wales(c)	Nugent	Bailey(s)	Boyd	Wood	Lupton	12
Close/c	Liddle	Waite	Hitchen(n)	Wales(c)	Nugent	Bailey(s)	Boyd	Wood	Lupton	13
Close/cp	Liddle	Waite	Hitchen	Wales(y)	Nugent	Bailey	Boyd	Wood/t	Lupton(s)	14
Close(z)(t)	Liddle	Waite(y)	Hitchen(n)	Wales	Nugent	Bailey	Pilkington	Wood	Boyd	15
Wellens	Topping	Waite	Hitchen/t	Wales	Nugent	Boyd	Pilkington	Wood	Lupton	16
Wellens	Topping	Waite(q)	Hitchen(x)	Wales	Nugent(d)	Boyd	Pilkington	Wood	Lupton	17
Wellens	Topping	Waite/t	Hitchen	Wales	Nugent	Boyd	Pilkington(d)	Wood	Lupton	18
Wellens(v)	Topping/t	Waite	Thompson(n)	Wales	Nugent	Boyd(e)	Pilkington(q)	Wood	Lupton	19
Wellens(v)	Topping	Waite	Hitchen/2t	Wales	Nugent	Boyd	Pilkington	Wood	Gaskell(F)(n)	20
Hatton	Topping	Waite(G)	Hitchen/t	Wales	Nugent	Boyd	Pilkington	Wood(C)	Lupton	21
Wellens	Topping	Hamer(G)	Hitchen	Wales/t	Nugent	Boyd	Pilkington	M Gaskell(f)	Lupton/t	22
Worsley	Topping(D)	Wales	Hitchen/2t	O'Keefe(q)	Nugent	Boyd(H)	Pilkington	Wood	Lupton	23
Wellens/cp	Brown	Waite	Hitchen	Wales/t	Boyd	Nugent	Pilkington	Wood	Lupton(J)	24
Worlsey	Brown	Wales	Hitchen(y)	Hamer	Nugent	Tchakoute(d)	Pilkington	Wood(F)	Boyd	25
Worlsey/c	Topping/t(D)	Wales	Hitchen	Waite/t	Nugent(K)	Boyd	Pilkington	M Gaskell	Lupton	26
Callaghan(t)	Eldoy(p)	Waite	Hitchen	Jackson	Nugent	Pruden	Bailey	Bayley	Lupton	A

REPLACEMENTS: a- S Humphreys b - M Sephton c - T Jackson d- R Bailey e - D Gaskell f - T Wood g - D Waite h - P Knowles i - J Sorby j - M Boyd k - M Keenaghan l - N Jones m - N Brooks n - P Dadswell o - C Walker p - P Bleasdale q - I Hamer r - K Toole s - A Pruden t - B Wellens u - N Ray v - D Carter w - C Wales x - B Thompson y - A McDonald z - K Davies A - S Pearson B - M Murphy C - S Worlsey D - D Brown E - A Hatton F- P Evans G - S O'Keefe H- M Gaskell

Chris Glynn topped the points scorers list with a lowly 55. The club had difficulty finding a consistent goal kicker and they struggled because of it.

Winger Mark Sephton topped the clubs try scoring for the seventh time with 9 tries which equals his best from the 1993-94 season.
Sephton also extends his all time career to 60 which puts him in the top three ever in senoir league rugby along with Eddie Saunders and Jeremy Guscott.

Liverpool suffered their worst ever home league defeats when they were beaten by 55 points twice. First they were beaten 55-0 by Nottingham at in November, two weeks later they were beaten 67-12 by Henley.

Won just once away from home all season when they beat Reading 31-10 in February.

LIVERPOOL ST. HELENS

LEAGUE STATISTICS
compiled by Stephen McCormack

SEASON	Division	P	W	D	L	F	A	Pts Diff	Lge Pts	Lge Pos	Most Points	Most Tries
89-90	2	11	8	2	1	154	106	48	18		66 Tosh Askew	6 Mark Sephton & Peter Buckton
90-91	1	12	0	0	12	88	349	-261	0		31 Andy Higgin	2 Mark Sephton & Peter Buckton
91-92	2	12	0	0	12	87	418	-331	0		26 Paul Ramsden	4 Mark Elliott
92-93	3	11	5	0	6	203	130	73	10		98 Andy Higgin	8 Mark Sephton
93-94	4	18	11	1	6	396	275	121	23		140 Simon Mason	9 Mark Sephton
94-95	4	18	10	3	5	374	243	134	23		155 Andy Higgin	7 Mark Sephton
95-96	4	18	11	1	6	471	343	128	23		120 Mark Wellens	14 Simon Humphreys
96-97	3	30	8	0	22	665	827	162	16		210 Paul Brett	14 Paul Brett
97-98	JN1	26	8	1	17	430	767	-337	17		85 Paul Brett	8 Mark Sephton
98-99	JN1	26	4	0	22	335	859	-524	8	14r	55 Chris Glynn	9 Mark Sephton

FACT FILE

Founded: 1857 (Merged 1986)
Nickname: LSH

Colours: Red, blue, white & black hoops/navy
Change colours: White with red & blue trim/navy.

GROUND

Address: Moss Lane (off Rainford Rd.) Windle, St. Helens. WA11 7PL.
Tel : 01744 25708
Capacity: 2300 Seated: 300 Standing: 2000

Directions: M6, leave at A580 (Haydock) towards Liverpool. After approx 4 miles, take A570 (right), immediate left, left again and follow lane straight ahead - the clubhouse will come into view on the left after 1/2 mile.
Nearest Railway Station: St Helens, 5mins by taxi

Car Parking: 200

Admission: Season tickets £60
Matchdays Adults £4 (incl prog)
Children/OAPs £1.

Club Shop: Yes.

Clubhouse: 3 bars & has food available.
Functions: Up to 100 seated can be catered.
Contact Alan Brown c/o Club

Training Nights: Tuesday & Thursday.

PROGRAMME
Size: A5 Pages: 20 + cover Price: £1
Editor: Ian Darlington Correspondence c/o Club.
01744 739620 (H) 01744 456387 (B)

ADVERTISING RATES
Full page £300

MORLEY R.F.C.

President	Allan Gray	c/o Morley RFC, Scatcherd Lane, Morley, WestYorkshire LS27 0JJ Tel: 0113 253 4387 Fax: 0113 253 4144
Chairman	Brian Falshaw	c/o Morley RFC, as above
Club Secretary	Dennis R Elam	26 The Roundway, Morley, Yorkshire LS27 0JS Tel/Fax 0113 252 4348
Chairman of Rugby	Chris Leathly	c/o Morley RFC, as above
Fixtures Secretary	Robert McCutcheon	c/o Morley RFC, as above

Morley failed to grasp the opportunity offered by the RFU and for the second successive season finished in the relegation zone. The euphoria of three straight wins to lead the table in September was quickly replaced by the realisation that we were in a relegation battle from early November. Three matches were lost with the last kick of the ball, when poor decision making gave visiting teams the opportunity to snatch victory or earn a draw. The most memorable was when Harrogate's lock Peter Taylor kicked a penalty from the touchline in the fourth minute of injury to give Harrogate a 22-21 victory and sealed Morley's fate.

Morley used 42 players in their starting line up in an effort to find a winning blend. Experienced campaigners Simon Smith and Paul Stewart each played in 23 league matches, whilst youngsters Chris Hall and Lance Hamilton both made try scoring debuts and went from strength to strength. Adam Standeven, despite missing five matches to injury, still managed to be joint top try scorer in the league with fifteen tries.

Morley's attention was distracted by a good run in the Tetley Bitter's Cup that saw them face the Cup holders, Saracens, in the Fourth Round. Although the result was predictable, the team and town enjoyed a memorable day.

Morley now look forward to next season in Jewson Two. We eagerly await friends old and new to welcome them to Scatcherd Lane. Already work parties have been in operation throughout the summer tidying up the ground and refurbishing the bar. Pre-season training started on June 7th under the watchful eye of new chairman of rugby Chris Leathley, with one aim in mind - promotion.

DENNIS ELAM

Club Captain for 1999-2000, Andy Swales, makes a break during the victory over Wharfedale.
Flankers Simon Smith (left) and David Hopton are ready to support. Photo courtesy of Yorkshire Post Newspapers

MORLEY

Match No.	Date	H/A	Comp.	Opponents	Result & Score	Att.	15	14	13	12	11
1	05.09	H	JN1	Liverpool StH	W 23-18	400	Standeven/tc2p	Hutchinson	Withington(n)(m)	Murray	Leathley
2	12.09	A	JN1	Harrogate	W 14-9	550	Standeven/t2p	Hutchinson	Bibb	Murray	Leathley
3	19.09	H	JN1	Wharfedale	W 29-17	400	Standeven(v)	Hutchinson	Bibb	A Sales/t	Leathley
4	26.09	A	JN1	Manchester	L 5-29	400	McCauly	Hutchinson	Bibb(y)	A Sales	Child/t
5	03.10	H	JN1	Nottingham	L 17-19	600	McCauly	Hutchinson/t	Bibb(t)	A Sales	Child
6	10.10	A	JN1	Camberley	L 24-33	400	Johnson	Hutchinson	Bone	A Sales(n)	Hall/t
7	24.10	H	JN1	Henley	L 10-13	600	Johnson	Hutchinson	Bone	A Sales(n)	Hall
8	31.10	H	JN1	Newbury	W 13-8	500	Johnson/t	Hutchinson(q)	Bone	Bibb	Hall
9	07.11	A	JN1	Lydney	L 10-35	500	Johnson	Standeven	Bone	Bibb(d)	Hall
10	21.11	H	JN1	Otley	L 20-25	700	Johnson/t	Standeven	Bone	Walker	Hall/2t
11	28.11	A	JN1	Reading	L 19-55	200	Johnson	Standeven/c(d)	Bone(B)	Walker	Hall
12	12.12	A	JN1	Birmingham S	L 7-35	150	Johnson	Standeven	Goddard/t	Walker(n)	Hall
13	19.12	H	JN1	Reading	L 14-17	500	Johnson	Barker	Bibb(w)	Bone	Hall
14	26.12	A	JN1	Otley	L 7-27	700	Johnson	Barker/t	Bone	A Sales	Hall
15	02.01	H	JN1	Lydney	D 13-13	400	Hall	Barker/t	Bone	A Sales	Standeven/t
16	16.01	A	JN1	Newbury	L 18-44	450	Hall/t	Barker	Bone	A Sales	Standeven/t
17	23.01	A	JN1	Henley	L 13-24	450	Hall/t(m)	Thompson	Bone	A Sales	Standeven/t
18	30.01	H	JN1	Camberley	W 39-22	400	Hall	Thompson/t(D)	Bone	Sales	Stabdeven/2t
19	06.02	A	JN1	Nottingham	L 11-19	400	Hall	Thompson	Naivalarua	A Sales	Standeven
20	13.02	H	JN1	Manchester	L 17-23	700	Hall	Thompson	Naivalarua	A Sales(m)	Standeven/t
21	20.02	H	JN1	Rosslyn Park	L 24-36	350	Hall/t	Thompson	Naivalarua	Bone	Standeven(m)
22	27.02	A	JN1	Wharfedale	L 14-38	750	Hall	Thompson/t	Naivalarua	Bone	Standeven/t
23	13.03	H	JN1	Harrogate	L 21-22	500	Hall	Thompson	Naivalarua/t	Bibb	Standeven/t
24	27.03	A	JN1	Liverpool StH	W 42-10	150	Hall/2t	Thompson/t	Naivalarua/t	Bibb(w)	Standeven/2t
25	03.04	H	JN1	Birmingham S	W 25-10	400	Hall	Thompson	Naivalarua/t	A Sales/t	Standeven/t
26	17.04	A	JN1	Rosslyn Park	L 19-42	500	Johnson(y)	Thompson	Navalarua/2t	A Sales	Standeven/t2c(t)
A	17.10	A	TBC	Otley	W 20-18	600	Johnson	Hutchinson	Bone	A Sales	Hall(b)
B	14.11	H	TBC	Maidenhead*	W 39-25	500	Johnson	Standeven	Bibb(G)	Walker	Hall/2t
C	10.01	H	TBC	Saracens	L 8-76	2,000	Hall/t	Barker(m)	Bone	A Sales	Standeven
D											

* after opponents name indicates a penalty try
Brackets after a player's name indicates he was replaced. eg (a) means he was replaced by replacement code "a" and so on.
/ after a player or replacement name is followed by any scores he made - eg /t, /c, /p, /dg or any combination of these

1998-99 HIGHLIGHTS

League debuts: George Hutchinson, Neil Murray, John Leathley, Steve Worsley, Paul Stewart, Jamie Wheelwright, Scott Wilson, Todd McCauly, Lee Child, Ian Worsley, Chris Hall, James Walker, Richard Goddard, Jon Skurr, Richard Thompson, Mark Burrows.

Ever Presents: None - most appearances Paul Stewart 21

Players used: 42 plus 2 as a replacement only

Most Points in a season:

Pts	Player	T	C	P	DG
119	T Bamber	1	24	21	1
95	A Standeven	15	4	4	-
40	C Hall	8	-	-	-
25	R Thompson	5	-	-	-

MATCH FACTS

10	9	1	2	3	4	5	6	7	8	
Bamber	Tiffin	Goodwin	Worsley	Szabo	Fletcher	Stewart	Smith	Hopton	Chippendale/t	1
Bamber/dg	Tiffin	Goodwin	Worsley(u)	Szabo	Fletcher	Pierre	Smith	Hopton	Chippendale(r)	2
Bamber/t3cp	Tiffin/t	Goodwin	Worsley(u)	Szabo	Fletcher	Pierre(i)	Smith	Hopton/t	Chippendal(r)	3
Bamber	Tiffin(x)	Goodwin	Worsley(u)	Szabo(q)	Stewart	Pierre	Smith	Hopton	Chippendal(r)	4
Bamber/2cp	I Worsley	Goodwin	Worsley(p)	Szabo	Fletcher	Stewart	Smith	Hopton	Tabua(l)	5
Bamber/2c	I Worsley(d)	Goodwin	Kneale/t	Szabo	Fletcher	Stewart	Kite	Hamilton/t	Smith/t	6
Bamber/cp	Tiffin	Ireland(e)	Kneale(f)	Szabo	Fletcher	Stewart	Kite(j)	Yule	Chippendale/t	7
M Sales/p	I Worsley/t	Goodwin	Worsley	Ireland	Chippendale	Stewart	Kite	Wheelwright(A/t)	Smith	8
M Sales	I Worsley	Goodwin	Worsley	Wilson	Chippendale	Stewart(z)	Kite/t	Wheelwright	Smith	9
Bamber/cp	I Worsley	Goodwin	Worsley	Wilson	Stewart	Fletcher(q)	Smith(C)	Hamilton	Chippendale	10
Bamber/c(D/t)	I Worsley	Goodwin(t)	Worsley	Wilson	Spence(r)	Stewart	Smith	Hopton	Chippendale/t	11
M Sales/c	I Worsley	Ireland	Worsley	Wilson	Pierre	Stewart	Spence	Hamilton	Smith(l)	12
M Sales/t3p	I Worsley(d)	Goodwin	Worsley	Wilson	Chippendale	Pierre	Spence(k)	Hamilton	Tabua	13
M Sales(c/c)	I Worsley(d)	Goodwin	Worsley(u)	Wilson	Chippendale	Pierre(i)	Spence	Hamilton	Tabua	14
Bamber/p	Tiffin	Goodwin	Kneale	Wilson(q)	Chippendale	Stewart	Spence	Hamilton	Tabua	15
Bamber/c2p	Tiffin(x)	Goodwin	Kneale(F)	Wilson	Chippendale	Pierre	Smith	Yule	Tabua(C)	16
Bamber/p	Tiffin	Sykes	Kneale	Wilson(t)	Burrows	Stewart	Smith	Skurr	Tabua(r)	17
Bamber/3cp	Tiffin	Sykes	Kneale	Wilson(e)	Burows/t	Stewart	Smith	Skurr/2t	Tabua(r)	18
Bamber/2p	Tiffin	Wilson(e)	Kneale	Sykes	Burrows	Stewart	Smith(A/t)	Skurr	Tabua	19
Bamber/4p	Tiffin	Wilson	Kneale	Sykes(g)	Burrows	Stewart	Smith(A)	Skurr	Tabua	20
Bamber/2c	Tiffin(x)	Wilson	Kneale(f/t)	Szabo	Pierre	Stewart	Smith/2t	Hamilton	Tabua(E)	21
Bamber/2c	Tiffin(x)	Sykes(s)	Worsley	Szabo	Pierre(l)	Stewart	Smith(z)	Hamilton	Tabua	22
Bamber/c3p	Tiffin	Wilson	Worsley(u)	Szabo	Fletcher	Stewart	Smith(r)	Hamilton	Tabua	23
Bamber/2cp	Tiffin	Sykes(s)	Worsley	Szabo	Fletcher	Stewart	Kite(j)	Hamilton	Tabua	24
Bamber/2c2p	Tiffin	Sykes	Worsley	Szabo(s)	Fletcher	Stewart(l)	Kite(j)	Hamilton	Tabua	25
M Sales	Tiffin(x)	Szabo	Worsley	Wilson(e)	Fletcher	Stewart	Kite	Hamilton	Tabua	26
Bamber/cp	Tiffin	Ireland(e)	Kneale	Szabo	Fletcher	Stewart	Kite	Hamilton(l/2t)	Smith	A
Bamber/t2c	Tiffin(o)	Goodwin	Kneale	Wilson	Fletcher	Stewart	Kite	Hamilton(f)	Smith(l)	B
Bamber/p	Tiffin(x)	Goodwin	Kneale(f)	Wilson(q)	Pierre	Stewart(l)	Spence(j)	Hamilton	Tabua	C

REPLACEMENTS:

	a- M Withington	b- J Leathley	c - T Bamber	d - J Tiffin	e - A Goodwin
f - S Worlsey	g - R Szabo	h - P Fletcher	i - P Stewart	j - S Smith	k - D Hopton
l - S Chippendale	m - C Johnson	n - C Bibb	o - D Campbell	p - J McNeish	q - N Sykes
r - J Kite	s - S Wilson	t - M Ireland	u - S Kneale	v - G Bone	w - A Sales
x - I Worsley	y - C Hall	z - T Tabua	A - L Hamilton	B - R Goddard	C - I Spence
D - J Barker	E - J Skurr	F - T Wilks			

Fly half Tom Bamber in his first full season with Morley tops the points scorers list for the first time. He also becomes only the second man after Jamie Grayshon to score over 100 points in a league season.

Full back/winger Adam Standeven tops the try scorers list for the second season running and takes his career total to 20. That places him third on the all time list behind Tony Clark and Ben Wade.

His total of 15 is a record in a season for a back.

Lee Child, Chris Hall and Richard Goddard all scored tries on their full league debuts.

MORLEY

LEAGUE STATISTICS
compiled by Stephen McCormack

SEASON	Division	P	W	D	L	F	A	Pts Diff	Lge Pts	Lge Pos	Most Points	Most Tries
89-90	ALN	10	8	0	2	169	115	54	16		78 Jamie Grayson	5 Paul White
90-91	3	12	9	1	2	210	118	92	19		50 Jamie Grayshon	5 Mark Faulkner
91-92	2	12	4	0	8	171	202	-31	8		57 Jamie Grayshon	4 Tony Clark
92-93	2	12	0	1	11	107	374	-267	1		66 Jamie Grayson	2 Tony Clark
93-94	3	18	6	0	12	245	334	-89	12		17 Jamie Grayson	8 Tony Clark
94-95	3	18	9	2	7	277	326	-49	20		166 Jamie Grayson	7 Tony Clark
95-96	3	18	9	2	7	336	328	8	20		206 Jamie Grayson	5 Ben Wade
96-97	3	30	22	0	8	928	572	356	44		195 Jamie Grayson	17 Ben wade
97-98	JN1	26	5	0	21	372	844	-472	10	13	78 Adam Standeven	5 Ian Tulloch Adam Standeven
98-99	JN1	26	7	1	18	468	643	-175	15	13	119 Tom Bamber	15 Adam Standeven

FACT FILE

Founded: 1878
Nickname: Maroons

Colours: Maroon & white quarters/maroon/maroon & white
Change colours: All Blue.

GROUND

Address: Scatcherd Lane, Morley, West Yorkshire, LS27 0JJ

Tel. 0113 253 3487 Ground 0113 252 7598 Office Fax: 0113 253 4144

Capacity: 3,250 Seated: 826 Standing: 2,400

Directions: From West; Leave M62 Jnc 27 Follow A650 towards Wakefield for 1.2miles turn left St Andrews Ave. Ground 0.3 miles on left. From East; Leave M62 Jnc 28 follow A650 towards Bradford for 1.7 miles, turn right into St Andrews Ave. Nearest Railway Station: Morley Low BR

Car Parking: 110 in & around ground

Admission:

Season Standing Adult £50, Family £100
Transfer to stand £1

Matchday Standing Adults £5, Children/OAPs £2
Transfer to stand £1

Club Shop: Yes, Manager Mr. Gill Mitchell 0113 253 3487

Clubhouse: Weekdays 6-11, Sat 12-11, Sun 12-4 & 8-11
Three bars with snacks & bar meals available

Functions: Capacity 200 - contact Sheila Tonge 0113 253 3487

Training Nights: Mondays & Thursdays

PROGRAMME

Size: A5 Pages: 16 Price: £1
Editor: Dennis Elam, 0113 252 4348

ADVERTISING RATES
Mono Page £300 1/2 page £175 1/4 page £100

NEW BRIGHTON F.C.

President	D Morgan	c/o New Brighton FC Reeds Lane, Moreton, Wirral CH46 3RH. 0151 677 2442
Chairman	H K Leyland	c/o New Brighton FC.
Secretary	Mrs B M Bowes	4 Murrayfield Drive, Moreton, Wirral CH46 3RS 0151 678 2654(Tel) 0151 678 3278 (Fax) e-mail: Beryl.Bowes@tesco.net
Fixtures Secretary	B M Murphy	43 Brookfield Gardens, West Kirby, Wirral L484EL 0151 625 8835 (H), 0151 637 0071 (B)
Press Officer	C C Bentley	47 Covertside, West Kirby, Wirral L48 9UH 0151 625 6188 (H)
Director of Coaching	L Connor	

It is, perhaps, reflective of New Brighton's aspirations, that third place in our first season of National Rugby is seen by players and supporters alike as a disappointment. Having won twenty of the 266 League games, including at least one victory over each of our opposition and only narrowly losing the other six, we know that the top spot and promotion were well within our grasp.
Three consecutive defeats just after Christmas, all to sides we had previously beaten, effectively put an end to our ambitions. These defeats included Nuneaton and Sandal, clubs that we had beaten 41-10 and 52-12 respectively, just a few weeks earlier. After those reverses, nine victories from our last ten matches were too little, too late, to interfere with Preston's march to the title - congratulations to them from Reeds Lane.
We lost in the third round of the Tetley's Cup, 23-34 at Waterloo, in a local derby. Although conceding two tries in as many minutes, we then matched them score for score, the result being in doubt until the final few minutes. The Cheshire Cup was retained with little trouble by beating Chester 47-18, in the Final.
Twelve of the squad took Cheshire, and one, Lancashire to the semi-finals of the Tetley's County Championship, but unfortunately there was to be no repeat of Cheshire's Championship victory of the previous season.
After seven years of captaining the club, Kevin Brookman has passed the reins over to Geoff Jones for the coming season. Along with our coach, Lol Connor, Kevin has overseen our rise from North West One and the club owe him a great debt of gratitude for all his efforts.
Finally, we welcome into our ranks Bedford Athletic, our old friends, Liverpool St. Helens and Morley and, most deservedly, Doncaster, whom we pipped on points difference 12 months ago.

NEW BRIGHTON F.C. 98-99 SQUAD - (L-R) **Back Row:** Karl Davies, Phil Gazzola, Nick Allott, Mark Donnington, Shaun Gallagher, Lee Hodgers, Jon Shudall. **Middle**: Frank Duff, Steve Dakin, Heather Cameron, Sean Kay, Jez Lamb, Steve Dorrington, Tom Mapp, Marcus Coast, Matt Bennett, Tony Atherton, Neville Waters. **Front**: Paul Brett, Ian Kennedy, Murray King, Joe Pinnington, Kevin Brookman, Geoff Jones, Andy Whalley, Simon Wright, Lawrie Connor

NEW BRIGHTON

Match No.	Date	H/A	Comp.	Opponents	Result & Score	Att.	15	14	13	12	11
1	05.09	H	J2N	Lichfield	W 45-7		Johnson/t	Whalley/3t	Kay	Coast/t(m)	Hancock
2	12.09	A	J2N	Kendal	W 17-12		Kennedy/t	Whalley	Kay	Coast/t	Hancock(a/t)
3	26.09	H	J2N	Sedgley Park	W 29-13		Kennedy/t	Whalley	Kay	Coast(m)	Johnson
4	03.10	A	J2N	Sheffield	W 18-13		Johnson	Kay	Ball	Coast	Whalley
5	10.10	H	J2N	Winnington P*	W 51-0		Johnson	Whalley	Ball	Coast	Kay/t
6	24.10	A	J2N	Aspatria	L 0-10		Kennedy	Whalley	Ball(c)	Coast	Johnson
7	31.10	H	J2N	Walsall	W 33-0		Johnson	Whalley	Ball	Coast	Kay(u)
8	07.11	A	J2N	Stourbridge	L 3-6		Mapp	Whalley	Ball	Coast	Johnson
9	21.11	H	J2N	Nuneaton	W 41-10		Mapp	Kay/t	Ball	Coast(u)	Johnson
10	28.11	H	J2N	Sandal	W 52-12		Mapp	Whalley	Ball	Coast/t	Kay/2t
11	05.12	A	J2N	Preston	W 15-9		Mapp	Whalley	Ball	Coast	Kay
12	12.12	H	J2N	Hinckley	W 54-0		Mapp	Whalley/t	Ball/3t	Coast/t	Kay/t(u)
13	19.12	A	J2N	Whitchurch	W 26-19		Mapp	Whalley	Brett/2t	Coast	Johnson
14	28.12	H	J2N	Preston	L 13-15		Mapp	Brett	King/c2p	Coast	Kay
15	02.01	A	J2N	Sandal	L 12-19		Mapp	Whalley	Brett	Coast/t	Kay
16	09.01	A	J2N	Nuneaton	L 3-6		Mapp(a)	Whalley	Brett	Coast	Kay
17	16.01	H	J2N	Stourbridge	W 16-15		Johnson	Whalley	Kay	Coast	Harman
18	23.01	A	J2N	Walsall	W 15-3		Mapp/t	Whalley	Kay	Coast(a)	Brett/t
19	30.01	H	J2N	Aspatria	W 12-3		Mapp	Brett	Kay	Coast	Whalley
20	06.02	A	J2N	Winnington P	W 26-14		Mapp/t	Brett/t	Kay	Coast	Harman/t
21	13.02	H	J2N	Sheffield	W 29-15		Mapp(n)	Whalley/t	Kay/t	Coast	Brett
22	27.02	A	J2N	Sedgley Park*	W 28-20		Kenndey	Harman	Brett/2c3p	Coast	Kay
23	13.03	H	J2N	Kendal	L 31-35		Mapp	Whalley	King/4cp	Coast	Brett(c)
24	27.03	A	J2N	Lichfield	W 61-24		Mapp	Whalley/t	King/t5c(c/t)	Coast/2t	Brett/3c
25	03.04	H	J2N	Whitchurch	W 44-27		Mapp/2t	Kay	Brett/t3cp	Coast/t	Whalley
26	17.04	A	J2N	Hinckley	W 29-22		Mapp/2t(C)	Whalley	Kay	Brett/t	Harman
A	19.09	H	TB1	Lichfield	W 33-8		Kennedy	Johnson(b/t)	Kay	Coast	Hancock
B	17.10	H	TB2	Nuneaton	W 25-10		Johnson	Whalley	Ball	Coast	Kay
C	14.11	A	TB3	Waterloo	L 23-34		Kennedy	Whalley(c/t)	Ball	Coast	Johnson

* after opponents name indicates a penalty try
Brackets after a player's name indicates he was replaced. eg (a) means he was replaced by replacement code "a" and so on.
/ after a player or replacement name is followed by any scores he made - eg /t, /c, /p, /dg or any combination of these

1998-99 HIGHLIGHTS

Ever Presents: None

Most appearances

25	Simon Wright, Mark Dorrington, Steve Dorrington (1), Marcus Coast
24	Nick Allott
23	Stuart Beeley, Geoff Jones (2), Kevin Brookman (2)

Players used: 31 plus 10 as replacement only.

Most Points in a season:

Pts	Player	T	C	P	DG
159	M King	1	32	30	-
151	I Kennedy	17	18	10	-
58	P Brett	6	8	4	-
40	S Kay	8	-	-	-
35	G Jones	7	-	-	-
35	M Coast	7	-	-	-

MATCH FACTS

10	9	1	2	3	4	5	6	7	8	
King/5c	Wright/t(l)	M Dorrington(q)	K Davies(i)	S Dorrington	Gallagher(j)	Allott	Jones(k)	Brookman/t	Beeley	1
King/c	Wright	M Dorrington	K Davies(i)	S Dorrington	Turley(p)	Gallagher	Jones	Brookman	Beeley	2
King/3p	Wright	M Dorrington	K Davies	S Dorrington	Gallagher/t(p)	Allott/t	Jones(k)	Brookman/t	Beeley	3
Kennedy/6p	Wright	M Dorrington	Grigg	S Dorrington	Gallagher	Allott(v)	Jones(w)	Brookman	Beeley	4
Kennedy2t5c2p	Wright(r)	M Dorrington/t	Grigg(e)	S Dorrington(s)	Gallagher/t	Allott(p)	Jones/t	Brookman(r)	Beeley	5
King	Wright	M Dorrington	K Davies	S Dorrington	Allott	Fox(p)	Jones(k)	Brookman	Hodges	6
King/2c3p	Wright	M Dorrington(s)	Grigg	S Dorrington	Allott(v/t)(e)	Bentley	Jones/2t	Brookman	Beeley/t(t)	7
King/p	Wright	M Dorrington	Grigg(e)	S Dorrington(o)	Allott	Bentley	Jones(w)	Brookman	Beeley	8
Kennedy/3t3c	Wright/t(r)	M Dorrington	Grigg(y)	S Dorrington(o)	Allott	Bentley	Jones/t	Shuddall/t	Beeley	9
Kennedy3t7cp	Wright(r)	M Dorrington	Grigg(z)	S Dorrington(s)	Gallagher	Allott	Lamb	Brookman	Beeley/t(g)	10
Kennedy/tcp	Wright	M Dorrington	Grigg	S Dorrington	Gallagher	Allott	Hodges(t)	Brookman	Beeley/t	11
Kennedy/t2c(d/5c	Carney	M Dorrington	D Davies(A)	S Dorrington(s)	Gallagher	Allott(p)	Jones/t	Shuddall	Hodges(h)	12
King/2c4p	Wright	M Dorrongton	Grigg	S Dorrington(s)	Allott(p)	Gallagher	Jones	Brookman	Beeley	13
Kennedy	Wright	M Dorrington	D Davies	S Dorrington	Allott	Gallagher	Jones	Brookman/t	Beeley	14
King/c(C)	Wright/t	M Dorrington	D Davies(y)	S Dorrington(s)	Bentley	Gallagher	Jones(t)	Brookman	Beeley	15
King/p	Wright(B)	M Dorrington	Grigg	Gazzola(f)	Allott	Gallagher	Jones(k)	Brookman	Beeley	16
King/c3p	Wright/t	M Dorrington	Grigg	S Dorrington	Allott(j)	Gallagher	Jones(k)	Brookman	Beeley	17
King	Wright(B)	M Dorrington/t	Grigg	S Dorrington(o)	Allott	Gallagher(j)	Jones(k)	Brookman	Beeley	18
King/4p	Wright	M Dorrington(o)	Grigg	S Dorrington	Allott	Gallagher	Jones	Brookman	Beeley	19
King/c3p	Wright	M Dorrington(o)	Grigg	S Dorrington	Allott	Gallagher	Jones	Brookman	Beeley	20
King/c4p	Wright(B)	M Dorrington	Grigg(y)	S Dorrington(o)	Allott	Gallagher(j)	Jones(k)	Brookman	Beeley/t	21
O'Connor	Wright/t(d)	M Dorrington(s)	Grigg(y)	S Dorrington	Allott	Turley(E)	Jones(t)	Brokman/t	Beeley(D)	22
Kennedy/t	Wright/t	Gazzola	K Davies	S Dorrington	Allott	Gallagher(j)	Jones/t	Brookman/t	Beeley(w)	23
Kennedy/3t	Wright	M Dorrington	K Davies(F)	S Dorrington(z)	Allott	Turley(D)	Lamb	Shuddall/t	Jones(h)	24
Kennedy/t	Wright(B)	M Dorrington	K Davies(z/t)	S Dorrington	Allott	Gallagher(j)	Shuddall(g)	Brookman	Beeley/t	25
King/3cp	Wright	M Dorrington	K Davies	S Dorrington(i)	Allott	Gallagher(E)	Jones/t	Brookman	Beeley	26
King/t4c	Wright	M Dorrington	K Davies	S Dorrington(o)	Allott(v)	Gallagher	Jones/t	Brookman	Beeley/t(t)	A
Kennedy/tc3p	Wright	M Dorrington	K Davies	S Dorrington	Allott	Gallagher(v)	Jones/t(w)	Brookman	Beeley	B
King/c2p(x)	Wright	M Dorrington	K Davies(i)	S Dorrington	Allott	Bentley	Jones/t	Brookman/t	Beeley(w)	C

REPLACEMENTS:

	a- S Johnson	b- A Whalley	c - S Kay	d - M ing	e - K Davies
f - S Dorrington	g - G Jones	h - K Brookman	i - J Grigg	j - C Turley	k - J Lamb
l - A Thompson	m - S O'Hare	n - I Kennedy	o - L McCourt	p - C Bentley	q - S Mooney
r - P Carney	s - P Gazzola	t - J Shuddall	u - R Harman	v - S Fox	w - L Hodges
x - T Mapp	y - A Probert	z - D Davies			
A - I Probert	B - M Bennett	C - S O'Connor	D - L Connor	E - M Hudson	

Murray King finished eight points ahead of Ian Kennedy as New Brighton's leading points scorer. King ended on 159 to Kennedy's 151.

Kennedy though did have the consolation of finishing as the clubs leading try scorer with a highly impressive 17. That put him in third place in the division's leading try scorers.

Lost just once at home, to Preston, in their first season at this level and finished a highly creditable third.

They were the only side in the division to win at Champions Preston.

Struggled to score tries away from home with just 31, the 7th best record in the division.

NEW BRIGHTON

LEAGUE STATISTICS

compiled by Stephen McCormack

SEASON	Division	P	W	D	L	F	A	Pts Diff	Lge Pts	Lge Pos	Most Points	Most Tries
89-90	North 2	10	0	1	9	93	187	-94	1	11		
90-91	North 2	10	2	0	8	78	187	-109	4	11r		
91-92												
92-93	NW 1	12	9	1	2	243	103	140	19	2		
93-94	NW 1	12	10	1	1	310	87	223	21	1p		
94-95	North 2	12	9	0	3	376	140	236	18	3		
95-96	North 2	12	10	1	1	232	105	127	21	1p		
96-97	North 1	21	14	1	6	484	381	103	29	3		
97-98	North 1	22	17	2	3	599	293	306	36	1p	243 Alex Guest	15 Ian Kennedy
98-99	N2N	26	20	0	6	703	329	374	40	3	159 Murray King	17 Ian Kennedy

FACT FILE

Founded: 1875

Colours: Light blue, navy blue & white quarters/black/black
Change colours:

GROUND
Address: Reeds Lane, Moreton, Wirral CH46 3RH
Tel/Fax: 0151 677 2442 e-mail: nbrugby@tesco.net
Capacity: 5,400 Seated: 400 Standing: 5,000

Directions: M53 Junc 1 direction for New Brighton, 1st turning left (sign posted club).
Approx 3/4 mile turn left into Reeds Lane
Nearest Railway Station: Leasome

Car Parking: 400 at ground

Admission: Season tickets - Adult £45.
Matchday - Adults £4. Children/OAPs £2

Clubhouse: Open 7 days,
Functions: Capacity 300. Contact C Cattrall c/o Club

Club Shop: Yes

Training Nights: Tuesday & Thursday. Women: Wednesday

PROGRAMME
Size: A5 Price: £1
Pages: 32 Editor: G C Stone

ADVERTISING RATES
Colour - Full page £300
Mono - Full page £200, Half £120, Qtr £70

NUNEATON R.F.C.

Chairman	Andy Ambrose	Unit 7 Tuttle Hill Ind Park, Nuneaton, Warks 01203 384012 (B), 01203 344010 (Fax)
Secretary	Maggie Mander	7 Farriers Way, Crowhill, Nuneaton, Warks, CV11 6UZ 01203 381803 (H), 0171 462 4315 (B), 0171 636 6915 (Fax)
Treasurer	TBA	
Fixtures Secretary	John Davies	3 Saints Way, Nuneaton, Warks, CV10 0UU 01203 370011 (H), 01203 344800 (B)
Club Coach	Harry Roberts	The Dog & Gun, Church Steet, Thurlaston, Leics. LE9 7TA 07971 284556 (Mobile)
President	Keith Howells	01203 348286/381803
Asst Fixture Sec	Dave Smith	01203 328835.
1st XV Manager	Dave Warden	01203 365777/328935

Finishing joint fifth in the league almost satisfied The Nuns' ambitions, but had it not been for injury problems affecting the latter games of the season, a higher position could have been obtained. Hopes are high for 1999/2000 to achieve a greater goal.

Harry Roberts was recruited at the beginning of December, 1998 when Darren Grewcock, who had been club coach for two seasons, left to pursue a career with Coventry FC. Harry brought with him extensive experience from his international playing career and this experience and skills are being instilled into players at all levels within the club.

Jez Harris joined the side at the start of the season and, whilst he is no longer keen to take to the field on a regular basis, he will be remaining to assist with coaching of the backs next season. Although Jez played only half a season, he still managed to come second as Jewson Kicker of the Year and actually won the Kicker of the Month three times during the season.

Ricky Hyslop joined part way through the season and performed excellently in the centre until hit by injury. Steve Carter had an amazing season and this was reflected by him being nominated Player of the Year at the annual Dinner. Marc Thomas has been appointed club captain for the new season and will be assisted by Steve Carter.

The Nuns have a very strong mini and junior section and this year several ex M&J players, who progressed to the colts, were joining the senior squad for training. Some of the colts, once old enough to be registered, actually made their first team debuts, including Stu Pierman, Jody Peacock, Ryan Banks. It is hoped to encourage these younger players next season by The Nuns partaking in the proposed MCA second XV and colts leagues. Simon Reid is welcomed back to the club as second XV captain following an extended spell of working overseas.

As well as nurturing the younger players, recruitment of new blood is in hand to replace Ricky Hyslop, who has m moved to Coventry, and Aidie Carlyle, who has taken a position as player coach with South Leicestershire, as well as to strengthen the current squad who intend staying on.

MAGGIE MANDER

Nuneaton 98-99 - Back Row: Lesley Ross (Physio), Dave Warden (1st XV Manager), George Mumford (Vice Chairman), Richard Gee, Glen Southwell, Stuart Gibson, Ewan McKay, Simon Jones, Aidie Carlyle, Al Roberts, Tej Kalirai, Craig Court, Steve Carter, Lee Clarke, Eddie Simkiss, Keith Howells (President), Andy Ambrose (Chairman), Maggie Mander (Secretary). Front: Steve Marshall, Paul Mitchell, Steve Wills, Jez Harris, Paul Sharp (Club Captain), Steve Doig (TNT - main sponsors), Darren Grewcock, Stuart Barden, Simon Reid, Marc Thomas, Ben Powis.

NUNEATON

Match No.	Date	H/A	Comp.	Opponents	Result & Score	Att.	15	14	13	12	11
1	05.09	H	J2N	Kendal	W 25-22		Reid(n)	Clark	Wills/t	Gee	Barden
2	12.09	A	J2N	Sedgley Park	D 22-22		Reid	Clark	Wills	Gee	Barden
3	26.09	H	J2N	Sheffield	L 14-39		Thomas	Clark	Wills(v)	Gee	Barden
4	03.10	A	J2N	Winnington P	W 28-7		Blackmore	Clark(c)	S Marshall(v)	Gee	Littlehales
5	10.10	H	J2N	Aspatria	W 42-20		Gee	Littlehales/t	Wills/t	Thomas/t	Barden
6	31.10	H	J2N	Stourbridge	L 13-23		Gee	Barden(t)	Wills	Thomas	Powis
7	07.11	H	J2N	Sandal	W 30-17		Gee	Littlehales(a)	Wills	Thomas/tdg	Powis
8	14.11	A	J2N	Walsall	W 20-10		Gee	A Marshall	Barden	Thomas/t	Powis
9	21.11	A	J2N	Sedgley Park	L 10-41		Gee	A Marshall	Barden	Thomas	Powis(t)
10	28.11	H	J2N	Preston	L 8-31		Gee(t)	Clark	Barden	Thomas	Powis
11	05.12	A	J2N	Hinckley	D 24-24		Thomas	Clark	Barden	Gee	Littlehales
12	12.12	H	J2N	Whitchurch*	W 24-15		Wills/2c(s)	Littlehales	Barden	Hyslop	Powis
13	19.12	A	J2N	Lichfield	W 25-7		Thomas	Littlehales	Hyslop	Gee/t	Powis(c)
14	28.12	H	J2N	Hinckley*	W 61-13		Thomas	Barden/2t	Gee/3t	Hyslop/t(t)	Blackmore
15	02.01	A	J2N	Preston	L 16-30		Thomas	Blackmore	Barden	Gee	Littlehales(p)
16	09.01	H	J2N	New Brighton	W 6-3		Thomas	S Marshall	Hyslop	Gee	Barden
17	16.01	A	J2N	Sandal	L 7-17		Thomas	Barden	Gee	Hyslop	S Marshall
18	23.01	A	J2N	Stourbridge	L 7-36		Thomas(b)	Littlehales	Gee	Hyslop	S Marshall
19	30.01	H	J2N	Walsall	W 30-15		Thomas/2c2p	A Marshall	Mitchell	Hyslop/t	S Marshall
20	06.02	A	J2N	Aspatria	W 23-17		Thomas/c2p	A Marshall	Mitchell	Hyslop/t	S Marshall/t
21	13.02	H	J2N	Winnington P	W 57-5		Thomas/2t6c	A Marshall	Mitchell(E)	Hyslop/2t	S Marshall
22	27.02	A	J2N	Sheffield	W 6-3		Thomas/2p	A Marshall	Baber	Hyslop	S Marshall
23	13.03	H	J2N	Sedgley Park	W 40-13		Thomas/5c	A Marshall	Baber	Barden(B)	S Marshall/t
24	27.03	A	J2N	Kendal	L 20-26		Thomas/2c2p	Barden	Mitchell	Hyslop/t	S Marshall/t
25	13.04	H	J2N	Lichfield	L 35-42		Thomas/c2p(p)	Barden	Baber/t	Hyslop/t	Blackmore
26	17.04	A	J2N	Whitchurch	L 3-35		Blackmore(d)	Barden	Mitchell(v)	Baber	S Marshall
A	19.09	A	TB1	Hinckley	W 24-20		Thomas/t2c	Clark	Wills/t	Barden	A Marshall
B	17.10	A	TB2	New Brighton	L 10-21		Gee	Littlehales	Wills/t(B)	Thomas	Powis/t

* after opponents name indicates a penalty try
Brackets after a player's name indicates he was replaced. eg (a) means he was replaced by replacement code "a" and so on.
/ after a player or replacement name is followed by any scores he made - eg /t, /c, /p, /dg or any combination of these

1998-99 HIGHLIGHTS

Ever Present:

Richard Gee

25	Richard Moore
24	Glen Southwell (1)
23	Craig Court (1)
22	Stuart Gibson (3)

Players used: 37 plus four as a replacement only

Most Points in a season:

Pts	Player	T	C	P	DG
135	J Harris	1	33	22	-
92	M Thomas	5	17	10	1
65	S Carter	13	-	-	-
35	R Hyslop	7	-	-	-
35	R Gee	6	1	1	-

MATCH FACTS

10	9	1	2	3	4	5	6	7	8	
Harris/2c2p	Grewcock/t(l)	Sharp(o)	Gibson	Court	Carlyle/t	Roberts	Kalarai(m)	Southwell	Carter	1
Harris/2cp	Grewcock	Moore	Gibson	Court	Sharp(e/t)	Roberts/t	Kalarai	Southwell	Carter/t	2
Harris/2c	Grewcock(r)	Moore	Mackay	Court(f)	Carlyle(e)	Roberts/t	Kalarai/t	Taylor	Carter	3
Harris/4c	Pittam(l)	Moore/t	Gibson	Court	Carlyle	Sharp(i)	Kalarai/t(u)	Southwell/t	Carter/t	4
Harris/4c3p	Pittam	Moore	Gibson	Court(h/t)	Sharp(w)	Roberts	Kalarai/t(u)	Southwell	Carter	5
Harris/c2p	Miles(r)	Moore	Gibson/t	Court	Carlyle(e)	Roberts	Simkiss(j)	Southwell	Carter	6
Harris/3c2p	Miles(l)	Moore/t	Gibson	Court	Sharp(h)	Roberts	Kalarai/t(k)	Southwell	Simkiss	7
Harris/cp	Miles(r)	Moore	Gibson	Court/t	Carlyle(e)	Roberts(z)	Kalarai	Southwell/t	Carter	8
Harris/cp	Mitchell	Moore	Gibson(x)	Court	Sharp(i)	Simkiss	Kalarai(h/t)	Southwell	Carter	9
Harris/p	Miles(l)	Moore	Gibson	Court	Carlyle	Roberts(e)	Simkiss	Southwell	Carter/t	10
Harris/3p	Mitchell(y)	Moore	Owen(f)	Court	Sharp(h)	Roberts	Kalarai/t(G)	Simkiss	Carter/2t	11
Gee	Miles(C)	Moore	Gibson/t	Bowell	Sharp	Roberts	Simkiss	Southwell	Carter/2t	12
Harris/tcp(s)	Miles(C)	Moore/t(A)	Gibson(x)	Court/t	Sharp(h)	Roberts	Simkiss	Southwell	Carter	13
Harris/8c	Miles/t(r)	Moore	Gibson(D)	Court(A)	Carlyle	Roberts(e)	Simkiss	Southwell/t	Carter	14
Harris/c3p	Miles(C)	Moore	Gibson	Court(D)	Carlyle	Roberts	Simkiss	Southwell	Carter/t	15
Harris/2p	Leedham	Moore	Gibson(D)	Court	Sharp	Carlyle	Simkiss	Southwell	Carter	16
Harris/c	Leedham(y)	Moore	Southwell(f)	Court	Sharp	Roberts(h)	Simkiss	Southwell	Carter/t	17
Harris/c	Miles(l)	Moore	Gibson(D)	Court(A)	Sharp	Roberts(h)	Kalarai/t	Southwell	Simkiss	18
Gee	Miles(C)	Moore/t	Gibson	Pearman/t	Carlyle	Roberts/t	Kalarai(k)	Southwell	Simkiss	19
Gee	Miles	Moore	Gibson(D)	Court(A)	Carlyle	Roberts	Simkiss/t(j)	Southwell	Carter	20
Gee/2t	Miles(r)	Moore	Southwell	Pearman(g/t)	Carlyle	Roberts(z)	Kalarai	Southwell	Carter/2t	21
Gee	Mitchell(y)	Moore	Gibson	Court	Carlyle	Roberts	Simkiss(j)	Southwell	Carter	22
Gee	Mitchell(y)	Moore	Gibson(D)	Court/t	Carlyle	Roberts/t	Kalarai(z)	Southwell/t	Carter/2t	23
Gee	Miles	Moore	Gibson(D)	Court	Carlyle(z)(A)	Roberts	Kalarai	Southwell	Mitchell	24
Gee/c	Mitchell(y)	Moore	Gibson(D)	Court/2t(A)	Carlyle	Roberts	Kalarai	Southwell	Mitchell(u/t	25
Gee/p	Miles	Moore	Gibson(D)	Court(A)	Sharp	Carlyle	Kalarai	Southwell	Banks	26
Gee	Mitchell	Moore	Gibson(q)	Court	Carlyle(e)	Roberts	Kalarai(z/t)	Southwell	Carter/2t	A
Harris	Pittam(y)	Moore	Gibson	Court	Carlyle(e)	Roberts	Kalarai(z)	Southwell	Carter	B

REPLACEMENTS:

	a- L Clark	b- S Wills	c - S Barden	d - J Harris	e - P Sharp
f - S Gibson	g - C Court	h - A Carlyle	i - A Roberts	j - T Kalarai	k - S Carter
l - P Mitchell	m - S Jones	n - B Powis	o - D Bowell	p - S Marshall	q - E Mackay
r - S Pittam	s - S Blackmore	t - J Littlehales	u - A Taylor	v - A Marshall	w - P Murphy
x - M Owen	y - P Miles	z - E Simkiss	A - S Pearman	B - D Carter	C - M Leedham
D - C Southwell	E - A Babar	F - R Atchison	G - G Southwell		

Jez Harris topped the points scorers list as he had previously done in league rugby for both Leicester and Coventry. He did though fail to land one of his landmark drop goals. He ended the season as a regular on the bench after starting 17 of the first 18 matches.

No 8 Steve Carter, previously with Rugby Lions, was the leading try scorer with 13 from 20 starts. This saw him average better than a try every other match.

Leading try scorer in the backs was centre Ricky Hyslop who joined Nuneaton half way through the season from nearby Coventry.

They finished a creditable fifth but still lost too many matches they should have won. With Harry Roberts at the helme they are expecting big things for the coming season.

NUNEATON

LEAGUE STATISTICS
compiled by Stephen McCormack

SEASON	Division	P	W	D	L	F	A	Pts Diff	Lge Pts	Lge Pos		Coach		Captain
89-90	3	11	4	0	7	127	196	-69	8	10	66	Russell Hensley	4	Michael Calverley
90-91	3	12	5	0	7	180	200	-20	10	7	39	Simon Reid	3	Bill Buffey/P Clayton
91-92	3	12	1	2	9	153	237	-84	4	12r	80	Vasile Ion	2	Colin Leake
92-93	D4N	12	2	0	10	138	269	-131	4	12				
93-94	D5N	12	4	1	7	122	200	-78	9	11				
94-95	D5N	12	4	0	8	129	161	-32	8	11				
95-96	D5N	12	4	1	7	176	329	-151	9	10	92	Warwick Masser	2	Darren Barry & Andy Brown, Paul Jones
96-97	D4N	26	8	1	7	457	667	-210	17	12	68	Marc Thomas & Gavin Henderson	9	Clive Bent
97-98	N2N	26	13	0	13	453	570	-117	26	7	141	Marc Thomas	7	Craig Court
98-99	N2N	26	14	2	10	596	533	66	30	5	135	Jez Harris	13	Steve Carter

FACT FILE

Founded: 1879
Nickname: Nuns

Colours: Red with white & black
Change colours: Green, white, black

GROUND

Address: Liberty Way, Attleborough Fields, Nuneaton, Warks. CV11 6RR.
Tel: 01203 383206
Capacity (all standing) No limit

Directions: From M6 follow A444 to Nuneaton, follow ring road towards M69/A5. Ring road enters Eastborough Way, club just off mini round about
Nearest Railway Station: Nuneaton, 5 mins by taxi

Car Parking: Ample parking within the ground

Admission: Matchday - Adults £4, OAPs £2, Children £1

Clubhouse: Normal licensing hours
Functions: Capacity up to 100 (seated).
Bookings thro' Club Secretary

Club Shop: Open Sat 12.30-2.30, Sun 10.30-12.00 & as required.
Contact Club Secretary.

Training Nights: Tuesday and Thursday.

PROGRAMME

Size: A5 Price: £1 Pages: 28 + cover
Editor: Andy Ambrose 01203 384012or
Maggie Mander, Club Sec.
ADVERTISING
Contact Andy Ambose, club chairman

Photograph courtesy of Coventry Evening Telegraph

SANDAL R.U.F.C.

President	Christopher Taylor	Woodside Farm, Woolley Edge, Wakefield 01924 830448 (H).
Chairman	C R Hoyland	1 Moorhouse Lane, Haigh, nr Barnsley S74 4DD 01924 830572 (H)
Director of Rugby	Steve Ackroyd	c/o Sandal RUFC Home Tel: 01924 256004
Dir. of Youth Rugby	Steve Smith	256 Bradford Rd., Wakefield WF1 2BA 01924 363918 (H)
Press Officer	Philip Harrison	46 Brandhill Drive, Crofton, Wakefield WF4 1PF 01924 863457
Secretary	Leonard Bedford	14 Lindale Mount, Alverthorpe, Wakefield, W. Yorks.WF2 0BH 01924 782263 (H)
Fixtures Secretary	Jack Adams	01924 373129
Match Sec.& Referees	Malcolm Pashley	01924 255020

With the major £1 million redevelopment of the clubhouse premises and facilities occupying a great deal of the club's energies off the field, this was always planned as a season of consolidation on the field, and so it proved.

The club started the season with two new coaches in charge, Tony Martin and Nick Powell, and their commitment to an open, flowing, entertaining style of attacking play was reflected in the number of points scored during the season - 873 - a club record of 25 years standing.

In the Jewson National League Division Two North, the club finished in seventh place, one place higher than the previous season. Thirteen games were won and thirteen lost, and 697 points were scored, nearly 50 per cent more than the previous season. However, a record number of points, 611, were conceded, and Sandal's defence will have to be tightened up considerably if a higher place in the League is ever going to be achieved.

In the Tetley's Bitter Cup Sandal progressed to the third round for the third season in a row, eventually going down to a full strength Bristol, but making many new friends on the day with a brave performance. Sandal reached the Final of the Yorkshire Cup for the second time in three years, losing by a late drop goal to winners Doncaster, whom Sandal meet next season in the League.

Skipper and play-maker Ian Shuttleworth was again leading points scorer with 314, and Ian also headed the try scoring list with sixteen touch downs. The ever-consistent Mark Wolff, with fifteen tries, was second in the table, and winger Andy Hodkinson third with thirteen. Leading forward try scorer was flanker Alex Ledger with nine. A total of 116 tries were scored in the season, the best for many years.

Sandal Saracens, unable to field anything like a settled side, enjoyed mixed fortunes in the North Merit Table, whilst Sandal Veterans, with a large and enthusiastic squad of players to select from, are amongst the strongest and best organised in the north. Sandal Ladies enjoyed their first competitive season in the RFUW Ladies Merit Table and look forward to even better things as they continue to flourish.

Sandal Mini and Juniors were as strong and as active as ever at every age-group, with two sides in particular, the U11s and U12s, enjoying exceptional seasons, both winning the Yorkshire Cup at their respective age groups as well as chalking up successes at both the London Saracens and Tynedale Festivals.

Sandal RUFC before their Yorkshire Cup quarter final v Sheffield, 8th May 1999.

Standing: Tony Martin (coach), Andy Hodkinson, Paul Philpott, Dan Tonkinson, Glynn Thompson, Jon-Lee Lockwood, Glenn Barker, Jason Mortimer, Mark Harrison, Adam Pogson, Ian Clappison, Richard Wade, Nick Powell (coach). **Seated:** Neil Barrett, Henry Sharp, Gary Swift, Andrew Metcalfe, Gary Lig, Ian Shuttleworth (captain), Ben Wheeler, Andrew Newton, Nigel Hoyle, Kristian Shuttleworth.

Photo courtesy of John Clifton Sports Agency, Wakefield.

SANDAL

Match No.	Date	H/A	Comp.	Opponents	Result & Score	Att.	15	14	13	12	11
1	05.09	H	J2N	Hinckley*	W 21-6		M Wolff/t	Davis	A Wolff	Metcalfe	Munn(k)
2	12.09	A	J2N	Aspatria	L 15-18		M Wolff	Davis(k)	A Wolff	Metcalfe	Munn
3	26.09	H	J2N	Whitchurch	W45-20		M Wolff/t	A Wolff/2t	Davis/t	Metcalfe	Hodkinson
4	03.10	A	J2N	Walsall	W39-32		M Wolff	A Wolff/t	Davis	Metcalfe	Hodkinson
5	10.10	H	J2N	Lichfield	W41-24		M Wolff(n)	A Wolff(a)	Davis	Metcalfe/t	Hodkinson
6	24.10	A	J2N	Stourbridge	L 3-19		Wheeler	Munn	Davis	Metcalfe	Hodkinson
7	31.10	H	J2N	Kendal	L 8-15		Wheeler(u)	Munn	Davis	Metcalfe	Hodkinson/t
8	07.11	A	J2N	Nuneaton	L 17-30		M Wolff/t	A Wolff(u)	Davis	Metcalfe	Munn
9	21.11	H	J2N	Sedgley Park	L 27-39		M Wolff/2t	Munn(t)	A Wolff/t	Metcalfe	Sharp
10	28.11	A	J2N	New Brighton	L 12-52		M Wolff(t)	Sharp	Davis/t	Metcalfe	A Wolff
11	05.12	H	J2N	Sheffield	W 38-5		M Wolff	A Wolff/t(k)	Davis	Metcalfe	Sharp/t
12	12.12	A	J2N	Preston	L 26-39		M Wolff	A Wolff	Davis	Metcalfe	Sharp
13	19.12	H	J2N	Winnington P*	W47-17		M Wolff/t	A Wolff	Lockwood/t	Metcalfe/dg	Sharp/2t(a)
14	28.12	A	J2N	Sheffield	L 9-31		M Wolff	A Wolff	Metcalfe	Lockwood	Sharp
15	02.01	H	J2N	New Brighton	W19-12		M Wolff/t	A Wolff/t	Lockwood	Metcalfe	Sharp
16	16.01	H	J2N	Nuneaton	W 17-7		M Wolff	Hodkinson	A Wolff(t)	Metcalfe/t	Sharp(z)
17	23.01	A	J2N	Kendal	L 3-25		M Wolff	A Wolff(u)	Lockwood	Metcalfe(z)	Hodkinson
18	30.01	H	J2N	Stourbridge	L 17-45		M Wolff/t	A Wolff/t	Lockwood/t	Metcalfe	Hodkinson
19	06.02	A	J2N	Lichfield*	W73-17		M Wolff/3t	A Wolff	Lockwood(u)	Metcalfe	Hodkinson/t
20	13.02	H	J2N	Walsall	W 43-5		M Wolff/t	Tomkinson/t	Lockwood(u)	Metcalfe/t	Hodkinson/t
21	27.02	A	J2N	Whitchurch	W29-13		M Wolff/t	Tomkinson/t	Lockwood	Metcalfe	Hodkinson
22	13.03	H	J2N	Aspatria	W 51-7		M Wolff/t	Tomkinson	Lockwood	Metcalfe	Hodkinson
23	20.03	A	J2N	Sedgley Park	L 15-49		M Wolff	Barrett	Tomkinson	Lockwood	Hodkinson/t
24	27.03	A	J2N	Hinckley	L 18-42		M Wolff	Sharp/t	A Wolff	Metcalfe	Hodkinson
25	03.04	A	J2N	Winnington P	W 53-6		K Shuttleworth/t	Tomkinson(E)	Lockwood	Metcalfe/t	Hodkinson/3t
26	17.04	H	J2N	Preston	L 11-36		M Wolff(E)	Tomkinson(x)	Lockwood	Metcalfe	Hodkinson/t
A	19.09	A	TB1	Malvern	W51-14		M Wolff	A Wolff	Davis	Metcalfe	Hodkinson/3t
B	17.10	H	TB2	Doncaster	W 6-3		M Wolff	A Wolff	Davis	Metcalfe	Hodkinson
C	14.11	A	TB3	Bristol	L 0-55		M Wolff	A Wolff	Davis	Metcalfe	Hodkinson

* after opponents name indicates a penalty try
Brackets after a player's name indicates he was replaced. eg (a) means he was replaced by replacement code "a" and so on.
/ after a player or replacement name is followed by any scores he made - eg /t, /c, /p, /dg or any combination of these

1998-99 HIGHLIGHTS

Ever Presents: None

Most appearances

25	Andrew Metcalfe & Nigel Hoyle
24	Jason Mortimer (1)
23	Steve Dykes, Mark Wolff
22	Ian SHuttleworth, Adam Pogson

Players used: 32 plus eight as replacement only

Most Points in a season:

Pts	Player	T	C	P	DG
246	I Shuttleworth	12	47	29	3
70	M Wolff	14	-	-	-
43	W Dixon	1	10	6	-
40	A Ledger	8	-	-	-
40	A Hodkinson	8	-	-	-
35	A Wolff	7	-	-	-

SANDAL

MATCH FACTS

10	9	1	2	3	4	5	6	7	8	
Shuttleworth/2p	Turton	Pogson	Newton	Hoyle	Thompson	Mortimer(i)	Wade(j)	Ledger/t	Dykes	1
Shuttleworth/4pdg	Turton	Pogson	Newton(m)	Hoyle(l)	Thompson	Mortimer	Wade(i)	Ledger	Dykes	2
Shuttleworth/6cp	Wheeler(b/t)	Pogson	Swift(d)	Hoyle/t(o)	Harrison(e)	Mortimer	Barnes(g)	Ledger	Dykes	3
Shuttleworth/2c5p	Wheeler/2t	Pogson	Newton(q)	Hoyle/t	Thompson	Mortimer	Wade(p)	Ledger	Dykes	4
Shuttleworth/5c2p	Turton	Pogson(s)	Newton(r)	Hoyle	Thompson	Harrison	Mortimer/t	Ledger/t	Wade(p/2t)	5
Shuttleworth//p	Turton	Clappison	Key(d)	Pogson	Thompson	Barker(i)	Mortimer(t)	Ledger	Dykes	6
Shuttleworth/p	Turton	Pogson	Swift	Hoyle	Thompson	Harrison(p)	Mortimer	Ledger	Dykes(g)	7
Shuttleworth/4p	Wheeler	Pogson	Newton	Hoyle(u)	Thompson(v)	Harrison	Mortimer	Ledger	Wade	8
Shuttleworth/2cp(u)	Wheeler	Pogson	Newton	Hoyle/t	Thompson	Mortimer	Wade	Ledger	Dykes	9
Dixon/tc	Wheeler	Pogson(y)	Newton(m)	Hoyle	Thompson	Barker	Mortimer(g)	Ledger	Dykes	10
Shuttleworth/cp(uc2p)	Wheeler	Pogson(y)	Swift(d)	Hoyle	Thompson	Barker	Mortimer(v)	Ledger/2t	Dykes(g/t)	11
Dixon/3c	Wheeler/t(z)	Pogson	Swift(d)	Hoyle(y)	Thompson/t(i)	Barker	Mortimer	Ledger/t	Wade/t	12
Dixon/3cp	Turton	Pogson(y)	Swift(q)	Hoyle/t	Thompson(i)	Barker	Wade(f)	Ledger/t	Dykes	13
Dixon/3p	Turton	Pogson(y)	Swift(q)	Hoyle	Thompson	Barker	Mortimer(i)	Ledger	Dykes	14
Shuttleworth/2c	Turton	Pogson	Swift/t	Hoyle	Thompson	Barker(i)	Mortimer(g)	Ledger	Dykes	15
Shuttleworth/tc	Turton	Pogson	Swift(q)	Hoyle	Thompson	Barker	Mortimer	Ledger/t	Dykes	16
Shuttleworth/p	Turton	Pogson(y)	Swift(r)	Hoyle	Thompson	Barker(i)	Mortimer	Wade(q)	Dykes	17
Shuttleworth/c	Turton	Pogson	Swift(d)	Hoyle(y)	Thompson(i)(g	)Barker	Mortimer	Ledger	Dykes	18
Shuttleworth/5t9c	Turton	Pogson(y)	Newton(q)	Hoyle	Thompson/t	Barker(i)	Mortimer	Ledger	Dykes(B)	19
Shuttleworth/2t4c	Turton	Pogson(y)	Newton(m)	Hoyle/t	Thompson	Barker(i)	Mortimer	Ledger(r)	Dykes	20
Shuttleworth/2t3cdg	Turton	Pogson	Newton(m)	Hoyle	Thompson	Harrison(p)	Mortimer	Ledger(g)	Dykes	21
Shuttleworth/2t3c2p(u/c2p)	Turton/t	Waterhouse	Newton	Hoyle	Thompson	Harrison(p)	Mortimer	Wade/t(h/t)	Dykes	22
Dixon(C/cp)	Wheeler/t	Clappison	Newton(m)	Hoyle(D)	Thompson	Barker(i)	Mortimer	Wade(h)	Dykes	23
Shuttleworth/p	Turton	Waterhouse(c)	Swift/t(d)	Hoyle	Thompson	Barker/t	Mortimer	Ledger	Dykes	24
Shuttleworth/3c4p	Turton	Clappison	Newton(r)	Hoyle/t(F)	Thompson	Harrison	Wade/t	Dunk	Dykes	25
Shuttleworth/pdg	Turton	Pogson(y)	Newton	Hoyle	Thompson	Harrison	Mortimer	Wade	Dykes	26
Shuttleworth/t5c2p	Wheeler/t	Pogson(y)	Swift	Hoyle	Thompson(p/t)	Mortimer	Wade(v)	Ledger	Dykes	A
Shuttleworth/pdg	Wheeler	Pogson	Swift	Hoyle	Thompson	Mortimer	Wade(p)	Ledger	Dykes	B
Shuttleworth	Wheeler	Pogson	Swift	Hoyle	Thompson	Barker	Mortimer	Ledger	Dykes	C

REPLACEMENTS:					
	a- P Munn	b- A Turton	c - A Pogson	d - A Newton	e - G Thompson
f - J Mortimer	g - R Wade	h - A Ledger	i - M Harrison	j - S Barnes	k - A Hodkinson
l - J Hanson	m - G Swift	n - B Wheeler	p - G Barker	q - A Key	r - G Lig
s - M Allchurch	t - J Lockwood	u - W Dixon	v - J Dunk	w - S Walker	x - H Sharp
y - I Clappison	z - D Tomkinson				
A - N Barrett	B - P McIntosh	C - G Oakley	D - C Waterhouse	E - P Philpott	F - D Angus

Stand off Ian Shuttleworth was again Sandal's leading points scorer.

Not content with just kicking the goals he also ended the season with 12 tries second only to Mark Wolff who led the way with 14. He scored them in 23 matches which saw him average better than a try every other match.

In the forwards new boy Alex Ledger was the leading try scorer with eight from openside flanker.

Scored 93 tries in the league which was only bettered by three teams in the division.

Need to improve on their away form which saw them win just four times on the road.

SANDAL

LEAGUE STATISTICS

compiled by Stephen McCormack

SEASON	Division	P	W	D	L	F	A	Pts Diff	Lge Pts	Lge Pos		Coach		Captain
89-90	North 2	10	4	1	5	151	112	39	9	7		M Shuttleworth		N Powell
90-91	North 2	10	9	0	1	190	74	116	18	2p		M Shuttleworth		M Hardcastle
91-92	North 1	10	5	0	5	140	115	25	10	4		M Shuttleworth		M Hardcastle
92-93	North 1	12	6	1	5	205	129	76	13	4		M Shutleworth		M Hardcastle
93-94	North 1	12	9	0	3	219	131	88	18	2		M Shuttleworth		A Turton
94-95	North 1	12	8	3	1	227	126	101	19	1p		M Shuttleworth		A Turton
												Most Points		**Most Tries**
95-96	D5N	12	6	0	6	244	198	46	12	6	110	Mark Hardcastle	6	Mark Wolff
96-97	D4N	26	15	1	10	618	573	45	31	5	248	Mark Hardcastle	9	Andrew Wolff & Mark Wolff
97-98	N2N	26	13	1	12	485	547	-62	25*	8	268	Ian Shuttleworth	9	Ian Shuttleworth
98-99	N2N	26	13	0	13	697	611	86	26	7	246	Ian Shuttleworth	14	Mark Wolff

FACT FILE

Founded: 1927
Nickname: The Milnthorpers

Colours: Maroon, gold & white hoops
Change colours: Gold with maroon & white hoops.

GROUND
Address: Milnthorpe Green, Standbridge Lane, Sandal, Wakefield, W. Yorks. WF27JD.
Tel: 01924 250661
Capacity: 1625 Seated: 75 Standing: 1500

Directions: From the M1, junction 39, take the A636 to Wakefield. After3/4 mile turn right at the roundabout into Ansdale Road, and after one mile the club will be found on the left.
Nearest Railway Station: Westgate, Wakefield.

Car Parking: 200 spaces are available within the ground.

Admission: Matchdays - Adults: £4 (League & Cup)
Children/OAPs: 1/2 price.

Clubhouse: New clubhouse. open during normal licensing hours, two bars, bar meals available. Fitness centre.
Functions: Up to 120 can be catered for.

Club Shop: Open matchdays & Sundays.
Manager - Howard Newton Tel. 01924 252411.

Training Nights: Tuesday and Thursday.

PROGRAMME Size: A5 Price: With admission Pages: 24 + cover
Editor: H H Newton 01924 252411

ADVERTISING RATES
Full page £200, 1/2 page £100 & 1/4 page £50

SEDGLEY PARK R.U.F.C.

President	Geof Roberts	Salesis Farm, Salesis Lane, Walmersley, Bury BL9 6TH 0161 764 6914 (H), 0161 834 1626 (B), 0161 833 2872 (Fax)
Chairman	David Smith	95 Bury Old Road, Whitefield, Manchester. 0161 280 2921 (H), 0161 280 3509 (B).
Club Secretary	Mark Mold	32 Vicarage Avenue, Cheadle Hulme, Cheadle, Ches. SK8 7JW 0161 486 0496 (H)
Treasurer	Peter Ratcliffe	22 Hilltop Avenue, Wilmslow, Cheshire SK9 2JE 01625 535542 (H)
Commercial Director	John Widdup	63 Greenleach Lane, Roe Green, Worsley M27 2RT 0161 702 9264 (H & Fax)
Commercial Manager	Leighton Hughes	c/o Sedgeley Park RUFC
Press Officer	John Lawrence	0161 723 2530(H).
Fixture Secretary	Ray Fallon	0161 724 7282 (H) 0831 460709 (M)

Very much mid table stuff, won twelve, drew one and lost thirteen. Satisfactory in some ways but much less than the off-field expectations. With magnificent facilities coming on stream more was hoped for.

Preston, Stourbridge, New Brighton and Whitchurch all did the double over Park but when on form Sedgley, could and did play expansive attractive rugby.

70 points against Winnington, 64 and 51 versus Hinckley and more than 35 on five other occasions gave a taste of what might have been.

In the Tetley's Cup wins over Bromsgrove, Manchester and Blackheath before falling to Wasps was the best ever run for Sedgley.

A new star emerged in Rob Moon at out-side half and Jon Duncan, Paul Morris and Mike Wilcock all had excellent scoring seasons. Rob Moon proved to be an excellent goal kicker but injuries to key players at full-back and in the forwards led to problems.

This year with Chris Radacuna leading the forwards and other new faces perhaps the talent obvious at Sedgley will be turned into points.

However the club with 22 teams from seven years of age upwards provides a constant stream of talent and the pressure for success from each and everyone at Park Lane will mean that the upward progress of the last ten years will continue.

'Park' captain, Rob Smith, gets the ball away during the Tetley's Bitter Cup match at Wasps.

SEDGLEY PARK

Match No.	Date	H/A	Comp.	Opponents	Result & Score	Att.	15	14	13	12	11
1	05.09	A	J2N	Stourbridge	L 17-32		Smythe	Webster/t	Wilcock/t	Taylor	Morris/t
2	12.09	H	J2N	Nuneaton	D 22-22		Howie	Webster	Horrocks	Wilcock/2t	Morris
3	26.09	A	J2N	New Brighton	L 3-29		Wilcock	Morris	Cohen(a)	Horrocks	Webster
4	03.10	H	J2N	Preston	L 19-27		Wilcock	Webster	R Moon	Cohen/t	Morris
5	10.10	A	J2N	Hinckley*	W 51-0		Wilcock/t	Smythe	R Moon/3tc	Cohen	Morris
6	24.10	H	J2N	Whitchurch	L 11-18		Wilcock	Smythe	R Moon	Cohen	Morris
7	31.10	A	J2N	Lichfield	W 28-17		Wilcock	Smyhte/t	R Moon/t	Cohen	Morris/t
8	07.11	H	J2N	Kendal	W 23-18		Smythe	Morris	Wilcock	Cohen	Howie(b/t)
9	21.11	A	J2N	Sandal	W 39-27		Smythe/t	Renwick	Horrocks	Wilcock/t	Webster/t
10	28.11	A	J2N	Sheffield	L 6-28		Smythe	Snape	Cohen	Wilcock	Webster
11	05.12	H	J2N	Winnington P	W 70-17		Smythe/t	Snape/t	S Moon	Cohen/4t	Webster(c/t)
12	12.12	A	J2N	Aspatria	L 25-30		Snape/t	Morris	Cohen/t	Horrocks	Webster
13	19.12	H	J2N	Walsall	W 24-11		Smythe	Morris	Horrocks(z)	Cohen/t	Lowe
14	27.12	A	J2N	Winnington P	W 16-15		Appleson/p	Snape	Cohen/t	Howie	Jew
15	02.01	H	J2N	Sheffield	W 35-8		Wilcock/t	Appleson	Horrocks	Cohen	Morris
16	16.01	A	J2N	Kendal	L 7-20		Wilcock	Hussey/c	Horrocks/t	Cohen	Snape(e)
17	23.01	H	J2N	Lichfield	W 39-10		Wilcock/2t	Hussey/t	Horrocks	Cohen	Morris(z)
18	30.01	A	J2N	Whitchurch	L 12-14		Wilcock	Morris	Hussey	Cohen	Appleson
19	06.02	H	J2N	Hinckley	W 64-17		Wilcock/t	Appleson	Horrocks/2t	Cohen(z)	Morris/2t
20	13.02	A	J2N	Preston	L 18-24		Wilcock	Morris	Horrocks	Cohen(z)	Appleson/t
21	27.02	H	J2N	New Brighton	L 20-28		Wilcock	Morris/t	Horrocks	Cohen	Appleson
22	13.03	A	J2N	Nuneaton	L 13-40		Wilcock	Hussey/tdg	Cohen/t	Horrocks	Morris
23	20.03	H	J2N	Sandal	W 49-15		Lomax	Morris	Horrocks/t	Cohen	Hussey/t
24	27.03	H	J2N	Stourbridge	L 24-43		Lomax/8p	Morris	Cohen(e)	Horrocks	Hussey
25	03.04	A	J2N	Walsall	L 10-24		Hussey	Morris/t	S Moon	Cohen	Snape
26	17.04	H	J2N	Aspatria	W 55-19		Appleson	Snape	Lomax/t2c	Morris/t	Hussey(r)
A	19.09	A	TB1	Bromsgrove	W 34-10		Smythe	Webster	Horrocks	Wilcock/t	Morris
B	17.10	H	TB2	Manchester	W 20-17		Wilcock	Morris/2t	R Moon	Cohen	Smythe/t
C	14.11	A	TB3	Blackheath	W 22-21		Smythe	Morris/2t	Wilcock	Cohen(v)	Webster
D	09.01	H	TB4	Wasps	L 3-53		Smythe(r)	Appleson(p)	Wilcock	Horrocks(v)	Morris

* after opponents name indicates a penalty try
Brackets after a player's name indicates he was replaced. eg (a) means he was replaced by replacement code "a" and so on.
/ after a player or replacement name is followed by any scores he made - eg /t, /c, /p, /dg or any combination of these

1998-99 HIGHLIGHTS

Ever Presents: None

Most appearances 25 James Wood

24	Andy Jackson (1), Jon Duncan (2)
22	Rob Smith (3), Ben Cohen (1)
21	Andy Kimmins (2), Paul Morris
20	Jim Johnston

Players used: 38 plus two as replacement only.

Most Points in a season:

Pts	Player	T	C	P	DG
150	R Moon	12	27	12	-
65	R Smith	3	13	8	-
65	J Duncan	13	-	-	-
57	M Appleson	1	11	10	-
45	M Wilcock	9	-	-	-
45	B Cohen	9	-	-	-

MATCH FACTS

10	9	1	2	3	4	5	6	7	8	
Appleson/c	Smith	Alcock	Woods	Jackson	Johnston(o)	Cremont(m)	Joesbury	Marshall(n)	Duncan	1
Appleson/2cp	Smith	Ledson(f)	Woods	Jackson	Johnston(m)	Cremont	Bond/t	Joesbury	Duncan	2
Appleson/p	Smith	Ledson	Woods	Jackson	Bamford	Cremont(i/t)	Kimmins(n)	Joesbury	J Ashcroft/t	3
Appleson/2c	Smith	Ledson	Woods	Jackson	Kimmins	Cremont(m)	Duncan/2t	Joesbury	J Ashcroft	4
Appleson/4c2p	Smith(p)	Ledson(f)	Woods(o)	Jackson	Kimmins	Johnston(j)	Duncan/2t	Joesbury	J Ashcroft(a)	5
Appleson/2p	Smith(u)	Ledson	Woods	Jackson	Kimmins	Johnston(j)	Joesbury(s/t)	Bond	Duncan	6
Appleson/2c3p	Smith	Ledson	Woods	Jackson	Kimmins	Cremont(s)	Joesbury	Bond	Duncan	7
R Moon/tc2p	Smith	Ledson	Woods	Jackson	Kimmins	Johnston	Joesbury	J Ashcroft	Duncan/t	8
R Moon/t4c2p	Smith	Ledson(f)	Woods(o)	Jackson	Kimmins(j)	Johnston(w)	Bond	Joesbury	Duncan/t	9
R Moon/2p	Smith	Alcock(x)	Woods(o)	Jackson	Kimmins	Johnston	Bond(y)	Duncan	Joesbury	10
Wilcock(p/t)	Smith/t7c2p	Alcock	Woods	Jackson/t(x)	Kimmins	Johnston	Joesbury	P Ashcroft(s)	Duncan	11
Howie	Smith/cp	Alcock(x)	Woods(o)	Jackson	Kimmins/t	Johnston	Joesbury(n)	Jones	Duncan/t	12
S Moon(d)	Smith/c4p	Alcock	Woods	Jackson	Kimmins	Johnston	P Ashcroft(k)	J Ashcroft/t	Duncan	13
R Moon/p	Smith/t	Alcock	Whitehouse(g)	Jackson	Kimmins(n)	Johnston	P Ashcroft(k)	J Ashcroft	Duncan	14
R Moon/t5c	Smith	Alcock	Woods	Jacksom	Kimmins/t	Johnston	P Ashcroft/t	J Ashcroft/t(n)	Duncan(k)	15
S Moon	Howie	Ledson(f)	Woods(o)	Jackson	Kimmins	Johnston	P Ashcroft(k)	J Ashcroft(n)	Duncan	16
S Moon(n)	Smith/t3cp	Alcock(x)	Woods(o)	Jackson	Kimmins	Johnston	Joesbury/t	P Ashcroft(w)	Duncan/t	17
R Moon/t	Smith/c	Alcock	Woods	Jackson	Raducanu	Kimmins	Joesbury	P Ashcroft/t	Duncan	18
R Moon/t7c	Smith(v)	Alcock(q)	Woods(o)	Jackson/t	Raducanu/t	Johnston(k)	J Ashcroft(t)	P Ashcroft	Duncan/.2t	19
R Moon/tp	Smith	Alcock(q)	Woods(o)	Jackson	Raducanu	Kimmins	J Ashcroft(i)	P Ashcroft	Duncan/t	20
R Moon/2c2p	Smith	Ledson(f)	Woods	Jackson	Raducanu/t	Kimmins	Hogg(s)	P Ashcroft	Duncan	21
R Moon	S Moon(e)	Alcock(x)	Woods(o)	Jackson	Johnston	Raducanu	Hogg(l)	Kimmins	J Ashcroft	22
R Moon/4c2p	S Moon/t	Ledson	Woods	Greene	Johnston	Raducanu/2t	J Ashcroft(w)	P Ashcroft/t(B)	Duncan/t	23
R Moon	S Moon	Greene(h)	Woods(o)	Ledson	Raducanu	Johnston(t)	J Ashcroft	P Ashcroft(B)	Duncan	24
R Moon/t	Smith	Ledson	Woods(o)	Jackson	Johnston	Kimmins	Joesbury	Duncan(w)	Hogg	25
R Moon/t3c	Smith	Greene(f)	Woods/t(o)	Jackson/t	Johnston	Raducanu/t	Kimmins	Cunliffe/t(y/t)	Duncan(s/t)	26
Appleson/3cp	Smith	Ledson	Woods	Jackson	Bamford	Kimmins/t	Bond/t	Bury	Duncan/2t	A
Appleson/cp	Smith	Ledson	Woods(o)	Jackson	Kimmins	Johnston	Joesbury	Bond(w)	Duncan	B
R Moon/2cp	Smith	Ledson	Woods	Jackson	Kimmins(j)	Johnson	J Ashcroft(w)(n)	Joesbury	Duncan/t	C
R Moon/p	Smith	Alcock(q)	Woods(o)	Jackson	Kimmins	Johnston	J Ashcroft	P Ashcroft(k)	Duncan	D

REPLACEMENTS:

	a- D Smythe	b- S Webster	c - P Morris	d - M Appleson	e - R Smith
f - M Alcock	g - J Woods	h - A Jackson	i - J Johnston	j - A Cremont	k - S Joesbury
l - J Duncan	m - J Bamford	n - S Bond	o - R Whitehouse	p - K Howie	q - P Ledson
r- B Cohen	s - J Ashcroft	t - A Kimmins	u - R Barraclough	v - S Moon	w - C Bury
x - C Greene	y - P Ashcroft	z - C Jew	A - K Hussey	B - D Hogg	

New Zealander Rob Moon topped the points scoring list with 150 in his first season for the club.

Leading try scorer was No 8 Jon Duncan with 13 whilst the leader in the backs was nine tries by Mike Wilcock and Ben Cohen.

Neil Lomax kicked eight penalties against Stourbridge late in the season.

Ben Cohen scored four tries in the match against Winnington Park in December

In that match against Winnington Park Rob Smith scored 25 points, a try, seven conversions and two penalties.

Sedgley Park ended the season as the third highest points scorers despite finishing in 8th place.

Lost home and away to Preston, New Brighton, Stourbridge and Whitchurch.

SEDGLEY PARK

LEAGUE STATISTICS
compiled by Stephen McCormack

SEASON	Division	P	W	D	L	F	A	Pts Diff	Lge Pts	Lge Pos		Coach		Captain
89-90	NW 1	10	2	0	8	91	132	-41	4	9		R Sharp		P Egan
90-91	NW 1	10	6	0	4	183	112	69	12	4		R Sharp		R Hall
91-92	NW 1	10	5	1	4	119	145	-26	11	6		V Baker		R Hall
92-93	NW 1	12	4	0	8	149	188	-36	6*	11		V Baker		P Renwick
93-94	NW 1	12	5	2	5	201	134	67	12	5		C Hebbut		R Hall
94-95	NW 1	12	12	0	0	421	60	361	24	1p		K Fletcher		P Egan
95-96	North 2	12	10	0	2	257	141	116	20	2p		K Fletcher		R KImmins
												Most Points		**Most Tries**
96-97	North 1	22	17	1	4	650	398	252	35	1p		K Fletcher		R Kimmins
97-98	N2N	26	14	2	10	655	595	109	30	5	97	Darren Weatherall	10	Jon Duncan Mike Wilcox
98-99	N2N	26	12	1	13	710	553	157	25	8	150	Rob Moon	13	Jon Duncan

FACT FILE

Founded: 1932
Nickname: Tigers

Colours: Claret with gold & black trimmings
Change colours: All Black.

GROUND

Address: Park Lane, Whitefield, Manchester M45 7DZ
Tel: 0161 766 5050 / 0161 796 2626 Website: www.sedgleyparkrugby.demon.co.uk
Capacity: 2,000 Seated: None Standing: 2,000

Directions: From M60, junction 17 onto A56 for Bury. take the left filter at the 2nd set of traffic lights, left at the next lights (Park Lane),ground 1/2 mile on left
Nearest Railway Station: Whitefield (Manchester Metro), take taxi about £2

Car Parking: 150 on ground, 150 nearby free.

Admission: Season tickets - Adult standing £45
Matchdays - Adult £5 incl. programme, Children Free

Clubhouse: Normal licensing hours, snacks & bar meals available
Functions: Capacity 150 - 2 function rooms & lounge
Contact John Grundy 0374 637064, 0161 280 5752

Club Shop: Yes, in club

Training Nights: Tuesday & Thursday (seniors) Juniors -Wed.

PROGRAMME

Size: A5 Price: £1 Pages: 40
Editor: Simon Tushingham 0161 796 7755 or 0161 796 2626

ADVERTISING RATES

Mono - Full page £170, half £90, Qtr £50

SHEFFIELD R.U.F.C.

Chairman	Bill Campbell	c/o Sheffield RUFC, Administration Office, Abbeydale Park Sports Club, Abbeydale Rd. South, Sheffield S17 3LG 01142 367023 (H) 01788 538124 (B)
President	Chris Pickering	26 Whirlow Court Road, Sheffield S11 9NT 0114 236 7452 (H) 0114 258 0783 (B)
Club Secretary	William Oliver	Cumberland House, Cumberland Street, SheffieldS1 4PT 0114 255 6817 (H), 0114 249 5501 (B), 0114 279 8804 (Fax)
Internal Admin	Richard Fedyk	0114 236 4785 (H), 01332 262951(B), 01332 262846 (Fax)
Coach	Paul Matthews	21 Batchelor Drive, Harrogate HG1 3EH 01423 566529 (H) 0113 276 8888 (B) 07801 641473 (M)
Fixtures Secretary		c/o Sheffield RUFC as above.Office Hours 09.30 -13.30 Tue to Thur incl. Tel: 0114 235 3414 Fax: 0114 226 5093

Sheffield began the season well and their early form suggested the possibility of a challenge for promotion but they fell away later, especially after Christmas, as the inconsistency of previous seasons re-appeared. The final position of sixth was four places higher than in 1997-98 but supporters were never sure whether they would be watching the team capable of beating the top two, Preston Grasshoppers (14-3) and Stourbridge (37-13), or the one that lost eleven league games, six of them by 20 points or more.

The deserved victory over champions Preston, in which full-back Rob Pound scored all the points, was the best performance of the season but even this highlighted the lack of consistency as it came in the middle of a run of six defeats (three at home) against lesser opposition.

Most of the improvement in the side could be attributed to the players signed during the close season. St. John Ellis, the ex Great Britain Rugby League centre, was the major acquisition and expected to make a big impact. He struggled, however, to adapt to playing Union for the first time and returned to R.L. with Doncaster in March. However, other newcomers in wing Jamie Bartle, who played every game, lock Martin Smith, flanker Mick Baillie and centre Andy Hulme all did well and new No 8 Matt Wood was a deserved winner of the Player of the Year award for his sterling defensive work.

Jamie Morley again captained and his strong running from centre brought him eighteen tries, ahead of Bartle with thirteen and Mark Allat with ten. Rob Pound again led the points scorers with 228

Sheffield Squad 1998-99

SHEFFIELD

Match No.	Date	H/A	Comp.	Opponents	Result & Score	Att.	15	14	13	12	11
1	05.09	A	J2N	Walsall	W 35-0		Pound/t2c2p	Bartle/t	Ellis	Morley/t	Allatt/t
2	12.09	H	J2N	Stourbridge	W37-13		Pound/3c2p	Bartle/t	Ellis/t	Morley/t	Allatt/2t
3	26.09	A	J2N	Nuneaton	W39-15		Pound/4c2p	Bartle/t	Ellis/t	Morley/t	Allatt
4	03.10	H	J2N	Sedgley Park*	L 13-18		Pound/c2p	Bartle	Ellis	Morley	Allatt
5	10.10	A	J2N	Preston	L 18-38		Pound/c2p	Bartle/t	Ellis	Morley	Allatt/t
6	24.10	H	J2N	Hinckley	W 13-6		Pound/c2p	Bartle	Ellis	Morley/t	Allatt
7	31.10	A	J2N	Whitchurch*	W20-12		Pound/cp	Bartle/t	Ellis	Morley	Allatt/t
8	07.11	H	J2N	Lichfield	W 21-7		Pound/c3p	Bartle	Ellis	Morley/t	Allatt
9	21.11	A	J2N	Kendal	L 16-24		Pound/2p	Bartle	Ellis	Morley	Allatt/t
10	28.11	H	J2N	Sedgley Park	W 28-6		Pound/2c3p	Bartle	Ellis	Morley	Allatt/t
11	05.12	A	J2N	Sandal	L 5-28		Pound(v)	Bartle	Ellis	Morley	Hewlett
12	12.12	A	J2N	Winnington P	W27-16		Ellis/2cp	Bartle/t	Morley/2t	Kaye	Allatt
13	19.12	H	J2N	Aspatria	W16-13		Ellis/2p	Bartle	Morley	Kaye	Allatt/t
14	28.12	H	J2N	Sandal	W 31-9		Ellis/2t	Bartle/t	Morley/t	Kaye	Allatt
15	02.01	A	J2N	Sedgley Park	L 8-35		Ellis	Bartle/t	Morley	Kaye(y)	Allatt
16	16.01	A	J2N	Lichfield	W32-24		Ellis	Bartle	Morley/3t	Kaye	Allatt/2t
17	23.01	H	J2N	Whitchurch	L 8-15		Ellis	Bartle/t	Morley	Kaye	Allatt
18	30.01	A	J2N	Hinckley	L 0-20		Ellis	Bartle	Morley(s)	Kaye	Allatt
19	06.02	H	J2N	Preston	W 14-3		Pound/t3p	Bartle	Ellis(B)	Kaye	Allatt
20	13.02	A	J2N	New Brighton	L 15-29		Pound/cp	Bartle	Morley/t	Kaye	Allatt(B)
21	20.02	H	J2N	Kendal	L 3-23		Pound/p	Bartle	Morley	Kaye(b)	Hulme
22	27.02	H	J2N	Nuneaton	L 3-6		Pound/p	Bartle	Morley	Hulme	Ellis
23	13.03	A	J2N	Stourbridge	L 25-45		Pound2c2p	Bartle/t	Morley	Hulme/t	Allatt
24	27.03	H	J2N	Walsall	W34-18		Pound/2c5p	Bartle	Morley/t	Hulme/t	Allatt(D)
25	03.04	A	J2N	Aspatria	W22-20		Hewlett	Bartle(p)	Morley/2t	Taylor2cp	Hulme/t
26	17.04	H	J2N	Winnington P	W 13-3		Pound/c2p(c)	Bartle	Morley	Taylor	Hume/t
A	19.09	A	TB1	Stourbridge	L 6-32		Pound/2p	Bartle	Ellis	Morley	Allatt

* after opponents name indicates a penalty try
Brackets after a player's name indicates he was replaced. eg (a) means he was replaced by replacement code "a" and so on.
/ after a player or replacement name is followed by any scores he made - eg /t, /c, /p, /dg or any combination of these

1998-99 HIGHLIGHTS

Ever Presents:
Jamie Bartle & David Holmes

25	Jamie Morley, Nick Crapper
23	Mick Baillie, Rob Pound (1)
22	Matt Wood, Dave Anderson (3)
21	Mark Allatt (1)

Players used: 30 plus 11 as replacement only.

Most Points in a season:

Pts	Player	T	C	P	DG
178	R Pound	2	27	38	-
75	J Morley	15	-	-	-
50	J Bartle	10	-	-	-
50	M Allatt	10	-	-	-
33	St J Ellis	4	2	3	-
20	M Baillie	4	-	-	-

MATCH FACTS

10	9	1	2	3	4	5	6	7	8	
Davies	Holmes	Anderson	Howard	Fearn(j)	Doran/t	Smith	Crapper	Baillie(i)	Watson	1
Davies	Holmes	Anderson	Howard(k)	Fearn	Doran	Smith	Crapper	Baillie	Watson	2
Burgess/t	Holmes	Venimore	Parkin(l)	Fearn	Watson	Smith	Crapper	Baillie/t	Wood	3
Burgess	Holmes	Venimore	Parkin(e)	Fearn	Watson	Smith	Crapper(m)	Baillie	Wood(n)	4
Burgess	Holmes	Anderson	Howard	Fearn	Smith(q)	Watson	Staley	Baillie	Crapper	5
Burgess	Holmes	Anderson	Parkin	Fearn	Smith	Doran	Watson	Baillie	Wood(r)	6
Davies	Holmes	Anderson	Parkin	Fearn	Watson	Smith	Crapper	Baillie(i)	Wood	7
Davies	Holmes/t	Anderson	Parkin(e)	Fearn	Watson	Smith	Crapper	Baillie	Wood	8
Davies	Holmes	Anderson	Parkin	Fearn	Smith	Watson	Crapper/t	Baillie	Wood	9
Davies/t	Holmes	Anderson	Parkin(e)	Fearn	Norris	Smith	Crapper	Baillie/t	Wood	10
Davies	Holmes	Anderson	Parkin(l)	Fearn(u)	Norris	Smith	Crapper	Baillie/t(t)	Wood(h)	11
Davies/t	Holmes	Anderson	Hetherington	Fearn	Smith	Norris(h)	Crapper	Baillie	Wood	12
Davies	Holmes	Anderson	Hetherington	Fearn	Smith(h)	Norris(t)	Crapper	Baillie/t(i)	Wood	13
Pound/4cp	Holmes	Anderson(u)	Hetherington(k)	Fearn	Smith(x)	Norris	Crapper(i)	Baillie	Wood	14
Pound/p	Holmes	Anderson	Hetherington(k)	Fearn(u)	Smith	Norris(h)	Crapper(n)	Baillie	Wood	15
Pound/2cp	Holmes	Anderson	Hetherington	Fearn	Smith	Norris	Crapper	Baillie	Wood	16
Pound/p	Holmes	Anderson(u)	Parkin	Fearn	Smith(h)	Norris	Crapper	Baillie	Wood	17
Pound	Holmes	Anderson	Parkin	Fearn(z)	Smith	Norris	Crapper	Baillie	Wood	18
Davies	Holmes(A)	Venimore	Parkin(e)	Fearn(d)	Watson	Norris	Crapper	Baillie(i)	Wood	19
Davies	Holmes(A)	Venimore	Parkin/t(e)	Fearn(d)	Norris	Watson	Crapper(i)	Baillie	Wood(x)	20
Davies	Holmes	Venimore	Parkin(e)	Anderson(j)	Norris	Watson(g)	Crapper	Baillie	Wood(n)	21
Davies	Holmes	Venimore	Parkin	Anderson	Watson	Norris	Crapper	Baillie	Wood	22
Davies	Holmes(o)	Venimore	Howard(k)	Anderson	Gresser(g/t)	Norris	Crapper	Baillie(C)	Wood	23
Davies	Holmes(o)	Venimore	Howard(k)	Anderson(f)	Gresser(E)	Norris	Crapper/t(C)	Cotton	Wood	24
Davies	Holmes	Venimore	Parkin	Anderson(f)	Norris	Joel	Cotton(F)	Raw	Crapper	25
Davies	Holmes(o)	Venimore	Howard	Anderson(f)	Norris	Joel(g)	Crapper	Cotton	Wood(C)	26
Davies(s)	Holmes	Anderson(u)	Howard(k)	Fearn	Doran	Smith	Crapper	Baillie(i)	Watson(G)	A

REPLACEMENTS:	a- R Pound	b- SJ Ellis	c - M Allatt	d - D Anderson	e - M Howard
f - T Fearn	g - M Smith	h - D Watson	i - A Cotton	j - J Littleton	k - A Parkin
l - C Hetherington	m - G Davies	n - D Staley	o - G Manuel	p - M Kaye	q - S Gravelle
r - J Norris	s - M Hewlett	t - I Beaumont	u - S Venimore	v - R Wring	w - K Holmes
x - I Gresser	y - R Keegan	z - A James	A - N Pearson	B - A hulme	C - J Raw
D - J Taylor	E - R Joel	F - M Hitchens	G - M Wood		

Rob Pound topped the points scorers list for a second successive season with 178 points from 23 starts.

Centre Jamie Morley topped the try scorers list for a second successive season with a club record 15 league tries from his 25 starts.

Sheffield conceded just 10 tries in their home league matches, that was easily the best record in the division. Kendal with 16 were next on the list.

Managed just 60 tries during the season. This included just 24 in their 13 home matches which put them second bottom in this catergory, only Winnington Park scored fewer with 22.

Jamie Morley scored their only hat trick of the season in the away win at Lichfield.

SHEFFIELD

LEAGUE STATISTICS

compiled by Stephen McCormack

SEASON	Division	P	W	D	L	F	A	Pts Diff	Lge Pts	Lge Pos	Most Points		Most Tries	
89-90	3	11	6	0	5	176	174	2	12	4	61	Robin Goodliffe	5	Kerry Morley
90-91	3	12	4	1	7	193	222	-29	9	10	108	Mark Rogers	7	Mark Rogers
91-92	3	12	5	1	6	146	228	-82	11	8	68	Chris Thompson	2	Ian Wright/Jamie Morley/ Kerry Morley
92-93	3	11	7	0	4	208	134	74	14	5	89	Mark Rogers	4	Stuart Juds/Jamie Morley
93-94	4	18	5	1	12	287	310	-23	11	9	150	Mark Rogers	4	Chris Saul/Paul Oldbury
94-95	D5N	12	5	0	7	156	197	-41	10	9	42	Jamie Morley	3	Mark Allatt/Martin Kirk
95-96	D5N	12	7	0	5	205	190	15	14	5	94	Jamie Morley	3	Dave Watson
96-97	D4N	26	11	2	13	484	483	1	24	8	167	J Morley	7	Darren Cairns/Mark Allatt
97-98	N2N	26	10	2	14	557	539	18	20*	10	243	Rob Pound	9	Jamie Morley/Mark Allatt
98-99	N2N	26	15	0	11	496	455	41	30	6	178	Rob Pound	15	Jamie Morley

FACT FILE

Founded: 1902

Colours: Blue & white hoops/navy blue/red.
Change colours: Red/navy blue/red.

GROUND

Address: Abbeydale Park Sports Club, Abbeydale Road South, Sheffield. S17 3LG
Tel 0114 236 7011
Capacity: 1200 Seated: 200 Standing: 1000

Directions: The club is on the A621 (Bakewell to Baslow road) out ofSheffield.
Nearest Railway Station: Sheffield (BR) Dore & Totley (local)

Car Parking: 200 spaces are available at the club.

Admission: Matchday Adult £3.

Clubhouse: Normal Licensing hours, snacks, bar meals & restaurant.
Functions: Up to 150 can be catered for.
Contact Gary Roberts 01142 367011

Club Shop: Open matchdays only.
Manager Ian Dawson 01246 250044 (B)

Training Nights: Tuesday and Thursday.

PROGRAMME

Size: A5 Price: £3 Pages: 48 + cover
Editor: C Roth, 01142 752575

ADVERTISING RATES

Full page £250, 1/2 page £125

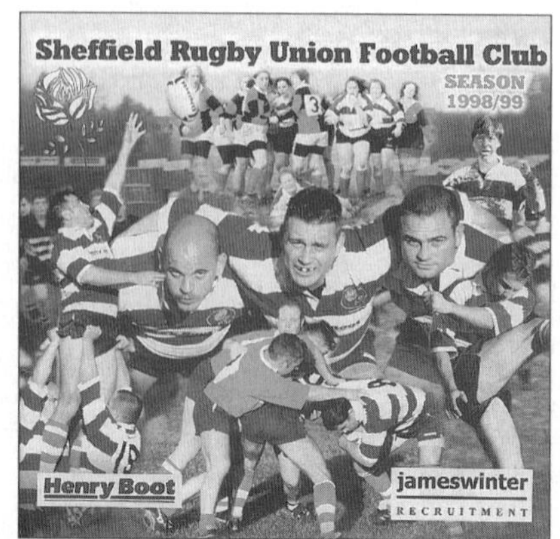

STOURBRIDGE R.F.C.

President	Roger Parkes	01299 896566
Chairman	Norman Robertson	16A Middlefield Lane, West Hagley, Stourbridge DY90PX 01562 886011 (H), 01384 455555 (B), 01384 455264 (Fax)
Secretary	Robert Browne	01562 882020 (H), 01905 763555 x4658 (B)
1st XV Manager	Nick Perry	36 Chawn Hill, Oldswinford, Stourbridge. 01384 375337 (H), 01789 400193 (B), 01789 400507 (Fax)
Director of Coaching	Stewart Jardine	25 Goldstone Road, Bridgnorth Shropshire. 01792 470044 (H)
Press Officer	Vernon Davies	36 Beckman Road, Pedmore, Stourbridge. 01562 883640 (H & Fax)

With the departure of Preston Grasshoppers and Lichfield in different league directions, Stourbridge is the only club to have remained in Jewson Two North, in one of its various forms, since the formation of the Leagues in 1987. Superficially, this seems to reflect an unusual consistency of performance but it hardly does justice to the quality of their challenge for promotion this season. They were a potent attacking force throughout, scoring 135 tries, the highest in all the National Leagues and a record for their own league, while the general recognition of the quality of their play was confirmed when Stewart Jardine won the prestigious Jewson Coach of the Year award. They only lost four league games, but since two of these were to Preston, there were no quibbles about the eventual destination of the promotion spot. Home form was particularly spectacular and, with only one game lost at Stourton all season, crowds were larger than ever.

This was generally acknowledged as Stour's best ever league squad and it was capably led by hooker Bob Merritt, the only `ever present'. With 99 league appearances he stands poised on the threshold of becoming the first Stourbridge player to complete a league century.

39 players were used in the 26 league games, six as replacements only, and to illustrate the overall competence of the side an unprecedented six try scorers reached double figures - Simon Baylie (prop 13), Richard Trigg (wing 13), Bob Merritt (hooker 12), Jamie Richardson (wing 12), Alan Dickens (scrum-half 11) and Jacob John (centre 11).

The appointment of Nick Tisdale as Schools Liaison Officer, aided by a grant from Sportsmatch, strengthened the links with the youth community as much as his grafting work in the engine room bulwarked the pack.

With Chris Mann unavailable or out of favour, place kicking was the side's Achilles heel until Simon Bailey, improbably, hit a rich streak of form in February and finally Mann regained form and fitness.

The strength in depth in the club remains impressive. All the five senior sides had a success rate of well above 70 percent and the Extras, representing the club in the North Midlands Cup, reached the final for a second successive year.

Stewart Jardine (coach), Darron Hall, Jon Watson, Simon Baylie, Nick Tisdale, Andy Freke, Jon Russell, Spencer Bradley, Rich Thompson, Richard Trigg, Adrian Parsons, Nick Perry (manager). Front: jon Hall, Jacob John, Alan Dickens, Pete Jones, Bob Merritt (capt.), Dave Timmingham, Nick Taylor, Hamish Pearson, Brett Milligan, Jamie Richardson.

STOURBRIDGE

Match No.	Date	H/A	Comp.	Opponents	Result & Score	Att.	15	14	13	12	11
1	05.09	H	J2N	Sedgley Park	W32-17		Taylor/t(k)	John/t	Pearson(j)	Parsons	Richardson
2	12.09	A	J2N	Sheffield	L 13-37		John(k)	Sherratt	Pearson	Parsons	Richarsson
3	26.09	H	J2N	Winnington P	W30-17		Taylor(d)	Trigg/2t	Pearson	John	Richardson
4	03.10	A	J2N	Aspatria	W42-21		England/3c2p	Richardson(j)	Parsons	John/t	Pearson/t(p)
5	10.10	H	J2N	Walsall	W52-20		England/p	Richardson(j)	Parsons	John	Pearson/t2c(p)
6	24.10	H	J2N	Sandal*	W 19-3		Taylor	Richardson(v)	Parsons	John/2c	Pearson(j)
7	31.10	A	J2N	Nuneaton	W23-13		Pearson/p	Richardson	John	Parsons	Timmington(r/t)
8	07.11	H	J2N	New Brighton	W 6-3		Pearson/2p	Sherratt	Johns	Parsons	Richardson
9	21.11	A	J2N	Preston	L 3-32		Tyalor(b)	Richardson	Parsons	Pearson/p	Trigg
10	28.11	H	J2N	Hinckley	W63-15		Pearson/t	Richardson/t	Milligan(v)	Parsons(b)	Trigg/3t
11	05.12	A	J2N	Whitchurch	W29-13		Taylor	Richardson(j)	Milligan	Parsons/2t	Trigg/2t(v)
12	12.12	H	J2N	Lichfield	W42-14		Taylor	Jones/t	John/t	Pearson/t	Trigg/2t
13	19.12	A	J2N	Kendal	W 20-7		England/cp	Richardson	John	Pearson	Trigg/t
14	28.12	H	J2N	Whitchurch	W42-19		Williams/2cp	Jones/3t	John	Pearson	Richardson/t
15	02.01	A	J2N	Hincklwy	W40-11		Williams/t5c	Richardson/3t	John	Pearson/t	Jones
16	09.01	H	J2N	Preston	L 10-25		Williams/cp	Richardson	John	Pearson	Sherratt(r)
17	16.01	A	J2N	New Brighton	L 15-16		Williams/cp	Richardson	Pearson	Milligan	Trigg(v)
18	23.01	H	J2N	Nuneaton	W 36-7		Pearson	Jones/t(u)	Richardson/t	John/t	Trigg/2t
19	30.01	A	J2N	Sandal	W45-17		Wylde	Pearson	Richardson	John/t	Jones(p)
20	06.02	A	J2N	Walsall	W37-11		Pearson(d)	Sherratt/t	Richardson/2t	John	Wylde(x)
21	13.02	H	J2N	Aspatria	W59-31		Wylde(j)	Richardson/2t	John/t	Parsons/t(r)	Sherratt/t
22	27.02	A	J2N	Winnington P	W 57-0		Wylde/t	Sherratt	John	Parsons(c)	Richardson(x)
23	13.03	H	J2N	Sheffield	W45-21		Pearson(a)	Richardson/t	John/t	Parsons(a)	Sherratt
24	27.03	A	J2N	Sedgley Park	W43-24		Pearson(a)	Richardson	John/t	Parsons(a)	Sherratt/t
25	03.04	H	J2N	Kendal	W18-15		Pearson(E)(D)	Richardson	John	Parsons	Sherratt
26	17.04	A	J2N	Lichfield*	W 74-0		Pearson(a/t)	Richardson	John/2t	Parsons/t	Sherratt/t
A	19.09	H	TB1	Sheffield	W 32-6		Taylor	Timmington/3t(j)	John	Pearson(F)	Trigg/t
B	17.10	A	TB2	Tynedale*	W30-22		Taylor/2cp	Richardson/t	John(G)	Parsons	Pearson/p
C	14.11	A	TB3	Lydney	L 5-41		Pearson	Richardsoon	John(x)	Meakin	Sherratt

* after opponents name indicates a penalty try
Brackets after a player's name indicates he was replaced. eg (a) means he was replaced by replacement code "a" and so on.
/ after a player or replacement name is followed by any scores he made - eg /t, /c, /p, /dg or any combination of these

1998-99 HIGHLIGHTS

Ever Presents: Rob Merritt

25	Jamie Richardson
24	Nick Tisdale, Alan Dickens, Simon Baylie
23	Jacob John (2), Hamish Pearson

Players used: 32 plus seven as a replacement

Most Points in a season:

Pts	Player	T	C	P	DG
112	S Baylie	14	15	4	-
82	D Lockley	1	5	4	7
65	R Trigg	13	-	-	-
60	R Merrett	12	-	-	-
59	J John	11	2	-	-
55	A Dickens	11	-	-	-
55	J Richardson	11	-	-	-

MATCH FACTS

10	9	1	2	3	4	5	6	7	8	
Lockley/3c2p	Dickens	Baylie(m)	Merritt/t	Phillips(l)	Watson	Freke	Gadd/t	W-Hughes(n)	Russell	1
Lockley/p	Dickens/t	Baylie	Merritt/t	Phillips	Tisdale	Watson	Gadd(o)	W-Hughes(q)	Russell	2
Lockley/cp	Dickens	Baylie	Merritt(t)	Ferguson(e)	Freke	Tisdale/t	W-Hughes(s)	Maurino/t	Gadd/t(f)	3
Milligan	Dickens	Baylie	Merritt	Phillips/t(l)	Freke/2t(o)	Tisdale	Gadd(h)	Bradley/t	Watson(m)	4
Milligan	Dickens/3t	Baylie/t	Merritt(m)	Phillips(l)	Freke/2t	Tisdale	Gadd(o)	Bradley/2t	W-Hughes(q)	5
Milligan	Dickens	Baylie/t	Merritt(m)	Ferguson(e)	Freke(o)	Tisdale	Maurino(i/t)	W-Hughes	Gadd	6
Milligan/t	Dickens	Baylie/t	Merritt(m)	Phillips(l)	G Taylor	Tisdale	Gadd/t(f)	Maurino	Russell	7
Milligan	Dickens	Baylie	Merritt	Phillips	Freke	Tisdale	Gadd(f)	Maurino	Russell	8
Milligan	Dickens	Baylie(l)	Merritt(w)	Phillips	Freke	Tisdale	Maurino	Bradley	Watson(i)	9
Lockley/6c2p	Dickens/t	Phillips/t(h/t)	Merritt/t(m)	Ferguson	Freke	Tisdale	Gadd(q)	Bradley	Russell	10
Lockley/2c	Dickens	Baylie/t	Merritt	Ferguson	Freke	Tisdale	Maurino	Bradley	Russell	11
Lockley/2cp	Dickens(j)	Baylie	Merritt(m)	Phillips/t(l)	Freke	Tisdale	Maurino	Bradley	Thomson(i/t)	12
Milligan	Dickens/t	Baylie/t	Merritt	Phillips	Freke	Tisdale	Russell	Maurino	Thomson(s)	13
Milligan/t	Dickens	Baylie/t	Merritt	Ferguson(e)	Freke	Tisdale	Russell	Bradley/t	Thomson(A)	14
Milligan	Dickens/t	Phillips	Merritt(m)	Ferguson(C)	Freke(f)	Tisdale	Maurino	Bradley	J Taylor(B)	15
Milligan	Dickens	Baylie/t	Merritt	Phillips	Freke(A)	Tisdale	Maurino	Bradley	Thomson(i)	16
John/t	Dickens	Baylie	Merritt/t	Phillips(l)	Freke	G Taylor(A)	Russell	Bradley	Thomson(g)	17
Lockley/3c	Dickens	Baylie	Merritt(m)	Ferguson(e)	G Taylor	Tisdale	Gadd/t	Bradley	Russell(q)	18
Lockley/5c	Dickens	Baylie/t	Merritt/t(w)	Ferguson(e)	G Taylor(f)	Tisdale/t	Gadd/2t(q)	Bradley	Russell/t	19
Lockley/t3c2p(u)	Dickens/t	Baylie(C)	Merritt(m)	Ferguson	G Taylor	Tisdale	Gadd)q)	Bradley	Russell	20
Mann/t2c2p(u/t)	Dickens	Baylie/2c	Merritt	Ferguson	G Taylor(q/t)	Tisdale	Gadd	Bradley/t	Russell	21
Mann(u/t)	Dickens/2t	Baylie/t7cp	Merritt/t(w)	Ferguson(C)	G Taylor/t	Tisdale	Russell(g)	Bradley/t	Maurino	22
Mann(u)	Dickens	Baylie/t3c3p	Merritt(m)	Ferguson	G Taylor	Tisdale/t	Gadd(B)	Bradley/t	Russell/t	23
Mann/t3c	Dickens/t(j)	Baylie/tc	Merritt/t	Ferguson(e)	G Taylor	Tisdale	Russell	Bradley	Maurino(B/t)	24
Mann/c2p	J Hall	Baylie	Merritt/2t	Ferguson(e)	G Taylor	Tisdale	Russell(g)	Bradley	Maurino	25
Mann/6c(u)	J Hall/t	Baylie/tc	Merritt/3t	Ferguson(e)	G Taylor	Tisdale	Russell	Mayrino	Thomson/t(g)	26
Lockley/2cp	Dickens	Baylie/t	Merritt	Phillips(l)	Freke	Tisdale	Russell	Maurino(g)	Watson(h)	A
Milligan	Dickens/t	Baylie	Merritt	Phillips	Freke(o)	Tisdale	Gadd(f)	Bradley/t	Maurino	B
Milligan(y)	J Hall/t	Starynskyj	D Hall	Ferguson(z)	Freke(A)	G Taylor	Gadd	W-Hughes	Watson(B)	C

REPLACEMENTS:

a- N Taylor; b- J John; c - H Pearson; d - A Parsons; e - S Phillips
f - J Watson; g - G Gadd; h - M Wyn-Hughes; i - J Russell; j - J Hall; k - R England
l - M Ferguson; m - D Hall; n - S Hill; o - G Taylor; p - D Sherratt; q - R Maurino
r - R Trigg; s - S Bradley; t - J Jeavons Fellows; u - B Milligan; v - P Jones; w - C Hurcombe
x - T Wilson; y - T Grenfell; z - S Homer; A - J Taylor; B - R Thomson; C - M Richardson
D - S Jardine; E - R Wylde; F - J Richardson; G - D Timmington; H - S Baylie

Prop Simon Baylie topped the clubs points scoring list with 112. Most of his points came from his 14 tries but late in the season he took over the kicking and did so very successfully for three matches.

In the try scoring fellow front row forward Rob Merritt was not far behind with 12. In all the front row contributed 29 tries during the season.

Veteran winger Richard Trigg scored 13 tries from just eight starts.

Stourbridge won 15 of their last 17 league matches, including their last nine, to put the pressure on Champions Preston.

They finished the season as leading points and try scorers with 895 and 135 respectively.

Lost just once at home when they were beaten 25-10 by Preston.

STOURBRIDGE

LEAGUE STATISTICS

compiled by Stephen McCormack

SEASON	Division	P	W	D	L	F	A	Pts Diff	Lge Pts	Lge Pos	Most Points	Most Tries
89-90	ALN	10	7	0	3	146	133	13	14	3	55 Murray Jones	4 John Wainwright
90-91	D4N	12	5	1	6	134	161	-27	11	8	53 Steve Baker	4 Mike Harris
91-92	D4N	12	6	0	6	163	137	26	12	6	34 Adrian Taft	5 Richard Trigg
92-93	D4N	12	5	1	6	161	144	17	11	9	108 Simon Pennington	2 Mark Wilson/Richard Trigg/Dale Smallman
93-94	D5N	12	6	0	6	162	188	-26	12	5	90 Chris Mann	5 Richard Trigg
94-95	D5N	12	6	0	6	166	174	-8	12	6	98 Chris Mann	4 Adrian James
95-96	D5N	12	6	0	6	200	177	23	12	7	100 Chris Mann	4 Richard Trigg
96-97	D4N	26	14	1	11	704	579	125	29	6	206 Chris Mann	15 Kevin Hickey
97-98	N2N	26	14	0	12	685	605	80	28	6	107 Chris Mann	14 Alan Dickens
98-99	N2N	26	22	0	4	895	413	482	44	2	105 Simon Baylie	13 Richard Trigg Simon Baylie

FACT FILE

Founded: 1876

Colours: Navy blue with narrow white bands
Change colours: Red & white hoops, trimmed navy blue

GROUND

Address: Bridgnorth Road, Stourton, Stourbridge, W. Midlands. DY7 6QZ
Tel: 01384 393889.
Capacity: 3500 Seated: 499 Standing: 3001

Directions: The ground is situated on the A458 (Bridgnorth road), two miles west of Stourbridge town centre. The ground is on the left hand side 1/2mile past the `Foresters Arms' public house.
Nearest Railway Station: Stourbridge Junction.

Car Parking: 200 spaces are available at the ground.

Admission: Matchday - Adults £5, including prog., U16 No charge

Clubhouse: Three bars and food is available.
Functions: Three rooms able to hold functions.
Contact Pam Purslow 01384 898142

Club Shop: None

Training Nights: Tuesday and Thursday.

PROGRAMME

Size: A5 Price: With admission
Pages: 40 plus cover
Editor: Vernon Davies 01562 883640

ADVERTISING RATES: Full page £100.

WALSALL R.F.C.

President	D E (Brains) Horton	c/o Walsall RFC, Broadway Ground, Delves Rd,Walsall WS1 3JY
Chairman	Barry J Bodilly	55A Highgate Road, Walsall. 01922 645330 (H)
Club Secretary	Caleb Tillott	6 Lichfield Road, Sandhills, Walsall Wood,Walsall. WS9 9PE 01543 372667 (H), 01922 613310 (Fax)
Fixtures Secretary	Tim Day	20 Daffodil Place, Walsall. WS5 3DN 01922 611729(H), 01922 613310 (Fax)
Press Officer	Howard Clews	4 Binbrook Road, Short Heath, Walsall. WV12 4TW 01902 631947 (H), 01922 613310 (Fax)
Director of Coaching	Arnie Evans	0121 353 1017 (H), 0121 378 1288 (B)
1st XV Manager	Bob Harknett	07050 157336 (Mob)

Walsall reviewed the 1997-98 season as one in which a number of ex-Colts were blooded and first teams with the lowest average age within memory were fielded. That was even more the case in 1998-99, when at times the average age of the three-quarter line was well below 21.

Injuries, both long and short term, took a heavy toll, notably shortening the season for the captain, Richard Mills, who nevertheless took his league record to exactly 1400 points in 167 appearances over ten years.

Just prior to the season Walsall lost to Coventry the services of Argentinian International back Luis Criscuolo, but obtained through him a friend and fellow-countryman, flanker Florencio Sequeira, who proved an engaging character both on and off the field. At the end of the season Walsall bade a fond farewell to Colin Jarvis, their former player and subsequent coach, who took them to successive promotions in 1995 and 1996, was working for a year in Australia when they were relegated in 1997, and resumed his role in 1998 but has now emigrated down-under. Bob Harknett, ex-Moseley and Worcester, succeeds him.

Of thirteen players to make league debuts, nine were ex-Colts including two aged eighteen, James Baker and Chris Mould, and three aged nineteen, Tom Ridgway, Mike Powell and Rob Emery. They all performed with distinction. Props Karl Jones and Steve Lea were ever-present in the league and were rested for just one game each all season.

Walsall's final league position of ninth accurately reflected their results, as they gathered seventeen of a possible 20 points from the five clubs who finished below them whilst gaining just two wins against the eight sides above them, at home 25-20 over Kendal - the result of the season - and 24-10 over Sedgley Park.

There was a First Round exit from the Tetley's Bitter Cup at Doncaster, but the Staffordshire Cup was won for the eighth time.

HOWARD CLEWS

Walsall 1st XV Squad 98-99 - L-R - **Back Row:** Alan Gillard (team asst.), Rod Dickson, Mike Powell, Richard Coleman, Mark Ellis, David Godfrey, Andy Walker, Richard Towe, Chris Mould, Julian Bambridge, Arnie Evans (Dir. of coaching), Colin Jarvis (1st XV coach), Stacey McQuenney (physio). **Front Row:** Jim Deare (team asst.), David Butler, Darren Robbins, Allan Mitchell, Steve Lea, Daren Haley, Richard Mills (capt.), Karl Jones, Tom Ridgway, Terry Finn, Rob Emery, Nick Rose. Photo courtesy Wolverhampton Express & Star

WALSALL

Match No.	Date	H/A	Comp.	Opponents	Result & Score	Att.	15	14	13	12	11
1	05.09	H	J2N	Sheffield	L 0-35		Marsh	Baker	Henwood	Towe	N Rose
2	12.09	A	J2N	Winnington P	W 24-3		Marsh	Baker	Henwood/t	Towe(r)	N Rose
3	26.09	H	J2N	Aspatria	W54-21		Marsh	N Rose/3t	Henwood	Finn	Mould/t
4	03.10	H	J2N	Sandal	L 32-39		Marsh/t(e)	N Rose(b)	Henwood	Finn/t	Mould
5	10.10	A	J2N	Stourbridge	L 20-52		Marsh/t	N Rose	Henwood	Towe	Mould/t
6	31.10	A	J2N	New Brighton	L 0-33		Marsh(B)	Finn(c)	Ridgway	Henwood	Mould
7	07.11	H	J2N	Preston	L 29-65		Marsh	Finn(c)	Henwood	Ridgway(b/t)	Mould
8	14.11	H	J2N	Nuneaton	L 10-20		Marsh	Ridgway	Henwood(v/2t)	Towe	Finn
9	21.11	A	J2N	Hinckley	W33-30		Marsh/2t	Finn	Ridgway	Towe	Mould(G)
10	28.11	H	J2N	Whitchurch	D 8-8		Marsh/t	Mould	Ridgway	Towe	Finn
11	05.12	A	J2N	Lichfield	W28-17		Marsh/t	Mould/t	Ridgway/t	Towe	Finn
12	12.12	H	J2N	Kendal	W25-20		A Walker	Mould/t	Ridgway	Towe	Finn(c)
13	19.12	A	J2N	Sedgley Park	L 11-24		A Walker/t	Mould	Ridgway	Towe	Finn(c)
14	28.12	H	J2N	Lichfield	W42-13		A Walker/2t	Mould	Henwood/t	Towe	N Rose
15	02.01	A	J2N	Whitchurch	W33-18		A Walker	N Rose/t(A)	Henwood	Towe	Mould/2t(a)
16	16.01	A	J2N	Preston	L 5-39		A Walker(H)	Mould/t	Ridgway	Henwood	Marsh
17	23.01	H	J2N	New Brighton	L 3-15		Marsh(r)	Finn(K)	Henwood	Towe	Mould
18	30.01	A	J2N	Nuneaton	L 15-30		Marsh	Finn/t	Henwood	Towe	Mould/t
19	06.02	H	J2N	Stourbridge	L 11-37		Marsh(K)	Mould	Henwood	Mills/2p(b)	Finn
20	13.02	A	J2N	Sandal	L 5-43		A Walker(u)	M Walker	Towe	Henwood	Mould(G)
21	20.02	H	J2N	Hinckley	W 14-13		A Walker	Mould	Towe	Finn/t	M Walker
22	27.02	A	J2N	Aspatria	L 0-47		A Walker(b)	Marshall	Wood	Finn	M Walker
23	13.03	H	J2N	Winnington P	W63-10		Wood/t	Ridgway/t(M)	Towe	Finn/3t	M Walker
24	27.03	A	J2N	Sheffield	L 18-34		Wood	N Rose	Ridgway/t	Finn	Linton
25	03.04	H	J2N	Sedgley Park	W24-10		Wood	N Rose/t	Ridgway/t	Finn	Mould
26	17.04	A	J2N	Kendal	L 8-44		Wood	Ridgway(M)	Finn	Towe/t	Mould
A	19.09	A	TB1	Doncaster	L 19-30		Marsh	Baker(v)	Henwood/t	Towe/t	Rose/c

* after opponents name indicates a penalty try
Brackets after a player's name indicates he was replaced. eg (a) means he was replaced by replacement code "a" and so on.
/ after a player or replacement name is followed by any scores he made - eg /t, /c, /p, /dg or any combination of these

1998-99 HIGHLIGHTS

Ever Presents: Karl Jones

24	Steve Lea (2)
23	David Godfrey (1)
21	Darren Haley (1)
20	Richard Mills (2), Chris Mould (1), Richard Coleman (1)

Players used: 34 plus nine as replacement only.

Most Points in a season:

Pts	Player	T	C	P	DG
124	R Mills	-	26	24	-
50	C Mould	10	-	-	-
44	D Butler	3	7	5	-
32	R Dickson	6	1	-	-
30	T Finn	6	-	-	-
30	R Marsh	6	-	-	-

MATCH FACTS

10	9	1	2	3	4	5	6	7	8	
Mills	Butler(n)	Lea	Robbins(o)	K Jones	Godfrey	Ellis(p)	Tillott(m)	Sequeira	Coleman	1
Mills/3cp	Butler/t(n)	Lea(t)	Haley	K Jones	Godfrey	Ellis(p)	M Jones	Sequeira/t	Coleman(s	2
Mills/3c2p(r)	Mitchell(e/c)	Lea(t)	Haley(x)	K Jones	Godfrey/t	Ellis(p)	M Jones(w)	Sequeira/2t	Coleman/t	3
Mills/3c2p	Mitchell/t	Lea(t)	Haley	K Jones	Godfrey	Ellis/t	M Jones(W)	Sequeira	Coleman	4
Mills/2c2p	Mitchell	Lea	Haley	K Jones	Godfrey	Ellis	M Jones(y)	Sequeira	Coleman	5
Mills	Mitchell(e)	Lea	Robbins(o)	K Jones	Godfrey	Ellis	Dickson	Sequeira	M Jones	6
Mills/3cp	Mitchell/2t	Lea(t)	Haley	K Jones	Godfrey	Ellis	Bambridge	Dickson/t(g)	M Jones(E	7
Mills	Mitchell	Emery(f)	Haley	K Jones	Godfrey	Ellis(F)	Burns(y)	Dickson	Coleman	8
Mills/3c4p	Mitchell	Emery(f)	Haley	K Jones	Godfrey	Powell	Burns	Dickson/t	Coleman	9
Mills/p	Butler(n)	Lea	Haley	K Jones	Godfrey	Powell(k)	Burns(m)	Dickson	Coleman	10
Mills/c2p	Butler	Lea	Haley/t	K Jones	Godfrey	Ellis	Dickson	Sequeira	Coleman	11
Mills/cp	Mitchell	Lea(t)	Haley/t	K Jones	Godfrey	Ellis(y/t)	Powell/t	Dickson	Coleman	12
Mills/2p(o)	Butler	Lea(C)	Haley	K Jones	Godfrey	Ellis	Owen(m)	Tillott(n)	Dickson	13
Mills/3c2p	Mitchell/t	Lea(t)	Haley(g)	K Jones	Godfrey	Ellis	Powell/t	Sequeira(l)	Dickson/t	14
Mills/2c	Mitchell(e)	Lea(t)	Robbins/2c	K Jones	Godfrey	Ellis(D)	Burns	Dickson/t	Coleman/t	15
Mills	Butler	Lea	Robbins(q)	K Jones	Godfrey	Harding(y)	Powell	Owen	Dickson	16
Mills/p	Butler	Lea	Haley	K Jones	Godfrey	Ellis(J)	Burns(D)	Sequeira	Dickson(o)	17
Mills/cp	Butler	Lea	Haley(q)	K Jones	Owen	Coleman	Burns(y)	Sequeira	Dickson	18
Shepherd	Butler(n)	Lea(t)	Haley	K Jones	Godfrey	Owen	Bambridge(g)	Tillott/t(L)	Coleman	19
Shepherd	Mitchell	Lea(C)	Haley	K Jones	Godfrey	Owen	Robbins(F/t)	Bambridge(L)	Coleman	20
Shepherd/3p	Mitchell(e)	Lea	Haley	K Jones	Ellis	Owen(k)	Powell	Dickson	Coleman	21
Shepherd	Butler(n)	Lea(t)	Haley(o)	K Jones	Ellis(y)	Owen(h)	Powell	Sequeira	Coleman	22
Shepherd	Butler/t5c2p	Lea	Haley(o)	K Jones	Godfrey/t	Powell	Dickson/2tc	Sequeira(i)	Coleman	23
Shepherd	Butler/tc2p	Lea	Haley	K Jones	Godfrey	Powell	Dickson	Sequeira	Coleman	24
Shepherd/2cp(d/c)	Mitchell	Lea	Haley	K Jones	Godfrey	Powell	Burns	Dickson(D)	Coleman/t	25
Mills/p	Mitchell	Lea(t)	Haley(g)	K Jones	Godfrey(i)	Powell	Burns(w)	Sequeira	Coleman	26
Mills/c(u)	Butler(n)	Lea(t)	Haley	K Jones	Godfrey	Ellis(p)	M Jones(j)	Sequeira/t	Coleman	A

REPLACEMENTS:

a- R Marsh, b- R Towe, c - N Rose, d - R Mills, e - D Butler
f - S Lea, g - D Robbins, h - D Godfrey, i - M Ellis, j - G Tillott, k - F Sequeira
l - R Coleman, m - M Jones, n - A Mitchell, o - M Lane, p - R Harding, q - D Haley
r - A Walker, s - A King, t - R Emery, u - T Finn, v - C Mould, w - R Dickson
x - G Green, y - J Bambridge, z - A Smallwood, A - T Ridgway, B - J McMurray, C - A Morton
D - G Owen, E - D Burns, F - M Powell, G - D Marshall, H - D Blakemore, J - M Reeve
K - M Walker, L - T Smith, M - D Linton

Richard Mills again tops the Walsall points scoring list. That was the ninth successive season he has done so.

Karl Jones was the clubs only ever present and has nowplayed in 51 of Walsall's last 52 league matches over two seasons.

The leading try scorer was new boy Chris Mould, the winger ran in 10 tries in his 20 starts. He became the third Walsall to reach double figures in a league campaign

They had a poor away record with just four wins. They managed just 25 tries on the road which was amongst the worst in the division.

Wingers Nick Rose and Terry Finn were the only two players to score hat tricks during the season.

WALSALL

LEAGUE STATISTICS

compiled by Stephen McCormack

SEASON	Division	P	W	D	L	F	A	Pts Diff	Lge Pts	Lge Pos	Most Points	Most Tries
89-90	ALN	10	2	0	8	143	183	-40	4		31 John Dowdswell	4 Simon Leaver & Matt McCluskey
90-91	ALN	12	5	0	7	149	176	-27	10		75 Richard Mills	3 Dave Wild & Nick Millward
91-92	D4N	12	3	1	8	139	187	-48	7		99 Richard Mills	4 Duncan Marshall
92-93	D4N	12	6	0	6	165	179	-14	12		90 Richard Mills	3 Mike Friar, Gary Till & Jon Rowe
93-94	D5N	12	7	0	5	166	148	18	14		81 Richard Mills	3 Gary Till
94-95	D5N	12	10	1	1	389	110	279	21		164 Richard Mills	11 Jon Rowe
95-96	4	13	10	0	8	406	324	82	20		193 Richard Mills	10 Malcolm Walker
96-97	3	30	8	0	22	640	980	-340	16		338 Richard Mills	8 Malcolm Walker
97-98	N2N	26	9	1	16	539	723	-183	19	11	220 Richard Mills	17 Richard Marsh
98-99	N2N	26	10	1	15	515	720	-205	21	9	124 Richard Mills	10 Chris Mould

FACT FILE

Founded: 1922

Colours: Scarlet/black/scarlet
Change colours: Royal blue & amber/blue/blue & amber

GROUND

Address: Broadway Ground, Delves Road, Walsall WS1 3 JY
Tel: 01922 626818 Fax 01922 613310
Capacity: 2,250 Seated: 250 Standing: 2,000

Directions: From NE (A38.A461) almost into Town centre, take ring Rd left, ground 2 miles on right.
From NW (M6) Jnc 9, go left and bear right at lights onto ring road, ground on left after 2miles.
From all points South, head for M6 Jct 7, take A34 Walsall, after 2 miles left onto ring road, ground half mile on left

Nearest Railway Station: Walsall BR 1.5 miles, hourly bus or taxi.

Car Parking: 100 adjacent to Clubhouse, 200 within 5 mins walk.

Admission: Match £5, inc programme, Members £3

Club Shop: Yes, contact Club Secretary

Clubhouse: Matchdays 12-11. Eves (except Wed), 8-11
Sun. 12-4.30. Snacks & bar meals available.

Functions: Capacity 130, Contact Keith Russell 01922 626818

Training Nights: Tuesday & Thursday

PROGRAMME

Size: A5 Price: Included in entry
Pages: 36 plus cover
Editor: Howard Clews 01902 631947

ADVERTISING RATES

Mono Full Page £150, Half £75

WHITCHURCH R.F.C.

President	John Henry Wynn	Fenns Wood, Whitchurch, Shropshire. 01948 780343
Chairman	Paul Kaminski	21 Kingsway, Whitchurch SY13 1EH 01948 662536(H), 01948 662889 (B)
Treasurer	Mark Smith	6 Smallbrook Rd., Whitchurch, Shropshire. 01948 664894
Secretary	Graham Kendall	Hibernia, Mile Bank, Whitchurch SY13 4JY 01948 666632 (H), 01244 321471 (B) 01244 320522 (Fax)
Fixture Secretary	Paul Kaminski	21 Kingsway, Whitchurch SY13 1EH 01948 662536(H), 01948 662889 (B)
Marketing	Ted Edgerton	30 Windmill Drive, Audlem, Crewe, Cheshire CW3 0BE 01270 812876

Whitchurch's aim was to compete in the professional surroundings of Jewson Two North with a truly amateur squad. The experience proved interesting both for players and committee. Having won Midlands Division One without loss the previous season we came down to earth with a `bump' with our first fixture at Preston Grasshoppers whom we congratulate on securing promotion to Jewson One.

Our initial defeats were sobering but the squad continued to train hard and results came our way. The season was very much one of ups and downs, losing games by the odd point in the last few minutes which we really might have won. The club enjoyed some success in the Tetley's Bitter Cup before going to Exeter where we were annihilated but gained from the experience. Our games at the end of the season against Preston Grasshoppers, New Brighton and Nuneaton secured our tenure in Jewson Two with the confidence to compete in 1999-2000.

It is probably fair to say that as the season developed the Whitchurch pack became one of the most respected in the league. We consider that we competed well and have made many friends whom we look forward to meeting again next year. It was a just reward to the players and the coaching staff to end the season on a high note, winning the North Midlands Cup by beating Stourbridge in a thrilling 19-15 final.

It is always a pleasure to look back on the season and note the success of our minis, juniors and colts. During the course of the season we managed to blood four of last year's colts with first team honours and look forward to continued development. Thanks are also extended for the contribution of two New Zealand students to the development of our squad.

Finally we extend our congratulations to Doncaster and Bedford Athletic on gaining promotion to Jewson Two North.

WHITCHURCH

Match No.	Date	H/A	Comp.	Opponents	Result & Score	15	14	13	12	11
1	05.09	A	J2N	Preston	L 7-50	Paton	Masters	Wynn	Marvel	MacGillivary
2	12.09	H	J2N	Hinckley	L 10-21	Paton	Masters	Wynn	Marvel	Dodd
3	26.09	A	J2N	Sandal	L 20-45	Masters	Lewis	Brookshaw(b)	M Hares	Paton
4	03.10	A	J2N	Lichfield	W 28-21	MacGillivary	Paton/t	Lewis	Maycock	Baker
5	10.10	H	J2N	Kendal	W 13-11	MacGillivary	Paton	Lewis	Maycock	Baker
6	24.10	A	J2N	Sedgley Park	W 18-11	MacGillivary	Baker	Wynn	Maycock	Lewis
7	31.10	H	J2N	Sheffield	L 12-20	MacGillivary	Baker	Wynn	Maycock	Lewis
8	07.11	A	J2N	Winnington P	W 26-10	MacGillivary/t	Baker	Wynn	Maycock/tcp	Lewis
9	21.11	H	J2N	Aspatria	L 8-20	MacGillivary	Baker(k)	Wynn	Maycock	Lewis/t
10	28.11	A	J2N	Walsall	D 8-8	MacGillivary	Wynn/t	Lewis	Canney/p	Paton(t)
11	05.12	H	J2N	Stourbridge	L 13-29	MacGillivary	Wynn(t)	Lewis	Canney/p	Paton
12	12.12	A	J2N	Nuneaton	L 15-24	MacGillivary	Wynn(a)	Lewis	Canney/tcp	Paton
13	19.12	H	J2N	New Brighton	L 19-26	Masters	MacGillivary	Lewis	Canney/c	Paton
14	28.12	A	J2N	Stourbridge	L 19-42	Masters	MacGillivary	Marvel	Canney/3p	Paton(s)
15	02.01	H	J2N	Walsall	L 18-33	Masters(b)	Maycock	Wynn	Marvel	Maycock
16	09.01	A	J2N	Aspatria	L 15-24	Lewis	Smith	Wynn/c	Marvel	Baker
17	16.01	H	J2N	Winnington P	W 36-17	Lewis/t(b)	Smith	Wynn	Canney/2c	Baker(x)
18	23.01	A	J2N	Sheffield	W 15-8	Lewis	Smith	Wynn	Canney/c	MacGillivary
19	30.01	H	J2N	Sedgley Park	W 14-12	Lewis	Smith/t	Wynn	Canney	MacGillivary
20	06.02	A	J2N	Kendal	L 10-26	Lewis	Baker	Wynn	Canney/c	Davies
21	13.02	H	J2N	Lichfield	W 24-19	Lewis	Baker	Wynn	Canney/c	Dodd
22	27.02	H	J2N	Sandal	L 13-29	MacGillivary/t	Smith	Wynn	Canney/c2p	Baker
23	13.03	A	J2N	Hinckley	L 11-26	MacGillivary	Smith	Canney/2p	M Hares	Ashton
24	27.03	H	J2N	Preston	L 16-20	MacGillivary	Paton	Wynn	Marvel	Ashton
25	03.04	A	J2N	New Brighton	L 27-44	Masters	Holloway	Wynn	Marvel	Paton
26	17.04	H	J2N	Nuneaton	W 35-3	Wynn/c	Dodd	Brookshaw	Driscoll	Holloway
A	19.09	H	TB1	Aspull	W 32-12	Masters	MacGillivary	Brookshaw	M Hares	Paton/t
B	17.10	H	TB2	Bedford Ath	W 23-15	MacGillivary	Baker	Wynn/2t	Maycock	Lewis
C	14.11	A	TB3	Exeter	L 19-81	MacGillivary	Baker	Wynn	Maycock	Lewis/t

* after opponents name indicates a penalty try
Brackets after a player's name indicates he was replaced. eg (a) means he was replaced by replacement code "a" and so on.
/ after a player or replacement name is followed by any scores he made - eg /t, /c, /p, /dg or any combination of these

1998-99 HIGHLIGHTS

Ever Present: Richard Lear

Most appearances:

24	John Canney (1)
23	Richard Wynn
22	Tom Pemberton
21	Phil Mullock

Players used: 37 plus seven as replacement only.

Most Points in a season:

Pts	Player	T	C	P	DG
145	J Canney	3	20	30	-
38	NMaycock	2	5	6	-
35	P Mullock	7	-	-	-
35	G Hazelton	7	-	-	-
30	S Bailey	6	-	-	-
30	R Lear	5	-	-	-

MATCH FACTS

10	9	1	2	3	4	5	6	7	8	
Canney(k)	Pemberton(j)	Howell	Barber(i)	Lear	Leonard	Pemberton	Charmley(h)	Appleby/t	N Owen	1
Canney/tcp	C Hares	Howell	Barber	Lear	Leonard	R Charmley	Owen	Appleby	Hayward	2
Wynn/cdg	Pemberton(D	)Hazelton/t	Barber	Lear	Leonard	Pemberton/t	Wills/t	Appleby	N Owen	3
Canney/2c3p	Wynn	Hazelton	Barber	Lear/t	Leonard/t	Pemberton	Wills(u)	Appleby	N Owen	4
Canney/c2p	Wynn	Hazelton	Barber	Lear	Leonard	Pemberton	Michie(p)	Appleby	N Owen	5
Canney/c2p	Mullock	Hazelton/2t	Bailey	Lear	Leonard	Pemberton	Wills	Appleby	Price	6
Canney/c	Mullock	Hazelton/t	Bailey	Lear	Leonard(r)	Pemberton	Wills/t(q)	Appleby	Michie(q)	7
Canney/2p(k)	Mullock	Howell(v)	Bailey(l)	Lear	T Charmley	T Owen	N Owen/t	Wills(u)	Price	8
Canney/p	Mullock(w)	Howell	Bailey(i)	Lear	T Charmley(n)	Pemberton	N Owen	Appleby(p)	Price	9
Maycock	Mullcok	Howell(o)	Bailey	Lear	T Charmley	Pemberton	Wills(q)	Appleby	Price	10
Maycock	Mullock	Howell/t	Bailey/t	Lear	T Charmley(d)	Pemberton	Wills	Appleby	Price(u)	11
Maycock	Mullock	Howell	Bailey/t	Lear	Leonard	Pemberton	Wills	Appleby	T Hares	12
Maycock/c	Mullock/t	Howell	Bailey/t	Lear/t	T Charmley	Pemberton	Wills	Appleby(g)	T Hares	13
Maycock	Mullock/t	Howell(o)	Barber	Lear	T Charmley	Leonard	Wills	Appleby(g)	T Hares(y/t	14
Canney/c2p	Mullock/2t	Howell	Bailey(c)	Lear	T Owen	R Charmley(B)	Wills	Appleby)q)	Price	15
Maycock/p	Mullock(C)	Howell/t	Bailey(c)	Lear	T Owen(e)	Pemberton/t	T Hares(u)	Wills	Price	16
Maycock/c	Mullock	Hazelton/2t	Bailey	Lear	T Charmley	Pemberton/t	T Hares(g)	Wills	Price/2t	17
Maycock/p	Mullock	Hazelton	Bailey(c)	Lear/t	T Charmley	Pemberton	T Hares	Wills/t	Price	18
Maycock/3p	Mullock	Hazelton	Bailey	Lear	T Charmley	Pemberton	T Hares	Wills	Price(g)	19
Maycock/p	Mullock	Hazelton	Bailey/t	Lear	T Charmley	Pemberton	N Owen	Wills	T Hares	20
Maycock/tc	Mullock	Hazelton/t	Bailey/t	Lear/t	Leonard(e)	Pemberton	N Owen	Michie	T Hares	21
Maycock	Mullock	Howell	Bailey	Lear	T Charmley	Pemberton	T Hares	Michie	N Owen	22
Mullock	Pemberton	Howell(v)	Bailey	Lear/t	T Charmley(d)	Pemberton	N Owen	T Hares	Price	23
Canney/c3p	Mullock/t	Howell(o)	Bailey	Lear	T Charmley	Pemberton	T Hares(m)	N Owen	Price	24
Canney/t3c2p	Mullock/t	Howell(o)	Barber	Lear	T Owen	Pemberton	M Hares	N Owen	Price(D/t)	25
Canney/c2p	Mullock/t	Howell(o)	Bailey/t(c)	Lear/t	Leonard	Pemberton/t	R Charmley(y)	M Hares	Dutton/t	26
Wynn/2cp	Pemberton/3t	Hazelton	Barber	Lear	Leonard	T Owen	N Owen	Appleby	Hayward(r)	A
Canney/c2p	Mullock	Hazelton	Bailey	Lear	Leonard(r)	Pemberton	Wills(u)	Appleby	Price	B
Canney/2p	Mullock(z)	Howell(A)	Bailey(c)	Lear	T Charmley(d)	Pemberton	Wills(f)	N Owen(u)	Price	C

REPLACEMENTS:

a- G Masters, b- R MacGillivary, c - K Barber, d - D Leonard, e - R Charmley,
f - P Appleby, g - N Owen, h - C Hayward, i - N Ashley, j - C Hares, k - A Dodd,
l - J Huxley, m - M Hares, n - T Owen, o - G Hazelton, p - M Wills, q - T Hares,
r - T Charmley, s - S Lewis, t - J Baker, u - A Michie, v - C Willis, w - M Smith,
x - L Davies, y - G Price, z - J Driscoll,
A - J Houston, B - D Hollins, C- R Gittings, D - J Canney

Fly half/centre John Canney was easily the leading points scorer for Whitchurch in their first season at this level.

Scrum half Phil Mullock and prop Giles Hazelton were leading try scorers with seven each. Next in the list were his front row team mates Simon Bailey and Richard Lear with six and five repectively.

Whitchurch had excellent away wins at Sedgley Park and Sheffield. They did though lose at home to sides they should have beaten - something they will need to rectify in the coming season.

Giles Hazelton scored his seven tries in just 10 league starts.

WHITCHURCH

LEAGUE STATISTICS

compiled by Stephen McCormack

SEASON	Division	P	W	D	L	F	A	Pts Diff	Lge Pts	Lge Pos
89-90	NMid 1	10	8	0	2	176	127	49	16	2
90-91	NMid 1	10	9	0	1	184	93	91	18	1p
91-92	Mid 2W	10	4	1	5	132	139	-7	9	6
92-93	Mid 2	11	4	0	7	156	130	26	8	9
93-94	Mid 2	12	10	1	1	178	85	93	21	1p
94-95	Mid 1	12	7	1	4	240	157	83	15	3
95-96	Mid 1	12	5	1	6	197	171	26	11	8
96-97	Mid 1	16	9	1	6	435	304	131	19	6
97-98	Mid 1	16	16	0	0	537	210	327	32	1p
98-99	N2N	26	9	1	16	450	559	-149	19	11

FACT FILE

Founded: 1936

Colours: Red/white/red
Change colours: White

GROUND

Address: Edgeley Park, Whitchurch SY13 1EU
Tel: 01948 663316 Fax: 01948 665508
Capacity: Unlimited Seated: None Standing: Unlimited

Directions: Follow by-pass (A41/A49) to the south of the town. Opposite Sir John Talbot school, access via Edgeley Road (on right).
Nearest Railway Station: Whitchurch (5 mins walk)

Car Parking: Free parking on ground

Admission: Matchday - Adults £3

Clubhouse: Regularly open
Functions: Yes. Contact Club

Club Shop: None

Training Nights: Tuesday & Thursday

PROGRAMME

Size: A5 Price: with entry Pages: 16/20
Editor: Dr. Alan Hares 01630 652135

ADVERTISING RATES

Mono Full page £100 Half £60 Qtr. £35

DIVISION FOUR NORTH

(CURRENTLY JEWSON NATIONAL LEAGUE TWO NORTH)

Previously also Area League North & Division Five North

RECORDS SECTION

Relegated clubs' Match Facts for season 1998-99

Hinckley	392/3
Lichfield	394/5
Winnington Park	396/7

The Last Ten Years 398

A breakdown showing the champions, runners-up, those relegated, who scored most - points, tries, conversions, penalties & drop goals in each of the last ten seasons in this division (or its equivalent)

All Time Team & Individual Records 399

A list of the various records for this division (or its equivalent) since the start of the league system.

Ten Year Record 400

A grid showing those clubs who have been part of this division (or its equivalent), and the league position they achieved for each of the last ten years

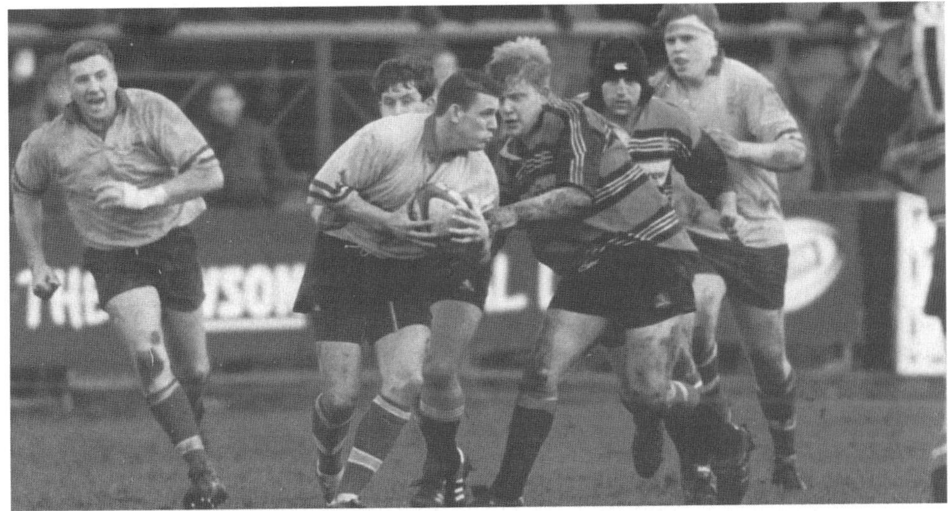

Sandal centre, Andrew Metcalfe, with the Nuneaton defence closing in, finds support in the shape of second row Glynn Thompson (left) and prop Adam Pogson (right). Photo courtesy of John Clifton Sports Agency, Wakefield.

Match No.	Date	H/A	Comp.	Opponents	Result & Score	Att.	15	14	13	12	11
1	05.09	A	J2N	Sandal	L 6-21		Curtis/2p	Brittain	Newman	Allen	A Duton
2	12.09	A	J2N	WHitchurch	W21-10		Curtis/c3p	Brittain(k)	Newman	Allen	A Dutton(j)
3	26.09	H	J2N	Lichfield	W 30-5		Curtis/2p	Harrison/t	Lennox/2c	Allen	A Dutton(o)
4	03.10	A	J2N	Kendal	L 0-36		Jenkins	Harrison	Lennox	Allen(v)	Anderson
5	10.10	H	J2N	Sedgley Park	L 0-51		Jenkins	Harrison	Newman	Allen	Anderson
6	24.10	A	J2N	Sheffield	L 6-13		Curtis/2p	Harrison	Newman(k)	Allen	Brittain
7	31.10	H	J2N	Winnington P	L 6-8		Curtis/2p	Harrison	Newman	Allen	Brittain
8	07.11	A	J2N	Aspatria	L 23-34		Jenkins(b)	Bunting(n)	Harrison/tc	Newman	Brittain
9	21.11	H	J2N	Walsall*	L 30-33		S Bennett/t	Harrison	Newman(A)	C Dutton	A Dutton
10	28.11	A	J2N	Stourbridge	L 15-63		S Bennett(a)	Harrison/2t	Lennox	C Dutton	A Dutton
11	05.12	H	J2N	Nuneaton	D 24-24		Harrison	Brittain/t	Dignan	C Dutton/t	A Dutton
12	12.12	A	J2N	New Brighton	L 0-54		Harrison	Brittain	Dignan	C Dutton	S Bennett
13	19.12	H	J2N	Preston	L 9-20		Harrison	Brittain/p	Dignan	C Duttin	A Dutton
14	28.12	A	J2N	Nuneaton	L 13-61		Bunting	Brittain/t	Dignan	C Dutton	Harrison
15	02.01	H	J2N	Stourbridge	L 11-40		Harrison	A Dutton(r/t)	Dignan	C Dutton	Brittain
16	23.01	A	J2N	Winnington P	W28-13		Harrison	Anderson/t	Dignan	Curtis/2c3p	Castle
17	30.01	H	J2N	Sheffield	W 20-0		Harrison	Anderson	Dignan	Curtis/cp	Castle
18	06.02	A	J2N	Sedgley Park*	L 17-64		Harrison(G)	Bramwel(k)	Dignan(i)	Curtis/c(z)	Castle/t
19	13.02	H	J2N	Kendal	L 14-15		Harrison	Anderson	C Bennett	C Dutton	Castle
20	20.02	A	J2N	Walsall	L 13-14		A Dutton	Bramwell	C Bennett(A)	C Dutton	Castle
21	27.02	A	J2N	Lichfield	L 24-29		Dignan	A Dutton/t	Newman	C Dutton(m/c)	Castle
22	06.03	H	J2N	Aspatria	W34-10		Brittain/3p	A Dutton/2t(E)	Harrison	C Dutton/t	Castle
23	13.03	H	J2N	Whitchurch	W26-11		Brittain/tc3p	A Dutton	Harrison/t	C Dutton	Castle(r)
24	27.03	H	J2N	Sandal	W42-18		Brittain/4c3p	Bott	C Bennett/t	Dignan(n)	Castle(F)
25	03.04	A	J2N	Preston	L 11-57		Brittain/t2p	Bott(C)	C Bennett	C Dutton(n)	Anderson
26	17.04	H	J2N	New Brighton	L 22-29		Brittain	Castle/t	Harrison(n)	C Bennett	Anderson
A	19.09	H	TB1	Nuneaton*	L 20-24		Curtis/2c2p	Harrison	Lennox	Allen	A Dutton

* after opponents name indicates a penalty try
Brackets after a player's name indicates he was replaced. eg (a) means he was replaced by replacement code "a" and so on.
/ after a player or replacement name is followed by any scores he made - eg /t, /c, /p, /dg or any combination of these

1998-99 HIGHLIGHTS

Ever Presents:
Richard Massarella, Phillip Massarella.

Most Appearances:

23	David Massarella (2)
22	Eddie Brittain
21	Neil Wells (1)

Players used: 40 plus seven as replacement only

Most Points in a season:

Pts	Player	T	C	P	DG
105	P Curtis	-	12	27	-
87	E Brittain	4	8	17	-
30	A Jones	6	-	-	-
29	A Harrison	5	2	-	-
25	P Green	5	-	-	-
20	A Goodall	4	-	-	-

MATCH FACTS

10	9	1	2	3	4	5	6	7	8	
C Massarella	R Masarella	P Massarella	D Massarella	Ashfield	Jones	R Walton	Goodall	Wells	Whittle	1
C Massarella	R Massarella	P Massarella	D Massarella	Ashfield	Jones/t	R Walton	Goodall/t	Wells(i)	Whittle	2
C Massarella/t	R Massarella	P Massarella/t	D Massarella/t	Ashfield	Jones/t	R Walton	Goodall	Wells	Whittle	3
C Massarella	R Massarella	P Massarella	D Massarella	Wayne(h)	Jones	R Walton	Burgess	Wells	Whittle(u)	4
C Masarella	R Massarella	P Massarella	D Massarella	Wayne	Jones	R Walton	Burgess	Wells	Whittle	5
C Massarella(k)	R Massarella	P Massarella	D Massarella	Wayne(p)	Stratford	R Walton	Goodall	Wells	T Walton	6
C Massarella(q)	R Massarella	P Massarella	D Massarella	Wayne	Jones	Green	Goodall	Wells	T Walton	7
Curtis/c3p	R Massarella	P Massarella	Whiteley(c)	Wayne(g)	Stratford	R Walton	Goodall/t	Wells(y)	T Walton	8
Curtis/2c2p	R Massarella	P Massarella	D Massarella	Stratford	Jones/t	R Walton/t(w)	Goodall	Wells(y)	T Walton	9
Curtis/cp	R Massarella	P Massarella(g)	D Massarella(x)	Stratford	Jones	R Walton	T Walton	Wells	Johnson	10
Curtis/3cp	R Massarella	P Massarella	D Massarella	Stratford(d)	Jones	R Walton	Bird	Wells	Wickham/t	11
Curtis(b)	R Massarella	P Massarella	Holyer	Ashfield	Jones	Stratford	Bird	Wells(B)	Wickham	12
Curtis/2p(b)	R Massarella	P Massarella	D Massarella	Stratford(d)	Jones	R Walton(w)	Wells	Johnson	Sanderson	13
Curtis/p	R Massarella	P Massarella	Hilyer	Stratford(d)	Jones	R Walton(w)	Sanderson	Wells(i)	Johnson/t	14
Curtis/2p(C)	R Massarella	P Massarella	D Massarella	Ashfield	Green	Stratford(f)	Johnson(y)	T Walton	Jones	15
Brittain	R Massarella/t	P Massarella	D Massarella	Ashfield	Green	Stratford	Wickham/t	Wells	Jones(B)	16
Brittain	R Massarella	P Massarella	D Massarella/t	Ashfield	Green	Stratford	Wickham	Wells(D)	Jones/2t	17
Brittain	R Massarella	P Massarella	D Massarella	Ashfield	Green	Stratford(t)	Johnson	Bird	Jones/t	18
Brittain/3p	R Massarella	P Massarella	D Massarella/t	Ashfield	Green	Stratford	Johnson	Bird(H)	Bennett	19
Brittain/c2p	R Massarella	P Massarella(G)	D Massarella	Ashfield	Green/t	Stratford(e)	Johnson	Bird(H)	Bennett	20
Brittain/c(n/t)	R Massarella	P Massarella	D Massarella(k)	Ashfield	Green/t	Stratford	Johnson	Bird(D)	Bennett/t	21
C Massarella	R Massarella	P Massarella	D Massarella(G)	Ashfield	Green/t	Burgess/t(h)	Wells	Whitton(u)	Goodall	22
C Massarella	R Massarella	P Massarella	D Massarella	Wayne	Green	Burgess/t	Wells(u)	Whitton	Goodall	23
C Massarella	R Massarella/2t	P Massarella	D Massarella	Ashfield(s)	Burgess	Stratford(w)	Wells/t	Bird	Goodall/t	24
C Massarella	R Massarella	P Massarella	D Massarella(L)	Ashfield(s)	Burgess	Stratford(w)	Wells	Bird(D)	Goodall	25
C Massarella	R Massarella	P Massarella	D Massarella	Ashfield	Burgess	Goodall/t	Wells(D)	Bird(w/2t)	T Walton	26
C Massarella	R Massarella(k)	P Massarella	D Massarella/t	Bates(d)	Jones	Stratford(f)	Goodall	Wells	Whittle	A

REPLACEMENTS:

a- E Brittain	b- C Masarella	c - D Massarella	d - K Ashfield	e - A Jones
f - R Walton	g - N Bates	h - S Stratford	i - T Walton	j - J Bramwell
k - G Jenkins	l - D Whiteley	m - A Harrison	n - G Lennox	o - Z Griffin
p - D Kitching	q - S Bennett	r - R Anderson	s - P Wayne	t - M Burgess
u P Williams	v - C Bennett	w - P Green	x - P Hilyer	y - T Sanderson
z - C Dutton	A - R Dignan	B - D Johnson	C - N Castle	D - D Whitton
E - A Bott	F - P Carwood	G - T Kilburn	H - W Johnson	

Promising youngster Phil Curtis ends the season as leading points scorer for the club with 105 despite missing the last eight matches of the season with injury.

Leading try scorer was second row forward Andrew Jones with six, just one behind him was fellow second rower Paul Gree with five from 10 starts.

Hinckley lost successive matches in February by single points and that proved vital in the end as they went back to Midlands One.

Although they finished third bottom they were relegated because the two sides at the bottom of Jewson National One were northern sides and had to go into Jewson Two South.

LICHFIELD

Match No.	Date	H/A	Comp.	Opponents	Result & Score	Att.	15	14	13	12	11
1	05.09	A	J2N	New Brighton	L 7-45		Antcliffe	Allen	Baker	Gray	Brown/t
2	12.09	H	J2N	Preston	L 15-30		Antcliffe/cp	Bennion/t	Baker	Gray/t	Brown
3	26.09	A	J2N	Hinckley	L 5-30		Antcliffe/t(j)	Bennion(i)	Gray	Ryan	Brown
4	03.10	A	J2N	Whitchurch	L 21-28		Antcliffe	Allen/t	Gray/t	Mitchell	Brown
5	10.10	A	J2N	Sandal	L 24-41		Antcliffe/2c	Mitchell/2t	Gray	Ryan	Brown
6	24.10	A	J2N	Kendal	L 3-35		Antcliffe/p	Mitchell	Gray(b)	Ryan	Brown
7	31.10	H	J2N	Sedgley Park	L 17-28		Antcliffe/t	Allen	Baker	Ryan(i)	Brown/2t
8	07.11	A	J2N	Sheffield	L 7-21		Antcliffe/t	Allen	Gray(w)	Cobdan	Brown
9	21.11	H	J2N	Winnington P	W 16-15		Antcliffe(y)	Allen	Mitchell	Cobdan(w)	Brown/t
10	28.11	A	J2N	Aspatria	L 0-66		Brown	Allen	Sey	Wilton	Lucas
11	05.12	H	J2N	Walsall	W 17-8		Antcliffe/t	Mitchell	Gray/t	Baker	Brown(y)
12	12.12	A	J2N	Stourbridge	L 14-42		Antcliffe	Mitchell/t(k)	Gray	Sebright	Brown
13	19.12	H	J2N	Nuneaton	L 7-25		Antcliffe	Mitchell	Gray	Baker	Brown
14	28.12	A	J2N	Walsall	L 13-42		Antcliffe	Clarke	Gray	Baker	Brown/t
15	02.01	H	J2N	Aspatria	L 20-27		Antcliffe	Baker	Gray/t	Cobdan	Brown
16	09.01	A	J2N	Winnington P	L 10-21		Antcliffe/cp	Baker	Gray	Cobdan	Brown/t
17	16.01	H	J2N	Sheffield*	L 24-32		Antcliffe(C)	Mitchell	Gray/t	Cobdan	Brown
18	23.01	A	J2N	Sedgley Park	L 10-39		Antcliffe(C)	Mitchell/t	Gray	Baker	Brown(i)
19	30.01	H	J2N	Kendal	L 5-17		Antcliffe	Mitchell(k)	Gray	Cobdan	Brown
20	06.02	H	J2N	Sandal	L 17-73		Antcliffe(y/c)	Mitchell	Gray/t	Baker/t	Brown(k)
21	13.02	A	J2N	Whitchurch*	L 19-24		Antcliffe/t2c	Mitchell/t	Gray	Cobdan	Brown
22	27.02	H	J2N	Hinckley	W 29-24		Antcliffe/c	Mitchell	Gray/t	Jones	Brown/t
23	13.03	A	J2N	Preston	L 5-46		Antcliffe	Bennion/t	Gray	Jones	Brown
24	27.03	H	J2N	New Brighton	L 24-61		Antcliffe/t2c	Bennion(c)	Gray/t	Jones/t	Brown
25	13.04	A	J2N	Nuneaton	W 42-35		Antcliffe	Mitchell/t	Gray/2t	Jones	Brown/t
26	17.04	H	J2N	Stourbridge	L 0-74		Antcliffe	Mitchell	Gray	Jones	Brown(k)
A	19.09	A	TB1	New Brighton	L 8-33		Antcliffe/p	Bennion	Gray/t	Baker	Brown

* after opponents name indicates a penalty try
Brackets after a player's name indicates he was replaced. eg (a) means he was replaced by replacement code "a" and so on.
/ after a player or replacement name is followed by any scores he made - eg /t, /c, /p, /dg or any combination of these

1998-99 HIGHLIGHTS

Ever Presents:
Neil Antcliffe & Matthew Brown

Most appearances:

24	John Hicks (1)
23	Richie Randolph (1), Andy Gray, Mark Broomhall
22	James Hitchen

Players used: 43 plus seven as replacement only

Most Points in a season:

Pts	Player	T	C	P	DG
58	G Thomas	1	16	7	-
57	N Antcliffe	6	9	3	-
50	A Gray	10	-	-	-
40	M Brown	8	-	-	-
30	J Mitchell	6	-	-	-
19	R Clarke	-	5	3	-

MATCH FACTS

10	9	1	2	3	4	5	6	7	8	
Thomas/c	Broomhall	Mackin	Dipple(h)	Tyler	Taylor	Grant	Davies(f)	Hitchen	Hicks(g)	1
W-Smith	Broomhall	Mackin(e)	Dipple(n)	O'Leary	Taylor	Grant	Davies	Hitchen	Randolph	2
Thomas	Broomhall	Mackin	Parker	Tyler	Taylor(p)	Grant	Davies(a)	Hitchen(o)	Randolph	3
Thomas/3c	Broomhall	Bishop(s)	Parker	Tyler	Grant	Hicks	Davies/t	Hitchen(r)	Randolph	4
Thomas/t(b/t)	Broomhall	Bryant	O'Leary	Reay(t)	Grant	Hicks	Davies	Hitchen(g)	Randolph	5
W-Smith	Broomhall	Cartwright	O'Leary(u)	Robinson	Grant	Hicks	Davies	Hitchen	Randolph	6
Thomas/c	Broomhall	Mackin(s)	Cartwright	Robinson	Grant	Hicks	Davies	Hitchen	Randolph	7
Thomas/c	Broomhall	Mackin(s)	Cartwright	Robinson	Hicks	Perry	Davies	v Block(v)	Randolph	8
Thomas/2p	Broomhall	Mackin/t	Cartwright(n)	Robinson	Hicks	Bourne	Davies	Hitchen	Randolph	9
Antcliffe(g)	Sebright	Mackin	Cartwright(p)	Bryant	Morris	Hicks	Bourne	Hitchen	Randolph	10
Thomas/2cp	Broomhall	Mackin	Parker(h)	Robinson	Morris	Hicks	Davies	Hitchen	Randolph	11
Thomas/2c	Broomhall/t	Mackin	Parker	Robinson	Morris	Hicks	Davies	Hitchen	Randolph	12
Thomas/c	Broomhall/t	Mackin	Parker(s)	Robinson	Morris(A)	Hicks	Davies	Haber(x)	Randolph	13
Thomas/p(i)	Broomhall	Bryant	Tyler	Robinson	Morris(A)	Hicks	Davies/t	Randolph	Bourne	14
Thomas/2c2p	Broomhall	Reay	Tyler	Bryant	Vaughan	Hicks	Bourne(z)	Davies	Randolph/t	15
McDonald(q)	Broomhall	Reay(d)	O'Leary	Bryant	Vaughan	Hicks	Bourne	Davies(v)	Randolph	16
Thomas/3cp	Broomhall	Reay/t(d)	O'Leary	Bryant	Vaughan	Hicks	Bourne	Hitchen(v)	Randolph	17
Thomas	Broomhall	Reay(d)	O'Leary	Bryant	Vaughan(z)	Hicks	Bourne(v)	Hitchen	Randolph/t	18
McDonald/t	Broomhall	Reay	O'Leary	Bryant	Vaughan(E)	Hicks	Bourne	Hitchen	Randolph	19
McDonald(l)	Broomhall	Mackin	O'Leary(n)	Robinson(s)	Reay(E)	Morris	Hicks	Hitchen	Haber/t	20
McDonald	Broomhall	Mackin	O'Leary	Robinson	Hicks	Morris	Harvey	Hitchen	Randolph	21
McDonald/c	Broomhall	Mackin	Roberts	Robinson	Morris	Vaughan	Hicks/t	Hitchen/t	Haber/t	22
Clarke	Broomhall	Mackin	Roberts	Bryant(t)	Morris	Haber(A)	Hicks(v)	Hitchen	Randolph	23
McDonald	Broomhall/t	Mackin	Parker(m)	Bryant(g)	Reay	Vaughan	Hicks	Hitchen	Randolph	24
McDonald	Clarke/4c3p	Mackin	Ho	Robinson	Reay(g)	Vaughan(E)	Hicks/t	Hitchen	Randolph	25
McDonald(l)	Clarke(D)	Mackin	Ho(n)	Bryant(t)	Reay(g)	Vaughan	Hicks	Hitchen	Randolph	26
W-Smith	Broomhall	Mackin	Dipple(n)	O'Leary(e)	Grant	Taylor	Davies	Hitchen	Randolph	A

REPLACEMENTS:

	a- J Hicks	b- J Allen	c - S Baker	d - V Mackin	e - D Tyler
f - R Randolph	g - S Haber	h - M Davis	i - I Cobdan	j - T Bartlett	k - S Bennion
l - L Whitby Smith	m - M O'Leary	n - W Parker	o - M Bishop	p - A Reay	q - J Mitchell
r - R Ingram	s - M Bryant	t - R Robinson	u - M Roberts	v - G Sey	w - G McDonald
x - D Bourne	y - R Clarke	z - J Morris			
A - D Vaughan	B - A Lewis	C - S Bag	D - J Massey	E - I Grant	

Gareth Thomas in his first season at the club topped the points scoring list with 58 points, one clear of full back Neil Antcliffe.

Centre Andy Gray topped the try scoring list with nine tries. That put him one clear of winger Matthew Brown.

Lichfield lost their first 12 away matches before winning mid week against Nuneaton 42-35.

Their only other wins were at home against Winnington Park and Hinckley.

WINNINGTON PARK

Match No.	Date	H/A	Comp.	Opponents	Result & Score	Att.	15	14	13	12	11
1	05.09	A	J2N	Aspatria	L 7-57		Shillabeer	Aitken	B Barton	M Patterson	Gibson(i)
2	12.09	H	J2N	Walsall	L 3-24		Shillabeer	Aitken	B Barton	M Patterson	Haesler
3	26.09	A	J2N	Stourbridge	L 17-30		Beswick	Aitken/t	M Patterson	Manicom(p)	Haesler
4	03.10	H	J2N	Nuneaton	L 7-28		Beswick	Aitken	M Patterson	Manicom	Haesler
5	10.10	A	J2N	New Brighton	L 0-51		Beswick	C Patterson	M Patterson(p)	Manicom	Haesler(d)
6	24.10	H	J2N	Preston	L 20-50		Beswick	Wright/t	M Patterson	Hartill	C Patterosn(n)(t)
7	31.10	A	J2N	Hinckley	W 8-6		B Barton/tp	Wright	M Patterson	Hartill	S Barton
8	07.11	H	J2N	Whitchurch	L 10-26		B Barton/cp	Wright	M Patterson	S Barton	Phoenix
9	21.11	A	J2N	Lichfield	L 15-16		B Barton/cp	Wright	Hartill	S Barton(b)	Phoenix
10	28.11	H	J2N	Kendal	L 13-54		S Barton	Wright	B Barton/tc2p	Hartill	Phoenix
11	05.12	A	J2N	Sedgley Park	L 17-70		B Barton/tc	Wright	M Patterson/t	Hartill	Phoenix
12	12.12	H	J2N	Sheffield	L 16-27		B Barton/2p	Wright	Hartill	M Patterson	Phoenix
13	19.12	A	J2N	Sandal	L 17-47		S Barton(E)	Watt	Hartill	M Patterson	Phoenix
14	27.12	H	J2N	Sedgley Park	L 15-16		B Barton/cp	Watt/t	Hartill	Myers	Beswick
15	02.01	A	J2N	Kendal	L 3-37		B Barton/p(D)	Watt(r)	Hartill	Myers	Beswick
16	09.01	H	J2N	Lichfield	W 21-10		B Barton/c3p	Watt/t	Hartill/t	Myers	Beswick
17	16.01	A	J2N	Whitchurch	L 17-36		B Barton/c	Watt(p/t)	Hartill	Myers/t	Beswick/t
18	23.01	H	J2N	Hinckley	L 13-28		Beswick	S Barton	Hartill	Myers	Wright/t(b)
19	30.01	A	J2N	Preston	L 8-60		S Barton	Kelly(q)	Hartill	Myers	Wright
20	06.02	H	J2N	New Brighton	L 14-26		S Barton	Beswick/t	Hartill(b)	Myers	Wright
21	13.02	A	J2N	Nuneaton	L 5-57		S Barton	Wright(b)	Hartill	Myers	Beswick
22	13.03	H	J2N	Stourbridge	L 0-53		Beswick	Watts	Hartill	S Barton	Wright
23	20.03	A	J2N	Walsall	L 10-63		Beswick	Watts	Hartill	S Barton	Wright
24	27.03	H	J2N	Aspatria	W 45-23		B Barton/3t5c	S Barton	Hartill	Myers(E)	C Patterson/t
25	03.04	H	J2N	Sandal	L 6-53		B Barton/2p	S Barton	Hartill	Myers(y)	C Patterson
26	17.04	A	J2N	Sheffield	L 3-13		B Barton/p	S Barton(r)	Hartill	Myers	C Patterson
A	19.09	A	TB1	Tynedale	L 10-47		Shillabeer	Aitken/t	M Patterson	S Barton(n)	Haesler(q)

* after opponents name indicates a penalty try
Brackets after a player's name indicates he was replaced. eg (a) means he was replaced by replacement code "a" and so on.
/ after a player or replacement name is followed by any scores he made - eg /t, /c, /p, /dg or any combination of these

1998-99 HIGHLIGHTS

Ever Present: Mike Bebbington

Most appearances:

23	Ben Barton
20	Dave Hartill, Ian Davies (5), Matt Dodds (2)
19	Danny Haddock

Players used: 44 plus eight as replacement only

Most Points in a season:

Pts	Player	T	C	P	DG
124	B Barton	6	14	22	-
32	N Yardley	5	2	1	-
15	J Pickering	3	-	-	-
15	M Dodds	3	-	-	-
10	I Davies	2	-	-	-
10	D Wright	2	-	-	-
10	T Cope	2	-	-	-
10	M Bebbington	2	-	-	-

MATCH FACTS

10	9	1	2	3	4	5	6	7	8	
Shaw/c	Agar(l)	Lakey	Green	Davies(j)	Bebbington	Cope/t	Haesler	Staley	Yardley(k)	1
Shaw/p(m)	Pickering	Lakey	Green	Davies	Haddock	Cope	Bebbington	Staley	Yardley(n)	2
Shaw/c	Pickering	Alcock	Dodds	Davies	Haddock	Bebbington	Sproston	Staley	Yardley/2t	3
B Barton(q/c)	Pickering(v)	Alcock(j)	Dodds(e)	Davies	Haddock	Bebbington	Sproston	Staley	Yardley(g)	4
Shaw	Agar(r)	Evans	Dodds(e)	Davies	Haddock	Bebbington	Sproston	Staley(s)	Bebbington	5
B Barton/cp	Pickering	Lakey	Dodds(i)	Davies/2t	Cope	Haddock	Sproston(s)	Yardley	Bebbington	6
Shaw	Agar	Lakey	Dodds	Davies	Cope(u)	Haddock	Sproston	Yardley(s)	Bebbington	7
Shaw	Pickering(r)	Lakey(v)	Dodds(e)	Davies	Cope/t	Haddock	Sproston	Richardson(h)	Bebbington	8
Shaw	Saverimutto	Alcock(d)	Green(o)	Davies	Haddock	Bebbington	Sproston(s)	Staley	Yardley/2t	9
Beswick	Saverimutto	Alcock(f)	Dodds	O'Keefe	Haddock	Cope	Yardley(s)	Staley	Bebbington	10
Beswick	Pickering	Alcock(d)	Dodds	O'Keefe/t	Faulkner(i)	Haddock	Sproston(g)	Staley	Bebbington	11
Beswick	Pickering/t	Alcock	Dodds/t(i)	O'Keefe(f)	Faulkner	Haddock	Sproston	Yardley	Bebbington	12
Shaw	Pickering/t	Davies	Dodds(i)	O'Keefe	Faulkner	D Green	Staley	Yardley/t2cp	Bebbington	13
Shaw	Pickering	Alcock(f)	Dodds	O'Keefe	Faulkner	Cope	Richardson	Yardley	Bebbington/t	14
Shaw	Agar	Alcock	Dodds	Davies	Faulkner	Cope	Richardson	Yardley	Bebbington	15
Shaw	Pickering	Faulkner(f)	Dodds(i)	O'Keefe	Cope	Haddock	Richardson	Yardley	Bebbington	16
Shaw(q)	Pickering(c)(i)	Faulkner	Dodds	O'Keefe(f)	Cope	Haddock	Richardson	Yardley	Bebbington	17
B Barton/p	Pickering/t(r)	Alcock	Dodds(i)	Davies	Faulkner	Haddock	Cope	Yardley(s)	Bebbington	18
B Barton/p	Pickering(x/t)	Faulkner	Dodds	Davies	Haddock	S Bebbington(d)	Bebbington(z)	Richardson	Jones	19
B Barton/3p	Sharples	Alcock(d)	Green(o)	Davies	Jennings	S Bebbington	Jones	Staley	Bebbington	20
B Barton(y)	Sharples(l)	Lakey	Dodds	Davies	Jennings(z)	S Bebbington	Jones/t	Staley	Bebbington	21
B Barton	Pickering(x)	Lakey	Wardell	Davies	Haddock	Bebbington	Richardson	Jones	Rooney	22
B Barton/cp	Pickering	Lakey	Dodds	Davies	Haddock	Bebbington/t	Richarson	Jones	Rooney	23
Beswick	Pickering(x/t)	Alcock(d)	Dodds/2t(e)	Davies	Haddock	Jennings(s)	Jones	Williams	Bebbington	24
Beswick	Sharples	Alcock	Dodds(e)	Davies	Haddock	Jennings(s)	Jones(z)	Williams(A)	Bebbington	25
Beswick	Sharples	Alcock(d)	Dodds	Davies	Cope(z)	Bebbington	Richardson(A)	Williams	Jones	26
Shaw(m)	Pickering	Alcock	Green/t	Davies	Haddock	Cope	Sproston	Staley	Bebbington	A

REPLACEMENTS:

a- M Shillabber, b- M Patterson, c - N Agar, d - C Lakey, e - M Green, f - I Davies, g - T Cope, h - G Staley, i - L Wardell, j - C Gleave, k - D Christmas, l - J Pickering, m - P Beswick, n - A Manicom, o - M Dodds, p - S Barton, q - C Patterson, r - C Blenkinsop, s - B Richardson, t - T Shaw, u - M Phoenix, v - D Alcock, w - N Archer, x - P Sharples, y - J Watt, z - M Plamer, A - E Rooney, C - D Yardley, D - W Sharpe, E - N Archer, F - D Green

Ben Barton was easily Winnington Park's leading points scorer with 124.

Barton was also the club's leading try scorer with six. After Barton the next best was three by two players.

Barton set a seasons high 25 points in the home win against Aspatria with three tries and five conversions

Park are releagated for the first time ever since the introduction of league rugby back in 1987-88. They started their career in North One, won promotion in the first season and have been in this division ever since.

Won just once away from home all season with an 8-6 win at Hinckley.

THE LAST TEN YEARS

1989-90

Champions	Runners-up	Relegated
Broughton Park	Morley	-

Most

Penalties: 15 Jamie Grayshon (Morley) | Points: 78 Jamie Grayshon (Morley) | Conversions: 8 Jamie Grayshon (Morley) | Tries: 5 Paul White (Morley) | D.Gs: 3 Jamie Grayshon (Morley)

1990-91

Champions	Runners-up	Relegated
Otley	Lichfield	Stoke on Trent, Birmingham Solihull

Most

Penalties: 28 Paul Grayson (Preston G) | Points: 105 Paul Grayson (Preston G) | Conversions: 17 Jon Howarth (Otley) | Tries: 16 Jon Walker (Otley) | D.Gs: 4 Richard Mills (Walsall)

1991-92

Champions	Runners-up	Relegated
Aspatria	Hereford	Vale of Lune, Northern

Most

Penalties: 25 Paul Grayson (Preston G) | Points: 127 Paul Grayson (Preston G) | Conversions: 13 Andrew harrison (Aspatria) | Tries: 7 Jimmy Miller (Aspatria) | D.Gs: 6 Paul Grayson (Preston G)

1992-93

Champions	Runners-up	Relegated
Harrogate	Rotherham	Towcestrians

Most

Penalties: 31 Simon Pennington (Stourbridge) | Points: 131 Ralph Zoing (Harrogate) | Conversions: 28 Ralph Zoing (Harrogate) | Tries: 9 Guy Easterby (Harrogate), Steve Baker (Harrogate) | D.Gs: N.A.

1993-94

Champions	Runners-up	Relegated
Rotherham	Preston Grasshoppers	Bradford & Bingley, Durham City

Most

Penalties: 23 Richard Mills (Walsall) | Points: 118 Kevin Plant (Rotherham) | Conversions: 22 Kevin Plant (Rotherham) | Tries: 8 John Dudley (Rotherham) | D.Gs: N.A.

1994-95

Champions	Runners-up	Relegated
Walsall	Kendal	Hereford, Barkers' Butts

Most

Penalties: 31 Richard Mills (Walsall) | Points: 164 Richard MIlls (Walsall) | Conversions: 29 Richard Mills (Walsall) | Tries: 11 Jon Rowe (Walsall) | D.Gs: N.A.

1995-96

Champions	Runners-up	Relegated
Wharfedale	Worcester	Broughton Park

Most

Penalties: 29 Alex Howarth (Wharfedale) | Points: 143 Alex Howarth (Wharfedale) | Conversions: 23 Alex Howarth (Wharfedale) | Tries: 10 Neil Hezeltine (Wharfedale), Spencer Bradley (Worcester) | D.Gs: 3 Warwick Masser (Nuneaton)

1996-97

Champions	Runners-up	Relegated
Worcester	Birmingham Solihull	Hereford, Stoke on Trent

Most

Penalties: 64 Steve Kerry (Preston G) | Points: 317 Steve Kerry (Preston G) | Conversions: 61 Tim Smith (Worcester) | Tries: 18 Nick Baxter (Worcester) | D.Gs: 9 Steve Kerry (Preston G)

1997-98

Champions	Runners-up	Relegated
Birmingham Solihull	Manchester	-

Most

Penalties: 62 Steve Swindells (Manchester) | Points: 398 Steve Swindells (Manchester) | Conversions: 91 Steve Swindells (Manchester) | Tries: 21 Matt Hoskin (Manchester) | D.Gs: 4 Ian Shuttleworth (Sandal), Rob Pound (Sheffield)

1998-99

Champions	Runners-up	Relegated
Preston Grasshoppers	Stourbridge	Hinckley, Lichfield, Winnington Park

Most

Penalties: | Points: | Conversions: | Tries: | D.Gs:

TEAM RECORDS

Highest score:	**101**	Manchester 101 Nuneaton 12, 25.4.98
Highest aggregate:	**113**	as above
Highest score by a losing side:	**38**	Nuneaton 40 Aspatria 38, 9.11.96
Highest scoring draw:	**33**	Nuneaton v Kendal, 25.1.98
Most consecutive wins:	**15**	Worcester 1996-97
Most consecutive defeats:	**18**	Stoke-on-Trent 1996-97
Most points for in a season:	**1029**	Manchester 1997-98
Least points for in a season:	**29**	Birmingham Solihull 1988-89
Most points against in a season:	**972**	Hereford 1996-97
Least points against in a season:	**67**	Roundhay 1987-88
Most tries for in a season:	**127**	Manchester 1997-98
Most tries against in a season:	**131**	Hereford 1996-97
Least tries for in a season:		
Least tries against in a season:		
Most conversions for in a season:	**98**	Manchester 1997-98
Most conversions against in a season:	**82**	Hereford 1996-97
Most penalties for in a season:	**73**	Sheffield 1996-97
Most penalties against in a season:	**60**	Winnington Park 1996-97
Least penalties for in a season:		
Least penalties against in a season:		
Most drop goals for in a season:	**10**	Preston Grasshoppers 1996-97
Most drop goals against in a season:	**8**	Aspatria 1996-97

INDIVIDUAL RECORDS

Most points in a season:	**398**	Steve Swindells (Manchester) 1997-98
Most tries in a season:	**21**	Matt Hoskin (Manchester) 1997-98
Most conversions in a season:	**91**	Steve Swindells (Manchester) 1997-98
Most penalties in a season:	**64**	Steve Kerry (Preston Grasshoppers) 1996-97
Most drop goals in a season:	**9**	Steve Kerry (Preston Grasshoppers) 1996-97
Most points in a match:	**44**	Jamie Morley, Sheffield v Lichfield 7.9.97
Most tries in a match:	**6**	Jason Slater, Kendal v Barkers Butts 14.1.95
Most conversions in a match:	**10**	Steve Swindells, Manchester v Nuneaton 25.4.98 Kevin Plant, Rotherham v Durham 19.2.94
Most penalties in a match:	**8**	Steve Baker, Stourbridge v Hereford 26.1.91
Most drop goals in a match:	**4**	Steve Kerry, Preston G. v Aspatria 7.9.96

TEN YEAR RECORD

Club	SEASONS									
	89-90	90-91	91-92	92-93	93-94	94-95	95-96	96-97	97-98	98-99
Aspatria	-	-	1	-	-	-	-	10	9	10
Barkers Butts	-	-	-	-	-	12	-	-	-	-
Birmingham Solihull	-	13	-	-	9	10	3	2	1p	-
Bradford & Bingley	-	-	-	-	13	-	-	-	-	-
Broughton Park	1	-	-	-	-	-	13	-	-	-
Durham City	4	10	10	8	12	-	-	-	-	-
Harrogate	-	6	7	1	-	-	-	-	-	-
Hereford	-	11	2	11	8	13	-	13	-	-
Hinckley	-	-	-	-	-	-	-	-	12	12r
Kendal	5	5	3	6	10	2	9	9	3	4
Lichfield	7	2	5	5	7	5	12	11	13	13r
Manchester	-	-	-	-	-	-	-	4	2p	-
Morley	2	-	-	-	-	-	-	-	-	-
New Brighton	-	-	-	-	-	-	-	-	-	3
Northern	8	7	13	-	-	-	-	-	-	-
Nuneaton	-	-	-	12	11	11	10	12	7	5
Otley	-	1	-	-	-	-	-	-	-	-
Preston Grasshoppers	6	3	4	3	2	3	8	3	4	1p
Rotherham	-	-	-	2	1	-	-	-	-	-
Sandal	-	-	-	-	-	-	6	5	8	7
Sedgley park	-	-	-	-	-	-	-	-	5	8
Sheffield	-	-	-	-	-	9	5	8	10	6
Stoke on Trent	11	12	-	4	6	7	11	14	-	-
Stourbridge	3	8	6	9	5	6	7	6	6	2
Towcestrians	-	-	9	13	-	-	-	-	-	-
Vale of Lune	-	-	13	-	-	-	-	-	-	-
Walsall	10	9	11	7	3	1	-	-	11	9
Winnington Park	9	4	8	10	4	8	4	7	14	14r
Wharfedale	-	-	-	-	4	1	-	-	-	-
Whitchurch	-	-	-	-	-	-	-	-	-	11
Worcester	-	-	-	-	-	-	2	1	-	-

JEWSON NATIONAL LEAGUE

TWO SOUTH

1998-99 Season

Review & statistics 402-405

1999-200 Fixtures 406

CLUBS

Barking	407
Bridgwater & Albion	411
Cheltenham	415
Clifton	419
Esher	423
Metropolitan Police	427
North Walsham	431
Norwich	435
Penzance & Newlyn	439
Plymouth Albion	443
Redruth	447
Tabard	451
Westcombe Park	455
Weston-super-Mare	459

Match Facts 1998-99

Havant 464/5

Division Four South Records

466-468

	P	W	D	L	F	A	PD	Pts	HOME W	HOME D	HOME L	HOME F	HOME A	HOME Tries For	HOME Pens For	HOME Tries Against	HOME Pens Against	AWAY W	AWAY D	AWAY L	AWAY F	AWAY A	AWAY Tries For	AWAY Pens For	AWAY Tries Against	AWAY Pens Against
Bracknell	26	23	1	2	631	317	314	47	13	0	0	315	113	35	31	10	18	10	1	2	316	204	36	27	24	18
Esher	26	23	0	3	864	308	556	46	12	0	1	545	112	77	22	8	20	11	0	2	319	196	34	38	19	26
North Walsham	26	22	0	4	627	306	321	44	12	0	1	348	112	49	15	12	13	10	0	3	279	194	40	14	20	26
Barking	26	19	1	6	644	327	317	39	11	1	1	381	117	53	25	13	14	8	0	5	263	210	32	23	22	27
Met Police	26	14	1	11	470	545	-75	29	8	1	4	293	228	37	21	29	19	6	0	7	177	317	22	12	44	13
Norwich	26	11	0	15	383	429	-46	22	8	0	5	263	171	31	23	21	15	3	0	10	120	258	16	6	28	29
Clifton	26	10	1	15	415	483	-68	21	5	0	8	257	240	29	28	25	26	5	1	7	158	243	13	24	31	17
Tabard	26	9	1	16	461	501	-40	19	5	1	7	241	219	26	27	24	20	4	0	9	220	282	26	19	34	24
Weston -s - Mare	26	9	1	16	415	588	-173	19	5	1	7	207	241	28	13	24	26	4	0	9	208	347	26	16	42	27
Bridgwater & Albion	26	8	2	16	463	624	-162	18	7	1	5	311	227	34	30	28	18	1	1	11	152	397	18	16	53	25
Redruth	26	8	1	17	503	652	-149	17	6	0	7	321	278	39	24	37	15	2	1	10	182	374	18	26	52	16
Plymouth	26	7	1	18	457	666	-209	15	6	0	7	266	291	33	19	40	16	1	1	11	191	375	21	19	50	26
Cheltenham	26	7	0	19	335	608	-273	14	5	0	8	194	247	16	33	27	27	2	0	11	141	361	14	18	44	28
Havant	26	7	0	19	361	675	-314	14	4	0	9	204	287	30	9	37	22	3	0	10	157	388	19	11	54	19

Review of the season 1998-1999

Bracknell won the Jewson Two South title at their first attempt. They spent most of the season just behind Esher and North Walsham but their consistency saw them take top spot after beating Esher at home. After that they maintained their composure and took the title by a point. Although they were not the division's top scorers, they did what they had to win the matches and came out on top in the close matches. They only lost twice all season and that was in their first two away matches. After that they were unbeaten all season with a draw at Barking the only time they did not take both points.

Esher were the division's glamour side rattling up the points and tries. They had three of the top six try scorers in the division and in John Gregory the leading points scorer. They slipped up on the road losing at Weston super Mare early in the season and then lost narrowly at home to North Walsham and away at Bracknell. They also had the best defensive record conceding just 27 tries in 26 league matches, but it was not to be and they will need to regroup and try again next season.

North Walsham surprised everybody with their exciting running game. In previous seasons they have always been a good side defensively but had trouble scoring tries. This time round they finished as second highest try scorers as new coach Jim McKay got the back division moving. They had the chance to put the pressure on Bracknell but went down 31-14 late in the season and with it their hopes of promotion.

Barking could not quite do it against the big sides. In six matches against the top three they managed just one win, against North Walsham at home. They were among the leading try scorers with contributions coming from both backs and forwards alike.

Met Police would not have been here but for the Allied Dunbar leagues increasing last season. But they took advantage of their reprieve and finished an excellent fifth. By their standards they had a settled side and with Andy Carter and Richard Galvin both in superb form they were a match for most on their day.

Norwich ended up sixth despite a bad mid season after a positive start in their first campaign at this level. Early on they shocked a few sides and were going well but a mid season collapse halted their progress. With the teams around them also erratic they manage to find their form again and finish a highly creditable sixth.

Clifton will be delighted with their seventh place, which was due mainly to their improved away form. They finished with three straight wins on their travels and overall won five and drew one. Part of their success was down to a much improved defence, which conceded far fewer tries this season.

Tabard had a disappointing campaign compared with the previous season. The side never quite found any consistent form with just five home wins all season. Mid season they had a run of ten matches without a win which saw them drop down the table after a promising start.

Weston super Mare started the season brightly and showing impressive form at home beating Esher and Tabard in winning their first five at home. Their home form then fell through the floor with just one win in the remainder of the season.

Bridgwater & Albion had a disappointing season changing coaches mid stream. They are now looking to appoint a Director of Rugby and lay the foundations for the club to move forward. They have had two below average seasons at this level and will be looking to improve next campaign.

Redruth had an up and down season; they scored plenty of tries but also conceded plenty as well. Some good home form saw them safe but if the are to avoid finishing in the bottom half again they need to try and improve their away form. They managed just two wins, at Clifton and Plymouth, compared with six home wins.

Plymouth, who only escaped the drop last year because there was no relegation, pushed their luck again this season. They had to win on the final day of the campaign to avoid going down. They travelled to Weston super Mare and came away with the right result and escaped again. Surely they do not want to be in the same situation next season as their luck could well run out a third time.

Cheltenham escaped on the last day of the season despite losing at Bracknell. Their survival was due to their two home wins in the previous matches against fellow strugglers Plymouth and Havant. Had a limited squad that was pushed to the limit through injury problems. They need to find a few experienced players to mould the side together and help them win the close encounters.

Havant were relegated after struggling all season. They had a problem scoring points and also conceding points, which is not a good recipe for success. Even though they improved late on the damage was already done, and although they won on the last day against Bridgwater & Albion with Cheltenham holding Bracknell to just a sixteen point defeat, Havant were relegated on points difference.

1998-99 RECORD REVIEW (Individual Records)

MOST POINTS - IN A SEASON

Former Richmond full back Jon Gregory became the second player to score 300 points in a season in the division but still finshed 60 points off the all time record. That was set by Newbury's Nick Grecian three seasons ago.

EVOLUTION OF RECORD

69	John Field	Askeans	1987-88
83	Simon Harvey	Clifton	1989-90
122	Melvin Badger	Weston-s-Mare	1990-91
129	Pete Russell	Havant	1991-92
133	Phil Belshaw	Reading	1993-94
176	Richard Perkins	Henley	1995-96
391	Nick Grecian	Newbury	1996-97

ALL-TIME RECORDS

391	Nick Grecian	Newbury	1996-97
313	Jonathan Gregory	Esher	1998-99
264	Nick Churchman	Tabard	1996-97
256	Rob Thirlby	Redruth	1997-98
253	James Shanahan	N Walsham	1997-98
248	Nick Thomson	Barking	1996-97
242	Nick Edmonds	Bridgwater & A	1997-98
239	Nick Churchman	Tabard	1997-98
223	Mark Slevin	Met Police	1996-97
217	Justin Azzopardi	Barking	1998-99

MOST PENALTIES - IN A SEASON

Esher's Jon Gregory set a new record for penalties in a season with 58 which beat Nick Churchman's old record by five.

EVOLUTION OF RECORD

13	John Field	Askeans	1987-88
15	Simon Harvey	Clifton	1989-90
27	Rob Ashworth	Havant	1990-91
34	Phil Belshaw	Reading	1993-94
53	Nick Churchman	Tabard	1996-97

ALL-TIME RECORDS

53	Nick Churchman	Tabard	1996-97
51	James Shanahan	N Walsham	1997-98
50	Nick Edmonds	Bridgwater & A	1997-98
45	Carson Russell	Bracknell	1998-99
44	Justin Azzopardi	Barking	1998-99
42	Mark Slevin	Met Police	1996-97
42	Nick Grecian	Newbury	1996-97
41	Rhys Oakley	Clifton	1998-99
41	Chris Sidwell	Redruth	1998-99
38	Nick Buoy	Henley Hawks	1997-98
38	Nick Churchman	Tabard	1997-98

MOST TRIES - IN A SEASON

Three players topped the try scoring list with 16 tries during last season and move into fifth on the division's all time list.

EVOLUTION OF RECORD

7	John Willis	Redruth	1988-89
8	Melvin Badger	Weston-s-Mare	1990-91
9	Will Knight	Havant	1991-92
12	Steve Titcombe	Sudbury	1992-93
27	Brian Johnson	Newbury	1996-97

ALL-TIME RECORDS

27	Brian Johnson	Newbury	1996-97
25	Craig Davies	Newbury	1996-97
19	Tom Holloway	Newbury	1996-97
17	Robert Thirlby	Redruth	1997-98
16	Nana Dontah	Esher	1998-99
16	James Shanahan	N Walsham	1998-99
16	Andy Carter	Met Police	1998-99
15	Steve Walklin	Plymouth	1997-98
15	Mark Venner	Henley	1997-98
15	Michael Corcoran	Esher	1998-99

MOST CONVERSIONS - IN A SEASON

Jon Gregory, Esher's full back, moves into number two on the all time list in his first season with the club but still over 40 behind Nick Grecian's record.
Bracknell's Carson Russell also in his first, and only season in the division, kicks 39 conversions and moves to No 4 on the all time list.

EVOLUTION OF RECORD

9	John Field	Askeans	1987-88
10	Simon Harvey	Clifton	1989-90
16	Simon Blake	Redruth	1990-91
23	Pete Russelll	Havant	1991-92
28	Mike Hamlin	London Welsh	1992-93
100	Nick Grecian	Newbury	1996-97

ALL-TIME RECORDS

100	Nick Grecian	Newbury	1996-97
52	Jon Gregory	Esher	1998-99
48	Robert Thirlby	Redruth	1997-98
39	Carson Russell	Bracknell	1998-99
38	Nick Thomson	Barking	1996-97
37	Mark Slevin	Met Police	1996-97
36	Jason Hoad	Camberley	1996-97
35	Nick Churchman	Tabard	1997-98
31	Nick Churchman	Tabard	1996-97
31	Phil Friel	N Walsham	1998-99

MOST DROP GOALS - IN A SEASON

Nobody managed more than three dropped goals during the season - way behind the division's record of 11 set the previous season by Bridgwater & Albions Nick Edmonds.

EVOLUTION OF RECORD

2	Andy Perry	Havant	1987-88
	Andy Perry	Havant	1988-89
6	Simon Harvey	Clifton	1989-90
10	Simon Cattermole	Weston-s-Mare	1996-97
11	Nick Edmonds	Bridgwater & Alb.	1997-98

ALL-TIME RECORDS

11	Nick Edmonds	Bridgwater & Alb.	1997-98
10	Simon Cattermole	Weston-s-Mare	1996-97
6	Simon Harvey	Clifton	1989-90
6	James Shanahan	N Walsham	1997-98

1998-99

JEWSON TWO SOUTH

MOST POINTS

POINTS			T	C	P	DG
313	Jonathan Gregory	Esher	7	60	70	0
217	Justin Azzopardi	Barking	6	26	44	1
216	Carson Russell	Bracknell	-	39	45	1
175	Chris Sidwell	Redruth	1	22	41	1
160	Jonathan Griffin	Norwich	4	25	27	3
158	Phil Friel	N Walsham	6	31	22	-
153	Rhys Oakley	Clifton	-	15	41	-
148	Nick Churchman	Tabard	4	19	29	1
144	Nick Edmonds	Bridgwater & A	-	18	34	2
118	Andy Carter	Met Police	16	10	6	-
115	Mark Armstrong	Weston	4	19	16	3
112	James Shanahan	N Walsham	16	7	4	2
97	James Herring	Met Police	1	10	23	1
89	Michael Corcoran	Esher	15	4	2	-
89	Richard Thompson	Plymouth	6	10	10	3
88	Phil Watters	Cheltenham	1	7	23	-

MOST PENALTIES

58	Jon Gregory	Esher
45	Carson Russell	Bracknell
44	Justin Azzopardi	Barking
41	Rhys Oakley	Clifton
41	Chris Sidwell	Redruth
34	Nick Edmonds	Bridgwater & A
29	Nick Churchman	Tabard
27	Jonathan Griffin	Norwich
23	James Herring	Met Police
23	Phil Watters	Cheltenham
22	Phil Friel	N Walsham
19	Matthew Watts	Cheltenham
16	Mark Armstrong	Weston s Mare
13	Nick Burt	Plymouth
13	Neil Coleman	Weston s Mare
11	Ralph Knibbs	Clifton
10	Micky Skinner	Tabard
10	Ben Nowak	Bracknell

MOST TRIES

16	Nana Dontah	Esher
16	Andy Carter	Met Police
16	James Shanahan	N Walsham
15	Michael Corcoran	Esher
14	David Bird	Weston s Mare
13	Andy Gollings	Bridgwater & A
13	Jim McKay	N Walsham
12	Ciaran Bird	Esher
11	Scott Gregory	Barking
11	Chris Greenhall	N Walsham
10	Steve Walklin	Plymoth 6, Redruth 4
8	Denville Ellerston	Havant
8	Paul Gastor	Met Police
8	Richard Gastor	Met Police
8	Howard Lamb	Bracknell
8	Phil Hopley	Bracknell
8	Steve Larkins	Redruth
8	Richard Goodwin	Esher

MOST CONVERSIONS

52	Jon Gregory	Esher
39	Carson Russell	Bracknell
31	Phil Friel	N Walsham
26	Justin Azzopardi	Barking
25	Jonathan Griffin	Norwich
22	Chris Sidwell	Redruth
19	Nick Churchman	Tabard
19	Mark Armstrong	Weston s Mare
18	Nick Edmonds	Bridgwater & A
15	Rhys Oakley	Clifton
15	Mark Slevin	Met Police
10	Andy Ashwin	Havant
10	Andy Carter	Met Police
10	James Herring	Met Police
10	Richard Thompson	Plymouth

MOST DROP GOALS

3	Jonathan Griffin	Norwich
3	Mark Armstrong	Weston s Mare
3	Richard Thompson	Plymouth
3	Richard Bailey	Esher
3	Ralph Knibbs	Clifton
2	Nick Edmonds	Bridgwater & Alb
2	Jamie Donaldson	Bridgwater & Alb
2	James Shanahan	N Walsham
2	Martin Thompson	Plymouth
2	Stewart Whitworth	Redruth

JEWSON NATIONAL TWO SOUTH FIXTURES 1999-2000

Away Teams

	HOME TEAMS	Barking	Bridgwater & Alb.	Cheltenham	Clifton	Esher	Metropolitan Police	North Walsham	Norwich	Penzance & Newlyn	Plymouth Albion	Redruth	Tabard	Westcombe Park	Weston-s-Mare	
1	Barking	X	25.09	25.03	11.09	09.10	20.11	26.02	18.12	29.01	30.10	15.01	28.08	04.12	15.04	1
2	Bridgwater & Albion	11.03	X	11.12	25.03	22.01	11.09	12.02	02.10	08.01	22.04	28.08	27.11	23.10	06.11	2
3	Cheltenham	04.09	15.04	X	08.04	25.09	30.10	18.03	15.01	26.02	09.10	29.01	04.12	20.11	18.12	3
4	Clifton	18.03	04.09	28.08	X	26.02	15.01	25.09	20.11	09.10	29.01	30.10	15.04	18.12	04.12	4
5	Esher	12.02	30.10	11.03	02.10	X	04.12	23.10	15.04	15.01	20.11	18.12	11.09	28.08	25.03	5
6	Metropolitan Police	08.01	18.03	22.01	06.11	22.04	X	27.11	11.03	11.12	08.04	04.09	23.10	02.10	12.02	6
7	North Walsham	02.10	09.10	11.09	11.03	29.01	18.12	X	04.12	30.10	15.01	20.11	25.03	15.04	28.08	7
8	Norwich	27.11	26.02	07.11	08.01	11.12	25.09	22.04	X	08.04	04.09	18.03	22.01	12.02	23.10	8
9	Penzance & Newlyn	23.10	20.11	02.10	12.02	06.11	15.04	22.01	28.08	X	18.12	04.12	11.03	25.03	11.09	9
10	Plymouth Albion	22.01	04.12	12.02	23.10	08.01	28.08	06.11	25.03	27.11	X	15.04	02.10	11.09	11.03	10
11	Redruth	06.11	08.04	23.10	22.01	27.11	25.03	08.01	11.09	22.04	11.12	X	12.02	11.03	02.10	11
12	Tabard	08.04	18.12	22.04	11.12	18.03	29.01	04.09	30.10	25.09	26.02	09.10	X	15.01	20.11	12
13	Westcombe Park	22.04	29.01	08.01	27.11	08.04	26.02	11.12	09.10	04.09	18.03	25.09	07.11	X	22.01	13
14	Weston-Super-Mare	11.12	15.01	27.11	22.04	04.09	09.10	08.04	29.01	18.03	25.09	26.02	08.01	30.10	X	14
		1	2	3	4	5	6	7	8	9	10	11	12	13	14	

BARKING R.U.F.C.

President	Gerald Mansfield	34 Spencer Road, Rainham, Essex RM13 8HB 0171 260 4904 (B) 01708 551073 (H)
Club Secretary	Jim Marner	Meadow View, Kirkham Road, Horndon-on-the-hill, Essex SS17 8QE 01708 858136 (B) 01268 490550 (H) 07957 328363 (M) 01708 858660 (F)
Treasurer	Keith Parker	Barking RFC Ltd., Gale St., Dagenham, Essex RM9 4TX 0181 595 7324 (Club)
Fixtures Secretary	Pauline Knight	89 Oxlow Lane, Dagenham, Essex RM9 5XD 0181 526 4637 (B) 0181 594 0025 (H)
Director of Rugby	Jeff Probyn	**Director of Coaching** Martin Jones **Senior Coaches:** Alan Evans & Steve Putts

A season that started with such promise for the first XV ended with only the Essex Sevens to show for their endeavours. The 1998/99 season will be sadly noteworthy for all the wrong reasons, notably the deaths of leading individuals at the club, most particularly the club president Bill Marshall and Derek Bacon, the club's first bar steward upon its move to its Gale Street HQ. Both will be missed and remembered for their contribution to the club's successes, which they each contributed to. Less seriously the club failed to improve on their finish in third position last year and actually slipped a place (ceding their title of most successful Eastern Counties side to North Walsham in the process).

Injuries to key players such as Justin Murphy in the front row, Macer Twydell at No 6 and Dean Cutting at scrum-half meant we had our strongest side (on paper) out about twice all season. Let's hope the close season sees at least three natural front row players sign for Barking - then watch us go!

On the field, the lame display put on during most of the match down in Redruth just before Christmas was painful to watch. Barking only awoke with twenty minutes to go in a contest they had sleep walked through to that point, by which time they had left themselves too much to do and went down 22-18 to the jubilant Cornishmen. The 56-20 home victory went some way towards showing Redruth why we ended five places above them come the end of the season.

The 19-24 home defeat to Esher still smarts as the team let themselves down with some poor tactical decisions at key moments. Esher proved themselves the most impressive visitors to Goresbrook over the course of the season.

Bracknell were let off the hook on their visit to Essex, when the home side failed to turn possession into points - which was to be the season's most common observation.

Bracknell played a very on-song Barkingside that day, but still looked a more lightweight proposition than Esher on their visit across London. The early season win (18-8) over a muscular North Walsham side promised much - but by the time Barking travelled to Norfolk for the rematch the home win was no surprise.

Of the other also rans only the Metropolitan Police threatened an upset upon their visit to Goresbrook.Ultimately it was the dropped points at home and the baffling away defeat at Redruth that cost Barking a serious tilt at the title.

During the heroic 65-9 Fourth Round Tetley's Bitter Cup defeat at Leicester, Barking resolutely refused to take the numerous penalties offered in the second half. Barking hunted for the elusive try (which would have been the most eloquent thank you to the 1,000 plus supporters who made the trip to Welford Road), but ultimately Fortress Leicester was impregnable on January 9th - but Barking's failure to score a try was not through lack of effort. JOHN DORAN

BARKING

Match No.	Date	H/A	Comp.	Opponents	Result & Score	15	14	13	12	11
1	05.09	H	J2S	Weston	W 21-9	Harries(i)	Green	Buckton	Mahoney	Gregory
2	12.09	A	J2S	Bracknell	L 8-23	Smith	Green	Buckton	Mahoney	Gregory/t
3	26.09	H	J2S	Cheltenham	W 24-5	Smith/p	Harries	Buckton	Turnell	Gregory(p)
4	03.10	A	J2S	Plymouth*	W 23-18	Smith	Gregory	Buckton	Turnell	Harries/t(a)
5	10.10	H	J2S	N Walsham	W 18-8	Turnell	Gregory/t	Buckton	Mahoney(t)	Green
6	24.10	H	J2S	Havant	W 40-3	Turnell	McDonald	Buckton	Mahoney(i)	Green/2t
7	31.10	A	J2S	Esher	L 6-26	Smith	McDonald	Buckton	Turnell	Gregory
8	07.11	H	J2S	Clifton	W 20-0	Smith(n)	Gregory	Buckton	Mahoney/t	Green
9	21.11	A	J2S	Bridgwater	W 31-16	Smith	Gregory/t	Buckton	Mahoney(t)	McDonald
10	28.11	H	J2S	Met Police	W 29-5	Smith	Gregory/2t	Buckton/t	Mahoney	McDonald
11	05.12	A	J2S	Tabard	W 22-13	Turnell	Gregory	Buckton/t	Mahoney	McDonald
12	12.12	H	J2S	Norwich	W 34-3	Smith	Gregory(p)	Buckton	Turnell	Stubbs/t
13	19.12	A	J2S	Redruth	L 18-22	Smith	Gregory/t	Buckton	Turnell	McDonald
14	28.12	H	J2S	Tabard	W 38-15	Smith	Gregory	Buckton	Mahoney	Green(p)(t)
15	02.01	A	J2S	Met Police	W 30-12	Smith(t)	Gregory/t	Buckton	Mahoney	Green
16	23.01	H	J2S	Esher	L 19-24	Smith(t)	Gregory	Buckton	Turnell	Stubbs
17	30.01	A	J2S	Havant	W 44-17	Smith/2t	Gregory/t	Buckton/t	Brightwell(n)	Stubbs
18	06.02	A	J2S	N Walsham	L 9-21	Smith	Gregory	Buckton	Brightwell	Stubbs
19	13.02	H	J2S	Plymouth	W 44-12	Smith/t	Gregory/2t(y)	Buckton	Brightwell	Green/3t
20	20.02	H	J2S	Bridgwater	W 25-0	G Cutting/t	Gregory	Buckton/t	Brightwell(A)	Green
21	27.02	A	J2S	Cheltenham	W 22-0	G Cutting/t2c	Gregory	Buckton	Brightwell(B)	Green
22	06.03	A	J2S	Clifton	W 19-11	Gregory/t	Green	Buckton/t	Brightwell	Siaw
23	13.03	H	J2S	Bracknell	D 13-13	Hadley	Gregory	Buckton	Cotterille	Green/t
24	27.03	A	J2S	Weston	W 16-8	Turnell/c	Gregory	Buckton(t)	Cotterille	Green
25	03.04	H	J2S	Redruth	W 56-20	Hadley/3c	Gregory	Turnell/3t	Cotterille(A)	Brightwell
26	17.04	A	J2S	Norwich	L 15-23	Hadley	Gregory	Buckton	Mahoney	Turnell
A	19.09	A	TB1	Clevendon	W 32-7	Smith	Gregory(a)	Buckton/t	Turnell(t)	Harries/t
B	17.10	A	TB2	Plymouth	W 18-13	Hadley	McDonald	Buckton/t	Mahoney(t)	Green/t
C	14.11	A	TB3	Swanage	W 36-6	Turnell//t	Gregory/2t(p)	Buckton(i)	Mahoney	Green
D	09.01	A	TB4	Leicester	L 6-65	Smith	Gregory	Buckton	Mahoney	Green

* after opponents name indicates a penalty try
Brackets after a player's name indicates he was replaced. eg (a) means he was replaced by replacement code "a" and so on.
/ after a player or replacement name is followed by any scores he made - eg /t, /c, /p, /dg or any combination of these

1998-99 HIGHLIGHTS

Ever Presents: None

Most appearances

25	John Buckton & Scott Gregory
22	Justin Azzopardi (1)
21	James Martin
20	Dean Cutting (2)

Players used: 38 plus two as replacement only.

Most Points in a season:

Pts	Player	T	C	P	DG
217	J Azzopardi	6	26	44	1
55	S Gregory	11	-	-	-
30	C Tate	6	-	-	-
30	P Green	6	-	-	-
26	T Hadley	1	6	3	-

MATCH FACTS

10	9	1	2	3	4	5	6	7	8	
Azzopardi/c3p	D Cutting	Blenkinsop	Murphy/t	Dunstan	Green/t	Twydell	Trowbridge	Everett	Martin	1
Azzopardi/p	D Cutting	Usher	Murphy(l)	Dunstan(m)	Baker(g)	Twydell	Green	Everett	Martin	2
Azzopardi/c3p(b)	D Cutting	Usher(e)	M-Stevens	Dunstan	Twydell/t(q)	Wright	Trowbridge	Everett/t	Green(r)	3
Azzopardi/tc2p	D Cutting	Usher(e)	Durkin	Dunstan	Twydell	Baker	Green(s)	Everett	Martin	4
Azzopardi/tp	D Cutting	Blenkinsop	Durkin	Dunstan	Twydell/t	Baker	Green(s)	Everett	Martin	5
Azzopardi/3c3p	Mahoney(d)	Blenkinsop(j)	Durkin/t	Dunstan	Twydell/t	Baker	Bury(g)	Everett/t	Martin	6
Azzopardi/2p	D Cutting	Usher	Durkin	Probyn(e)	Twydell	Baker	Green	Everett(q)	Martin	7
Azzopardi/2c2p	D Cutting	Usher	Durkin	Blenkinsop	Twydell	Baker	Green(r)	Bury	Martin/t	8
Azzopardi/2c4p	D Cutting	Blenkinsop	Tate	Probyn(j)	Twydell	Baker/t	Trowbridge(q)	Everett/t	Martin	9
Azzopardi/t3cp	D Cutting	Usher	Tate	Dunstan	Twydell	Baker	Trowbridge(x)	Everett	Martin	10
Azzopardi/2cp	D Cutting	Orwell	Tate/t(w)	Dunstan*	Twydell	Baker	Bury(m)	Everett/t(g)	Martin	11
Azzopardi/c4p	D Cutting	Blenkinsop(j)	Morris/t	Probyn	Twydell	Wright(q)	Trowbridge	Everett	Martin/2t	12
Azzopardi/c2p	D Cutting/t	Usher	Tate	Probyn	Twydell	Wright	Bury	Everett	Martin	13
Azzopardi/2tcpd	D Cutting	Usher	Murphy(v/t)	Blenkinsop	Twydell	Baker(q/t)	Trowbridge	Everett/t	Stone/t	14
Azzopardi/2c2p	D Cutting	Blenkinsop	Tate/t(f)	Probyn/t(k)	Twydell	Baker	Bury	Goodey/t	Stone(g)	15
Azzopardi/3p	D Cutting	Blenkinsop	Murphy(v)	Dunstan/t	Twydell/t	Baker	Trowbridge	Everett(x)	Bury	16
Azzopardi/t4c2p	D Cutting(b)	Blenkinsop	Tate(f)	Dunstan	Bury(C)	Baker	Trowbridge(x)	Everett	Martin/t	17
Azzopardi/3p	Mahoney	Usher	Tate	Dunstan	Twydell	Baker	Trowbridge	Goodey	Martin	18
Azzopardi/c(z/c)	D Cutting	Blenkinsop(j)	Murphy(w)	Dunstan	Stone(y)	Baker	Trowbridge	Everett/t	Martin/t(x)	19
Hadley/2c2p	Mahoney	Usher	Murphy	Dunstan	Stone	Baker	Trowbridge	Everett	Martin/t	20
Hadley/tp	Mahoney	Blenkinsop	Murphy	Probyn/t	Bury	Stone	Trowbridge	Everett	Martin(k)	21
Hadley/c(c/c)	Mahoney	Usher	Murphy	Blenkinsop	Martin	Baker/t(h)	Trowbridge	Goodey	Bury	22
Azzopardi/p	D Cutting/t	Blenkinsop	Tate(f)	Probyn	Bury	Stone	Trowbridge	Goodey	Martin	23
Azzopardi/3p(d)	Mahoney	Usher(m)	Murphy(v)	Blenkinsop	Stone/t	Bailey	Trowbridge	Goodey	Knowles	24
Mahoney/t	D Cutting	Usher	Tate	Blenkinsop/2t	Stone(C)	Bailey/2t	Trowbridge	Goodey/t(s)	Martin/t(r)	25
Azzopardi	D Cutting	Usher	Tate/3t	Blenkinsop	Stone	Bailey	Trowbridge	Goodey	Martin	26
Azzopardi/t3c2p	D Cutting	Usher(u)	M-Stevens	Blenkinsop(m)	Twydell	Baker	Everett/t	Knowles(g)	Martin	A
Azzopardi/c2p	D Cutting	Blenkinsop	Murphy	Probyn	Twydell	Baker	Bury	Everett	Martin	B
Azzopardi/t4cp	D Cutting	Usher	Tate	Blenkinsop(m)	Twydell	Baker	Bury/t	Knowles	Martin(D)	C
Azzopardi/2p(n)	D Cutting	Usher(e)	Tate(f)	Probyn	Twydell	Baker	Trowbridge	Everett(x)	Martin(q)	D

REPLACEMENTS: a - P Green, b - P Mahoney, c - J Azzopardi, d - D Cutting, e - N Blenkinsop
f - J Murphy, g - N Trowbridge, h - P Everett, i - N Smith, j - G Usher, k - J Baker
l - S Durkin, m - J Probyn, n - L Turnell, o - J Mount Stevens, p - D McDonald, q - B Bury
r - S Knowles, s - J Shearing, t - M Brightwell, u - V Ludden, v - C Tate, w - D Morris
x - P Goodey, y - B Siaw, z - G Cutting
A - G Stannard, B - C Cotterille, C - M Twydell, D - B Stone

New boy Justin Azzopardi finished leading points scorer in his first season for the club.
His 217 points made him the second highest scorer in the division after Esher's Jon Gregory.

Leading try scorer was winger Scott Gregory who ran in 11 tries in 25 league matches, he also scored two in the Tetley Bitter Cup.

Lost just once at home when they were beaten narrowly by Esher.

Only lost to Norwich and Redruth of the sides finishing below them in the league.

Only beat North Walsham out of the sides that finished above them in the division.

BARKING

LEAGUE STATISTICS
compiled by Stephen McCormack

SEASON	Division	P	W	D	L	F	A	Pts Diff	Lge Pts	Lge Pos		Coach		Captain
89-90	Lon 2N	10	5	1	4	141	151	-10	11	4		T Wright		T Reader
90-91	Lon 2N	10	8	0	2	147	94	53	16	3		T Wright		T Reader
91-92	Lon 2N	10	7	1	2	187	140	47	15	2p		M LOvett		T Reader
92-93	Lon 1	12	6	1	5	183	171	12	13	7				
93-94	Lon 1	12	10	1	1	290	149	141	21	1p				
94-95	D5S	12	7	0	5	223	190	33	14	5		M Lovett		D Cutting
												Most Points		**Most Tries**
95-96	D5S	12	8	0	4	243	187	56	16	4	51	Lee Evans	6	P Green, C Tate, D Cutting
96-97	D4S	26	16	1	9	740	496	244	33	3	248	Nick Thompson	14	Chris Tate, N Thomson
97-98	N2S	26	19	0	7	762	450	312	38	3	69	Andy Tunningley	12	J Murphy, P Goodey
98-99	N2S	26	19	1	6	644	327	317	39	4	217	Justin Azzopardi	11	Scott Gregory

FACT FILE

Founded: 1930

Colours: Cardinal and grey
Change colours: Blue or Yellow

GROUND

Address: Goresbrook, Gale St., Dagenham, Essex RM9 4TY
Tel: 0181 595 7324 Website: www.brufc.freeserve.co.uk
Capacity: 2,000 - all uncovered standing

Directions: From Dartford Tunnel, follow A13 (London bound). Past the Ford works, continue for 2 miles to 2nd r'about (beneath a flyover). 4th exit and return back on A13 in opposite direction. The ground is half a mile on the left hand side. From M11 - At end of M11 take A406 EAST bound towards the A13. Onto A13, signposted Dartford Tunnel, and ground is 4 miles on the left.
Nearest Railway Station: Becontree (District Line - Upminster direction). Turn right on leaving the station into Gale Street. The ground is 1 mile on the left.

Car Parking: 200 spaces available at ground

Admission: Season Tickets (members only) £30.
Matchday: Members £3 Non-members: £5.00

Club Shop: Manager L Consiglio 0181 984 1114
Clubhouse: Normal Licensing hours, snacks available.
Functions: Capacity 120.

Training Nights: Tuesdays & Thursday (seniors).
Juniors: Monday & Wednesday

PROGRAMME Size: A5 Price: With admission Pages: 22 plus cover
Editor: John Doran, 15 Lake Gardens, Dagenham RM10 8NV
0181 593 9095 (H) 0171 676 4678 (B) 0171 676 4679 (F)

ADVERTISING RATES Colour only
Full Page £250 Half Page £150

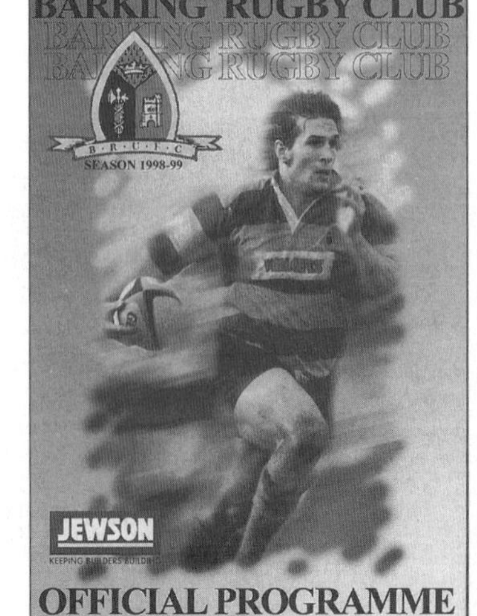

BRIDGWATER & ALBION R.F.C.

President	Richard Bell	c/o the club office 01278 424883 (B) 01278 425944 (Fax)
Club Secretary	Tony Pomeroy	Hafod-Y-Gan, Newton Road, North Petherton, Somerset TA6 6SN Tel: 01278 662181 Fax: 01278 662178
General Manager	Julian Graham	c/o the club office Tel: 01278 423900 (Club) Fax: 01278 446608
Fixtures Secretary	Ralph Sealey	12 Capes Close, Stanwell, Bridgwater, Somerset. TA7 9AA Tel: 01278 444757 (H)

Despite the euphoria at winning the Somerset Worthington Cup again, the season was not one to remember. Our League form was reasonable at home after a very shaky start to the season, but, the visit to Clifton apart, a disaster away from home. As a result, we were destined to be flirting with the basement of the League Table for all of the season.

Following two `coaching regimes' in 1997/98, it was hoped that the appointment of Kevin Short, a local headmaster, as head coach would be the making of the team for 1998/99. However, this did not work out and Paul Westgate, a teacher at Kings College, Taunton, was invited to take charge in mid season. He started well, becoming Jewson `Manager of the Month' at his first attempt, but his school commitments mean that he cannot continue as head coach for the coming season, although he will continue to be involved. The club has appointed Dr. Tom Hudson as director of rugby and Dave Robson as head coach from June 1999. We are looking for great things from these men who, with Jack Rowell, guided Bath to the top of the tree in English club rugby.

These appointments, together with that of a full-time club manager, are hoped to move Bridgwater into the Millennium as one of the major clubs in the South West. Our club facilities are second to none and we hope for a team to match.

Our club manager took over at a very difficult time. The previous manager, Roy Chidgey, had been very ill and unfortunately died in March. He had worked for the club for many years and was well known to all those who played at Bridgwater. His successor, Julian Graham, is maximising the use of the clubhouse and hopefully raising sufficient money to fund a team to play at the highest levels.

There will undoubtedly be some new faces taking the field for Bridgwater and Albion RFC this season. We are confident they will do well.

BRIDGWATER & ALBION

Match No.	Date	H/A	Comp.	Opponents	Result & Score	15	14	13	12	11
1	05.09	H	J2S	Tabard	L 14-20	Triggoll	Williams	Webber	Vodden	Buller
2	12.09	A	J2S	Norwich	L 11-21	Triggoll	Veale	Webber	Vodden	Buller/t
3	26.09	H	J2S	Redruth*	W 26-9	Triggoll	Gollings	Webber	Vodden	Buller
4	03.10	A	J2S	Weston	L 19-24	Triggoll	Veale(b/t)	Webber	Vodden	Buller
5	10.10	H	J2S	Bracknell	L 25-42	Triggoll	Gollings/t	Webber	Vodden/t	Buller
6	31.10	H	J2S	Plymouth	D 16-16	Triggoll	Williams	Webber	Buller	Gllings
7	07.11	A	J2S	N Walsham	L 10-21	Triggoll	Gollings/t	Webber	Buller	Hamilton
8	14.11	A	J2S	Cheltenham	L 16-23	Triggoll/t	Williams	Webber	Buller	Gollings
9	21.11	H	J2S	Barking	L 16-31	Triggoll	Veale	Webber	Vodden	Gollings/t
10	28.11	A	J2S	Esher	L 0-49	Triggoll	Veale	M Ranson	Vodden	Buller
11	05.12	H	J2S	Clifton	W 28-10	Triggoll	Veale	Webber/t	Vodden/t	Gollings/t
12	12.12	H	J2S	Havant	W 33-7	Triggoll/t	Veale	Webber	Vodden/2t	Gollings
13	19.12	A	J2S	Met Police	D 18-18	Triggoll	Veale	Webber/t	Buller	Gollings/t
14	28.12	A	J2S	Clifton	W 22-10	Triggoll	Gollings/t	Webber	Buller	Veale
15	02.01	H	J2S	Esher	L 14-18	Triggoll	Veale	Webber	Buller	Gollings/t
16	16.01	H	J2S	N Walsham	L 16-31	Triggoll	Gollings	Webber	Buller(n)	Veale
17	23.01	A	J2S	Plymouth	L 10-48	Triggoll	Gollings/t	Webber	Vodden	Buller/t
18	30.01	H	J2S	Cheltenham	W 32-6	Triggoll/t	Gollings	Webber/t	Buller	Veale/t
19	06.02	A	J2S	Bracknell	L 0-38	Triggoll	Gollings	Vodden(i)	M Ranson	Veale(m)
20	13.02	H	J2S	Weston	W 25-10	Triggoll	Gollings	Webber	Veale	Gwilliam
21	20.02	A	J2S	Barking	L 0-25	Triggoll	Gollings	M Ranson	Hanson	Hamilton
22	27.02	A	J2S	Redruth	L 17-49	Triggoll	Gollings	Webber	Brock	M Ranson
23	13.03	H	J2S	Norwich	W 18-10	Triggoll	Veale	Webber	Vodden	Gollings
24	27.03	A	J2S	Tabard	L 15-39	Triggoll	Gollings/t	Webber	Buller(v)	Veale
25	03.04	H	J2S	M Police	W 48-17	Donaldson/t	Gollings/2t	Webber/dg	Buller/t	Triggoll/t(v)
26	17.04	A	J2S	Havant	L 14-32	Triggoll	Gollings	Webber	Buller	Veale
A	19.09	A	TB1	Guildford & God	W 28-18	Triggoll	Veale	Vodden	Webber	Buller/t
B	17.10	H	TB2	Rosslyn Park	L 15-49	Triggoll/t	Buller(E/t)	Veale	Webber	Gollings

* after opponents name indicates a penalty try
Brackets after a player's name indicates he was replaced. eg (a) means he was replaced by replacement code "a" and so on.
/ after a player or replacement name is followed by any scores he made - eg /t, /c, /p, /dg or any combination of these

1998-99 HIGHLIGHTS

Ever Presents: Simon Triggoll

Most appearances

24	Jerry Barnes (1), Andy Webber (1)
23	Ewan Murchison (1)
22	Andy Gollings (1), Ewan Murchison (1)

Players used: 38 plus eight as replacement only.

Most Points in a season:

Pts	Player	T	C	P	DG
144	N Edmonds	-	18	34	2
61	J Donaldson	1	7	12	2
60	A Gollings	12	-	-	-
25	E Murchison	5	-	-	-
20	S Triggoll	4	-	-	-
18	A Webber	3	-	-	1

MATCH FACTS

10	9	1	2	3	4	5	6	7	8	
Edmonds/3p	S Ranson(c)	Barnes/t(f)	C Milkins	Parkes	Curry	Perry	Sluman	Hanson(A)	Murchison	1
Edmonds/2p	Livingstone(i)	Barnes	C Milkins(p)	Harris	Rackman	Curry	Sluman	Hanson	Murchison	2
Edmonds/2c2p2dg	Livingstone(i)	Barnes	Innells(e)	Parkes	Rackman	Perry	Sluman	Gibbs	Murchison/t	3
Edmonds/c4p	Ranson	Barnes(z)	Innells	Parkes	Rackman	Curry	Perry	Gibbs(m)	Murchison	4
Edmonds/2c2p	Livingstone(i)	Harris	Innells	Barnes	Curry	Perry	Sluman/t	Hanson(B)	Murchison	5
Donaldson/p(a/p)	Bradford	Barnes/t	Bell	Parkes	Rackman	Curry	Sluman	Ranson	Murchison/t	6
Donaldson	Bradford	Barnes	Bell	Parkes	Rackman	Curry	Sluman	Ranson	Murchisont/t	7
Donaldson/p(a/p)	Bradford/t	Barnes(l)	Bell	Parkes	Rackman	Curry	Sluman(m)	Ranson	Murchison	8
Edmonds/2p	Bradford	Barnes	Innells	Parkes	Rackman	Waddon(h)	Gibbs/t(o)	Hanson	Murchison	9
Donaldson(a)	S Ranson(c)	Parkes(d)	Bell	Masters	Rackman	Curry	Batchelor	Hanson	Murchison	10
Donaldson/cpdg	Bradford	Barnes/t	Innells	Parkes	Rackham	Passmore	Gibbs	Sluman	Murchison	11
Edmonds/4c(k)	Bradford(i)	Barnes	Innells	Masters	Rackman(q)	Curry	Gibbs/t	Sluman(o)	Murchison/t	12
Donaldson/c2p	Bradford	Barnes	Innells	Parkes	Rackman	Curry	Gibbs(s)	Sluman(o)	Murchison	13
Donaldson/2cp	Bradford	Barnes	Innells(e)	Parkes/t	Rackman	Curry	Gibbs/t	Kingdon	Murchison	14
Donaldson(2pdg)	Bradford	Barnes	Innells	Parkes	Rackman	Curry	Gibbs	Kingdon	Batchelor	15
Donaldson/c3p	Bradford/t(i)	Barnes	Innells	Parkes(r)	Rackman	Curry	Batchelor	Kingdon(t)	Murchison	16
Edmonds	S Ranson	Barnes	Innells	Parkes	Rackman	Curry	Batchelor	Hills	Murchison	17
Donaldson/2cp	Bradford	Barnes(f)	Fitzpatrick/t	Masters	Curry(g)	Waddon	Batchelor	Hills/t	Murchison	18
Webber	Bradford	Parkes	Fitzpatrick	Masters	Curry	Waddon	Batchelor(y)	Hills	Murchison	19
Edmonds/c6p	S Ranson	Barnes	Fitzpatrick	Masters	Rackman	Waddon	Hanson	Hills	Murchison/t	20
S Bradford	S Ranson	Barnes	Fitzpatrick(q)	Masters	Curry(r)	McGuire(o)	Parkes(C)	Hills	Murchison	21
Edmonds/2cp	S Ranson(c)	Barnes	Innells	Masters	Rackman	Curry/t	Hanson(o)	Hills/t	Murchison	22
Edmonds/6p	S Ranson(c)	Barnes(u)	Innells	Parkes(r)	Rackman	Curry	Batchelor(m)	Hills	Murchison	23
Edmonds/cp	Bradford(i)	Barnes	Fitzpatrick	Parkes(r)	Rackman	Curry/t	Batchelor	Hills	Murchison	24
Edmonds/5c	S Ranson/t(c)	Barnes(f)	Milkins	Masters	Rackman	Curry	Batchelor/t	Hills(w)	Murchison	25
Edmonds/3p	S Ranson(x)	Barnes	Milkins	Masters	Rackman	Curry	Richards(j)	Hills	Batchelor/t	26
Edmonds/t2c2pdg	Livingstone	Barnes(z)	Innells	Parkes	Curry	Rackman	Sluman/t	Perry	Murchison	A
Donaldson	Livingstone(c)	Barnes	Innells(e)	Norris	Perry(D)	Curry/t	Sluman	Hanson	Murchison	B

REPLACEMENTS:

	a- N Edmonds	b - A Gollings	c - S Bradford	d - J Barnes	e - N Bell
f- D Parkes	g - M Rackman	h - M Curry	i - S Ranson	j - E Murchison	k - J Donaldson
l - B Norris	m - C Hanson	n - D Vodden	o - J Batchelor	p - K Innells	q - S Passmore
r - D Masters	s - J Kingdon	t - M Hills	u - C Milkins	v - M Ranson	w - C Richards
x - L Dickinson	y - K Pechacek	z - T Harris			
A - B Thirwell	B - M Lloyd	C - A Webber	D - L Waddon	E - A Williams	

Nick Edmonds in what was probably his last season of rugby ended up as Bridgwater & Albion's leading points scorer yet again.

The leading try scorer was new boy Andy Gollings who ran in 12 tries from the wing. He finished seven clear of his nearest rival, back row forward, Ewan Murchison.

Won just once on the road last season when they were 22-10 winers at Clifton.

Away from home they managed just 152 points, the third lowest total in the division behind Norwich and Cheltenham.

BRIDGWATER & ALBION

LEAGUE STATISTICS

compiled by Stephen McCormack

SEASON	Division	P	W	D	L	F	A	Pts Diff	Lge Pts	Lge Pos		Coach		Captain
89-90	SW2	10	2	1	7	122	158	-36	5	11R		J Davies		A J Harris
90-91	SW-SC	10	7	0	3	145	105	30	14	3		J Davies		A J Harris
91-92	SW-WC	10	8	0	2	266	74	192	16	2p		G Cooper		N P Edmonds
92-93	SW2	12	9	0	3	243	114	129	18	3		G Cooper		N P Edmonds
93-94	SW2	12	9	0	3	251	135	116	18	4		G Cooper		N P Edmonds
94-95	SW2	12	10	0	2	238	127	111	20	2p		G Cooper		N P Edmonds
95-96	SW1	12	8	0	4	241	195	46	16	4		D Egerton		G M Buller
												Most Points		**Most Tries**
96-97	SW1	22	18	0	4	794	318	476	36	1p	278	Nick Edmonds	17	Nick Gwilliam
97-98	N2S	26	12	0	14	535	664	-129	24	8	242	Nick Edmonds	6	Ian Veale
98-99	N2S	26	8	2	16	463	624	-162	18	10	144	Nick Edmonds	13	Andy Gollings

FACT FILE

Founded: 1875
Nickname: Bridgey

Colours: Black, scarlet & amber hoops
Change colours: All white

GROUND

Address: College Way, Bath Road, Bridgwater, Somerset. TA6 4TZ.
Tel: 01278 423900 Fax: 01278 446608
Capacity: 5,000 Seated: 630 Standing: Covered 500, Uncovered 3,870

Directions: The ground is sign-posted from the A38 and A39
Nearest Railway Station: Bridgwater (BR) (Bristol to Exeter line). 10 minute walk to the ground.

Car Parking: 400 spaces available at ground

Admission: (1997-98 Prices)
Season tickets - Adults £56, Children/OAPs £28
Matchdays - Adult £5, Children/OAPs £2.50

Club Shop: Matchdays only 12-5.
Contact Lionel Porter c/o the club

Clubhouse: Open normal licensing hours, snacks available.
Functions capacity 300,contact Jon Brinkman 01278 423900

Training Nights: Tuesday & Thursday

PROGRAMME

Size: A5 Price: £1 Pages: 8 editorial plus ads & cover.
Editor: Anthony Pomeroy (Club Secretary)

ADVERTISING: Contact Julian Graham c/o the club

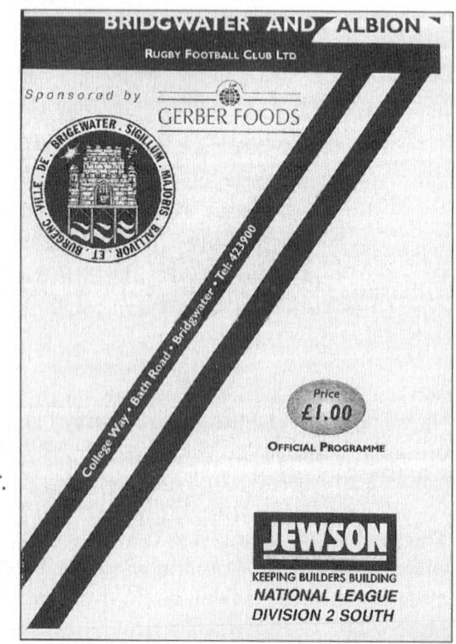

CHELTENHAM R.F.C.

President	Keith Plain	Foxhole Farm, Kinsham, Tewkesbury, Glos GL20 6JG 01684 772096 (H & Fax)
Chairman	Stephen Ratcliffe	10 Waterside Close, Andoversford, Cheltenham, Glos. 01242 820824 (H), 01242 233430 (B)
Fixtures Secretary	Mike Edwards	2 Greenbank Cottages, Guiting Power,Cheltenham, Glos 01451 850232 (H), 01452 387664 (B), 01452 892040 (Fax)
Press Officer	Tom Parker	39 Long Mynd Avenue, Cheltenham GL51 5QT 01242 694299 (H & Fax)
Club Secretary	David Evans	Cliff Cottage, Leckhampton Hill, Cheltenham GL53 9QG 01242 514519 (H), 01452 509555 (B)

It has been a disappointing season for Cheltenham, who just managed to keep a place in the National League Two (S), after some nail biting games, especially towards the end of the season.

Whether the club would be relegated or not was not decided until the club completed their only double, against Havant. It was a game which will live long in the memories of the courageous team, as well as a record number of spectators.

A try in the fifth minute of injury time by winger Paul Edwards just ensured Cheltenham's continuance on the national scene, with Havant doomed to relegation by the smallest margin.

Cheltenham lost some players at the start of the season, but two stalwarts, Malcolm Preedy and Don Caskie, retired - and then became club coaches. They have worked hard and long and even turned out to play on several occasions, to add to the very small squad.

Leading the team was Rob York (30), who showed leadership qualities and has been elected for a second season.

The club will be looking for some players to strengthen their numbers, and, with most of the existing squad stating their intention to stay with the club, the prospects must be good.

Early injuries caused many team changes and it was not until November 14th that the first win, against Bridgwater, was recorded.

Several games were lost by vary narrow margins, but victories late in the season over Plymouth and Havant put fresh life into a team, and they battled hard against Bracknell, who topped the league, to lose by only 3-10.

Two players, skipper Rob York and back row Adam Tarplee, played for Gloucestershire against Cornwall at Twickenham in the final.

Cheers all round from players and replacements of Cheltenham RFC, after doing the double over Havant, and learning they had retained a place in Nation League Two south for another season.

Match No.	Date	H/A	Comp.	Opponents	Result & Score	Att.	15	14	13	12	11
1	05.09	A	J2S	Plymouth*	L 13-26		Watters/c2p	Edwards	Pitman(g)	Long	Ainscow
2	12.09	H	J2S	N Walsham	L 7-32		Watters/c	Edwards	Spurway	Long	Bright
3	26.09	A	J2S	Barking	L 5-24		Watters	Ainscow	Johnson	Lee	Edwards
4	03.10	H	J2S	Esher	L 25-30		Watters/c6p	Fereday	Lee	Spurway	Bright
5	10.10	A	J2S	Clifton	L 14-36		Watters/3p	Fereday(h)	Lee	Lambert	Edwards
6	31.10	A	J2S	M Police	L 9-32		Lee/3p	Edwards(i)	Pitman	Lambert(t)	Sarghini
7	07.11	H	J2S	Tabard	L 9-10		Watters/3p	Edwards	Lambert	Pitman	Sarghini
8	14.11	H	J2S	Bridgwater	W 23-16		Watters/tc2p	Edwards	Pitman	Caskie	Sarghini
9	21.11	A	J2S	Norwich	L 0-28		Watters	Sarghini	Pitman(j)	Lambert	Edwards
10	28.11	H	J2S	Redruth	W 22-12		Watters/4p	Edwards/t	Pitman	Turner/t	Sarghini
11	05.12	A	J2S	Weston*	L 17-32		Watters/2cp	Sarghini	Pitman/t	Caskie	Mudway
12	12.12	H	J2S	Bracknell	L 11-15		Watters/2p	Edwards	Pitman	Turner	Sarghini
13	19.12	A	J2S	Havant	W 21-13		Watters	Sarghini	Pitman	Turner/t	Edwards
14	28.12	H	J2S	Weston	L 16-30		Lee(q)	Edwards	Pitman	Turner	Mudway
15	02.01	A	J2S	Redruth	L 12-25		Harper/t	Edwards	Lambert	Turner	Pitman
16	16.01	A	J2S	Tabard	W 18-6		Sarghini	Edwards	Pitman(x)	Turner/2t	Knight
17	23.01	H	J2S	M Police	L 9-22		Sarghini	Fereday	Tucker	Turner	Edwards
18	30.01	A	J2S	Bridgwater	L 6-32		Sarghini	Edwards	Tucker	Turner	Fereday
19	06.02	H	J2S	Clifton	L 14-19		Sarghini/t	Fereday	Tucker	Turner	Edwards
20	13.02	A	J2S	Esher	L 23-49		Sarghini	Edwards	Tucker	Turner	Fereday
21	20.02	H	J2S	Norwich	W 17-8		Sarghini	Fereday	Caskie	Turner	Edwards
22	27.02	H	J2S	Barking	L 0-22		Sarghini	Mudway	Caskie	Turner	Edwards
23	13.03	A	J2S	N Walsham	L 0-29		Sarghini	Tucker	Caskie(z)	Turner	Fereday
24	27.03	H	J2S	Plymouth	W 26-19		Sarghini	Edwards	Caskie/t	Turner	Tucker/t
25	03.04	H	J2S	Havant	W 15-12		Wheatley(a/c)	Tucker	Caskie	Turner	Edwards/t
26	17.04	A	J2S	Bracknell	L 3-19		Wheatley(a)	Edwards	Tucker	Turner	Sarghini(A)
A	19.09	A	TB1	M Police	L 8-34		Watters/p	Edwards	Lee	Johnson	Bright

* after opponents name indicates a penalty try
Brackets after a player's name indicates he was replaced. eg (a) means he was replaced by replacement code "a" and so on.
/ after a player or replacement name is followed by any scores he made - eg /t, /c, /p, /dg or any combination of these

1998-99 HIGHLIGHTS

Ever Presents: None - most appearnces

24 Adam Tarplee
23 Paul Edwards (1)
22 Peter Lodge, Matt Mudway, Rob York, Greg Newcombe

Players used: 39 plus 4 as a replcement only

Most Points in a season:

Pts	Player	T	C	P	DG
88	P Watters	1	7	23	-
73	M Watts	-	5	19	2
23	M mudway	4	-	1	-
20	I Fox	4	-	-	-
17	R Knight	-	1	5	-

MATCH FACTS

10	9	1	2	3	4	5	6	7	8	
Turner	Mudway	Venna(f)	Brown	Gilder	York	Lodge	Clifford	Tarplee	Clarke	1
Turner	Mudway(i/t)	Gilder	Newcombe	Strudwick(c)	Gibson	Lodge	Clarke	Clifford	York	2
Long	Mudway/t	Venna	Newcombe	Gilder	Gibson	Lodge	Clarke	Tarplee	York	3
Long	Mudway	Venna(l)	Newcombe(n)	Gilder	Gibson	Lodge/t	Clifford	Tarplee	Clarke(m)	4
Long	Mudway/t(r)	Venna(l)	Freebury	Gilder	Gibson	Lodge	Clifford	Tarplee	Mico	5
Long	Mudway	Venna	Newcombe	Gilder	Gibson	Lodge	York	Tarlee	Mico(e)	6
Turner	Mudway	Bayliss(c)	Newcombe	Gilder	Gibson	Burton	Clarke	Tarlee	York	7
Long	Mudway/t	Bayliss	Newcombe	Gilder	Gibson	Burton	York/t	Tarplee	Mico	8
Watts	Mudway	Gilder(f)	Freebury	Bayliss	Gibson	Burton	York	Tarplee	Mico	9
Watts	Mudway	Gilder	Newcombe	Bayliss	Gibson	Lodge(s)	York	Tarplee	Mico	10
Turner(b)	Harper	Gilder	Newcombe	Strudwick	Clink	Lodge	York	Tarplee	Mico(e)	11
Watts	Mudway	Gilder	Newcombe	Bayliss(f)	Clink	Lodge	York	Tarplee	Burton/t(m)	12
Watts/2p	Mudway/t	Gilder(c)	Newcombe	Bayliss(f)	Clink	Lodge	York/t	Tarplee	Mico	13
Watts/c3p	Harper	Venna	Newcombe	Strudwick	Clink	Lodge	York	Tarplee	Mico/t	14
Watts/c	Mudway/t	Venna	Newcombe	Bayliss(d)	Clink	York	Clarke	Tarplee(w)	Mico(o)	15
Watts/cpdg	Mudway	Strudwick	Newcombe	Bayliss	Burton	Lodge	York	Tarplee	Mico(q)	16
Watts/pdg(i)	Mudway/p(u)	Strudwick(l)	Newcombe	Bayliss	Burton	Lodge	Clarke(v)	Bridgens	Mico	17
Watts/2p	Harper(u)	Strudwick	Newcombe	Bayliss	Burton	Lodge	Clarke(y)	Tarplee	Mico	18
Watts/3p	Harper	Strudwick	Newcombe	Bayliss	Clink	Lodge	York	Tarplee	Burton	19
Watts/2c3p	Harper(u)	Preedy	Newcombe	Bayliss	Burton/t	Lodge	York	Tarplee/t	Mico(e)	20
Watts/4p(x)	Harper/t	Preedy	Newcombe	Bayliss	Burton	Lodge	Clarke(m)	Tarplee	York	21
Knight	Harper	Preedy	Newcombe	Bayliss	Crabb	Lodge	York(m)	Tarplee(e)	Burton	22
Knight	Mudway	Preedy(d)	Newcombe	Bayliss	Crabb	Lodge	York	Tarplee	Clarke	23
Knight/c3p	Mudway	Preedy	Newcombe	Bayliss	Crabb	Lodge/t	Clarke(s)	Tarplee	York	24
Knight/p	Mudway	Preedy(d)	Newcombe	Bayliss/t	Crabb	Lodge	Clarke	Tarplee	Burton	25
Knight/p	Mudway	Gilder	Newcombe	Bayliss	Crabb	Lodge	York	Tarplee	Burton	26
Long	Mudway	Venna(p)	Newcombe	Gilder	Gibson/t	Lodge	Clarke	Clifford	York	A

REPLACEMENTS:					
	a- P Watters	b- P Edwards	c - J Venna	d - S Gilder	e - R Clarke
f - M Strudwick	g - B Spurway	h - P Bright	i - D Caskie	j - S Lee	k - K Cuthbert
l - M Preedy	m - S Mico	n - R Freebury	o - R Knight	p - N Bayliss	q - J Lambert
r - R Harper	s - T Clink	t - S Davis	u - M Kelly	v - A Ahnad	w - T Meadows
x - R Tucker	y - J Bridgens	z - G Wheatley	A - C Fereday		

Phil Watters scored a season high 20 points in the home defeat against Esher last October.

Cheltenham avoided the drop thanks to a superior points differnce over Havant.

Two home wins late in the season over fellow strugglers Plymouth and Havant turned their season round.

Cheltenham were the lowest scorers in the division.

They were also the lowest try scorers with just 30, 12 behind Clifton who managed 42.

Leading points scorer was Full Back Phil Watters who scored 88 points despite playing in less than half Cheltenham's league matches.

Scrum half Matt Mudway and centre Ian Fox were the joint leading try scorers with just four each.

Won twice away from home at Havant and Tabard.

CHELTENHAM

LEAGUE STATISTICS

compiled by Stephen McCormack

SEASON	Division	P	W	D	L	F	A	Pts Diff	Lge Pts	Lge Pos		Coach		Captain
89-90	ALS	10	2	0	8	107	201	-94	4	9		R Akenhead		D Kearsey
90-91	D4S	12	2	0	10	150	240	-90	4	13r		R Akenhead		P Sargison
91-92	SW1	10	6	0	4	164	142	22	12	4		J Moore		
92-93	SW1	12	6	0	6	221	197	24	12	6				
93-94	SW1	12	11	0	1	312	119	193	22	2				
94-95	SW1	12	11	1	0	275	112	163	21	1p				
												Most Points		**Most Tries**
95-96	D5S	12	6	0	6	194	173	21	12	6	30	Phil Stanlake	4	Derrick Morgan
96-97	D4S	26	15	2	9	599	420	179	34	5	114	Mike Crisp	8	Ian Turner
97-98	N2S	26	14	1	11	627	516	111	29	5	117	Mike crisp	13	Rob York
98-99	N2S	26	7	0	19	335	608	-273	14	13	88	Phil Watters	4	Ian Turner, Matt Mudway

FACT FILE

Founded: 1889

Colours: Red & black shirts.
Change colours: White

GROUND

Address: Prince of Wales Stadium, Tommy Taylors Lane, Cheltenham, Glos GL50 4NJ
Tel: 01242 525393
Capacity: 2500 Seated: 500 Standing: Uncovered 2000

Directions: M5 Jnc 10, 1.5 miles A4019 over t/lights to r'about, turnleft Kingsditch Lane, 1st right, right into Windyridge Rd at end turn right,200 yds turn right. Grd on right 500 yds.
Nearest Railway Station: Cheltenham (Taxi or bus)

Car Parking: 300 on ground no charge

Admission: Season - Adults Member £45, V-P £60,
Matchday - Adults £5 (including programme),
Children/OAPs £2.50

Clubhouse: Normal Licensing hours, snacks available.
Functions available,capacity 100

Club Shop: Open match-days, Manager J G Pitman 01242 525393

Training Nights: Tuesday & Thursday

PROGRAMME

Size: A5 Price: 50p with entry Pages: 24 + cover
Editor: T Parker 01242 694299

ADVERTISING RATES
Colour - Full page £250
Mono - Full Page £150, Half £100, Qtr £50

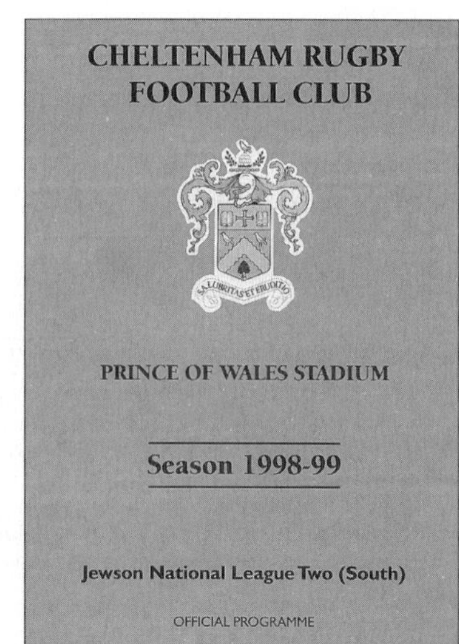

CLIFTON R.F.C.

Chairman	John Raine	1 Shumack House, High Street, Pensford BS18 4NN 01761 490717 (H), 01761 221190 (B)
Secretary	Roger Bealing	13 Frobisher Road, Ashton, Bristol. BS3 3AU. 01761 963 1832 (H), 01761 961 1532 (Fax)
Rugby Chairman		c/o Clifton RFC, Station Rd., Henbury, Bristol BS10 7TT 0117 950 4723, 0117 950 2855 (Fax)
Press Officer/ Fixtures Secretary/ Administrator	Brian Ben Jordan	17 RoyalClose, Henbury, Bristol BS10 7XP 0117 950 4723 (H), 0117 950 2855 (Fax)
Commercial Manager	Roger Jordan	39 Summerhouse Lane, Thornwell, Chepstow NP65SJ 01291 624883 (H), 01291 629246 (Fax)
Director of Coaching	Peter Polledri	8 Lampeter Road, Bristol BS9 3QQ 0117 962 8480 (H), 0117 929 8521 (B)

As Christmas approached it looked as if the Clifton would again have to endure their annual battle against relegation. After twelve games they had only recorded three wins but could count themselves unlucky to have lost two others to the final kick of the game. The turning point in the season came in the away game at Tabard just before Christmas. Looking a well beaten side at the break they staged a remarkable second half come-back deservedly to draw and gain their first away point for over a year. Over the next few weeks the side slowly grew in confidence and consistency going on to record a further seven wins including a remarkable five away from home. The deserved reward was a finish in the top half of the table.

A youthful squad was boosted at the start of the season by the arrival of the experienced Ralph Knibbs and Andy Blackmore from Coventry and fly half James Dunlop from Henley. Unfortunately Dunlop suffered a knee injury after only three games and the club lacked a natural replacement until Simon Hogg taking a break from teaching duties returned to the side at Christmas.

Dave Bennett again proved he is a class act at full back while Dale Jefferies and the ever improving Barnaby Kent were exciting partners for Knibbs in the centre. Winger Alan Barnes was the leading try scorer though try scoring proved a problem for Clifton throughout the season. Gozie Ezulike and Chris Randall shared the other win spot. Mark Harraway established himself as first choice scrum half until injury struck and Nick Lloyd proved reliable cover.

The strength of the side was up front where Tony Hussey, Quentin Webster and Andy Stephens formed a solid front row while Nick Cooper and latterly Alex Adams proved excellent partners for Blackmore. Flanker Eddie Smith was player of the season returning to the side after a shoulder injury which kept him out of the rugby for two seasons. Simon Burton, Ben McCarthy. Rhys Oakley and Mark Wyatt, who returned to the club from Plymouth mid season, proved a forceful backrow.

Oakley was the find of the season. Still a schoolboy he came into the side in late September and proved adaptable as a player appearing in every position in the back two rows of the pack. He grew in stature as the season progressed. His other attribute is to kick goals and he became Clifton's second highest point scorer in a season with 156. He is surely a player who in time will make an impact in the game at a higher level.

Looking to the future coach Peter Polledri will be hoping to build upon the development the side made during the second half of the season.

L-R - Back Row: Gozie Ezulike, Mark Harraway, Andy Collins, Eddue Smith, Stuart Roberts, Alex Adams, Alan barnes, Nick Cooper, Andy Blackmoor, Ralph Knibbs (Captain), Peter Polledri (Dir. of Coaching) **Front Row:** Justin Morris, Duncan Jeffrey, Barnaby Kent, Andy Stephens, Tony Hussey, Rhys Oakley, Mark Wyatt, Nick Lloyd, Mark Lloyd, Jason Packer

CLIFTON

Match No.	Date	H/A	Comp.	Opponents	Result & Score	Att.	15	14	13	12	11
1	05.09	H	J2S	Norwich	L 8-17		Bennett	Barnes	Knibbs/p	Tarasuik(k)	Ezulike/t
2	12.09	A	J2S	Redruth	L 18-25		Bennett	Barnes/2t	Knibbs/c2p	Tarasuik	Ezulike
3	26.09	H	J2S	Weston	W 16-11		Bennett	Hodges	Knibbs	Jeffries	G-Jones
4	03.10	A	J2S	Bracknell	L 12-22		Bennett	Barnes	Jeffries	Knibbs	G-Jones
5	10.10	H	J2S	Cheltenham	W 36-14		Bennett	Barnes	Knibbs/dg	Jones(s)	G-Jones
6	24.10	A	J2S	Plymouth	L 11-22		Bennett/t	Barnes	Knibbs	Jeffries	Ezulike(n)
7	31.10	H	J2S	N Walsham	L 14-15		Bennett	Barnes	Knibbs	Jeffries	G-Jones
8	07.11	A	J2S	Barking	L 0-20		Bennett	Barnes	Knibbs	Jeffries(b)	Ezulike
9	21.11	H	J2S	Esher	L 19-29		Bennett	Barnes/t	Knibbs/3p	Jeffries	Randall(s)
10	28.11	H	J2S	Havant	W 26-7		Bennett	Roberts	Knibbs/2c4p	Jeffries	Randall(a)
11	05.12	A	J2S	Bridgwater	L 10-28		Bennett(s)	Barnes	Knibbs/cp	Jones	Randall
12	12.12	H	J2S	M Police	L 19-20		Bennett	Barnes(s)	Knibbs/dg	Jeffries	Randall/t
13	19.12	A	J2S	Tabard*	D 24-24		Bennett	Barnes/t	Knibbs	Jeffries	Randall
14	28.12	H	J2S	Bridgwater	W 24-12		Bennett	Barnes(s)	Knibbs/t	Jeffries(s)	Randall
15	02.01	A	J2S	Havant	W 6-0		Bennett	Jeffrey	Knibbs	Roberts(C)	Randall
16	23.01	A	J2S	N Walsham	L 3-26		Bennett	Barnes	Knibbs	Barnaby	Randall(A)
17	30.01	H	J2S	Plymouth	W 24-12		Roberts	Barnes	Knibbs	Barnaby	Ezulike
18	06.02	A	J2S	Chelltenham	W 19-14		Bennett	Barnes/t	Knibbs	Barnaby	Randall(s)
19	13.02	H	J2S	Bracknell	L 20-34		Bennett	Barnes/t(s/t)	Knibbs	Barnaby	Ezulike
20	20.02	A	J2S	Esher	L 3-41		Bennett	Barnes	Knibbs	Barnaby	Ezulike
21	27.02	A	J2S	Weston	W 22-7		Bennett	Barnes	Knibbs/2t	Barnaby/t	Ezulike
22	06.03	H	J2S	Barking	L 11-19		Bennett	Barnes(s)	Knibbs	Barnaby	Ezulike
23	13.03	H	J2S	Redruth	L 15-20		Bennett/t	Barnes	Knibbs(s)	Barnaby	Ezulike
24	27.03	A	J2S	Norwich	W 16-6		Bennett	Hodges	Knibbs/dg	Barnaby	Jeffrey
25	03.04	H	J2S	Tabard	W 39-20		Roberts	Ezulike/t	Knibbs	Barnaby/t	Barnes
26	17.04	A	J2S	M Police	W 14-8		Carswell	Barnes	Knibbs	Barnaby/t	Ezulike
A	19.09	H	TB1	Esher	L 3-60		Bennett	Barnes	Knibbs/p	Tarasuik(E)	Ezulike

* after opponents name indicates a penalty try
Brackets after a player's name indicates he was replaced. eg (a) means he was replaced by replacement code "a" and so on.
/ after a player or replacement name is followed by any scores he made - eg /t, /c, /p, /dg or any combination of these

1998-99 HIGHLIGHTS

Ever Presents: Ralph Knibbs

24	Tony Hussey (1)
23	David Bennett, Andy Blackmore, Quentin Webster (1), Eddie Smith (1)
22	Alan Barnes
21	Rhys Oakley (1), Andy Stephens (1)

Players used: 42 plus 4 as replacement only.

Most Points in a season:

Pts	Player	T	C	P	DG
153	R Oakley	-	15	41	-
67	R Knibbs	3	5	11	3
30	A Barnes	6	-	-	-
20	E Smith	4	-	-	-
15	B Kent	3	-	-	-
15	Q Webster	3	-	-	-

MATCH FACTS

10	9	1	2	3	4	5	6	7	8	
Jamieson(n)	Burrows(l)	Hussey	Stephens	Collins(j)	Cooper	Blackmore	McCarthy(m)	Robinson	Smith	1
Dunlop	Harraway	Hussey	Stephens	Trollope(o)	Cooper	Blackmore	McCarthy	Robinson(m)	Smith	2
Dunlop	Harraway(b)	Hussey/t	Stephens	Webster	Cooper	Blackmore/t	Robinson	Burton	Oakley/2p	3
Dunlop(d)	Harraway	Hussey	Stephens	Webster	Cooper(c)	Blackmore	Robinson(m)	Burton	Oakley/4p	4
Burrows/t	Harraway	Hussey	Stephens	Webster	Cooper	Blackmore	Weatherall/t(i/t)	Burton/t	Oakley/2c3p	5
Burrows	Harraway	Hussey	Stephens	Webster	Cooper	Blackmore	Smith	Burton	Oakley/2p	6
Burrows	Morris	Webster	Stephens	Shortman	Cooper	Lakin	Smith/t	Burton	Oakley/3p	7
Burrows(t)	Harraway	Hussey	Stephens	Webster	Cooper	Blackmore	Smith	McCarthy(p)	Oakley(u)	8
Burrows	Harraway	Hussey	Stephens	Webster/t	Cooper	Blackmore	Smith	McCarthy(p)	Pekacek	9
Burrows	Harraway/t	Hussey	Stephens	Webster(j)	Cooper	Blackmore	Smith/t(v)	Burton	Pekacek	10
Burrows	Harraway(t)	Hussey	Stephens(r)	Webster/t(j)	Cooper	Blackmore	Burton(q)	McCarthy	Smith	11
Burrows	Harraway	Hussey	Stephens	Webster(j)	Oakley/2p	Blackmore	Burton	McCarthy/t	Smith	12
Burrows	Harraway	Hussy	Stephens(r)	Webster(j)	Oakley	Blackmore	Powell	McCarthy	Smith	13
Hogg	Harraway/t	Hussey	Hardy	Webster(j)	Oakley(g)	Blackmore	Smith	McCarthy	Wyatt	14
Hogg	Harraway	Webster	Hardy(y)	Shortman	Cooper	Blackmore	Smith	McCarthy	Oakley/2p	15
Hogg	Harraway	Hussey	Stephens	Webster(j)	Cooper	Oakley/p	Smith	McCarthy(x)	Wyatt	16
Hogg/t	Harraway(w)	Hussey	Stephens(r)	Webster	Cooper	Oakley	Smith	Oakley/c4p	Wyatt/t	17
Hogg	Lloyd	Hussey	Hardy(y)	Webster(j)	Cooper	Blackmore	Smith	Oakley/c4p	Wyatt(h)	18
Carswell	Lloyd(d)	Hussey	Jennings/t(r)	Webster(j)	Cooper	Blackmore	Smith	McCarthy	Oakley/cp(p)	19
Carswell	Lloyd	Hussey	Jennings(f)	Webster	Cooper(x)	Adams	Burton	Oakley/p	Smith(h)	20
Hogg	Lloyd	Hussey	Stephens	Webster	Adams	Blackmore	Smith	Oakley/2cp	Wyatt	21
Hogg(d)	Lloyd/t	Hussey	Stephens	Webster	Adams	Blackmore	Oakley/2p	McCarthy	Smith	22
Carswell	Lloyd(t)	Hussey	Stephens	Webster/t	Adams	Blackmore	Smith	Oakley/cp	Wyatt(h)	23
Carswell	Lloyd	Hussey	Stephens/t	Webster	Adams	Blackmore	Oakley/c2p	McCarthy	Smith(B)	24
Morris	Lloyd	Hussey	Stephens(D)	Collins	Adams	Blackmore	Smith/t(z/t)	Oakley/4c2p	Wyatt/t	25
Morris	Lloyd	Hussey	Stephens	Webster	Adams	Blackmore	Smith	Oakley/3p	Wyatt(h)	26
Dunlop	Harraway	Hussey	Stephens(r)	Shortman(o)	Cooper	Blackmore	Weatherall	Robinson(q)	Smith	A

REPLACEMENTS:

	a- A Barnes	b-B Tarasuik	c - G Ezulike	d - H Burrows	e - Hussey
f - Stephens	g - N Cooper	h - B McCarthy	i - E Smith	j - G Shortman	k - D Perres
l - M Harraway	m - J Weatherall	n - D Glyn Jones	o - Q Webster	p - S Burton	q - R Oakley
r - G Hardy	s - S Roberts	t - J Morris	u - K Pekacek	v - R Amphlett	w - N Lloyd
x- P Polledri	y - M Jennings	z - M Lloyd	A - H Aftab	B - M Wyatt	C - K Barnaby
D - S Packer	E - D Jeffries				

18 year old Rhys Oakley topped the points scoring list in his first season of senior rugby, with 153 points.

That put him in seventh place in the division's leading scorers, this season.

Winger Alan Barnes leads the try scoring list with six tries.

Clifton finished a creditable seventh after a strong finish that saw them win their last three matches.

Clifton actually picked up more points away from home with 11 compared to the 10 they won at home.

Although they finished seventh they were 13th in the try scoring list.

CLIFTON

LEAGUE STATISTICS

compiled by Stephen McCormack

SEASON	Division	P	W	D	L	F	A	Pts Diff	Lge Pts	Lge Pos	Most Points	Most Tries
89-90	ALS	10	8	1	1	240	122	118	17		83 Simon Harvey	6 Mark Trott & Mark Wyatt
90-91	D3	12	6	1	5	172	186	-14	13		32 Phil Cue	8 Dan Cottrell
91-92	D3	12	9	0	3	298	132	166	18		100 Simon Hogg	8 Matt Brain
92-93	D3	11	4	2	5	206	175	31	10		71 Simon Hogg	5 Mark Wyatt & Doug Woodman
93-94	D4	18	16	2	0	477	205	272	34	1p	222 Simon Hogg	16 John Phillips
94-95	D3	18	5	1	12	242	344	-102	11		116 Simon Hogg	4 Matt Brain & Mark Wyatt
95-96	D4	18	7	2	9	283	298	-15	16		87 Simon Hogg	5 Malcolm Crane
96-97	D3	30	4	0	26	518	1347	-829	8		80 Simon Hogg	13 Mark Buckingham
97-98	N2S	26	7	1	18	414	611	-197	15	11	58 Gareth Pugh	9 Janik Hendriksz
98-99	N2S	26	10	1	15	415	483	-68	21	7	153 Rhys Oakley	6 Alan Barnes

FACT FILE

Founded: 1877
Nickname: The Club

Colours: Lavender, black and white hoops.
Change colours: Yellow

GROUND

Address: Station Road, Cribbs Causeway, Henbury, Bristol BS10 7TP.
Tel: 0117 950 0445 Fax: 0117 950 2855
Capacity: 2,500 Seated: 250 Standing: 2,250

Directions: Leave M5 at J17, taking dual carriageway A4018 towards Bristol (ignore signs to Regional Shopping Centre). Coaches go to 2nd r'about and take bus lane. Entrance to ground on right. Cars go on to next r'about (Old Crow P.H.) & return down other side of dual carriageway. Pass BP petrol station & take next left (signed Clifton RFC). Right at end of lane & ground entrance is on left. The way to ground is signed on dual carriageway.
Nearest Railway Station: Bristol Parkway, taxi 15 minutes

Car Parking: 250 spaces on the ground.

Admission: Season ticket - Adults £40
Matchday - Adults £5, OAPs £2.50, Children Free

Clubhouse: Normal licensing hours, bar meals available.
Functions: Capacity 150

Club Shop: Yes, manager Mike Anderton 0117 968 8092

Training Nights: Monday & Wednesday

PROGRAMME

Size: A5 Price: £1 Pages: 40 + cover.
Editor: Ben Jordan 0117 950 4723

ADVERTISING RATES:
Full page £300, half £125

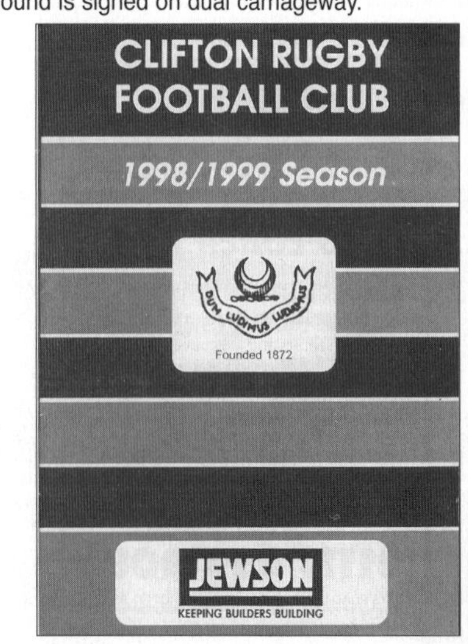

ESHER R.F.C.

President	R C Howard	
Chairman	Tim Bale	
Club Secretary	Wally Grey	
Director of Rugby	Hugh McHardy	
Rugby Managers	John Inverdale, Bob Stratton & David Page	
Fixtures Secretary	Simon Gardner	01962 869846 (H).
1st XV Manager/ Press Officer	David Page	35 Misty's Field, Walton on Thames,Surrey KT12 2BG 01932 886197 (H - Tel/Fax), 0973 488142 (M)

Correspondence to:
c/o Esher RFC,
The Rugby Ground,
369 Molesey Road,
Hersham,
Surrey KT12 3PF
01932 220295 (B)

As Carl Lewis so memorably put it `Show me the guy who came second, and I'll show you the first loser'. So it was with Esher last season. The sporting analogies are endless, from Crisp in the Grand National to Newcastle in the Premiership, but the position you occupy at the finishing line is all that counts in the end. Leading all the way until the closing rounds, the knock-out punch was delivered when Bracknell won the crucial match by the narrowest of margins, and, perhaps against the odds, did magnificently well to beat North Walsham and draw with Barking in subsequent weeks. For that alone, they deserved their promotion, and in the end Esher's weaknesses in certain key areas counted against them. A season that promised so much and contained several high spots, notably the Tetley Bitter Cup run that culminated in a match against Harlequins, ultimately finished in frustration and disappointment.

However, the pluses were many. On the playing side, Jon Gregory deservedly won the award for best player and best goalkicker in the league, and there were several other individuals, notably Nana Dontoh, Mark Butterworth and Paul Brady, who could lay claim to the former title. Equally important though was the amount of local support that emerged, attracted by the quality of the play on offer. An interesting statistic was the vastly superior points difference Esher enjoyed compared to most other sides in the top five divisions. Rising attendances - which included taking nearly 1,500 supporters to the Harlequins match - generated extra income, which but for a regrettable contretemps with North Walsham that incurred substantial legal expenses would have ensured the club broke even for the season. That in itself is no mean feat for any club at this level.

So to the future, which as with so many recent seasons still has any number of question marks hanging over it. In a highly competitive part of the country, Esher's playing resources will depend largely on decisions that are made by clubs higher up the pecking order. However with Hugh McHardy and Peter Taylor still at the helm, and placing greater emphasis on fun and enjoyment tan on another night of scrummaging, the heart of the club will continue to beat vibrantly. Promotion must be the aim this time, with the completion of a new clubhouse running an equal priority. All clubs in this league had better make the most of the original 1927 showers in the early part of the season. They won't be there for much longer.

Esher still manage to smile even though they missed out on promotion

ESHER

Match No.	Date	H/A	Comp.	Opponents	Result & Score	Att.	15	14	13	12	11
1	05.09	H	J2S	Redruth	W 44-3		Gregory/4c2p	Marchant(r)	Alexander/t	Dixon	Dontah/2t
2	12.09	A	J2S	Weston	L 22-24		Gregory/t5cp	Marchant	Alexander	Old	Dontah
3	26.09	H	J2S	Bracknell	W 27-6		Gregory/c4p	Marchant	Alexander	Dixon	Martin
4	03.10	A	J2S	Cheltenham	W 30-25		Gregory/tc5p	Marchant(w)	Old	Dixon	Martin
5	10.10	H	J2S	Plymouth	W 61-18		Gregory/p(a/t)	Corcoran(d)	Alexander	Dixon/2t	Dontah/4t
6	24.10	A	J2S	N Walsham	W 13-10		Gregory/c2p	Corcoran	Alexander	Dixon	Dontah
7	31.10	H	J2S	Barking	W 26-6		Gregory/c3p	Corcoran	Alexander(a)	Dixon	Dontah/t
8	07.11	H	J2S	Havant	W 63-6		Gregory/5c	Corcoran/4t	Alexander(q)	Marchant	Dontah2t(b)
9	21.11	A	J2S	Clifton	W 29-19		Gregory/c4p	Corcoran	Alexander(a)	Dixon	Dontah
10	28.11	H	J2S	Bridgwater	W 49-0		Gregory/4c2p	Corcoran	Alexander/t	Dixon(a)	Dontah/t
11	04.12	A	J2S	M Police	W 30-9		Gregory/3c3p	Corcoran	Alexander	Dixon	Dontah/t
12	12.12	H	J2S	Tabard	W 18-10		Gregory/c2p	Corcoran	Alexander	Dixon(C)	Dontah
13	19.12	A	J2S	Norwich	W 23-7		Gregory/c2p	Corcoran/t(D)	Alexander	Dixon	Dontah
14	28.12	H	J2S	M Police	W 53-6		Gregory/t5cp	Corcoran/t	Alexander	Dixon(E)	Dontah/3t
15	02.01	A	J2S	Bridgwater	W 18-14		Gregory/c2p	Corcoran/t	Alexander	Clouston	Dontah
16	16.01	A	J2S	Havant	W 25-10		Gregory	Corcoran/t	Alexander/t	Marchant	Sandilands(D)
17	23.01	A	J2S	Barking	W 24-19		Gregory/c4p	Corcoran	Alexander	Marchant	Dontah
18	30.01	H	J2S	N Walsham	L 11-12		Gregory/2p	Corcoran	Alexander	Marchant	Dontah
19	06.02	A	J2S	Plymouth	W 34-15		Gregory/t3cp(D)	Corcoran/t	Alexander	Marchant	Dontah
20	13.02	H	J2S	Cheltenham	W 49-23		Greenyer	Corcoran/4t4c2p	Alexander(G)	Marchant/t	Dontah(F)
21	20.02	H	J2S	Clifton	W 41-3		Gregory/2t4cp	Corcoran/t	Sandilands	Marchant	Dontah
22	27.02	A	J2S	Bracknell	L 11-16		Gregory/2p	Corcoran	Alexander	Marchant(b)	Dontah
23	13.03	H	J2S	Weston	W 70-19		Gregory/t7c2p	Corcoran/t(G)	Alexander/t	Dixon/t	Dontah
24	27.03	A	J2S	Redruth	W 33-15		Gregory/3c4p	Corcoran	Alexander	Dixon	Sandilands/2t(c/t)
25	03.04	H	J2S	Norwich*	W 33-0		Gregory/4c	Sandilands	Alexander	Dixon/t	Dontah/t(w)
26	17.04	A	J2S	Tabard	W 27-13		Gregory/4p	Corcoran	Alexander	Dixon	Sandilands
A	19.09	A	TB1	Clifton	W 60-3		Gregory/t7c2p	Marchant/2t	Alexander/t	Dixon	Dontah
B	17.10	H	TB2	Tabard	W 41-3		Gregoryt3c5p	Corcoran/t	Alexander	Dixon	Dontah/t(a)
C	14.11	H	TB3	Harrogate	W 42-17		Gregory/2t3c2p	Corcoran	Alexander	Dixon(a)	Dontah
D	09.01	A	TB4	Harlequins	L 10-46		Gregory/cp	Corcoran	Alexander	Clouston	Dontah

* after opponents name indicates a penalty try
Brackets after a player's name indicates he was replaced. eg (a) means he was replaced by replacement code "a" and so on.
/ after a player or replacement name is followed by any scores he made - eg /t, /c, /p, /dg or any combination of these

1998-99 HIGHLIGHTS

Ever Presents: None - most appeances

25	Jonathan Gregory.
24	Jeff Alexander
23	Richard Bailey
22	Alastair Meadows(1)

Players used: 34 plus 3 as replacement only.

Most Points in a season:

Pts	Player	T	C	P	DG
313	J Gregory	7	52	24	-
89	M Corcoran	15	4	2	-
80	N Dontah	16	-	-	-
60	C Bird	12	-	-	-
40	R Goodwin	8	-	-	-
35	M Butterworth	7	-	-	-

MATCH FACTS

10	9	1	2	3	4	5	6	7	8	
Bailey	Bird	White	Waddington/t(m)	Agnew/t(n)	Meadows	Mole(o)	Owen	Brady/t	Butterworth(p)	1
Bailey	Bird	Cormack(s)	Waddington	Busby	Burrage(t)	Mole	Bird	Brady	Owen(l)	2
Bailey/dg	Bird/t	White	Waddington(m)	Baird(g)	Towns	Mole	Bird/t	Owen	Butterworth	3
Bailey/dg	Bird	White	Bennett	Agnew(v)	Towns	Mole	Burrage(h)	Bird/t	Owen	4
Bailey/4c	Goodwin/t	White(n)	Waddington	Cormack	Towns/t(i)	Meadows	Owen	Bird(o)	Butterworth/t	5
Bailey	Goodwin	White	Waddington	Agnew	Mole	Meadows	Owen	Brady(p)	Butterworth	6
Bailey	Goodwin/t(d)	White/t	Waddington(m)	Agnew(v)	Meadows	Towns	Bird(j)	Brady	Butterworth	7
Bailey/dg	Bird/t	Cormack(e)	Bennett(f)	Agnew	Meadows	Towns(t/t)	Bird/t	Brady	Owen	8
Bailey	Bird(q)	White	Waddington/t	Cormack(g)	Meadows/t	Towns/t	Mole(A)	Brady	Owen	9
Bailey	Goodwin(d)	White	Bennett(f/t)	Cormack(n)	Meadows/t	Towns(i)	Owen/t	Bird/2t	Butterworth	10
Bailey	Goodwin/t(d)	White	Bennett(f)	Cormack	Meadows	Towns(i)	Bird/t	Brady	Butterworth	11
Bailey	Bird(q/t)	Baird	Waddington(m)	Cormack	Meadows/t	Mole(t)	Bird(A)	Brady	Butterworth	12
Bailey	Goodwin(d)	Cormack	Bennett(f)	Agnew(n)	Meadows/t	Towns(j)	Bird/t(A)	Brady	Butterworth	13
Bailey	Bird(q/t)	Cormack	Waddington(m)	Agnew	Meadows(i)	Towns	Hankey(A)	Bird/t	Butterworth/t	14
Bailey(F)	Goodwin	Cormack	Bennett(f)	Busby(g)	Meadows	Mole	Bird	Davison(j)	Butterworth/t(t)	15
Butterworth/t	Bird/t	Cormack(e)	Bennett(f)	Agnew	Meadows(t)	Mole	Bird/t	Brady(l)	Owen	16
Butterworth/t	Bird(q)(q/t)	Cormack	Waddington	Agnew(e)	Meadows	Town(i)	Owen(p)	Brady	Butterworth/t	17
Butterworth	Goodwin/t	Cormack(e)	Bennett	Agnew	Meadows	Mole(t)	Owen	Bird	Butterworth	18
Bailey/t	Bird	White(v)	Holland(m/t)	Agnew	Meadows	Towns(i)	Owen/t(A)	Brady	Butterworth	19
Bailey	Bird(q/t)	White(g)	Bennett(z)	Cormack	Meadows(j)	Mole	Bird/t	Brady	Buterworth	20
Bailey	Goodwin(d)	Cormack	Holland(H)	Agnew(n)	Meadows	Towns/t(i)	Owen/t	Brady	Butterworth/t(A)	21
Bailey	Goodwin	Cormack	H-Evans	Agnew	Meadows	Towns(p/t)	Owen	Brady	Butterworth	22
Bailey/t	Bird(J)	White(s)	H-Evans(z)	Cormack	Mole(o)	Towns/t	Owen/2t	Brady/t	Butterworth(A/t	23
Bailey	Bird	White	H-Evans(m)	Cormack	Meadows(t)	Mole	Owen	Brady(B)	Butterworth	24
Bailey	Bird(q)	White/t(g)	Bennett(H)	Cormack	Meadows	Mole	Bird/t	Davison	Butterworth(B)	25
Bailey)a)	Bird(q/t)	White(g)	H-Evans(m)	Cormack/t	Meadows(j)	Mole	Bird(k)	Davison	Butterworth/t	26
Bailey	Bird/2t	White/t	Waddington(x)	Baird(n)	Towns(j)	Mole	Bird	Brady(y)	Butterwoth/t	A
Bailey	Goodwin(d)	White	Waddington(m)	Cormack(n)	Mole(t)	Meadows/t	Owen	Brady(o)	Butterworth	B
Bailey	Goodwin/2t(d)	White/t(v)	Waddington/t	Agnew	Meadows	Towns(i)	Bird	Brady	Butterworth	C
Bailey	Goodwin(d/t)	Cormack	Waddington(m)	Agnew(n)	Meadows	Towns(i)	Owen(A)	Bird(k)	Butterworth	D

REPLACEMENTS:

a- K Marchant, b- S Dixon, c - N Dontah, d - J Bird, e - A White,
f - N Waddington, g - C Agnew, h - A Meadows, i - P Mole, j - S Owen, k - P Brady,
l - M Butterworth, m - M Bennett, n - R Busby, o - C Burrage, p - C Bird, q - R Goodwin,
r - P Martin, s - J Baird, t - J Towns, u - M Old, v - D Cormack, w - M Corcoran,
x - G Bell, y - O Hall, z- W Holland, A - J Davison, B - P Vaughan, C - T Sanderson,
D - J Greenyer, E - T Clouston, F - J Butterworth, G - A Sandilands, H - M Humphreys Evans, J - D Bailey

Former Richmond full back Jonathan Gregory scored an impressive 313 points and was the leading scorer in the division.

Winger Nana Dontah topped the try scorers list by one ahead of fellow winger Michael Corcoran.

Leading the way in the forwards was flanker Ciaran Bird with 12.

Esher ended the season as the leading points and try scorers in the division.

At home they conceded a division low eight tries. They conceded just 112 points which was joint lowest in the division.

Lost just once at home to North Walsham.

Away from home they had the best record in the division with 22 out of 26 points.

ESHER

LEAGUE STATISTICS
compiled by Stephen McCormack

SEASON	Division	P	W	D	L	F	A	Pts Diff	Lge Pts	Lge Pos	Most Points	Most Tries
89-90	L2S	10	3	0	7	84	107	-23	6	8		
90-91	L2S	10	5	1	4	149	139	10	11	6		
91-92	L2S	10	5	0	5	153	146	7	9	6		
92-93	L2S	12	7	0	5	201	189	12	14	3		
93-94	L2S	12	10	2	0	382	95	287	22	1p		
94-95	L1	12	10	0	2	344	132	212	20	2		
95-96	L1	12	9	0	3	280	159	121	18	3		
96-97	L1	13	12	0	1	458	171	287	24	1p		
97-98	N2S	26	18	1	7	651	448	203	37	4	92 Ray Dudman	12 Mark Butterworth
98-99	N2S	26	23	0	3	864	308	566	46	2	313 Jon Gregory	16 Nana Dontah

FACT FILE

Founded: 1923-24
Nickname: The EE's
Colours: Black and amber
Change Colours:

GROUND

Address: The Rugby Ground, 369 Molesey Road, Hersham, Surrey KT12 3PF
Tel: 01932 220295 (Office), 01932 254627 (Fax), 01932 224834 (Clubhouse)
Capacity: 3,000 Seated: 1,200 Standing: Uncovered 1,800

Directions: M25 Junc 10, A3 to London. After 1 mile left to Walton-on-Thames (A245), after 1/4 mile right at lights into Seven Hills Road (B365).Turn right at r/about into Burwood Road & follow into Hersham Village, bear right into Molesey Road. After railway bridge (Hersham BR) ground 300yds left.
Nearest Railway Station: Hersham (Waterloo-Woking line)

Car Parking: 1,000 on ground

Admission: Season - £35. Matchdays £5 incl. programme
14-16 yr old £2 Children u14/OAPs Free.

Clubhouse: Open matchdays & training nights
Snacks & bar meals available.
Functions: Up to 180, contact Phil Beebe 01932 220295

Club Shop: Open matchdays & training days.
Contact Tim Bale 01932 220295

Training Nights: Monday & Thursday 7pm

PROGRAMME

Size: A5 Price: With admission Pages: 28 + cover
Editor: Dick Ralph 01932 702958
ADVERTISING RATES
Colour - Full page £375, Half £250, Qtr £150
Mono - Full page £350, Half £210, Qtr £125

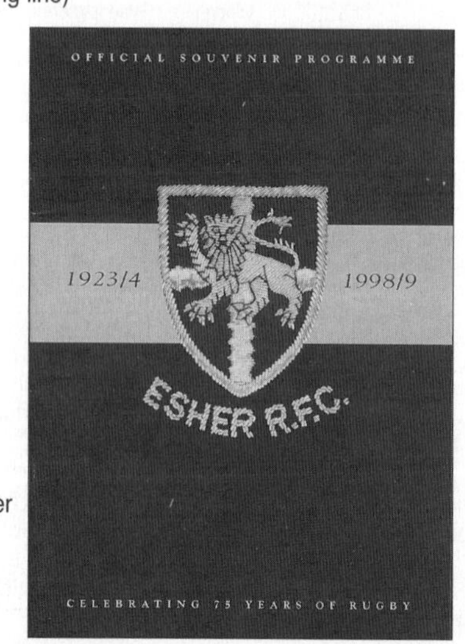

METROPOLITAN POLICE R.F.C.

Club Secretary	Neil Sinclair	Room 1707, New Scotland Yard, London SW1H 0BG 020 8977 4569 (H) 020 7230 4711 (B) 07971 048966 (M)
Fixtures Secretary	Simon Gill	Room 1707, New Scotland Yard, London SW1H 0BG 020 7230 2187 (B) 07971 044405 (M)
Press Secretary	Contact either of the above.	Fax: 020 7230 3255

President	**Chairman**	**Coach**	**Registration**
Sir Paul Condon QPM	Dick Cullen	Jon Taylor 0402 742376 (Mobile)	John Packer 020 8429 1935(H)

The 75th Anniversary season will be regarded as one of consolidation tinged with success.
Following on from the nadir of 1998 when the club's status was only preserved by the machinations of the RFU, there was much joy at the unequivocal fifth place in Jewson National League Two (South). This reflected well on the work of Jon Taylor and his coaching team Gordon Raybould, Phil Spittles and the occasional consultant drafted in throughout the season. Accolades are also deserved for those who have taken the club into a new era, possibly eight or nine years overdue, of recruiting quality players who are not exclusively Metropolitan Police officers.
The season began with a very successful tour to Australia, playing very high calibre opposition. Many observers felt the Met players performed above themselves; the League season was to prove that they had previously been under-performing. An added bonus of the tour was that the team spirit engendered in the Antipodes was sustained into the domestic season.
After an uninspiring opening to the League programme, including an abject performance in defeat at Tabard, the season developed into one of burgeoning success and confidence. Only Esher & Barking proved to be consistently better than the Met. along with Bracknell who won both League fixtures and knocked the Met. out of the Third Round of the Tetley's Bitter Cup.
The pay-off has been increased playing membership and enthusiasm for the forthcoming season and players gaining representative honours for British Police, Middlesex, Hertfordshire and Hampshire.
An interesting statistic: in 26 league games only 33 penalties were kicked. Either opponents were very disciplined or the Met's kickers were very poor!

METROPOLITAN POLICE

Match No.	Date	H/A	Comp.	Opponents	Result & Score	Att.	15	14	13	12	11
1	05.09	A	J2S	Havant	W 13-11		Carter	P Gastor	Ferry	S Gastor	Weatherley
2	12.09	A	J2S	Tabard	L 10-17		Walsh	P Gastor	Ferry	S Gastor/t	Weatherley
3	26.09	H	J2S	Norwich	W 21-12		Carter/t(n)	Wakeford	Ferry	S Gastor/t	Evans
4	03.10	A	J2S	Redruth	W 26-10		Carter/2t	P Gastor	Ferry	S Gastor/t	Evans(p)
5	10.10	H	J2S	Weston	W 43-22		Carter	P Gastor/t	Ferry	S Gastor(a)	Wakeford
6	24.10	A	J2S	Bracknell	L 5-11		Carter	P Gastor	Ferry	S Gastor/t	Weatherley
7	31.10	H	J2S	Cheltenham	W 32-9		Carter/3t	P Gastor	Ferry	S Gastor/t	Weatherley
8	07.11	A	J2S	Plymouth	W 20-13		Carter/t	P Gastor	Ferry	S Gastor	Richards
9	21.11	H	J2S	N Walsham	W 31-8		Carter	P Gastor	Ferry	S Gastor/t(q)	Weatherley
10	28.11	A	J2S	Barking	L 5-29		Carter(b)	P Gastor	Ferry(x)	S Gastor	Evans
11	04.12	H	J2S	Esher	L 9-30		Carter	P Gastor	Ferry	S Gastor	Richards(a)
12	12.12	A	J2S	Clifton	W 20-19		Carter/2t	P Gastor	Ferry	Richards	Weatherley
13	19.12	H	J2S	Bridgwater	D 18-18		Carter	Richards(a)	Fery	S Gastor/t	P Gastor/t
14	27.12	A	J2S	Esher	L 6-53		Carter	Richards	Ferry	Walsh	Weatherley
15	02.01	H	J2S	Barking	L 12-30		Carter	P Gastor(A)	Richards	S Gastor	Weatherley
16	09.01	A	J2S	N Walsham	L 6-42		Carter	Thomas	Richards	Walsh	Care
17	16.01	H	J2S	Plymouth	W 26-12		Carter/c2p	P Gastor/t	Ferry	S Gastor/t	Richards
18	23.01	A	J2S	Cheltenham	W 22-9		Carter/2cp	P Gastor/t(q)	Ferry	Richards	Weatherley
19	31.01	H	J2S	Bracknell	L 6-18		Carter/2p	Richards	Ferry	S Gastor	Weatherley
20	06.02	A	J2S	Weston	W 24-14		Carter/2tc	Thomas	Ferry	Lenthall	Richards
21	13.02	H	J2S	Redruth	W 33-15		Carter/t2c	P Gastor/2t	Ferry	S Gastor	Richards/t
22	27.02	A	J2S	Norwich	L 3-41		P Gastor	Evans	Ferry	S Gastor(D)	Richards
23	13.03	H	J2S	Tabard	W 39-28		Carter/t2c	Richards	Ferry	S Gastor(l)	Weatherley/3t
24	27.03	H	J2S	Havant	W 15-12		Carter/2tcp	Richards	Ferry	S Gastor	Weatherley
25	03.04	A	J2S	Bridgwater	L 17-48		Carter/tc	Jenkins	McLoughlin	Lenthall/t(E)	Richards
26	17.04	H	J2S	Clifton	L 8-14		P Gastor	Weatherley/t	Ferry	S Gastor	Richards(F)
A	19.09	H	TB1	Cheltenham	W 34-8		P Gastor	Evans(p/t)	Ferry	S Gastor	Weatherley
B	17.10	H	TB2	Wimborne	W 25-14		Carter	P Gastor	Ferry	S Gastor/2t	Wakeford(a)
C	14.11	A	TB3	Bracknell	L 6-13		Carter	P Gastor	Ferry	S Gastor	Weatherley(p)

* after opponents name indicates a penalty try
Brackets after a player's name indicates he was replaced. eg (a) means he was replaced by replacement code "a" and so on.
/ after a player or replacement name is followed by any scores he made - eg /t, /c, /p, /dg or any combination of these

1998-99 HIGHLIGHTS

Ever Presents: Colin Hall

25	Jim Panter(1), Jamie Canham (1).
23	Ross Ferry, Andy Carter

Players used: 37 plus 4 as replacement only.

Most Points in a season:

Pts	Player	T	C	P	DG
118	A Carter	16	10	6	-
97	J Herring	1	10	23	1
50	M Slevin	1	15	4	1
40	P Gastor	8	-	-	-
35	S Gastor	7	-	-	-
30	G Tovey	6	-	-	-

MATCH FACTS

10	9	1	2	3	4	5	6	7	8	
Slevin/tp	Jenkins	Booth(j)	Jeffrey(i)	Warlow	Canham	Thompson	Panter	Tovey/t(k)	Hall	1
Slevin/cdg	Jenkins(m)	Booth(G)	Instance	Warlow	Canham	McClenaghan(k)	Panter	Tovey	Hall	2
Slevin/3c	Fryar/t	Banaghan(c)(i)	Jeffrey	Warlow	Canham	Thompson	Panter	Thorpe(r)	Hall	3
Slevin/3c	Jenkins	Barham	Instance(d)	Warlow	Canham(r)	Thompson	Panter	Tovey/t(k)	Hall	4
Slevin/5cp(n)	Jenkins(i)	Rhymes	Jeffrey	Marsey	Hall/t	Thompson/t	Panter(k)	Tovey/3t(v)	Galvin	5
Slevin	Fryar(b)	Davies(u)	Jeffrey	Rhymes	Canham	Hall	Panter	Tovey	Galvin	6
Slevin/3c2p(n)	Fryar(b)	Davies(u)	Jeffrey(i)	Rhymes(e)	Canham	Hall	Panter(k)	Tovey	Galvin	7
Herring/2c2p	Fryar(b)	Davies	Jeffrey	Marsey(e)	Canham	Hall/t	Panter	Tovey	Galvin	8
Herring/c3p	Jenkins(m)	Davies(z)	Jeffrey/t(i)	Rhymes(e)	Canham	Hall	Panter/t	Tovey/t(k)	Galvin	9
Herring	Fryar(b)	Davies(u)	Instance(d)	Rhymes(e)	Canham	Thompson(k)	Panter	Tovey	Hall/t	10
Herring/2pdg	Fryar	Rhymes	Jeffrey(i)	Davies(z)	Canham	Hall	Panter	Tovey	Galvin(b)	11
Herring/2c2p	Jenkins	Sang	Instance(d)	Davies	Canham	Hall	Panter	Thorpe(h)	Galvin	12
Herring/c2p	Jenkins(A)	Davies	Jeffrey	Sang(t)	Canham	Hall	Panter	Tovey	Galvin	13
Herring/2p	Fryar(o)	Davies	Jeffrey(i)	Rhymes(z)	Canham	Hall	Panter	Tovey	Galvin(k)	14
Herring/4p	Jenkins	Sang(w)	Instance	Rhymes(e)	Canham	Hall	Panter	Thorpe	Galvin	15
Herring/2p	Jenkins	Sang	Instance	Warlow	Canham	Hall	Panter	Tovey	Galvin	16
Herring/p	Jenkins	Davies	Jeffrey/t	Sang	Canham	Hall	Panter	Tovey	Galvin	17
Herring	Jenkins(A/t)	Sang	Jeffrey/t(i)	Davies(t)	Canham(B)	Hall	Panter	Thorpe	Galvin	18
Herring	Jenkins	Sang(t)	Jeffrey	Davies	Canham	Hall	Panter	Tovey(k)	Galvin	19
Herring/t2cp	Jenkins	Rhymes(z)	Instance(d)	Davies	Canham	Hall	Strickler	Panter	Galvin	20
Herring/2c(y)	Jenkins(A)	Sang(t/t)	Instance(d)	Davies	Canham	Hall	Strickler	Thorpe(g)	Galvin	21
Herring/p	Care(b)	Rhymes	Lenthall	Davies	Canham	Hall	Sang(B)(k)	Panter	Williams(r)	22
P Gastor/t	Jenkins/t	Rhymes(z)	Instance(d)	Davies	Canham	Hall	Williams(B/t)	Panter	Galvin	23
P Gastor	Jenkins(m)	Sang	Jeffrey(i)	Davies(t)	Canham	Hall	Strickler(k)	Panter	Galvin(C)	24
P Gastor/t	Care	Rhymes	Instance	Barham(v)	Canham	Hall	Strickler	Panter	Williams	25
Herring/p(y)	Care	Rhymes	Instance(d)	Davies	Canham	Hall	Panter	Thorpe(B)	Williams(r)	26
Slevin/tc4p(n)	Fryar/t	Banaghan	Jeffrey(i)	Warlow	Canham	Thompson	Panter	Thorpe(s)	Hall/t	A
Herring/2c2p	Jenkins/t(m)	Davies	Instance(d)	Marsey	Canham	Thompson	Galvin	Tovey(k)	Hall	B
Herring/2p	Fryar(b)	Davies	Instance	Warlow(u)	Canham	Hall	Panter	Thorpe(f)	Galvin	C

REPLACEMENTS:

	a- E Weatherley	b- R Jenkins	c - M Booth	d - D Jeffrey	e - I Warlow
f - P Thompson	g - J Panter	h - G Tovey	i - K Instance	j - P Harvey	k - J Thorpe
l - K Walsh	m - G Fryar	n - J Herring	o - A Lenthall	p - P Wakeford	q - R Evans
r - R Galvin	s - E Cudmore	t - R Rhymes	u - B Marsey	v - G Raybould	w - M Davies
x - P Richards	y - N Thomas	z - S Sang	A - B Care	B - J Strickler	C - M Williams
D - S Stockton	E - G Chesterton	F - J McLoughlin			

With regular kicker Mark Slevin out for most of the season Andy Carter and James Herring shared the kicking.
Carter added to his total with 16 tries to end the season as leading points and try scorer for the club.

Met Police had a good start to the season and finished well. But in the middle they managed just one win in seven to lose their way.

After finished bottom last season fifth place was a tremendous improvement.

They managed just one win against the teams that finished above them when they beat North Walsham at home 31-8.

Gareth Tovey, Andy Carter and Eddie Weatherley all scored hat tricks in league matches.

METROPOLITAN POLICE

LEAGUE STATISTICS
compiled by Stephen McCormack

SEASON	Division	P	W	D	L	F	A	Pts Diff	Lge Pts	Lge Pos	Most Points	Most Tries
89-90	ALS	10	9	0	1	255	74	181	18	1p	34 John Kerr	4 Paul Galvin/John Kerr
90-91	D3	12	4	0	8	130	188	-58	8	12r	74 Derek Lamour	4 Kevin Walsh/J Bailey/ S O'Reilly
91-92	D4S	12	3	0	9	149	195	-46	6	10	32 Derek Lamour	3 Ross Ferry
92-93	D4S	12	4	1	7	201	207	-6	9	9	Mark Wood	Andy Carter
93-94	D5S	12	5	0	7	167	174	-7	10	10	82 Andy Carter	7 Andy Carter
94-95	D5S	12	5	0	7	183	175	8	10	7	90 Mark Slevin	7 Andy Carter
95-96	D5S	12	2	1	9	130	204	-74	5	12	50 Mark Slevin	4 Ross Ferry
96-97	D4S	26	14	1	11	661	558	103	29	7	223 Mark Slevin	11 Richard Galvin
97-98	N2S	26	2	0	24	320	941	-621	4	14	116 Mark Slevin	5 Mark Slevin
98-99	N2S	26	14	1	11	470	545	-75	29	5	118 Andy Carter	16 Andy Carter

FACT FILE

Founded: 1923
Nickname: Mets

Colours: Blue and white hoops.
Change colours: All green

GROUND

Address: Met Police (Imber Court) Sports Club, Ember Lane, East Molesey, Surrey KT8 0BT
Tel: 0181 398 1267 Fax 0181 398 9755
Capacity: 3,250 Seated: 750 Standing: 2,500

Directions: M25 Jnc 12, M3 towards London Jnc 1, take A308 to Hampton Court, turn right over bridge A309 to next roundabout, turn right into Ember Court Rd, club at end.
Nearest Railway Station: Esher, turn right ground entrance 600 yds

Car Parking: 200 within ground

Admission: £4, Children/OAP £1

Clubhouse: Normal licensing hours, snacks & meals available.
Functions available

Club Shop: No

Training Nights: Monday & Thursday

PROGRAMME

Size: A5 Price: With entry Pages: 12 plus cover
Editor: Neil Sinclair 020 7230 4711 (B)

ADVERTISING RATES
Contact John Packer 0181 429 1935

NORTH WALSHAM R.F.C.

President	George Bradford	Half Acre, Horning Road, Hoveton, Norfolk. 01692 630426 (H)
Chairman	Nick Beardshaw	Grove Cottage, Aylsham Road, Swanton Abbott. 01692 538298 (H)
Club Secretary	Yvonne Baines	Rose Dene, Crown Road, Buxton, Norwich NR10 5EH 01603 712969 (H)
Press Officer	Tony Marcantonio	The White House, Southwood Road, Beighton,Norwich. NR13 3AB. 01493 751837 (H & Fax)
Fixtures Secretary	K T Jarvis	The Chilterns, 2D Millfield Road, North Walsham.NR28 0EB. 01692 406429 (H), 01263 732341 (B)
Marketing Manager	Chris Fletcher	01692 538808 (Tel & Fax)
Shop Manager	Chris Fletcher	as above

After several seasons in the middle lower and reaches of the table North Walsham with basically the same squad as the previous year suddenly found a new belief and for a long time looked likely contenders for promotion finally having to settle for a best ever third place behind Bracknell and Esher.

The season started well with four wins on the trot before successive defeats at the hands of Barking and Esher, a one point win in the most atrocious conditions at Clifton and a poor performance and a heavy defeat at Met Police concentrated minds. The following week a home win against Tabard started a club record run of fifteen successive wins including two hard games against local rivals Norwich with the home fixture attracting the biggest crowd ever seen at a rugby match in Norfolk. Any hope of grabbing the top spot disappeared at Bracknell when the champions elect deservedly took the points. Records were broken during the season. A new attitude towards the game instilled by coach Jim McKay brought new club records, highest ever total points and tries scored and lowest ever points conceded with only the absence of a front line kicker causing concern. Kiwi Kenny Dodds, a dynamic No 8, was voted player of the year.

With a high average age in the side the lookout was on for youngsters. Johnny Wyatt spent many hours on the bench but could always be relied upon when the call came. Dominic Crossley and student Tim Lowles both filled wing berths but the find of the season was prop Spencer Williams who arrived as a loose head but by the end of the season was a regular on the other side.

Sadly for Walsham but to the relief of opponents Ian Fox has decided to retire. Credit must go to Club Captain Phil Anthony who despite not always getting into the starting line up never let his enthusiasm flag.

Walsham's blindside, Grant Furlong, in action against Cheltenham. Photo courtesy Eastern Daily Press

NORTH WALSHAM

Match No.	Date	H/A	Comp.	Opponents	Result & Score	15	14	13	12	11
1	05.09	H	J2S	Bracknell	W 17-3	Dillon	C Greenhall	Kingsmill	N Greenhall/2c	McKay/t
2	12.09	A	J2S	Cheltenham	W 32-7	Dillon	C Greenhall/t(n)	Fox	N Greenhall/t(b/c)	McKay/t
3	26.09	H	J2S	Plymouth	W33-17	C Greenhall(a)	Crossley	Kingsmill	N Greenhall	McKay/t
4	03.10	H	J2S	Havant	W47-17	C Greenhall/t	Crossley	Kingsmill	N Greehall(a/2t)	McKay/2t
5	10.10	A	J2S	Barking	L 8-18	C Greenhall	Crossley	Kingsmill	N Greenhall/t	McKay
6	24.10	H	J2S	Esher	L 10-13	C Greenhall	Crossley	Fox	N Greenhall	McKay/t
7	31.10	A	J2S	Cheltenham	W15-14	C Greenhall	Brand	Fox	N Greenhall/dg	McKay/t
8	07.11	H	J2S	Bridgwater	W21-10	Dillon/2p	Brand/t	Kingsmill	Fox	McKay/t
9	21.11	A	J2S	M Police	L 8-31	Dillon	C Greenhall	Fox	N Greenhall(b)	McKay/t(n)
10	28.11	H	J2S	Tabard	W 21-7	Dillon	Kingsmill/t	Fox	N Greenhall	C Greenhall/t(p)
11	05.12	A	J2S	Norwich	W 15-6	Dillon	Kingsmill	Fox/t	N Greenhall	C Greenhall
12	12.12	H	J2S	Redruth	W25-10	Dillon/p	Kingsmill/t	Fox(w)	N Greenhall	C Greenhall/t
13	19.12	A	J2S	Weston	W 13-5	Dillon	Crossley	Kingsmill	N Greenhall	Lowles(n)
14	28.12	H	J2S	Norwich	W 13-0	Dillon	Kingsmill(n)	Fox	N Greenhall	C Greenhall/t(p)
15	02.01	A	J2S	Tabard	W27-17	Dillon	Brand/t	Fox	Kingsmill	N Greenhall/t
16	09.01	H	J2S	M Police	W 42-6	Dillon	Brand/t	Fox/t	Kingsmill	C Greenhall/2t(p/t)
17	16.01	A	J2S	Bridgwater	W31-16	Dillon/t(l)	Crossley/t	C Greenhall	N Greenhall/t	Kingsmill
18	23.01	H	J2S	Clifton	W 36-3	Dillon	C Greenhall/t	Fox	Kingsmill/t	McKay/t
19	30.01	A	J2S	Esher	W12-11	C Greenhall	Kingsmill	Fox	N Greenhall	McKay
20	06.02	H	J2S	Barking	W 21-9	C Greenhall/t	Kingsmill/t	Fox	N Greenhall	McKay
21	13.02	A	J2S	Havant*	W47-10	C Greenhall(a)	Kingsmill	Fox	N Greenhall(w/c)	McKay/t
22	27.02	A	J2S	Plymouth	W23-11	C Greenhall	Crossley(W/t)	Kingsmill	N Greenhall	McKay
23	13.03	H	J2S	Cheltenham	W 29-0	C Greenhall/t	Kingsmill	Fox	N Greenhall	McKay/t
24	27.03	A	J2S	Bracknell	L 14-31	C Greenhall(l)	Kingsmill/t(t)	Fox	N Greenhall(n)	McKay
25	03.04	H	J2S	Weston	W43-17	C Greenhall	Brand/3t	Fox	Kingsmill/2t	McKay
26	17.04	A	J2S	Redruth	W34-17	C Grennall(t)(l/t)	Brand	Fox	Kingsmill(A)	McKay/t
A	19.09	A	TB1	Launceston	L 18-32	Dillon(l)	C Greenhall	Fox/t(p)	Kingsmill	Brand

* after opponents name indicates a penalty try
Brackets after a player's name indicates he was replaced. eg (a) means he was replaced by replacement code "a" and so on.
/ after a player or replacement name is followed by any scores he made - eg /t, /c, /p, /dg or any combination of these

1998-99 HIGHLIGHTS

Ever Presents: None

Most appearances

25	James Shanahan
24	C Greenhall, Rex Hargrave, John Morfoot, Stuart Loose (1).
22	Tony Kingsmill (2), Jeff van Poortvliet

Players used: 30 plus six as a replacement only.

Most Points in a season:

Pts	Player	T	C	P	DG
158	P Friel	6	31	22	-
112	J Shanahan	16	7	4	2
65	J McKay	13	-	-	-
55	C Greenhall	11	-	-	-
32	T Kingsmill	6	1	-	-
26	S Dillon	3	1	3	-
25	K Dodds	5	-	-	-

MATCH FACTS

10	9	1	2	3	4	5	6	7	8	
Shanahan/dg	Friel/t	Loose	Byrne	Yaxley(i)	Hargrave	Morfoot(j)	Anthony	v Poortvliet(k)	Dodds	1
Shanahan/2t	Wyatt	Loose	Yaxley	Nobbs(e)	Hargrave	Morfoot(o)	Furlong(m)	Walters	Dodds/t	2
Shanahan/dg	Friel/2t2c2p	Loose	Byrne/t	Leonard(i)	Hargrave	Morfoot	Anthony	v Poortvliet	Dodds(k)	3
Shanahan/t	Friel/4c3p(s)	Loose(r)	Byrne(f)	Leonard	Hargrave	Morfoot	Furlong	v Poortvliet	Anthony(m)	4
Shanahan	Friel/p	Loose	Byrne	Leonard	Hargrave	Morfoot	Furlong	v Poortvliet	Anthony	5
Shanahan	Wyatt(c)	Loose	Byrne/t(f)	Leonard(i)	Fletcher(t)	Morfoot	Furlong	v Poortvliet	Anthony	6
Shanahan(a/c)	Friel(l)	Loose(v)	Byrne(u)	Yaxley(i)	Anthony	Morfoot/t	Furlong	v Poortvliet	Purling	7
N Greenhall	Wyatt	Loose	Kenworthy	Leonard(v)	Hargrave	Morfoot	Furlong	v Poortvliet/t	Purling(g)	8
Shanahan/p	Wyatt	Loose	Byrne(u)	Scott(q)	Hargrave	Morfoot(z)	Furlong(t)	Malone	Anthony	9
Shanahan/3c	Wyatt	Loose	Byrne(u)	Scott(i)	Hargrave	Morfoot	Furlong	v Poortvliet	Dodds/t(t)	10
Shanahan/2t	Friel	Loose	Byrne(u)	Scott	Hargrave	Morfoot	Anthony(t)	v Poortvliet	Dodds	11
Shanahan/tc	Wyatt	Loose	Kenworthy	Scott(q)	Hargrave	Furlong	Anthony(z)	v Poortvliet	Dodds/t(x)	12
Shanahan/t2p	Friel/c	Loose	Byrne	Scott(v)	Hargrave	Furlong	Malone(g)	v Poortvliet	Dodds	13
Shanahan/p	Friel	Loose	Byrne	Scott(v)	Hargrave	Morfoot(g)	Furlong/t	v Poortvliet	Dodds	14
Shanahan	Friel/t2cp	Loose/t	Byrne	Scott(v)	Hargrave	Morfoot(g)	Furlong	Dodds	Purling	15
Shanahan	Friel/3c2p	Loose	Byrne	Scott/t	Hargrave	Morfoot	Furlong	v Poortvliet	Dodds	16
Shanahan/t	Friel/3c	Williams(d)	Byrne/t	Scott	Hargrave	Morfoot	Furlong(t)	v Poortvliet	Dodds(z)	17
Shanahan/3c	Wyatt	Loose	Dodds	Williams	Hargrave/t	Morfoot	Furlong	v Poortvliet	Purling(z)	18
Shanahan	Friel/4p	Loose	Byrne	Scott	Hargrave(z)	Morfoot	Furlong(g)	v Poortvliet	Dodds	19
Shanahan	Friel/c3p(l)	Loose	Byrne	Scott(v)	Hargrave	Morfoot	Furlong(g)	v Poortvliet	Dodds	20
Shanahan/3t	Friel/t5c(l)	Williams	Byrne	Scott	Hargrave(z)	Morfoot	Anthony(k)	v Poortvliet	Dodds/t	21
Shanahan/t	Friel/tp	Loose	Kenworthy	Williams	Hargrave	Morfoot	Anthony(k)	Dodds/t	Purling	22
Shanahan/t	Friel/3cp	Loose	Byrne(u)	Williams(q)	Hargrave	Morfoot	Furlong	v Poortvliet/t	Purling(h)	23
Shanahan	Friel/3p	Loose	Byrne(u)	Williams(y)	Hargrave	Morfoot	Furlong(g)	v Poortvliet	Dodds	24
Shanahan/t	Friel/4c(l)	Loose	Byrne(u)	Williams(y)	Hargrave	Morfoot	Anthony(x)	v Poortvliet	Purling/t	25
Shanahan/2t	Friel/3cp	Loose	Byrne(u/t)	Williams	Hargrave	Morfoot(k)	Anthony	v Poortvliet	Dodds	26
Shanahan	Friel/c2p	Loose	Yaxley(e/t)	Leonard	Hargrave	Bowyer(m)	Furlong	Walters	Dodds	A

REPLACEMENTS:

	a- S Dillon	b- T Kingsmill	c - P Friel	d - S Loose	e - M Byrne
f - M Yaxley	g - P Anthony	h - K Dodds	i - R Nobbs	j - L Walters	k - G Furlong
l - J Wyatt	m - D Malone	n - A Brand	o - J Bowyer	p - D Crossley	q - K Leonard
r - B Colman	s - M Scott	t - M Purling	u - M Kenworthy	v - S Williams	w - T Lowles
x - T Malone	y - M Scott	z - J Marlee	A - D Cooke		

Scrum half Phil Friel topped the points scorers chart with 158 points.

Fly half James Shanahan finished as leading try scorer for North Walsham and in the division where he shared the lead with Esher's Nana Dontah.

Player coach Jim McKay was not far behind with 13 in his first, and only, season at the club.

North Walsham ended the season with the least points against, 306 compared with Esher's 308.

Lost just once at home when they were beaten by Esher 13-10 in October.

Mid season Walsham put together a 14 match unbeaten run and in all lost just one of their last 17 matches.

NORTH WALSHAM

LEAGUE STATISTICS
compiled by Stephen McCormack

SEASON	Division	P	W	D	L	F	A	Pts Diff	Lge Pts	Lge Pos		Coach		Captain
89-90	Lon 1	10	9	0	1	231	94	137	18	1p		D Brunton		S Rossi
90-91	D4S	12	5	2	5	170	180	-10	12	6		P Bryant		M Goodall
91-92	D4S	12	5	0	7	153	152	1	10	7		P Bryant		B Gardner
92-93	D4S	12	4	0	8	125	209	-84	8	11				
93-94	D5S	12	5	2	5	120	173	-53	12	8				
94-95	D5S	12	7	1	4	233	190	43	15	4		R Flatters		N Greenall
												Most Points		**Most Tries**
95-96	D5S	12	3	1	8	149	212	-63	7	11	51	Tony Kingsmill	3	Smith
96-97	D4S	26	10	1	15	426	605	-179	21	10	70	James Shanahan	10	Tom Rains
97-98	N2S	26	12	1	13	431	373	58	25	7	253	James Shanahan	8	James Shanahan Adain Brand
98-99	N2S	26	22	0	4	627	306	321	44	3	158	Phil Friel	16	James Shanahan

FACT FILE

Founded: 1962 **Colours**: Green with 1wide black & 2 narrow white bands/black/green.

Nickname: Walsh **Change colours:** All white **Away colours:** Blue with 2 white & 1 red hoop/white/red

GROUND

Address: Norwich Road, Scottow, Norwich, NR10 5BU
Tel: 01692 538808 (Office & Fax) 01692 538461 (Clubhouse)
Capacity: 1,000 Seated: 160 Standing: 1,000

Directions: From Norwich take B1150 to North Walsham, go through Coltishall towards N Walsham. Ground is on left just past "Three Horseshoes" Pub
Nearest Railway Station: North Walsham

Car Parking: Ample at ground

Admission: 98-99 - Adults £4 inc programme 99-00 - TBA

Clubhouse: Open matchdays & training nights.
Snacks & barmeals available

Functions Capacity 80, contact Chris Fletcher

Club Shop: Yes; Manager Chris Fletcher 01692 538808

Training Nights: Tuesday & Thursday 7.30pm

PROGRAMME

Size: A5 Price: With Entry
Pages: 44 + cover
Editor: Tony Marcantonio 01493 751837

ADVERTISING RATES
Contact Chris Fletcher 01692 538808

NORWICH R.F.C.

President	Chris Gillham	27 Camberley Road, Norwich NR4 6SJ Tel: 01603 458439 (H) 01473 284428 (B)
Club Secretary	Tracey Bailey	'Oakdene', Church Hill, Reedham, Norfolk NR10 4JL Tel: 01603 871773 (H)
Fixtures Secretary	Iain Blaxhall	15 Suters Drive, Thorpe St. Andrew, Norwich NR8 6UU Tel: 01603 860029 (H) 01603 632194 (B)

Norwich Rugby Football Club's first season in the National League was the culmination of years of hard work by the club's management and coaching staff. The first fifteen squad always knew that their first season would not be easy and the new experience would be a year of learning and development in this higher standard of rugby.

Norwich acquired new members, Pinegar, Williams, Smith, Wells, and Orgais, some with National League experience, and these together with the promotion team provided the nucleus of a strong squad for their first Nation League campaign. Unfortunately, Owen Coyne was unavailable due to work commitments, and this was a big blow to the Norwich team, Coyne having years of previous National League experience.

The first of the season saw Norwich winning the majority of their games including good away victories at Clifton and Redruth. Injury problems after Christmas saw eight players out of action for a long period, however, the team pulled together and new members from the junior teams in the club provided able replacements. The younger players equipped themselves well to National League rugby and will be looking to establish themselves as squad members for the new season.

Norwich ended their first season sixth in the National League and retained the Eastern Counties Cup. Mooney, the first fifteen captain, and his squad can be very pleased with their inaugural season in the National League, and the whole team are looking forward to the new season under new First Team coach Steve Worrall.

Norwich Squad 1989-99

Match No.	Date	H/A	Comp.	Opponents	Result & Score	Att.	15	14	13	12	11
1	05.09	A	J2S	Clifton	W 17-8		Griffin/2cp	Steed	Wells	O'Sullivan	Smith
2	12.09	H	J2S	Bridgwater*	W21-11		Griffin/c3p	Steed/t	Wells	O'Sullivan	Smith
3	26.09	A	J2S	M Police	L12-21		Griffin/c	Bracey	O'Sullivan	Thomas(n)	Smith/t
4	03.10	H	J2S	Tabard	W31-20		Lenihan	Steed	O'Sullivan/t	Orgias/t	Smith
5	10.10	A	J2S	Havant	L12-25		Lenihan	Steed/t	O'Sullivan/t	Orgias	Smith
6	24.10	A	J2S	Redruth	W12-10		Wells	Steed	O'Sullivan	Orgias/t	Smith
7	31.10	H	J2S	Weston	W 16-6		Wells	Steed/t	Orgias	O'Sullivan	Smith
8	07.11	A	J2S	Bracknell	L 6-16		Dwyer	Steed	Orgias(o)	O'Sullivan	Smith
9	21.11	H	J2S	Cheltenham	W 28-0		Wells	Steed/t(b)	O'Sullivan(j)	Bracey	Smith
10	28.11	A	J2S	Plymouth	W23-12		Orgias	Steed	Thomas	Bracey/t	Smith
11	05.12	H	J2S	N Walsham	L 6-15		Orgias	Steed	Thomas	O'Sullivan	Smith
12	12.12	A	J2S	Barking	L 3-34		Orgias	Steed	Thomas	O'Sullivan	Smith
13	19.12	H	J2S	Esher	L 7-23		Griffin/c	Steed	O'Sullivan	Orgias/t	Thomas
14	28.12	A	J2S	N Walsham	L 0-13		Griffin	Steed	O'Sullivan	Orgias	Thomas
15	02.01	H	J2S	Plymouth	W 35-5		Griffin/2t2c2p	Steed	Orgias/2t	Thomas	Smith
16	16.01	H	J2S	Bracknell	L15-19		Orgias	Stubbs	Thomas	O'Sullivan	Smith/2t
17	23.01	A	J2S	Weston	L 5-23		Orgias	Stubbs	Thomas	O'Sullivan	Smith/t
18	30.01	H	J2S	Redruth	W22-20		Orgias/t	Stubbs/t	O'Sullivan(i)	Thomas/t	Smith/t
19	06.02	H	J2S	Havant	L12-21		Griffin/c	Stubbs	Thomas/t	Orgias(a)	Smith
20	13.02	A	J2S	Tabard	L12-29		Griffin	Stubbs	Orgias(a)	Thomas(i)	Smith
21	20.02	A	J2S	Cheltenham	L 8-17		Holmes	Stubbs/t	O'Sullivan	Thomas	Bracey
22	27.02	H	J2S	M Police*	W 41-3		Holmes	Bracey	Cocker	Thomas/2t	Smith/t
23	13.03	A	J2S	Bridgwater	L10-18		Stubbs	Ratcliffe	O'Sullivan	Thomas	Smith
24	27.03	H	J2S	Clifton	L 6-16		Holmes/2p(u)	Stubbs	Cocker	Orgias	Smith
25	03.04	A	J2S	Esher	L 0-33		Griffin(w)	Stubbs	Cocker	Orgias(u)	Smith(o)
26	17.04	H	J2S	Barking	W23-15		Griffin/2c3p	Stubbs	Orgias	Coyne(i)	O'Sullivan
A	19.09	H	TB1	Winchester*	L15-23		Griffin/cp	Bracey/t	Wells	O'Sullivan	Ratcliffe

* after opponents name indicates a penalty try
Brackets after a player's name indicates he was replaced. eg (a) means he was replaced by replacement code "a" and so on.
/ after a player or replacement name is followed by any scores he made - eg /t, /c, /p, /dg or any combination of these

1998-99 HIGHLIGHTS

Ever Presents: None

Most appearances

25	Jonathan Griffin
23	Ed Marjoram (1), Ben Everitt
22	Lee Smith

Players used: 32 plus one as replacement only.

Most Points in a season:

Pts	Player	T	C	P	DG
160	J Griffin	4	25	27	3
30	L Smith	6	-	-	-
30	G Orgias	6	-	-	-
25	J Thomas	5	-	-	-
20	E Steed	4	-	-	-
20	J Carmichael	4	-	-	-

MATCH FACTS

10	9	1	2	3	4	5	6	7	8	
Dwyer/t	Mooney/t	Marjoram	Ogle	Everitt	Loveday	Pinnegar	Carmichael	Gibbs	Woodhouse	1
Dwyer	Mooney	Marjoram	Ogle	Everitt	Loveday	Pinnegar	Carmichael	Gibbs	Woodhouse(h)	2
Dwyer	Mooney	Everitt(d)	Vavasour	Scott	Bradford	Farthing	Carmichael	Gibbs	Loveday/t	3
Griffin/2c4p	Mooney	Everitt	Ogle	Marjoram	Loveday	Bradford	Carmichael/t	Gibbs(h)	Woodhouse	4
Griffin/c	Mooney	Everitt	Ogle	Marjoram	Loveday	Bradford	Carmichael	Williams	Woodhouse	5
Griffin/tc	Mooney(h)	Bailey(r)	Ogle	Everitt	Loveday	Pinnegar	Carmichael	Williams(q)	Woodhouse(f)	6
Griffin/c3p	Holmes	Everitt	Ogle	Marjoram(p)	Loveday	Pinnegar	Williams(g)	Hill	Gibbs	7
Griffin/pdg	Holmes	Everitt	Ogle	Marjoram(p)	Farthing(e)	Loveday	Williams(g)	Hill	Gibbs	8
Griffin/t2c2pdg	Holmes	Everitt	Vavasour	Bailey(c/t)	Farthing	Loveday	Carmichael	Hill	Woodhouse	9
Griffin/2c2pdg	Holmes/t	Everitt	Vavasour	Marjoram	Farthing	Loveday	Carmichael	Hill	Gibbs	10
Griffin/2p	Holmes	Everitt	Vavasour(d)	Marjoram(p)	Farthing	Loveday	Carmichael	Hill	Woodhouse	11
Griffin/p	Holmes	Everitt	Ogle(s)	Marjoram	Farthing	Loveday	Gibbs	Williams	Woodhouse	12
Hughes	Mooney	Everitt	Hillier(d)	Marjoram	Farthing(l)	Loveday	Williams	Hill	Woodhouse	13
Hughes	Mooney	Everitt	Hillier	Marjoram	Loveday	Pinnegar(l)	Williams	Hill	Gibbs(g)	14
Hughes	Mooney	Everitt	Ogle	Marjoram(k)	Loveday	Pinnegar	Williams/t	Hill	Woodhouse	15
Griffin/cp	Holmes	Everitt	Ogle	Marjoram	Loveday	Farthing	Williams	Gibbs	Woodhouse	16
Griffin	Mooney	Everitt	Ogle	Marjoram	Pinnegar	Farthing(v)	Williams	Gibbs(e)	Woodhouse	17
Griffin	Holmes/c	Everitt	Ogle	Marjoram	Farthing	Loveday	Williams	Gibbs	Carmichael(g)	18
Cocker	Holmes	Everitt	Vavasour	Marjoram	Farthing	Pinnegar	Carmichael/t	Williams	Gibbs	19
Cocker	Mooney(w)	Everett/t	Ogle(k)	Marjoram	Piinnegar	Farthing	Carmichael/t(q)	Williams(f)	Woodhouse	20
Griffin/p	Mooney	Everitt	Ogle	Marjoram	Pinnegar	Farthing	Carmichael	Gibbs	Williams	21
Griffin/4cp	Mooney/t	Everitt	Vavasour(s)	Marjoram	Pinnegar	Farthing(l)	Williams	Hill(t)	Woodhouse/t	22
Holmes	Mooney	Everitt	Vavasour	Marjoram	Pinnegar	Farthing(v)	Carmichael/t	Hill(f)	Woodhouse/t	23
Hughes	Mooney	Woodhouse	Vavasour(s)	Marjoram	Bradford	Farthing	Carmichael	De Villiers	Gibbs	24
Hughes	Mooney	Woodhouse	Vavasour	Marjoram	Bradford	Farthing	De Villiers	Gibbs	Carmichael	25
Hughes	Mooney	Woodhouse	Ogle	Marjoram	Pinnegar/t	Loveday(m)	Carmichael(q)	De Villiers	Williams/t	26
Dwyer	Holmes	Everitt	Vavasour	Scott	Pinnegar	Bradford	Carmichael	Gibbs	Loveday	A

REPLACEMENTS:					
	a- B O'Sullivan	b- E Dwyer	c - E Marjoram	d - A Ogle	e - J Carmichael
f - T Gibbs	g - S Woodhouse	h - D Williams	i - C Bracey	j - J Thomas	k - S Vavasour
l - J Bradford	m -M Farthing	n - G Orgias	o - J Ratcliffe	p - D Bailey	q - S Hill
r - C Angell	s - M Hillier	t - R de Villiers	u - O Coyne	v - M Loveday	w - M Holmes

Full back/stand off Jonathan Griffin was easily the leading points scorer with 160. The next best was 130 points behind.

Matt Holmes was the only other player to kick any points.

The leading try scorers were Glen Orgias and Lee Smith with six each.

Norwich in their first season at this level finished a higly creditable sixth.

Their main problem last season was scoring points with just 383 from their 26 matches. That was the third worst record in the division after the bottom two Havant and Cheltenham.

Defensively they had the fifth best record in the division.

NORWICH

LEAGUE STATISTICS

compiled by Stephen McCormack

SEASON	Division	P	W	D	L	F	A	Pts Diff	Lge Pts	Lge Pos	Coach	Captain
89-90	Lon 2N	10	4	1	5	163	145	18	9	7		
90-91	Lon 2N	10	4	0	6	89	153	-64	8	7		
91-92	Lon 2N											
92-93	Lon 2N	12	6	2	4	182	131	51	14	5		
93-94	Lon 2N	12	6	1	5	143	122	21	13	6		
94-95	Lon 2N	12	6	1	5	188	132	56	13	5		
95-96	Lon 2N	12	10	0	2	250	72	178	20	1p		
96-97	Lon 1	13	9	1	3	267	181	86	19	2		
											Most Points	Most Tries
97-98	Lon 1	16	15	0	1	525	151	374	30	1p	120 Jonathon Griffin	16 Jim McKay
98-99	N2S	26	11	0	15	383	429	-46	22	6	160 Jonathon Griffin	6 Lee Smith, Glen Orgias

FACT FILE

Founded:

Colours: Green, maroon & gold
Change colours: White

GROUND

Address: Beeston Hyrne, North Walsham Road, Norwich NR12 7BW
Tel: 01603 426259 / 454561
Capacity: 1,000 Seated: None Standing: 1,000

Directions: Follow the outer ring road and turn onto the B1150 (signed Coltishall/North Walsham). Go over two sets of traffic lights and the ground is 400 yards on the left.
Nearest Railway Station: Norwich

Car Parking: 1,000 at ground

Admission: Matchday tckets £4

Clubhouse: Normal licensing hours.
Snacks & bar meals available.
Functions Up to 100, contact Jenny Chenery 01603 426259

Club Shop: Yes contact Lizzy Mason 01603 426259

Training Nights: Tuesday & Thursday nights

PROGRAMME

Size: A5 Pages: 24 + cover Price: With admission
Editor: Ian Coxhead, 01603 259508

ADVERTISING RATES
Contact Alan Boswell 01603 218001

PENZANCE & NEWLYN R.F.C.

President	Dicky Evans	01736 351104	c/o Penzance & Newlyn RFC, Westholme, Alexandra Road, Penzance, Cornwall. TR18 4LY
Chairman	David James	01736 351568	
***Club Administrator**	Terry Drew	01736 351104 / 364227	
***Chief Executive**	Martin Scrase	01736 351104	

* Full time at club address

We won promotion from South-West One to Jewson Two South by virtue of a better points difference than Launceston.

Everything hinged on the last match of the season. We were playing Torquay and Launceston were playing Gloucester Old Boys.
Going into the match we were fourteen points down on Launceston, and although Launceston defeated their opponents by 88-19, we beat Torquay 131-5 leaving us with a better points difference of 45.
This was the only time that we headed the table. The most important whistle is the final one!
Good teams are built around long periods. The main objective we set ourselves at the beginning of the season was to win the league. The problem was time, because we were starting with a new team. At the end of the 1997-98 season we replaced several players. By December, it seemed that things were taking shape and the team's potential was about to be realised. Players were getting used to each other, reading each other's body language and thoughts. By the end of the season we were defeating sides by huge scores, and our season's average in the league was 50 points a match.
The team's performance outside the league was also significant. In November 1998 we played the Fijian national side and, although losing 5-51, we acquitted ourselves well. We played in the Tetley's Bitter Cup for the first time in the club's history. We defeated Marlow (A) 44-10 in the Preliminary Rounds, we beat Cambridge (H) 32-13 in the Second Round and lost in the Third Round to Jewson One opponents, Reading (21-5), a match in which we badly missed out top try scorers in Nacaniela Saumi and Richard Newton. We reached the final of the Cornwall Cup for the first time in 23 years where we beat Launceston 34-16. On the path there we beat Redruth in the First Round 38-23 and Camborne in the Semi-Final 23-13.
Over the season we scored 1336 points, including 194 tries. Not bad!

PENZANCE & NEWLYN

Match No.	Date	H/A	Comp.	Opponents	Result & Score	15	14	13	12	11
1	12.09	H	SW1	Maidenhead	W 30-18	Saumi/t2c2p	Pollard/t	Sibson	Evans	Newton
2	26.09	A	SW1	Keynsham	W 25-14	Olonga(a/cp)	Pollard	Sibson	Gadsdon	Newton
3	03.10	H	SW1	Stroud	W 43-10	Saumi/3c4p	Sibson	Gadsdon	Evans/t	Newton/t
4	10.10	A	SW1	Berry Hill	W 70-17	Saumi/2t	Sibson(c/t)	Gadsdon/t	Evans/t	Newton/3t
5	24.10	H	SW1	Salisbury	W 34-16	Pollard/t	Redgrave/t	Gadsdon	Evans/t	Randall
6	07.11	H	SW1	Matson	W 31-0	Saumi/3c	Richards/t	Gadsdon	Evans/t	Newton/2t
7	21.11	A	SW1	Barnstaple	L 10-18	Saumi/cp	Sibson/t	Olonga	Evans	Newton
8	28.11	A	SW1	Torquay	W 48-25	Saumi/5c	Pollard/t	Richards	Evans/t	Newton/2t
9	05.12	A	SW1	Launceston	L 6-12	Saumi/2p	Richards	Gadsdon	Evans	Newton
10	12.12	H	SW1	Old Patesians	W 42-16	Saumi/6c	Redgrave/t	Gadsdon	Sibson	Newton/2t
11	19.12	H	SW1	Barnstaple	W 18-12	Saumi/cp	Redgrave/t	Gadsdon	Sibson	Newton/t
12	09.01	A	SW1	Matson	W 17-10	Saumi/2cp	Redgrave	Gadsdon	Sibson	Newton
13	16.01	H	SW1	Launceston	W 19-9	Saumi/3p	Redgrave/t	Gadsdon	Sibson	Newton/t
14	23.01	A	SW1	Salisbury	W 90-14	Saumi/t11cp	Sibson	Gadsdon/2t	Evans/t	Newton/3t
15	30.01	H	SW1	Berry Hill	W 92-0	Saumi/4t11c	Redgrave/t	Gadsdon	Evans/3t	Newton/3t
16	06.02	A	SW1	Stroud	W 59-7	Saumi/2t7c	Redgrave/t	Gadsdon	Evans	Richards/t
17	13.02	H	SW1	Keynsham	W 61-0	Saumi/3c	Redgrave/t	Gadsdon	Evans/2t	Richards/t
18	20.02	A	SW1	Gloucester OB	W 20-7	Saumi/cp	Redgrave	Gadsdon	Evans	Richards
19	27.02	A	SW1	Maidenhead	W 50-15	Saumi/t6cp	Redgrave/3t	Gadsdon	Evans/t	Richards/t
20	13.03	H	SW1	Gloucester OB	W 104-8	Saumi/2t13cp	Redgrave/4t	Gadsdon/t	Evans/t	Richards/t
21	27.03	A	SW1	Old Patesians	W 83-12	Saumi/3t9c	Redgrave/4t	Gadsdon/t(f/t)	Evans/3t	Richards/t
22	17.04	H	SW1	Torquay	W 131-5	Saumi/3t13c	Redgrave/4t	Gadsdon/t(f/t)	Evans/3t	Richards/t
A	05.09	A	TB1	Marlow	W 44-10	Saumi/2t2c	Sibson/t	Gadsdon	Evans	Newton/t
B	19.09	H	TB2	Cambridge	W 32-13	Saumi/t2cp	Pollard	Sibson	Pascoe	Newton/3t
C	17.10	A	TB3	Reading	L 5-21	Pollard	Sibson	Gadsdon	Evans	Newton

* after opponents name indicates a penalty try
Brackets after a player's name indicates he was replaced. eg (a) means he was replaced by replacement code "a" and so on.
/ after a player or replacement name is followed by any scores he made - eg /t, /c, /p, /dg or any combination of these

1998-99 HIGHLIGHTS

Ever Prseents: Chris Mills

21	Nat Saumi (1)
20	Olonga
18	Roderick

Players used: 30 plus one as replacement only

Most Points in a season:

Pts	Player	T	C	P	DG
339	N Saumi	17	97	20	-
194	Olonga	33	10	1	2
105	Redgrave	21	-	-	-
100	R Newton	20	-	-	-
85	Evans	17	-	-	-
25	K Moseley	5	-	-	-
25	P Gadsdon	5	-	-	-

MATCH FACTS

10	9	1	2	3	4	5	6	7	8	
Moyle	Roderick	Thomas	Laity	Williams	Mruk	Moseley	Goldsmith/t	Bick	Mills	1
Evans	Pascoe	Thomas	Laity	Williams	Yelland	Moseley	Atkinson	Bick	Mills/t	2
Olonga/t	Pascoe	Harvey	Laity	Williams	Yelland	Moseley/t	Lawrence	Bick	Mills	3
Olonga/2t7c	Roderick	Harvey	Porte	Williams	Mruk	Moseley/t	Lawrence	Bick	Mills	4
Olonga/t2c	Pascoe	Harvey/t	Porte(b/t)	Williams	Yelland	Moseley	Atkinson	Bick	Mills	5
Olonga	Roderick/t	Harvey	Laity	Williams	Yelland	Moseley	Lawrence	Atkinson	Mills	6
Moyle	Roderick	Harvey	Laity	Williams	Yelland	Mruk	Lawrence	Atkinson	Mills	7
Olonga	Pascoe/t	Harvey	Laity	Thomas	Atkinson	Mruk	Goldsmith	Bick/t	Mills/t	8
Olonga	Roderick	Harvey	Laity	Thomas	Atkinson	Moseley	Bearman	Bick	Mills	9
Olonga/3t	Roderick	Thomas	Laity	Williams	Atkinson	Moseley	Bearman	Bick	Mills	10
Olonga/dg	Roderick	Harvey	Laity	Williams	Atkinson	Moseley	Lawrence	Bick	Mills	11
Olonga/t	Roderick	Thomas	Laity	Williams	Atkinson	Moseley	Goldsmith	Lawrence	Mills	12
Olonga	Roderick	Harvey	Andrew	Thomas	Mruk	Moseley	Atkinson	Bick	Mills	13
Olonga/3t	Roderick	Thomas	Andrew	Williams/t	Mruk	Moseley	Atkinson(d/t)	Bick/t	Mills	14
Olonga/3t	Roderick	Harvey	Bush	Thomas	Mruk	Moseley	Atkinson	Bick	Mills	15
Olonga/5t	Roderick	Thomas	Andrew	Williams	Mruk	Moseley	Atkinson	Bick	Mills	16
Olonga/4t	Roderick/t	Thomas	Andrew	Williams	Atkinson	Mruk/t	Goldsmith	Bick	Mills/t	17
Olonga/2t	Roderick/t	Harvey	Andrew	Thomas	Mruk	Moseley	Goldsmith	Atkinson	Mills	18
Olonga/t	Roderick	Thomas	Laity	Williams	Atkinson	Mruk	Goldsmith	Bick	Mills	19
Olonga/t	Roderick	Thomas	Laity	Williams/t	Atkinson/t	Moseley/2t	Goldsmith	Bick/t	Mills	20
Olonga/3t	Roderick	Thomas(g/t)	Laity	Williams	Atkinson	Moseley/t	Goldsmith/t	Bearman(e/t)	Mills/t	21
Olonga/3t	Roderick	Harvey/t	Andrew	Thomas	Atkinson	Moseley/t	Goldsmith/t	Bick/t	Mills/t	22
Moyle	Roderick	Thomas	Laity	Williams	Mruk	Moseley/2t	Goldsmith/2t	Bick	Mills	A
Evans	Roderick	Harvey	Porte	Williams	Mruk	Moseley	Goldsmith/t	Bick	Mills	B
Olonga	Roderick	Harvey	Laity	Williams	Yelland	Moseley	Lawrence(h/t)	Bick	Mills	C

REPLACEMENTS: a- N Saumi b- Laity c - Richards d - Nicholas e - Bick f - Sibson g - Harvey h - Atkinson

Winger Redgrave scored 15 tries in the last fopur matches of the season.

Fly half Olonga scored 25 tries in the last nine matches of the season.

Full back Nat Saumi scored 42 points in the 92-0 home win over Berry Hill.
In other matches he scored 41 and 39 as he amassed 339 points in the league.

Won all 11 home matches but did lose away at Barnstaple and Launceston.

Topped the 100 points in their last two home matches of the season against Gloucester OB and Torquay.

PENZANCE & NEWLYN

LEAGUE STATISTICS

compiled by Stephen McCormack

SEASON	Division	P	W	D	L	F	A	Pts Diff	Lge Pts	Lge Pos	Coach	Captain
89-90	Dev &C'wall	36	16	2	20	462	681	-219	32	1p	P Greaves	J Dean
90-91	Western Cos.	34	16	1	17	560	484	76	32	8	P Greaves	J Dean
91-92	Western Cos.	34	20	2	12	791	399	392	40	5	P Greaces	J Dean
92-93	Western Cos.	38	25	0	13	975	510	465	50	4	P Greaves	A Bick
93-94	Western Cos.	37	26	0	11	686	428	258	52	4	P Greaves	A Bick
94-95	Western Cos.	33	24	0	9	787	400	387	48	4	P Greaves	A Bick
95-96	Western Cos.	38	22	1	15	923	685	238	45	3p	R Tonkin	A Ellery
96-97	SW 2	31	25	0	6	1074	441	633	50	1p	R Tonkin	M Murrish
97-98	SW 1	39	26	1	12	1102	716	386	53	4	M Ring/P Johnson	M Murrish
98-99	SW1	32	26	0	6	1336	464	872	52	1p	P Johnson	A Bick

FACT FILE

Founded: 1875

Colours: Black, white & red hoops
Change colours: Black with red collar

GROUND

Address: Westholme, Alexandra Road, Penzance, Cornwall. TR18 4LY
Tel: 01736 351568 / 364227 Fax: 01736 351104 e-mail: pirates@city2000.net
Capacity: 4,010 Seated: 558 Standing - Covered: 750 Uncovered: 2,702

Directions: Follow the sea road (via the harbour) until mini roundabout at Beachfield Hotel (Newlyn end of promenade), then turn right and the ground is 400 yards up on the left.
Nearest Railway Station: Penzance, 250 yds from town centre

Car Parking: Limited at ground. Car Park on promenade for 300 cars. Off street parking available.

Admission: Season tickets - Adults £85 Sen. Citizens £45
Matchday - Standing: Adults £5, Se. Cit./Students £2
Seated: £6 & £3

Clubhouse: Open every evening 7-11, Sun 12-3 & matchdays 12-11.
4 bars with snacks & bar meals available.
Corporate hospitality & Functions available.

Club Shop: At club - open during the week incl. matchdays

Training Nights: Monday, Tuesday & Thursday

PROGRAMME

Size: A5 Price: 50p
Pages: 48 Editor: Martin Scrase

ADVERTISING RATES (all + V.A.T.)
Page £300; 1/2 £160; 1/4 £90; 1/8 £50

PLYMOUTH ALBION R.F.C.

Director of Rugby	Andy Johnson	c/o Plymouth Albion RFC, Beacon Park, Plymouth PL2 3JP 01752 777454 (Club), 01752 777454 (Fax)
Press Officer	Paddy Marsh	Hardwick Farmhouse, Drunken Bridge Hill, Plymouth PL7 1UG 01752 343631 (H), 01752 773187 (B)
Club Secretary	Geoff Morris	c/o Plymouth Albion RFC, Beacon Park, Plymouth PL2 3JP 01752 777454 (Club) 01752 661640 (H) 01752 305639 (B)
Fixtures Secretary	Terry Brown	c/o Plymouth Albion RFC, as above 01752 837742 (H), 01752 777454 (B), 01752 777454 (Fax)

After narrowly missing relegation the previous season, Albion had another difficult campaign only securing their National League status with a last day win at Weston-Super-Mare.

Led again by Richard Thompson, the early signs were encouraging as Albion opened with league victories against Cheltenham and Havant and a cup win over local rivals Redruth. They narrowly missed topping the league when after making the long journey to North Walsham indiscipline lost them the game.

In an attempt to strengthen the side, Director of Rugby Andy Johnson brought in South Africans Rory Watts (scrum half) and Roger Thompson (flanker). Watts took over the goal kicking and finished the season as the most consistent in the league, although not kicking enough for an end of season award.

After suffering a heavy defeat at Esher, Albion lost vital league points at Bridgwater and Tabard when late kicks cost them a victory and a draw respectfully.

Two defeats by Redruth at the turn of the year were followed by a trip to Norwich on January 2nd. Player availability meant the team had to go up and back to East Anglia on match day, a situation created by a lack of fixture planning at Twickenham. For the last three months of the season Albion had to either play teams at the top of the league or fighting for points at the bottom.

Defeat at bottom of the table Havant in mid-March put Albion in serious danger of relegation. A loss at Cheltenham two weeks later followed by a predictable defeat by champions Bracknell meant they went into the last game with their destiny still in their own hands.

A totally committed team performance at Weston-Super-Mare saw Albion through to their only league victory away from home and left them with plenty to do behind the scenes in the summer.

Paddy Marsh

Plymouth Albion lock, Ian Goldsmith (scrum cap) supported by from L-R: Lee Thomas (scrum half), Cullam Osborne (lock), Mark Manton (prop) and Steve Dyer (flanker) during their match v Esher in February.

Photo: Mike Cox

PLYMOUTH ALBION

Match No.	Date	H/A	Comp.	Opponents	Result & Score	Att.	15	14	13	12	11
1	05.09	H	J2S	Chelteham	W 26-13		M Thompson	Walklin/2t	Burt/tc3p	Hodge	Enticknap
2	12.09	H	J2S	Havant	W 22-5		M Thompson/3p	Walklin/t	Hodge	Williams	Enticknap
3	26.09	A	J2S	N Walsham	L 17-33		Awad	Walklin	Hodge	Burt/3p	Williams/t
4	03.10	H	J2S	Barking	L 18-23		M Thompson	Walklin	Burt	James	Hodge
5	10.10	A	J2S	Esher	L 18-61		M Thompson	Hooper/t	R Thompson/c2p	Burt/t	Hodge
6	24.10	H	J2S	Clifton*	W 22-11		Awad	Hooper/t	Hodge	R Thompson/t2cp	Walklin(w)
7	31.10	A	J2S	Bridgwater	D 16-16		Awad	Hooper	R Thompson/t2p	Hodge	James
8	07.11	H	J2S	M Police	L 13-20		Awad/t	Enticknap	Hodge	R Thompson/tp	Williams
9	21.11	A	J2S	Tabard	L 13-16		R Thompson	Walklin	Burt/c2p	Hodge	Enticknap(B)
10	28.11	H	J2S	Norwich	L 12-23		R Thompson	Walklin/t	Burt/c	Ridley	Rees/t
11	05.12	A	J2S	Redruth	L 8-24		Rees(c)	S Thomas(b)	Ridley	R Thompson	Williams
12	12.12	H	J2S	Weston	W 27-18		R Thompson	Rees	Burt	Ridley/t	Williams(D)
13	19.12	A	J2S	Bracknell	L 13-24		R Thompson	S Thomas(a)	Ridley	Burt	Rees
14	28.12	H	J2S	Redruth	L 17-25		M Thompson	R Thompson	Ridley/t	James	Rees
15	02.01	A	J2S	Norwich	L 5-35		R Thompson	Rees	James	Ridley	Hodge(D)
16	09.01	H	J2S	Tabard	W 23-22		R Thompson	S Thomas	Ridley/t	James	Hodge
17	16.01	A	J2S	M Police*	L 12-26		R Thompson	Hooper	Ridley	James	Rees/t
18	23.01	H	J2S	Bridgwater	W 48-10		R Thompson/6cp	S Thomas(B)	Hodge	Ridley	Hooper
19	30.01	A	J2S	Clifton	L 12-24		Watts/p(w)(c)	S Thomas	Ridley	Hodge	Hooper
20	06.02	H	J2S	Esher	L 15-34		R Thompson	S Thomas(d)	Burt/cp	Ridley/t	Rees(y)
21	13.02	A	J2S	Barking	L 12-44		Awad	S Thomas(v)	Ridley/t	Burt/c	Hooper
22	27.02	H	J2S	N Walsham	L 11-23		R Thompson/2p	Hodge	Ridley	Burt	Rees
23	13.03	A	J2S	Havant	L 12-29		R Thompson	Rees	Ridley	Burt/c	Hooper
24	27.03	A	J2S	Cheltenham	L 19-26		Rees(t)(G)	Hooper	Ridley	Burt/c3p	Underwood
25	03.04	H	J2S	Bracknell	L 12-64		Hodge	Enticknap	Ridley	Burt/c	Underwood
26	17.04	A	J2S	Weston	W 34-17		M Thompson	Rees	Ridley/t	Burt/2cp	Hooper
A	19.09	H	TB1	Redruth	W 32-18		M Thompson/t2c	Walklin/t	Hodge	Burt/p(e)	Underwood(r/t)
B	17.10	H	TB2	Barking	L 13-18		R Thompson/cp	Walklin/t	Burt/p	Hodge	Hooper

* after opponents name indicates a penalty try
Brackets after a player's name indicates he was replaced. eg (a) means he was replaced by replacement code "a" and so on.
/ after a player or replacement name is followed by any scores he made - eg /t, /c, /p, /dg or any combination of these

1998-99 HIGHLIGHTS

Ever Presents: Stuart Coleman

Most appearances:

24	Richard Thompson
23	Steve Pooley
22	Lee Thomas (1)
21	Mark Manton (4), Martin Thompson (1)

Players used: 34 plus 6 as replacement only.

Most Points in a season:

Pts	Player	T	C	P	DG
89	Roger Thompson	6	10	10	3
69	N Burt	2	10	13	-
50	R Watts	1	9	9	-
34	M Thompson	2	-	6	2
30	M Ridley	6	-	-	-
30	Roger Thompson	6	-	-	-

MATCH FACTS

10	9	1	2	3	4	5	6	7	8	
R Thompson	L Thomas	Coleman	Pooley(p)	Brooks(n)	Osborne	Stevens(m)	Trollope(o)	Dyer	Durbin(l)	1
R Thompson/dg	L Thomas	Coleman	Pooley/t(p)(h)	Manton	Osborne	Goldsmith(s)	Trollope(l)	Dyer	Durbin(m)	2
R Thompson/dg	L Thomas	Coleman	Pooley(u)	Manton	Goldsmith(m)	Osborne	Durbin	Dyer	Wyatt(k)	3
R Thompson/p	L Thomas/t	Coleman	Pooley/t	Manton	Halton(o)	Osborne	Durbin(x/t)	Dyer	Wyatt	4
Awad	Watts	Coleman	Pooley	Manton	Osborne	Goldsmith(m)	L Thomas	Dyer(z)	Wyatt(j)	5
M Thompson	L Thomas	Coleman	Pooley(u)	Manton	Osborne	Stevens(o)	Durbin(m)	Trollope	Wyatt	6
M Thompson	Watts	Coleman	Pooley(u)	Manton	Osborne	Goldsmith	Durbin(k)	L Thomas/t	Wyatt(j)	7
M Thompson	Watts	Coleman	Pooley	Manton	Osborne	Stevens(o)	Trollope(A)	L Thomas	Wyatt	8
M Thompson	Watts	Coleman	Beddow	Manton	Halton	Goldsmith	L Thomas	Dyer/t	Thompson	9
M Thompson	Watts	Coleman	Beddow(g)	Manton	Goldsmith(i)	Halton(j)	L Thomas	Dyer	Thompson	10
M Thompson/dg	Watts	Coleman	Pooley	Manton/t	Osborne(C)	Halton(j)	L Thomas	Dyer	Thompson	11
Watts/3c2p	L Thomas	Coleman	Pooley	Manton	Stevens	Goldsmith	Thompson/t	Dyer	Wyatt/t	12
Watts/c2p	L Thomas	Coleman	Pooley	Manton	Goldsmith	Halton	Thompson/t	Dyer	Wyatt	13
Watts/2cp	L Thomas(d)	Coleman	Pooley	Manton/t	Goldsmith(j)	Halton(i)	Thompson	Dyer	Russell	14
M Thompson	Watts	Coleman(h)	Pooley	Manton	Osborne/t(q)	Halton	Stevens	Thompson	Russell	15
M Thompson/t	Watts/2c3p	Coleman	Pooley	Manton	Halton	Osborne(o)	Thompson	Dyer(k)	Russell	16
M Thompson(f)	Watts/c(d)	Coleman	Pooley	Manton	Halton	Osborne(j)	Thompson	Dyer	Russell	17
M Thompson/dg	L Thomas	Coleman/t	Pooley	Manton/2t	Halton	Osborne	Thompson/2t	Dyer	Russell/t	18
M Thompson/3p	L Thomas	Coleman	Pooley	Manton	Halton	Osborne	Thompson	Dyer(k)	Gldsmith(j)	19
M Thompson	L Thomas	Coleman	Pooley/t	Manton(h)	Halton(i)	Stevens	Thompson	Dyer	Goldsmith	20
M Thompson	L Thomas	Coleman	Pooley(u)	Brooks(n)	Osborne	Halton	Thompson/t	Dyer	Goldsmith(	21
M Thompson/t	L Thomas	Coleman	Pooley	Manton	Goldsmith	Osborne	Trollope	Thompson	Durbin	22
M Thompson(D)	L Thomas	Coleman	Pooley/t(u)	Manton	Halton	Osborne	Thompson	Dyer/t	Goldsmith	23
R Thompson/dg	L Thomas	Coleman	Pooley(u)	Brooks(F)	Halton(i)	Goldsmith	Scott(A/t)	Trollope	Chubb	24
R Thompson/t	Hooper	Coleman(F)	Beddow(g)	Brooks(n)	Halton(j)	Goldsmith(i)	Thompson	Trollope/t	Chubb	25
R Thompson/2tc	L Thomas/t	Coleman	Pooley(u)	Brookes(n)	Halton	Owens	Thompson(j)	Trollope	Durbin/t	26
R Thompson	L Thomas	Coleman	Pooley	Manton	Stevens	Goldsmith	Durbin(m)	Dyer(k/t)	Wyatt	A
M Thompson	Watts(E)	Coleman	Pooley	Manton	Osborne	Stevens(m)	Durbin(o)	L Thomas(t)	Wyatt	B

REPLACEMENTS:

	a- M Thompson	b- S Walklin	c - N Burt	d - S Hodge	e - P Enticknap
f - L Thomas	g - S Pooley	h - P Brooks	i - C Osborne	j - S Stevens	k - A Trollope
l - M Wyatt	m - J Halton	n - M Manton	o - I Goldsmith	p - C Roberts	q - R Williams
r - R Williams	s - I Harrison	t - S Awad	u - M Beddow	v - J Underwood	w - E James
x - R Watts	y - G Hooper	z - J Gratrix	A - R Thompson	B - C Rees	C - N Woodman
D - S Thomas	E - M Scott	F - M Street	G - K Owens		

Richard Thompson follows brother Martin to top the Plymouth points scoring list.

The top try scorer title was shared by three players, Richard Thompson was joined by new boys Martin Ridley and Roger Thompson.

Along with Bridgwater Plymouth had the worst away record in the division with just three points taken out of 26.

Their only away win was in their last match of the season when they won at Weston super Mare to avoid being relegated.

Conceded 40 tries at home which was the most by any side in the division.

Although Plymouth had the worst away record they still managed to be the 7th highest scorers on the road.

PLYMOUTH ALBION

LEAGUE STATISTICS

compiled by Stephen McCormack

SEASON	Division	P	W	D	L	F	A	Pts Diff	Lge Pts	Lge Pos	Most Points		Most Tries	
89-90	D2	11	5	0	6	206	164	42	10		36	Charlie Gabbitas	4	Ian Russell & Steve Walklin
90-91	D2	12	4	0	8	129	210	-81	8		44	Kevin Thomas	2	Charlie Gabbitas
91-92	D2	12	3	0	9	153	209	-56	6		62	Mark Slade	2	by five players
92-93	D3	11	0	0	11	130	305	-175	0		26	Martin Thompson	3	Mark Haimes
93-94	D4	18	9	0	9	286	416	-130	18		90	Martin Thompson	5	Roger Bailey
94-95	D4	18	4	2	12	324	381	-57	10	8	129	Martin Thompson	6	Steve Walklin
95-96	D4	18	4	0	14	268	545	-277	8		61	Mark Slade	6	Steve Walklin
96-97	D4S	26	14	1	11	709	591	118	29		131	Martin Thompson	12	Steve Walklin
97-98	N2S	26	6	0	20	472	756	-284	12		131	Martin Thompson	15	Steve Walklin
98-99	N2S	26	7	1	18	457	666	-209	15	12	89	Richard Thompson	6	Richard Thompson, Martin Ridley & Roger Thompson

FACT FILE

Founded: 1876
Nickname: Albion

Colours: White with broad cherry band edged with green.
Change colours: Red.

GROUND

Address: Beacon Park, Beacon Park Road, Plymouth, PL2 3JP
Tel: 01752 777454 Fax 01752 777454
Capacity: 3,000 Seated: 500 Standing: 2,500

Directions: On approaching Plymouth follow signs for Plymouth Argyle FC. 200 yards past Safeway Superstore at 3rd traffic lights turn right, turn left at Cherry Tree Pub into Langstone Rd, ground 500yards on right.
Nearest Railway Station: Plymouth North Road

Car Parking: 50 within ground

Admission: Matchday - Seated Adults £3.
Standing Adults £2.50, Children/OAPs £1.25.

Clubhouse: Normal licensing hours. Snacks & bar meals available
Functions: Capacity 120, contact Squash Club 01752 777454

Club Shop: Open matchdays only. Other times from bar staff
Manager Maggie Fuge 01752 777454

Training Nights: Tuesday & Thursday

PROGRAMME

Size: A5 Price: £1 Pages: 36 + cover
Editor: John Crow 01752 219836

ADVERTISING RATES

Colour - Full page £300, Half £175, Qtr £100
Mono Full page £175, Half £90, Qtr £50

REDRUTH R.F.C.

President	W J `Bill' Bishop OBE	Lafrowda, Tregolls Road, Truro TR1 1LE
Secretary	Ivor Horscroft	The Firs, South Tehidy, Camborne TR14 0HU 01209 612244 (H & B) 01209 612203 (Fax)
Fixtures Secretary	Denzil Williams	13 Boskennal Drive, Hayle, TR27 4DX 01736 752795 (H)
Rugby Secretary	Simon Blake	Oakland, Albany Court, Redruth TR15 2NY 01209 215401
Treasurer	Jerry Penna	01209 211520 (H), 01209 216988 (B)
Press Officer	David Penberthy	10 Little Treloweth, Treloweth Gardens, pool, Redruth TR15 3QA 01209 217488 (H) 01392 448845 (B)

Once again, National League status was preserved and the usual mid season crisis disrupted the progress of the team. The crisis this time came in the form of the entire coaching panel resigning. However, this was quickly resolved and Barry Trevaskis, the former Bath and Cornwall winger, took the helm ably assisted by Dai Morgan who re-thought his original decision to resign. Next season they will be joined by Will Davies a former England Schools U16s coach.

On the field, Steward Whitworth was captain and new players in the form of Steve Larkins, Nick Edyvean, Daniel Locke and Andy Hicks joined the club. An early victory at home against Clifton was followed by a disastrous run of defeats. The rot was sensationally halted just prior to Christmas when table toppers Barking were the visitors. A truly committed performance from the team saw a well deserved victory achieved. This was followed by an equally deserved win at Plymouth.

At this time prolific try scorer Steve Walklin joined the club and immediately made his presence felt. Single point defeats at the hands of Weston caused concern but a well earned victory at Clifton guaranteed our national status once again.

Stewart Whitworth and Steve Larkins represented the County in the Championship final at Twickenham with both making telling contributions, Larkins kicking three penalties and Whitworth scoring an injury time try to seal a deserved victory over Gloucestershire.

The Colts had a tremendous season and retained the County Colts trophy and progressed to the Fifth Round of the National tournament. Ex-player Rob Thirlby's progress at Saracens, and with the England U21's and full England 7's squad, was followed with great interest.

Next season the club celebrates its 125th anniversary and an improved league position and progression in the Tetley's Bitter Cup are wanted. With the new coaching team and an improved squad everything is possible.

David Penberthy.

REDRUTH

Match No.	Date	H/A	Comp.	Opponents	Result & Score	Att.	15	14	13	12	11
1	05.09	A	J2S	Esher	L 3-44		Edyvean	Gomez(m)	S Whitworth	Hambly	Hussey
2	12.09	H	J2S	Clifton	W 25-18		Edyvean/t	Gomez	S Whitworth	Hambly/t	Hussey
3	26.09	A	J2S	Bridgwater	L 9-21		Edyvean	Finch(s)	S Whitworth	Hambly	Hussey
4	03.10	H	J2S	M Police	L 10-26		Gomez/t(c)	Hussey	Doyle	Hambly	Finch
5	10.10	A	J2S	Tabard	L 13-47		Edyvean	Hicks(w)	Hussey	Hambly	Finch
6	24.10	H	J2S	Norwich	L 9-12		Gomez	Edyvean(r)	S Whitworth	Hambly	Hussey
7	31.10	A	J2S	Havant	L 9-14		Sidwell/3p	Pengilly	Larkins	Hambly	Hussey
8	07.11	A	J2S	Weston	D 16-16		Sidwell/c3p	Gomez	Larkins	Hambly	Hussey
9	21.11	H	J2S	Bracknell	L 25-34		Sidwell/2c2p	Hussey/t	Larkins/t	Harding	Mead
10	28.11	A	J2S	Cheltenham	L 12-22		Sidwell/4p	Hussey	Larkins	Harding	Finch(a)
11	05.12	H	J2S	Plymouth	W 24-8		Sidwell/c2pdg	Edyvean(r)	Larkins/t	Harding	Hussey/t
12	12.12	A	J2S	N Walsham	L 10-25		Edyvean/t	Pengilly	Hussey	Stephens	Finch
13	19.12	H	J2S	Barking	W 22-18		Sidwell/3p	Edyvean/t	Larkins	Harding	Hussey/t
14	28.12	A	J2S	Plymouth	W 25-17		Sidwell/2c2p	Edyvean/t	Larkins	Harding	Finch
15	02.01	H	J2S	Cheltenham	W 35-12		Sidwell/3c2p	Hussey	Stephens	Harding	Edyvean/t
16	16.01	H	J2S	Weston	L 28-34		Sidwell/t2c3p	Edyvean(C)	Larkins	Harding	Hussey
17	23.01	H	J2S	Havant	W 46-13		Sidwell/3c	Walklin/2t	Larinks/2t	Harding(a)	Hussey(l)
18	30.01	A	J2S	Norwich	L 20-22		Sidwell/cp	Walklin/t	Larkins/t	Stephens	Edyvean
19	06.02	H	J2S	Tabard	L 16-21		Sidwell/c3p	Walklin	Larkins	Stephens	Edyvean
20	13.02	A	J2S	M Police	L 15-33		Sidwell	Walklin/t	Larkins	Harding/t	Edyvean
21	20.02	A	J2S	Bracknell	L 10-37		Larkins/cp	Walklin	Harding	Stephens(b)	Edyvean/t
22	27.02	H	J2S	Bridgwater	W 49-17		Larkins/t4c2p	Walklin/t	Harding	Hambly(v)	Edyvean
23	13.03	A	J2S	Clifton	W 20-15		Larkins/5p	Walklin(m)	Harding	Hambly/t(c)	Edyvean
24	27.03	H	J2S	Esher	L 15-33		Larkins/cp	Walklin	Harding/t	Hambly	Edyvean
25	03.04	A	J2S	Barking	L 20-56		Sidwell/cp	Walklin/t	Larkins/t	Hambly	Edyvean(m)
26	17.04	H	J2S	N Walsham	L 17-34		Sidwell/2cp	Walklin	Harding/t	Larkins/t	Edyvean
A	19.09	A	TB1	Plymouth	L 18-32		Edyvean/t	Pengilly/t(r)	S Whitworth	Hambly	Gomez

* after opponents name indicates a penalty try
Brackets after a player's name indicates he was replaced. eg (a) means he was replaced by replacement code "a" and so on.
/ after a player or replacement name is followed by any scores he made - eg /t, /c, /p, /dg or any combination of these

1998-99 HIGHLIGHTS

Ever Presents: None

Most appearances

24	StewartWhitworth , Matthew Gray (1)
22	Andy Hawken (1)
21	Chris Sidwell (1)
20	Nick Edyvean (2)

Players used: 32 plus 4 as replacement only.

Most Points in a season:

Pts	Player	T	C	P	DG
175	C Sidwell	1	22	41	1
79	S Larkins	8	6	9	-
30	N Edyvean	6	-	-	-
30	A Joint	6	-	-	-
30	S Walklin	6	-	-	-

MATCH FACTS

10	9	1	2	3	4	5	6	7	8	
Sidwell/p	C Whitworth(n)	Douch	C-Griffiths(o)	Cowie	O'Sullivan	Gray/t(p)	Hawken	Navin	Lock	1
Sidwell/2c2p	Hicks	Douch	C-Griffiths(o)	Cowie	O'Sullivan	Gray(p)	Hawken	Navin	Lock	2
Sidwell/3p(m)	Hicks	Douch	Rutter(f)	Cowie	O'Sullivan	Gray	Hawken(p)	Navin	Lock	3
S Whitworth	C Whitworth	Douch	C-Griffiths	Cowie	O'Sullivan	Gray	Lock	Navin/t(p)	Hawken	4
Sidwell/c2p	C Whitworth	Douch	Rutter	Cowie(n)	O'Sullivan	Gray(y)	Lock	Navin(t/t)	Hawken	5
Sidwell/3p	C Whitworth(q)	Douch	Rutter	Croker(y)	Joint	O'Sullivan(t)	Lock	Navin	Hawken(i)	6
S Whitworth	C Whitworth(q)	Douch	Rutter	Croker(y)	O'Sullivan	Gray	Lock	Navin	Hawken	7
S Whitworth	Hicks(d/t)	Douch	Rutter	Moyle(n)	Joint	Gray	Hawkne	Navin	Lock	8
S Whitworth	C Whitworth(q)	Moyle	Rutter	Croker	O'Sullivan/t(t)	Gray	Joint	Navin	Lock	9
S Whitworth	Hicks	Douch	Rutter	Croker	O'Sullivan	Gray	Joint(t)	Navin	Lock(j)	10
S Whitworth/dg	C Whitworth	Douch	Rutter(y)	Cowie	Sampson(A)	Gray	O'Sullivan	Navin	Hawken	11
Harding	C Whitworth	Douch/t	Rutter	Croker	O'Sullivan(A)	Gray	Joint	Navin	Griffiths(B)	12
S Whitworth/dg	C Whitworth	Douch	Trivett	Cowie(y)	Joint(A)	Gray	Hawken	Navin	Lock	13
S Whitworth	C Whitworth	Douch	Trivett(o)	Moyle	Joint/2t	Gray	Hawken	Boase	Lock	14
S Whitworth	C Whitworth/dg	Douch	Rutter	Moyle	Joint/t	Gray	Hawken/t	Boase/t	Lock(k)	15
S Whitworth	C Whitworth	Douch	Rutter	Moyle	O'Sullivan/2t(t)	Gray	Hawken	Boase	Lock	16
S Whitworth	C Whitworth/t	Douch	Trivett/2t	Moyle(n)	Joint/t	Gray(h)	Navin	Boase	Hawken	17
S Whitworth	Hicks	Douch	Rutter	Croker	Joint	Gray(h/t)	Lock(k)	Boase	Hawken	18
S Whitworth	Hicks	Douch	Rutter(f)	Croker(y)	Joint(h)	Gray	Navin	Boase/t	Hawken	19
S Whitworth	C Whitworth	Moyle	Rutter(f)	Cowie(e)	O'Sullivan	Gray	Navin/t	Boase	Hawken	20
S Whitworth	C Whitworth(q)	Douch	C-Griffiths(y)	Moyle(n)	O'Sullivan	Gray	Lock(t)	Navin	Hawken	21
S Whitworth	C Whitworth(q)	Douch/t	Trivett(f)	Moyle(n)	O'Sullivan	Gray	Joint/2t(A)	Navin	Griffiths/t(l)	22
S Whitworth	C Whitworth	Douch	Trivett(f)	Moyle(g)	O'Sullivan	Gray	Hawken	Boase	Griffiths(k)	23
S Whitworth	C Whitworth	Douch	Trivett(f)	Moyle(g)	O'Sullivan/t	Gray(p)	Hawken	Boase	Griffiths	24
S Whitworth	C Whitworth	Douch	Rutter	Croker(D)	Joint	O'Sullivan(E)	Hawken	Boase(B/t)	Griffiths	25
S Whitworth	C Whitworth	Douch	Rutter	Croker	O'Sullivan	Gray(z)	Navin(y)	Boase	Hawken	26
Sidwell/c2p(u)	Hicks	Douch	Rutter(f)	Cowie(n)	O'Sullivan	Gray	Hawken	Nain	Lock	A

REPLACEMENTS:					
	a- N Edyvean	b- N Hambly	c - C Sidwell	d - C Whitworth	e - N Douch
f - J Clifton-Griffiths	g - E Cowie	h - S O'Sullivan	i - M Gray	j - A Hawken	k - J Navin
l - D Lock	m - J Pengilly	n - N Croker	o - A Rutter	p - A Joint	q - A Hicks
r - A Finch	s - G Doyle	t - S Griffiths	u - K Harding	v - C Stephens	w - D Furse
x - D Moyle	y - L Trivett	z - J Sampson	A - I Boase	B - M Ellis	C - S Walklin
D - I Wright	E - N Pryor				

Chris Sidwell finished top of the scoring list in his first full season. He scored 175 points which was the 4th highest total in the division.

Centre Steve Larkins, in his first season with the club, was the leading try scorer with eight.

Redruth finished the season badly with just two wins in their last nine league matches.

Steve Larkins scored a season high 19 points in the 49-17 against Bridgwater & Albion.

Redruth conceded 37 tries at home, only Plymouth with 40 conceded more.

2nd row forward Andy Joint twice scored two tries in a match.

REDRUTH

LEAGUE STATISTICS

compiled by Stephen McCormack

SEASON	Division	P	W	D	L	F	A	Pts Diff	Lge Pts	Lge Pos		Most Points		Most Tries
89-90	ALS	10	7	0	3	151	84	67	14		34	Gary Wills & Peter Harrison	4	Jon Bowden & Marcel Gomez
90-91	D4S	12	12	0	0	225	79	145	24		95	Simon Blake	6	Andy Knowles
91-92	D3	12	6	1	5	155	123	32	13		80	Kevin Thomas	2	by four players
92-93	D3	11	7	2	2	175	125	50	16		89	Kevin Thomas	6	Andy Knowles
93-94	D3	18	2	0	16	178	488	-310	4		71	Simon Blake	2	Mark Rose & Chris Whitworth
94-95	D4	18	6	2	10	309	387	-78	14		179	Simon Blake	4	Simon Blake
95-96	D4	18	7	2	9	358	392	-34	16		126	Stu Whitworth	8	Peter Congo
96-97	D3	30	7	0	23	565	1116	-551	14		120	Ian Morgan	10	Peter Congo
97-98	N2S	26	10	0	16	720	580	140	20	9	256	Rob Thirlby	17	Rob Thirlby
98-99	N2S	26	8	1	17	503	652	-151	17	11	175	Chris Sidwell	8	Steve Lakins

FACT FILE

Founded: 1875
Nickname: The Reds

Colours: Red with a green band
Change colours: Green with a red band

GROUND

Address: The Recreation Ground, Redruth, Cornwall TR15 1SY
Tel: 01209 215520 Fax: 01209 314438 web: redruth-rfc.cornwall.eu.org
Capacity: 15,000 Seated: 670 Standing: 14,330

Directions: A30 West through Cornwall, leave at Redruth exit over roundabout, down through council estate, 1/4 mile to crossroads, then left.
Nearest Railway Station: Redruth, walk thro Town Centre, down Green Lane grd at end, 10 mins

Car Parking: 50 on ground, 500 on Industrial Estate - free.

Admission: Season ticket - Adults £60, OAP/children £35
Matchday - Adults standing £5, seated £6, u16 Free

Clubhouse: Evenings 7-11, matchdays 12-11, Sun 12-2, 7-11.
Three bars, with snacks & bar meals available.
Functions catered for contact Social Committee

Club Shop: Open home matchdays.
Manageress Christina Thomas 01209 215520

Training Nights: Mondays & Wednesdays

PROGRAMME

Size: A5 Price: £1 Pages: 44
Editor: Nick Serpell 01579 348853
ADVERTISING RATES
Full page £250, Half page £130, Qtr page £70

TABARD R.F.C.

Chairman	Ross Hopcroft	100 Manor Road, Barton-le-Clay, Bedfordshire MK45 4WR
Secretary	Mrs P Mitchell	48 Hill Rise, Rickmansworth, Herts. WD3 2NZ 01923 490133
Fixtures Secretary	Campbell Carmichael	10 Chandos Road, Borehamwood, Herts. 0181 953 9006 (H)
1st XV Manager	Geoff Bird	1 Kendalls Close, Radlett, Herts 01923 852465 (H), 01923 852655 (B), 01923 852465 (Fax)
Director of Rugby	Tim Smithers	
Press Officer	Peter Cook	0181 207 5564 (H), 0171 250 7499 (B)

Tabard had a bright start to the season, winning their first three league matches in fine style before coming unstuck against Norwich. They quickly overcame this setback however, but then the increased demands of the modern game began to take effect as injuries built up and the middle part of the season was sparse indeed. A succession of losses, albeit some by the narrowest of margins, like Plymouth, where Tabard won the try count four to two but still lost an exciting encounter by one point, gave Tabard cause for concern. However, the run was broken by perhaps the most satisfying win of the season, at least as far as Tabard's travelling supporters were concerned, with a superb away victory over Redruth, by 21 points to 16. Further victories over Norwich and Bridgwater meant that Tabard finished top of the bottom half of the table but this was not quite as high as expected.

There were also some close league games, the most notable being against Bracknell, at Bracknell, where the team looked like winning almost to the end, until a late penalty gave Bracknell the game by 15 points to 12.

In the Pilkington Cup Tabard beat a keen Wimbledon side before meeting their demise at the hands of Esher. In this encounter Tabard were never able to get going, whereas in the league two exciting games took place, albeit with Esher victorious each time.

Nick Churchman was again the highest points scorer for the club with 162, somewhat below his usual massive scores but this did reflect a season beset by injury, and centre Andy Pinnock topped the tries with seven.

Tabard entered their `A' XV in the Hertfordshire President's Cup and had a good run including defeating the holders, Old Albanians, before narrowly losing to Cheshunt.

L-R - Back Row: Bryan Green (Coach), Rob Botterman, Matt Collie, Bob Lloyd, Peter Luders, John Sayers, Mick Finnie, Simon Lascelles, Richard Malone, Nick Hood, Nick Turner, Geoff Bird (Manager), Andy Pinnock, Tim Andrews (Coach). Front Row: Jag Johal, Mike Hanson, Basra Singh, Jim Nolan, Steve Armstrong, Mick Skinner, Mak Sharp, Simon Dogbe, Andy Dudley, Ian McMullen.

TABARD

Match No.	Date	H/A	Comp.	Opponents	Result & Score	Att.	15	14	13	12	11
1	05.09	A	J2S	Bridgwater	W 20-14		Pinnock/t	Bejak	Luders	Moretti	Dogbe/t
2	12.09	H	J2S	M Police*	W 17-10		Pinnock	Dogbe	Luders	Moretti	McMullen(n/t)
3	26.09	A	J2S	Havant*	W 29-11		Hewson	Dickinson	Pinnock/t	Moretti	McMullen
4	03.10	A	J2S	Norwich*	L 20-31		Hewson	Dickinson	Pinnock(c)	Moretti	McMullen
5	10.10	H	J2S	Redruth	W 47-13		Hewson/2t	Dickinson/t	Pinnock/t	Moretti(u)	McMullen/t
6	24.10	A	J2S	Weston	L 6-8		Hewson(w)	McMullen(n)	Pinnock	Moretti	Bejak
7	31.10	H	J2S	Bracknell	L 6-18		Dudley	Bejak	Pinnock	Moretti	Dickinson
8	07.11	A	J2S	Cheltenham	W 10-9		Dudley	Bejak	Pinnock	Moretti	Dickinson
9	21.11	H	J2S	Plymouth	W 16-13		Dudley/t	Dickinson	Pinnock	Moretti	Bejak
10	28.11	A	J2S	N Walsham	L 7-21		Dudley	Dickinson	Pinnock	Moretti	Bejak
11	05.12	H	J2S	Barking	L 13-22		Dudley	Bejak/t	Pinnock	Moretti	Dickinson
12	12.12	A	J2S	Esher	L 10-18		Dudley	Dickinson	Pinnock	Moretti	McMullen
13	19.12	H	J2S	Clifton	D 24-24		Dudley/t	McMullen(b)	Pinnock	Moretti	Dickinson/t
14	27.12	A	J2S	Barking	L 15-38		Dudley(a)	Bejak/t	Larkin	Moretti	Dickinson
15	02.01	H	J2S	N Walsham	L 17-27		Dudley	Luders	Pinnock/t	Moretti	Dickinson
16	09.01	A	J2S	Plymouth	L 22-23		Dudley	Luders	Pinnock	Moretti	Dickinson
17	16.01	H	J2S	Cheltenham	L 6-18		Dudley	Dickinson(x)	Pinnock	Moretti	Luders
18	23.01	A	J2S	Bracknell	L 12-15		Dudley	Dickinson	Pinnock	Luders	Turner
19	30.01	H	J2S	Weston	L 3-6		Dudley	Dickinson	Pinnock	Luders	Turner
20	06.02	A	J2S	Redruth	W 21-16		Dudley	Dickinson	Pinnock/t	Moretti	Turner/t
21	13.02	H	J2S	Norwich	W 29-12		Dudley/t(c)	Dickinson	Pinnock	Moretti	Turner/t
22	27.02	H	J2S	Havant	L 11-14		Dudley	Dickinson/t	Pinnock	Moretti(A)	Turner
23	13.03	A	J2S	M Police	L 28-39		Hewson	Dickinson/t	Pinnock	Dudley/t	Turner
24	27.03	H	J2S	Bridgwater*	W 39-15		Dudley	McMullen	Pinnock	Luders	Turner/2t
25	03.04	A	J2S	Clifton	L 20-39		Andrews(A)	Dogbe	Pinnock	Moretti	Turner
26	17.04	H	J2S	Esher	L 13-27		Dudley	McMullen	Pinnock/t	Luders	Turner(G)
A	19.09	H	TB1	Wimbledon	W 26-23		Hewson/t	Dogbe	Pinnock	Moretti	Dickinson
B	17.10	A	TB2	Esher	L 3-41		Hewson	Dickinson	Pinnock	Moretti	McMullen

* after opponents name indicates a penalty try
Brackets after a player's name indicates he was replaced. eg (a) means he was replaced by replacement code "a" and so on.
/ after a player or replacement name is followed by any scores he made - eg /t, /c, /p, /dg or any combination of these

1998-99 HIGHLIGHTS

Ever Presents: None

Most appearances

25	Andy Pinnock (1)
24	Basra Singh (1)
23	Mark Sharp (2)
21	Jim Nolan (1)

Players used: 34 plus 7 as replacement only.

Most Points in a season:

Pts	Player	T	C	P	DG
148	N Churchman	4	19	29	1
56	M Skinner	2	8	19	-
30	A Pinnock	6	-	-	-
25	J Dickinson	5	-	-	-
25	G Hewson	3	2	2	-
22	S Andrews	1	1	5	-

MATCH FACTS

10	9	1	2	3	4	5	6	7	8	
Churchman/cp(l)	Skinner/t	Singh	Sharp	Nolan	Malone	Bickle	Hanson	Johal	Armstrong	1
Churchman/c	Andrews	Singh(o)	Sharp/t	Nolan	Malone	Bickle	Hanson	Johal	Armstrong	2
Churchman/2c5p	Skinner	Singh	Sharp	Nolan	Malone	Bickle	Williams(p)	Johal	Armstrong	3
Churchman/t2c2p	Skinner(m)	Singh	Sharp	Nolan	Malone	Bickle	Williams	Johal	Hanson	4
Churchman/6c	Andrews/t(t)	Singh	Sharp/t(q)	Nolan	Malone	Bickle	Hanson	Johal	Metcalfe(k)	5
Churchman/2p	Andrews	Singh	Sharp	Nolan	Malone	Bickle	Hanson	Johal(v)	Metcalfe	6
Churchman/2p	Skinner	Singh	Sharp	Nolan	Tyler	Bickle	Hanson(v)	Johal	Metcalfe	7
Churchman/tcp	Skinner	Singh	Sharp	Nolan	Tyler	Lascelles	Sayers	Hanson	Metcalfe	8
Churchman/c3p	Skinner	Singh(o)	Sharp	Nolan	Malone	Tyler	Sayers(i)	Johal	Metcalfe	9
Churchman/c	Skinner	Singh	Sharp/t	Trippick(g)	Malone	Tyler(z)	Sayers	Hanson	Metcalfe	10
Churchman/p	Skinner/t	Nolan	Sharp	Singh	Malone(j)	Tyler	Sayers	Hanson	Metcalfe(p)	11
Churchman/tcp	Skinner	Singh	Botterman	Nolan	Finnie	Tyler	Sayers(z)	Johal	Hanson	12
Andrews/t2p(u)	Skinner/p	Nolan	Botterman(f)	Trippick	Finnie	Tyler	Sayers	Johal	Metcalfe(z)	13
Andrews	Skinner/cp	Nolan	Sharp	Trippick(e)	Finnie	Tyler	Sayers	Johal(z)	Metcalfe/t	14
Hewson	Skinner/2cp	Nolan	Sharp	Singh	Finnie(h)	Tyler/t	Sayers	Evans	Metcalfe	15
Hewson/tc	Christal/t(m)	Nolan	Sharp	Singh	Malone	Tyler	Sayers	Evans	Armstrong/t	16
Hewson/2p	Andrews	Nolan	Sharp	Singh	Malone	Tyler	Sayers(o)	Evans(j)	Armstrong(s)	17
Hewson/c	Andrews	Nolan	Sharp	Singh	Malone	Tyler(y)	Sayers	Johal/t(i)	Armstrong/t	18
Churchman/p	Andrews	Nolan(B)	Sharp	Singh	Malone	Finnie(C)	Sayers	Johal(i)	Armstrong	19
Churchman/c2pdg	Andrews	Singh	Sharp	Trippick	Malone	Finnie	Evans	Hanson	Armstrong	20
Churchman/2c3p(l)	Andrews/2p	Trippick	Sharp	Singh	Malone	Lascelles	Evans	Hanson	Armstrong	21
Hewson	Andrews/2p	Trippick	Botterman(f)	Singh	Malone	Lascelles	Evans	Hanson(F)	Armstrong	22
Churchman	Andrews/cp(d/p)	Trippick(r)	Sharp	Singh	Malone	Lascelles	Sayers(j/t)	Hood(i)	Armstrong/t	23
Churchman/3p(m)	Skinner/2c2p	Nolan	Sharp	Singh	Malone	Lascelles	Sayers(i)	Johal/t(E)	Armstrong	24
Churchman(u)	Skinner/2c2p	Nolan	Sharp(q)	Singh(D)	Finnie	Lascelles/t	Sayers/t	Johal(i)	Armstrong	25
Lloyd	Skinner	Nolan	Sharp	Singh	Malone(y)	Lascelles	Sayers	Johal(E)	Armstrong	26
Churchman/c3p	Skinner	Singh	Sharp/t	Nolan	Malone	Bickle	Hanson/t	Johal	Armstrong	A
Churchman/p	Andrews	Singh	Sharp	Nolan	Malone	Bickle	Hanson	Johal	Metcalfe	B

REPLACEMENTS:					
	a- A Pinnock	b- C Bejak	c - P Luders	d - M Skinner	e - B Singh
f - Sharp	g - J Nolan	h - D Malone	i - M Hanson	j - J Johal	k - S Armstrong
l - G Hewson	m - S Andrews	n - J Dickinson	o - M Trippick	p - M Cripps	q - R Botterman
r - C Collinson	s - A Metcalfe	t - G West	u - B Larkin	v - J Sayers	w - A Dudley
x - N Turner	y - M Finnie	z - M Evans	A - B Lloyd	B - D Sullivan	C - J Fincham
D - M Colme	E - N Hood	F - S Lane	G - S Dogbe		

Fly half Nick Churchman topped the scoring list yet again with 148 points in a season interrupted by injury.

Leading the try scorers with six was new boy Andy Pinnock who joined the club during last summer from Havant.

Tabard had a mid season collapse with 11 matches without a win that included 10 defeats and a draw.

At home Tabard managed just 26 tries at home, only Cheltenham with 16 scored less.

TABARD

LEAGUE STATISTICS
compiled by Stephen McCormack

SEASON	Division	P	W	D	L	F	A	Pts Diff	Lge Pts	Lge Pos		Coach		Captain
89-90	Lon3NW	10	10	0	0	264	75	189	20	1p		I Jones		T Smithers
90-91	Lon 2N	10	6	0	4	116	122	-6	12	4		T Smithers		N Churchman
91-92	Lon 2N	10	9	1	0	167	59	108	19	1p		T Smithers		M Richards
92-93	Lon 1	12	10	1	1	230	127	103	21	1p				
93-94	D5S	12	6	2	4	183	136	47	14	3				
94-95	D5S	12	7	0	5	207	208	-1	14	6		I Jones		R Malone
												Most Points		**Most Tries**
95-96	D5S	12	4	1	7	195	244	-49	9	9	112	Nick Churchman	3	Giles Hewson Nick Churchman
96-97	D4S	26	10	3	13	511	557	-46	23	8	264	Nick Churchman	8	Nick Churchman
97-98	N2S	26	14	0	12	556	532	-24	28	6	239	Nick Churchman	11	Nick Churchman
98-99	N2S	26	9	1	16	461	501	-40	19	8	148	Nick Churchman	6	Andy Pinnock

FACT FILE

Founded: 1951
Nickname: Tabs

Colours: Navy with broad yellow band edged with red.
Change colours: Blue, gold & red quadrants.

GROUND

Address: Cobden Hill, Radlett, Hertfordshire, WD7 7LN
Tel. Nos. 01923 855561
Capacity: 1,000 Seated: None Standing: 1,000

Directions: On A5183 Watling Street, from Elstree turn right after entryinto Radlett, blind entrance by high brick wall nearly opposite "Cat & Fiddle"Pub.
Nearest Railway Station: Radlett

Car Parking: 250 spaces adjacent to ground

Admission: Adult standing £4, Children/OAPs £2

Clubhouse: Matchdays & training eves only. Bar meals available.
Functions: Contact Nick Gray 0831 668204

Club Shop: Open Saturdays only

Training Nights: Tuesday & Thursday

PROGRAMME

Size: A5 Price: with entry Pages: 16 + cover
Editor: Ross Hopcroft

ADVERTISING RATES (Last Years Rates)
Colour Full page £300, Half page £150, Qtr page £75

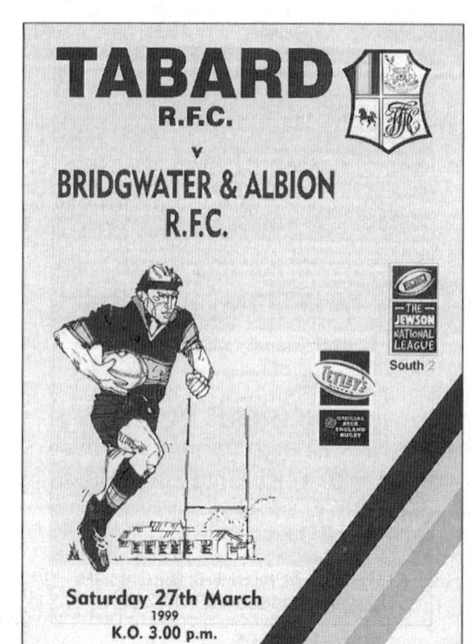

WESTCOMBE PARK R.F.C.

President	Peter G Hudson, Fairfield, 9 Downs View Close, Pratts Bottom, Kent BR6 7SU
Chairman	John Yeates, Coppers, Farthing Street, Downe, Kent BR6 7JB 01689 857495
Secretary	Geoff Boyd, 7 Hawfield Bank, Orpington, Kent BR6 7TA. 01689 839171 (H) 0958 402295 (M)
Treasurer	Terry Hadaway,Hilbre, Main Road, Knockholt,Kent TN14 7LD. 01959 532067(H) 0181 308 7024(B)
Chairman of Rugby Playing/Fixtures Secretary	John Bellinger, 32A Courtyard, Eltham London SE9 5QE 0181 850 7280 (H) 0171 481 5507 (B) 0171 3773116 (Fax)
Chairman of Marketing	Robin Taylor, 24 Pinchbeck Road, Green Street Green, Orpington, Kent BR6 6DR 01689 855052 (H) 0181 319 7768 (B) 0374 212029 (M) 0181 3197784 (B Fax) 01689 600717 (H Fax)
1st XV Manager/Publicity	John Ward Turner, Westerham Lodge, Westerham Road, Keston Kent BR2 6DA Tel 01689 854868, Fax 01689 860246, Mob. 0402
Match Secretary:	Chriss Snape, 01322 3830-22 (H) 01293 535331 (B)
Club Coaches	Fraser Thomson, 01689 607052 & Peter Danckert, 0181 309 1241

The Club was founded in 1904 when nineteen year old Dudley Roughton, though physically handicapped and unable to play himself, formed a team from his friends and relations, many ofwhom were in their teens and new to the game. Westcombe Park have maintained the name of their original location,near Greenwich before fmoving to Goddington Dene, Orpington in 1990. The sports club offer rugby, football, tennis and cricket on a 23 acre site with a large clubhouse and new changing accommodation built in 1990

The Club is well known for it's mini and junior rugby and have been running their own mini festival for 26 years, staging the Kent Festival twice in recent years.

In the last two seasons the club has played entertaining rugby in losing only one league game, winning the Kent Cup twice and losing to Bracknell 14-21 in last seasons Tetley Bitter Cup. It would be invidious to pick out individual players for mention especially as try scoring was shared out equally between backs and forwards!

'Combe were slow to start when the Leagues first appeared starting in London South East 3 in 1989-90 and gaining promotion into London Two South where they remained until season 1997-98 on several occasions just missing promotion by one game. In 1997-98 under the captaincy of Nick Hayler and the Coaching of Fraser Thomson and Danny Vaughan 'Combe had a magnificent season winning all 15 of their league games with a massive 565 points difference to be promoted to London One.

Season 1998-99 with the team now being captained by Rupert Chitty and coached by Fraser Thomson and Peter Danckert, started badly losing to Staines in the first league game by one point, however 'Combe went on to win every league game thereafter with a average of 44 points a game. A slip up by Staines beaten surprisingly by Cheshunt let 'Combe back into the frame and with a vastly superior points difference they won the league and promotion into Jewson National Two South. The final icing on the cake for season 1998-99 was to win for the second consecutive season the Kent County Cup, by beating Sevenoaks 40 points to 15.

Westcombe Park RFC 1stXV Squad Season 1998/99

WESTCOMBE PARK

Match	Date	H/A	Comp	Opponents	Result &Score	**Point Scorers**
1	05-09	H	TBC	Staines	W 40-20	Daniel(2t)Coates(2t4c4p)
2	12-09	H	L1	Staines	L 28-29	Daniel(t)Welch(t)Chitty(t)HarrisM(t)Coates(1t2p)
3	19-09	H	TBC	Bracknell	L 14-21	Subbiani(t)Coates(t2cpt)
4	26-09	A	L1	Sudbury	W 33-20	Smith(t)Subbiani(t)Anderson(t)Chitty(t)Coates(t4c)
5	03-10	H	L1	Woodford	W 46-20	Subbiani(t)Jervis(t)Daniel(t)Anderson(t)Chitty(2t)Coates(t4cp)
6	10-10	A	L1	Southend	W 62-10	Jervis(t)HarrisR(t)Dawson(2t)Hayward(t)Richardson(2t) Coates(t7cppt)
7	24-10	H	L1	Ruislip	W 24-0	Smith(t)Watts(t)Anderson(t)Coates(t2c)
8	31-10	A	L1	Cheshunt	W 48-16	Smith(t)Watts(t)Jenkins(t)Jervis(t)Dawson(t)Chitty(t)Hayward(t) Coates(2c3p)
9	07-11	H	L1	Thurrock	W 38-20	Dawson(t)HarrissS(t)Chitty(2)Coates(cp)Smith(pt)
10	21-11	A	L1	Thanet Wanderers	W 27-8	Jervis(t)Anderson(t_)Goodwin(t)Coates(3c2p)
11	28-11	H	L1	Charlton Pk	W 73-0	McCarthy(t)Jervis(t)Watts(t)Wech(t)Richardson(t)Hayward(2t) Chitty(t)Coates(t9c)Chitty(t)Goodwin(t)
12	09-01	A	L1	Guildford & Godalming	W 44-14	Goodwin(t)Chitty(t)Beckett(t)Hennessy(2cp)Smith(4tc)
13	16-01	H	L1	O Colfeians	W 48-8	Smith(2t)Hennessy(t4c)Welch(t)Dawson(t)HarrissS(t)Chitty(t)HarisM(t)
14	24-01	A	KC	Blackheath	W 20-8	Smith(cp)Welch(t)HarrissS(t)Goodwin(t)
15	30-01	A	L1	O Mid-Whitgiftians	W 43-6	Smith(t)McCarthy(2t)Jervis(t4c)Sheehan(t)Welch(t)
16	06-02	H	L1	Basingstoke	W 51-10	Smith(t2c)Hennessy(c)McCarthy(t)Subbiani(t)Welch(2)Richardson(2t) Goodwin(t)HarrisM(t)
17	14-02	A	KC	Canterbury	W 34-14	Hennessy(t2c)Sheehan(t)Welch(t)HarrissS(t)Goodwin(t)Chitty(t)
18	27-02	A	L1	Harlow	W 43-15	Coates(t4c)Jervis(t)Subbiani(2t)HarrissS(2t)Goodwin(t)
19	07-03	H	KC	Maidstone	W 29-6	Coates(t2c)Bates(t)Jenkins(t)Richardson(t)Goodwin(t)
20	13-03	H	L1	Wimbledon	W 59-5	Coates(7c)Hennessy(3t)Sheehan(t)Jervis(t)Subbiani(4)
21	21-03	A	KC	Lordswood	W 58-7	Smith(2t3c)Subbiani(t)Jervis(tc)Hennessy(t)Sheehan(t)Hayler(t) Hayward(t)Richardson(t)Chitty(t)
22	27-03	A	L1	Sutton & Epsom	W 39-33	Coates(2p4c)Hennessy(t)Jervis(t)Sheehan(t)Welch(t)Richardson(t)
23	18-04	A	KC	Sevenoaks	W 40-15	Coates (5c)Subbiani(t)Richardson(t)Goodwin(2t)Welch(t)HarrissS(t)

Players used: 38

Ever Present: Rupert Chitty (Captain) and Dom Jenkins all games including friendlies and Cup games. Rupert Chitty, Dom Jenkins, Mike Harris and Stuart Anderson for all league games.

Most points in the season for all games played:

Player	Pts	T	C	P	DG
Coates	222	10	62	16	-
Smith	97	16	7	1	-
Hennessy	80	11	11	1	-
Goodwin	75	15	-	-	-
Jervis	71	11	8	-	-
Chitty	70	14	-	-	-
Welch	55	11	-	-	-
Richardson	55	11	-	-	-

1998-99 HIGHLIGHTS

To be London One league champions in our first appearance with an average of 44 points per game was a huge bonus to Westcombe Park and we look forward to our first season in Jewson National Two South.
Westcombe Park were also winners of the Kent County Cup, for the second consecutive year

Four Tries in a Match:
Ben Smith v Guildford & Godalming 9/1
Subbiani v Wimbledon 13/3

Hat Trick of tries in a Match:
Hennessey v Wimbledon 13/3

	15	14	13	12	11	10	9	8	7	6	5	4	3	2	1	
1	Coates	Subbiani	Jenkins	McCarthy	Daniel	Sheehan	Welch	Harris M	Chitty	Sole	Harriss S	Hayward	Anderson	Clarke	Beck	1
2	Coates	Subbiani	Jenkins	McCarthy	Daniel	Sheehan	Welch	Harris M	Chitty	Sole	Hariss S	Hayward	Anderson	Clarke	Beck	2
3	Coates	Subbiani	Jenkins(F)	Bates (C)	Daniel	Sheehan	Welch	Harris M	Chitty	Sole	Harriss S	Hayward	Cordier	Dawson(A)	Hayler(W)	3
4	Smith	Subbiani	Jenkins(K)	Bates	Daniel	Coates	Welch	Harris M	Chitty	Sole	Richardson(D)	Hayward	Anderson(E)	Dawson(A)	Cordier	4
5	Smith	Subbiani	Jenkins	Jervis	Daniel	Coates	HarrisR	Harris M	Chitty	Sole	Jones(G)	Hayward	Anderson(E)	Dawson(H)	Hayler	5
6	Coates	Watts	Jenkins	Jervis	Daniel	Sheehan	HarrisR)	Harris M	Chitty	Sole	Harriss S(N)	Hayward	Anderson	Dawson(H)	Hayler	6
7	Smith	Watts	Jenkins	Jervis	Hennessy	Coates	Welch(O)	Harris M	Chitty	Hayward	Harriss S(D)	Richardson	Anderson	Dayani	Hayler	7
8	Smith	Watts	Jenkins	Jervis	McCarthy	Coates	Welch	Harris M	Chitty	Clifton	Harriss S	Richardson(H)	Anderson	Dawson	Hayler(E)	8
9	Smith	Watts	Jenkins	Jervis	McCarthy	Coates	Welch	Harris M	Chitty(N)	Clifton	Harriss S	Hayward	Anderson	Dawson(A)	Campbell(B)	9
10	Smith	Watts	Jenkins	Jervis	McCarthy	Coates	Welch	Harris M	Chitty	Goodwin	Harriss S(N)	Hayward	Anderson	Dawson(A)	Hayler	10
11	Coates	Watts	Jenkins	Jervis	McCarthy	Sheehan	Welch	Harris M	Chitty	Goodwin	Richardson	Hayward	Anderson	Dawson	Hayler(E)	11
12	Smith	Beckett	Jenkins	McCarthy(F)	Hennessy	Sheehan	Welch	Harris M	Chitty	Goodwin	Harriss S	Hayward	Anderson	Dawson(A)	Hayler	12
13	Smith	Beckett	Jenkins	McCarthy(Q)	Hennessy	Sheehan	Welch	Harris M	Chitty	Hayward(R)	Harriss S	Richardson	Anderson	Dawson(H)	Hayler	13
14	Smith	McCarthy	Jenkins	Jervis	Beckett	Sheehan	Welch	Harris M	Chitty	Goodwin(R)	Harriss S	Hayward	Anderson	Dawson(H)	Hayler(P)	14
15	Smith	Subbiani	Jenkins	Jervis	McCarthy	Sheehan	Welch	Harris M	Chitty	Goodwin(R)	Harriss S	Hayward	Anderson	Dawson(S)	Hayler(J)	15
16	Smith	Subbiani	Jenkins	McCarthy(F)	Hennessy	Sheehan	Welch	Harris M(R)	Chitty	Goodwin	Harriss S	Richardson	Anderson	Dawson(S)	Campbell(B)	16
17	Hennessy	McCarthy	Jenkins	Bates	Daniel(U)	Sheehan	Welch	Chitty	Hayward	Goodwin	Harriss S	Richardson	Anderson	Dawson	Hayler(J)	17
18	Coates	Subbiani	Jenkins	Jervis	Smith	Sheehan	Welch	Harris M	Chitty	Goodwin	Harriss S	Hayward	Anderson	Widdett(A)	Campbell(B)	18
19	Coates	Subbiani	Jenkins	Bates	Smith	Sheehan	Welch	Harris M	Chitty	Goodwin	Richardson	Hayward(G)	Anderson	Widdett(A)	Hayler	19
20	Coates	Hennessy	Jenkins	Bates	Smith	Sheehan	Welch	Harris M	Chitty	Goodwin	Richardson	Hayward	Anderson	Widdett(V)	Campbell	20
21	Smith	Subbiani(T)	Jenkins(F)	Jervis	Hennessy	Sheehan	HarrisR	Harris M	Chitty	Goodwin(H)	Richardson	Hayward	Anderson	Widdett(V)	Hayler (J)	21
22	Coates	Subbiani(T)	Jenkins	Jervis	Hennessy	Sheehan	Welch	Harris M	Chitty	Goodwin	Richardson	Hayward	Anderson	Dawson(S)	Hayler	22
23	Coates	Subbiani	Jenkins	Jervis(T)	Hennessy	Sheehan	Welch	Harris M	Chitty	Goodwin	Richardson	Hayward	Anderson	Dawson(S)	Hayler	23

REPLACEMENTS: A - Clarke; B - Hayler; C - McCarthy; D - Jones; E - Cordier; F - Bates; G - Harriss S; H - Dayani; J - Campbell; K - Rolfe; L - Hayward; M - Sheehan: N - Richardson; O - Harris R; P- Beck; Q - Jervis; R - Sole; S - Widdett; T - Smith; U - Beckett; V - Dawson; W - Uncles

WESTCOMBE PARK

LEAGUE STATISTICS
compiled by John Ward Turner

SEASON	Division	P	W	D	L	F	A	Pts Diff	Lge Pts	Lge Pos	Coach	Captain
89-90	Lon 3SE	10	9	1	0	227	89	138	19	1p	C Chapman	F Thomson
90-91	Lon 2S	10	7	1	2	178	114	64	15	2	C Chapman	F Thomson
91-92	Lon 2S	10	8	0	2	214	130	84	20	3	C Chapman	F Thomson
92-93	lon 2S	12	9	1	2	279	135	144	19	2	C Chapman	F Thomson
93-94	Lon 2S	12	10	1	1	259	130	129	21	2	F Thomson	P Harris
94-95	Lon 2S	12	7	1	4	228	177	51	15	4	F Thomson	G Mayor
95-96	Lon 2S	12	7	0	5	317	196	121	14	5	F Thomson	G Mayor
96-97	Lon 2S	12	7	0	5	414	228	186	14	4	F Thomson	J Hayday
97-98	Lon 2S	15	15	0	0	703	138	565	30	1p	F Thomson/D Vaughan	N Hayler
98-99	Lon 1	16	15	0	1	706	201	505	30	1p	F Thomson/P Danckert	R Chitty

FACT FILE

Founded: 1930
Nickname: "Combe"

Colours: Navy blue, with white hoops, blue shorts
Change colours: White, with blue hoops, blue shorts

ADDRESS: Goddington Dene, Goddington Lane, Orpington, Kent BR6 9SX
Tel: 01689 834902 **Fax:** 01689 822116
Capacity: 2000 standing

Directions: From M25 - exit at J4. At next round-about exit A244 (Orpington), at 40 MPH sign (2.8 miles from M25) turn right into Goddington Lane, opposite the Highway.
From A20 - Leave A20 at Crittall's Corner (Orpington A224). Take A224 to Orpington, Sevenoaks Way, Continue into Court Road, following sign, M25-Sevenoaks. After six sets of lights turn LEFT into Goddington Lane (opposite Volvo show room)
From Croydon - follow A232 into Orpington, over War Memorial roundabout, up Spur Road to A224. Turn Right into Court Road at lights, 1/4 mile turn Left into Goddington Lan e as above.
Nearest Station: Orpington (Taxis/Buses), Chelsfield (10mins. walk)

Car Parking: 200, Special events: 2500

Admission: By programme

Club Shop: Open Saturdays & Sundays
Manager Jane Hadaway. 01959 532067

Clubhouse: Normal licensing hours, snacks and bar meals.
Functions Rooms available for up to 200
Contact House Manager: 01689 834902

Trianing Nights: Tuesdays and Thursdays.

PROGRAMME Size: A5 **Price:** £2.00 **Pages:** 20
Editor: Contact: John Ward Turner
Tel:01689 854868 Fax 01689 860246

ADVERTISING RATES
Full Page: £150.00, 1/2 page: £100.00 1/4 Page: £55.00 plus VAT

WESTON super MARE R.F.C.

President	J W Brentnall	c/o Messers J W Ward, 37 The Boulevard, Weston super Mare 0117 922 0208 (H), 01934 413545 (B)
Chairman	W A Poole	19 Worlebury Park Road, Worlebury, W-s-M. 01934 626870 (H)
Hon. Secretary	S Sharp	10 Southview, Yatton, nr. Bristol 01934 876285 (Tel & Fax) - Daytime only.
Hon. Treasurer	R Holder	74b Clevedon Rd., W-s-M. 01934 414929 0831 828611 (Mobile)
Fixture/Match Secretary	M Shergold	34 Flamingo Cres., Worle, W-s-M. 01934 521701 (H) 641618 (B)
Club Coach	M Reece	27 Addison Grove, Taunton, Somerset TA2 6JG 01823 332101 (H), 0802 663888 (Mob)
1st XV Manager	H C Hope	24 Feniton, Clovelly Rd., Worle, W-s-M. BS22 0LN 01934 511834 (H)

Weston with their good friends from North Walsham hold the distinction of being the longest surviving members of National League Two South. We were both promoted at the same time for season 90/91. We have seen many changes over the years with teams being promoted and demoted. Recent years have been quite dramatic particularly on the financial front. Weston's aims for last season were very simple. 1. To maintain our league status. 2. To remain solvent. I suppose we achieved both.

Unfortunately, money seems to be the key to success. Just look at league positions for last season and maybe draw your own conclusions. West Country sides would appear to be the poor cousins.

Prior to the start of the season a number of 1st XV players from our small squad were not available for one reason or another and there was a lack of real optimism i n the camp. However, a lively spirited display away to Barking for the start of the season was encouraging. This was followed with a totally unexpected victory at home over promotion seeking opponents Esher. This victory was achieved with grim determination and a strong will to win.

A win over Ipswich in the Tetley's Cup gave the club a better start than we thought possible. Looking back we were doing well, but lacked consistency. However, we did enough to enter the `comfort zone' by the end of January. We were looking to finish in a creditable sixth place. There was bitter disappointment towards the end of the season when over a dozen 1st team squad players were injured and two players sidelined after being sent off.

We lost to our old adversaries Bridgwater RFC in the semi final of the Somerset Cup in a high scoring game. There was a general feeling that the standard of refereeing was not as good as it should have been, and we hope for improvements next season.

Congratulations to captain Graham Buller for receiving his Somerset County Cap and always leading the club's side from the front and to Neil Colman for being versatile enough to play in all the back positions during the season; also to Dave Bird for being top try scorer with eighteen tries as well as being chosen Player of the Year for the third consecutive season. It is a pity that some other senior players could not follow his excellent commitment and attitude to the game of rugby.

The club's major success of the season culminated in our excellent colts side lifting the County Cup for the first time in twenty years. A number of these players will be contesting for places in our league side. With the right blend of experience and youthful enthusiasm I feel a degree of optimism for next season. On that note `Here's to next season - World Cup and all'.

CLAYTON HOPE

Back Row: Russ Main, Jon Pitt, James Hedges, Ardene Miller, Mark Perry, Stuart Board, Duncan Rainey.

3rd Row: Robert Hedges, Barry Popham, Mervyn Down, Jon Cornish, Simon Thompson, Ian Wintle, Jarad Collard, Barry Sparks, Tony Russell.

2nd Row: Graham Hill, Danny Murphy, Mick Reede (Coach), Graham Buller (Captain), John Brentall (President), Andy Gaulton, Neil Coleman.

Front Row: Dave Steele, Andy Steele, Paul Denham, Tony Down, Jim Wiseman, Dave Jones, Dave Bird.

WESTON SUPER MARE

Match No.	Date	H/A	Comp.	Opponents	Result & Score	Att.	15	14	13	12	11
1	05.09	A	J2S	Barking	L 9-21		Murphy(a)	Wiseman	Collard	Miller	D Steele
2	12.09	H	J2S	Esher	W 24-22		Murphy	D Steele	Havard	Collard	Wise/t
3	26.09	A	J2S	Clifton	L 11-16		Murphy	Wise	Collard	Havard	Jordan
4	03.10	H	J2S	Bridgwater	W 24-19		Murphy	D Steele	Collard	Havard	Jordan
5	10.10	A	J2S	Met Police*	L 22-43		Murphy	Wise	Collard	Havard	Jordan
6	24.10	H	J2S	Tabard	W 8-6		Wiseman	Wise	Collard	Venn	Jordan
7	31.10	A	J2S	Norwich	L 3-16		Wiseman(g)	Wise	Collard	Coleman	Jordan
8	07.11	H	J2S	Redruth	D 16-16		Collard	Wise/t	Venn	Coleman	Jordan
9	21.11	A	J2S	Havant	W 25-15		Collard	Wise	Havard	Coleman	Wiseman
10	28.11	A	J2S	Bracknell	L 6-24		D Steele	Wise	Havard	Coleman	Wiseman
11	05.12	H	J2S	Cheltenham	W 32-17		D Steele	Wise/t	Havard	Coleman	Wiseman
12	12.12	A	J2S	Plymoputh	L 18-27		Venn	Taylor	Havard	Coleman	Jordan
13	19.12	H	J2S	N Walsham	L 5-13		D Steele	Wise	Havard	Coleman(y)	Jordan
14	28.12	A	J2S	Cheltenham	W 30-16		Venn	Wise	Havard	Coleman/t	Jordan/2t
15	02.01	H	J2S	Bracknell	L 10-20		Venn	Wise	Havard/t(q)	Bamsey	Jordan(p)
16	09.01	H	J2S	Havant*	L 19-27		Hiles	Wise	Havard	Venn	Jordan/t
17	16.01	A	J2S	Redruth*	W 34-28		Hiles	Wise	Venn(x)	Bamsey	Jordan
18	23.01	H	J2S	Norwich*	W 23-5		Hiles	Wise	Venn	Bamsey	Jordan
19	30.01	A	J2S	Tabard	W 6-3		D Steele	Wiseman	Venn	Havard	Wise
20	06.02	H	J2S	Met Police	L 14-24		D Steele/t	Wise	Venn	Havard/t	Jordan
21	13.02	A	J2S	Bridgwater	L 10-25		D Steele	Wise	Venn	Havard	Jordan
22	27.02	H	J2S	CLifton	L 7-22		D Steele(j)	Morris	Bamsey	Coleman	Taylor
23	13.03	A	J2S	Esher	L 19-70		D Steele/t	Sharp	Coleman	Venn(z)(A)	Morris
24	27.03	H	J2S	Barking	L 8-16		Coleman	Wise	Venn	Bamsey	Sharp
25	03.04	A	J2S	N Walsham	L 17-43		Coleman	Taylor	Miller	Bamsey	D Steele
26	17.04	H	J2S	Plymouth	L 17-34		Hiles	Wise	Bamsey	Miller/t	Rainey/t
A	19.09	H	TB1	Ipswich	W 34-26		Murphy	Wise	Collard	Havard	D Steele/2t
B	17.10	H	TB2	Bracknell	L 15-43		Murphy	Wise	Collard	Bamsey	Jordan

* after opponents name indicates a penalty try
Brackets after a player's name indicates he was replaced. eg (a) means he was replaced by replacement code "a" and so on.
/ after a player or replacement name is followed by any scores he made - eg /t, /c, /p, /dg or any combination of these

1998-99 HIGHLIGHTS

Ever Presents: None

Most appearances
25 Neil Coleman (1), David Bird, Graham Buller
23 Mervyn Down
22 Andy Gunningham
19 Tony Down (3)

Players used: 38 plus five as replacement only

Most Points in a season:

Pts	Player	T	C	P	DG
115	M Armstrong	4	19	16	3
70	D Bird	14	-	-	-
65	N Coleman	3	4	13	1
25	L Walsh	5	-	-	-
20	P Redman	4	-	-	-

MATCH FACTS

10	9	1	2	3	4	5	6	7	8	
Coleman/3p	Down	Gunningham(b)	Press	Down	Main	Pitt	Cornish	Sparks	Buller	1
Coleman/c4p	Down	Gunningham	Bird	Down	Main/t	Pitt	Cornish(d)	Martin(c)	Buller	2
Coleman/2p	Down	Gunningham	Bird/t	Down	Main	Pitt	Ashley	Sparks	Buller	3
Coleman/t3p	Down	Gunningham	Bird/t	Down/t	Buller	Pitt	Ashley	Sparks	Walsh	4
Coleman/2cp	Down	Gunningham/t)(b)	Bird(h)	Down	Cornish	Buller	Sparks(i)	Ashley(g)	Walsh/t	5
Coleman/dg	Down/t	Gunningham(b)	Bird	Down	Main	Pitt	Buller	Redman(k)	Walsh	6
Armstrong/p	Down	Gunningham	Bird	Down	Main	Pitt	Buller	Cornish	Walsh	7
Armstrong/c3p	Down	Gunningham	Bird	Down	Main	Pitt	Buller	Cornish	Walsh(l)	8
Armstrong/t2c2p	Down	Gunningham	Bird/t	Down	Main	Buller	Fear	Clapp	Walsh/t	9
Armstrong/2p	Down	Gunningham	Bird	Down	Pitt(c)	Buller	Clapp	Redman	Walsh	10
Armstrong/2cp	Down/t	Gunningham	Bird/t	Popham	Clapp(c)	Buller	Fear(i)	Redman/t	Walsh/t	11
Armstrong/c2p	Down	Gunningham(b)	Bird/t	Down	Clapp	Buller	Fear(c)	Redman/t(i)	Walsh	12
Armstrong	Down	Gunningham	Bird/t(h)	Down	Pitt	Buller	Clapp	Redman	Walsh(n)	13
Armstrong/cp	Down	Gunningham	Bird/t	Down(b)	Buller	Clapp	Fear	Redman/t	Walsh	14
Coleman	Down	Gunningham	Bird	Popham(o)	Pitt(r)	Buller	Clapp	Redman	Walsh/t	15
Armstrong/2c(t)	Down	Gunningham(o)	Bird	Popham	Pitt(r)	Buller	Clapp(n)	Redman/t	Walsh	16
Armstrong/3cp	Coleman/t	Gunningham	Bird/3t	Down	Buller	Main(c)	Clapp(n)	Redman	Walsh	17
Armstrong/tcpdg	Coleman	Gunningham	Bird	Down	Pitt	Buller	Clapp	Redman	Walsh/t	18
Armstrong/pdg	Coleman	Gunningham	Bird	Down	Pitt(r)	Buller	Clapp(n)	Redman	Walsh	19
Armstrong/2c	Coleman(x)	Gunningham	Bird	Down(b)	Pitt(r)	Buller	Clapp	Redman	Walsh	20
Armstrong/cp	Coleman(x)	Gunningham(o)	Bird/t	Down	Pitt	Buller	Clapp	Redman	Walsh	21
Armstrong/c	Down	Popham	Bird/t	Down(o)	Pitt	Main	Clapp	Collins(u)	Buller	22
Armstrong/t2c	Down/t	Popham	Bird(h)	Down	Main	Buller	Sparks	Fear(v)	Clapp	23
Armstrong/p	Down	Popham	Bird/t	Down	Main(w)	Buller	Weatherall(v)	Fear	Clapp	24
Armstrong/tc(A)	Gaulton(E/t)	Popham	Bird	Down	Gary Buller	Cornish(B)	Weatherall	Board(C)	Clapp/t	25
Coleman/c	Down	Gunningham(b)	Bird/t(C)	Down	Pitt	Buller	Weatherall(c)	Fear	Clapp	26
Coleman/c4p	Down	Gunningham	Bird	Down(b)	Main/t	Pitt	Cornish(d/t)	Martin	Buller	A
Coleman	Down	Gunningham/t	Bird	Down	Pitt	Buller/2t	Clapp(s)	Sparks(e)	Walsh	B

REPLACEMENTS:					
	a-Denham	b-Popham	c-Sparks	d-Walsh	e-Press
f-Cornish	g-D Steele	h-Hill	i-Collins	j-Bamsey	k-Clapp
l-Redman	m-Venn	n-Fear	o-A Steele	p-Taylor	q-Hiles
r-Main	s-Wiseman	t-Coleman	u-Weatherall	v-Board	w-Pitt
x-T Down	y-Venn	z-Collard	A- Renwick	B - M Perry	C - D Burge
					E - J Morris

Mark Armstrong finished top points scorer for the second season running, while in the try stakes hooker David Bird ran away with it scoring 14 tries, nine better than his nearest rival.

Weston started the season well enough but lost their way by the end culminating in seven straight defeats.

Early in the season they beat Esher which in the end proved vital for the London club as they missed out on promotion by just a single point.

In January they were awarded penalty tries in three successive league matches.

They only managed the 'double' over Cheltenham last season. After winning at Havant they lost the return at home.

WESTON super MARE

LEAGUE STATISTICS

compiled by Stephen McCormack

SEASON	Division	P	W	D	L	F	A	Pts Diff	Lge Pts	Lge Pos		Most Points		Most Tries
89-90	SW1	10	8	0	2	186	133	53	16	2p	66	Melvin Badger	8	Chris Brown
90-91	D4S	12	6	0	6	192	182	10	12	5	122	Melvin Badger	8	Melvin Badger
91-92	D4S	12	4	0	8	175	215	-40	8	9	39	Jarad Collard	5	Paul Whatley & Charlie Larkin
92-93	D4S	12	4	1	7	154	226	-72	9	10	81	Paul Thatcher	3	Barry Sparks
93-94	D5S	12	7	0	5	163	180	-17	14	5	91	Paul Thatcher	2	Neil Coleman & Robert Chamberlain
94-95	D5S	12	8	0	4	194	160	34	16	3	119	Paul Thatcher	2	Mark Venner & Alan Baskerville
95-96	D5S	12	10	0	2	207	123	84	20	2	105	Paul Thatcher	5	Mark Venner
96-97	D4S	26	11	0	15	482	515	-33	22	9	164	Paul Thatcher	8	Graham Biller
97-98	N2S	26	10	0	16	468	651	-183	20	10	76	Mark Armstrong	5	Matthew Hiles
98-99	N2S	26	9	1	16	415	588	-173	19	9	115	Mark Armstrong	14	David Bird

FACT FILE

Founded: 1875
Nickname: Seasiders

Colours: Royal blue with red and white hoops
Change colours: To be decided

GROUND

Address: Recreation Ground, Drove Road, Weston Super Mare, North Somerset BS233PA
Tel: 01934 623118 Tel/Fax: 01934 625643
Capacity: 6,499 Seated: 499 Standing - Covered: 300 Uncovered: 5,700

Directions: M5 Jnc 21, follow new road into Weston, follow signs for town centre
Nearest Railway Station: Weston Super Mare, 100 yards from ground

Car Parking: 200 at ground, 50+ nearby

Admission: Season ticket from £30 - £45, OAPs £20, Junior £15.
Matchday £5, Children/OAPs £2

Club Shop: Open Sat & Sun matchdays.

Clubhouse: Every evening (except Sunday) 7.00-11.00, matchdays 12.00-11.00, Sundays 12.00-3.00.
Snacks & bar meals available.
Functions: Capacity 100 +, contact Club Manager

Training Nights: Tuesday & Thursday

PROGRAMME

Size: A5 Price: £1 Pages: 16 + cover
Editor: Jon Cornish (Waterside Printers) 01275 340090, 343916 (Fax)

ADVERTISING RATES
Colour Full page £250
Mono - Full page £170, half £90

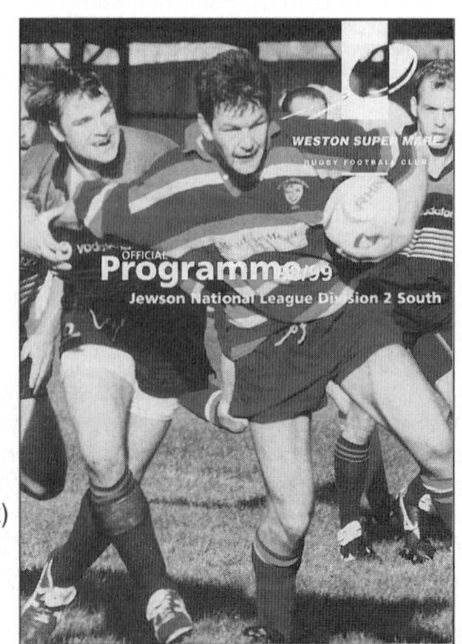

DIVISION FOUR SOUTH

(CURRENTLY JEWSON NATIONAL LEAGUE TWO SOUTH

Previously also Area League South& Division Five South

RECORDS SECTION

Relegated clubs' Match Facts for season 1998-99

Havant 464/65

The Last Ten Years 466

A breakdown showing the champions, runners-up, those relegated, who scored most - points, tries, conversions, penalties & drop goals in each of the last ten seasons in this division (or its equivalent)

All Time Team & Individual Records 467

A list of the various records for this division (or its equivalent) since the start of the league system.

Ten Year Record 468

A grid showing those clubs who have been part of this division (or its equivalent), and the league position they achieved for each of the last ten years

Clifton's scrum half, Nick Lloyd, passing during their match against Barking with Eddie Smith in support.

HAVANT

Match No.	Date	H/A	Comp.	Opponents	Result & Score	Att.	15	14	13	12	11
1	05.09	H	J2S	M Police	L 11-13		Andrew(l)	Hill	McCormac	Boydell	Draper(k)
2	12.09	A	J2S	Plymouth	L 5-22		Beacham	Andrew	Davies	Boydell	Crunow/t
3	26.09	H	J2S	Tabard	L 11-29		Dudley/p	Andrews/t	French	Boydell	Hill
4	03.10	A	J2S	N Walsham	L 17-47		Dudley	Andrew	French	Hill/t	Stapleton
5	10.10	H	J2S	Norwich	W 25-12		Dudley/t	Andrew	Claffey/t	Boydell	Hill
6	24.10	A	J2S	Barking	L 3-40		Dudley	Andrew	McCormac	Shaw	Jewitt
7	31.10	H	J2S	Redruth	W 14-9		Andrew	Hill	Claffey	Boydell	Jewitt/t(s)
8	07.11	A	J2S	Esher	L 6-63		Dudley	Andrew	Boydell(a)	Claffey	Shaw(t)
9	21.11	H	J2S	Weston	L 15-25		Andrew	Wybro/2t	Hill	Boydell(j)	French
10	28.11	A	J2S	Clifton	L 7-26		French(M)	Wybro	Boydell	Claffey	Elleston/t
11	05.12	H	J2S	Bracknell	L 17-30		Andrew	Wybro	Claffey	A Russell	Elleston/t
12	12.12	A	J2S	Bridgwater	L 7-33		Andrew	Wybro	Claffey	A Russell	Elleston/t
13	19.12	H	J2S	Chelteham	L 13-21		Andrew	Wybro	Claffey/t	A Russell	Elleston
14	28.12	A	J2S	Bracknell	L 13-39		Elleston/t	Andrew	Boydell	A Russell	Dudley
15	02.01	H	J2S	Clifton	L 0-6		Elleston	Andrew	Boydell	A Russell	Wybro
16	09.01	A	J2S	Weston	W 27-19		Elleston	Wybro	Boydell	A Russell(i)	Andrew
17	16.01	H	J2S	Esher	L 10-25		Irwin	Andrew	A Russell	Jones(a)	Elleston
18	23.01	A	J2S	Redruth	L 13-46		French	Andrew	A Russell	Irwin	Elleston
19	30.01	H	J2S	Barking	L 17-44		French	Andrew	A Russell(x/t)	Irwin	Elleston/t
20	06.02	A	J2S	Norwich	W 21-12		French	Andrew	Boydell	Irwin	Jewitt/t
21	13.02	H	J2S	N Walsham	L 10-47		French	Elleston/2t	Boydell(J)	A Russell	Jewitt
22	27.02	A	J2S	Tabard	W 14-11		Irwin	Wybro	Boydell	A Russell	French/t
23	13.03	H	J2S	Plymouth	W 29-12		French	Elleston/t	Boydell	A Russell	Jewitt(D)
24	27.03	A	J2S	M Police	L 12-15		French	Wybro/t	Boydell	A Russell(j/t)	Jewitt(M)
25	03.04	A	J2S	Cheltenham	L 12-15		French	Wybro	Boydell	Claffey	Elleston(x)
26	17.04	H	J2S	Bridgwater	W 32-14		French	Elleston	Boydell/t	Clafey/t	Jewitt/2t
A	19.09	A	TB1	Spartens	W 24-10		Andrew	Curnow(a)	Davies	Boydell	Jewitt/t(t)
B	17.10	A	TB2	Henley Hawks	L 19-100		Dudley/t	Andrew	McCormac(z)	Shaw	Fench

* after opponents name indicates a penalty try
Brackets after a player's name indicates he was replaced. eg (a) means he was replaced by replacement code "a" and so on.
/ after a player or replacement name is followed by any scores he made - eg /t, /c, /p, /dg or any combination of these

1998-99 HIGHLIGHTS

Ever Presents: None - most appearances

20	Syd Claffey
19	Rob Andrew(1)
18	Steve Boydell, Alex Knight-Barnard (2), Adrian Mitchell (3).
17	Harry Harrison (2), Will Knight (1).

Players used: 49 plus 4 as replacement only.

Most Points in a season:

Pts	Player	T	C	P	DG
60	S Claffey	4	8	8	-
41	A Ashwin	-	10	6	1
40	D Elleston	8	-	-	-
30	H Harrison	6	-	-	-
25	P Russell	-	5	4	1
25	A Jewitt	5	-	-	-

MATCH FACTS

10	9	1	2	3	4	5	6	7	8	
P Russell/dg(j/p)	Jones	Ad Mitchell(m)	Powell(n)	Burns	Harrison/t	W Knight	Raubenheimer	Reeve	Hart	1
Claffey(b)	Jones	K-Barnard(d)	Cowan(e)	Burns	Matthews	W Knight	Raubenheimer(r)	Reeve	Hart(q)	2
Claffey/p	Jones	K-Barnard	Powell	Burns	Harrison	W Knight	Raubenheimer	Cox(i)	Hart(v)	3
P Russell/2cdg	Claffey	Ad Mitchell	Powell	Drew	Kell(f)	W Knight	Hart	Reeve	Pearce(h/t)	4
P Russell/cp	Jones	K-Barnard/t	Howard	Ad Mitchell	Harrison	Kell	Hart/t	Reeve(h)	Pearce(r)	5
Claffey/p	Jones	K-Barnard	Moore	Ad Mitchell	Harrison	Cattermole(B)	Hart	Raubenheimer	Davenport	6
P Russell/2c	Jones	K-Barnard(u)	Moore(y)	Ad Mitchell	Kell	Cattermole	Hart	Raubenheimer	Pearce	7
P Russell/2p	Jones	K-Barnard(u)	Howard	Ad Mitchell	Harrison	Kell	Davenport(z)	Cox	Hart(A)	8
Ashwin	Coulson	K-Barnard	Ad Mitchell	Mills	Kell	Brown	Hart	Cox	Pearce(h/t)	9
Ashwin/c	Coulson	K-Barnard	Ad Mitchell(y)	Mills(G)	Kell	Knight	Raubenheimer	At Mitchell	Hart(p)	10
Ashwin/2cp	Jones	Drew(o)	Howard	Ad Mitchell	Kell	Harrison(g)	Hart/t	At Mitchell	Pearce(h)	11
Ashwin/c	Coulson	Ad Mitchell(o)	Howard	Drew	Kell	Brown	Cox(C)	R Knight(N)	Raubenheimer	12
Ashwin/p	Coulson	K-Barnard	Howard	Drew	Kell	Harrison/t	W Knight	R Knight	Pearce	13
Claffey/p	Coulson	Holland	Howard(H)	Drew	Kell	Matthews	Reeve/t	R Knight	Whittle	14
Ashwin	Coulson	K-Barnard	Mills	Drew	Kell	Matthews(f)	Whittle	Reeve(F)	W Knight	15
Claffey/3c2p	Coulson	K-Barnard	Mills/t(d)	Drew	Harrison/2t	W Knight	Kell	Raubenheimer	Oldham	16
Claffey	Coulson/t	K-Barnard	Mills(d)	Drew	Harrison	W Knight(i)	Kell	Raubenheimer	Oldham/t	17
Claffey/p	Coulson/t	K-Barnard	Mills	Drew	Harrison(B)	W Knight	Kell	Raubenheimer	Oldham(i)	18
Claffey/2cp	Coulson	Drew	Howard	Ad Mitchell	W Knight	Matthews(H)	Raubenheimer(N)	Reeve	Whittle(L)	19
Claffey/3c	Coulson	K-Barnard	Howard(P)	Ad Mitchell	Harrison/t	W Knight/t	Raubenheimer	Reeve	Oldham	20
Claffey(K)	Coulson	Drew	Howard	Ad Mitchell	Harrison(k)	W Knight(p)	Raubenheimer(B)	Reeve	Oldham	21
Ashwin/2c	Jones/t	K-Barnard(R)	Ad Mitchell	Drew	Harrison	W Knight	Raubenheimer	Reeve	Oldham	22
Ashwin/3cp	Jones(E)	K-Barnard	Ad Mitchell/t(y)	Drew	Harrison/t	W Knight	Whittle	Reeve/t	Oldham	23
Ashwin/c	Coulson(c)	K-Barnard	Ad Mitchell	Drew	Kell	Harrison	Whittle	Reeve	Oldham	24
Ashwin/3pdg	Coulson(c)	K-Barnard	Ad Mitchell	Drew	Harrison	W Knight	Raubenheimer(k)	Reeve	Oldham	25
Ashwin/2cp	Jones	Drew(G)	Howard	Ad Mitchell	Harrison	W Knight	Whittle	Reeve	Oldham(k/t)	26
Claffey/c4p	Jones	K-Barnard/t	Powell	Drew(Q)	Harrison	Kell(v)	Hart	Reeve	W Knight	A
Claffey/2c	Jones/t	K-Barnard/t	Howard	Ad Mitchell	Harrison	W Knight	Hart	Cox	Pearce(r)	B

REPLACEMENTS:

	a- S Hill	b- P Russell	c - D Jones	d - Adrian Mitchell	e - J Powell
f - H Harrison	g - W Knight	h - D Raubenheimer	i -M Reeve	j - S Claffey	k - M kell
l - A Beacham	m - S Sang	n - C Cowan	o - A Knight-Barnard	p - R Matthews	q - D Cox
r - J Davenport	s - B Dudley	t - N French	u - P Drew	v - B Pearce	w - S Stapleton
x - A Jewitt	y - D Howard	z - B Cattermole	A - S Walsh	B - N Whittle	C - Anthony Mitchell
D - R Wybro	E - J Coulson	F - I Brown	G - J Holland	H - S Mills	

Syd Claffey in his first season of league rugby with Havant ended the season as leading poins scorer with just 60 points.

Another new boy, Denville Elleston, ended the season as leading try scorer with eight in just 15 starts.

Havant were relegated by points difference from Cheltenham. They needed to score another 42 points against Bridgwater to have had a better record than Cheltenham.

Havant ended the season with the worst home record in the division, while away from home they had a better record than Bridgwater, Redruth, Plymouth and Cheltenham.

With 49 they used more players than any other side in the division.

THE LAST TEN YEARS

Season	Champions	Runners-up	Relegated
1989-90	**Metropolitan Police**	Clifton	-

Most
Penalties: 15 Simon Harvey (Clifton)
Points: 83 Simon Harvey (Clifton)
Conversions: 10 Simon Harvey (Clifton)
Tries: N.A.
D.Gs: 6 Simon Harvey (Clifton)

Season	Champions	Runners-up	Relegated
1990-91	**Redruth**	Basingstoke	Maidenhead, Cheltenham

Most
Penalties: 27 Rob Ashworth (Havant)
Points: 122 Melvin Badger (Weston-s-Mare)
Conversions: 16 Simon Blake (Redruth)
Tries: 8 Melvin Badger (Weston-s-Mare)
D.Gs: N.A.

Season	Champions	Runners-up	Relegated
1991-92	**Havant**	Basingstoke	Sidcup, Ealing

Most
Penalties: 24 Pete Russell (Havant)
Points: 129 Pete Russell (Havant)
Conversions: 23 Pete Russell (Havant)
Tries: 9 Will Knight (Havant)
D.Gs: 4 Paul Tincknell (Weston-s-Mare)

Season	Champions	Runners-up	Relegated
1992-93	**Sudbury**	London Welsh	Thurrock

Most
Penalties: 31 Simon Pennington (Stourbridge)
Points: 123 Steve Dybler (Sudbury)
Conversions: 28 Ralph Zoing (Harrogate)
Tries:12 Steve Titcombe (Sudbury)
D.Gs: N.A.

Season	Champions	Runners-up	Relegated
1993-94	**Reading**	Lydney	Southend, Maidstone

Most
Penalties: 34 Phil Belshaw (Reading)
Points: 133 Phil Belshaw (Reading)
Conversions: N.A.
Tries: N.A.
D.Gs: 5 Paul Tincknell (Weston-s-Mare)

Season	Champions	Runners-up	Relegated
1994-95	**London Welsh**	Lydney	Sudbury, Basingstoke

Most
Penalties: 31 Paul Thatcher (Weston-s-Mare)
Points: 119 Paul Thatcher (Weston-s-Mare)
Conversions: N.A.
Tries: N.A.
D.Gs: N.A.

Season	Champions	Runners-up	Relegated
1995-96	**Lydney**	Weston-s-Mare	Camborne

Most
Penalties: 28 Paul Thatcher (Weston-s-Mare), Richard Larkin (Askeans)
Points: 176 Richard Perkins (Henley)
Conversions: 27 Richard Perkins (Henley)
Tries: 10 Richard Perkins (Henley), Tommy Adams (Camborne)
D.Gs: 4 Simon Cattermole (Weston-s-Mare)

Season	Champions	Runners-up	Relegated
1996-97	**Newbury**	Henley	Berry Hill, Askeans, High Wycombe, Charlton Park

Most
Penalties: 53 Nick Churchman (Tabard)
Points: 391 Nick Grecian (Newbury)
Conversions: 100 Nick Grecian (Newbury)
Tries: 27 Brian Johnson (Newbury)
D.Gs: 10 Simon Cattermole (Weston-s-Mare)

Season	Champions	Runners-up	Relegated
1997-98	**Camberley**	Henley	-

Most
Penalties: 51 James Shanahan (N. Walsham)
Points: 256 Rob Thirlby (Redruth)
Conversions: 48 Rob Thirlby (Redruth)
Tries: 17 Rob Thirlby (Redruth)
D.Gs: 11 Nick Edmonds (Bridgwater)

Season	Champions	Runners-up	Relegated
1998-99	**Bracknell**	Esher	Havant

Most
Penalties:
Points:
Conversions:
Tries:
D.Gs:

TEAM RECORDS

Highest score:	**95**	Camberley 95 Askeans 17, 16.11.96
Highest aggregate:	**112**	as above
Highest score by a losing side:	**34**	Redruth 34 Otley 41, 21.9.96
Highest scoring draw:	**25**	Henley v Metropolitan Police, 5.4.97
Most consecutive wins:	**25**	Newbury 1996-97
Most consecutive defeats:	**20**	Metropolitan Police 1997-98
Most points for in a season:	**1170**	Newbury 1996-97
Least points for in a season:	**64**	Maidstone 1989-90
Most points against in a season:	**1140**	Charlton Park 1996-97
Least points against in a season:	**61**	Reading 1993-94
Most tries for in a season:	**167**	Newbury 1996-97
Most tries against in a season:	**166**	Charlton Park 1996-97
Least tries for in a season:		
Least tries against in a season:		
Most conversions for in a season:	**103**	Newbury 1996-97
Most conversions against in a season:	**95**	Charlton Park 1996-97
Most penalties for in a season:	**66**	Camberley 1997-98
Most penalties against in a season:	**65**	Plymouth Albion 1997-98
Least penalties for in a season:		
Least penalties against in a season:		
Most drop goals for in a season:	**14**	Bridgwater 1997-98
Most drop goals against in a season:	**8**	Metropolitan Police 1997-98

INDIVIDUAL RECORDS

Most points in a season:	**385**	Nick Grecian (Newbury) 1996-97
Most tries in a season:	**27**	Brian Johnson (Newbury) 1996-97
Most conversions in a season:	**96**	Nick Grecian (Newbury) 1996-97
Most penalties in a season:	**58**	Jonathan Gregory (Esher) 1998-99
Most drop goals in a season:	**11**	Nick Edmonds (Bridgwater) 1997-98
Most points in a match:	**34**	Chris Spencer, Henley v Charlton Park 12.4.97
		Michael Corcoran Esher v Cheltenham 13.2.99
Most tries in a match:	**5**	Eddie Weatherley, Met. Police v Askeans 8.2.97
		Nick Temperley Clifton v Met Police 28.02.98
Most conversions in a match:	**11**	Nick Grecian, Newbury v Charlton Park 25.1.97
Most penalties in a match:	**7**	Carson Russell, Bracknell v N Walsham 27.3.99
Most drop goals in a match:	**4**	Simon Cattermole, Weston-s-M. v Berry Hill 16.11.96

TEN YEAR RECORD

Club	SEASONS									
	89-90	90-91	91-92	92-93	93-94	94-95	95-96	96-97	97-98	98-99
Askeans	-	-	-	-	-	-	8	14	-	-
Barking	-	-	-	-	-	5	4	3	3	4
Basingstoke	8	2	2	5	11	13	-	-	-	-
Berry Hill	-	-	-	7	7	11	5	11	-	-
Bracknell	-	-	-	-	-	-	-	-	-	1p
Bridgwater & Albion	-	-	-	-	-	-	-	-	8	10
Camberley	-	-	-	-	-	-	7	4	1p	-
Camborne	4	4	6	4	4	8	13	-	-	-
Charlton Park	-	-	-	-	-	-	-	13	-	-
Cheltenham	9	13	-	-	-	-	6	5	5	13
Clifton	2	-	-	-	-	-	-	-	11	7
Ealing	-	10	13	-	-	-	-	-	-	-
Esher	-	-	-	-	-	-	-	-	4	2
Havant	5	8	1	-	-	-	-	-	12	14r
Henley	-	-	-	-	-	9	3	2	2p	-
High Wycombe	-	-	5	8	9	10	10	12	-	-
London Welsh	-	3	3	2	6	1	-	-	-	-
Lydney	-	-	-	3	2	2	1	-	-	-
Maidenhead	-	12	-	-	-	-	-	-	-	-
Maidstone	10	11	8	12	13	-	-	-	-	-
Metropolitan Police	1	-	10	9	10	7	12	7	14	5
Newbury	-	-	-	-	-	-	-	1	-	-
North Walsham	-	6	7	11	8	4	11	10	7	3
Norwich	-	-	-	-	-	-	-	-	-	6
Plymouth Albion	-	-	-	--	-	-	-	6	13	12
Reading	-	-	-	-	1	-	-	-	-	-
Redruth	3	1	-	-	-	-	-	-	9	11
Salisbury	11	-	-	-	-	-	-	-	-	-
Sidcup	-	-	12	-	-	-	-	-	-	-
Southend	7	9	11	6	12	-	-	-	-	-
Sudbury	6	7	4	1	-	12	-	-	-	-
Tabard	-	-	-	-	3	6	9	8	6	8
Thurrock	-	-	-	13	-	-	-	-	-	-
Weston-super-Mare	-	5	9	10	5	3	2	9	10	9

JEWSON NATIONAL LEAGUE ANNUAL AWARDS 1998-99

The Awards Winners line up after their presentations.

Henley's captain, Matt Maudsley, and Director of Rugby, Tony Macarthur, hold the Jewson National One Trophy, having just been presented with it by Lindsay Poston of Jewson

Coach of the Year

Nigel Dudding

Henley Hawks

Congratulations to Henley's Nigel Dudding for picking up his second consecutive Jewson Coach of the year award. Last season Nigel picked up the award when Henley were promoted from Jewson Two South. This season he has gone one better and taken Henley straight through Jewson National One as champions.

He has got his side playing a quick exciting brand of rugby, which is certainly good entertainment. We will be sad to lose Nigel and his club and we wish them well for next season as they take on Allied Dunbar Two.

Runner-up: Alex Keay - Manchester
3rd placed: Tim Herman & Kent Bray - Rosslyn Park

Player of the Year

David Pears

Wharfedale

David Pears made an immediate impact when he joined Wharfedale last October. At the time they were having a bad time with results not quite going their way. The introduction of Pears steadied the ship and put them on an even keel. They rapidly got back to winning ways and climbed the table to finish a very creditable 7th.

After all his injury problems of the past it was good to see him come through the season unscathed. He even turned out for Harlequins in the Allied Dunbar Premiership against Leicester. When they had an injury crisis.

Runner-up: Mark Venner - Henley
3rd placed: Dave Muckalt - Reading

Goalkicker of the Year

Steve Swindells

Manchester

Steve is another double winner as last season he picked up awards as Manchester gained promotion from Jewson Two North. During Manchester's two promotion seasons his kicking has been instrumental in their success and he is probably the most consistent kicker in first class rugby in this country and that includes the top two divisions.

Runner-up: Guy Gregory - Camberley
3rd placed: Chris Atkinson - Nottingham

All photographs courtesy of
PRESTIGE
PHOTOGRAPHY
Solihull

Nigel Dudding
(Henley)
receives the Jewson National One Coach of the Year award from Jonathon Davies

Stewart Jardine
(Stourbridge)
receives the Jewson National Two North Coach of the Year award from Peter Hindle

Jim McKay
(North Walsham)
receives the Jewson National Two Sourh Coach of the Year award from Alan Peacock

NATIONAL TWO NORTH

NATIONAL TWO SOUTH

Coach of the Year

Stewart Jardine

Stourbridge

Stewart, in his third full season at Stourbridge, has got them playing an exciting XV man game. They end up the season as the leading try scorers with a highly impressive 135. They ended the season with six players in double figures in the try scoring chart including two of their front row.

Runner-up: John Morgan - Preston Grasshoppers
3rd placed: Peter Kremer - Kendal.

Jim McKay

North Walsham

Jim McKay, who also plays as well as coaching, picks up the award in his first season at this level. He joined North Walsham in the summer from local rivals Norwich and has made a huge difference. North Walsham were an average run on the mill side who were good defensively but did not score enough tries. Jim has changed all that he has kept the defence but has turned them into on of the most exciting sides in the division and they finished up as second highest try scorers.

Runner-up: Paul Rendall - Bracknell
3rd placed: Hugh McHardy - Esher

Player of the Year

Michael Lough

Preston Grasshoppers

Michael Lough has been instrumental in helping to guide Preston to the Jewson Two North title. He has not only scored tries, 27 in 26 matches, but also made many more as well. The 22-year-old is in his second season with Preston and has taken a job locally and settled in well at the club who have made him feel at home.

Runner-up: Andy Gray - Lichfield
3rd placed: Casey Mee - Kendal

Jonathan Gregory

Esher

Jonathan was in his first season with Esher after being with Richmond. He was not just Esher's leading points scorer he was an exciting runner who is happy coming into the line to use his running skills to open up defences, and he did that well as his wingers will testify. He is a real level headed player and a credit to the game.

Runner-up: Howard Lamb - Bracknell
3rd placed: Andy Carter - Met Police

Goalkicker of the Year

Ian Kennedy

New Brighton

Ian took over the kicking duties after Murray King got injured and did a tremendous job himself till he good injured and missed a month of the season. On his return though he left the kicking to Murray King but by then he had established a strike rate over 70% and headed the table.

Runner-up: Jez Harris - Nuneaton
3rd placed: Stephen Stoddart - Aspatria

Jonathan Gregory

Esher

Jonathan picks up another award to go with his player of the year title. He will not be thanking his wingers who were prolific finishing first and fourth in the try scoring list and making him kick no end of conversions from the touchline.

Runner-up: Chris Sidwell - Redruth
3rd placed: Carson Russell - Bracknell

NORTHERN DIVISION

NORTHERN DIVISION	Officials & League Secretaries	474
NORTH ONE	League table & Fixture Grid	475
	Clubs	476
NORTHERN DIVISION	1998-99 League Tables	481
	1999-2000 Fixture Grids	484
	Clubs (in alphabetical order)	492

Northern Division Structure 1999-200

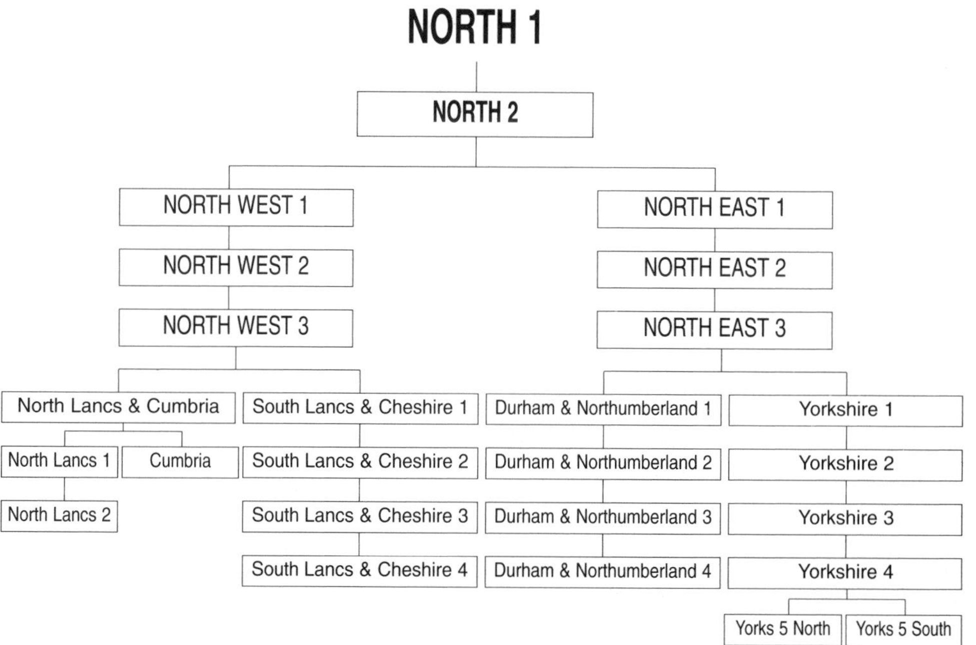

NORTHERN DIVISION OFFICIALS

Bob Archer **Chairman**
Brookfield House, Scotland Head, Winlaton Tyne & Wear NE21 6PL. 0191 414 3532 H

Les Bentley **Secretary/NE Co-ordinator/Yorks Rep**
32 Moorhead Terrace, Shipley, W Yorks BD18 4LB 01274 585460 H

Mike Lord **NW Coordinator/Cheshire Rep**
68 Hoole Road, Hoole, Chester CH2 3NL 01244 312702

Lee Hetherington **Treasurer/Durham Rep**
97 Kells Lane, Low Fell, Gateshead NE9 5XX. 0191 4219487 (H); 0191 2674393 (B)

Jack Hamer **Cumbria Rep**
55 Rush Green Road, Lymm, Cheshire WA13 9PS. 01925 755584 (H); 01515 548675 (B)

Dudley Gibbs **Northumberland Rep**
Sandy Ford, Healy, Nr Riding Mill, Northumberland NE44 6BA. 01434 682496 (H)

I Hodgeson **Lancashire Rep**
Kimberley End, 22 Capesthorn Close, Holmes Chapel, Cheshire CW4 7EW. 01477 533406 H

LEAGUE SECRETARIES

A Johnson **North 1**
6 Rugby Drive, Tytherington, Macclesfield, Cheshire SK10 2JD 01625 614697 H/F

M S Smith **North 2**
The Lowe, Wainstalls, Halifax, W Yorks HX2 7TR 01422 882879 H/F

I Clarke **North East 1**
46 Eastwood Gardens, Low Fell, Gateshead, Tyne & Wear NE9 5UB 01914 218271 H; 0191 232 5091x 4087 (B)

A Bentley **North East 2**
15 Sycamore Drive, Cleckheaton, West Yorkshire BD19 6AP 01274 969364 (H); 01274 861101 (B)

G Gravil **North East 3**
6 Grampian Way, Thorne, Doncaster, S Yorks DN8 5YL 01405 813642 H

W F Cooper **Yorkshire 1**
"Moorcroft" Lucy Hall Drive, Baildon, Shipley W Yorks BD17 5BG. 01274 584355

R Lewis **Yorkshire 2**
33 Swift Way, Sandal, Wakefield W Yorks WF2 6SQ. 01924 253049 H

J Cooper **Yorkshire 3**
8 Otterwood Park, Foxwood Hill, Acomb, York YO12 3JS 01904 797858 H; 01904 452773 B

G Mapplebeck **Yorkshire 4**
33 Oakley St, Thorpe, Wakefield, W Yorks WF3 3DX 01924 828809 H; 0113 245 7205 B

Mrs K McNally **Yorkshire 5**
28 Cherry Tree Rd, Armthorpe, Doncaster, S. Yorkshire DN3 2HP 01302 834252 (H)

J Ker **Durham & Northumberland 1**
4 Anlaby Close, Billingham, Cleveland RS23 3RA 01624 560536 (H)

Mrs J Baty **Durham & Northumberland 2**
5 Brooklands, Ponteland Northumberland NE20 9LZ 01661 823527 H

A R Brown **Durham & Northumberland 3**
22 Mill Crescent, Hebburn, Tyne & Wear NE31 1UQ 01914 693716

J Ker (as D & N 1) **Durham & Northumberland 4**

I Hodgeson **North West 1**
Kimberley End, 22 Capesthorn Close, Holmes Chapel, Cheshire CW4 7EW 01477 533406 H

Ken Punshon **North West 2**
24 Newcombe Rd Holcombe Brook, Nr Bury, Lancs 01204 884886 H

Ian Scott Brown **North West 3**
umsholme, Pendleview, Grindleton Nr Clitheroe, Lancs BB7 4QU 01200 440102 H; 01254 582749 B; 0973 819222 M

Roger Bott **North Lancs & Cumbria**
123 Albert Rd West, Heaton, Bolton, Lancs BL1 5ED 01204 841376 H

Bill Hopkinson **Cumbria**
Far Hey Farm, Littleborough, Rochdale, Lancs OL15 9NS 01706 279879 H; 01706 47474 EXT 4531 B

Colin Barton **North Lancs 1**
4 Oulderhill Drive, Rochdale, Lancs OL11 5LB 01706 350312 H

Vic Thomas **North Lancs 2**
5 Portree Close, Winton, Eccles, Manchester M30 8LX 0161 788 7274 H

Mike Massey **South Lancs & Cheshire 1**
Fieldside, Grange Rd, Bowden, Cheshire WA14 3EE 0161 928 2997 H

Brian Minor **South Lancs & Cheshire 2**
45 Gorton St., Peel Green, Eccles, Manchester M30 7LZ 0161 789 4867 H

Vic Thomas (as North Lancs 2) **South Lancs & Cheshire 3**

Ken Potter **South Lancs & Cheshire 4**
Lindisfarne, 97 The Farthing, Ashley Park, Chorley, Lancs PR7 1SH 01257 267411 H; 01695 51205 F

NORTH ONE

1998-1999 LEAGUE TABLE

	P	W	D	L	F	A	PD	Pts	
Doncaster	22	18	1	3	550	214	336	37	
Northern	22	18	0	4	530	316	214	36	
Tynedale	22	15	0	7	573	298	275	30	
Middlesborough	22	15	0	7	499	300	199	30	
Blaydon	22	13	2	7	453	308	145	28	
Hull Ionians	22	10	0	12	422	492	-70	20	
Stockton	22	10	0	12	338	426	-88	20	
Macclesfield	22	10	0	12	339	434	-95	20	
Wigton	22	9	2	11	375	479	-104	20	
Widnes	22	4	2	16	269	567	-298	10	
*Broughton Park	22	3	2	17	355	592	-237	6	(-2)
Bridlington	22	2	1	19	244	521	-277	5	

1999-2000 FIXTURE GRID

	Blaydon	Bradford & Bingley	Driffield	Hull Ionians	Macclesfied	Middlesbrough	Northern	Stockton	Tynedale	Widnes	Wigton	Winnington Park
Blaydon		12.02	11.09	02.10	11.03	25.03	08.04	11.12	23.10	22.01	20.11	08.01
Bradford & Bingley	09.10		08.01	11.12	26.02	25.09	20.11	18.03	08.04	23.10	04.09	22.01
Driffield	18.03	27.11		25.09	15.01	06.11	25.03	29.01	26.02	15.04	09.10	18.12
Hull Ionians	26.02	15.04	11.03		27.11	15.01	11.09	06.11	09.10	18.12	29.01	25.03
Macclesfield	25.09	02.10	20.11	08.01		18.03	22.01	04.09	11.12	12.02	08.04	23.10
Middlesbrough	04.09	11.03	22.01	20.11	11.09		23.10	08.04	08.01	02.10	11.12	12.02
Northern	18.12	15.01	04.09	18.03	06.11	29.01		09.10	25.09	27.11	26.02	15.04
Stockton	15.04	11.09	23.10	22.01	25.03	18.12	12.02		20.11	11.03	08.01	02.10
Tynedale	29.01	18.12	02.10	12.02	15.04	27.11	11.03	15.01		25.03	06.11	11.09
Widnes	06.11	29.01	11.12	08.04	09.10	26.02	08.01	25.09	04.09		18.03	20.11
Wigton	15.01	25.03	12.02	23.10	18.12	15.04	02.10	27.11	22.01	11.09		11.03
Winnington Park	27.11	06.11	08.04	04.09	29.01	09.10	11.12	26.02	18.03	15.01	25.09	

BLAYDON R.F.C.

Chairman: Jack Massey **Hon. President:** Bruce Strickland
Secretary John E Archibald 17 Sarrsyde Close, Whickham, Newcastle upon Tyne NE16 5UB
0191 488 8362 (H)
Fixture Secretary Jim Huxley Tel: 0191 488 7280
GROUND **Address:** Crow Trees Ground, Hexham Road, Swalwell, Newcastle upon Tyne NE163BM
Tel: 0191 420 0505 Tel/Fax: 0191 420 0506
Capacity: 1,500 Covered seating: 500 Uncovered standing: 1,000
Directions A1 north past Gateshead Metro Centre, take next exit for Swalwell
Car Parking: 400 spaces approx. at the ground Nearest Railway station: Newcastle Central
Admission £3 incl. programme
Clubhouse Open every day - normal licensing hours. Health Club 7am - 10pm every day. **Club Shop:** Yes open with clubhouse.
Colours: Scarlet and white **Programme -** Size: A5 Pages: 10 Price: with admission

BRADFORD & BINGLEY R.F.C.

President R Allen 7 Birchdale, Bingley BD16

Secretary J N Greaves West Bank, 9 The Grove, hipley, Bradford BD18 4LD

Fixture Secretary J Oates 16 Foulds Terrace, Bingley BD16 4LZ

Ground **Address:** Wagon Lane, Cottingley Bridge, Bingley, W. Yorks. BD16 1LT
Tel: 01274 775441/ 775443 Fax: 01274 775442

Directions: M62 onto M606 to Bradford ring road, right to 2nd roundabout, left onto A650 for 5 miles to Bingley, right by Beckfoot School onto Wagon Lane, ground 200 yards along.

Nearest Railway Station: Bingley Car Parking: Approx. 300 spaces at ground

Colours: Red, amber & black hoops/black **Change colours:** All black

Training Nights: Tuesday & Thursday

DRIFFIELD F.C.

Founded: 1926

President Mike Sellers Low Kaythorpe, Rudston, Driffield YO25 0JD 01262 420237
Chairman John Harrison 9 Parsonage Close, Nafferton, Driffield YO25 0LH 01377 253032
Hon. Secretary Stephen Edwards Cedar Cottage, St. Johns Road, Driffield, E. Yorks. YO25 7RS
Tel: 01377 253757 (H) 01653 697820 (B)
Fixture Sec. John Leason Tel: 01377 254036
Director of Rugby Stuart Cooper 1 Orchard Drive, Middleton, Driffield YO25 9UW

Ground Address Kelleythorpe, Driffield, E. Yorks. YO25 9DW Tel: 01377 256598
Capacity: Unlimited - all uncovered standing

Directions: South of Driffield town centre, between Market Weighton Road roundabout and Beverley Road roundabout.
Nearest Station: Driffield, 1 mile from ground.
Car Parking: Unlimited car parking at ground.

Admission: Matchday £3.00 including programme. No season tickets available.
Clubhouse: Open Tues & Thurs evs., matchdays & Sun morning. **Club Shop:** Open Sunday morning.
Colours: Red, navy & white/navy/red **Change colours:** All red **Training Nights:** Tuesday & Thursday
Programme: **Size**: A5 **Pages**: 20 **Price**: With admission **Editor**: John Harrison (Chairman)
Advertising: Contact editor

HULL IONIANS R.U.F.C.

Founded: 1989

President B Appleyard c/o the club
Chairman G Cuthbertson c/o the club
Secretary P Sharp 38 Corby Park, North Ferriby, E Yorks. HU14 3AY
Tel: 01482 631819 (H) 01753 840605 (B) 0788 7842252 (M)
Treasurer S Dent c/o the club
Fixture Secretary J Clayton 45 Cheshunt Ave., Willerby HU10 6PD Tel: 01482 651667
Ground Address Brantingham Park, Brantingham Road, Elloughton, E. Yorks. HU15 1HX
Tel: 01482 667342 Fax: 01482 666695 Capacity: 2,500 Covered Seating: 224
Directions: Leave M62 East onto A63. At first junction take slip road, at top of slip road turn right & follow signs to Brough. After 1 mile take 2nd left turn to Brantingham. At end of lane turn right , club on right after 1/2 mile.
Nearest Railway Station: Brough **Car Parking:** Spaces for 120 cars at club
Admission: Matchday £3
Clubhouse: 2 bars, 3 sponsors' rooms, gym & sports hall. Function rooms for 10-250
Club Shop: open training days & matchdays. Manager: Mark Kelk.
Programme Size: A5 Pages: 30 Price: inclusive with admission.
Editor: B Norman 01482 666014 Advertsing: £180 per page
Colours: Red, white, green & blue quarters/blue/red **Change colours:** Blue shirts
Training Nights: Tuesday & Thursday Nickname: "Is"

MACCLESFIELD R.U.F.C.

Founded: 1877

President M E Richardson High Ash Farm, Wildboarclough, Macclesfield SK10 2E 01260 500964
Chairman I Wooldridge 23 Cherington Crescent, Macclesfield SK11 8LA 01625 618777
Secretary A Johnson 6 Rugby Drive, Tytherington, Macclesfield SK10 2JD 01625 614697
Treasurer D A J Taylor 77 Manchester Road, Macclesfield SK10 2JP

Ground Priory Park, Priory Lane, Prestbury, Macclesfield, Cheshire SK10 4AF
Tel: 01625 827899 Fax: 01625 827899
Capacity: 5,500 Covered Seating: 200
Directions About 1 mile west of Town Centre on the B5087 - Macclesfield to Alderley Edge road
Nearest Railway Station: Macclesfield (in town centre) **Car Parking**: Spaces for 250 cars at ground
Admission: £3.50 including programme
Clubhouse: Open Saturdays & Sundays & every night except Wed. & Sunday
Club Shop: Open Saturady & Sunday & Tues & Thursday evenings.
Programme: Size: A5 Pages: 32 Price: £1 Editor: G A Allen
Advertising: O/S Back Cover £350 I/S Back Cover £160 Full page: £100 1/2 Page £
Colours: Blue and white narrow hoops **Change colours:** Red/black/white vertical stripes
Nickmame: The Silkmen **Training Nights:** Tuesday & Thursday

MIDDLESBROUGH R.U.F.C.

Founded: 1872

President: Peter Riley, 01642 892789 (H) **Chairman:** Dave Waddington, 01642 701535 (H)
Secretary Don Brydon 20 West Wood Ave., Linthorpe, Middlesbrough, TS5 5PY 01642 819954(H)
Fixture Secretary John Haddon 5 Wycherley Avenue, Linthorpe, Middlesbrough. Tel 01642 821126(H) 677181 (B) 606458 (Fax)
Director of Rugby Paul Hodder 18 Pinewood Close, Hartlepool, TS27 3QU. Tel 01429 280890
Press Officer Mike Read Orchard House, Thimbleby, Northallerton, DL6 3PY. Tel 01609 883525(H) 01642 242753(B) 01642 246326 (Fax)
Match Secretary Andy Murray 10 Sandwood Park, Guisborough, TS14 8EH. Tel 01287 637803
Ground Acklam Park, Green Lane, Acklam, Middlesbrough, TS5 7SL, Tel 01642 851370(Office) 818567(Bar) 851379(Fax)
Directions A19 take A1130 exit to M'Bro. L. at small r/about, R. at bollards to Croft Ave, straight across traffic lights to Green Lane, club 600 yards on R.
Nearest Railway Station: Middlesbrough **Car Parking:** Yes - Ample - Free
Admission: Matchday £3.00 **Club Shop** Yes open Tues/Wed/Thurs evenings & Sunday morning
Clubhouse Open every evening, plus Thurs-Sunday lunch time with bar meals available
Colours: Maroon with two gold hoops/Maroon **Change Colours:** Sky Blue **Training Nights:** Tuesday & Thursday
Programme Size A5 - Pages 28 - Price with admission - Editor Don Brydon Tel 01642 819954(H)
Advertising Walter Hibbert, 50 Lufton Avenue, Hartlepool, TS26 9QW. Tel 01429 297947

NORTHERN F.C.

Founded: 1875

President Bill Midgley 17 Beaumont Drive, Whitley Bay, Tyne & Wear NE25 9UT 0191 281 8981
Chairman Keith Irving Smallburn East, Ponteland, Northumberland NE20 0AD 0191 217 0485
Hon. Secretary Robert Gibson c/o Samuel Phillips & Co, 52 Westgate Road, Newcastle-upon-Tyne. 0191 232 8451 Fax: 0191 232 7664
Fixture Sec. Richard Kain 13 Polwarth Rd., Newcastle-upon-Tyne NE3 5ND 0191 217 0362 (H) 0191 273 7965 x 148 (B)
Press Officer Jon Curry c/o Northern FC
Ground Address McCracken Park, Great North Road, Gosforth, Newcastle-upon-Tyne NE3 2DG
Tel: 0191 236 3369 Fax: 0191 236 6288
Capacity: 1,300 Covered Seats: 300 Uncovered Standing: 1,000
Directions: From south & west, A1 Western by-pass north, then leave at exit B1318 "City North Gosforth" for 3/4. Ground on left. From north, B1318, ground 3/4 mile on left.
Nearest Station: Regent Centre (Metro), connection to Newcastle Central (BR)
Car Parking: 200 spaces adjacent to clubhouse
Admission: Matchday £3.00
Clubhouse: Bar & clubhouse open 7 days a week **Club Shop:** Open every day, full kit stocked.
Colours: Red, navy & white/navy/red **Change colours:** White/navy/red **Nickname**: "North" **Training Nights:** Mon & Thur
Programme: **Size**: A5 **Pages**: 36 **Price**: With admission **Editor**: Bill Davidson- contact at club
Advertising: Contact Bill Davidson

STOCKTON R.F.C.

Founded: 1863

Chairman John Maloney Castlegate Insurance Brokers, Yarm Lane, Stockton-on-Tees TS18 3NA Tel: 01642 615611
President Dr T McCarthy 2 Crooks Barn Lane, Horton, Stockton-on-Tees TS20 1LW 01642 550776
Secretary Keith Kelly 45b Kestrel Close, Stockton-on-Tees 01642 556818
Treasurer: Arthur Dodgson 14 Eden way, Billingham TS22 5HU 01642 533002

Ground address Horton Sports & Social Club, Station Road, Horton TS20 1PE Tel: 01642 554031
Capacity: 500 Covered Seating: 100 Uncovered Standing: 400
Directions: Follow A19 north, over Tees Bridge, take 3rd exit (signposted Norton, Billingham), turn left, then at roundabout turn right & immediately right again into Station Road.
Nearest Railway Station: Billingham Car Parking: At rear of Sports ground

Admission: Matchday: £3
Club Shop: Yes, in clubhouse.
Programme Size: A5 Pages: Varies Price: with admission Editor: Alan Todd
Colours: Red shirts/white shorts/blue stockings **Change colours:** Blue shirts
Training Nights: Monday & Thursday

TYNEDALE R.F.C.

Founded: 1876

President Richard Halford Lynwood, Crabtree Rd., Stocksfield NE43 7SX 01661 842428
Hon. Secretary Neil Foster 2 Tyneview Terrace, Corbridge, Northumberland NE45 5AJ
01434 632262 (H) 01434 605441 (B) 01434 607141 (F) 0467 407706 (M)
Hon. Treasurer Andrew Cuthbertson 6 Windsor Terrace, Corbridge, Northumberland NE45 5DF
01434 633713 (H) 01434 634557 (B) 01434 634558 (F) 07712 676663 (M)
Hon. Fixture Secretary Craig Johnston 44 Kingsgate Terrace, Hexham NE46 3EP 01434 607696 (Tel/Fax)

Ground Address: Tynedale Park, Station Rd., Corbridge, Northumberland NE45 5AY
Tel: 01434 632997 Office: Tel/Fax: 01434 632996
Capacity: Unlimited Covered Seats: 350 Car Parking: plentiful, within ground
Directions: From A69 westbound: 2nd exit at Styford roundabout (signed Corbridge) follow signs for Hexham. Cross single lane bridge to roundabout. First exit signed gateshead. 250 yds to left fork into Station Road - 150 yards to entrance.
Nearest Railway Station: Corbridge, next to ground entrance
Admission £3 adult.
Clubhouse: Open Mon & Thur 6.30-11, matchdays & Sun lunch. Private functions & special events.
Club Shop: open on matchdays **Training Nights:** Monday & Thursday, 7pm.
Colours: Royal blue & white hoops/white/royal blue **Change colours:** Navy blue, narrow yellow & white hoops/white/navy
Programme Size: A5 Pages: 32 Price: With admission Editor: D F Hamilton 01661 852017
Advertising: Contact Neil Foster (Hon. Sec.)

WIDNES R.U.F.C.

Founded: 1924

President	John Parle	12 Woodland Avenue, Widnes, Cheshire. Tel 0151 4249159
Chairman	Brian D. Ward	Ashling, 3 Tree Bank Close, Runcorn. Tel 01928 563902
Secretary	John McCann	2 Ash Priors, Widens, Cheshire. WA8 4NH Tel 0151 4232549
Treasurer	Peter Barrow	76 Lunts Heath Road, Widnes, Cheshire. Tel 0151 4240760
Rugby Chair	Paul Woodward	29 Foxley Heath, Widnes, Cheshire. Tel 0151 4234613

Ground Heath Road, Widnes, Cheshire, WA8 7NU. Tel 0151 4242575
Capacity: 1500, all uncovered standing

Directions From M62 J7, A568 South to A5080, go West to Traffic Lights then South to ground.
From M56 J12 to Runcorn and North to Widnes
Nearest Railway Station: Widnes North - Runcorn
Car Parking: 100 cars

Admission £3 League matches (Inc. Programme)
Clubhouse: Open Evenings Monday-Friday / All day Saturday & Sunday

Colours: Red & Black **Change Colours:** Amber **Training Nights:** Tuesday & Thursday
Programme Size A5 Pages 32 Price with admission

WIGTON R.U.F.C.

Founded: 1883

President	M Sunter	Tel: 01697 478081 (H)
Chairman	A H Robson	Tel: 01697 342310 (H) 01228 545810 (B)
Hon. Secretary	A Lynch	Tel: 01697 343436 (H)

All correspondence - c/o Wigton R.U.F.C., Lowmoor Rd., Wigton, Cumbria CA7 9QT

Ground Address Lowmoor Road, Wigton, Cumbria CA7 9QT Tel: 01697 342206
Capacity: Unlimited Covered seats: 100

Directions: M6 (North), take Junction 41 sign-posted Wigton, or A595 Carlisle to Cockermouth - both roads bring you to Wigton junction. Follow road for half a mile, club is the first stop.
Nearest Station: Wigton
Car Parking: Unlimited car parking at ground.

Training Nights Monday & Wednesday
Programme Advertising: Contact R Aird, 01697 344969
Admission:
Clubhouse: Yes **Club Shop:** Yes
Colours: Green shirts/white shorts **Change colours:** All white

WINNINGTON PARK R.F.C. see Page 396 for 98-99 match details

Founded: 1907

President: R D Glenisten, 29 Brookside, Weaverham, Northwich, Cheshire, CW8 3HR 01606 851705 (H), 01565 632391 (B)

Chairman: Brian Patterson, Highcliffe House, Cliff Road, Acton Bridge, Northwich CW8 3QP 01606 851110 (H) 01606 724366 (B)

Club Secretary: J C W Downham 216 London Road, Leftwich, Northwich, Cheshire.CW9 8AQ 01606 48962 (H), 01565 633294 (B)

Fixtures Secretary: C F Gleare, Westerley, West Rd, Weaverham, Northwich,Ches. CW8 3HH 01606 853999 (H) 01925 752016 (B)

Press Officer: Club Secretary

Address: Burrows Hill, Hartford, Northwich, Cheshire. CW8 3AA. Tel: 01606 74242
Capacity: 5000 Seated: 200 Standing: 5000

Directions: 1 mile from Hartford turn off A556, signed Hartford, near Blue Weaver bridge. Turn right at church, left at the lights, right at T junction, then next left. Burrows Hill ground is second on the right.
Nearest Railway Station: Hartford. **Car Parking:** 500 spaces on the ground, 500 nearby, no charge.

Admission: Season tickets - Adult £30 Matchdays - Adults £3 Children U13 Free. OAPs: £1

Clubhouse: Open matchdays & training nights, snacks available. Functions: Up to 190 people can be catered for. **Club Shop:** No

Colours: Royal & navy blue **Change colours:** Red **Nickname**: Park **Training Nights:** Tuesday and Thursday

Programme: Size: A5 Price: With admission. Pages: 28 plus cover. Editor: John Palmer 01608 75817
Advertising Rates Full page £150, half page £75.

BLACKPOOL RUFC

celebrate winning the North Lancs & Cumbria league and gaining promotion to North West 3.

WEST PARK RFC (ST. HELENS)

were joint winners (with Wigan) of the Lancashire Trophy and runners-up in North West 1

NORTHERN DIVISION FINAL LEAGUE TABLES 1998-99

NORTH TWO

	P	W	D	L	PF	PA	PD	Pts
Bradford & Bing.	22	17	1	4	535	328	207	35
Driffield	22	14	1	7	483	290	193	29
Blackburn*	22	15	1	6	485	319	166	29
Morpeth	22	14	0	8	406	274	132	28
Vale of Lune	22	12	1	9	474	303	171	25
Chester	22	12	0	10	452	399	53	24
Huddersfield	22	11	0	11	362	385	-23	22
W Pk Bramhope	22	9	0	13	276	276	0	18
Lymm	22	8	0	14	271	399	-128	16
Alnwick	22	7	1	14	305	395	-90	15
Percy Park	22	6	1	15	348	603	-255	13
York	22	4	0	18	265	691	-426	8

NORTH EAST ONE

	P	W	D	L	PF	PA	PD	Pts
Darlington M Pk	18	18	0	0	729	223	506	36
Halifax	18	14	1	3	402	269	133	29
Old Crossleyans	18	11	0	7	372	312	60	22
Horden	18	8	1	9	427	442	-15	17
Goole	18	8	0	10	326	304	22	16
Keighley	18	7	1	10	288	369	-81	15
Beverley	17	7	0	10	274	317	-43	14
Pontefract	18	5	1	12	345	446	-101	11
Old Brodleians	17	5	0	12	259	392	-133	10
Durham City	18	4	0	14	247	595	-348	8

06.02.99 Beverley v O Brodleians match declared void.

NORTH EAST TWO

	P	W	D	L	PF	PA	PD	Pts
Darlington	18	18	0	0	693	192	501	36
Redcar	18	15	1	2	458	248	210	31
Cleckheaton	18	11	1	6	364	238	126	23
Hull	18	9	0	9	318	286	32	18
Pocklington	18	9	0	9	284	329	-45	18
Wheatley Hills	18	8	1	9	259	284	-25	17
North Ribblesdale	18	7	0	11	309	346	-37	14
Hartlepool Rovers	18	5	1	12	266	433	-167	11
Roundhegians	18	4	0	14	248	478	-230	8
Gateshead	18	2	0	16	197	562	-365	4

NORTH EAST THREE

	P	W	D	L	PF	PA	PD	Pts
Selby	18	14	2	2	423	206	217	30
W H'pool TDSOB	18	15	0	3	382	222	160	30
Westoe	18	13	1	4	437	258	179	27
Ashington	18	9	1	8	419	338	81	19
Yarnbury	18	9	1	8	310	326	-16	19
Ripon	18	8	0	10	306	288	18	16
Ryton	18	7	1	10	305	381	-76	15
Bradford Salem	18	6	0	12	308	340	-32	12
Sunderland	18	5	0	13	263	417	-154	10
Thornensians	18	1	0	17	135	512	-377	2

NORTH WEST ONE

	P	W	D	L	PF	PA	PD	Pts
Aldwinians	18	17	0	1	651	148	503	34
West Pk St Helens	18	15	0	3	568	209	359	30
Penrith	18	12	0	6	425	295	130	24
Caldy	18	10	1	7	296	263	33	21
Kirkby Lonsdale	18	8	1	9	309	345	-36	17
Birkenhead Park	18	7	0	11	245	422	-177	14
Oldershaw	18	6	1	11	272	397	-125	13
Aspull	17	5	0	12	217	337	-120	10
Ashton on Mersey	18	4	1	13	184	485	-301	9
Vagabonds (IoM)	17	3	0	14	210	476	-266	6

NORTH WEST TWO

	P	W	D	L	PF	PA	PD	Pts
Stockport	18	15	2	1	495	187	308	32
Altrincham Kersal	18	12	2	4	449	200	249	26
Leigh	18	10	1	7	401	317	84	21
Egremont	17	10	0	7	256	292	-36	20
Carlisle	18	9	1	8	361	303	58	19
Wilmslow	18	7	2	9	353	369	-16	16
Fleetwood	18	6	0	12	260	371	-111	12
Northwich	18	5	2	11	198	352	-154	12
Netherhall	18	5	1	12	216	286	-70	11
Merseyside Police*	17	4	1	12	181	493	-312	7

* Points deducted

NORTH WEST THREE

	P	W	D	L	PF	PA	PD	Pts
Wigan	18	17	0	1	639	88	551	34
Workington	18	14	1	3	429	147	282	29
Warrington	18	13	1	4	572	174	398	27
Rochdale	18	12	0	6	390	179	211	24
St Benedict's*	18	10	0	8	152	279	-127	16
Rossendale	18	7	0	11	190	289	-99	14
Calder Vale	18	5	2	11	245	473	-228	12
Cockermouth*	18	6	0	12	265	390	-125	10
Sandbach	18	4	0	14	181	558	-377	8
Old Salians*	18	0	0	18	92	578	-486	-2

Amended table - St Benedicts have been deducted 2 x 2 points for failing to fulfil fixtures on due dates

YORKSHIRE ONE

	P	W	D	L	PF	PA	PD	Pts
Hud'field YMCA	18	17	0	1	665	160	505	34
Castleford*	18	15	0	3	506	215	291	28
Northallerton*	18	12	0	6	321	243	78	22
Wath on Dearne	18	10	0	8	273	322	-49	20
West Leeds	18	8	1	9	351	330	21	17
Ilkley	18	6	1	11	321	384	-63	13
Leodiensians	18	6	1	11	281	440	-159	13
Bramley Ph'nix P*	18	6	2	10	249	382	-133	12
Malton and Norton	18	4	0	14	246	485	-239	8
Old Otliensians	18	3	1	14	165	417	-252	7

Amended table.

YORKSHIRE TWO

	P	W	D	L	PF	PA	PD	Pts
Scarborough	17	15	1	1	372	121	251	31
Hemsworth	18	12	1	5	460	250	210	25
Halifax Vandals	18	11	2	5	294	180	114	24
Sheffield Oaks	18	10	1	7	219	204	15	21
Sheffield Tigers*	18	9	1	8	281	283	-2	17
Dinnington O.B.	18	7	1	10	275	318	-43	15
Hullensians	18	7	1	10	235	319	-84	15
Moortown	17	6	0	11	171	231	-60	12
Barnsley*	18	5	0	13	237	422	-185	8
Stanley Rodillians	18	3	0	15	172	388	-216	6

Moortown v Scarborough will not be played

YORKSHIRE THREE

	P	W	D	L	PF	PA	PD	Pts
York Railway Inst	18	15	0	3	358	176	182	30
Heath	18	13	1	4	396	156	240	27
Baildon	18	12	1	5	355	241	114	25
Leeds Corinthians	18	9	1	8	397	213	184	19
Hessle	18	9	1	8	395	265	130	19
Skipton	18	9	0	9	307	404	-97	18
Stocksbridge	18	7	0	11	262	245	17	14
Wetherby	18	7	0	11	223	311	-88	14
Old Modernians	18	6	0	12	217	295	-78	12
Wibsey	18	1	0	17	72	676	-604	2

YORKSHIRE FOUR

	P	W	D	L	PF	PA	PD	Pts
Old Rishworthians	18	16	1	1	526	93	433	33
Knottingley*	18	17	0	1	669	130	539	32
Mosborough	18	10	1	7	273	261	12	21
Aireborough*	18	9	3	6	324	208	116	19
Burley	18	9	1	8	267	361	-94	19
Marist	18	6	0	12	154	299	-145	12
Hornsea*	18	6	1	11	254	419	-165	11
Garforth	18	5	1	12	151	341	-190	11
Ossett	18	5	0	13	191	382	-191	10
Rowntree	18	3	0	15	227	542	-315	6

YORKSHIRE FIVE

	P	W	D	L	PF	PA	PD	Pts
Rotherham Clifton	14	11	0	3	370	92	278	22
Edlington Granby	14	11	0	3	276	133	143	22
Adwick le Street	14	10	0	4	294	103	191	20
Knaresborough	14	8	0	6	191	168	23	16
Wickersley Exel	14	8	0	6	220	217	3	16
Rawmarsh	14	5	0	9	192	256	-64	10
De La Salle OB (Sh)	14	2	0	12	132	337	-205	4
Withernsea	14	1	0	13	128	497	-369	2

NORTH EAST 3

Durham & Northumberland 1 | Yorkshire 1

Durham & Northumberland 2 | Yorkshire 2

Durham & Northumberland 3 | Yorkshire 3

Durham & Northumberland 4 | Yorkshire 4

Yorks 5 North | Yorks 5 South

DURHAM/NORTHUMBERLAND ONE

	P	W	D	L	PF	PA	PD	Pts
Medicals	18	17	0	1	473	170	303	34
Acklam	18	15	0	3	411	168	243	30
Whitby	18	11	0	7	278	215	63	22
Billingham	18	9	2	7	303	241	62	20
Novocastrians	18	8	1	9	304	304	0	17
Winlaton Vulcans	18	7	2	9	270	276	-6	16
Whitley Bay Rock.	18	7	1	10	208	347	-139	15
Consett	18	6	0	12	322	320	2	12
North Shields	18	4	0	14	129	382	-253	8
Blyth	18	3	0	15	197	472	-275	6

DURHAM/NORTHUMBERLAND TWO

	P	W	D	L	PF	PA	PD	Pts
Houghton	16	13	2	1	308	131	177	28
Seghill	16	13	1	2	388	151	237	27
Bishop Auckland	16	13	0	3	315	198	117	26
Gosforth	16	11	1	4	405	166	239	23
Chester le Street*	16	6	0	10	188	318	-130	10
Hartlepool*	16	5	0	11	211	358	-147	8
Ponteland	16	3	0	13	160	335	-175	6
Barnard Castle	16	3	0	13	158	368	-210	6
Guisborough*	16	3	0	13	190	298	-108	4

DURHAM/NORTHUMBERLAND THREE

	P	W	D	L	PF	PA	PD	Pts
Wallsend	18	16	1	1	623	189	434	33
Richmondshire*	18	14	1	3	400	131	269	27
Seaton Carew	18	12	0	6	355	175	180	24
W Hartlepool Ams	18	11	0	7	281	228	53	22
Wearside	18	8	2	8	253	255	-2	18
Sedgefield	18	8	2	8	214	307	-93	18
Hartlepool Athletic	18	5	0	13	205	520	-315	10
Wensleydale*	18	5	1	12	207	366	-159	9
Seaham	18	4	0	14	213	383	-170	8
Hartlepool BBOB	18	3	1	14	162	359	-197	7

DURHAM/NORTHUMBERLAND FOUR

	P	W	D	L	PF	PA	PD	Pts
Jarrovians	8	6	1	1	158	80	78	13
Durham Constabulary	8	5	0	3	160	102	58	10
Prudhoe Hospital	8	5	0	3	120	97	23	10
Newton Aycliffe	8	2	1	5	110	160	-50	5
Yarm	8	1	0	7	33	142	-109	2

Shildon Town have been withdrawn

* denotes points deducted

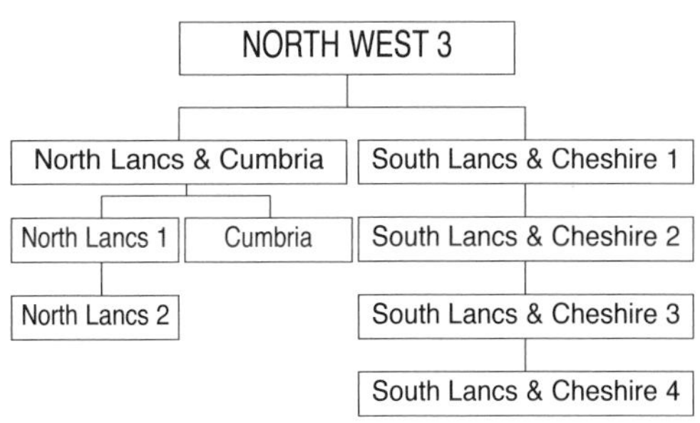

NORTH LANCS/CUMBRIA

	P	W	D	L	PF	PA	PD	Pts
Blackpool	18	17	0	1	658	148	510	34
Oldham	18	12	1	5	441	202	239	25
Tyldesley	18	11	3	4	392	299	93	25
Ormskirk	18	11	0	7	489	280	209	22
Trafford MV	18	10	0	8	378	239	139	20
Vickers Sports	18	9	0	9	299	321	-22	18
Furness	18	7	1	10	283	359	-76	15
Windermere	18	7	0	11	289	407	-118	14
Ambleside	18	2	1	15	191	637	-446	5
Keswick	18	1	0	17	179	707	-528	2

NORTH LANCS ONE

	P	W	D	L	PF	PA	PD	Pts
De La Salle	18	16	1	1	471	157	314	33
Bury	18	14	0	4	331	234	97	28
Bolton	18	12	0	6	397	224	173	24
Ashton-u-Lyne	18	10	0	8	256	256	0	20
Eccles	18	9	1	8	267	210	57	19
Heaton Moor	18	9	0	9	273	210	63	18
Old Bedians	18	8	0	10	264	287	-23	16
Colne & Nelson	18	5	0	13	195	416	-221	10
Broughton	18	3	0	15	214	411	-197	6
Chorley	18	3	0	15	198	461	-263	6

NORTH LANCS TWO

	P	W	D	L	PF	PA	PD	Pts
Burnage	12	11	1	0	325	78	247	23
Th'nton Cleveleys	12	9	0	3	262	142	120	18
North Manchester*	12	9	0	3	307	139	168	14
Littleborough	12	5	2	5	192	168	24	12
Clitheroe	12	4	1	7	167	180	-13	9
Lostock	12	2	0	10	116	299	-183	4
Montell Carrington	12	0	0	12	78	441	-363	0

CUMBRIA

	P	W	D	L	PF	PA	PD	Pts
Millom	14	12	0	2	333	113	220	22
Moresby	13	10	0	3	387	97	290	18
Upper Eden	12	8	0	4	406	214	192	16
Greengarth	14	5	1	8	244	195	49	11
Carnforth	14	5	1	8	157	268	-111	11
Silloth	14	5	0	9	146	423	-277	10
Whitehaven	14	4	0	10	119	379	-260	8
Creighton*	13	4	0	9	163	266	-103	6

SOUTH LANCS/CHESHIRE ONE

	P	W	D	L	PF	PA	PD	Pts
St Edward's O.B.	18	16	0	2	566	179	387	32
Wallasey	18	13	0	5	318	259	59	26
Southport	18	12	0	6	403	244	159	24
Birchfield (Lancs)	18	11	1	6	345	256	89	23
Wirral	18	10	1	7	462	317	145	21
Eagle	18	8	0	10	174	293	-119	16
Newton-le-Willows	18	7	0	11	267	365	-98	14
Crewe & Nantwich	18	6	0	12	193	373	-180	12
Ruskin Park	18	4	0	14	196	458	-262	8
Old Anselmians	18	2	0	16	241	421	-180	4

SOUTH LANCS/CHESHIRE TWO

	P	W	D	L	PF	PA	PD	Pts
Dukinfield	16	14	0	2	500	167	333	28
St Mary's OB	15	13	0	2	353	131	222	26
Bowdon	16	9	1	6	222	292	-70	19
Shell Stanlow	16	9	0	7	267	220	47	18
Congleton	16	9	0	7	245	207	38	18
Sefton	16	7	1	8	222	208	14	15
Marple	16	5	0	11	124	229	-105	10
Prenton	16	3	2	11	109	278	-169	8
Parkonians	15	0	0	15	71	381	-310	0

SOUTH LANCS/CHESHIRE THREE

	P	W	D	L	PF	PA	PD	Pts
Moore	14	12	2	0	328	138	190	26
Douglas (I.O.M.)	14	9	0	5	319	229	90	18
Helsby*	14	8	1	5	276	175	101	15
Port Sunlight	13	7	1	5	161	196	-35	15
Vulcan	14	6	1	7	228	299	-71	13
Liverpool Coll. OB	14	5	1	8	190	213	-23	11
Hoylake	13	3	0	10	245	324	-79	6
Didsbury Toc H	14	2	0	12	154	327	-173	4

SOUTH LANCS/CHESHIRE FOUR

	P	W	D	L	PF	PA	PD	Pts
Halton	10	7	1	2	273	132	141	15
Runcorn	10	7	1	2	180	58	122	15
Orrell Anvils*	10	7	1	2	336	112	224	13
Mossley Hill A.C.	10	4	1	5	108	169	-61	9
Holmes Chapel	10	3	0	7	96	231	-135	6
Hightown	10	0	0	10	78	369	-291	0

Amended table. Lucas have been withdrawn.

NORTH TWO

	Aldwinians	Alnwick	Blackburn	Bridlington	Broughton Pk	Chester	D'ton Mowden	Huddersfield	Lymm	Morpeth	Vale of Lune	West Park
Aldwinians		23.10	26.02	20.11	09.10	18.03	11.12	08.01	25.09	22.01	04.09	???
Alnwick	29.01		09.10	08.01	06.11	25.09	???	11.12	26.02	20.11	18.03	04.09
Blackburn	02.10	12.02		22.01	25.09	04.09	08.01	20.11	18.03	23.10	???	11.12
Bridlington	15.01	27.11	06.11		18.12	09.10	18.03	04.09	29.01	15.04	26.02	25.09
Broughton Park	12.02	22.01	11.03	???		11.12	02.10	11.09	25.03	08.01	20.11	23.10
Chester	11.09	11.03	25.03	12.02	15.04		22.01	23.10	18.12	02.10	08.01	20.11
Darlington Mowden	15.04	18.12	27.11	11.09	26.02	06.11		11.03	15.01	25.03	29.01	09.10
Huddersfield	27.11	15.04	15.01	25.03	18.03	29.01	25.09		06.11	18.12	09.10	26.02
Lymm	11.03	02.10	11.09	23.10	04.09	???	20.11	22.01		12.02	11.12	08.01
Morpeth	06.11	15.01	29.01	11.12	27.11	26.02	04.09	???	09.10		25.09	18.03
Vale of Lune	25.03	11.09	18.12	02.10	15.01	27.11	23.10	12.02	15.04	11.03		22.01
West Park	18.12	25.03	15.04	11.03	29.01	15.01	12.02	02.10	27.11	11.09	06.11	

NORTH WEST ONE

	Altrincham	Ashton	Aspull	Birkenhead Pk	Caldy	Kirkby Lons.	Oldershaw	Penrith	Stockport	West Park St H
Altrincham Kersal		02.10	23.10	08.01	20.11	29.01	15.04	26.02	11.12	11.09
Ashton on Mersey	15.04		11.12	11.03	12.02	20.11	25.09	15.01	08.01	09.10
Aspull	27.11	25.09		12.02	15.01	25.03	09.10	18.12	11.09	06.11
Birkenhead Park	25.03	26.02	09.10		06.11	11.09	15.01	27.11	02.10	18.12
Caldy	11.09	02.10	29.01	18.12		26.02	06.11	25.03	23.10	27.11
Kirkby Lonsdale	18.12	11.12	11.03	25.09	09.10		12.02	06.11	15.04	15.01
Oldershaw	26.02	29.01	23.10	08.01	27.11	02.10		11.09	20.11	25.03
Penrith	23.10	20.11	15.04	11.12	25.09	08.01	11.03		29.01	12.02
Stockport	06.11	11.03	12.02	15.01	25.03	27.11	18.12	09.10		25.09
West Park St Helens	29.01	08.01	20.11	15.04	11.03	23.10	11.12	02.10	26.02	

NORTH WEST TWO

	Carlisle	Egremont	Fleetwood	Leigh	Netherhall	Northwich	Vagabonds IoM	Wigan	Wilmslow	Workington
Carlisle		20.11	29.01	12.02	08.01	11.12	11.03	23.10	15.04	25.09
Egremont	18.12		11.09	06.11	25.03	12.02	09.10	27.11	25.09	15.01
Fleetwood	09.10	11.03		25.09	27.11	15.01	18.12	06.11	12.02	25.03
Leigh	02.10	08.01	26.02		23.10	15.04	11.12	29.01	20.11	11.03
Netherhall	06.11	11.12	15.04	15.01		25.09	12.02	18.12	11.03	09.10
Northwich	25.03	02.10	23.10	27.11	26.02		06.11	11.09	29.01	18.12
Vagabonds (I.O.M.)	11.09	29.01	20.11	25.03	02.10	08.01		26.02	23.10	27.11
Wigan	15.01	15.04	08.01	09.10	20.11	11.03	25.09		11.12	12.02
Wilmslow	27.11	26.02	02.10	18.12	11.09	09.10	15.01	25.03		06.11
Workington	26.02	23.10	11.12	11.09	29.01	20.11	15.04	02.10	08.01	

NORTH WEST THREE

	Blackpool	Ca;der Va;e	Cockermouth	Rochdale	Rossendale	Sandbach	St Benedict's	St Edward's OB	Wallasey	Warrington
Blackpool		29.01	25.03	23.10	08.01	11.09	20.11	02.10	27.11	26.02
Calder Vale	09.10		06.11	25.09	12.02	18.12	11.09	25.03	15.01	27.11
Cockermouth	11.12	08.01		20.11	15.04	02.10	26.02	23.10	11.03	29.01
Rochdale	15.01	26.02	18.12		09.10	27.11	02.10	11.09	06.11	25.03
Rossendale	06.11	02.10	27.11	29.01		25.03	23.10	26.02	18.12	11.09
Sandbach	11.03	20.11	12.02	15.04	11.12		29.01	08.01	25.09	23.10
St Benedict's	18.12	11.03	25.09	12.02	15.01	09.10		27.11	25.03	06.11
St Edward's O.B.	12.02	11.12	15.01	11.03	25.09	06.11	15.04		09.10	18.12
Wallasey	15.04	23.10	11.09	08.01	20.11	26.02	11.12	29.01		02.10
Warrington	25.09	15.04	09.10	11.12	11.03	15.01	08.01	20.11	12.02	

NORTH LANCS/ CUMBRIA

	Amblesode	De :a Sa;;e	Firmess	Millom	Oldham	Ormskirk	Trafford MV	Tyldesley	Vickers Sports	Windermere
Ambleside		29.01	08.01	23.10	11.12	20.11	11.09	02.10	26.02	15.04
De La Salle	09.10		11.03	11.12	15.04	25.09	15.01	18.12	06.11	12.02
Furness	06.11	11.09		26.02	02.10	09.10	18.12	25.03	27.11	15.01
Millom	15.01	25.03	25.09		11.09	12.02	06.11	27.11	18.12	09.10
Oldham	25.03	27.11	12.02	11.03		15.01	25.09	06.11	09.10	18.12
Ormskirk	18.12	26.02	29.01	02.10	23.10		27.11	11.09	25.03	06.11
Trafford MV	11.03	23.10	20.11	08.01	26.02	15.04		29.01	02.10	11.12
Tyldesley	12.02	20.11	11.12	15.04	08.01	11.03	09.10		15.01	25.09
Vickers Sports	25.09	08.01	15.04	20.11	29.01	11.12	12.02	23.10		11.03
Windermere	27.11	02.10	23.10	29.01	20.11	08.01	25.03	26.02	11.09	

NORTH LANCS ONE

	Ashton-u-Lyne	Bolton	Broughton	Burnage	Bury	Colne & Nelson	Eccles	Heaton Moor	Old Badians	Thornton Cleve.
Ashton-under-Lyne		06.11	11.12	25.09	12.02	18.12	15.01	11.03	15.04	09.10
Bolton	08.01		20.11	11.12	11.03	23.10	12.02	15.04	29.01	25.09
Broughton	25.03	18.12		12.02	09.10	27.11	06.11	25.09	11.09	15.01
Burnage	26.02	25.03	02.10		06.11	11.09	27.11	29.01	23.10	18.12
Bury	02.10	11.09	29.01	08.01		26.02	25.03	23.10	20.11	27.11
Colne & Nelson	20.11	15.01	15.04	11.03	25.09		09.10	11.12	08.01	12.02
Eccles	23.10	02.10	08.01	15.04	11.12	29.01		20.11	26.02	11.03
Heaton Moor	11.09	27.11	26.02	09.10	15.01	25.03	18.12		02.10	06.11
Old Bedians	27.11	09.10	11.03	15.01	18.12	06.11	25.09	12.02		25.03
Thornton Cleveleys	29.01	26.02	23.10	20.11	15.04	02.10	11.09	08.01	11.12	

NORTH LANCS TWO

	Chorley	Clitheroe	Didsbury Toc H	Littleborough	Lostock	Montell Carr.	Nth Manchester
Chorley		29.01	11.03	25.09	23.10	06.11	08.01
Clitheroe	09.10		08.01	11.03	11.12	12.02	25.09
Didsbury Toc H	20.11	11.09		12.02	06.11	15.01	25.03
Littleborough	15.01	20.11	23.10		29.01	25.03	26.02
Lostock	12.02	25.03	26.02	09.10		11.09	20.11
Montell Carrington	26.02	23.10	25.09	11.12	08.01		29.01
North Manchester	11.09	15.01	11.12	06.11	11.03	09.10	

CUMBRIA

	Carnforth	Creighton	Greengarth	Keswick	Moresby	Silloth	Upper Eden	Whitehaven
Carnforth		08.01	06.11	09.10	11.12	25.09	11.03	12.02
Creighton	11.09		09.10	20.11	06.11	25.03	12.02	15.01
Greengarth	26.02	29.01		25.03	25.09	23.10	08.01	20.11
Keswick	29.01	11.03	11.12		23.10	08.01	25.09	06.11
Moresby	25.03	26.02	15.01	12.02		20.11	09.10	11.09
Silloth	15.01	11.12	12.02	11.09	11.03		06.11	09.10
Upper Eden	20.11	23.10	11.09	15.01	29.01	26.02		25.03
Whitehaven	23.10	25.09	11.03	26.02	08.01	29.01	11.12	

SOUTH LANCS/ CHESHIRE ONE

	Birchfield	Crewe & Nant.	Dukinfield	Eagle	Merseyside Pol.	Newton-le-Will.	Old Salians	Southport	St Mary's OB	Wirral
Birchfield (Lancs)		29.01	20.11	23.10	25.09	12.02	15.04	11.03	08.01	11.12
Crewe and Nantwich	09.10		11.03	06.11	25.03	25.09	12.02	18.12	27.11	15.01
Dukinfield	18.12	11.09		27.11	15.01	06.11	25.09	09.10	25.03	12.02
Eagle	15.01	08.01	15.04		12.02	09.10	11.12	25.09	20.11	11.03
Merseyside Police	26.02	11.12	23.10	02.10		11.09	08.01	15.04	29.01	20.11
Newton-le-Willows	02.10	26.02	08.01	29.01	11.03		20.11	11.12	23.10	15.04
Old Salians	27.11	02.10	26.02	25.03	06.11	18.12		15.01	11.09	09.10
Southport	11.09	20.11	29.01	26.02	27.11	25.03	23.10		02.10	08.01
St Mary's O.B.	06.11	15.04	11.12	18.12	09.10	15.01	11.03	12.02		25.09
Wirral	25.03	23.10	02.10	11.09	18.12	27.11	29.01	06.11	26.02	

SOUTH LANCS/ CHESHIRE TWO

	Bowdon	Congleton	Douglas (IoM)	Ellesmere Port	Marple	Moore	Old Anselmians	Prenton	Ruskin Park	Sefton
Bowdon		11.03	12.02	09.10	25.09	18.12	15.04	15.01	11.12	06.11
Congleton	11.09		15.01	06.11	09.10	25.03	02.10	18.12	26.02	27.11
Douglas (I.O.M.)	02.10	23.10		27.11	08.01	26.02	20.11	25.03	29.01	11.09
Ellesmere Port	29.01	08.01	15.04		20.11	02.10	11.12	11.09	23.10	26.02
Marple	26.02	29.01	06.11	18.12		11.09	23.10	27.11	02.10	25.03
Moore	20.11	11.12	25.09	12.02	11.03		08.01	09.10	15.04	15.01
Old Anselmians	27.11	12.02	18.12	25.03	15.01	06.11		25.09	11.03	09.10
Prenton	23.10	20.11	11.12	11.03	15.04	29.01	26.02		08.01	02.10
Ruskin Park	25.03	25.09	09.10	15.01	12.02	27.11	11.09	06.11		18.12
Sefton	08.01	15.04	11.03	25.09	11.12	23.10	29.01	12.02	20.11	

SOUTH LANCS/ CHESHIRE THREE

	Halton	Helsby	Hoylake	Liverpool Coll.	Parkonians	Port Sunlight	Runcorn	Vulcan
Halton		25.03	20.11	11.09	12.02	09.10	15.01	06.11
Helsby	11.12		11.09	15.01	06.11	12.02	09.10	11.03
Hoylake	11.03	08.01		29.01	25.09	11.12	06.11	23.10
Liverpool Collegiate	08.01	25.09	09.10		11.03	06.11	12.02	11.12
Parkonians	23.10	26.02	15.01	20.11		11.09	25.03	29.01
Port Sunlight	29.01	23.10	25.03	26.02	08.01		20.11	25.09
Runcorn	25.09	29.01	26.02	23.10	11.12	11.03		08.01
Vulcan	26.02	20.11	12.02	25.03	09.10	15.01	11.09	

SOUTH LANCS/ CHESHIRE FOUR

	Capenhurst	Crosby Vag.	Hightown	Holmes Chapel	Lucas Mersey.	Mossley Hill	Orrell Anvils
Capenhurst		06.11	15.01	20.11	25.03	12.02	11.09
Crosby Vagabonds	26.02		11.09	12.02	20.11	09.10	25.03
Hightown	25.09	08.01		26.02	29.01	11.12	23.10
Holmes Chapel	11.03	23.10	06.11		08.01	25.09	29.01
Lucas Merseyside	11.12	11.03	09.10	11.09		06.11	15.01
Mossley Hill A.C.	23.10	29.01	25.03	15.01	26.02		20.11
Orrell Anvils	08.01	11.12	12.02	09.10	25.09	11.03	

NORTH EAST ONE

	Beverley	Darlington	Goole	Halifax	Horden	Keighley	Old Crossleyans	Percy Park	Redcar	York
Beverley		29.01	11.12	08.01	11.03	15.04	20.11	23.10	02.10	26.02
Darlington	09.10		25.09	15.04	12.02	11.03	11.12	20.11	15.01	08.01
Goole	25.03	26.02		29.01	27.11	08.01	23.10	02.10	11.09	20.11
Halifax	06.11	27.11	09.10		15.01	12.02	25.09	25.03	18.12	11.09
Horden	11.09	02.10	15.04	23.10		20.11	08.01	29.01	26.02	11.12
Keighley	27.11	11.09	06.11	02.10	18.12		29.01	26.02	25.03	23.10
Old Crossleyans	18.12	25.03	15.01	26.02	06.11	09.10		11.09	27.11	02.10
Percy Park	15.01	18.12	12.02	11.12	09.10	25.09	11.03		06.11	15.04
Redcar	12.02	23.10	11.03	20.11	25.09	11.12	15.04	08.01		29.01
York	25.09	06.11	18.12	11.03	25.03	15.01	12.02	27.11	09.10	

NORTH EAST TWO

	Cleckheaton	Durham City	Hull	North Rib'dale	Old Brodleians	Pocklington	Pontefract	Selby	West Hartlepool	Wheatley Hills
Cleckheaton		15.01	27.11	09.10	26.02	18.12	02.10	06.11	25.03	11.09
Durham City	23.10		11.09	08.01	29.01	25.03	20.11	27.11	26.02	02.10
Hull	15.04	11.03		11.12	20.11	12.02	29.01	25.09	23.10	08.01
North Ribblesdale	29.01	06.11	25.03		02.10	27.11	23.10	18.12	11.09	26.02
Old Brodleians	25.09	09.10	18.12	12.02		06.11	11.09	15.01	27.11	25.03
Pocklington	20.11	11.12	02.10	15.04	08.01		26.02	11.03	29.01	23.10
Pontefract	12.02	18.12	09.10	15.01	11.03	25.09		25.03	06.11	27.11
Selby	08.01	15.04	26.02	20.11	23.10	11.09	11.12		02.10	29.01
West Hartlepool	11.12	25.09	15.01	11.03	15.04	09.10	08.01	12.02		20.11
Wheatley Hills	11.03	12.02	06.11	25.09	11.12	15.01	15.04	09.10	18.12	

NORTH EAST THREE

	Ashington	Gateshead	Hartlepool Rvrs	Huddersfield	Medicals	Ripon	Roundhegians	Ryton	Westoe	Yarnbury
Ashington		26.02	29.01	02.10	23.10	15.04	08.01	11.09	11.12	20.11
Gateshead	25.09		08.01	23.10	20.11	11.03	15.04	12.02	29.01	11.12
Hartlepool Rovers	09.10	06.11		18.12	11.12	12.02	11.03	15.01	15.04	25.09
Huddersfield	12.02	15.01	20.11		15.04	25.09	11.12	09.10	08.01	11.03
Medicals	15.01	18.12	25.03	27.11		09.10	25.09	06.11	11.09	12.02
Ripon	27.11	11.09	02.10	26.02	29.01		23.10	25.03	20.11	08.01
Roundhegians	06.11	27.11	11.09	25.03	26.02	15.01		18.12	02.10	09.10
Ryton	11.03	02.10	23.10	29.01	08.01	11.12	20.11		26.02	15.04
Westoe	25.03	09.10	27.11	06.11	11.03	18.12	12.02	25.09		15.01
Yarnbury	18.12	25.03	26.02	11.09	02.10	06.11	29.01	27.11	23.10	

DURHAM NTHUMBERLAND ONE

	Acklam	Billingham	Consett	Houghton	Novocastrians	Seghill	Sunderland	Whitby	Whitley Bay	Winlaton Vulc.
Acklam		08.01	26.02	02.10	11.03	23.10	11.12	20.11	29.01	15.04
Billingham	06.11		11.09	18.12	15.01	25.03	09.10	25.09	27.11	12.02
Consett	25.09	11.03		09.10	25.03	27.11	18.12	12.02	06.11	15.01
Houghton	12.02	20.11	29.01		25.09	08.01	11.03	15.04	23.10	11.12
Novocastrians	11.09	23.10	11.12	26.02		29.01	15.04	08.01	02.10	20.11
Seghill	15.01	11.12	15.04	06.11	09.10		12.02	11.03	18.12	25.09
Sunderland	25.03	29.01	20.11	11.09	27.11	02.10		23.10	26.02	08.01
Whitby	18.12	26.02	02.10	27.11	06.11	11.09	15.01		25.03	09.10
Whitley Bay	09.10	15.04	08.01	15.01	12.02	20.11	25.09	11.12		11.03
Winlaton Vulcans	27.11	02.10	23.10	25.03	18.12	26.02	06.11	29.01	11.09	

DURHAM NTHUMBERLAND TWO

	Barnard Castle	Bishop Auck.	Blyth	Chester le Street	Gosforth	Hartlepool	North Shields	Ponteland	Richmondshire	Wallsend
Barnard Castle		26.02	23.10	08.01	29.01	02.10	11.09	25.03	20.11	27.11
Bishop Auckland	25.09		11.12	11.03	15.04	20.11	15.01	09.10	08.01	12.02
Blyth	15.01	25.03		09.10	26.02	11.09	27.11	18.12	02.10	06.11
Chester le Street	06.11	11.09	29.01		02.10	26.02	25.03	27.11	23.10	18.12
Gosforth	09.10	27.11	25.09	12.02		25.03	18.12	06.11	11.09	15.01
Hartlepool	12.02	18.12	11.03	25.09	11.12		06.11	15.01	15.04	09.10
North Shields	11.03	23.10	15.04	11.12	20.11	08.01		12.02	29.01	25.09
Ponteland	11.12	29.01	20.11	15.04	08.01	23.10	02.10		26.02	11.03
Richmondshire	18.12	06.11	12.02	15.01	11.03	27.11	09.10	25.09		25.03
Wallsend	15.04	02.10	08.01	20.11	23.10	29.01	26.02	11.09	11.12	

DURHAM NTHUMBERLAND THREE

	Durham	Guisborough	Hartlepool Ath	Jarrovians	Seaham	Seaton Carew	Sedgefield	Wearside	Wensleydale	West Hartlepool
Durham		26.02	02.10	09.10	25.03	11.09	15.01	06.11	27.11	18.12
Guisborough	25.09		11.09	12.02	27.11	25.03	09.10	15.01	18.12	06.11
Hartlepool Athletic	12.02	11.03		15.01	06.11	27.11	18.12	25.03	09.10	25.09
Jarrovians	29.01	02.10	23.10		11.09	26.02	06.11	18.12	25.03	27.11
Seaham	11.12	15.04	08.01	11.03		20.11	25.09	12.02	15.01	09.10
Seaton Carew	11.03	11.12	15.04	25.09	18.12		12.02	09.10	06.11	15.01
Sedgefield	23.10	29.01	20.11	08.01	26.02	02.10		27.11	11.09	25.03
Wearside	08.01	23.10	11.12	20.11	02.10	29.01	15.04		26.02	11.09
Wensleydale	15.04	20.11	29.01	11.12	23.10	08.01	11.03	25.09		12.02
West Hartlepool	20.11	08.01	26.02	15.04	29.01	23.10	11.12	11.03	02.10	

DURHAM NTHUMBERLAND FOUR

	Hartlepool BB	Newton Aycliffe	Prudhoe Hosp.	Shildon Town	Yarm
Hartlepool B.B.O.B.		20.11	25.09	12.02	???
Newton Aycliffe	25.03		12.02	11.12	26.02
Prudhoe Hospital	29.01	09.10		26.02	06.11
Shildon Town	09.10	???	23.10		15.01
Yarm	11.12	23.10	11.03	???	

YORKSHIRE ONE

	Bradford Salem	Castleford	Hemsworth	Ilkley	Leodiensians	Northallerton	Scarborough	Thornensians	Wath on Dearne	West Leeds
Bradford Salem		29.01	15.04	08.01	02.10	11.12	11.09	23.10	26.02	20.11
Castleford	09.10		12.02	11.03	18.12	15.04	15.01	11.12	06.11	25.09
Hemsworth	27.11	02.10		23.10	26.02	20.11	25.03	29.01	11.09	08.01
Ilkley	06.11	11.09	15.01		25.03	02.10	18.12	26.02	27.11	09.10
Leodiensians	12.02	20.11	25.09	11.12		08.01	09.10	15.04	15.01	11.03
Northallerton	25.03	27.11	18.12	12.02	06.11		25.09	11.03	09.10	15.01
Scarborough	11.03	23.10	11.12	20.11	29.01	26.02		08.01	02.10	15.04
Thornensians	15.01	25.03	09.10	25.09	27.11	11.09	06.11		18.12	12.02
Wath on Dearne	25.09	08.01	11.03	15.04	23.10	29.01	12.02	20.11		11.12
West Leeds	18.12	26.02	06.11	29.01	11.09	23.10	27.11	02.10	25.03	

YORKSHIRE TWO

	Bramley Ph'nix	Dinnington OB	Halifax Vand.	Heath	Hullensians	Malton & Nort.	Old Oldiensians	Sheffield Oaks	Sheffield Tigers	York Railway
Bramley Phoenix		25.03	18.12	25.09	11.09	06.11	15.01	12.02	27.11	09.10
Dinnington O.B.	06.11		11.03	15.04	15.01	09.10	11.12	25.09	18.12	12.02
Halifax Vandals	08.01	15.04		29.01	12.02	25.09	20.11	11.12	23.10	11.03
Heath	11.09	27.11	02.10		18.12	06.11	26.02	09.10	25.03	15.01
Hullensians	27.11	09.10	12.02	25.09		25.03	11.03	15.01	06.11	18.12
Malton and Norton	23.10	02.10	20.11	26.02	11.03		08.01	15.04	29.01	11.12
Old Otliensians	29.01	26.02	08.01	11.12	11.09	23.10		20.11	02.10	15.04
Sheffield Oaks	26.02	25.03	29.01	23.10	27.11	18.12	02.10		11.09	06.11
Sheffield Tigers	20.11	15.01	11.12	08.01	09.10	12.02	15.04	11.03		25.09
York Railway	02.10	11.09	23.10	20.11	25.03	27.11	29.01	08.01	26.02	

YORKSHIRE THREE

	Baildon	Barnsley	Hessle	Knottingley	Leeds Corinth.	Moortown	Old Rishworth.	Skipton	Stanley Rod.	Stocksbridge
Baildon		12.02	15.01	09.10	25.09	11.12	11.03	20.11	15.04	08.01
Barnsley	02.10		26.02	11.09	15.04	08.01	20.11	29.01	23.10	11.12
Hessle	23.10	25.09		12.02	11.03	15.04	11.12	08.01	20.11	29.01
Knottingley	29.01	11.03	02.10		11.12	20.11	15.04	23.10	08.01	26.02
Leeds Corinthians	26.02	27.11	11.09	25.03		23.10	08.01	02.10	29.01	20.11
Moortown	25.03	06.11	27.11	18.12	15.01		09.10	11.09	26.02	02.10
Old Rishworthians	11.09	18.12	25.03	27.11	06.11	29.01		26.02	02.10	23.10
Skipton	18.12	09.10	06.11	15.01	12.02	11.03	25.09		11.12	15.04
Stanley Rodillians	27.11	15.01	18.12	06.11	09.10	25.09	12.02	25.03		11.09
Stocksbridge	06.11	25.03	09.10	25.09	18.12	12.02	15.01	27.11	11.03	

YORKSHIRE FOUR

	Airsborough	Burley	Edlington G.	Hornsea	Marist	Mosborough	Old Modernians	Rotherham Clif.	Wetherby	Wibsey
Aireborough		11.03	20.11	02.10	23.10	15.04	11.12	26.02	08.01	29.01
Burley	11.09		08.01	26.02	29.01	20.11	15.04	11.12	23.10	02.10
Edlington Granby	18.12	06.11		27.11	11.09	09.10	15.01	02.10	26.02	25.03
Hornsea	12.02	25.09	15.04		08.01	11.12	11.03	29.01	20.11	23.10
Marist	15.01	09.10	11.03	06.11		25.09	12.02	15.04	11.12	18.12
Mosborough	27.11	18.12	29.01	25.03	26.02		06.11	23.10	02.10	11.09
Old Modernians	25.03	27.11	23.10	11.09	02.10	08.01		20.11	29.01	26.02
Rotherham Clifton	25.09	25.03	12.02	09.10	27.11	15.01	18.12		11.03	06.11
Wetherby	06.11	15.01	25.09	18.12	25.03	12.02	09.10	11.09		27.11
Wibsey	09.10	12.02	11.12	15.01	20.11	11.03	25.09	08.01	15.04	

YORKSHIRE FIVE NORTH

	Garforth	Knaresborough	Leeds Round.	Ossett	Rowntree	Wakefield C.
Garforth		25.03	20.11	09.10	11.09	12.02
Knaresborough	11.12		25.09	11.03	12.02	09.10
Leeds Roundheads	11.03	15.01		06.11	09.10	11.09
Ossett	29.01	20.11	26.02		25.03	15.01
Rowntree	08.01	23.10	29.01	11.12		26.02
Wakefield Cougars	23.10	29.01	08.01	25.09	06.11	

YORKSHIRE FIVE SOUTH

	Adwickle Street	Danum Phoenix	De La Salle OB	Rawmarsh	Sheffield Med.	Wickersley Exel	Withernsea
Adwick le Street		11.09	25.03	29.01	26.02	23.10	15.01
Danum Phoenix	08.01		20.11	25.09	23.10	29.01	25.03
De La Salle OB	11.12	11.03		08.01	29.01	25.09	26.02
Rawmarsh	09.10	15.01	11.09		20.11	26.02	12.02
Sheffield Medicals	06.11	12.02	09.10	11.03		11.12	11.09
Wickersley Exel	12.02	09.10	15.01	06.11	25.03		20.11
Withernsea	25.09	11.12	06.11	23.10	08.01	11.03	

Northern Division Clubs

ACKLAM RUFC
Durham & Northumberland 1
Ground Address: Talbot Park, Saltersgill Avenue, Middlesborough, ClevelandTel: 01842 321397
Club Secretary: Paul Pearson, 32 Foxgloves, Coulby Newham, Middlesborough, Cleveland. TS8 0XA Tel: (H) 01642 597195 (W) 01325 461231
Fixtures Secretary: Jim Ward, 108 Guisborough Road, Nunthorpe, Middlesborough, TS7 0JD
Club Colours: Black, green and white

ADWICK-LE-STREET RUFC
Yorkshire 5 South
Ground Address: Church Lane Playing Fields, Adwick-le-Street, Doncaster, South Yorkshire
Tel: 01302 723550 (HQ Foresters Arms)
Brief Directions: 4 miles north of Doncaster on A638 Wakefield Road. Just off south bound A1 (Doncaster turn off at Redhouse) Ground directly opposite Adwick Railway Station.
Club Secretary: R J Terry, 7 Cranfield Drive, Skellow, Doncaster, South Yorkshire. DN6 8RS
Tel: (H) 01302 727580 (W) 01977 669201
Fixtures Secretary: M A Leach-Flanagan, 31 Alexandra Road, Bentley, Doncaster, South Yorkshire.
Tel: (H) 01302 872429
Club Colours: Navy with White/Royal Hoops

AIREBOROUGH RUFC
Yorkshire 4
Ground Address: Nunroyd Park, Yeadon, Leeds, LS19
Tel: 01943 878299
Brief Directions: From Leeds follow signs for Airport. Then for Guiseley - Club is approx 1 mile from Jct 600 R/about on the A65 - Leeds/Ilkley Road.
Club Secretary: M Harper, 32 Aire View, Yeadon, West Yorkshire
Tel: (H) 01132 504219 (W) 01132 505151
Fixtures Secretary: Mr Paul Markie, 1 Hillside Rise, Guiseley, Leeds LS20 9DJ
Tel: (H) 01943 879363 (W) 01274 693622
Club Colours: Maroon and white hoops - Black shorts

ALNWICK RUFC
North 2
Ground Address: Greensfield, St James, Alnwick, Northumberland
Tel: 01665 602342
Brief Directions: A1 slip (South) of Alnwick signed Alnwick from N/castle, after slip 1st left, club 300 yds on left. From Edinburgh, after slip straight over cross roads, Greensfield Ave as above
Club Secretary: Mr. R. Todd, Linden House, Lesbury, Alnwick, Northumberland, NN66 3QW
Tel: 01665 830898
Fixtures Secretary: John Answorth
Tel: (H) 01665 605196 (W) 01665 510505
Club Colours: Royal blue jersey with gold lion rampant badge

ALTRINCHAM (KERSAL) RFC
North West 1
Ground Address: Stelfox Avenue, Timperley, Altrincham, Cheshire
Tel: 0161 972 9157
Brief Directions: M56 J3, take road towards Altrincham, after 3 miles 3rd exit off roundabout, Stelfox Ave 100 yds on right
Club Secretary: Dominic Leach, 5 Lisson Grove, Hale, Altrincham, Cheshire. WA15 9AE
Tel: (H) 0161 941 3085 (W) 0161 929 1851
Fixtures Secretary: George Brugnoli, 231 Brooklands Road, Sale, Greater Manchester.
Tel: (H) 0161 973 0194 (W) 0385 261743
Club Colours: Black, red & white hoops

AMBLESIDE
North Lancs & Cumbria
Ground Address: Galava Park, Borrans Road, Ambleside, Cumbria LA22 0UL.
Tel: 015394 32536
Brief Directions: M6 Juct 36 A591 Widermere-Ambleside. Turn for Coniston, Hawkshead at Waterhead lights, ground .5 mile on left.
Club Secretary: Mrs. J eanette. Irwin, Flat 2, Orrest Drive, Windermere LA23 2LF.
Tel No: 015394 42025
Fixtures Secretary: Mr. N. Fecitt, Hart Head Farm, Rydal, Ambleside, Cumbria.
Tel No: (H) 015394 33772 (
Club Colours: Black & Amber.

ASHINGTON J.W.C. RFC
North East 3
Ground Address: Recreation Ground, Ellington Road, Ashington, Northumberland
Tel: 01670814123
Brief Directions: 1 mile north west of Ashington town centre on A1068. Map available on request
Club Secretary: Albert Armstrong, 25 Dundale Drive, Cramlington, Northumberland. NE23 2GA.
Tel: (H) 01670 736891 (W) 01670 533303
Fixtures Secretary: A Armstrong
Tel: (H) 01670 736891 (W) 01670 533303
Club Colours: Royal blue and amber hoops, white shorts.

ASHTON ON MERSEY RUFC
North West 1
Ground Address: Banky Lane, off Carrington Lane, Ashton on Mersey, Cheshire
Tel: 0161 973 6637
Brief Directions: M63 J63 Carrington Spur, towards Carrington, right at lights, left at T junction, club 300 yards on right
Club Secretary: Barry Piper, 25 Pinford Road, Worsley, Manchester, M28 7DZ
Tel: (H) 0161 790 0674
Fixtures Secretary: P.Stokes.
Tel: (H) 0161 941 5641
Club Colours: Maroon and white hoops with Navy shorts

ASHTON-UNDER-LYNE RFC
North Lancs 1
Ground Address: Pavilion, Gambrel Bank, St Albans Avenue, Ashton-Under-Lyne. OL6 8TU

Tel: 0161 330 1361
Brief Directions: From Market Square Ashton, Henrietta Street to Broadoak Hotel, straight on to St Albans Avenue
Club Secretary: Mr Dennis Gee, 26 Burnedge Lane, Grasscroft, Oldham. OL4 4EA
Tel: (H) 01457 872823 (W) 0161 303 9482
Fixtures Secretary: Paul Newton. Tel No: 0161 344 5873
Club Colours: Red, amber and black hoops,black shorts,red socks

ASPULL RFC
North West 1
Ground Address: Woodshaw Park, Woods Road, Aspull, Wigan, Lancs
Tel: 01942 831611
Club Secretary: Graham Bennett, 11 Prestbury Avenue, Marus Bridge, Wigan, Lancs. WN3 6SG
Fixtures Secretary: G W Gregson
Tel: (H) 01257 421421 (W) 01772 267898 (F) 01772 885262
Club Colours: Sky and navy hoops

BAILDON RUFC
Yorkshire 3
Ground Address: Jenny Lane, Baildon, Shipley, West Yorks. BD17 6RS
Tel: 01274 582644
Brief Directions: A650 to centre of Shipley, follow Baildon signs in village centre, roundabout 3rd exit then left on Jenny Lane
Club Secretary: Mr G Porter, 100 Cliffe Avenue, Baildon, BRadford. BD17 6PD.
Tel: 01274 419596
Fixtures Secretary: Roger Shuttleworth, 11 The Crescent, Otley, West Yorks.
Tel: (H) 01943 467058
Club Colours: Red, white and black hoops

BARNARD CASTLE RUFC
Durham & Northumberland 2
Ground Address: The Clubhouse, 7 Birch Road, Barnard Castle, Co Durham, DL12 8JR. Tel: 01833 631766
Ground: The Demesnes(off Newgate), Barnard Castle.
Brief Directions: Head into Town centre. At Market Cross follow signs for Bowes Museum. Take turn at Catholic Church (Birch Road). Clubhouse is on left (approx 100 yds)
Club Secretary: Tim Worley, 17 Newgate, Barnard Castle, Co Durham. DL12 8NQ
Tel: (H) 01833 637608 (W) 01833 690305
Fixtures Secretary: Mr. David Jackson c/o Headlam Hall Hotel, Headlam, Nr. Darlington, Co. Durham, DH2 3HA.
Tel: 01325 730238
Club Colours: All black.

BARNSLEY RUFC
Yorkshire 3
Ground Address: Shaw Lane, Barnsley, South Yorkshire. S70 6HZ
Tel: 01226 203509
Brief Directions: M1 J37, towards Barnsley, through 1st major lights, 2nd turning right into Shaw Lane, ground on right after school
Club Secretary: Mick Marshall, 4 Westbourne Grove, Barnsley. S75 1AE
Tel: (H) 01226 771473
Fixtures Secretary: Steve Lumb, 49 Wood Lane, Carlton, Barnsley, S71 3JQ. Tel: 01226 726542
Club Colours: Red, white and navy blue hoops

BEVERLEY RUFC
North East 1
Ground Address: Beaver Park, Norwood, Beverley. HU17 9HT
Tel: 01482 870306
Brief Directions: Through Beverley centre, follow signs for Hornsea, ground is just before level crossing behind Lady le Gros pub
Club Secretary: Andrew Winter, 4 The Vineyards, Leven, Beverley, East Yorkshire
Tel: (H) 01964 543981
Fixtures Secretary: Rob Jenner
Tel: (H) 01482 868944
Club Colours: Green, brown and white

BILLINGHAM RUFC
Durham & Northumberland 1
Ground Address: Greenwood Road, Billingham
Brief Directions: From A19, follow signs to Belasis Hall Technology Park, Greenwood Road. Goround adjacent to the north.
Club Secretary: J M Ker, 4 Anlaby Close, Billingham. TS23 3RA
Tel: (H & Fax) 01642 560536
Fixtures Secretary: Colin Wakenshaw
Tel: (H) 01642 647813
Club Colours: Green and white hoops, white and green shorts

BIRCHFIELD (LANCS) RUFC
South Lancs & Cheshire 1
Ground Address: Albright & Wilson Recreational Club, Birchfield Road, Widnes, Cheshire. WA8 0TB
Tel: 0151 424 3222
Brief Directions: From M62 Junct. 7, follow A57 (Warrington) . Turn right at first set of lights, then right at T junction, 1st left at roundabout onto Birchfield Rd. Ground is 250 yds on the right.
Club Secretary: Stuart Ashton, 11 Eltham Close, Widnes, Cheshire. WA8 3RG
Tel: (H) 0151 424 6344
Fixtures Secretary: Kevin McDonnell, 20 Newlyn Gardens, Penketh, Warrington. WA5 2UX.
Tel: (H) 01925 722440 (W) 0151 424 4109 (M) 0802 400333
Club Colours: Maroon and black

BIRKENHEAD PARK FC
North West 1
Ground Address: Upper Park, Park Road North, Birkenhead. L41 8AA
Tel: 0151 652 4646
Brief Directions: M53 J4, take 4th exit off roundabout onto B5151 to Birkenhead, after 8 miles turn right at 4th lights into Upton Rd/Park Rd Nth, ground 0.5 miles on right
Club Secretary: Peter Greville, 2 Howbeck Close, Oxton, Birkenhead L43 6TH
Tel Nos: 0151 653 6070 (W) 0151 653 5424(H)
Fixtures Secretary: R C Hardman
Tel: (H) 0151 652 5204
Club Colours: Red, white and blue hoops

BISHOP AUCKLAND RUFC
Durham & Northumberland 2
Ground Address: West Mills Playing Fields, Bridge

Road, Bishop Auckland, Co Durham. DL14 7JH
Tel: 01388 602922
Brief Directions: Leave Bishop Auckland Market Place on Old Road to Crook via Toronto and turn left at Rugby Club sign, just before Crossing River Wear. Three quarters along this road (Bridle Road)
Club Secretary: Keith Wilkinson, 7 Victoria Avenue, Bishop Auckland, Co Durham. DL14 7JH
Tel: (H) 01833 605768
Fixtures Secretary: Ron Williamson, 19 Waddington Street, Bishop Auckland, Co Durham, DL14 6HG
Tel: (H) 01388 600059
Club Colours: Navy and sky blue

BLACKBURN RUFC

North 2
Ground Address: Ramsgreave Drive, Blackburn, Lancs. BB1 8NB
Tel: 01254 247669 - Fax: 01254 246834
Brief Directions: M6 J31, follow signs to Blackburn, left at Moat House Hotel, club on left after 1 mile
Club Secretary: Nick Westhead, 9 Paris, Ramsgreave, Blackburn, Lancs, BB1 9BJ.
Tel: 01284 248574
Fixtures Secretary: Andy Whalley, 5 Heys Court, Oswaldtwistle, Accrington, Lancs, BB5 3BN
Tel: 01254 875037
Club Colours: Blue top, white shorts

BLACKPOOL RUFC

North West 3
Ground Address: Fleetwood Road, Norbreck, Blackpool, Lancashire
Tel: 01253 853308
Brief Directions: M55 J4, right onto A583, right onto Whitegate Drive (still A583), bear right onto Devonshire Rd B5214, club on right 0.5 mile past Red Lion pub
Club Secretary: Cliff Wainscott, 15 Stafford Avenue, Poulton-Le-Fylde, Lancashire. FY6 8BJ
Tel: (H) 01253 885151
Fixtures Secretary: M Spowart, 3 Plymouth Rd., Blackpool. FY3 7JS
Tel No: 01253 393448
Club Colours: Red & blue squares

BLYTH RFC

Durham & Northumberland 2
Ground Address: Plessey Road, Blyth, Northumberland
Tel: 01670 352063
Brief Directions: From the south take A19 through Tyne Tunnel, continue on this until you pass Cramlington, take A1061 turn off into Blyth
Club Secretary: Mr S Hall,18 Fairfield Avenue, Blyrth, NE24 3HW
Tel: 01670 356362
Fixtures Secretary: Mr Neil Richardson, 12 Banbury Way, Blyth,NE24 3TY
Tel: (H) 01670 353605
Club Colours: Black and green hoops, black shorts

BOLTON RUFC

North Lancs 1
Ground Address: Mortfield Pavilion, Avenue Street, Bolton. BL1 3AW
Tel: 01204 363710
Brief Directions: Head out of Bolton on Chorley Old Road, signposted near Morrisons supermarket
Club Secretary: David Powell, 31 Harvest Drive, Crosses Farm, Whittle-Le-Woods, Chorley, PR6 7QL.
Tel: (H) 01257 234746
Fixtures Secretary: David Patchett
Tel: (H) 017064 826298
Club Colours: Red and white hoops, black shorts

BOWDON RUFC

South Lancs & Cheshire 2
Ground Address: The Club House, Clay Lane, Timperley, Cheshire, WA15 7AF.
Brief Directions: M56 J6, follow signs to Hale, after 1.5 turn right at lights onto Delahays Rd, through next set of lights, after 0.5 mile up Thorley Ln turn R. at Mini R/about Clay Lane. Club on left.
Club Secretary: Myles Kitchener, 67 Crofton Avenue, Timperley, Altrincham, Cheshire, WA15 6BZ
Tel: 0161 973 3003H - 01244 672531W
Fixtures Secretary: Frank Norton, 36 Green Walk, Timperley. Altrincham, Cheshire, WA15 6JN.
Tel: 0161 980 8195 H - 01925 834639W
Club Colours: Claret, white and black

BRADFORD SALEM RFC

Yorkshire 1
Ground Address: Shay Lane, Heaton, Bradford. BD9 6SL
Tel: 01274 496430
Brief Directions: From Bradford centre take A650 (Towards Keighley) along Manningham Lane. Left at 'The Park' (pub) and up hill turn right at top , past shops into Shay Lane. Ground is 100 yds on left.
Club Secretary: Mrs A Wheeler, 25 Ashwell Road, Heaton, Bradford BD9 4BA
Tel: 01274 487517
Fixtures Secretary: John Dobson
Tel: (H) 01274 487517
Club Colours: Royal blue, gold, black hoops, black shorts, blue socks

BRAMLEY RUFC

Yorkshire 2
Ground Address: The Warrels, Grosmount Terrace, Warrels Road, Bramley, Leeds. LS13 3NY
Tel: 0113 257 7787
Club Secretary: Andrew Hurdley, Hall Farm, Hall Road, Little Preston, Leeds. LS26 8UT
Tel: (H) 0113 286 0131 (W) 01274 741433
Fixtures Secretary: Brian Parkin
Tel: (H) 0113 256 3127
Club Colours: Green with black and gold band

BRIDLINGTON RUFC

North 2
Ground Address: Dukes Park, Queensgate, Bridlington
Tel: 01262 676405
Brief Directions: Follow signs to Bridlington, 1st traffic lights keep in n/s lane, right at roundabout, left at next lights, ground is 0.25 mile on right
Club Secretary: John Chambers, 31 Quay Road, Bridlington To15 2AR
Tel:01262 672088
Fixtures Secretary: James Armstrong, 57 St Johns Street, Bridlington YO15 2AR
Tel: 01262 671218
Club Colours: Blue, yellow hoop around middle

BROUGHTON PARK FC

North 2
Ground Address: Chelsfield Grove, Off Mauldeth Rd West, Chorlton-cum-Hardy Manchester. M21 7SU Tel:

0161 8812481 Web: http://www.nwnet.co.uk/dean/
Brief Directions: M56 J3, follow signs to Manchester A5103 (straight on) for 3 miles, left at Mauldeth Road West, ground is 0.75 mile on right
Club Secretary: Barry Allen, 1 Deanbank Avenue, Manchester M19 2EZ
Tel: 0161 224 0889
E-mail: barrya@dean.newnet.co.uk
Fixtures Secretary: Tom Barber, 48 Pauldon Road, Manchester M23 8PD
Tel: (H) 0161 998 8936 (W) 0161 226 2501
Club Colours: Black and white hoops

BROUGHTON RUFC
North Lancs 1
Ground Address: Yew Street, Broughton, Salford. M7 9HL
Tel: 0161 743 0902
Club Secretary: Mr Gary Goward, 13 Leigh Avenue, Swinton, Manchester, M27 5RD
Tel: (H) 0161 281 3354
Fixtures Secretary: Peter Raymond Smith, 33 Kirtley Avenue, Monton Green, Eccles, Manchester, M30 9PU
Tel: (H) 0161 788 8098 (W) 0161 908 6075
Club Colours: Blue with yellow, red, yellow stripe midway

BURLEY RFC
Yorkshire 4
Ground Address: Club House, Abbey Road, Leeds. LS5 3NG
Tel: 0113 275 7400
Brief Directions: Take A65 from Leeds city centre, Clubhouse 100 yds on left past Kirkstall Abbey opposite Vesper Gate pub
Club Secretary: R.K.N.Jones, 377 Burley Road, Leeds LS4 2SP
Tel: 01132 742769
Fixtures Secretary: John Sanderson 3 Southolme Close, Leeds LS5 3LP
Tel: (H) 01132 787772
Club Colours: Maroon and white

BURNAGE RFC
North Lancs 1
Ground Address: Varley Park, Battersea Road, Heaton Mersey, Stockport. SK4 3EA
Tel: 0161 432 2150
Brief Directions: J.1 on M60 1st left onto A5145, 1st Left after Crown Pub into Station Road, bends to right into Battersea Road - Club at bottom.
Club Secretary: Mr T Gregory, 22 Berwick Avenue, Heaton Mersey, Stockport. SK4 3AA
Tel: (H) 0161 443 2761 (W) 01706 861341
Fixtures Secretary: Dave Harper, 11 Fulmer Gardens , Bamford, Rochdale OL11 5RB
Tel: 01706 632232
Club Colours: Black

BURY RUFC
North Lancs 1
Ground Address: Radcliffe Road, Bury, Lancashire
Tel: 0161 764 1528
Brief Directions: Leave M660 at J.17 follow A56 towards Bury. After 4 miles turn left at junction with Radcliffe Road. Club immediately on right.
Club Secretary: G J Hilton, 66 Twiss Green Lane, Culcheth, Warrington, Cheshire WA3 4DQ
Tel: (H) 01925 762119
Fixtures Secretary: S. Treadgold, 68 Palatine Drive, Walmersley, Bury, Lancs.
Tel: 0161 7970959
Club Colours: Red, gold and blue hoops, navy blue shorts, red stockings

CALDER VALE RUFC
North West 3
Ground Address: Holden Road, Reedley, Burnley, Lancashire. BB10 2LE
Tel: 01282 424337
Brief Directions: M65 J12, right to to Brierfield, through one set of traffic lights, Holden Road on left approx a quarter mile on left by Oaks Hotel
Club Secretary: Mr W K Seed, 30 Moorland Drive, Brierfield, Nelson. BB9 5ER
Tel: (H) 01282 614172
Fixtures Secretary: Mr M Wilton, 93 Talbot Drive, Brier Cliffe, Burnley, Lancs. BB10 2RT
Tel: (H) 01282 457963
Club Colours: Royal blue and gold hoops

CALDY RFC
North West 1
Ground Address: Paton Field, lower Caldy crossroads, Wirral
Tel: 0151 6258043
Brief Directions: M56-M53-Jct 2-B5139-A540
Club Secretary: R.B. Flashman, 26 Milton crescent, Heswall, Wirral L60 5ST
Tel: 0151 342 5300
Fixtures Secretary: K Doolan
Tel: (H) 0151 3480119
Club Colours: Sable, claret, silver and gold

CAPENHURST RUFC
South Lancs & Cheshire 4
Ground Address: BNFL Sports Ground, Capenhurst, Chester, CH1 6ER.
Tel: 0151 3473494
Brief Directions: From Liverpool M53, A41 turn R. at lights to Capenhurst, L. at R/about, over railway bridge past BNFL Wks. Ground on R. From Warrington/Cheshire M56 to end R. at R/about, L. to Capenhurst. T-Jncn turn L. Past BNFL Ground on R.
Club Secretary: Ted Roberts, 8 Chichester Street, Chester, CH1 4AD.
Tel: 01244 378789
Fixtures Secretary: John Lewis, 42 Kingsmead, Chester, CH2 1EF.
Tel: 01244 380320
Club Colours: Blue & White

CARLISLE RFC
North West 2
Ground Address: The Rugby Ground, Warwick Road, Carlisle
Tel: 01228 521300
Brief Directions: M6 J43 on A69, head towards Carlisle, through 3 sets of lights,
Pass Carlisle United AFC 200 yards on right
Club Secretary: N J Laycock, 90 Greystone Road, Carlisle. Cumbria, CA1 2DD
Tel: (H & F) 01228 522895 e-mail: nlaycock@freenet.co.uk
Fixtures Secretary: D D Morton, 14 Naworth Drive, Lowry Hill, Carlisle, Cumbria
Tel: (H & Fax) 01228 515486 (Mobile) 0585 546803
Club Colours: Red, white & blue irregular hoops, blue shorts

CARNFORTH RFC
Cumbria
Ground Address: Carnforth High School, Kellet Road, Carnforth, Lancashire
Club Secretary: P.D.Wetherill, 13 Hill St., Carnforth, Lancs. LA5 9DY
Tel: 01524 73587
Fixtures Secretary: Steve Vose, 15 Clifton Drive, Bare, Morcambe, Lancs
Tel: (H) 01524 832041
Club Colours: Green and black hoops

CASTLEFORD RUFC
Yorkshire 1
Ground Address: Willow Bridge Lane, Whitwood, Castleford
Tel: 01977 554762
Brief Directions: M62E towards Hull, exit J31, 2nd turn left off roundabout, approx 1 mile through traffic lights, ground on right hand side
Club Secretary: M.Connell, 30 Church Avenue, Swillington , Leeds, LS26 8QH
Tel: (H) 0113 286 5231
Fixtures Secretary: Mr E Mills
Tel: (H) 01977 515784
Club Colours: Red and blue quarter shirts, blue shorts.hoops

CHESTER RUFC
North 2
Ground Address: Hare Lane, Littleton, Chester CH3 7DB
Tel: 01244 336017
Brief Directions: From A55 (Chester Outer Ring Rd), take A51 then 1st left into Hare Lane.
Club Secretary: P W Rhodes, The Hollies, Off Carriage Drive, Frodsham, Cheshire. WA6 6EF
Tel: (H) 01928 731485
Fixtures Secretary: C Cawthorn, 21 Oaklands Ave, Tattenhall, Cheshire CH3 9QU Tel: (H) 01829 770498
Club Colours: Red and blue

CHESTER-LE-STREET RFC
Durham & Northumberland 2
Ground Address: Donald Owen Clarke Centre, Riverside Park, Chester-Le-Street, Co Durham
Tel: 0191 3871995
Brief Directions: Take A1(M) to Chester-Le-Street, follow directions to County Cricket Ground, Rugby Club is situated adjacent to ground in the Donald Owen Clarke Centre
Club Secretary: Mr. David Kilkenny, 64 Highfield Rise, Chester-Le-Street, Co Durham, DH3 3UX.
Tel: (H) 0191 3888357
Fixtures Secretary: Graham Rodger, Fife Avenue, Chester-Le-Street, Co Durham
Tel: (H) 0191 389 1713
Club Colours: Navy blue shirts and shorts, red socks

CHORLEY
North Lancs 2
Ground Address: Brookfields, Chancery Road, Astley Village, Chorley, Lancashire PR71XP.
Tel: 01257 268806
Brief Directions: Exit M61 J.8 towards Chorley acorss 1st R/about. Right at 2nd R/about past hospital on left. Left at next R/about into Chancery Road. Club on the right after 200 yards.
Club Secretary: Sean Riches, 12 Middlewood Close, Eccleston, Chorley, Lsncs PR7 5QG
Tel: (H) 01257 450651
Fixtures Secretary: Dave Nickeas, 7 Morris Close, Stokes Hall, Leyland, Lancs., PR5 2FD.
Tel: (H) 01772 451171
Club Colours: Black and white hoops, Red

CLECKHEATON RUFC
North East 2
Ground Address: The Pavilion, Moorend, Cleckheaton, West Yorkshire. BD19 3UD
Tel: 01274 873410
Brief Directions: Off J.26 M62 - take road to Dewsbury and in 200 yards turn left into Cleckheaton Sports Club.
Club Secretary: Ian Worley, 342 Whitehall Road, Westfield, Wyke, Bradford, BD12 9DP.
Tel: (H) 01274 677526
Fixtures Secretary: Peter Lawton, 5 York Place, Cleckheaton, BD19 3PA.
Tel: 01274 864155
Club Colours: Red and white hoops, black shorts

CLITHEROE RUFC
North Lancs 2
Ground Address: Littlemoor Park, Littlemoor Road, Clitheroe, Lancs
Tel: 01200 422261
Brief Directions: A59 Turn off signed Clitheroe & Barrow. Turn Right before garden centre. Ground on Left after 200 yards.
Club Secretary: John Hyde, Moor Hey Cottage, Knowle Green, Longridge, Preston
Tel: (H) 01254 878402
Fixtures Secretary: Phil Isherwood
Tel: (H) 01200 23781 (W) 01282 777368
Club Colours: Maroon and gold

COCKERMOUTH RUFC
North West 3
Ground Address: `Grasmoor', Strawberry How, Cockrmouth, Cumbria.
Brief Directions: A66 Cockermouth. Follow road to town. Quarter mile take R. fork pass Shell garage. 50 yards turn R. Lortun Road. Half mile pass cemetery turn L. into Strawberry How Road 100 yds Clubhouse, drive/enterance on the right.
Club Secretary: Chris Garrard, "Bent Dyke", Bent Ash Lonning Eaglesfield, Nr Cockermouth, Cumbria. CA13 0SF
Tel: (H) 01900 822835
Fixtures Secretary: A Quarry, 14 Collinfield, Kendal, Cumbria.
Tel: (H) 01539 731640
Club Colours: Black and amber hoops, black shorts

COLNE & NELSON RUFC
North Lancs 1
Ground Address: Holt House, Harrison Drive, Colne, Lancashire, BB8 9SF
Tel: 01282 863339
Club Secretary: Keith Thornton, 261 Brunshaw Road, Burnley, Lancs. BB10 4QR
Tel: (W) 01282 717673
Fixtures Secretary: H. Lambert, 13 Townley Street, Colne, Lancs, BB8 9LF
Tel: 01282 860095
Club Colours: All black

CONGLETON RUFC

South Lancs & Cheshire 2
Ground Address: Hankinson's Field Clubhouse , 78 Park Street, Congleton, Cheshire. CW12
Tel: 01260 273338
Brief Directions: Follow signs to Leisure centre
Club Secretary: Dennis Thorley, 46 Bladon Crescent, Alsager, via Stoke-on-Trent. ST7 2BG
Tel: (H) 01270 878293 (W) 0161 223 1301 Ext 3132
Fixtures Secretary: Ken Williams, 2 Sprink Lane, Buglawton, Congleton, CW12
Tel: (H) 01260 279202
Club Colours: Red, white, red, black hoops,black shorts

CONSETT & DISTRICT RFC (PHOTO ABOVE)

Durham & Northumberland 1
Ground Address: Belle Vue Park, Medomsley Road, Consett, Co Durham
Tel: 01207 590662 (admin) or 503600
Brief Directions: Behind and to the side of Consett Civic Centre only 400m from centre of Consett
Club Secretary: Mark Swinney,32 The Close, Shotley Bridge Co.Durham DH8 0DE
Tel No: 01207 500788
Fixtures Secretary: Paul Dixon, 2 Greencroft Road, Delves Lane, Consett DH8 7DY. Tel No: 01207 500906
Club Colours: Black and amber hoops.with red trim(Unique Design)

CREIGHTON RUFC

Cumbria
Ground Address: Carrs Field, Caxton Road, off Newton Road, Carlisle
Tel: 01228 521169
Brief Directions: Follow signs to Cumberland Infirmary, 400 yards past on right hand side
Club Secretary: David J Thomlinson, 146 Moorhouse Road, Carlisle
Tel: (H) 01228 535111 (W) 01228 524379
Fixtures Secretary: Ian Langley, Kiln Green House, Aikton, Wigton, CA7 0HY.
Tel: 0169973 449900
Club Colours: Navy blue, red collars and cuffs, white shorts, red sock

CREWE AND NANTWICH RUFC

South Lancs & Cheshire 1
Ground Address: Crwe Vagrants Sporets Club, Newcastle Road (A500), Willaston, Nantwich, Cheshire. CW5 7EP
Tel: 01270 569506
Brief Directions: Situated on A500, opposite The Horseshoe pub, 2 miles east of Nantwich and 6 miles from J16 M6
Club Secretary: Alan Jones, 9 Gingerbread Lane, Nantwich, Cheshire. CW5 6NH
Tel: (H & W) 01270 625737
Fixtures Secretary: Bob Christie
Tel: (H) 01270 629637 (after 8 p.m.) (W) 01270 624160
Club Colours: Black Jersey with broad white band

CROSBY VIKINGS RFC

South Lancs & Cheshire 4
Ground Address: The Memorial Ground, St.Anthony's Road, Liverpool L23 3TW
Brief Directions: Currently groundsharing with Waterloo F.C. Directions on Waterloo's page.
Club Secretary: M.Flett, Lanvollon, 17 Fulwood Park, Aigburth, Liverpool L17 5AD. Tel No: 0151 728 7807
Fixtures Secretary: John Rimmer, 2 Chapel Meadow, Longton, Preston, PR4 5NR
Tel No: 01772 614277
Club Colours: Red/white/green.

DANUM PHOENIX RUFC

Yorkshire 5 South
Ground Address: Armthorpe Road, Doncaster, South Yorkshire, DN9 3DG.
Tel: 01302 831388
Brief Directions: From M18 J4 to Doncaster, left at 2nd R/about, right at next R/about. Ground 1 mile on left. From A1M, A630 into Doncaster, anticlockwise round ring road 1st R/about right.
Club Secretary: Will Hircock, The Cottage, Cusworth Village, Doncaster, DN5 7TR
Tel: (H) 01302 780331 (M) 0385 522238 (W) 01302 727595
Fixtures Secretary: Graham Kitchen, 18 Broadway, Dunscroft, Doncaster, DN7 4AA. Tel: (H) 01302 844700
Club Colours: Black with red and yellow band on chest

DARLINGTON MOWDEN PARK RFC

North 2
Ground Address: 22 Yiewsley Drive, Darlington DL3 9XS
Tel: 01325 465932
Brief Directions: From A1(M) follow A68 into Darlington, follow signs to Staindrop, left to Barnes Road, merges into Fulthorpe Ave, 2nd right is Yiewsley Drive
Club Secretary: D.A.Lowe, c/o Charltons, 27A Market Place, Richmond,North Yorkshire.
Fixtures Secretary: George Nevill, 44 Leith Road, Darlington Co Durham DL3 8BG
Tel: (H) 01325 469001
Club Colours: Red,white and blue

DARLINGTON RFC

North East 1
Ground Address: Blackwell Meadows, Grange Road, Darlington. DL1 5NR
Tel: 01325 363777
Brief Directions: From south take A66, DRFC directly off Blands Corner roundabout. From north take A68 to Darlington and continue to A66 junction at Blands Corner roundabout at Blackwell
Club Secretary: Mr Andrew P F Foster, Cadogan, 45 Hartford Road, Darlington. Co. Durham DL3 8HF
Tel: (H) 01325 466501 (Mbl) 0468 661266 (FAX) 01325 466501

Fixtures Secretary: Mr David Gardner, Balder View, Cotherstone, Barnard Castle, Co.Durham DL12 9NR
Tel: (H) 01833 650543 (W) 01833 690305
Club Colours: Scarlet with Black & White Hoop

DE LA SALLE (SALFORD) RUFC
North Lancs & Cumbria
Ground Address: Lancaster Road, Salford 6
Tel: 0161 789 2261
Brief Directions: Sth: off M602 Eccles Jcn 2 follow Salford past Hope Hsptl on rt, next lights left onto Lancaster Rd. From Nth: A580 East Lancs Rd towards Salford, right at Lancaster Rd, club halfway on right
Club Secretary: John Malone, 57 Hayfield Road, Salford. M6 8QA
Tel: (H) 0161 281 6011
Fixtures Secretary: Jim Collins
Tel: (H) 0161 281 3761 (W) 0161 775 7928
Club Colours: Red and gold hoops

DE LA SALLE (SHEFFIELD) RUFC
Yorkshire 5 South
Ground Address: Rear of Beauchief Hall, Abbey Lane, Sheffield, S8
Brief Directions: Come off ring road at the Norton roundabout, turn right down Bocking Lane to the roundobout at the bottom, turn left club sign 3/4 mile on left hand side.
Club Secretary: James Halliday, Mayfield House, 443 Greystones Road, Sheffield, S11 7BY
Fixtures Secretary: Ryley Wing, Robin Cottage, 82 Carr Lane, Dronfield.
Club Colours: Yellow and green hoops

DIDSBURY TOC H RFC
North Lancs 2
Ground Address: Ford Lane, Didsbury, Manchester
Tel: 0161 446 2146
Brief Directions: M62 to M63 Stockport, take M56 turnoff, follow signs to Northenden, left at lights, right at next lights, right at next lights, through village and turn right into Ford Lane
Club Secretary: Peter J M Bradley, 8 Barnard Avenue, Heaton Moor, Stockport. SK4 4ED
Tel: (H) 0161 432 0496 (W) 0161 788 9611
Fixtures Secretary: Roy Knight, 4 Snowdon Street, Heathershaw, Oldham, OL8 1LE
Tel: (H) 0161 345 3735
Club Colours: Black jersey with broad amber band

DINNINGTON RUFC
Yorkshire 2
Ground Address: Lodge Lane, Dinnington, Sheffield, South Yorkshire. S31 7PB
Tel: 01909 562044
Brief Directions: M1 J.31 Take A57 towards Worksop. Turn left B6060 2nd Traffic Lights after one and a half miles turn left on Lodge Lane.
Club Secretary: Bill Gilbody, 16 Devonshire Drive, North Anston, Sheffield. S25 4AQ
Tel: (H) 01909 562997
Fixtures Secretary: Bill Gilbody
Tel: (H) 01909 562997
Club Colours: Blue, gold, black and white hoops

DOUGLAS (I.O.M.) RUFC
South Lancs & Cheshire 2
Ground Address: The Clubhouse, Port-E-Chee, Douglas, Isle of Man
Tel: 01624 676493
Brief Directions: Leave Douglas via Peel Road to Quaterbridge, ground on right. FROM AIRPORT. Head for Douglas turn left at Quarterbridge roundabout, ground on the Right.
Club Secretary: P E Garrett,12 Meadow Crescent, Saddlestone, Douglas, Isle of Man
Tel: (H) 01624 629037 (W) 01624 681230
Fixtures Secretary: T. Ward, 1 Harbour View, Onchan, Isle of Man. 1MJ 2AJ
Tel: (H) 01624 673005 01624647647
Club Colours: Maroon with gold band

DUKINFIELD RUFC
South Lancs & Cheshire 1
Ground Address: Blocksages Playing Fields, Birch Lane, Dukinfield, Cheshire
Tel: 0161 343 2592
Brief Directions: On B6170 between Hyde and Ashton-under-Lyne, next to the baths
Club Secretary: Ernie Taylor, 52 Gower Road, Hyde, Cheshire. SK14 5AD
Tel: (H) 0161 3669541 (W) 01706 47422
Fixtures Secretary: Alan Hilton, Old St,Georges Vicarage, Pennine View, Heyrod, stalybridge, Cheshire.
Tel: (H) 0161 338 3410
Club Colours: Royal blue and gold hoops

DURHAM CITY RFC
North East 2
Ground Address: Hollow Drift, Green Lane, Durham City. DH1 3JU
Tel: 0191 386 1172
Brief Directions: Take A1M, then A690, straight across 1st roundabout, left at next roundabout, left at traffic lights, after 300 yards turn left into Green Lane, opposite Durham Prison
Club Secretary: Mr R Elston, 18 Mayorswell Field, Claypath, Durham City. DH1 1JW
Tel: (H) 0191 386 3245 (W) 01207 507001
Fixtures Secretary: Mr J Thompson
Tel: (H) 01388 528071 (W) 01388 762522
Club Colours: Blue and gold hoops, white shorts

DURHAM CONSTABULARY RUFC
Durham & Northumberland 3
Ground Address: Durham Constabulary Police HQ, Aykley Heads, Durham. DH1 5TT
Tel: 0191 3864929 Ext 2295
Brief Directions: Ground is to the north west of the city, approaching on A167 or A1(M) join A691 and then B6532, Police HQ is well signposted, ground adjacent to HQ
Club Secretary: Mr Peter Davis, 22 Rickleton Avenue, Chester-Le-St, Co Durham, DH3 4AE
Tel: (H) 0191 3890848
Fixtures Secretary: Mr Keith Marston.Tel No: 01207 529052
Club Colours: Royal blue and gold quarters, black shorts

EAGLE RUFC
South Lancs & Cheshire 1
Ground Address: Thornton Road, Great Sankey, Warrington
Tel: 01925 632926 Sat. Emergencies Tel: 0976 288560
Brief Directions: A57 west from Warrington towards Liverpool onto the dual carriageway, where road splits at roundabout take left hand road (A562) and at lights turn left into Thornton Rd

Club Secretary: Vince Sandwell, 23 Waterworks Lane, Winwick, Warrington
Tel: (H) 01925 650367 (W) 01925 830007 (M) 0976 288560
Fixtures Secretary: Dave Unsworth
Tel: (H) 01925 727505
Club Colours: Black and white hoops

EDLINGTON AND GRANBY RUFC

Yorkshire 4
Ground Address: Granby Road WMC, Broomhouse Lane, Edlington, Doncaster, South Yorkshire
Brief Directions: A1(M) J36, A630 in direction of Rotherham for 0.25 mile, left at traffic lights, then 2nd left, right at T junction, Granby club and ground are 0.25 mile on left
Club Secretary: Keith Richards, 5 Markham Square, Edlington, Doncaster, South Yorkshire, DN4 9LS
Fixtures Secretary: Colin Ford, 56 Roberts Road, Edlington, Doncaster, DN12 1JG.
Club Colours: Yellow shirts, black shorts and socks

EGREMONT RUFC

North West 2
Ground Address: Bleach Green, Egremont, Cumbria
Tel: 01946 820645
Brief Directions: M6 J36, follow A595 north towards Workington, Egremont is approx 4 miles south of Whitehaven
Club Secretary: Mr Luke Murphy, 13 Sunnyside, Castle Croft, Egremont, Cumbria. CA22 2BS
Fixtures Secretary: Mr Mark Finlinson, Winder Farm, Nr Frizington, Cumbria.
Tel: (H) 01946 862023
Club Colours: Black and gold

ELLESMERE PORT RUFC

South Lancs & Cheshire 4
Ground Address: The Shell Club, Chester Road, Whitby, Ellesmere Port, Cheshire.
Tel: 0151 2007050 or 7080
Brief Directions: M56, M53 J.8. A5117 toStrawberry Pub. Left in half mile to clubhouse.
Club Secretary: Mr. A.R.J. Dale, 12 Archers Way, Ellesmere Port, Cheshire, CH66 2RY.
Tel: 0151 2001860 Fax: 0151 2001860
Fixtures Secretary: Mr. G. Fenion, 19 Belgrave Drive, Ellesmere Port, Cheshire, CH65 7EJ.
Tel: 0151 3573841
Club Colours: Black with single Red/Yellow Hoops, Black shorts

FLEETWOOD RUFC

North West 2
Ground Address: Broadwaters, Melbourne Avenue, Fleetwood, Lancs, FY7 8AY
Tel: 01253 874774
Brief Directions: Turn off M55 to Blackpool at Fleetwood/Kirkham exit, A585 to Fleetwood, 1st exit off roundabout at Nautical College, sharp left at tram tracks into Crescent, follow round to Melbourne Ave
Club Secretary: B Olsen, 32 Huntingdon Road, Thornton Cleveleys , Lancs FY5 1SR
Tel: (H) 01253 854758 (W) 01253 866336
Fixtures Secretary: A,Thompson, 67 Levens Drive, Poulton -le-Fylde, Lancs. FY6 8EZ
Club Colours: Green and gold hoops

FURNESS RUFC

North Lancs & Cumbria
Ground Address: Strawberry Grounds, Abbey Road, Barrow-in-Furness, Cumbria
Tel: 01229 825226
Brief Directions: At 3rd R/about on Dalton bypass take L. exit for hospital. At mini R/about turn R. onto Abbey Road after approx 1 mile turn L. into Croslands Park Road, entrance 100 yards on R.
Club Secretary: I. McAllister, 14 Jesmond Avenue, Barrow in Furness, Cumbria, LA13 9AW.
Tel: 01229 839806
Fixtures Secretary: D. Troughton, Greystones House, Greystones Lane, Dalton in Furness, Cumbria, LA15 8PX.
Tel: 01229 462586
Club Colours: Blue and white hoops

GARFORTH RUFC

Yorkshire 5 North
Ground Address: Garforth Community College, Lidgett Lane, Garforth, Leeds. LS25 1LJ
Brief Directions: A63 Leeds to Selby road, left into Lidgett Lane, school on right, into main gate, proceed to changing facilities at back of school buildings
Club Secretary: George Shaw, 34 Rose Court, Garforth, Leeds. LS25 1NS
Tel: (H) 0113 286 7193 (W) 01274 732707
Fixtures Secretary: John Daw
Tel: (H) 0113 286 7338
Club Colours: Red, yellow, blue and black quarters, shorts and socks black

GATESHEAD RFC

North East 3
Ground Address: Hedley Lawson Park, Eastwood Gardens, Low Fell, Gateshead. NE9 5UB
Tel: 0191 4200207
Brief Directions: Travelling north A167 into Gateshead, pass 2 sets main lights, turn right Joicey Rd, 2nd left Eastwood Gdns. Travelling south A167, left Springfield Hotel, phone box turn left
Club Secretary: M A Nunn, 30 Limetrees Gardens, Low Fell, Gateshead. NE9 5BE
Tel: (H) 0191 4203089
Fixtures Secretary: Dr.W.D,Hetherington, 97 Kells Lane, Lowfell, Gateshead NE9 5XX.
Tel (H) 0191 4219487
Club Colours: Red,Navy and sky narrow hoops , white shorts

GOOLE RUFC

North East 1
Ground Address: Westfield Bank Sports Complex , Westfield Lane, Hook, Goole, North Humberside. DN14 5PW
Tel: 01405 762018
Brief Directions: M62 J36, straight through 2 sets of traffic lights, continue on road out of Goole, right towards Hook just before Boothferry bridge into Westfield Lane
Club Secretary: I R Higgins, 14 The Meadows, Howden, Goole, North Humberside. DN14 7DX
Tel: (H) 01430 430037 (W) 01405 768621
Fixtures Secretary: P Shand, 4 Kings Close, Pontefract, West Yorks WF8 3PD
Tel: (H) 01977 780652 (W) 01977 703357
Club Colours: Navy blue and gold quarters

GOSFORTH RFC
Durham & Northumberland 2
Ground Address: Bullocksteads Sports Ground, Ponteland Road, Kenton Bank Foot, Newcastle-upon-Tyne NE13 8AH Tel: 0191 286 0088
Brief Directions: Turn off A1 at Airport, go westwards approx one mile and the ground is on right hand side of Ponteland Road.
Club Secretary: Trevor Hogg, 11 Launceston Close, Kingston Park, Newcastle-upon-Tyne. NE3 2XX Tel: (H) 0191 271 1120
Fixtures Secretary: Malcolm Bell, 3 Lansdowne Gardens, Stakeford, Northumberland NE62 5LF
Tel: 01670 851652
Club Colours: Green and white hoops, white shorts, hooped socks.

GREEN GARTH RUFC
Cumbria
Ground Address: Greengarth Hostel, Holmbrook, Cumbria
Tel: 01946 725800
Club Secretary: Robert Eales, 20 Wholehouse Road, Scale, Cumbria. CA20
Tel: (H) 019467 28734
Fixtures Secretary: Steven Edgare
Tel: (H) 019467 841534
Club Colours: Maroon and gold

GREYHOUND
Cumbria
Ground Address: City Sports Ground, Grandstand Road, Hereford HR2 7RL
Tel: 01432 272921
Club Secretary: A Braithwaite, 1 Marlbrooke Road, Redhill, Hereford HR2 7PU
Tel: (H) 01432 272921
Fixtures Secretary: N. Greening, 9 Old School Lane, Hereford HR1 1EU
Tel: (H) 01432 356579

KESWICK RUFC
Ground Address: Davidson Park, Keswick, Cumbria
Tel: 017687 72823
Brief Directions: Follow road past town centre towards West, turn left towards the lake and Borrowdale, then right past lakes Feod Hall
Club Secretary: A. J. Branthwaite, 15 St. Herbert Street, Keswick, Cumbria CA12 4DF
Tel: (H) 017687 74234
Fixtures Secretary: P. Harper, 7 The Hawthorns, Keswick, Cumbria CA12 4LL
Tel: (H) 017687 72668
Club Colours: Navy, green, gold hoops, white shorts, RED SOCKS.

GUISBOROUGH RUFC
Durham & Northumberland 3
Ground Address: Belmangate, Guisborough, Cleveland. TS14 7BB
Tel: 01287 632966
Brief Directions: A19 to A174 Parkway. Leave at slipway at Marton to A172 to R/about. Through town, turn R at memorial. Continue straight into Belmangate.
Club Secretary: Dennis F Childs, 32 Boston Drive, Marton, Middlesborough. TS7 8LZ
Tel: (H) 01642 314081
Fixtures Secretary: J. Weastell, 18 Sudbury, Marton, Middlesex, TS8 9XZ Tel: (H) 01642 317220
Club Colours: Black and amber

HALIFAX RUFC
North East 1
Ground Address: Standeven Memorial Ground, Ovenden Park, Keighley Road, Ovenden, Halifax, West Yorkshire. HX2 8AR
Tel: 01422 365926
Brief Directions: From Halifax town centre take main road to Keighley (A629), HRUFC is approx 2.5 miles from town centre on right behind Moorside Junior School
Club Secretary: M S Smith, The Lowe, Wainstalls, Halifax, West Yorkshire. HX2 7TR
Tel: (H) 01422 882879 (W) 0850 233019
Fixtures Secretary: Glyn Kenyon, 18 Watkinson Rd, Illingworth, Halifax
Tel: (H) 01422 245193
Club Colours: Dark blue, light blue and white bands

HALIFAX VANDALS RUFC
Yorkshire 2
Ground Address: Warley Town Lane, Warley, Halifax, West Yorkshire
Tel: 01422 831704
Club Secretary: Martin Pritchard, 5 Nursery Nook, Hebden Bridge, Halifax HX7 8NA Tel No: 01422 845840
Fixtures Secretary: Nigel Riley. Tel No: 01422 360822
Club Colours: Blue and white thin hoops, navy blue shorts

HALTON RUFC
South Lancs & Cheshire 3
Ground Address: ICI Recreation Ground, Liverpool Road, Widnes, Cheshire
Tel: 0151 424 2355
Brief Directions: Frm M62 J7, A57 W'ington, rt at 1st lights, rt at T jcn, rt after 4th pelican, rt at lights, club on lft. Frm R'corn Brge, towncentre slip, under flyover, lft at r'bout, over next r'bout, rt at lights, club on lft
Club Secretary: S.G.Dennett. 267 Lunts Heath Road,Widnews, CheshireWA8 5BB Tel Nos: 01514243978 (H) 07050 191715 (W)
Fixtures Secretary: D Dyer
Tel: (H) 0151 424 6944
Club Colours: Narrow blue and white horizontal stripes

HARTLEPOOL ATHLETIC RFC
Durham & Northumberland 3
Ground Address: Oakesway Estate, Hartlepool, Co Durham. TS24 0RE
Tel: 01429 274715
Brief Directions: Leave A19 at A179 Hartlepool turn off, follow signs for Headland, ground 3 miles from A19
Club Secretary: Jim Ainslie, 10 Regent Street, Hartlepool, Co Durham. TS24 0QN
Tel: (H) 01429 260003
Fixtures Secretary: John Bentham, 22Tempest Rd., Hartlepool,Co.Durham.TS24 9QH
Tel: (H) 01429 281012
Club Colours: Sky blue

HARTLEPOOL BOYS BRIGADE OLD BOYS RFC
Durham & Northumberland 4
Ground Address: Old Friarage, Headland, Hartlepool (Ground only)
Brief Directions: From north or south, A19, take A179 Hartlepool exit, straight over 4 roundabouts, left at T junction, take left fork, Il Ponte pub, left at fire station,

right onto seafront, ground on left
Club Secretary: G K Faint, 11 Nesbyt Road, Hartlepool. TS24 9NB
Tel: (H) 01429 265674
Fixtures Secretary: I Mulrooney, 6 Carr Street, Hartlepool
Tel: 01429 272254
Club Colours: White with broad black band, black shorts

HARTLEPOOL RFC
Durham & Northumberland 2
Ground Address: Mayfield Park, Easington Road, Hartlepool. TS24 9BA
Tel: 01429 266445
Brief Directions: Leave A19 north of town on A179 over 2 roundabouts, right at 3rd, ground 500m on left
Club Secretary: Mr D,Jones, 14 Turnberry Crescent, Hartlepool TS 27 3PX
Tel: (H) 01429 231125
Fixtures Secretary: Ken Thompson
Tel: (W) 01642 279880
Club Colours: Maroon and White Change Colours: Black and white

HARTLEPOOL ROVERS
North East 3
Ground Address: The Friaridge, Low Warren, Westview Road, Hartlepool, TS24 0BP
Tel: 01429 267741
Brief Directions: Take A19 to the A179 turn off. Follow A1049 (Bypass Hartlepool) for 4 miles to the headland.
Club Secretary: Bill Dale, 21 Knapton Avenue, Billingham, Stockton-on-Tees. TS22 5DJ
Tel: (H) 01642 863791
Fixtures Secretary: Tony Lowe, Alma House, Junction Rd., Stockton-on-Tees. TS20 1PJ. Tel: (H) 01624 530697
Club Colours: White shirts, black shorts, red socks

HARTLEPOOL (WEST) TECHNICAL DAY SCHOOL OLD BOYS RUFC
North East 2
Ground Address: Grayfields, Wiltshire Way, Hartlepool
Tel: 01429 238548
Brief Directions: From A19 take A179 to Hartlepool, right at roundabout, continue for approx 2 miles, left into estate, right at T junction, club on left after 0.5 mile
Club Secretary: D Bramley, 63 Hutton Avenue, Hartlepool
Tel: (H) 01429 263157
Fixtures Secretary: A Cheshire
Tel: (H) 01429 234659
Club Colours: Blue and white

HEATH RUFC
Yorkshire 2
Ground Address: North Dean, Stainland Road, West Vale, Halifax. HX4 8LS
Tel: 01442 372920
Brief Directions: M62 J24, follow Halifax signs at bottom of hill (end of dual c'way), turn left towards Stainland, clubhouse approx 500m on left through used car lot
Club Secretary: Peter Burton, 10 Castle Lane, Ripponden, Sowerby Bridge, W.Yorks. HX6 4JY
Tel No: 01422 824847
Fixtures Secretary: Gary Mason
Tel: (H) 01422 349271 (W) 01422 371909
Club Colours: Emerald, gold and claret

HEATON MOOR RUFC
North Lancs 1
Ground Address: Green Lane, Heaton Moor, Stockport
Tel: 0161 432 3407
Brief Directions: M63 J12, taking A5145 for Didsbury, at 1st set of traffic lights turn right (signed B5169 Heaton Moor/Reddish), Green Lane is 5th road on right
Club Secretary: Peter Jackson, 35 Stanley Road, Heaton Moor, Stockport
Tel: (H) 0161 442 9061 (W)01612471571
Fixtures Secretary: J.Jeskins.
Tel Nos: 0161 436 4867 (H) 0161 485 4372 (W)
Club Colours: Black, red and gold

HELSBY RUFC
South Lancs & Cheshire 3
Ground Address: Helsby Sports and Social Club, Chester Road, Helsby, Cheshire
Tel: 01928 722267
Brief Directions: Head west along M56 J14, left at roundabout, continue for 1 mile to lights, go straight ahead and pass the Helsby Arms pub, club is next turning on left
Club Secretary: C.Johnson, Greenfields, Primrose Lane,Alvaney,Cheshire WA69BS
Tel: 01928 724180 (H) 01928 598849 (W)
Fixtures Secretary: A Ryder, 64 Chester Road, Helsby, Warrington, Cheshire
Tel: (H) 01928 723733
Club Colours: Black and gold hoops

HEMSWORTH RUFC
Yorkshire 1
Ground Address: Moxon Fields, Lowfield Road, Hemsworth, Pontefract, West Yorkshire. WF9 4JT
Tel: 01977 610078
Brief Directions: Pontefract Road from Town centre turn right after passing Hemsworth School.
Club Secretary: M ark Roberts, The Elms, Stockingate, South Kirkby, Pontefract. WF9 3QX
Tel: (H) 01977 644379
Fixtures Secretary: N.Jennings, 8 Churchfield Terrace, Cudworth, Barnsley.
Club Colours: Navy blue quarters, navy blue shorts and socks

HESSLE RUFC
Yorkshire 3
Ground Address: Livingstone Road, Hessle, East Yorkshire
Tel: 01482 643430
Brief Directions: Follow M62/A63 to Hull, 2 miles after traffic lights take Humber Bridge turn off, 2nd left at r'bout to Hessle Foreshore, 1st right into Woodfield Ln, follow into L'stone Rd
Club Secretary: T J Sleight, 69 Tranby Avenue, Hessle. HU13 0PX
Tel: (H) 01482 643262
Fixtures Secretary: P K Denton
Tel: (H) 01482 561338
Club Colours: Green, black and white irregular hoops

HIGHTOWN RUFC
South Lancs & Cheshire 4
Ground Address: The Hightown Club, Sandy Lane, Hightown, Merseyside. L38 Tel: 0151 929 2330

Brief Directions: Main Liverpool/Southport Rd (was By-Pass) sign posts for Hightown left hand side before railwlay bridge
Club Secretary: J D Barker, 28 Parkfield Road, Waterloo, LiverpoolL22 4RH Tel: (H) 0151 474 0514
Fixtures Secretary: R. Baker, 17 Mornington Avenue, Crosby, Liverpool, L23 0SA. Tel: 0151 920 7387
Club Colours: Blue, white and brown Hoops

HOLMES CHAPEL RUFC

South Lancs & Cheshire 4
Ground Address: RPR Sports & Social Club, Brookl;ands, Holmes Chapel, CW4 8BE
Tel: 01477 532018
Brief Directions: Ground is on A54 (Holmes Chapel - Congleton Rd) on outskirts of village just beyond Railway Station
Club Secretary: Steve Ranger, 16 Balmoral Drive, Holmes Chapel, Cheshire. CW4 7HY
Tel: (H) 01477 533765 (W) 0850 003869
Fixtures Secretary: John Leary
Tel: (H) 01606 554614 (W) 01606 593411
Club Colours: Blue and gold hoops

HORDEN WELFARE RUFC

North East 1
Ground Address: Northumberland Street, Horden, Peterlee, County Durham
Tel: 0191 5863501
Brief Directions: A19 into Peterlee, follow signs for Horden, left onto Sunderland Rd, turn right at Bell Hotel, 100 yards to club house
Club Secretary: Joseph Watson, Clairemont, Sunderland Rd., Horden, Peterlee, Co. Durham. SR8 4PF.
Tel No: 0191 5861042
Fixtures Secretary: John Fenwick, 1 Leyburn Place, Co Durham SR8 4BD
Tel: (H) 0191 5866540
Club Colours: Maroon and Sky Blue hoops, black shorts

HORNSEA RUFC

Yorkshire 4
Ground Address: Clubhouse, Westwood Avenue, Hornsea. HU18 1BB
Tel: 01964 534181
Brief Directions: Leave Hornsea on Atwick road. Turn left onto Westwood Avenue, opposite school playing fields.
Club Secretary: Ralph Voke, 8 Carlton Avenue, Hornsea, East Yorks, HU18 1JG
Tel: (H) 01964 534850
Fixtures Secretary: Roger Mc Latchie, 18 Shaftsbury Avenue, Hornsea, East Yorks.
Tel: (H) 01964 534497
Club Colours: Black with green and white hoops across chest

HOUGHTON RUFC

Durham & Northumberland 1
Ground Address: Dairy Lane, Houghton le Spring, Tyne & Wear
Tel: 0191 5841460
Brief Directions: Situated on A1052, Houghton to Chester-le-Street road, opposite Houghton Police Station, 0.25 mile west of A690
Club Secretary: Mrs. Lorraine Walls, 38 Hopgarth Gardens, Chester-Le-Street, Co. Durham, DH3 3RH
Tel: 0191 3883642
Fixtures Secretary: John Felton, 37 Larchwood, Harraton, Washington, Tyne & Wear, NE38 9BT.
Tel: (H) 0191 4161467
Club Colours: Black shirts with white hoop, black shorts, black socks

HOYLAKE RUGBY FC

South Lancs & Cheshire 3
Ground Address: Melrose Avenue, Hoylake, Wirral, Merseyside
Tel: 0151 632 2538
Brief Directions: M53 exit for West Kirkby and Moreton, travel through to Hoylake, left at roundabout, cross over level crossing at Hoylake Station and follow direction signs
Club Secretary: Mr D Western, The White Cottage, 118 Irby Road, Heswall, Wirral, Merseyside. L61 6XG
Tel: (W) 0151 648 3208
Fixtures Secretary: P. Lea, 7 Albert Road, West Kirby, Wirral, Merseyside.
Tel: 0151 625 3647
Club Colours: Red, green and white hoops

HUDDERSFIELD RUFC

North East 3
Ground Address: Lockwood Park, Brewery Drive, Lockwood, Huddersfield. HD1 3UR
Tel: 01484 423864 Fax: 01484 469880
Brief Directions: Leave Huddersfield town centre on A616 signed Holmfirth, 0.75 mile straight across lights on B6108 signed Meltham, left after 300yds into ground
Club Secretary: Ian D Cleave, c/o Club
Tel: 01484 306045
Fixtures Secretary: Simon Irving
c/o club
Tel No: 01484 469801
Club Colours: Claret , gold and white.

HULL RUFC

North East 2
Ground Address: Haworth Park, Emmott Road, Hull. HU6 7AB
Tel: 01482 802119
Brief Directions: Follow ring road signs onto Beverley Road Hull, the ground is signposted from there
Club Secretary: D J Ward, 78 St Margarets Avenue, Cottingham, Hull. HU16 5NB
Tel: (H) 01482 842292 (W) 01482 325242
Fixtures Secretary: Steve Watson, 236 Bracknell Avenue, Hull HU5 4QG
Tel: 01482 341946
Club Colours: Black with gold and red band

HULLENSIANS RUFC

Yorkshire 2
Ground Address: Springhead Lane, Anlaby Common, Hull
Tel: 01482 651086
Brief Directions: A63 (Boothferry Road) into Hull. Left turn oppositeGreen Arrow garage and turn right at T junction. Then left at roundabout into Springfield Way and first right into Springfield Lane.
Club Secretary: Peter Francis Jones, 5 Sherwood Drive, Chanterlands Avenue, Hull HU5 4DP
Fixtures Secretary: Tim Robinson, 79 Huntly Drive, Chanterlands Avenue, Hull.HU5 4DP
Tel: (H) 01482 348181 (W) 01482 323631
Club Colours: Red and black

ILKLEY RUFC
Yorkshire 1
Ground Address: Stacks Field, Denton Road, Ilkley, West Yorkshire. LS29 0AD
Tel: 01943 607037
Brief Directions: From lights in town, turn towards the river down Brook Street, the ground is visible 300 metres on right
Club Secretary: J.K. Bernard, 36 Dale View,Ilkley, West Yorks. LS29 9BP
Tel No: 01943 602945
Fixtures Secretary: J.E.Martin. Tel No: 01943 607732
Club Colours: Red, white and black hooped shirts ,white shorts

JARROVIANS RUFC
Durham & Northumberland 3
Ground Address: Lukes Lane Estate, Hebburn, Tyne & Wear
Tel: 0370 964 113
Brief Directions: North end of A1(M)/A194(M), continue north along A194, at 1st roundabout turn left, then immediate right, follow road along full length, ground on right
Club Secretary: M.B.W.McCoy, 61 Frobisher Street, Hebburn, Tyne & Wear NE31 2XE
Tel: 0191 428 2750
Fixtures Secretary: Dave King., 53 Peterborough Way, Fellgate, Jarrow, Tyne & Wear
Tel: (H) 0191 4891611
Club Colours: Black and amber hoops

KEIGHLEY RUFC
North East 1
Ground Address: Skipton Road, Utley, Keighley, West Yorkshire. BD20 6DX
Tel: 01535 602174
Brief Directions: Access to ground is from former A629 from Keighley to Skipton, ground is on right travelling north just on outskirts of town. NB no access from present A629 Aire V'ly rd
Club Secretary: M T Greaves, Holmlea, Summerhill Lane, Steeton, Keighley, West Yorkshire. BD20 6RX
Tel: (H) 01535 653192 (W) 01535 605646
Fixtures Secretary: J Midgley
Tel: 01535 214545 (W) 01535 605311
Club Colours: Scarlet, white and green hoops

KIRKBY LONSDALE RUFC
North West 1
Ground Address: The Club House, Underley Park, Kirkby Lonsdale, via Carnforth, Lancs
Tel: 015242 71780
Brief Directions: M6 J36, 1st left turn signpost town centre, keep left sign KL RUFC Old Hutton, 0.5 mile turn right
Club Secretary: Richard Harkness, Meadowgarth, Fairbank, Kirkby Lonsdale, Via Carnforth, Lancs
Tel: (H) 015242 71137 (W) 015242 72111
Fixtures Secretary: Paul Newell, Primrose Cottage, Thorns Lane, Sedbergh Cumbria
Tel: 015396 20091
Club Colours: Red, black and amber hoops and socks, black shorts

KNARESBOROUGH RUFC
Yorkshire 5 North
Ground Address: Hay-A-Park, Park Lane, off Chain Lane, North Yorkshire
Tel: 01423 862525
Brief Directions: Follow A59 to centre of Knaresborough, at traffic lights by Board Inn turn north, away from Calcutt (signpost), take 2nd right, at school, follow on to end of road
Club Secretary: Antony Merrin, 73 West End Avenue, Harrogate, N. Yorks HG2 9BX Tel: 01423 569245
Fixtures Secretary: Steve McGrail, 33 Westville Oval, Harrogate, N.Yorks. Tel: 01423 522521
Club Colours: Blue and gold hooped shirts, navy shorts and socks

KNOTTINGLEY RUFC
Yorkshire 3
Ground Address: Knottingley RUFC, Howards Field, Marsh Lane, Knottingley. WF11 9DE
Tel: 01977 672438
Brief Directions: Onto A645 main road toward Knottingley, turn off at town hall/St Botolophs Church, follow road 500m past Cherry Tree pub, turn left just before lights at bridge to Howards Field
Club Secretary: Adrian Carley, 50 Womersley Road, Knottingley, West Yorkshire Tel: (H) 01977 677690
Fixtures Secretary: John Alexander Tel: (H) 07899 732757
Club Colours: Blue and white shirts, blue shorts and socks.

LEEDS CORINTHIANS RUFC
Yorkshire 3
Ground Address: Nutty Slack, Middleton District Centre, Leeds. 10-4RA
Tel: 0113 2711574
Brief Directions: M62 J28 to Leeds or M1 city centre to Dewsbury follow signs for A653, turn onto Middleton ringroad at Tommy Wass pub, right at 1st r'bout and go to rear of supermarket onto shale track to club
Club Secretary: Glenn Maynard, 60 Middleton Park Grove, Leeds 10 4BQ
Tel: 0113 2711728
Fixtures Secretary: Mr G Mapplebeck
Tel: (H) 01924 828809 (W) 0113 2457205
Club Colours: Black with gold trim

LEEDS ROUNDHEADS RUFC
Yorkshire 5 North
Ground Address: Chandos Park, Chandos Avenuue, Leeds, LS8 1QX.
Brief Directions: From ringroad/A61 R/about go into Leeds down Harrogate Road, through lights (2sets) turn L. down Lidgett Lane (opp. St. Gemmas Hospice). Chandos Avenue is half mile on R.
Club Secretary: Jenny MacDonald-Smith, Fairfield, Almscliffe Drive, Huby, Leeds, LS17 0HB.
Tel: 01423 734871
Fixtures Secretary: Les Jackson, 4 Gledhow Wood Avenue, Leeds, LS8 1NY.
Tel: 0113 2665544 (Fax & Phone)
Club Colours: Royal Blue/White/Yellow

LEIGH RUFC
North West 2
Ground Address: Round Ash Park, Hand Lane, Pennington, Leigh WN7 3NA
Tel: 01942 673526 or 01924 516024
Brief Directions: Pennington area of Leigh off St. Helens Rd on to Beech Walk. Club & grounds Hand Lane - continuation of Beech Walk.
Club Secretary: A J Westwell, 140 Chestnut Drive South, Leigh, Lancs. WN7 3JY. Tel: 01942 671017
Fixtures Secretary: Tom Hughes, 2 Launceston Drive, Hindley Green, Wigan, Lancs. Tel: (H) 01942 257427
Club Colours: Black with amber hoops

LEODIENSIAN RUFC
Yorkshire 1
Ground Address: Crag Lane (off King Lane), Alwoodley, Leeds. LS17 5PR
Tel: 0113 2673409
Brief Directions: Leeds ringroad (outer) to Moortown Sainsburys, from Sainsburys travel away from Leeds on King Lane for 0.75 mile, ground on left hand side
Club Secretary: John Hastie, 132 Buckstone Avenue, Alwoodley, Leeds. LS17 5ET
Tel: (H) 01132 689881
Fixtures Secretary: Michael Crook
Tel: (H) 01132 260455 (W) 01535 636116
Club Colours: Navy blue and gold

LITTLEBOROUGH RUFC
North Lancs 2
Ground Address: Deep Lane, Rakewood, Hollingworth Lake, Littleborough, Lancashire. OL15 0AP
Tel: 01706 370220
Brief Directions: Take J21 off M62 .Left at r'about, rt at traffic lights and left into Kiln Lane. Then take left into Wild Horse Lane, rt at mini r'bout follow signs to Hollingworth Lake. Rt to Rakewood at Fish pub.
Club Secretary: Darren Mave, 11 Buersil Avenue, Balderstone, Rochdale.
Tel: 01706 32466
Fixtures Secretary: Mr Harry Hanson
Tel: (H) 0161 872 2141
Club Colours: Green, black and amber

LIVERPOOL COLLEGIATE OLD BOYS RUFC
South Lancs & Cheshire 3
Ground Address: Liverpool Cricket Club, Aigburth Rd., Grassendale, Liverpool.19
Brief Directions: M62 Follow Queens Drive to Aigburth Road (Ohone secretary if further details are needed)
Club Secretary: M Hesketh, 37 Hattons Lane, Childwall, Liverpool 16.
Tel: 0151 475 8495
Fixtures Secretary: L.Brown. 2 Barchester Drive, Riverside Park Otterspool, Liverpool L16 7QR
Club Colours: Light blue, dark blue quarters

LOSTOCK RFC
North Lancs 2
Ground Address: Lostock Lane, Lostock, Bolton, Lancashire
Brief Directions: M61 J6, turn right at roundabout on A6027 to Horwich, 1 mile on turn right before traffic lights, ground on left at BAC Lostock
Club Secretary: R Fletcher, 19 Shaftesbury Avenue, Lostock, Bolton. BL6 4AP
Tel: (H) 01204 698362
Fixtures Secretary: B.Jubb, 5 Lower Makinson Fold, Horwich, Bolton BLG 7PD
Tel: 01204 696998
Club Colours: All Black

LUCAS
South Lancs & Cheshire 4
Ground Address: No Details?
Brief Directions: No Details?
Club Secretary: No Details?
Fixtures Secretary: No Details?
Club Colours: No Details?

LYMM RFC
North 2
Ground Address: Crouchley Lane, Lymm, Cheshire. WA13 0AT
Tel: 01925 753212
Brief Directions: M6 J20 to Lymm, 1.5 miles right at T junction, 0.5 mile turn right into Crouchley Lane, club 200 yds on right
Club Secretary: Jophn Cartwright, 12 Parke Gate Road, Stockton Heath, Warrington, WA4 2AP.
Fixtures Secretary: Chris Monks
Tel: (H) 01925 262904
Club Colours: Black, green, white

MALTON & NORTON RUFC LTD
Yorkshire 2
Ground Address: The Gannock, Old Malton, Malton, North Yorkshire
Tel: 01653 694657
Brief Directions: From A64 York to Scarborough - take bypass and enter Malton on the Pickering road, club is on left. From Malton head towards Old Malton and club is on right
Club Secretary: C J Whincup, Arboretum, Keld Head Hall, Middleton Road, Pickering. YO18 8NR

Tel: (H) 01751 477170
Fixtures Secretary: J Q Knock
Tel: (H & W) 01904 421105
Club Colours: Black shorts, red, white and black hooped shirts, black socks

MARIST RUFC
Yorkshire 4
Ground Address: Cranbrook Avenue, Cottingham Road, Hull Tel: 01482 859216
Brief Directions: From M62 follow signs for Universities, then continue to Cranbrook Avenue along Cottingham Road
Club Secretary: Mick Jones, 52 Ferriby Road, Hessle, HU13 0HT
Tel BNo: 01482 643362
Fixtures Secretary: Ralph Ayre, 92 Aukland Ave, Cottingham Road, Hull HU6
Tel: (H) 01482 804166
Club Colours: Blue & white

MARPLE RUFC
South Lancs & Cheshire 2
Ground Address: Wood Lane Playing Fields, Marple, Stockport
Brief Directions: Changing Rooms at Ridge College Marple, A626 into Marple, turn right into Cross Lane at Bowling Green pub, turn left into Buxton Lane, Ridge College on the right
Club Secretary: Richard Hammersley, 9 Ridge Avenue, Marple, Stockport SK6 7HJ
Tel: 0161 427 5881
Fixtures Secretary: N Hawkley, 109 Woodville Drive, Marple , Stockport
Tel: 0161 449 9985
Club Colours: Red and black Change Colours: Black

MEDICALS RFC
North East 3
Ground Address: Cartington Terrace, Heaton, Newcastle
Tel: 0191 2761473
Club Secretary: D.W.Reeve, 3 Station Road North, Forest Hall, Newcastle. NE12 0AR.
Fixtures Secretary: Dr A Ramshaw, 19 Douglas Avenue, Gosforth, Newcastle. NE3 4XD
Club Colours: Maroon with white shorts, maroon & white socks

MERSEYSIDE POLICE RUFC
South Lancs & Cheshire 1
Ground Address: Police Sports Ground, Riversdale Road, Aigburth, L'pool 19, Merseyside
Tel: 0151 427 2200
Brief Directions: Turn into Riversdale Road from Aigburth Road (A561) at Liverpool Cricket Club - half mile on Left before the river.
Club Secretary: D/Sgt Eric Sheppard, 38 Lynmouth Road, Aigburth, L'pool Merseyside. L17 6AW
Tel: (H) 0151 475 9386
Fixtures Secretary: Andrew Doyle. Tel no: (H) 0151 230 0495
Club Colours: Blue, black and white quarters

MILLOM RUFC
North Lancs & Cumbria
Ground Address: Wilson Park, Haverigg, Millom, Cumbria. LA18 4LU
Tel: 01229 770401
Brief Directions: Upon entering Haverigg, past Harbour pub towards the beach and play area, pass the Inshore Rescue Station, club house is 200m down the tarmac lane
Club Secretary: G Edward Whitfield, 13 Willowside Park, Haverigg, Millom, Cumbria. LA18 4PT
Tel: (H) 01229 774876
Fixtures Secretary: Ian Shovelton
Tel: (H) 01229 773743
Club Colours: Blue and white

MONTELL CARRINGTON
North Lancs 2
Ground Address: Carrington Works, Manchester Road, Carrington, Manchester M31 4AJ
Club Secretary: Tony Kelly, The Vine, 133 Washway Road, Sale, M33 1UD.
Tel: 0161 973 0139
Fixtures Secretary: As Above
Club Colours: Red and yellow quarters

MOORE RUFC
South Lancs & Cheshire 2
Ground Address: The Clubhouse, Moss Lane, Moore, Warrington. WA4 6UU
Tel: 01925 740473
Brief Directions: A56 from M56 towards Warrington, left at 1st set of traffic lights, right into Moss Lane in Moore Village
Club Secretary: John Stockton, 3 Hayes Lane, Appleton, Warrington. WA4 3DA
Tel: (H) 01925 266025 (W) 0161 973 1505
Fixtures Secretary: P J Woollacott
Tel: (H) 01925 266576 (W) 0161 228 6282
Club Colours: Black with gold band

MOORTOWN RUFC
Yorkshire 3
Ground Address: Far Moss, off The Avenue, Alwoodley, Leeds, West Yorkshire
Tel: 0113 2678243
Brief Directions: From the ring road turn up past the entrance to Sainsburys, 1.5 miles turn right onto The Avenue, 0.5 mile turn right into Far Moss
Club Secretary: Graham Spark, 7 Hall Cliffe Grove, Horbury, Wakefield. WF4 6DE
Tel: (H) 01924 271808
Fixtures Secretary: Clive Forbes, 19 The mount, Alwoodley, Leeds. LS17 RH
Tel: (H) 0113 2269490
Club Colours: Maroon with green and white hoops, blue shorts.

MORESBY RUFC
Cumbria
Ground Address: Walkmill Park, Old Pit Road, Moresby Parks, Whitehaven, Cumbria
Tel: 01946 695984
Brief Directions: M6 Junction 40 (Penrith) A66 for 35 miles. Turn left onto A595 for approx 7 miles, then left up Swallow Brow. Ground is approx 2 miles.
Club Secretary: Thomas Callan, 15 Burton High Close, Harras Moor Park, Whitehaven, Cumbria CA28 6SD
Tel: 01946 694583
Fixtures Secretary: Syd Bray, 19 Sneckyeat Road, Hensingham, Cumbria
Tel: 01946 694199
Club Colours: Red shirts, white shorts

MORPETH RFC (50TH ANNIVERSARY)
North 2
Ground Address: Grange House Field, Mitford Road, Morpeth. NE61 1RJ
Tel: 01670 512508
Brief Directions: North from Newcastle on A1 from Morpeth centre travelling north, left after telephone exchange onto Mitford Road, entrance on right past the school
Club Secretary: Ken Fraser, Solway House, De Merley Road, Morpeth. NE61 1HZ
Tel: (H) 01670 511208 (W) 01642800800
Fixtures Secretary: Bill Hewitt, The Birches, Lane End Farm, Felton, Northumberlamd
Tel: (H) 01670 787757
Club Colours: Red, wite and navy irregular hoops, navy shorts.

MOSBOROUGH RUFC
Yorkshire 4
Ground Address: Mosborough WMC, Station Road, Mosborough, Sheffield, 19
Tel: 0114 248 5546
Brief Directions: M1 J30, take A616 towards Sheffield, at 2nd set of lights turn right, clubhouse on left
Club Secretary: Lawrence S Hannon, 12 Stonegravels Croft, Halfway, Sheffield. S19 5HP
Tel: (H) 0114 248 8425 (W) 01246 854650
Fixtures Secretary: S C Collins
Tel: (H) 0170 953 1732
Club Colours: Black and white hooped shirts, black shorts

MOSSLEY HILL RUFC
South Lancs & Cheshire 4
Ground Address: Mossley Hill Road, Liverpool 18
Tel: 0151 7244377
Brief Directions: From M62 take ring road towards Liverpool Airport. Turn left onto Allerton Road, right onto Rose Lane (at Tescos) Ground is behind Church at top of Rose Lane.
Club Secretary: Mr A Pealing, 48 Heathfield Park, Widnes. Wa8 9WY
Fixtures Secretary: Mr J Parr, 30 Ridgtor Road, Liverpool 25
Tel: (H) 0151 4287625
Club Colours: Maroon and gold quarters or hoops

NESTLE ROWNTREE RUFC
Yorkshire 5 North
Ground Address: Nestle UK (York) , Mille Crux, Haxby Road, York
Tel: 01904 623933
Brief Directions: From York outer ring road (A1237), take New Earswick turn off thr r'about. Through the village and ground is on left, 1/2 mile from the 3rd small r'about.
Club Secretary: Ashleigh Walters, 26 Kerver Lane, Dunnington, York YO19 5SH
Tel: 01904 489286 (H) 01904 602274
Fixtures Secretary: Grahem Lavender, 52 Wilton Rise, Holgate, York
Tel: (H) 01904 626897
Club Colours: Red, black and white quarters

NETHERHALL
North West 2
Ground Address: Netherhall Park, Netherhall Road, Maryport
Brief Directions: A66 to Cockermouth Head to Workington, right at roundabout for Maryport, turn left off bypass head into Maryport, right at lights A596 to Carlisle, club 400yds on right
Club Secretary: Paul Bartlett, 66 Garborough Close, Crosby, Maryport. CA15 6RZ
Tel: (H) 01900 818420
Fixtures Secretary: L Rumney
Tel: (H) 01900 811440
Club Colours: Claret and gold

NEWTON AYCLIFFE RUFC
Durham & Northumberland 4
Ground Address: Newton Aycliffe Sports Club, Moore Lane, Newton Aycliffe, Co Durham. DL5 5AG
Tel: 01325 312768
Brief Directions: Enter Newton Aycliffe on Central Ave, at the roundabout turn L. on Shafto Way take 3rd L. (Creighton Rd) then lst R. Moore Lane, carry on to the end of the road.
Club Secretary: Mr Sean Carroll, 91 Washington Crescent, Newton Aycliffe, Co Durham. DL5 4BE
Tel: (H) 01325 320874 (M) 0973 371971
Fixtures Secretary: Mr Charles Heslop, 35 Holly Hill, Shildon, Co. Durham, DL4 2DB.
Tel: 0976 305287
Club Colours: Green, amber and maroon

NEWTON-LE -WILLOWS RUFC
South Lancs & Cheshire 1
Ground Address: Crow Lane East, Newton-le-Willows, Merseyside Tel: 01925 224591
Brief Directions: M6 J23, take signs for Newton A49, continue down Ashton Rd (A49) until mini roundabout with Oak Tree pub on right, right into Crow Lane, club 300 yds on right
Club Secretary: David Hughes, 127 Birley St., Newton-le-Willows, Merseyside Wa12 9UN.
Tel no: 01925 221304
Fixtures Secretary: Steve Kruger, 2 Camelot Close, Newton-le-Willows, Merseyside.
Tel No: 01925 221937
Club Colours: Royal blue and gold hoops

NORTH MANCHESTER & OLDHAM COLLEGES RUFC
North Lancs 2
Ground Address: Greengate/Victoria Avenue East, Moston, Manchester Tel: 0161 682 9234
Club Secretary: Brian H Stott, 8 Barlea Avenue, New Moston, Manchester. M40 3WL
Tel: (H) 0161 682 0541 (W) 0161 681 1582
Fixtures Secretary: Jason Malone
Tel: (H) 0161 653 5020
Club Colours: Green, black and white hoops

NORTH RIBBLESDALE RUFC
North East 2
Ground Address: Grove Park, Lower Greenfoot, Settle, North Yorkshire
Tel: 01729 822755
Brief Directions: Leave A65 at roundabout on southern outskirts of town, into town turning right at Falcon Manor Hotel, ground 0.25 mile on left
Club Secretary: C.V.Sharpe, 1 Mains Road,Rathmell, nr Settle, N.Yorks BD24 0LH
Tel NO: 01729 840679
Fixtures Secretary: R.T.Graveson. Tel Nos: (H)01729 823559 (W) 01729 825252
Club Colours: Royal blue and white. Change Colours: Maroon

NORTH SHIELDS RFC
Durham & Northumberland 2
Ground Address: Preston Playing Fields, Preston Village, North Shields, Tyne & Wear
Tel: 0191 257 7352
Brief Directions: From Tyne Tunnel (south) or A1/A19 (north) take A1058, follow signs for Tynemouth, club is situated next to Tynemouth Swimming Baths
Club Secretary: David Daniels, 1 Highcross Road, North Shields, Tyne & Wear
Tel: (H) 0191 252 6395 (W) 0191 253 1329
Fixtures Secretary: A,G, Shield, 9 Cresswell Avenue, North Shields, Tyne & Wear NE29 9BQ
Tel No: 0191 259 0402
Club Colours: Royal blue and white hoops, white shorts

NORTHALLERTON RUFC
Yorkshire 1
Ground Address: Brompton Lodge, Northallerton Road, Brompton, Northallerton, North Yorkshire. DL6 2PZ
Tel: 01609 773496
Brief Directions: Brompton Road. Left at filling station. Club 1/4 mile on left.
Club Secretary: D Middlemiss, 13 Quaker Lane, Northhallerton, Yorks.
Tel: (H) 01609 779945
Fixtures Secretary: A Bradley, 15 Borrowby Ave., Northallerton, N. Yorkshire.
Tel: (H) 01609 772743
Club Colours: Green, amber and white

NORTHWICH RUFC
North West 2
Ground Address: Moss Farm Reception Centre, Moss Farm, Moss Road, Winnington, Northwich, Cheshire.
Tel: 01606 79987
Brief Directions: Follow directions from Northwich town centre to swimming pool
Club Secretary: Dave Sargent, 12 Sydney Street, Greenbank, Northwich, CW8 4AP. Tel: (H) 01606 783335
Fixtures Secretary: Paul Hughes, 14 Woodland Road, Hartford, Northwich, CW8 1NS
Tel: (H) 01606 76817 (W) 01270 616391
Club Colours: Black shirts, black shorts

NOVOCASTRIANS RFC LTD
Durham & Northumberland 1
Ground Address: Sutherland Park, The Drive, High Heaton, Newcastle upon Tyne. NE7 7SY
Tel: 0191 2661247
Brief Directions: From A19 or N'castle Central Motorway take A6127M and A1058 signed N'castle - Tynemouth. Exit on slip road A188 to Killingworth. NVOS. RFC signs at The Drive. Club on left.
Club Secretary: Brian Chater, 100 Malvern Road, Preston Grange, North Shields, Tyne & Wear. NE29 9ES
Tel: (H) 0191 2576885
Fixtures Secretary: Bob Fay
Tel: (H) 0191 4873393 (W) 0191 3862714
Club Colours: Red, black and white hoops

OLD ALDWINIANS RUFC
North 2
Ground Address: Audenshaw Park, Droylsden Road, Audenshaw, Manchester. M34 5SN Tel: 0161 3011001
Brief Directions: East of Manchester, at junction of the A662 /635 Nr. Snipe Retail Park.
Club Secretary: Mr Chris Daly, 60 Green Lane, Hollingworth, Hyde, Cheshire. SK14 8JQ
Tel: (P&F 01457 762402 e.mail.Aldwinians@aol.com.
Fixtures Secretary: Alan Whalley, 190 Greenside Lane, Droylsden, Manchester. M35 6RR. Tel: (H)0161 3700921 (W)0161 2231353 Ext 246
Club Colours: Red and white narrow hoops. Blue shorts/socks

OLD ANSELMIANS RUFC
South Lancs & Cheshire 2
Ground Address: Malone Field, Eastham Village Road, Eastham, Wirral Tel: 0151 327 1613
Brief Directions: M53 J5, take A41 towards Birkenhead, approx 400yds turn right into Eastham Village Rd, follow road for 0.5 mile, clubhouse on left opposite shops
Club Secretary: Tony Neville, 33 Stapleton Avenue, Greasby, Wirral. L49 2QT
Tel: (H) 0151 678 4154 (W) 0151 350 1696
Fixtures Secretary: Tony McArdle
Tel: 0151 342 1470
Club Colours: Blue, gold and white hoops

OLD BEDIANS RFC
North Lancs 1
Ground Address: Underbank Farm, Millgate Lane, East Didsbury, Manchester. M20 5QX
Tel: 0161 445 8862
Club Secretary: Mr Ian Wilson, 7 Brooklands Close, Denton, Manchester. M34 3PL
Tel: (H) 0161 320 3392 (W) 0161 287 7760 (Fx) 287 7761
Fixtures Secretary: G Tucker
Tel: (H) 0161 445 2358
Club Colours: Royal blue shirts, white shorts

OLD BRODLEIANS RUFC
North East 2
Ground Address: Woodhead, Denholme Gate Road, Hipperholme, Halifax
Tel: 01422 202708
Brief Directions: M62 J26, follow A58 signs to Halifax, after 3.75 miles turn right at Hippodrome lights, continue up hill for 0.5 mile, club on left about 250 yds after Shell petrol station
Club Secretary: Mr Simon Heaton, Sutcliffe Wood Farm, Woodbottom Lane, Hove Edge, Brighouse. HD6 2QW
Tel: (H) 01484 721628 (W) 01274 700115
Fixtures Secretary: Mr M Hey, 2 Sunnybank Cres., Sowerby Bridge, Halifax.
Tel: (H) 01422 839614 (W) 01924 490803
Club Colours: Black, red and white shirts, black shorts

OLD CROSSLEYANS RUFC
North East 1
Ground Address: Standeven House, Broomfield Avenue, Halifax, West Yorkshire. HX3 0JF
Tel: 01422 363000
Brief Directions: M62 Exit 24. A629 towards Halifax at 3rd set of lights. Left at A646 towards Rochdale /Burnley. Left at 2nd mini roundabout.
Club Secretary: Richard A Davies, 4 Warley Dene, Holme Road, Warley, Halifax. HA2 7RS
Tel: (H) 01422 832218
Fixtures Secretary: Derek Ainley
Tel: (H) 01422 368233
Club Colours: Blue, white and amber

OLD MODERNIANS RUFC

Yorkshire 4
Ground Address: The Clubhouse, Cookridge Lane, Cookridge, Leeds, West Yorkshire. LS16 7ND
Tel: 0113 267 1075
Brief Directions: A660 north from Leeds until 1/4 mile past junction with A6120 ring road at Lawnswood. Fork left at cockridge, ground 2 miles on right
Club Secretary: J.C,Bracewell, 8m Holly Park, Huby LS17 0BT
Tel No: 01423 734782
Fixtures Secretary: D Carter
Tel: (H) 0113 267 9718
Club Colours: Red and black hoops shirts and socks, black shorts

OLD OTLIENSIANS RUFC

Yorkshire 2
Ground Address: Chaffer's Field, Pool Road, Otley, West Yorkshire LS21
Tel: 01943 461476
Brief Directions: From Otley town centre, take A659 to Harrogate, turn right at Stephen Smiths Garden Centre, follow sign to clubhouse
Club Secretary: D Taylor Esq, 39 The Whartons, Otley, West Yorkshire. LS21 2AG
Tel: (H) 01943 850913 (W & FAX) 01423 553075
Fixtures Secretary: Dr A S Normanton
Tel: (H) 01642 723199 (W) 01642 467144
Club Colours: Navy blue, royal blue and white narrow hoops

OLD RISHWORTHIAN RUFC

Yorkshire 3
Ground Address: The Clubhouse, Copley, Halifax, West Yorkshire. HX3 0UG
Tel: 01422 353919
Brief Directions: M62 J24 follow signs to Halifax, at roundabout take 2nd exit, 2 miles turn left to Sowerby Bridge, enter Copley, turn left at Volunteer pub, follow road into Copley village, club on left
Club Secretary: D W Butler, Keepens, Shaw Lane, Holywell Green, Halifax. HX4 9DH
Tel: (H) 01422 371672 (W)0113 204 3300
Fixtures Secretary: R Wadsworth, Abbotsroyd Cottage, Rochdale Rd, Barkisland, Halifax, West Yorks.
Tel: (H) 01422 822113 (W) 01484 845740
Club Colours: Maroon, white and black hoops

OLDERSHAW RUFC

North West 1
Ground Address: Belvidere Recreation Ground, Belvidere Road, Wallasey, Cheshire.
Tel: 0151 638 4379
Brief Directions: J.1 M53 to New Brighton, turn 2nd R. after golf club, 2nd L. into Grove Rd, turn R. at traffic lights. Ground is half mile on right hand side.
Club Secretary: Mr. A. P. Grabe, 19 Beresford Road, Wallasey, Cheshire, CH45 0JJ.
Tel: 0151 5131470H - 0151 5129535W.
Fixtures Secretary: Mr Peter Purland. 63 Croxteth Road, Liverpool, L8 3SF.
Tel: 0151 733 4854 H
Club Colours: Navy blue with gold hoops Navy blue shorts

OLDHAM RUFC

North Lancs & Cumbria
Ground Address: Manor Park, Bryth Road, Bardsley, Oldham. OL8 2TJ Tel: 0161 624 6383
Brief Directions: Off the main A627 Oldham to Ashton road, behind Bardsley Church
Club Secretary: T J Brown, 12 Tilton Street, Oldham. OL1 4JA
Tel: (H) 0161 620 1878
Fixtures Secretary: T Park, 79 Crofton Avenue, Timperley, Cheshire
Tel: 0161 832 4551
Club Colours: Red and white hoops , navy shorts

ORMSKIRK RUFC

North Lancs & Cumbria
Ground Address: Green Lane, Ormskirk, Lancs. L39
Tel: 01695 572523
Brief Directions: Adjacent A59 at junction with A570 opposite the Fiveways Pub.
Club Secretary: A.Allan, Ormskirk RUFC,Green Lane, Ormskirk,Lancs.
Tel No: 01257 422130
Fixtures Secretary: A.Barton. Tel : 01257 253051
Club Colours: Green & Blue Hoops

OSSETT RUFC

Yorkshire 5 North
Ground Address: Ossett Cricket and Athletic Club, Springmill, Queens Terrace, Ossett, West Yorkshire
Tel: 01924 273618
Brief Directions: M1 J40, A638 to Wakefield, right at 1st lights, turn right up to Spring Mill after 0.5 mile
Club Secretary: D J Dearnley, 4 Crown Point Close, Kingsway, Ossett. WF5 8RH
Tel: (H) 01924 278991
Fixtures Secretary: I Whitehead
Tel: (H) 01924 274345
Club Colours: Black shirts with narrow red and white hoops, black shorts

PARKONIANS RUFC

South Lancs & Cheshire 3
Ground Address: H Martin Curphey Memorial Ground, Holm Lane, Oxton, Birkenhead, Wirral, Merseyside. L43 2HU
Tel: 0151 652 3105
Brief Directions: M53 J3, A552 for Birkenhead, turn off into Holm Lane at the Swan Hotel, club is 200m on left
Club Secretary: Mr P L Mullen, 8 Deerwood Crescent, Little Sutton, South Wirral. L66 1SE
Tel: (H) 0151 339 1270 (W) 0151 448 6280
Fixtures Secretary: Mr E Potter
Tel: (W) 0151 609 0202
Club Colours: Maroon, blue and white jerseys,stockings and white shorts

PENRITH RUFC

North West 1
Ground Address: Winters Park, Penrith, Cumbria CA11 4RG.
Tel: 01768 863151 (Secretary) - 01768 843462 (Steward)
Brief Directions: M6 J40, A66 east for 0.5 mile, A686 east for 0,5 mile, PRUFC on left just past Police HQ
Club Secretary: Keith Davis, Ivy Bank, 59 Lowther Street, Penrith, Cumbria. CA11 7UQ
Tel: (H) 01768 866089
Fixtures Secretary: Willie Mounsey, The Luham, Edenhall, Penrith, Cumbria.
Tel: (H) 01768 881202
Club Colours: Myrtle green and white hooped shirts, white shorts.

PERCY PARK RFC
North East 1
Ground Address: Percy Park RFC, The Clubhouse, Preston Avenue, North Shields, Tyne & Wear. NE29
Tel: 0191 2575710
Brief Directions: Take east exit signed Tynem'th/N. Shields/ W'tley Bay onto A1058 1 mile north of Tyne Tunnel at the r'bout with A19/A1, rt at baths 2 r'bouts later, 0.5mile lft, club 400yds lft
Club Secretary: A C Baker, 30 The Garth, Winlaton, Tyne & Wear. NE21 6DD
Tel: (W) 0191 4144869 (Fax) 0191 4148672
Fixtures Secretary: Andy Donaghy, 71 Davison Avenue, Whitley Bay, Tyne & Wear
Club Colours: Black and white hoops, black shorts, black & white socks

POCKLINGTON RUFC
North East 2
Ground Address: Percy Road, Pocklington, East Yorkshire. YO4 2QB
Tel: 01759 303358
Brief Directions: Pocklington is situated 13 miles east of York off the A1079 towards Hull, ground located near town centre
Club Secretary: I Johnston, Fern Lea, 39 Percy Road, Pocklington, East Yorkshire. YO4 2LZ
Tel: (H) 01759 302967
Fixtures Secretary: Adrian Wilson
Tel: (H) 01759 305014
Club Colours: Navy and white quarters

PONTEFRACT RFC
North East 2
Ground Address: Moor Lane, Carleton, Pontefract, West Yorkshire. WF8 3RX
Tel: 01977 702650
Brief Directions: Exit A1 at Darrington, follow signs for Pontefract, 2 miles to Moor Lane which is 1st left after 30mph sign on outskirts of Pontefract
Club Secretary: R Peacock, 12 Fair View, Carleton, Pontefract, West Yorkshire. WF8 3NT
Tel: (H) 01977 702284 (W) 01977 677421
Fixtures Secretary: M Higgitt, The Chimes, Common Lane, Upton, Pontefract. WF9 !DF.
Tel: (H) 01977 643605
Club Colours: Royal blue shirts and shorts

PONTELAND RUGBY FOOTBALL CLUB
Durham & Northumberland 2
Ground Address: Ponteland Leisure Centre, Callerton Lane, Ponteland, Northumberland. NE20 9EG
Tel: 01661 825441
Brief Directions: From north or south, enter village via A696, at lights by Diamond Inn turn to follow river, entrance to Sports Centre 150 yards on left just after zebra crossing
Club Secretary: G.G.Baty, 5 Brooklands, Ponteland, Northumberland.NE20 9LZ Tel: 01661 823527
Fixtures Secretary: T.W.Snaith. Tel No: 0191 2689315
Club Colours: Maroon shirts with a black and white hoop, white shorts, maroon socks with a white top

PORT SUNLIGHT RFC
South Lancs & Cheshire 3
Ground Address: Bromborough Playing Fields, Green Lane, Bromborough, Wirral
Tel: 0151 334 3677
Brief Directions: A41 to Eastham, playing fields at Bromborough, Wirral
Club Secretary: Alan Haigh, 13 Charlotte's Meadow, Bebington, Wirral. L63 3JH
Tel: (H) 0151 334 1304 (W) 0151 231 3132
Fixtures Secretary: Chris Dodd
Tel: (H) 0151 608 7022
Club Colours: Black and white narrow hoops

PRENTON RUFC
South Lancs & Cheshire 2
Ground Address: The Clubhouse, Prenton Dell, Prenton Dell Road, Prenton, Wirral, Merseyside. L43 3BS
Tel: 0151 608 1501
Brief Directions: M53 Jct 3 Follow signs to Birkenhead. Pass under railway bridge(A551) 200 yds sign for golf range, Preston Dell Rd with club entrance half a mile on right.
Club Secretary: Paul Foster, 8 Rake Close, Upton, Wirral, Merseyside. L49 0XD
Tel: (H) 0151 678 6643
Fixtures Secretary: Paul Bennett, 2 Aston Wood Road, Birkenhead L42 6DJ
Tel : 0151 7644 9775
Club Colours: Maroon, gold and black

PRUDHOE HOSPITAL RFC

Durham & Northumberland 4
Ground Address: Prudhoe Hospital Sports & Social Club, Prudhoe, Northumberland
Brief Directions: A695 from Blaydon to Hexham, turn off for Prudhoe, look for Hospital sign on left just before Falcon pub on the right
Club Secretary: G Bridgewater, 15 Paddock Wood, Prudhoe, Northumberland. NE42 5BJ
Tel: (H) 01661 832772
Fixtures Secretary: E.Walton,54 Moorlands, Prudhoe, Northumberland. NE42 5LS
Club Colours: Blue and red quarters, white collar, white shorts, red socks

RAWMARSH RUFC

Yorkshire 5 South
Ground Address: Rawmarsh Leisure Centre, Barbers Avenue, Rawmarsh, Rotherham, South Yorkshire
Tel: 01709 719952
Brief Directions: From Sheffield or Doncaster approach the Rotherham ring road.Take A630 and enquire at Mushroom Garage.
Club Secretary: Alan Parker, 3 McManus Avenue, Rawmarsh, Rotherham
Tel: (H) 01709 522795
Fixtures Secretary: Eric Perkins, 21 Harding Avenue, Rawmarsh, Rotherham.
Tel: 01709 526786
Club Colours: Black, maroon and amber hoops. Change: Black & amber trim.

REDCAR RUFC

North East 1
Ground Address: McKinlay Park, Green Lane, Redcar. TS10 3RW
Tel: 01642 482733 (FAX) 01642 480830
Brief Directions: From A19 take A174 east towards Saltburn, take 2nd left (B1269), over level crossing, 1st right to coast road, continue to Green Lane on right at end of houses
Club Secretary: Keith Jeffrey, 11 Woodbridge Close, New Marske TS11 8HP
Tel: 01642 477977
Fixtures Secretary: Dave Pearson, 36 Henry Street, Redcar, Cleveland
Tel: 01642 473786
Club Colours: Black and Red

RICHMONDSHIRE RUFC

Durham & Northumberland 2
Ground Address: The Playing Fields, Theakston Lane, Richmond, North Yorkshire. DL10 4LL
Tel: 01748 850515
Brief Directions: A6136 out of Richmond, pass bus station approx 500 yards turn right, club situated on left approx 100 yards from junction
Club Secretary: Mr Russell Lord, 12 Whitefields Walk, Richmond, North Yorkshire. DL10 7DE
Tel: (H) 01748 824273 (W) 01904 525844
Fixtures Secretary: Bob Dixon
Tel: (H) 01748 825360
Club Colours: Red, gold and white hoops

RIPON RUFC

North East 3
Ground Address: Mallorie Park, Ripon, North Yorkshire. HG4 2QD
Tel: 01765 604675
Brief Directions: Mallorie Park is off main Ripon - Pateley Bridge Road, follow signs for Pateley Bridge via Skellbank
Club Secretary: M P P Viner, 9 Northlands Avenue, Earswick , York. YO32 9FS.
Tel: 01904 750686
Fixtures Secretary: A W Proud
Tel: (H) 01765 605474 (W) 0113 292 6846
Club Colours: White, light blue and dark blue hoops, blue shorts

ROCHDALE RUFC

North West 3
Ground Address: Moorgate Avenue, Bamford, Rochdale, Lancs. OL11 5LU
Tel: 01706 46863
Brief Directions: From Rochdale: B6222 to Bury past Cemetary Hotel, Moorgate Ave 3rd on right. From M62: J20 A627(M) to Rochdale, over 2nd r'bout B6452 left into B6222 at Cemetary Hotel
Club Secretary: John McManus, 27 Hunstanton Drive, Brandlesholme, Bury, Lancs. BL8 1EG
Tel: (H) 0161 761 4371 (W) 0161 740 4993 (F) 795 8094
Fixtures Secretary: Michael Deasey
Tel: (H) 01706 356094 (W) 01706 353208
Club Colours: Maroon and white hoops

ROSSENDALE RUFC

North West 3
Ground Address: Marl Pits Sports Ground, Newchurch Road, Rawtenstall, Lancashire
Tel: 01706 229152
Brief Directions: M66, A56, follow A682 St Mary's Way through 2 sets of traffic lights, right at 2nd set onto Newchurch Road, Marl Pits 0.5 mile on right
Club Secretary: Alec Graham, 14 Hardman Close, Cowpe, Rosssendale, Lancs.BB4 7DL
Tel: 01706 225078
Fixtures Secretary: T erry Kelly, 111Broadway, Haslingden, Rossendale ,Lancs.
Tel: 01706 217361
Club Colours: Maroon and white

ROTHERHAM CLIFTON

Yorkshire 4
Ground Address: Change at Rotherham Rugby Club and play on Hemingthorpe PLaying Fields.
Brief Directions: M1 Jct 33. Follow Rotherway for 1/2 mile to roundabout. Take 2nd exit for Bawtry.AtTraffic lights straight on up hill to roundabout. First left to town centre and ground is 1 mile on right.
Club Secretary: Paul C Richardson, 22 Boswell Street, Broom, Rotherham S^% 2ED , Tel No: 01709 517823
Fixtures Secretary: As above
Club Colours: Maroon & Sky Blue Hoops, navy blue shorts.

ROUNDHEGIANS RUFC

North East 3
Ground Address: Memorial Ground, Chelwood Drive, Roundhay, Leeds. LS8 2AT
Tel: 0113 266 7377
Brief Directions: A61 to junction with Street Lane, follow Street Lane towards Roundhay Park, Chelwood Drive is a road off Street Lane
Club Secretary: Philip A Hobson, 3 Ashgrove Mount, Kippax, Leeds. LS25 7RD
Tel: (H) 0113 286 7106 (W) 01422 362461
Fixtures Secretary: Glen English

Tel: (H) 01924 265858
Club Colours: Green, black and white hooped shirts, black shorts

RUNCORN RFC

South Lancs & Cheshire 3
Ground Address: Halton Sports, Murdishaw Avenue, Runcorn. WA7 6HP
Brief Directions: M56,A56,A533, Runcorn,Murdishaw,Halton Arms Pub off Murdishaw Avenue.
Club Secretary: Jeff Gore, 26 Tarnbeck, Norton, Runcorn, Cheshire WA7 6SF
Tel: (H) 01928 712284
Fixtures Secretary: Tony Elliot. Tel No: 01928 715091
Club Colours: Blue and White Hoops

RUSKIN PARK RUFC

South Lancs & Cheshire 2
Ground Address: Ruskin Drive, St Helens
Tel: 22893
Brief Directions: Turn off A580 onto A570 towards St Helens. Travel approx one mile and turn right into Dentons Green Lane. Ruskin Drive is 500 metre on left.
Club Secretary: Brian Ball, 10 Broadway, Eccleston, St.Helens, Lancs WA10 5DE Tel No: 01744 611955
Fixtures Secretary: Geoff White
Tel: (H) 01744 6634235
Club Colours: Royal blue, black and white hoop

RYTON RUFC

North East 3
Ground Address: Main Road, Barmoor,l Ryton, Tyne & Wear. NE40 3AG
Tel: 0191 413 3820
Brief Directions: On B6317 road to the west of Ryton, B6317 Ryton Road signposted from A695
Club Secretary: Gordon Wright, 57 Middle Row, Stargate, Ryton ,Tyne & Wear
Tel 0191 4131986 Mobile 07931 860858
Fixtures Secretary: Ian Nesbitt, 118 Middle Drive, Ponteland, Newcastle upon Tyne NE20 9DW Tel: 01661 823629
Club Colours: Royal blue or green

SALIANS (FORMERLY OLD SALIANS) RUFC

South Lancs & Cheshire 1
Ground Address: Rookwood, Clarendon Crescent, Sale, Cheshire
Brief Directions: M63 junction signposted to Sale B5166, at traffic lights turn right (Dane Road), Clarendon Crescent is 0.5 mile down Dane Road on the left
Club Secretary: Simon Dewsnip, 51 Park Avenue, Sale, Cheshire M33 6HU
Tel: 0161 282 1664
Fixtures Secretary: Bob Redmond, 15 Beeston road, SAale, Cheshire.
Tel: 0161 9766115
Club Colours: Blue shirts with white hoop, blue shorts

SANDBACH RUFC

North West 3
Ground Address: Bradwall Road, Sandbach, Cheshire. CW11 9AP
Tel: 01270 762475
Brief Directions: M6 J17, follow signs for Sandbach, turn right after 100 yds opposite Texaco garage, follow Offley Rd for 0.25 mile, turn right signed Bradwall, club 400 yards on right
Club Secretary: Andrew Maddock, 40 Mortimer Drive, Sandbach, Cheshire. CW11 4HS
Tel: (H) 01270 759538 (W) 0113 204 4000
Fixtures Secretary: George Elphick. Tel No: 01782 510751
Club Colours: Green and red

SCARBOROUGH RUFC

Yorkshire 1
Ground Address: The Clubhouse, Scalby Road, Scarborough, North Yorkshire. YO12 6EE
Tel: 01723 363039
Brief Directions: Main Whitby Road out of Scarborough, approx 2 miles
Club Secretary: Mrs S E Hanson, The Clubhouse, Scalby Road, Scarborough
Tel: (W) 01723 363039
Fixtures Secretary: Mr. J.B. Beanland c/o club address.
Tel: (H & Fax) 01723 367023
Club Colours: Maroon, navy and white

SEAHAM

Durham & Northumberland 3
Ground Address: New Olrive Playing Fields Club, 27 Cornelia Terrace, Seaham, Co Durham
Tel: 0191 581 2331
Brief Directions: Come down A19 or A1, follow signs for Seaham, once in Seaham follow signs for harbour and ask for directions to club (everyone knows where it is)
Club Secretary: Mrs Carol Pinter, 37 Stavordale St., Dawdonn, Seaham Co.Durham SR 7 7LS
Tel: (W) 01915 815836
Fixtures Secretary: Alan Mason
Tel: (H) 0191 520 0282 (W) 0191 279 4342
Club Colours: Red jersey, white shorts, red socks

SEATON CAREW RUGBY UNION FOOTBALL CLUB

Durham & Northumberland 3
Ground Address: Hornby Park, Elizabeth Way, Seaton Carew, Hartlepool. TS25 2AZ
Tel: 01429 260945
Brief Directions: From A19 take A689 to Hartlepool, right at Owton Lodge pub onto B1276 to Seaton Carew seafront area, turn right and go along seafront past golf club, club on right in Elizabeth Way.
Club Secretary: Paul McManus, 9 Ruswarp Grove, Seaton Carew, Hartlepool. TS25 2BA
Tel: (H) 01429 296327 (W) 01429 268821
Fixtures Secretary: Andrew Sedgwick. Tel Nos: 01429 261995 (H) 01429 266544 (W) 01429 524411(Fax)
Club Colours: Maroon and amber hooped shirts& socks, black shorts

SEDGEFIELD RUFC

Durham & Northumberland 3
Ground Address: Sedgefield Community College, Sedgefield, Stockton-on-Tees, Cleveland
Tel: 01740 621097
Club Secretary: Mr N Hetherington, 1 The Meadows, Sedgefield, Stockton-on-Tees, Cleveland
Tel: (H) 01740 621179 (W) 0836 292665
Fixtures Secretary: Mr M Price
Tel: (H) 01740 622792
Club Colours: Red and black quarters

SEFTON RUFC

South Lancs & Cheshire 2
Ground Address: Thornhead Lane, Leyfield Road, West Derby, Liverpool. L12 9EY
Tel: 0151 228 9092
Brief Directions: End of M62 take A5058 towards Bootle, at A57 turn right, left at lights, right in front of hospital, left at Bulldog pub (Leyfield Road), right into lane by electricity substation
Club Secretary: Roy Spencer, 8 Stoneycroft Close, Liverpool L13 0AT.
Tel: (H) 0151 228 9833
Fixtures Secretary: B Houghton
Tel: (H) 0151 428 3740
Club Colours: Red and white hooped shirts/socks, blue shorts

SEGHILL RFC

Durham & Northumberland 1
Ground Address: Welfare Park, Seghill, Cramlington, Northumberland
Tel: 0191 2370414
Brief Directions: A19 through Tyne Tunnel, take sliproad for Seghill, right at junction, left at next junction, right at mini r'bout then 2nd left, right at T junction, car park 150yds on right
Club Secretary: John Barlow, 32 Manor Drive, Benton, Newcastle, NE7 7XN. Tel: (H & FAX) 0191 2668341
Fixtures Secretary: Geoffrey Fenwick, 20 Wheatfield Grove, Benton , Newcastle
Tel: (H) 0191 2665146
Club Colours: Scarlet and black hooped shirts and socks, white shorts

SELBY RUFC

North East 2
Ground Address: Sandhill Lane, Leeds Road, Selby. YO8
Tel: 01757 703608
Brief Directions: Situated off Sandhill Lane, 1 mile west of town centre off A63 Leeds road
Club Secretary: Richard Besley, 20 Rowan Close, Thorpe Willoughby, Selby. YO8 9FJ
Tel: (H) 01757 708816 (W) 01757 292067 (M) 07977 385086
Fixtures Secretary: Michael Sullivan, 2 The Link, Selby, YO8
Tel: (H) 01757 709545
Club Colours: Green, red and gold narrow hoops

SHEFFIELD OAKS RUFC

Yorkshire 2
Ground Address: Malin Bridge Sports and Social Club, 22A Stannington Rd, Sheffield. S6 5TA
Tel: 01142 345349
Brief Directions: M1 J36 into Sheffield (north), A61 to Hillsborough Ground, 1st available right after Hillsborough Ground, Bradfield Rd, to Holme Lane, left at end of Holme Ln, 1st right after petrol station
Club Secretary: Kay Grayson,13 Hill Close, Stannington, Sheffield S6 6BH
Tel No: 0114 2339209
Fixtures Secretary: Glyn Davies
Tel: (H) 01142 2335829
Club Colours: Gold with royal blue hoops

SHEFFIELD TIGERS RUFC

Yorkshire 2
Ground Address: Door Moor, Hathersage Road, Sheffield. S17 3AB
Tel: 0114 236 0075
Brief Directions: About 5 miles south west of Sheffield city centre on the A625 signed Hathersage. Ground just after Dore Moor Inn.
Club Secretary: Alick Bush, 210 Bradway Road, Sheffield. S17 4PE
Tel: (H) 0114 2361129 (W) 0114 2716950
Fixtures Secretary: Chris Mills, 380 Richmond Road, Sheffield S13 8LZ
Tel: (H) 0114 264 6150
Club Colours: Maroon and gold hoops, black shorts

SHILDON TOWN

Durham & Northumberland 4
Ground Address:
Brief Directions: Please phone fixtures secretary
Club Secretary: Gillian Bowman, 49a Jubilee Road, Shildon, Co. Durham
Tel: 01388 778421
Fixtures Secretary: Peter Plews, 14 Alexandra Street, Shildon, Co. Durham DL4 2EY
Tel: 01388 777334
Yarm
Ground Address: No Details?
Brief Directions: No Details?
Club Secretary: No Details?
Fixtures Secretary: No Details?
Club Colours: No Details?

SILLOTH RUFC

Cumbria
Ground Address: Old Marshalling Yard,Eden Street, Silloth, Cumbria.CA5 4HE
Tel: 016973 32299
Brief Directions: Lies in the centre of town
Club Secretary: David Henderson, 8 Beaconsfield Terrace, Silloth, Cumbria. CA5 4HE
Tel: (H) 016973 31076
Fixtures Secretary: Richard Smith
Tel: (H) 016973 31936
Club Colours: Green and black hoops

SKIPTON RFC

Yorkshire 3
Ground Address: Coulthurst Memorial Grounds, Carleton New Road, Skipton, North Yorkshire. BD23 2AZ
Tel: 01756 793148
Brief Directions: Locate Skipton Railway Station - opposite car park, turn onto Carleton New Road, club 1st right after railway bridge
Club Secretary: Andrew Clark, 33 High St.,Gargrave, North YorKs Bd23 3RA
Tel No: 01758 749565
Fixtures Secretary: Paul Tyson, 24 Rombalds Drive, Skipton.BD23 2SP
Tel; 01756 797661 or 0421 979143
Club Colours: Cardinal red shirts, white shorts

SOUTHPORT RUFC

South Lancs & Cheshire 1
Ground Address: Waterloo Road, Hillside, Southport, Merseyside
Tel: 01704 569906
Brief Directions: From north - through S/port via Lord St, past station on right, ground on right 50 yds after crossing. From south, A565 to S/port, straight through 3 lights, ground on left
Club Secretary: Ann Shorrock, 28a Alexander Rd.,Southport, Merseyside.PR9 9EZ

Tel: 01704 537420
Fixtures Secretary: Mrs Margaret Jackson
Tel: (H) 01704 578362
Club Colours: Red, black, amber hoops

ST BENEDICTS RFC

North West 3
Ground Address: Newlands Avenue, Mirehouse, Whitehaven, Cumbria,
Club House attached to St.Benedicts Social Club, Meadow Rd.
Mirehouse, Whitehaven, Cumbria.
Brief Directions: M6 to jct 40 (Penrith) A66 to A595 to Whitehaven-Barrow by pass and Pelican garage.Straight on to hospital over rouindabout then 1st rt down hill to green. Club by church.
Club Secretary: Stephen House, 12 Castlerigg Close, Mirehouse, Whitehaven, Cumbria. CA28 9RJ
Fixtures Secretary: Ian Maguire. 9 Grisedale Close, Mirehouse, Whitehaven, Cumbria. CA28 8DF
Club Colours: Black, emerald and amber.

ST EDWARDS OLD BOYS RUFC

North West 3
Ground Address: Bishops Court, North Drive, Sandfield Park, West Derby, Liverpool. L12 2AR
Tel: 0151 228 1414
Brief Directions: To end of M62, traffic lights, right onto Queens Drive (A5080), downhill through lights, right at next lights onto Alder Rd, left onto Eaton Rd, playing fields on left
Club Secretary: Simon J Smith, 107 Church Road, Woolton, Liverpool. L25 6OB
Tel: (H) 0151 428 2799 (W) 0151 227 3869
Fixtures Secretary: B Reilly, 130 Quarry Street, Woolton, Liverpool, L25
Tel: (H) 0151 428 3296 (W) 0151 283 3300
Club Colours: Royal blue shirt with gold band, white shorts, royal blue socks

ST MARYS OLD BOYS RUFC

South Lancs & Cheshire 1
Ground Address: Sandy Lane, off Gorsey Lane, Hightown, Merseyside
Tel: 0151 929 2020 HQ: 17 Moor Lane, Crosby. L23
Tel: 0151 924 1774
Brief Directions: Gorsey Lane is off a small road linking Little Crosby and Hightown, and can be reached from the A565 heading from Liverpool or Southport
Club Secretary: Mr Paul McCann 3 Dumfries Way, Melling Mount, Kirkby
Tel: (H) 0151 5480659
Fixtures Secretary: Mr Peter Moore
Tel: (H) 017048 78537
Club Colours: Maroon, yellow and blue hoops

STANLEY RODILLIANS RUFC

Yorkshire 3
Ground Address: Manley Park, Lee Moor Road, Stanley, Wakefield, West Yorkshire. WF3 4EF
Tel: 01924 823619
Brief Directions: M62 J30, head towards Wakefield, turn right opposite Gordons Tyres, top of hill turn right, past double junction on left, turn left just after Lee Moor pub
Club Secretary: R J Matthews, 27 Newlands Walk, Stanley, Wakefield. WF3 4DT
Tel: (H) 01924 828727
Fixtures Secretary: I Young
Tel: (H) 0113 282 6743 (W) 01742 671131
Club Colours: Green, black and white hoops

STOCKPORT RUFC

North West 1
Ground Address: Bridge Lane Memorial Ground, Headlands Road, Bridge Lane, Bramhall, Stockport, Cheshire. SK7 3AN
Tel: 0161 439 2150
Club Secretary: Michael William Drew, 191 Moor Lane, Woodford, Stockport, Cheshire. SK7 1PF
Tel: (H) 0161 439 5439 (W) 01625 525256
Fixtures Secretary: M J Wroe
Tel: (H) 0161 440 8536
Club Colours: Red, green and white hoops

STOCKSBRIDGE RUFC

Yorkshire 3
Ground Address: Stone Moor Road, Bolsterstone
Tel: 0114 288 5078
Brief Directions: A616 to Deepcar, go up hill at side of Royal Oak and opposite King & Miller, right to the top of hill, park in village square opposite Castle Inn
Club Secretary: Julian McGowan, 12 Keats Grove, Penistone, Sheffield. S30 6GU
Tel: (H) 01226 765814
Fixtures Secretary: C Lambert
Tel: (H) 0114 288 5223 (W) 0831 141732
Club Colours: Royal blue with two white hoops

SUNDERLAND RFC

Durham & Northumberland 1
Ground Address: Ashbrooke West Lawn, Sunderland, Tyne & Wear. SR2 7HH
Tel: 0191 528 4536
Brief Directions: A19 tow'ds Sunderland, exit Durham/S'land jcn, east 2.5 mls on Durham Rd to Barnes Htl, right then left into Qn Alex'a Rd, over 1st r'bout, 1st left W'bank Rd, left Ashbrk Rd, club 200yds left
Club Secretary: Mr J C Martin, 11 Roker Park Terrace, Sunderland, Tyne & Wear. SR6 9LY
Tel: (H) 0191 567 7045
Fixtures Secretary: Mr A Scott-Gray
Tel: (H) 0191 522 6188
Club Colours: Red,black & Gold hoops, white shorts

THORNENSIANS RUFC

Yorkshire 1
Ground Address: Clubhouse, Coulman Road, Thorne, Doncaster, South Yorkshire
Tel: 01405 812746
Brief Directions: M18 J6 signed Thorne, 1 mile to town, left at traffic lights, right at crossroads, left at Church, club on left past school
Club Secretary: J.B.Platt c/o Clubhouse, Thornensians RUFC
Tel No: 01405 740191 (H)
Fixtures Secretary: Bob Hutchinson
Tel: (H) 01405 813757
Club Colours: Blue, black and white hoops

THORNTON CLEVELEYS RUFC

North Lancs 1
Ground Address: Fleetwood Road North, Thornton Cleveleys, Lancashire
Tel: 01253 854104
Brief Directions: J3 M55 A585 to Fleetwood, turn right at second roundabout (~6/7 miles), ground on left ~1 mile
Club Secretary: Dr. Phil Horsfield, 336 Fleetwood Road North, Thornton Cleveleys, Lancs FY5 4LQ
Tel No: 01253 868537
Fixtures Secretary: Mrs Pam Horsfield as Secretary
Club Colours: Red, black and amber hoops

TRAFFORD (METROVICK) RFCC
North Lancs & Cumbria
Ground Address: Macpherson Park, Finney Bank Road, Sale, Cheshire. M33 1LR
Tel: 0161 973 7061
Brief Directions: M63 J7, head for Altrincham, at 1st traffic lights turn right (Glebelands Rd), Finney Bank Rd is 0.5 mile along on right
Club Secretary: Mr Des French, 8 Shandon Avenue, Northenden, Manchester. M22 4DP
Tel: (H) 0161 902 9963
Fixtures Secretary: Mr M Pringle, Flat 4, 109 Edge Lane, Stretford, Manchester M32 8PU
Tel: (H) 0161 286 1775 (W) 0161 877 7760
Club Colours: Black and white hooped shirts, white shorts, black and white socks

TYLDESLEY RUFC
North Lancs & Cumbria
Ground Address: Well Street, Tyldesley M29 8HW
Tel: 01942 882967
Brief Directions: From A580 (East Lancs Road) take A577 (Mosley Common Road) until the start of the one way system, take a left down Well Street
Club Secretary: Mr H Hughes, 7 Finstock Close, Winton, Eccles, Manchester. M30 7NP
Tel: (H) 0161 707 8096 (W) 0161 600 4563
Fixtures Secretary: Mr A W Jones
Tel: (H) 01942 876938 (W) 01942 883348
Club Colours: Royal blue shirts, white shorts

UPPER EDEN RUFC
Cumbria
Ground Address: Pennine Park, Westgarth Road, Kirkby Stephen, Cumbria CA17 4DW Tel: 017683 71585
Brief Directions: M6 J38, 12 miles to Kirkby Stephen, turn left by Spar shop (Westgarth), straight on to top of estate. A66 turn off at Brough, 4 miles to K. Stephen, right just after shop
Club Secretary: Stuart Reed, 4 Eastview Cottages, Redmayne Road, Kirkby Stephen Tel: (H) 017683 72528
Fixtures Secretary: Graham Park, Manour Holme, Winton, Kirkby Stephen, Cumbria
Tel: (H) 017683 71424
Club Colours: Black and white hoops

VAGABONDS (I.O.M.) RUFC
North West 2
Ground Address: Mike Hailwoods Centre , Glencrutchery Road, Douglas, Isle of Man. IM2 6DA
Tel: 01624 661996
Brief Directions: Ask for T.T. Grandstand in Douglas.
Club Secretary: Stewart Halliday, 10 Kirkby Hall, Saddlestone, Braddan, Isle of Man. IM2 1PA
Tel: (H) 01624 624 421
Fixtures Secretary: Stephen Wilson, 49 St. Catherines Close, Douglas, Isle of Man IM1 4JB
01624 673029
Club Colours: White with black and yellow chest band, black shorts

VALE OF LUNE RUFC
North 2
Ground Address: Powderhouse Lane, Lancaster. LA1 2TT
Tel: 01524 64029
Brief Directions: M6 J34 for Lancaster, follow signs for A589 Morecambe, approx 0.5 mile after crossing River Lune, turn right down Scale Hall, left at junction, ground 50yds on right
Club Secretary: Peter Atkinson, 12 Moorside Road, Brookhouse, Lancaster, LA2 9PJ. Tel: (H) 01524 770152
Fixtures Secretary: Fred Swarbrick, 116 Prospect Street, Lancaster, LA1 3BH.
Tel: (H) 01524 37601 (W) 01524 64055
Club Colours: Cherry and white hoops, blue shorts, cherry and white socks

VICKERS RUFC
North Lancs & Cumbria
Ground Address: Hawcoat Park, Hawcoat Lane, Barrow in Furness, Cumbria Tel:01229 825296
Brief Directions: M6 Jct 36. A590 to Barrow and follow signs for Furness General Hospital. Turn right at lights after hospital, ground is 200 yards on left.
Club Secretary: Mr A T Mason, 48 Crosslands Park, Barrow in Furness, Cumbria LA13 9NH Tel: (H) 01229 821624
Fixtures Secretary: Mr N. Smith, 48 Norland Ave. Barrow in Furness, Cumbria
Tel: 01229 828234
Club Colours: Maroon and white shirts, white shorts and maroon socks.

VULCAN RUFC
South Lancs & Cheshire 3
Ground Address: The Sportsfield, Wargrave Road, Newton-le-Willows, Merseyside
Tel: 01925 224180
Brief Directions: Wargrave Rd is a continuation of Victoria Rd which is off Crow Lane West (A572)
Club Secretary: Mr D. W. Lodge, 19 Pipit Ave, Newton-Le-Willows, Merseyside, WA12 9RG
Tel: (H) 01925 225108
Fixtures Secretary: Mr M. Holland, 4 Wayfarers Drive, Newton-Le-Willows, Merseyside, WA12
Tel: (H) 01925 229201
Club Colours: Black and amber

WAKEFIELD COUGARS RUFC
Yorkshire 5 North
Ground Address: Wakefield Cougars RUFC, College Grove, Eastmoor Road,Wakefield. WF1 3RR Tel : 01924 374801
Brief Directions: M1 Jct41. Take A650 to City centre. Left at Queen Elizabeth GS to Wakefield Rd.Ground 250 yds.M62 Jct30 .A642 to centre. Rt at Lights after hospital to Eastmoor Rd.Grd 300yds.
Club Secretary: Alex Judson, 2 Windsor Crescent, Wrenthorpe, Wakefield WF1 2BS.
Tel No: (H) 01924 361358 (M) 0976 976153
Fixtures Secretary: Bill Halstead. (H) 01274 872710 (FAX) 01274 865975
Club Colours: Black & Gold. Alternative : Red.

WALLASEY RUFC
North West 3
Ground Address: Cross Lane, Leasowe Road, Wallasey, Wirral, Merseyside. L45 8NS
Tel: 0151 638 1486
Brief Directions: Exit 1 on M53 towards Wallasey, take 2nd slip road to A551, turn right at lights
Club Secretary: J A Burton, 14 Seaview Lane, Irby, Wirral, Merseyside. L61 3UL
Tel: (H) 0151 648 4341 (W) 0161 236 3707

Fixtures Secretary: A Rae, 8 Inchcape Rd, Wallasey, Wirral, Merseyside L45 8JR
Tel: (H) 0151 638 6903
Club Colours: Red, black, white hoops Change: Black

WALLSEND RFC
Durham & Northumberland 2
Ground Address: Benfield Community Association Sam Smiths Pavilion, Benfield School Campus, Benfield Road, Walkergate, Newcastle. NE6 4NU Tel: 0191 265 9357.
Brief Directions: Just off A1058 Newcastle-Tynemouth (Coast rd), turn on to C127 to Benfield School, club at rear of school
Club Secretary: Brian J Thirlaway, 29 Belmont Close, Battle Hill Estate, Wallsend, Tyne & Wear. NE28 9DX
Tel: (H) 0191 234 4877
Fixtures Secretary: Bob Lowery, 27 Boyd Road, Wallsend, Tyne & Wear NE28 7 SG
Tel: (H) 0191 234 2400
Club Colours: Myrtle green jerseys with gold trim, white shorts.

WARRINGTON RUFC
North West 3
Ground Address: Bridge Lane, Appleton, Warrington
Tel: 01925 264591
Brief Directions: J20 M6. Follow A50 Warrington 2m. At lights turn left, after 1 1/2 mls 2 sets of lights, left at 2nd set, under bridge first right into Bridge Lane, 1/4m on right.
Club Secretary: G P Robinson, 8 Bellhouse Lane, Warrington. WA4 2SD
Tel: (H) 01925 261644
Fixtures Secretary: R. Turner, 62 Fairfield Road, Stockton Heath, Warrington, WA4 2UU
Club Colours: Red, green, white

WATH-UPON-DEARNE RUFC
Yorkshire 1
Ground Address: Moor Road, Wath-Upon-Dearne, Rotherham
Tel: 01709 872399
Brief Directions: Moor Road is adjacent to Wath Swimming Baths on the main Rotherham to Barnsley (A630) road
Club Secretary: Mr S Poxton, 19 Packham Way, Wath-Upon-Dearne, Rotherham, South Yorkshire. S63 6BR
Tel: (H) 01709 874154 (W) 01226 282549
Fixtures Secretary: Mr S Corns
Tel: (H) 01709 874911
Club Colours: Blue with maroon and gold bands

WEARSIDE RUFC
Durham & Northumberland 3
Ground Address: Fulwell Quarry Reclamation Site, Newcastle Road, Sunderland, Tyne & Wear
Brief Directions: Leave A19, follow A184 (Newcastle rd) into Sunderland passing Regal Greyhound Stadium on left, turn right at roundabout to changing rooms
Club Secretary: S. F. Thompson, 87 Beach Road, South Shields, Tyne And Wear. NE 33 2LZ
Tel: (H) 0191 497 5013
Fixtures Secretary: G. Curtis, 6 Ainthorpe Close, Tunstall, Sunderland, Tyne And Wear. SR3 2DA
Tel: (H) 0191 5235094 (W) 0191 2595117
Club Colours: Royal blue and scarlet hoops, white shorts, red socks

WENSLEYDALE RUFC
Durham & Northumberland 3
Ground Address: Cawkhill Park, Wensley Road, Leyburn, North Yorkshire. DL8 5AR
Tel: 01969 623067
Brief Directions: To Leyburn then Take the Wensley/West Witton Road. The club is 1 mile west of Leyburn on the A684
Club Secretary: Graham Jameson, 7 Fearby Rd., Masham, Ripon, N.Yorkshire.HG4 4ES
Tel NO: 01765 689185 (H) 0802 253060
Fixtures Secretary: E Lowther
Tel: (H) 01748 88473 (W) 01748 884473
Club Colours: Black and amber hoops

WEST HARTLEPOOL AMATEUR RFC
Durham & Northumberland 3
Ground Address: Hartlepool Sixth Form College, Blamelock Road, Hartlepool, Cleveland.
Brief Directions: Changing facilites and pitches by the Catcote Road entrace to the College.
Club Secretary: Tony Wilson, 27 Suggitt Street, Hartlepool, Cleveland, TS26 8IY.
Tel: 01429 279322H - 07788 972827M
Fixtures Secretary: Graham Frankland, 39 Parklands Way, Hartlepol, Cleveland.
Tel: 01429 261716
Club Colours: Royal Blue with Red & White trim.

WEST LEEDS RUFC
Yorkshire 1
Ground Address: Blue Hill Lane, Wortley, Leeds. LS12 4NZ
Tel: 0113 2639869
Brief Directions: From M621 to Leeds outer ring road take A6110 and turn right at second roundabout . After Ringways, turn right at lights follow road leftt at Fawcett Lane and club is half a mile on left
Club Secretary: Ms Jill Dowson, 21 Butterbowl Road, Leeds. LS12 5JE
Tel: (H) 0113 279 6220 (W) 0113 2436606
Fixtures Secretary: Colin Edwards
Tel: (H) 0113 2522487
Club Colours: Navy, old gold and white

WEST PARK BRAMHOPE RUFC
North 2
Ground Address: The Sycamores, Bramhope, Leeds. LS16 9JR Tel: 0113 2671437
Brief Directions: From Leeds city centre take A660 sign posted Skipton & Otley, at Bramhope village turn left at roundabout direct to Club
Club Secretary: Noel Barker, 3 Greystones Close, Aberford, Leeds,LS25 3AR
Tel/Fax:(H) 0113 2813238
Fixtures Secretary: Rob Storey, 7 Moseley Wood Way, Cookridge, Leeds LS16 7HN .
Tel No: 0113 2675266
Club Colours: Black and gold

WEST PARK (ST HELENS) RFC
North West 1
Ground Address: 'Redrocks',Prescot Road, St Helens, Merseyside WA10 3AG
Tel: 01744 26138
Brief Directions: From St Hellens town center follow signs to Liverpool, clubhouse situated 11/2 miles out of town on lefthand bend just after GRange public house.nent. Alight at Eccleston Hill
Club Secretary: John B Fletcher, Cellduminn, 7 Kings Road, Taylor Park, St Helens. WA10 3HT
Tel: (H) 01744 755895 (W/Fax) 01744 617372
Fixtures Secretary: David Appleton,41 Mitchell Road,St Helens. WA10 3EX
Club Colours: Green and gold hoops

WESTOE RFC
North East 3
Ground Address: Dean Road, South Shields, Tyne & Wear. Tel: 0191 456 1506
Brief Directions: Map available
Club Secretary: J R Wells, 240 Mowbray Road, South Shields. NE33 3NW
Tel: (H) 0191 4552260
Fixtures Secretary: D Allen, 118 Harton House Road (E), South Shields, NE34 6DZ
Tel: (H) 0191 4569531 (W), 0191 456115
Club Colours: Red, sky and dark blue hoops

WETHERBY RUFC
Yorkshire 4
Ground Address: Grange Park, Wetherby, West Yorkshire
Tel: 01937 582461
Brief Directions: From Wetherby town centre head for A1 south, pass Police station on left, Jarvis Hotel on right, head for A1 south, having crossed A1 take left turn into Grange Park
Club Secretary: Gerry Davies, 'Fellside', Langwith Valley Road, Colingham LS22 5DH
Tel No: 01937 572405
Fixtures Secretary: Simon Kelly, 1 Milnthorpe Way, Bramham, Wetherby LS23 6TQ
Tel: (H) 01937 841058
Club Colours: Red and white hoops, white shorts

WHEATLEY HILLS DONCASTER RUFC
North East 2
Ground Address: Wheatley Hills Sports Ground, Brunel Road, York Road Industrial Estate, Doncaster. DN5 8PT
Tel: 01302 781472
Brief Directions: A638 into Doncaster, turn right at B & Q depot, 1st right, follow road to bottom, club on right
Club Secretary: Eddie Wenninger, 60 Whitton Close, Bessacarr, Doncaster DN4 7RD
Tel: 01302 537636 (H) 01246 414651 (W)
Fixtures Secretary: Chris Whitehouse, 11a Hillfold, South Elmsall, Wakefield.
Tel No: 01977 644303
Club Colours: Maroon and gold quartered shirts, maroon shorts

WHITBY HARLEQUINS RUFC
Durham & Northumberland 1
Ground Address: Showfield, White Leys Road, Whitby, North Yorkshire. YO21 1L8
Tel: 01947 602008
Brief Directions: North West side of river, towards Sandend off Stakesby Road
Club Secretary: Mr F Howarth, 18 Lime Grove, Whitby, North Yorkshire
Tel: (H) 01947 600692
Fixtures Secretary: Mr T Cook
Tel: (H) 01947 600614
Club Colours: Maroon and black

WHITEHAVEN RUFC
Cumbria
Ground Address: The Playground, Richmond Terrace, Whitehaven, Cumbria. CA28 7QR
Tel: 01946 695253
Brief Directions: Behind the Whitehaven Sports Centre and next to Jacksons Timber Yard.
Club Secretary: Mr E McConnell, 38 Loop Road South, Whitehaven, Cumbria. CA28 7SE
Tel: (H) 01946 692225
Fixtures Secretary: Mr. G. Blaney, 82 Rannerdale Drive, Whitehaven, Cumbria, CA28 6LA.
Tel: 01946 591908
Club Colours: Maroon and white hoops white shorts

WHITLEY BAY ROCKCLIFF RFC
Durham & Northumberland 1
Ground Address: Lovaine Avenue, Whitley Bay, Tyne & Wear. NE25 8RW Tel: 0191 2513704
Brief Directions: Turn off Hillsheads Road at the pelican crossing at the Safeways store. Club is signposted.
Club Secretary: Martin Page, 25 Hillcrest, Whitley Bay, Tyne And Wear, NE25 9AD. Tel: (H) 0191 2510748
Fixtures Secretary: Mr D Bennett, 4 Millfield Gardens, Tynemouth, Tyne And Wear.
Tel: (H) 0191 2572174
Club Colours: Cardinal red shirts with gold trim, white shorts

WIBSEY RUFC

Yorkshire 4
Ground Address: Northfiel Road, Wibsey, Bradford. BD6 Tel: 01274 671643
Brief Directions: From top of M606 take 2nd exit towards Odsal roundabout, take 4th exit at side of Police station, 0.75 mile on left joined onto White Swan pub
Club Secretary: Martin Spencer,143 High Street, Wibsey, Bradford. BD6
Tel: (H) 01924 463736 (W) 01274 776000
Fixtures Secretary: Mr Paul Knowles, 125 Poplar Grove, Bradford. BD7 4JX.
Tel: 01274 576373
Club Colours: Red and green hoops

WICKERSLEY (Formerly Wickersley Exel)

Yorkshire 5 South
Ground Address: Wickersley Comprehemsively School, Bawtry Road, Wickersley,Rotherham, South Yorkshire.
Brief Directions: M18 Junction 1. Follow sign for Rotherham. About 2 miles up dual carriage way, Wickersley Comprehensive on left.
Club Secretary: Brian SWancott, 19 Crossgate,Mexborough. South Yorkshire. S64 0JU
Tel No: 01709 581577 (H) 07970 905371(M)
Fixtures Secretary: Steve Houghton, 150 Pear Tree Avenue, Bramley, Rotherham, South Yorks.S66 2NF
Tel Nos: 01709 531758 (H) 0498 825644(M)
Club Colours: Navy shirts, black shorts. Change: Amber shirts, black shorts

WIGAN RUFC

North West 2
Ground Address: Douglas Valley, Wingates Road, Leyland Mill Lane, Wigan. WN1 2SA
Tel: 01942 242556
Brief Directions: M6 J27, follow signs to Standish, take A49 towards Wigan, 2 miles, 1st left after Cherry Gardens Hotel into Leyland Mill Lane, then signposted
Club Secretary: Graham Heeley, 30 Darley Road, Hawkley Hall, Wigan. WN3 5PS
Tel: (H) 01942 201360 (W) 01625 503050
Fixtures Secretary: David Clarke
Tel: (H) 01942 207771
Club Colours: Black and white irregular hoops

WILMSLOW RUFC

North West 2
Ground Address: Memorial Ground, Kings Road, Wilmslow. SK9 6JF
Tel: 016625 522274
Brief Directions: Kings Road is off the A538 - Wilmslow to Altrincham, approx 4 miles from the M56 junction, on the left as you enter the town.
Club Secretary: David Pike, 12 Fairbourne Drive, Wilmslow, Cheshire. SK9 6JF
Tel: (H) 01625 525616
Fixtures Secretary: J. Harries, 6 Stockton Road, Wilmslow SK9 6EU
Tel No: 01625 524359 (H) 01625 530175 (W)
Club Colours: Sky blue with maroon & white hoops, white shorts

WINDERMERE RUFC

North Lancs & Cumbria
Ground Address: Dawes Meadow, Longlands, Bowness on Windermere, Cumbria. LA23 3AS
Tel: 015394 43066
Brief Directions: Drive towards Bowness & the lake from Windermere, coming in to Bowness, right just before cinema, right again past the bowling club, clubhouse is on the right.
Club Secretary: J C Stephenson, 46 Craig Walk, Windermere. LA23 2JT
Tel: (W) 015394 45448
Fixtures Secretary: K E Williams, 40A Main Road, Windermere, LA23 1DY
Tel: (H) 015394 42389
Club Colours: Amber and black

WINLATON VULCANS RFC

Durham & Northumberland 1
Ground Address: Axwell View Playing Fields, Winlaton, Blaydon-on-Tyne. NE21 6EU
Tel: 0191 4142502
Brief Directions: From A1 take exit past Metro Centre signed Swalwell, take signs for Blaydon, just past Blaydon Pool turn left, continue up Shibdon Bank for 0.5 mile, club on left
Club Secretary: Steve Foley, 62 Silverdale Drive, Winlaton Blaydon-on-TYne NE 216EN
Tel No: 0191 4146894 (H) 0191 2112015 (W)
Fixtures Secretary: Ian Bilclough, 7A Tyne Street, Winlaton, Blaydon-on-Tyne
Tel: (H) 0191 4147723
Club Colours: Black shirts with white collars, black shorts and black socks

WIRRAL RFC

South Lancs & Cheshire 1
Ground Address: Old Wirralians Memorial Ground, Thornton Common Road, Clatterbridge, Wirral, Merseyside Tel: 0151 334 1309
Brief Directions: M53 J4, B5151 to Clatterbridge, past hospital on right, o.5 mile take left at crossroads, into Thornton Common Road
Club Secretary: Chris Whorton, 47 Meadow Lane, Willaston, Cheshire. L64 2TY
Tel: 0151 327 5312
Fixtures Secretary: Mr A Hignett
Tel: (H) 0151 327 1309
Club Colours: Maroon and white hoops

WITHERNSEA RUFC

Yorkshire 5 South
Ground Address: Plough Inn, Hollym, nr. Withernsea, East Yorkshire. HU19 2RS
Tel: 01964 612049
Brief Directions: Main road from Hull to Patrington, turn left into Hollym village at the crossroad, ground at rear of Plough
Club Secretary: Mr A C Ellis, Clifton Lodge, Sand-le-Mare, Tunstall,Iroos, Nr HullHU 12 0JQ
Fixtures Secretary: Mr D Thompson, 13 Manor Garth, Keyinham, HU12 9SQ.
Tel: (H) 01964 624094
Club Colours: White and blue hoop

WORKINGTON RFC

North West 2

Ground Address: Ellis Sports Ground, Mossbay Road, Workington. CA14 3XZ

Tel: 01900 602625

Brief Directions: Adjacent to B5296, 0.5 mile south of town centre, 1st right after traffic lights at T A Centre

Club Secretary: M J Heaslip, 32 Elizabeth St, Workington. CA14 4DB

Tel: (H) 01900 66339 (W) 01900 65656 (FAX) 01900 67587

Fixtures Secretary: K.Greenhow, 45 St Andrews Road,Stainburn, Workington.

Tel: 01900 870670

Club Colours: Black and white hoops Change Colours: Green & White Hoops

YARNBURY (HORSFORTH) RFC

North East 3

Ground Address: Brownberrie Lane, Horsforth, Leeds

Tel: 0113 2581346

Brief Directions: Follow signs on Leeds outer ring road (A6120) to Horsforth. Turn north onto Low Lane at T junction turn left then third exit off the roundabout

Club Secretary: Paul Trigg, 3 Moorland Gardens, Moortown, Leeds. LS17 6JT

Tel: (H) 0113 2251389

Fixtures Secretary: John Riley, 65 Broadgate Lane, Horsforth, Leeds, LS18 5AB

Tel: (H) 0113 2589131 (W) 01924 441818

Club Colours: Blue, black and white uneven hoops

YORK RAILWAY INSTITUTE RUFC

Yorkshire 2

Ground Address: Railway Institute Sports Ground, New Lane, Acomb, York. YO2 4NU

Tel: 01904 798930

Brief Directions: From A1237 York ringroad, take B1224 signposted Acomb for 1.5 miles, after the Church of the Latter Day Saints on the right, take the 1st on the right (New Lane), sports ground at end

Club Secretary: Bryn D Bates, 16 Beech Place, Strensall, York. YO3 5AS

Tel: 01904 491296 (H) 01904 622112 (W)

Fixtures Secretary: W F Cooper, Moorcroft, Lucy Hall Drive, Baildon, Shipley

Tel: (H) 01274 584355

Club Colours: Royal blue and white hooped shirts, black shorts, royal blue socks

YORK RUFC

North East 1

Ground Address: Clifton Park, Shipton Road, York YO3 6RE

Tel:01904 623602

Brief Directions: Turn south off York outer ring road (A10) towards York city centre on A19 from Thirsk, club situated on right after about 1.75 miles

Club Secretary: Brian McClure, 15 Stubden Grove, York. YO30 4UY

Tel: (H) 01904 691026

Fixtures Secretary: Jim Dunwell, The Granery, 1Swan Close, Deighton, York YO19 6NY

Tel: 01904 728848(H)

Club Colours: Green, black and white hoops with black shorts and socks

MIDLAND DIVISION

MIDLAND DIVISION	Officials & League Secretaries	520
MIDLAND ONE	League table & Fixture Grid	521
	Clubs	522
MIDLAND DIVISION	1998-99 League Tables	528
	1999-2000 Fixture Grids	531
	Clubs (in alphabetical order)	538

Midland Division Structure 1999-2000

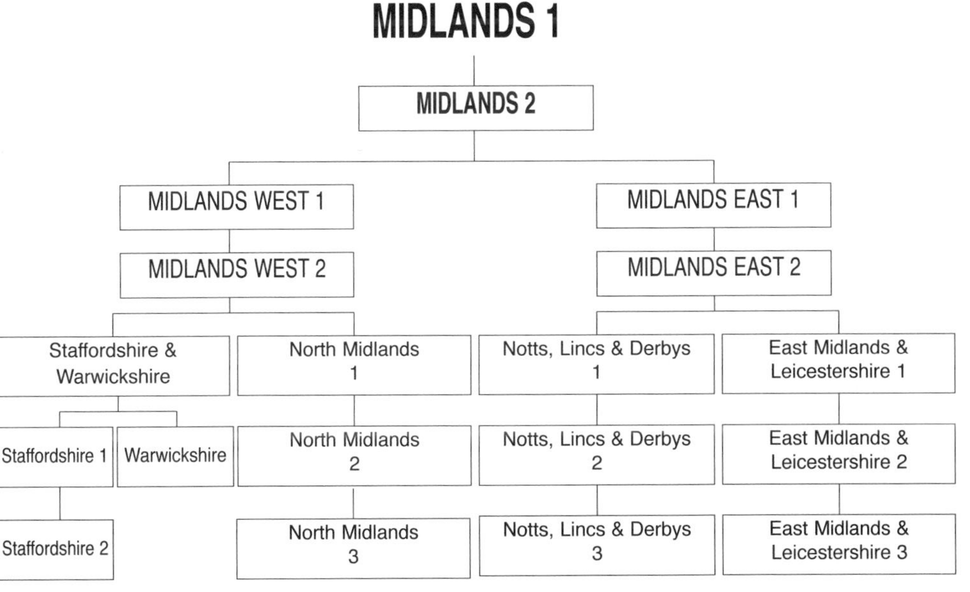

OFFICIALS
MIDLAND DIVISION

David I Robins **Chairman**
The Clubhouse, Upper Chase Rd, Malvern WR14 2BU 01684 564826 (H) 01684 560247 (B) 01684 893125 (F)

LEAGUE SECRETARIES

Mike Bracey **Midlands 1**
154 Manor Road, Barton-le-Clay, Bedford MK45 4NU 01582 881237 (H)

Geoff Goodall **Midlands 2**
38 Presthills Rd., Hinckley, Leics LE10 1AJ 01455 238742 (H) 01203 562650 (B)

Bob Ingledew **Midlands East 1**
15 Martin Close, Bedford MK41 7JY 01234 407521

Brian Johnston **Midlands West 1**
9 Nursery Close, Atworth, Melksham, Wilts SN12 8HX 01225 790658 (H) 01249 442771 (B) 01249 442865 (F)

Philip Osborne **Midlands East 2**
Ashthorne, Teeton Rd., Ravensthorpe, Northampton NN6 8EJ 01604 770772 (H) 01327 705785 (B)

Nigel Banwell **Midlands West 2**
16 Riverside Close, Upton upon Severn, Worcester WR8 0JN 01684 592046 (H)

Keith Dale **Staffordshire & Warwickshire 1**
14 St Anthony's Drive, Newcastle, Staffs ST5 2JE 01782 615770 (H) 01782 615235 (F)

Bruce Braithwaite **Staffordshire**
4 Badgers Croft, Eccleshall, Staffs ST21 6DS 01785 851114 (H) 01785 277330 (B) 01785 277224 (F)

Ray Roberts **Warwickshire**
261 Alwyn Rd., Bilton, Rugby, Warks CV22 7RP 01788 810276 (H) 01788 816520 (B)

John McNally **North Midlands 1**
490 Brook Lane, Moseley, Birmingham B13 0BZ 0121 604 6180 (H) 0121 783 7232 (B) 0121 789 8306 (F)

Alun Humphreys **North Midlands 2**
26 Low Fold Close, St Johns, Worcester WR2 5UE 01905 422522 (H

Terry Wheeler **North Midlands 3**
14 Wollescote, Pedmore, Stourbridge, W Midlands DY9 7JJ 01384 832647 (H) 0121 423 4000 (B)

David Tribee **Notts, Lincs & Derbys 1**
42 Charnwood Drive, Ripley, Derbyshire DE5 3TB 01773 512719 (H)

Paul Cobbin **Notts, Lincs & Derbys 2**
60 Loughborough Road, Hathern, Leicestershire LE12 5JA 01509 646354 (H) 01509 842893 (F)

David H Murphy **Notts, Lincs & Derbys 3**
The Old Carpenters Arms, 32 High St, Little Bytham, Grantham, Lincs NG33 4QX 01780 410692 (H)

Clive Elliott **East Midlands & Leicestershire 1**
9 Wavertree Close, Cosby, Leics LE9 1TN 0116 2841746 (H) 01788 544 508 (B) 0850 441382 (M) 01788 568711 (F)

Peter Howard **East Midlands & Leicestershire 2**
Caudle View,Church Lane, Thorpe, Langton, Leics LE16 7TR 01858 545227 (H) 01455 610747 (B)

Kevin Curtis **East Midlands & Leicestershire 3**
21 Potton Road, St Neots, Huntingdon, Cambs PE19 2NP 01480 3900066 (H)

MIDLAND ONE

1989-1999 LEAGUE TABLE

	P	W	D	L	PF	PA	PD	Pts	
Bedford Athletic	16	15	0	1	569	163	406	30	
Scunthorpe	16	15	0	1	590	187	403	30	
Dudley	15	13	0	2	391	205	186	26	
Banbury	16	12	0	4	492	255	237	24	
Broadstreet	16	10	1	5	342	248	94	21	
Kenilworth	16	10	0	6	386	245	141	20	
Burton	16	9	1	6	308	229	79	19	
Belgrave	15	9	0	6	279	215	64	18	
*Hereford	16	9	0	7	355	258	97	16	(-2)
Syston	16	7	0	9	273	323	-50	14	
Barkers Butts	16	5	1	10	233	373	-140	11	
Camp Hill	16	5	0	11	209	377	-168	10	
Westleigh	16	4	1	11	222	470	-248	9	
Stoke on Trent	16	3	2	11	217	351	-134	8	
Wolverhampton	16	4	0	12	223	493	-270	8	
Mansfield	16	1	0	15	154	479	-325	2	
Leighton Buzzard	16	1	0	15	150	522	-372	2	

1999-2000 FIXTURE GRID

	Banbury	Barkers Butts	Belgrave	Broadstreet	Burton	Camp Hill	Dudley Kingswinford	Hereford	Hinckley	Kenilworth	Lichfield	Longton	Newbold	Scunthorpe	Stoke on Trent	Syston	Westleigh/Wigston
Banbury			20.11		11.12				15.01		26.02		23.10	25.03	11.09		02.10
Barkers Butts	06.11			25.09		09.10					27.11		25.03	08.01	29.01		26.02
Belgrave		11.09			09.10		25.03	27.11	06.11	29.01		08.01				26.02	
Broadstreet	27.11		02.10			06.11					08.01		11.09	29.01	26.02		25.03
Burton		02.10		23.10			11.09	08.01	27.11	26.02		29.01				25.03	
Camp Hill	08.01		23.10		20.11						29.01		02.10	26.02	25.03		11.09
Dudley Kingswinford	09.10	11.03		08.04		25.09					06.11			27.11	08.01		29.01
Hereford	12.02	20.11		11.12		15.01	23.10			11.09		25.03				02.10	
Hinckley		23.10		20.11		11.12	02.10	29.01		25.03		26.02				11.09	
Kenilworth	08.04	15.01		12.02		11.03	11.12				25.09			09.10		20.11	
Lichfield			11.12		15.01			11.03	12.02				20.11	11.09	02.10		23.10
Longton	11.03	11.12		15.01		12.02	2.11			02.10	08.04					23.10	
Newbold			08.04		25.09		26.02	06.11	09.10	08.01		27.11				29.01	
Scunthorpe			15.01		12.02			08.04	11.03			25.09	11.12		23.10		20.11
Stoke on Trent			12.02		11.03			25.09	08.04	06.11		09.10	15.01				11.12
Syston	25.09	12.02		11.03		08.04	15.01				09.10			06.11	27.11		
Westleigh/Wigston			11.03		08.04			09.10	25.09	27.11		06.11	12.02			08.01	

BANBURY

Founded: 1925

Hon. Secretary: Bryan A Davies, 34 Horton View, Banbury. OX16 9HP Tel: 01295 262027
President: John Phillips, c/o Banbury RUFC, Bodicote Park, Banbury. OX15 4AF 01295 279000
Chairman: Roy Evans, Whineray, Thorpe Rd., Chacombe, Oxon. 01295 710853
Rugby Director: Peter Payne, 14 Lillington rd., Leamington Spa, Warwicks. 01926 888308
Commercial Manager: Peter May, c/o Banbury RUFC as above. 01295 279000 (B) 01295 263862

Ground Address: Bodicote Park, Oxford Road, Banbury, Oxon. Tel/Fax: 01295 279000
Capacity: 3,400 Covered Seating: 366 Uncovered Standing: 3,000
Directions: M40 Junct. 11. Follow the signs to A41260 towards hospital & Adderbury. The ground is approx. 3 miles south of town, on the left. Nearest Railway Station: Banbury
Car Parking: 500 +spaces available on the ground.
Admission: £3 with programme for league matches. Season tickets are available.
Clubhouse: Yes **Club Shop:** Open matchdays only.
Programme: Size: A5 Pages: 24 Price: with admission Editor: Norman Lacey
Advertising rates: Full page £100
Colours: Navy & white hooped shirts, navy shorts **Change colours:** Red, with single navy & white hoop, navy shorts
Training Nights: Monday & Wednesday **Nickname:** Bulls

BARKERS' BUTTS RFC

Founded: 1947

President R E Hobson 63 Tilewood Ave., Coventry CV5 7GT 01203 468679
Chairman R A White 36 Westcotes, Coventry CV4 9BD 01203 469875
Treasurer M White 36 Westcotes, Coventry CV4 9BD 01203 469875
Fixture Secretary H Paine 43 Sutton Ave., Coventry CV5 7EG 01203 474261
Sponsorship Sec. J Saltmarsh 8 Conway Ave., Tilehill Village, Coventry CV4 9HZ 01203 474454
Hon. Secretary R G Coward c/o Barkers' Butts RFC (see below)

Ground: Pickford Grange Lane, Allesley, Coventry CV5 9AR Tel: 01676 522192/523633 Fax: 01676 523470
Capacity: 1000 - all uncovered standing. Use Coventry RFC for special matches
Directions: A45 from Coventry - take Meriden turn - 200 yds turn left - ground 100 yds on right.
From Birmingham & M42 take A45 towards Coventry. Turn right to Meriden & follow for 2 miles.
Nearest Railway station: Birmingham International or Coventry
Car Parking: 200 spaces available at ground
Matchday admission: £2
Clubhouse: Open daily 7-11pm, Sat. 12-11 & Sun 12-4 **Club Shop:** open 1-5 sat & 12-2 Sun.
Colours: Royal blue and amber **Change colours:** All red Training Nights: Tuesday & Thursday
Programme: Size: A3 Pages: 32 Price: £1 Editor: J Saltmarsh (as above)
Advertising: Contact editor £125 full page £75 half page

BELGRAVE RFC

Founded: 1883

President C Hawkins 16 Wellbrook Ave., Sileby, Leics. LE12 7QQ 01509 814833
Chairman W Clarke 9 Ulverscroft Drive, Groby, Leics. LE6 0YA 0116 232 2122
Secretary M J Goddard Grange Court, 271A Birstall Rd., Birstall, Leics. 0116 267 7383
Fixture Secretary K Hick 3 Coplow Cres., Syston, Leics. 0116 260 8617
Marketing M Cox Cliffe Road, Birstall, Leics. 0116 267 2535

Ground Address Belgrave Pastures, Thurcaston Road, Abbey Lane, Leicester Tel/Fax: 0116 266 3033
Capacity: 1,000 - all uncovered standing
Directions From M1 take A46 by-pass, exit at A6 to Leicester. Ground opposite McDonalds.
From town centre take St Margarets Way leading to Abbey Lane. At 4th set of lights turn left into Thurcaston Rd. Nearest Railway Station: London Road, Leicester
Car Parking 50 spaces at ground, 200+ on road nearby
Admission Matchdays £2
Programme: Size: A5 Price: £2 Pages: 22+ cover Editor: M Cox
Advertising: Contact M Cox - Marketing
Colours: Red & black hooped shirts, black shorts
Training Nights: Monday & Wednesday **Nickname:** The Graves

BROADSTREET RFC

Founded: 1929

President D Branston 114 Earle Court, Bell Green, Coventry CV7 7GX 01203 663866
Chairman G Watts 15 Coopers Walk, Bubbenhall, Coventry CV8 3JB 01203 301838(H) 01203 633336(B)
Secretary C J McGint 14 Glendower Ave., Whoberley, Coventry CV5 8BE
01203 679261 (H) 00353 7323155 (H) 00353 7323349 (F) 07801 869730 (M)
Coach R Harcourt 69 Heather Road, Binley Woods, Coventry CV3 2DD 01203 542788
Fixture Secretary D Wilkinson 4 Court Leet, Binley Woods, Coventry 01203 543548 (H)
Ground The Ivor Preece Field, Brandon Rd., Binley, Coventry CV3 2AW Tel: 01203 453982 (Club) 01203 451706 (Caretaker)
Capacity: 1,250 Covered Seating: 50 Uncovered Standing: 1,200
Directions M6 Junct. 2, follow signs for banbury, Stratford & Warwick along the Coventry Eastern By-pass. Ground entrance is between TGI Friday & Morrisons supermarket at the Binley Woods roundabout.
Nearest Railway Station: Coventry **Car Parking:** 200 spaces FOC on ground.
Admission: Matchdays - £2 including programme Season tickets not available. **Club Shop: Yes**
Clubhouse: Most eves plus Sat & Sun lunchtimes. Available for private functions - contact K Tyrell 01203 451706.
Programme: Size: A5 Pages: 32 + cover Price: with admission Editor: C J McGinty (Sec.)
Advertising Rates: £100 full page, £75 half page Mono colour only. Also matchday packages available
Colours: White with red & green bands, green shorts. **Change colours:** Red with white & green bands, green shorts
Training Nights: Tuesday & Thursdays 6.45pm. **Nickname**: `The Street'

BURTON R.F.C.

Founded: 1870

President R A Clark 1 Leedhams Croft, Walton on Trent DE2 8NW 01283 712682
Secretary J D Lowe 20 The Chevin, Stretton, Burton upon Trent DE13 0XU Tel/Fax: 01283 534422
Treasurer D G Gill c/o Smith Cooper & Partners, Peel House, Lichfield st., Burton upon Trent DE14 3SQ
Tel: 01283 561621 Fax: 01283 510216
Fixture Secretary P E Richard 20 Olton Road, Mickleover, Derby DE5 5PL Tel: 01332 516901 (H)
Coaching J E French 193 Newton Rd., Burton upon Trent DE15 0TU Tel: 01283 548774

Ground: Peel Croft, Lichfield Street, Burton upon Trent, Staffs. DE14 3RH Tel: 01283 564510
Capacity: 2,150 Covered Seats: 350 Covered Standing: 400
Directions: In the centre of Burton, adjacent to Safeways supermarket
Nearest Railway station: Burton upon Trent **Car Parking:** Limited in ground, plenty of public parking nearby.
Admission Matchdays: £3 Season tickets: £20, non-members £40
Clubhouse Open training nights, matchdays & Sundays
Club Shop Open matchdays, tarining evenings & Sun (12-1pm). Contact John Roberts
Colours: White with black diagonal band/white/black **Change colours:** Black/white/black
Training Nights Tuesday & Thursday **Nickname:** 'The Crofters'
Programme **Size:** A5 **Pages:** 22 **Price:** 50p **Advertising:** Contact editor (see below)
Editor: D J Bowen, 15 Newton Leys, Winshill, Burton upon Trent DE15 0DW Tel: 01283 547533

CAMP HILL R.F.C.

Founded: 1893

Chairman Alistair Hayward 0468 335944 (B - Mobile)
Asst. Chairman Martin Crutchley 0121 745 4454 (H/B)
Treasurer R L Lewin
Secretary Alan D Murray 40 Robin Hood Lane, Hall Green, Birmingham B28 0LN
Tel: 0121 744 3804 e-mail: murray@alandonald@freeserve.co.uk
Fixture Secretary Graham Scutt 130 Longmore Road, Solihull, West Mids. Tel: 0121 744 4495

Ground: Haslucks Green Road, Shirley, Solihull, West Mids. Tel: 0121 744 4175
Capacity: 2-3,000 - all uncovered standing
Directions: Haslucks Green Road is off Stratford Road (A34) - at the city centre end of Shirley - Junction 4 of M42
Nearest Railway station: Shirley, 10 minute walk
Car Parking: 300 spaces at ground
Admission £2.50 league games, £1.50 others, includes matchday programme
Clubhouse Open every evening & weekend lunchtimes. Snacks available. **Club Shop:** Open with clubhouse
Colours: Maroon & light blue **Change Colours:** All red
Training Nights: Monday & Wednesday (Seniors) Tues & Thur (Ladies) Sun (Minis) **Nickname:** 'Camps'
Programme **Size:** A5 **Pages:** 40 **Price:** With admission **Editor:** Alan Murray
Advertising: Contact Alan Murray

DUDLEY KINGSWINFORD R.F.C.

Founded: 1927

Honorary Secretary David Evans 156 Common Road, Wombourne, West Midlands WV5 0LX
Tel: 01902 894463

Ground Heathbrook, Swindon Road, Wallheath, Kingswinford, W. Mids. DY6 0AW Tel/Fax: 01384 287006
Capacity: 4,000+ Covered Seating: 50 Uncovered Standing: 4000

Directions: Just off the A449 at Wallheath, midway between Kidderminster and Wolverhampton.
Nearest Railway Station: Stourbridge or Wolverhampton
Car Parking: Spaces for 300+ at the ground

Admission: Matchday: £3, OAPs £1, u16 Free. No season tickets available.
Clubhouse: Open 7 days per week, from 7pm weekdays, 1-11 Saturdays & 12-3 Sundays.
Club Shop: Open Momday & Thursday 7.30-9.30 pm, Sat. 1-4.30pm & Sun. 12-2pm

Programme: Size: A5 Pages: 20 Price: incl with admission
Editor: Martin Chard, Colcroft, High St., Wallheath.
Advertising; £65 Full page, £40 half page
Colours: Cambridge blue and navy hoops
Change colours: Royal blue and white hoops
Training Nights: Monday & Thursday 7.30pm
Nickname: "D.K"

HEREFORD R.F.C.

Founded: 1870

Secretary Peter Greenow, Hackford House, Dinedor Cross, Hereford HR2 6PD
Tel: 01432 870874 (H)
Fixture Secretary Fred Walsh, 32 Chandos Street, Whitecross, Hereford
Tel: 01432 351560 (H) 07970 012544 (Mob)
Treasurer A Whitfield, 47 Pengrove Road, Hereford HR2 1PT
Tel: 01432 359770 (H) 01432 274544 (B)

Ground Wyeside, Hereford HR4 9UT Tel: 01432 273410

Directions Follow the ring road to Ross-on-Wye, turn right before the bridge over the River Wye, first left after 'The Antelope' into Broomy Hill, first left again into a narrow lane, the club is on the riverside.

Club Colours Red and black

HINCKLEY

Founded: 1893

President A Gildroy 3 Shelley Gardens, Hinckley, Leics LE10 1TA 01455 449894 (H) 01455 238333 (B)
Chairman P Williams 5 Knighton Close, Broughton astley, Leics. 01455 - 634483 (Fax) 285897 (H) 631222 (B)
Secretary J M J Kind `The Pebbles`, 156 Station rd., Earl Shilton, Leics. LE9 7GD 01455 847158 (H - Fax/Tel)
Rugby Chairman D Whitton 20 Welford Court, Knighton, Leicester LE2 6ER 0116 270 0816 (H)
Fixture Secretary F Farndon 20 Torridon way, Hinckley, Leics. LE10 0UH 01455 636671 (H)

Ground Address: Leicester Road, Hinckley. Tel: 01455 615010
Capacity: 1,000 - all uncovered standing **Car Parking**: 200 on ground, 200+ nearby
Directions: From the M69 take A5 towards Tamworth. Right at 1st r'about. Follow road over 3 r'abouts then turn right at 4th. The club is 300 metres on the right. Nearest Station: Hinckley
Admission: Matchday - Adults £3 Season tickets not available
Clubhouse: Tuesday & Thursday 7-11. Saturday 12-late. Sundays 12-3. Snacks & bar meals available
Functions: Capacity 200. Contact Carole Davies 01455 890939(H) or at the club
Club Shop: Open matchdays & Sun. Contact C Morgan 01455 271801
Training Nights: Tuesday & Thursday
Programme Size: A5 Price: TBA Pages: 32 + cover Editor: Mike Kind 01455 847158
Advertising Rates Mono: Full page £150, Half page £80, Quarter £45 Colour: By quote
Colours: Black & amber hoops, black shorts **Change colours:** Red & green hoops

KENILWORTH R.F.C.

Founded: 1924

President	Chris Holmes	36 Lunn Ave., Kenilworth CV8 2DS 01203 713313
Chairman	Chris Elgar	7 Wordsworth Drive, Kenilworth CV8 2TB 01926 852587
Secretary	Wille Whitesmith	4 Glasshouse Lane, Kenilworth CV8 2AJ 01926 859465 (H) 01926 851113 (B)
Treasurer	John Davies	24 Thirlestone Close, Kenilworth CV8 2DW 01926 857962
Fixtures Secretary	Graham Billinger	7 Saville Grove, Kenilworth Kenilworth CV8 2PR 01926 851914

Ground Jack Davies Memorial Ground, Glasshouse lane, Kenilworth CV8 2AJ
Tel: 01926 853945 Fax: 01926 851394 e-mail: iges@compuserve.com
Capacity: Unknown

Directions A452 off A46. At roundabout take last exit onto Birches lane; ground is about 1/2 mile on the right.
Nearest Railway station: Coventry   Car Parking: Plenty at the ground

Admission Charges vary   No season tickets are available

Clubhouse Tue, Wed & Thur 7-11pm, Fri 6-11pm, Sat 12-12, Sun 12-3pm   **Club Shop:** Open as clubhouse

Colours: Yellow & blue/dark blue   **Change colours:** All red

Training Nights: Tues, Wed & Thur.   **Nickname:** "Kens"

Programme Size: A5   Pages: 20+   Price: Varies   Editor: Chris Holmes 01203 713313
Advertising: Page: £100   Half: £60   Quarter: £35

KENILWORTH RFC

Warwickshire Sevens Winners 1999

Back Row (L-R):
David Ashworth (Man.)
Don Carrick
James Fitzpatrick
Dave Rowlett
John New
Mark Bennett

Front Row (L-R):
David Bourne
Simon Givens
Mark Poulton
Tony Munro

LICHFIELD R.U.F.C.

Founded: 1874

President Dave Beck 129 Birmingham Road, Lichfield. Tel: 01543 251702 (H)

Chairman Roger Fathers c/o Lichfield RUFC

Club Secretary Maurice Keenan 61 Noddington Lane, Whittington, Lichfield WS14 9PA Tel: 01543 432804 (H)

Treasurer Paddy N Martin 11 Church Road, Shenstone, Lichfield WS14 0NE Tel: 01543 480045(H)

Ground Address: Cooke Fields, Tamworth Road, Lichfield, Staffs. WS14 9JE Tel: 01543 263020
Capacity: 5,000   Seated: 200   Standing: 4,800

Directions: Take the A51 out of Lichfield towards Tamworth. After approx. two miles, and after crossing the A38, the ground is on the left behind the 'Horse & Jockey' public house.
Nearest Railway Station: Lichfield City or Lichfield Trent Valley

Car Parking: 1,000 spaces are available on the ground.

Admission: Season tickets - Adults £35   Matchday - Adults £2 Children/OAPs £1

Clubhouse: Normal licensing hours, snacks & bar meals available. Functions: Capacity 200   **Club Shop:** Yes

Programme Size: A5   Price: £1   Pages: 20   Editor: David Lewis 01664 464047
Advertising: Contact Editor

Colours: Myrtle green/navy blue/red   **Change colours:** Myrtle green & yellow hoops/navy blue/red.

Training Nights: Tuesday and Thursday.   **Nickname**: Myrtle Greens

LONGTON R.F.C.

Founded: 1952

President	Martin Hamer	
Chairman/ Fixture Secretary	Brent Rawlings	20 Fernlea Grove, Weston Coyney, Stoke-on-Trent, Staffs. ST3 5HT 01782 335317
Secretary	John Till	The Old Barn, Peacock Lane, Hanchurch, Stoke-on-Trent ST4 8RZ 01782 657660 (H) 01782 291672 (B) 01782 291799 (Fax)
Coach	Tom Wainwright	

Ground Roughcote Lane, Caverswall, Stoke-on-Trent, Staffs. ST11 9EG Tel: 01782 394449
Capacity: 250 - all uncovered standing

Directions: A50 from Stoke to Uttoxeter, Meir/Leek turn off (A520) through Weston Coyney and right hand turn to ground (signed)
Nearest Railway station: Stoke-on-Trent Car Parking: Plenty on ground
Admission: to be arranged

Clubhouse: Open matchdays & training nights **Club Shop**: Limited amount of merchandise available from clubhouse

Colours: Black and amber **Change colours:** Blue
Training Nights: Tuesday & Thursday
Programme: Size: A5 Pages: Vary Price: £1

NEWBOLD-ON-AVON R.F.C.

Founded:1894

President	K Foster	32 Mulberry Rd., Rugby CV22 5TD	01788 814489
Chairman	T Andrews	67 York St., Rugby CV21 2BS	01788 569074
Treasurer	A Williams	45 Pinfold St., Rugby CV21 2JD	01788 561814
Hon. Secretary	R Hall	8 Belmont Road, Rugby CV22 5NZ	01788 334757
Match/Fixture Sec.	P Bale	135 Norman Rd., Rugby CV21 1DW	01788 560014
Press Officer	S Brown	17 Cheshire Close, Lutterworth LO17 4YE	01788 550476

Ground: The Clubhouse, Parkfield Road, Newbold-on-Avon, Rugby, Warks. CV21 1EZ
Tel: 01788 565811 e-mail: newbold.rfc@virgin.net Web site: http://freespace.virgin.net/newbold.rfc
Capacity: 1,500 Covered Seats: 100

Directions: M6, Junction 1 to Rugby. After 1/2 mile, at large landscaped r'about turn right (3rd exit) to Newbold village (1.5 miles). At crossroads, Parkfield Road is straight over, clubhouse 300 metres on the right.
Nearest Railway station: Rugby **Car Parking:** Ample at the ground

Clubhouse: Bar, lounge, Avon suite, gymnasium
Club Shop: Shopkeeper - P Reed (Snr). Sells a good range of merchandise & equipment.
Training Nights: Monday & Wednesday (Seniors). Colts: Tues & Thurs. **Nickname:** 'The Bold'
Colours: Red and black quarters **Change colours:** Blue & gold
Programme: **Size:** A5 **Pages:** 8 **Price:** £1.00 **Editor:** Jamie Dodd

SCUNTHORPE R.U.F.C.

Founded: 1929

President	Jim Lynch	3 Neath Road, Scunthorpe	01724 844403
Chairman	Alan Taylor	49a Moorwell Road, Scunthorpe	01724 866960
Secretary	Andy Bagshaw	41 Grammar School Road, Brigg 01652 652031 (B) 01652 659354 (Fax)	01652 657300 (H)
Treasurer	John Graham	11 High Street, Winterton	01724 732520

Ground: Heslam Park, Ashby Road, Scunthorpe Tel: 01724 843013
Capacity: 1000 all uncovered standing
Directions: End of M181, 3rd exit to `Berkeley' Roundabout, 3rd exit Kingsway to 'Beefeater' Roundabout, 3rd exit into Ashley Road, 400 meteres on left 'Haslem Park'
Nearest Railway Station: Scunthorpe Car Parking: Spaces for 100 cars at ground
Admission: Matchday: £2
Clubhouse: Open evey day 12-2.30pm & 5-11pm
Club Shop: Open Saturday lunchtime & Sunday morning
Programme: Size: A4 Price: 50p Editor: Mal Yates
Colours: Green shirts with 2 narrow black bands bordered by 2 narrow white bands/black
Change colours: Red shirts with bands as above
Training Nights: Tuesday & Thursday Colts: Wed Women: Thur. **Nickname**: The Greens

STOKE-ON-TRENT R.U.F.C.

Founded: 1884

President M Mosley 21 Castleton Road, Lightwood, Stoke-on-Trent ST3 7TD 01782 313662 (H)
Chairman Stephen Beck 10 Hillside Close, Fulford, Stoke-on-Trent ST11 9RU 01782 398090 (H)
Secretary D Potts Oaks Cottage, Moddershall Oaks, Moddeshall, Nr Stone, Staffs. ST15 0TR 01782 373309 (H) 01782 715555 (B)
Fixture Secretary Eric Hardisty 29 Kingstone drive, Stone, Staffs. ST15 0EJ 01785 813641 (H)
Chairman of Playing J Cheadle Laburnum Cottage, Sandon Road, Hilderstone, Stone, Staffs ST15 8SF 01889 505445 (H)

Ground Hartwell Lane, Barlaston, Stoke-on-Trent ST15 8TL Tel: 01782 372807
Capacity: 2,120 Seated: 120
Directions From North - M1, take A38, then A50, then A520 toward Stone. Follow road to Barlaston & club is 1 mile on left
- M6 J15, A34 south, then follow road to Barlaston & club is thro' village on the right.
From South - M6 J 14, A34 north then directions as above.
Nearest Railway station: Barlaston Car Parking: 200 spaces at club
Admission Matchday: £3 Season ticket: £30
Clubhouse: Open Tues, thur, Sat & Sun. Available for private hire - capacity 250 **Club Shop:** Open matchdays & Sundays
Training Nights: Tuesday & Thursday Nickname: "Potters"
Programme Size: A5 Pages: 20 Price: with entry Editor: Paul Sheldon
Advertising: Page £75, Half £50, Quarter: £30

SYSTON R.F.C.

Founded: 1887

President G. Stonehouse 81 Glebe Rd, Queniborough, Leics, LE7 3FH. Tel 0116 2605858
Chairman A.C. Edgeley 37 Pembroke Avenue, Syston, Leics, LE7 2BZ. Tel 0116 2600398
Secretary J.D. Newton 62 Fosse Way, Syston, Leics, LE7 1NE Tel 0116 2694647
Fixture Secretary I. Thorpe 12 Perseuerance Rd, Birstall, Leics, LE4 4AU Tel 0116 2267750

GROUND **Address:** Barkby Road, Queniborough, Leicester, LE7 3FE.
Tel 0116 2601223 e-mail EDGELEY@THE CURRANT BUN.com
Directions: Contact Secretary for map

Training Nights Monday & Thursday
Colours Shirts Navy with Saxe (Light Blue) Hoops - Navy Shorts
Change Colour Shirts Red

WESTLEIGH/WIGSTON R.F.C.

(LEICESTER LIONS) **Westleigh** (Founded 1904) & **Wigston** (Founded 1946) merged 1999
(name change still to be confirmed)

Secretary Steve Benton, 5 Ramsdean Avenue, Wigston, Leicester LE18 1DX
0116 212 6571 (H) 0116 255 6776 (B) 0116 255 6940 (F)).
Fixture Secretary Nigel Biswell, Cedar Lodge, Rollaston Road, Skeffington, Leicestershire.
0116 259 6616 (Day)
Grounds: **Westleigh Park**, Lutterworth Road, Blaby, Leicestershire LE8 3DPTel: 0116 277 1010
Directions: M1/M69 J21, B4114 to Narborough, left at Foxhunter pub r'about, over next r'about, left at next r'about, ground 150 yds on left.
Wigston Park, Leicester Road, Countesthorpe, Leicester LE18 3QUTel: 0116 277 1153.
Directions: From outer ring road rake B5366 (Saffron Lane) to South Wigston, then Countesthorpe Road - signed Countesthorpe & ground is approx 1 mile on left.
Admission By programme **Programme:** Size: A5 Pages: 20 Price: TBA
Clubhouse Mon (Wigston), Thur (Westleigh), matchdays & Sun am (both)
Training Nights Monday at Wigston, Thursday at Westleigh.
Colours Black, white and purple quarters

MIDLAND DIVISION FINAL LEAGUE TABLES 1998-99

MIDLANDS TWO

	P	W	D	L	PF	PA	PD	Pts
Longton	16	14	0	2	400	154	246	28
Newbold	16	12	2	2	374	177	197	26
Ampthill	16	13	0	3	352	197	155	26
Old Laurentians	16	9	1	6	431	249	182	19
Kettering	16	8	2	6	305	197	108	18
Sutton Coldfield	16	8	2	6	318	269	49	18
Newport	16	8	0	8	298	304	-6	16
Luctonians	16	8	0	8	298	310	-12	16
Nottingham Mods	16	8	0	8	253	317	-64	16
Stockwood Park	16	7	1	8	303	287	16	15
Derby	16	6	1	9	225	294	-69	13
Huntingdon	16	6	1	9	242	315	-73	13
Lincoln	16	6	0	10	224	310	-86	12
Bromsgrove	16	5	1	10	262	229	33	11
Stafford*	16	6	1	9	240	321	-81	11
Towcestrians	16	4	0	12	168	524	-356	8
Leamington	16	2	0	14	164	403	-239	4

MIDLANDS EAST ONE

	P	W	D	L	PF	PA	PD	Pts
Wellingborough	16	15	0	1	547	163	384	30
Dunstablians	16	14	0	2	501	185	316	28
Ilkeston	16	12	1	3	440	119	321	25
Spalding	16	11	1	4	380	147	233	23
N'hmptn O Scouts	16	11	0	5	314	245	69	22
Stoneygate	16	9	0	7	255	280	-25	18
Peterborough	16	8	0	8	336	268	68	16
Newark*	16	9	0	7	271	347	-76	16
Old Northamptonians	16	7	0	9	287	351	-64	14
Long Buckby	16	7	0	9	250	318	-68	14
Lutterworth*	16	7	0	9	246	300	-54	12
N'hmptn Mens O	16	5	0	11	236	319	-83	10
Paviors	16	5	0	11	215	338	-123	10
Stewarts & Lloyds	16	5	0	11	182	308	-126	10
Oadby Wyggest'ns	16	5	0	11	178	324	-146	10
Vipers	16	3	0	13	132	478	-346	6
Coalville	16	2	0	14	125	405	-280	4

MIDLANDS WEST ONE

	P	W	D	L	PF	PA	PD	Pts
Malvern	16	14	1	1	594	145	449	29
Selly Oak	16	14	0	2	465	214	251	28
Old Coventrians	16	11	0	5	360	205	155	22
Shrewsbury	16	10	0	6	241	204	37	20
O Leamingtonians	16	9	1	6	295	239	56	19
Old Halesonians*	16	10	1	5	256	261	-5	19
Bedworth	16	7	1	8	225	247	-22	15
Stratford-Upon-Avon	16	7	1	8	251	300	-49	15
Keresley*	16	8	0	8	295	219	76	14
Kings Norton	16	7	0	9	197	247	-50	14
Evesham	16	7	0	9	218	288	-70	14
Woodrush	16	5	2	9	217	336	-119	12
Aston Old Edwardians	16	5	2	9	218	344	-126	12
Telford	16	5	1	10	195	328	-133	11
Leek	16	5	0	11	249	337	-88	10
Willenhall	16	4	2	10	131	268	-137	10
Ludlow	16	1	2	13	149	374	-225	4

MIDLANDS EAST TWO

	P	W	D	L	PF	PA	PD	Pts
Luton	16	15	0	1	644	116	528	30
South Leicester	16	15	0	1	513	131	382	30
Leicester Forest	16	14	0	2	550	170	380	28
Loughborough	16	12	1	3	379	186	193	25
Kibworth	16	12	0	4	451	244	207	24
Matlock	16	10	0	6	290	233	57	20
Glossop	16	8	1	7	300	283	17	17
Kesteven	16	8	0	8	287	268	19	16
Buxton	16	8	0	8	214	312	-98	16
Long Eaton	16	6	0	10	204	343	-139	12
Ashbourne	16	5	0	11	212	330	-118	10
Stamford	16	5	0	11	184	430	-246	10
Amber Valley	16	5	0	11	114	382	-268	10
Grimsby	16	4	1	11	212	372	-160	9
West Bridgford	16	3	1	12	183	341	-158	7
Biggleswade	16	2	1	13	155	385	-230	5
Nottingham Casuals	16	1	1	14	130	496	-366	3

MIDLANDS WEST TWO

	P	W	D	L	PF	PA	PD	Pts
Newcastle (Staffs)	16	14	0	2	508	187	321	28
Birmingham Exiles	16	14	0	2	395	166	229	28
Nuneaton Old Eds	16	13	0	3	424	165	259	26
Kidderminster	16	11	2	3	442	153	289	24
Old Yardleians	16	11	0	5	451	198	253	22
Southam	16	10	0	6	281	250	31	20
Old Saltleians	16	9	0	7	302	269	33	18
Tamworth	16	8	0	8	176	272	-96	16
Berkswell & Balsall	16	6	2	8	203	244	-41	14
Pershore	16	6	1	9	206	338	-132	13
Edwardians	16	5	1	10	139	206	-67	11
Stoke Old Boys	16	5	0	11	154	277	-123	10
Dixonians	16	5	0	11	206	381	-175	10
Warley	16	5	0	11	135	378	-243	10
GPT Coventry	16	4	1	11	177	348	-171	9
Manor Park	16	3	0	13	197	415	-218	6
Erdington*	16	3	1	12	154	303	-149	3

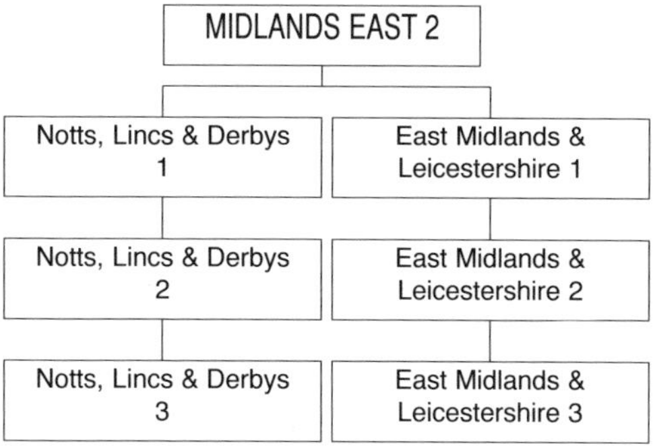

MIDLANDS EAST 2

Notts, Lincs & Derbys	East Midlands & Leicestershire
Notts, Lincs & Derbys 1	East Midlands & Leicestershire 1
Notts, Lincs & Derbys 2	East Midlands & Leicestershire 2
Notts, Lincs & Derbys 3	East Midlands & Leicestershire 3

NOTTS/LINCS/DERBY ONE

	P	W	D	L	PF	PA	PD	Pts
Ashfield	14	12	1	1	349	86	263	25
Belper	14	12	0	2	262	157	105	24
Sleaford	14	9	0	5	239	167	72	18
Melbourne	14	8	1	5	349	154	195	17
Keyworth	14	8	1	5	288	208	80	17
Bakewell Mann's	14	8	1	5	253	200	53	17
Dronfield	14	8	0	6	237	183	54	16
Market Rasen	14	7	0	7	226	221	5	14
Worksop	14	5	2	7	230	202	28	12
Southwell	14	6	0	8	181	190	-9	12
Mellish	14	5	1	8	200	227	-27	11
Boots Athletic	14	5	1	8	175	222	-47	11
Castle Donington	14	4	0	10	132	296	-164	8
Leesbrook	14	3	0	11	154	342	-188	6
Stamford College	14	1	0	13	107	527	-420	2

NOTTS/LINCS/DERBY TWO

	P	W	D	L	PF	PA	PD	Pts
Barton & District	13	11	0	2	275	117	158	22
Nottinghamians	13	10	2	1	280	123	157	22
Rolls Royce	13	9	1	3	285	251	34	19
East Retford	13	8	0	5	298	157	141	16
East Leake	13	7	1	5	271	159	112	15
Cleethorpes	13	7	0	6	170	145	25	14
Chesterfield	13	7	0	6	168	178	-10	14
Boston	13	6	1	6	202	166	36	13
Skegness	13	6	0	7	193	156	37	12
Hope Valley*	13	7	0	6	172	182	-10	12
Notts Constabulary	13	4	0	9	159	166	-7	8
Cotgrave	13	3	1	9	140	283	-143	7
Meden Vale	13	3	0	10	104	185	-81	6
Bourne*	13	0	0	13	46	495	-449	-2

NOTTS/LINCS/DERBY THREE

	P	W	D	L	PF	PA	PD	Pts
Bolsover	18	16	0	2	401	154	247	32
Tupton	18	13	1	4	350	187	163	27
Burton Joyce	18	10	0	8	280	227	53	20
Univ. Of Derby	18	9	1	8	265	270	-5	19
Appleby Frod'ham	18	8	1	9	253	231	22	17
Ollerton	18	8	1	9	190	232	-42	17
Yarborough Bees	18	7	0	11	232	304	-72	14
Bingham	18	6	1	11	240	276	-36	13
Horncastle	18	5	1	12	197	365	-168	11
Gainsborough	18	5	0	13	186	348	-162	10

EAST MIDLANDS/LEICS ONE

	P	W	D	L	PF	PA	PD	Pts
Market Bosworth	22	21	0	1	724	160	564	42
Loughboro Stdnts*	22	19	0	3	818	187	631	36
Wigston	22	15	1	6	613	210	403	31
Melton Mowbray	22	12	0	10	432	360	72	24
Oakham	22	12	0	10	436	409	27	24
Rushden & Higham	22	12	0	10	401	399	2	24
Daventry	22	9	0	13	323	509	-186	18
N'hmpton Casuals	22	6	2	14	260	354	-94	14
St Ives (Midlands)	22	6	1	15	293	547	-254	13
Nhmptn BBOB*	22	7	0	15	215	664	-449	12
Bedford Swifts	22	5	0	17	220	569	-349	10
Bedford Queens*	22	6	0	16	239	606	-367	10

EAST MIDLANDS/LEICS TWO

	P	W	D	L	PF	PA	PD	Pts
Wellingboro O.G.	21	18	0	3	777	207	570	36
Old Newtonians	22	17	2	3	678	175	503	36
Bugbrooke	22	15	1	6	452	301	151	31
Ayleston St James	22	13	1	8	361	329	32	27
Brackley*	22	13	1	8	458	356	102	23
Ashby	22	11	0	11	313	278	35	22
Aylestonians*	21	12	0	9	401	275	126	20
Oundle*	22	8	1	13	303	518	-215	15
Deepings	22	6	1	15	320	580	-260	13
St Neots	21	4	2	15	252	573	-321	10
Vauxhall Motors	21	3	1	17	214	496	-282	7
Colworth House*	20	4	0	16	221	662	-441	6

EAST MIDLANDS/LEICS THREE

	P	W	D	L	PF	PA	PD	Pts
Corby	16	15	0	1	592	117	475	30
Biddenham	16	13	2	1	357	97	260	28
Thorney	16	8	3	5	396	225	171	19
Nhmptn Heathens	16	8	2	6	304	332	-28	18
Kempston	16	8	1	7	330	184	146	17
Anstey	16	6	2	8	200	254	-54	14
Aylestone Athletic	16	3	1	12	168	502	-334	7
Westwood*	16	4	0	12	174	309	-135	6
Burbage*	16	1	1	14	71	572	-501	1

* Points deducted

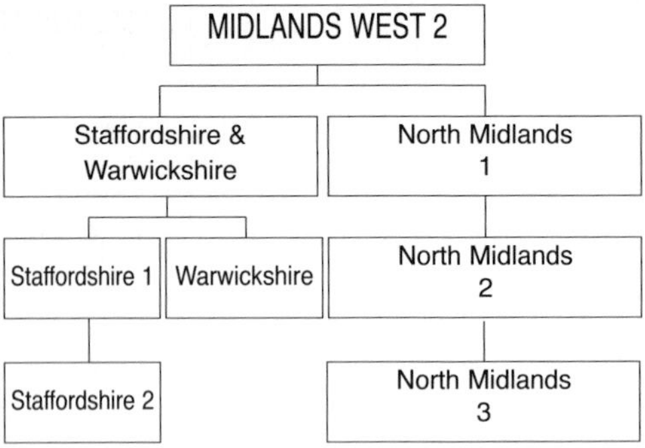

MIDLANDS WEST 2

Staffordshire & Warwickshire

North Midlands 1

Staffordshire 1

Warwickshire

North Midlands 2

Staffordshire 2

North Midlands 3

STAFFORDSHIRE/WARWICKSHIRE

	P	W	D	L	PF	PA	PD	Pts
Silhillians	16	14	0	2	528	120	408	28
Wednesbury	16	13	1	2	318	129	189	27
Trinity Guild	16	13	1	2	350	166	184	27
Earlsdon	16	12	1	3	426	194	232	25
Spartans (Mids)*	16	11	0	5	336	181	155	20
Trentham	16	9	1	6	296	182	114	19
Dunlop	16	8	3	5	199	217	-18	19
Shipston On Stour	16	8	1	7	304	215	89	17
Handsworth	16	8	0	8	379	195	184	16
Burntwood	16	7	2	7	353	250	103	16
Coventry Welsh	16	6	1	9	296	302	-6	13
Claverdon	16	5	1	10	181	248	-67	11
Pinley	16	5	0	11	145	411	-266	10
Alcester*	16	4	2	10	233	365	-132	6
GEC St. Leonards	16	3	0	13	220	441	-221	6
Harbury	16	3	0	13	143	447	-304	6
Coventry Saracens	16	0	0	16	59	703	-644	0

STAFFORDSHIRE

	P	W	D	L	PF	PA	PD	Pts
Uttoxeter	10	9	0	1	364	62	302	18
Bloxwich	10	9	0	1	322	36	286	18
Linley	10	8	0	2	305	108	197	16
Cannock	10	7	0	3	265	134	131	14
Wheaton Aston	10	6	0	4	218	139	79	12
Barton u N'wood	10	5	0	5	180	200	-20	10
Whittington	10	4	0	6	217	242	-25	8
Rugeley	10	3	0	7	135	216	-81	6
Market Drayton	10	3	0	7	72	231	-159	6
Eccleshall	10	1	0	9	71	300	-229	2
Michelin	10	0	0	10	19	500	-481	0

WARWICKSHIRE

	P	W	D	L	PF	PA	PD	Pts
Atherstone	16	15	0	1	742	61	681	30
Rugby St Andrews	16	13	1	2	554	138	416	27
Old Wheatleyans	16	11	2	3	509	206	303	24
Ford	16	8	0	8	248	481	-233	16
Standard	16	7	1	8	411	245	166	15
Coventry Tech	16	6	1	9	196	328	-132	13
Old Warwickians*	16	6	1	9	232	456	-224	11
Coventrians*	16	2	0	14	123	564	-441	2
Shottery*	16	1	0	15	123	659	-536	-2

NORTH MIDLANDS ONE

	P	W	D	L	PF	PA	PD	Pts
Bridgnorth	22	20	0	2	651	226	425	40
Droitwich	22	19	1	2	748	205	543	39
Upton On Severn	22	17	1	4	629	283	346	35
Five Ways O.E.	22	13	0	9	496	379	117	26
Redditch	22	12	0	10	470	396	74	24
Ledbury	22	11	0	11	354	369	-15	22
Bromyard	22	10	0	12	391	426	-35	20
Old Griffinians	22	9	0	13	474	537	-63	18
Yardley & District	22	9	0	13	349	513	-164	18
Bishops C & O.V.	22	6	0	16	298	453	-155	12
Tenbury*	22	4	0	18	217	754	-537	6
Birchfield	22	1	0	21	321	857	-536	2

NORTH MIDLANDS TWO

	P	W	D	L	PF	PA	PD	Pts
Veseyans	24	18	1	5	531	294	237	37
Cleobury Mortimer	24	16	2	6	467	240	227	34
Ross On Wye	24	14	0	10	432	384	48	28
Harborne	24	13	2	9	396	372	24	28
Aldridge*	24	14	1	9	414	346	68	27
Birmingham CS*	24	12	2	10	331	274	57	24
Stourport*	24	12	0	12	369	303	66	22
Bournville	24	10	0	14	413	469	-56	20
Kynoch	24	7	2	15	359	425	-66	16
Clee	24	4	3	17	196	480	-284	11
Wulfrun	24	3	0	21	245	760	-515	6
Bredon Star	24	2	1	21	233	850	-617	5
Oswestry*	24	24	0	0	1012	201	811	-42

* Points deducted

MIDLAND DIVISION FIXTURE GRIDS 1999-2000

MIDLANDS TWO

	Ampthill	Bromsgrove	Derby	Huntingdon	Kettering	Leighton Buzz.	Lincoln	Luctonians	Malvern	Mansfield	Newport	Nottingham M.	Old Laurentians	Stockwood Pk	Sutton Coldfield	Wellingborough	Wolverhampton
Ampthill					15.01	23.10	20.11		11.12	08.04	12.02		11.03	02.10			
Bromsgrove	27.11			08.01	08.04				11.03	06.11	25.09	29.01	09.10				
Derby	11.09	20.11		02.10				12.02				23.10			11.03	15.01	11.12
Huntingdon	09.10				12.02	20.11	11.12		15.01	25.09	11.03		08.04				
Kettering			08.01			26.02	25.03	06.11	11.09					29.01	27.11	09.10	
Leighton Buzzard		15.01	09.10					08.04				11.12		06.11	25.09	11.03	12.02
Lincoln		12.02	06.11			08.01		25.09						27.11	09.10	08.04	11.03
Luctonians	26.02	02.10		25.03						29.01		11.09	08.01			20.11	23.10
Malvern			27.11			29.01	26.02	09.10						08.01	06.11	25.09	08.04
Mansfield			25.03		11.12	02.10	23.10		20.11		15.01		12.02	11.09			
Newport			29.01		23.10	25.03	11.09	27.11	02.10					26.02	08.01		
Nottingham Moderns	06.11			27.11	11.03		15.01		12.02	09.10	08.04		25.09				
Old Laurentians			26.02		20.11	11.09	02.10		23.10		11.12			25.03	29.01		
Stockwood Park		11.12	25.09	23.10				11.03				20.11			08.04	12.02	15.01
Sutton Coldfield	25.03	23.10		11.09				15.01		26.02		02.10				11.12	20.11
Wellingborough	29.01	11.09		26.02						08.01	06.11	25.03	27.11				02.10
Wolverhampton	08.01	25.03		29.01	25.09					27.11	09.10	26.02	06.11				

MIDLANDS WEST ONE

	Aston Old	Bedworth	Birmingham Ex	Evesham	Keresley	Kings Norton	Leamington	Newcastle (Stfs)	Old Coventrians	Old Halesonians	Old Leamington	Selly Oak	Shrewsbury	Stafford	Stratford u Avon	Telford	Woodrush
Aston Old					09.10	25.09		06.11		08.01		29.01	27.11	25.03	26.02		
Bedworth	11.09		09.10	27.11			06.11		08.01		29.01					26.02	25.03
Birmingham Exiles	02.10			08.01		23.10	27.11		29.01		26.02					25.03	11.09
Evesham	20.11				15.01	11.12		12.02	25.03		11.09					02.10	23.10
Keresley		23.10	20.11					08.01		26.02		25.03	29.01	02.10	11.09		
Kings Norton		02.10			06.11			27.11		29.01		26.02	08.01	11.09	25.03		
Leamington	23.10			29.01	11.12	20.11			26.02		25.03					11.09	02.10
Newcastle (Staffs)		20.11	11.12				15.01			25.03		11.09	26.02	23.10	02.10		
Old Coventrians	11.12				12.02	15.01		11.03			02.10		08.04			23.10	20.11
Old Halesonians		15.01	12.02	08.04			11.03		25.09			23.10		11.12	20.11		
Old Leamingtonians	15.01				11.03	12.02		08.04		09.10			25.09			20.11	11.12
Selly Oak		12.02	11.03	25.09			08.04		09.10		06.11			15.01	11.12		
Shrewsbury		11.12	15.01	11.03			12.02			11.09		02.10		20.11	23.10		
Stafford		08.04	25.09	06.11			09.10		27.11		08.01					29.01	26.02
Stratford-Upon-Avon		11.03	08.04	09.10			25.09		06.11		27.11			12.02		08.01	
Telford	12.02				08.04	11.03		25.09		06.11		27.11	09.10				15.01
Woodrush	11.03				25.09	08.04		09.10		27.11		08.01	30.10		29.01		

MIDLANDS WEST TWO

	Berkswell & B	Bridgnorth	Dixonians	Edwardians	Kidderminster	Leek	Ludlow	Nuneaton Old	Old Saltleians	Old Yardleians	Pershore	Silhillians	Southam	Stoke Old Boys	Tamworth	Warley	Willenhall
Berkswell & Balsall		25.03		20.11						26.02		15.01	11.09	02.10	23.10		11.12
Bridgnorth				15.01					08.04		25.09	11.03	23.10	20.11	11.12		12.02
Dixonians	25.09	06.11			12.02	11.03	08.04			09.10			27.11			15.01	
Edwardians			26.02		11.09			29.01	27.11		08.01	06.11				25.03	09.10
Kidderminster	06.11	08.01				25.09	09.10			27.11			29.01	26.02	25.03		
Leek	27.11	29.01		02.10			06.11			08.01			26.02	25.03	11.09		
Ludlow	08.01	26.02		23.10						29.01			25.03	11.09	02.10		20.11
Nuneaton Old	08.04	09.10	20.11		15.01	12.02	11.03			25.09						11.12	
Old Saltleians	12.02		02.10		20.11	11.12	15.01	11.09			25.03					23.10	
Old Yardleians		11.09		11.12					11.03			12.02	02.10	23.10	20.11		15.01
Pershore	11.03		23.10		11.12	15.01	12.02	02.10		08.04						20.11	
Silhillians			11.09		23.10	20.11	11.12	25.03	29.01		26.02					02.10	
Southam				12.02				06.11	25.09		09.10	08.04		11.12	15.01		11.03
Stoke Old Boys			08.01	11.03				27.11	09.10		06.11	25.09			12.02		08.04
Tamworth			29.01	08.04				08.01	06.11		27.11	09.10				26.02	25.09
Warley	09.10	27.11			11.03	08.04	25.09			06.11			08.01	29.01			
Willenhall			25.03		02.10	23.10		26.02	08.01		29.01	27.11				11.09	

STAFFS & WARWICKS

	Alcester	Atherstone	Burntwood	Claverdon	Coventry Welsh	Dunlop	Earlsdon	GPT Coventry	Handsworth	Manor Park	Pinley	Shipston on S	Spartan (Mids)	Trentham	Trinity Guild	Uttoxeter	Wednesbury
Alcester				25.09	09.10		06.11		27.11		08.01			26.02	25.03	29.01	
Atherstone	02.10			23.10		27.11		08.01		29.01		26.02	25.03				11.09
Burntwood	11.09	09.10				06.11		27.11		08.01		29.01	26.02				25.03
Claverdon			02.10		06.11		27.11		08.01		29.01			25.03	11.09	26.02	
Coventry Welsh		20.11	23.10				08.01		29.01		26.02			11.09	02.10	25.03	
Dunlop	23.10			20.11	11.12			29.01		26.02		25.03	11.09				02.10
Earlsdon		11.12	20.11			15.01			26.02		25.03			02.10	23.10	11.09	
GPT Coventry	20.11			11.12	15.01		12.02			25.03		11.09	02.10				23.10
Handsworth		15.01	11.12			12.02		11.03			11.09			23.10	20.11	02.10	
Manor Park	11.12			15.01	12.02		11.03		08.04			02.10	23.10				20.11
Pinley		12.02	15.01			11.03		08.04		25.09				20.11	11.12	23.10	
Shipston On Stour	15.01			12.02	11.03		08.04		25.09		09.10		20.11				11.12
Spartans (Midlands)	12.02			11.03	08.04		25.09		09.10		06.11					27.11	15.01
Trentham		08.04	11.03			25.09		09.10		06.11		27.11	08.01		12.02		
Trinity Guild		25.09	08.04			09.10		06.11		27.11		08.01	29.01				26.02
Uttoxeter		11.03	12.02			08.04		25.09		09.10		06.11		11.12	15.01		
Wednesbury	11.03			08.04	25.09		09.10		06.11		27.11			29.01		08.01	

STAFFS ONE

	Bloxwich	Cannock	GEC St Leon'ds	Linley	Wheaton Aston	Whittington
Bloxwich		25.09	11.12	26.02	20.11	29.01
Cannock	08.01		12.02	09.10	27.11	11.12
GEC St. Leonards	11.03	20.11		25.09	29.01	26.02
Linley	27.11	29.01	08.01		11.03	20.11
Wheaton Aston	12.02	26.02	09.10	11.12		08.01
Whittington	09.10	11.03	27.11	12.02	25.09	

STAFFS TWO

	Barton under	Eccleshall	Gnosall	Market Drayton	Michelin	Rugeley	Stone
Barton under		11.09	11.03	15.01	20.11	12.02	09.10
Eccleshall	08.01		11.12	09.10	11.03	20.11	12.02
Gnosall	27.11	25.03		11.09	12.02	09.10	15.01
Market Drayton	25.09	29.01	23.10		11.12	11.03	20.11
Michelin	26.02	27.11	??.??	25.03		15.01	11.09
Rugeley	23.10	26.02	29.01	27.11	25.09		25.03
Stone	29.01	23.10	25.09	26.02	08.01	11.12	

WARWICKSHIRE

	Coventrians	Coventry Sar.	Coventry Tech.	Ford	Harbury	O. Warwickians	O. Wheatleyans	Rugby St A.	Shottery	Standard
Coventrians		18.12	02.10	29.01	20.11	26.02	23.10	25.09	25.03	11.12
Coventry Saracens	11.09		08.01	02.10	26.02	23.10	29.01	11.12	20.11	25.03
Coventry Technical	15.01	25.09		23.10	25.03	20.11	26.02	09.10	11.12	18.12
Ford	09.10	15.01	12.02		11.12	25.03	20.11	06.11	18.12	25.09
Harbury	11.03	06.11	27.11	15.04		08.01	11.09	15.01	09.10	12.02
Old Warwickians	06.11	12.02	11.03	27.11	25.09		15.04	18.12	15.01	09.10
Old Wheatleyans	12.02	09.10	06.11	11.03	18.12	11.12		27.11	25.09	15.01
Rugby St Andrews	08.01	15.04	29.01	26.02	02.10	11.09	25.03		23.10	20.11
Shottery	27.11	11.03	15.04	11.09	29.01	02.10	08.01	12.02		06.11
Standard	15.04	27.11	11.09	08.01	23.10	29.01	02.10	11.03	26.02	

NORTH MIDLANDS ONE

	Bromyard	Cleobury Mort.	Droitwich	Erdington	Five Ways OE	Ledbury	Old Griffinians	Redditch	Upton on Severn	Veseyans
Bromyard		11.03	25.09	12.02	09.10	15.01	06.11	18.12	27.11	25.03
Cleobury Mortimer	11.09		06.11	25.09	18.12	12.02	27.11	09.10	25.03	15.01
Droitwich	26.02	08.01		20.11	02.10	15.04	29.01	11.12	23.10	11.03
Erdington	02.10	26.02	18.12		27.11	09.10	25.03	15.01	11.09	06.11
Five Ways O.E.	29.01	20.11	12.02	15.04		11.12	23.10	11.03	08.01	25.09
Ledbury	23.10	02.10	27.11	29.01	25.03		11.09	06.11	26.02	18.12
Old Griffinians	08.01	15.04	09.10	11.12	15.01	11.03		25.09	20.11	12.02
Redditch	20.11	29.01	25.03	23.10	11.09	08.01	26.02		02.10	27.11
Upton On Severn	15.04	11.12	15.01	11.03	06.11	25.09	18.12	12.02		09.10
Veseyans	11.12	23.10	11.09	08.01	26.02	20.11	02.10	15.04	29.01	

NORTH MIDLANDS TWO

	Aldridge	Birchfield	Brimingham CS	Bishops Castle	Bourneville	Harborne	Ross on Wye	Stourport	Tenbury	Yardley & Dist
Aldridge		11.09	08.01	02.10	29.01	23.10	26.02	20.11	25.03	11.12
Birchfield	26.02		08.01	20.11	02.10	25.03	29.01	11.12	18.12	23.10
Birmingham C.S.	06.11	11.03		15.01	27.11	09.10	15.04	12.02	25.09	11.09
Bishops Castle &	25.09	20.11	25.03		29.01	11.12	23.10	18.12	15.01	26.02
Bournville	11.03	02.10	27.11	15.04		12.02	11.09	06.11	09.10	08.01
Harborne	15.01	25.03	09.10	11.12	18.12		26.02	25.09	12.02	20.11
Ross On Wye	27.11	29.01	15.04	23.10	11.09	08.01		11.03	06.11	02.10
Stourport	09.10	11.12	12.02	18.12	06.11	25.09	15.01		11.03	25.03
Tenbury	15.04	23.10	11.09	26.02	08.01	20.11	02.10	27.11		29.01
Yardley & District	12.02	18.12	06.11	25.09	11.03	15.01	27.11	09.10	15.04	

NORTH MIDLANDS THREE

	Bredon Star	Chaddesley C	Clee	Essington	Greyhounds	Kynoch	Old Shrewsbury
Bredon Star		11.09	18.12	25.03	02.10	15.01	20.11
Chaddesley Corbett	11.12		23.10	20.11	18.12	25.03	02.10
Clee	25.09	12.02		09.10	11.09	08.01	27.11
Essington	27.11	11.03	15.01		12.02	25.09	11.09
Greyhounds	08.01	25.09	11.12	23.10		11.03	15.01
Kynoch	09.10	27.11	02.10	18.12	20.11		12.02
Old Shrewsbury	11.03	08.01	25.03	11.12	09.10	23.10	

MIDLANDS EAST ONE

	Dunstablians	Ilkeston	Long Buckby	Luton	Lutterworth	Newark	Northampton M	Northampton O	Oadby	Old Northampt	Paviors	Peterborough	South Leicester	Spalding	Stewarts & L	Stoneygate	Towcestrians
Dunstablians			11.09	09.10			27.11	08.01			06.11	29.01	25.03		26.02		
Ilkeston	23.10			20.11	08.01	29.01				26.02				25.03		11.09	02.10
Long Buckby		09.10			06.11	27.11			25.09	08.01				29.01		26.02	25.03
Luton			02.10				08.01	29.01	23.10		27.11	26.02			11.09		
Lutterworth	20.11			11.12		26.02				25.03	15.01			11.09		02.10	23.10
Newark	11.12			15.01			11.03			11.09	12.02			02.10		23.10	20.11
Northampton Mens		15.01	20.11		12.02			25.03	11.12			11.09	23.10		02.10		
Northampton Old		12.02	11.12		11.03	08.04			15.01			02.10	20.11		23.10		
Oadby	02.10	06.11			27.11	08.01				29.01				26.02		25.03	11.09
Old Northamptonains	15.01			12.02			08.04	25.09			11.03			23.10		20.11	11.12
Paviors		11.12	23.10				29.01	26.02	20.11			25.03	11.09				
Peterborough		11.03	15.01		08.04	25.09			12.02	09.10			11.12		20.11		
South Leicester		25.09	11.03		09.10	06.11			08.04	27.11				08.01		29.01	
Spalding	12.02			11.03			25.09	09.10			08.04	06.11				11.12	15.01
Stewarts & Lloyds		08.04	12.02		25.09	09.10			11.03	06.11			15.01	27.11			
Stoneygate	11.03			08.04			09.10	06.11			25.09	27.11			08.01		12.02
Towcestrians	08.04			25.09			06.11	27.11			09.10	08.01	26.02		29.01		

MIDLANDS EAST TWO

	Amber Valley	Ashbourne	Ashfield	Buxton	Coalville	Glossop	Grimsby	Kesteven	Kibworth	Leicester Forest	Long Eaton	Loughborough	Market Bos.	Matlock	Stamford	Vipers	West Bridgford
Amber Valley		11.09	09.10	08.01				06.11		27.11			26.02	29.01	25.03		
Ashbourne					08.01	25.09	09.10		06.11		27.11	29.01				26.02	25.03
Ashfield		02.10		29.01		23.10		27.11		08.01			25.03	26.02	11.09		
Buxton		11.12				15.01	12.02		04.03		08.04		23.10	02.10	20.11		
Coalville	15.01		12.02	25.09				04.03		08.04		23.10				20.11	11.12
Glossop	02.10				29.01		06.11		27.11		08.01	26.02				25.03	11.09
Grimsby	23.10		20.11		26.02				08.01		29.01	25.03				11.09	02.10
Kesteven		23.10		26.02		20.11	11.12			29.01			11.09	25.03	02.10		
Kibworth	20.11		11.12		25.03			15.01			26.02	11.09				02.10	23.10
Leicester Forest		15.01			09.10	12.02	04.03		08.04		25.09		20.11		11.12		
Long Eaton		20.11		25.03		11.12	15.01		12.02				02.10	11.09	23.10		
Loughborough	11.12		15.01		11.09			12.02		04.03		02.10				23.10	20.11
Market Bosworth	12.02		04.03	09.10				08.04		25.09				06.11		11.12	15.01
Matlock		12.02			06.11	04.03	08.04		25.09		09.10	27.11			15.01		
Stamford		04.03			27.11	08.04	25.09		09.10		06.11	08.01				29.01	
Vipers	04.03		08.04	06.11				25.09		09.10			08.01	27.11			12.02
West Bridgford	08.04		25.09	27.11				09.10		06.11			29.01	08.01	26.02		

NOTTS, LINCS DERBY ONE

	Bakewell	Barton & Dist.	Belper	Boots Athletic	Castle Don	Dronfield	Keyworth	Market Rasen	Melbourne	Mellish	Nott. Casuals	Nottinghamians	Sleaford	Southwell	Worksop
Bakewell		25.03		09.10		06.11			08.01		26.02	27.11	29.01		
Barton & District			25.09		09.10		06.11	27.11		08.01				29.01	26.02
Belper	02.10				06.11		27.11	08.01		29.01				26.02	25.03
Boots Athletic		02.10	23.10			27.11			29.01		25.03	08.01	26.02		
Castle Donington	23.10			20.11			08.01	29.01		26.02				25.03	02.10
Dronfield		23.10	20.11		11.12				26.02		02.10	29.01	25.03		
Keyworth	20.11			11.12		15.01		26.02		25.03				02.10	23.10
Market Rasen	11.12			15.01		12.02				02.10		11.03		23.10	20.11
Melbourne		11.12	15.01		12.02		11.03	25.09			20.11		23.10		
Mellish	15.01			12.02		11.03			09.10			25.09		20.11	11.12
Nottingham Casuals		20.11	11.12		15.01		12.02		25.03		23.10		02.10		
Nottinghamians		12.02	11.03		25.09		09.10	06.11		27.11				08.01	
Sleaford		15.01	12.02		11.03		25.09	09.10		06.11	11.12				
Southwell	12.02			11.03		25.09			06.11			09.10	27.11		15.01
Worksop	11.03			25.09		09.10			27.11		29.01	06.11	08.01		

NOTTS, LINCS DERBY TWO

	Bolsover	Boston	Chesterfield	Cleethorpes	Cotgrave	East Leake	East Relford	Hope Valley	Leesbrook	Meden Vale	Notts Constab	Rolls Royce	Skegness	Stamford Coll.	Tupton
Bolsover		02.10			20.11		15.01	12.02	23.10		11.12		11.03		
Boston			09.10		11.12		12.02	11.03	20.11		15.01		25.09		
Chesterfield	25.09			20.11		23.10				11.12		12.02		15.01	11.03
Cleethorpes	06.11	27.11							08.01	12.02		25.09		11.03	09.10
Cotgrave			27.11	29.01		08.01	25.09	09.10			11.03		06.11		
East Leake	09.10	06.11		11.12						15.01		11.03		12.02	25.09
East Retford			29.01	25.03		26.02		27.11		02.10			08.01	23.10	
Hope Valley			26.02	02.10		25.03				23.10		11.12	29.01	20.11	
Leesbrook			06.11		15.01	27.11	11.03	25.09			12.02		09.10		
Meden Vale	27.11	08.01			26.02				29.01			09.10		25.09	06.11
Notts Constabulary			08.01	26.02		29.01	09.10	06.11		25.03			27.11		
Rolls Royce	29.01	26.02			02.10		20.11		25.03		23.10				08.01
Skegness			25.03	23.10		02.10				20.11		15.01		11.12	12.02
Stamford College	08.01	29.01			25.03				26.02		02.10	06.11			27.11
Tupton	26.02	25.03			23.10		11.12	15.01	02.10		20.11				

NOTTS, LINCS DERBY THREE

	Appleby Frod.	Bingham	Bourne	Burton Joyce	Gainsborough	Horncastle	North Kesteven	Ollerton	Univ of Derby	Yarborough B
Appleby Frodingham		11.09	26.02	02.10	29.01	23.10	08.01	20.11	08.04	11.12
Bingham	11.03		08.01	26.02	20.11	02.10	08.04	29.01	11.12	23.10
Bourne	25.09	06.11		18.12	12.02	27.11	09.10	25.03	15.01	11.09
Burton Joyce	12.02	25.09	20.11		08.04	29.01	11.12	23.10	11.03	08.01
Gainsborough	09.10	18.12	02.10	27.11		25.03	15.01	11.09	06.11	26.02
Horncastle	15.01	12.02	08.04	09.10	11.12		11.03	08.01	25.09	20.11
North Kesteven	06.11	27.11	29.01	25.03	23.10	11.09		26.02	18.12	02.10
Ollerton	18.12	09.10	11.12	15.01	11.03	06.11	25.09		12.02	08.04
University Of Derby	27.11	25.03	23.10	11.09	08.01	26.02	20.11	02.10		29.01
Yarborough Bees	25.03	15.01	11.03	06.11	25.09	18.12	12.02	27.11	09.10	

EAST MIDLANDS/ LEICS ONE

	Bedford Swifts	Biggleswade	Daventry	Loughborough	Melton Mowb.	N'hampton BB	Northampton	Oakham	Old Newtonians	Rushden & H	St Ives (Mids)	Wellingborough
Bedford Swifts		04.09	11.03	25.09	12.02	09.10	22.01	18.03	08.01	20.11	15.04	11.12
Biggleswade	25.03		18.03	11.03	08.01	25.09	20.11	12.02	15.04	09.10	11.12	22.01
Daventry	11.09	15.01		06.11	26.02	18.12	02.10	27.11	29.01	08.04	23.10	04.09
Loughborough	26.02	11.09	08.01		20.11	12.02	15.04	09.10	11.12	22.01	25.03	18.03
Melton Mowbray	02.10	06.11	25.09	18.12		27.11	29.01	08.04	23.10	04.09	15.01	11.03
Northampton BBOB	29.01	26.02	20.11	02.10	15.04		11.12	22.01	25.03	18.03	11.09	08.01
Northampton	23.10	18.12	12.02	27.11	09.10	08.04		04.09	15.01	11.03	06.11	25.09
Oakham	15.01	02.10	15.04	29.01	11.12	23.10	25.03		11.09	08.01	26.02	20.11
Old Newtonians	06.11	27.11	09.10	08.04	22.01	04.09	18.03	11.03		25.09	18.12	12.02
Rushden & Higham	18.12	29.01	11.12	23.10	25.03	15.01	11.09	06.11	26.02		02.10	15.04
St Ives (Midlands)	27.11	08.04	22.01	04.09	18.03	11.03	08.01	25.09	20.11	12.02		09.10
Wellingborough	08.04	23.10	25.03	15.01	11.09	06.11	26.02	18.12	02.10	27.11	29.01	

EAST MIDLANDS LEICS TWO

	Ashby	Ayleston St J	Aylesonians	Bedford Queens	Biddenham	Brackley	Bugbrooke	Corby	Deepings	Oundle	St Neots	Vauxhall M
Ashby		09.10	06.11	15.01	25.03	27.11	11.03	18.12	26.02	08.04	11.09	29.01
Ayleston St James	12.02		27.11	18.12	11.03	08.04	22.01	25.03	23.10	11.09	02.10	15.01
Aylestonians	22.01	08.01		25.03	12.02	11.09	11.12	11.03	20.11	02.10	23.10	15.04
Bedford Queens	20.11	15.04	04.09		23.10	11.03	11.09	02.10	08.01	12.02	22.01	11.12
Biddenham	04.09	25.09	09.10	29.01		06.11	15.04	15.01	18.03	27.11	11.12	26.02
Brackley	08.01	11.12	18.03	25.09	22.01		02.10	12.02	15.04	23.10	20.11	04.09
Bugbrooke	25.09	06.11	08.04	18.03	18.12	26.02		29.01	09.10	15.01	04.09	27.11
Corby	15.04	04.09	25.09	26.02	20.11	09.10	23.10		11.12	22.01	08.01	18.03
Deepings	02.10	29.01	15.01	27.11	11.09	18.12	12.02	08.04		25.03	11.03	06.11
Oundle	11.12	18.03	26.02	09.10	08.01	29.01	20.11	06.11	04.09		15.04	25.09
St Neots	18.03	26.02	29.01	06.11	08.04	15.01	25.03	27.11	25.09	18.12		09.10
Vauxhall Motors	23.10	20.11	18.12	08.04	02.10	25.03	08.01	11.09	22.01	11.03	12.02	

EAST MIDLANDS LEICS THREE

	Anstey	Aylestone Ath	Brixworth	Colworth House	Kempston	Northampton	Thorney	Westwood
Anstey		08.01	23.10	09.10	27.11	26.02	25.03	15.01
Aylestone Athletic	25.09		09.10	15.01	26.02	23.10	27.11	25.03
Brixworth	12.02	29.01		20.11	08.01	25.03	02.10	27.11
Colworth House	29.01	02.10	26.02		25.03	27.11	08.01	12.02
Kempston	11.03	20.11	25.09	11.12		15.01	12.02	09.10
Northampton	20.11	12.02	11.12	11.03	02.10		29.01	25.09
Thorney	11.12	11.03	15.01	25.09	23.10	09.10		20.11
Westwood	02.10	11.12	11.03	23.10	29.01	08.01	26.02	

Midland Division Clubs

ASHFIELD R.U.F.C. Winners of Notts, Lincs & Derbys Div. 1 1998-99

BAKEWELL MANNERIANS R.U.F.C. 1st XV, March 1999

ALCESTER RFC

Staffs & Warwicks 1
Ground Address: Birmingham Road, King's Coughton, Alcester, Warwickshire. B49 5QF Tel: 01789 764061
Brief Directions: The Ground is situated on the West side of the A435 between Studley and Alcester approx. 1 mile north of Alcester at Kings Coughton.
Club Secretary: Mrs. Karyl Rees, 2 Wain Close, Captains Hill, Alcester, Warks.
Tel: 01789 764188
Fixtures Secretary: Alan Brookes, 20 Alauna Avenue, Alcester, Warwicks., B49 6AN.
Tel: (H) 01789 764076
Club Colours: Red and black jerseys with black shorts

ALDRIDGE RFC

North Midlands 2
Ground Address: Bourne Vale, Little Hardwick Road, Aldridge, West Midlands WS9 0SQ
Tel: 0121 353 2856
Brief Directions: Sign posted off Little Hardwick Road. Situated at the end of Bourne Vale.
Club Secretary: Mark Field, 47 Canberra Road, Walsall WS5 3NN Tel: (H) 01922 637588
Fixtures Secretary: Alex Reed, 4a Rectory Road, Sutton Coldfield, West Midlands B75 7AL
Tel: (H) 0121 240 8245
Club Colours: Black, Maroon & Gold hoops, black shorts

AMBER VALLEY RUFC

Midlands East 2
Ground Address: Pye Bridge, Lower Somerscotes, Alfreton, Derbyshire DE55 1NF. Tel: 01773 541308
Brief Directions: M1 J28 follow A38 towards Derby, 2 miles B600 to Somrtcotes, follow B600 towards Selston club 2 miles on left.
Club Secretary: Mr.A.Clarke, 98 Hickton Road, Swanwick, Alfreton, Derbyshire, DE55 1AG
Fixtures Secretary: Mr.A.Pickworth, 53 Ashton Close, Swanwick, Derbyshire, DE55 1HG
Club Colours: Black, maroon and amber

AMPTHILL & DISTRICT

Midlands 2
Ground Address: Dillingham Park, Woburn Road, Ampthill, Bedford. MK45 2HX
Tel: 01525 403303
Brief Directions: Ground on right approaching Ampthill from Woburn
Club Secretary: Mrs. Helene E Wright,74 Willow Way, Ampthill, Bedford MK45 2SP
Tel: 01525 754551
Fixtures Secretary: Tony Phillips, 17 Osprey Road, litwick, Beds. Tel: 01525 754517
Club Colours: Maroon and amber

ANSTEY RFC

East Midlands & Leicester 3
Ground Address: Bennion Road, Beaumont Leys, Leicester
Brief Directions: From A46 (Leicester Western Bypass) take Anstey/Beaumont Leys exit. Follow signs to shopping centre, turn beside police station.
Club Secretary: Chris Apperley, 97 Link Road, Anstey, Leicester. LE7 7BZZ
Tel: (H) 0116 234 0293
Fixtures Secretary: Doug Spokes, 338 Thurcaston Road, Leicester. LE4 2RD
Club Colours: Black shirt with scarlet & emerald V, black shorts and socks.

APPLEBY FRODINGHAM

Notts Lincs & Derby 3
Ground Address: Brumby Hall Social Club, Ashby Road, Scunthorpe
Brief Directions: R Garner, 26 Glanville Avenue, Scunthorpe, Lincs DN17 1DE
Club Colours: Black, White coller/Black/Black

ASHBOURNE RUFC

Midlands East 2
Ground Address: The Recreation Ground, Ashbourne. DE6 1EJ
Brief Directions: From the centre of town, keep in right hand lane at junction, go straight on, playing field is 100 yds on right
Club Secretary: Peter J Fuller, Ednaston Lodge Farm, Ednaston, Derby. DE6 3BA
Tel: (H) 01335 360381 (W) 0845 6044610
Fixtures Secretary: Andrew bailey, Yeldersley Hall, Ashbourne DE6 1LS Tel: 01335 343432 (H&B)
Club Colours: Navy and old gold hoops

ASHBY RFC (NEW NAME FOR OLD ASHBEIANS RFC)

East Midlands & Leicester 2
Ground Address: Nottingham Road, Ashby, Leicester LE65 1DJ
Tel: 01530 413992
Brief Directions: M42 junction 13, signposted Ashby (A50), right at next roundabout, signposted Lount Breedon (A453)
Club Secretary: John Mitchell, 50 Pennine Way, Ashby, Leicester LE65 1EW. Tel: (H) 01530 415284
Fixtures Secretary: J Grimsley, Tel: (H) 01530 414531
Club Colours: Maroon and light blue hoops with navy blue shorts

ASHFIELD (AMALGAMATED SWANS & SPARTANS)

Midlands East 2
Ground Address: Oddicroft Lane off A38, Kingsmill Road East, Suttton in Ashfield, Nottingham
Brief Directions: M1 J28, follow signs to Mansfield A38, go through 3 sets of traffic lights, turn right (fire station opposite), follow road for 300 metres until school on right hand side of road
Club Secretary: Stephen Trainer, 12 Belfry Close, Broadlands Park, Kirkby in Ashfield, Notts. NG17 8NS
Tel: (H) 01623 400411 (W) 0115 965 7276
Fixtures Secretary: John Chambers, 12 Berry Hill Lane, Mansfield, Nottingham NG18 4BQ.
Tel: 01623 641391
Club Colours: Navy , amber and red hoops

ASTON OLD EDWARDIANS FC

Midlands West 1
Ground Address: Sunnybank Avenue, Perry Common, Birmingham. B44 0HP
Tel: 0121 373 5746
Brief Directions: Off College Road (A453) approx 1 mile south of Chester Road (A452)
Club Secretary: Mrs G. Grundy, 31 Fredrick Rd, Sutton Coldfield, W. Midlands
Tel: 0121 354 5840
Fixtures Secretary: Mr Tony Stafford, 54 Station Rd, Marston Green, Solihull B37 7BA
Tel: (H) 0121 684 2653
Club Colours: Red, white and green hooped jerseys, white shorts

ATHERSTONE RFC

Staffs & Warwicks 1
Ground Address: Ratcliffe Road, Atherstone, Warks
Tel: 01827 714934
Brief Directions: Drive into town centre, turn at Midland Bank into Ratcliffe Road, clubhouse approx 0.75 mile down on left
Club Secretary: David Boal, Thurmaston House, 74 South Street, Atherstone, Warks. CV9 1DZ
Tel: (H) 01827 713145
Fixtures Secretary: Keith Berry, 10 Goodere Drive, Polesworth, Tamworth, Staffs B78 1BZ
Tel: (H) 01827 893138
Club Colours: Black and White

AYLESTONE ATHLETIC RFC

East Midlands & Leicester 3
Ground Address: Victoria Park Pavilion, Victoria Park, Leicester
Brief Directions: From City centre take A6 London Road to Market Harborough three quarters mile out on right hand side - changing rooms at Pavilion.
Club Secretary: Robert Jackson, 23 Cherry Tree Avenue, Leicester Forest East, Leicester LE3 3HP
Tel: (H) 0116 299 3847 - M07803 890334
Fixtures Secretary: Tommy Clay, 56 Cranfield Road, Leicester LE2 8QQ
Tel: (H) 0116 224 6808
Club Colours: Navy and scarlet hoops

AYLESTONE ST JAMES RFC

East Midlands & Leicester 2
Ground Address: Covert Lane, Scraptoft, Leicester
Tel: 01162 419202
Brief Directions: Out of Leicester on A47 Uppingham Rd, left into Scraptoft Lane, top of lane go directly on to Covert Lane, 2nd clubhouse on left
Club Secretary: K Wiridge, 5 Canons Close, Narborough, Leicestershire. LE9 5FC
Tel: (H) 01162 866481 (W) 01162 608187 (Fx) 640543
Fixtures Secretary: P Chapman
Tel: (H) 01162 431826
Club Colours: Blue and white hoops, navy shorts

AYLESTONIANS RFC

East Midlands & Leicester 2
Ground Address: Knighton Lane East, Leicester
Tel: 0116 2834899
Club Secretary: Clive Cooper, 31 Rockingham Close, Leicester
Tel: (H) 0116 2740922
Fixtures Secretary: RombMitcham.Tel No: 0116 2831357
Club Colours: Red, white and blue hoops

BAKEWELL MANNERIANS RUFC

Notts Lincs & Derby 1
Ground Address: The Showground, Coombs Road, Bakewell, Derbyshire
Brief Directions: Follow the `Agricultural Centre' signs from the A6. The pitch is on the right in front of the centre. Changing is at the Pavilion across the river via the footbridge.
Club Secretary: Martin Pearce, 37 Burton Edge, Bakewell, Derbyshire, DE45 1FQ.
Tel: 01629 813154
Fixtures Secretary: Rod Bell, Nether Croft, Eaton Place, Baslow, Derbys. DE45 1RW.
Tel: 01246 583564
Club Colours: Navy, light blue and white hoops, navy shorts

BANBURY RUFC

Midlands 1
Ground Address: Bodicote Park, Oxford Road, Banbury, Oxon
Tel: 01295 263862 (Ground) 01295 256298 (Clubhouse)
Brief Directions: M40 J11, follow signs town centre, hospital, Adderbury, continue to follow signs hospital, Adderbury, Ground on right 1.5 mile south of hospital on A4260
Club Secretary: Bryan A Davies, 34 Horton View, Banbury, Oxon. OX16 9HP
Tel: (H) 01295 262027
Fixtures Secretary: Roger Croft
Tel: (H) 01295 258289
Club Colours: Dark blue and white hoops

BARKERS' BUTTS RFC

Midlands 1
Ground Address: Pickford Grange Lane, Allesley, Coventry. CV5 9AR
Tel: 01676 522192
Brief Directions: A45 from Coventry to Birmingham, take left to Merden, 40yds turn left into Pickford Grange Lane, Club entrance 100yds on right
Club Secretary: R.G.Coward, c/o club at address above.
Fixtures Secretary: R.Hill
Tel: (H) 01676522887
Club Colours: Royal Blue and Amber, Navy Shorts

BARTON & DISTRICT RUFC

Notts, Lincs & Derby 1
Ground Address: Mill Lane, Barrow-on-Humber, North Lincolnshire
Brief Directions: To Barton, Right at mini roundabout, throughBarton market place, out of Barton approx 1 1/2 milesto Barrow, right at roundabout next sharp right into ground.
Club Secretary: T Phipps, 4 West Alridge, Barton-on Humber
Tel: (H) 01652 632373 (W) 01724 847888
Fixtures Secretary: Graham Briggs, 99 Farthings Road, Barton
Tel No: 01652 634187 (H)
Club Colours: Red and white hoops

BARTON-UNDER-NEEDWOOD

Staffordshire 2
Ground Address: Holland Sports & Social Club, Efflinch Lane, Barton-Under-Needwood, Staffs
Tel: 01283 712937
Club Secretary: G. Steen, 8 Gawain Grove, Stretton, Burton on Trent, Staffs DE13 0GN
Tel: (H) 0585 098257
Fixtures Secretary: N. Rigby, 67 Arden Road, Barton-Under-Needwood, Staffs DE13 8LE
Tel: (H) 01283 716528 (W) 0121 3537833

BEDFORD QUEENS RUFC

East Midlands & Leicester 2
Ground Address: Bedford Sports & Hockey centre, Chester Road, Queens Park, Bedford M K40 3BY
Tel: 01234 211151
Brief Directions: Central Bedford, over bridge, towards Queens Park near Post Office..
Club Secretary: Llewellyn John, 36 Goldington Avenue, Bedford, Beds. MK40 3BY
Tel: 01234 305145
Fixtures Secretary: Andy Radnor
Tel: (H) 01462 816175 (W) 0385 372897
Club Colours: Maroon and white hoops, navy blue shorts, maroon socks.

BEDFORD SWIFTS RUFC

East Midlands & Leicester 1
Ground Address: Bedford Athletics Stadium, Barkers Lane, Bedford, MK41 9SA
Tel: 01234 351115
Brief Directions: From A1, A428 west to Birmingham and Northampton on outskirts of Bedford follow signs left to Bedford Athletics Stadium or Priory Country Park
Club Secretary: Trevor N Stewart, 64 Ravensden Road, Renhold, Bedford. MK41 0JY
Tel: (H) 01234 771828
Fixtures Secretary: Matthew Norris, Flat 5, 1 Dynevor Road, Bedford, MK40 2DB.
Tel: (H)01234 327862 (B)0411 418229
Club Colours: Gold and royal blue hooped shirts, navy shorts

BEDWORTH RUFC

Midlands West 1
Ground Address: Rectory Fields, Smarts Road, Bedworth. CV12 0BP
Tel: 01203 312025
Brief Directions: M6 Jvt3. Bedworth turn off A444 bypass, left at the bottom of slip road then left at Cross Keys pub into Smarts Road
Club Secretary: David Hatfield, 17 New Road, Ash Green, Coventry. CV7 9AS
Tel: (H) 01203 365160 (W) 01203 362399
Fixtures Secretary: Alan Sheppard
Tel: (H) 01203 353434
Club Colours: Emerald Green jerseys, white shorts

BELGRAVE RFC

Midlands 1
Ground Address: Belgrave Pastures, Thurcaston Road, Abbey Lane, Leicester.
Tel: 0116 2663033
Brief Directions: Ground situated where A6 Loughborough Road meets the Abbey Lane, opposite Mcdonalds
Club Secretary: Michael John Goddard, Grange Court, 271A Birstall Road, Birstall, Leics. LE4 4DJ
Tel: (H) 0116 2677383 (W) 0802 263676
Fixtures Secretary: Kevin Hick
Tel: (H) 0116 2608617 (W) 0116 2739501
Club Colours: Red and black hoops, black shorts

BELPER RUFC LTD

Notts, Lincs & Derby 1
Ground Address: Herbert Strutt School Fields, Derby Road, Belper, Derbyshire.
Brief Directions: Ground is off A6 in Belper between Safeways supermarket and Babbington Hospital - near town centre.
Club Secretary: Mike Phelan, 5 Derby Road, Lower Kilburn, Belper, Derbyshire.
Tel: 01332 780203
Fixtures Secretary: Adrian Young, 65 Silverburn Drive, Oakwood, Derby,
Tel: (H) 01332 830877 - (W) 01159 860464
Club Colours: Black and white hoops

BERKSWELL & BALSALL RFC

Midlands West 2
Ground Address: Honiley Road, Meek End, Nr Balsall Common, Coventry
Brief Directions: From Birmingham or Balsall Common follow main road to Warwick (A4111 (Not road to Kennilworth). Ground approx I mile on right with entrance in Honiley Road.
Club Secretary: John Utley, 265 Station Road, Balsall Common , Coventry CV7 7EG
Tel: 01676 532463
Fixtures Secretary: K.Ballinger, 340 Kenilworth Road, Balsall Common, Coventry CV7 7ER
Tel: 01676 533020
Club Colours: Red and black shirts, black shorts

BIDDENHAM RFC
East Midlands & Leicester 2
Ground Address: The Biddenham Pavilion, Biddenham, Beds
Brief Directions: Enter Biddenham on A428 and turn right at Roundabout. Club is at the end of the road .
Club Secretary: Andrew Pryor, 43 Main Road, Biddenham, Bedfordshire. MK40 4BD
Tel: (H) 01234 328278 (W) 01234 350812
Fixtures Secretary: Jez Bird, 120 deep Spinney, Biddenham, Beds. MK40 4QN Tel No: 0403 344376 (M) 04325 135340 (Pager)
Club Colours: Bottle green and old english cream quarters, green shorts.

BIGGLESWADE RUFC
East Midlands & Leicester 1
Ground Address: Langford Road, Biggleswade, Beds. SG18 9RA
Tel: 01767 312463
Brief Directions: On the A6001 Biggleswade to Henlow road, approx 1 mile from Biggleswade by the Broom turn off, on the right hand side coming from Biggleswade
Club Secretary: Mike Williams, 8 Laurel Way, Ickleford, Hitchin, Herts. SG5 3UP
Tel: (H) 01462 624925 (W) 01462 443091
Fixtures Secretary: Mike Pearson
Tel: (H) 01480 385077
Club Colours: Navy blue shirts with red hoop and navy blue shorts

BINGHAM RUFC
Notts, Lincs & Derby 3
Ground Address: The Town Pavilion, Brendan Grove, Wynhill, Bingham, Notts. Tel: 01949 832874
Club Secretary: John Perry, 29 Cogley Lane, Bingham, Notts. Tel: (H) 01949 837777
Fixtures Secretary: R J Williams,
Tel: (H) 01636 8233076
Club Colours: Green & red hoops.

BIRCHFIELD RUFC
North Midlands 2
Ground Address: Burford Rd Playing Fields, 143 Kingstanding Rd, Kingstanding, B44 8JU
Brief Directions: M6 J7 A34 towards Birmingham, A452 towards Sutton Coldfield, ground on Kiingstanding road B4138 1/2mile from A453 junction. B'ham A-Z Ref 4B page 48
Club Secretary: Amanda Cadman, 45 Hall Rd, Warley, West Mids, B67 6SQ
Tel: (H) 0121 565 3621
Fixtures Secretary: Robert Chapman, 44 Olton Croft, Accocks Green, B'ham, B27 6PG
Tel: (H) 0121 604 3694
Club Colours: Green and black hoops

BIRMINGHAM CITY CIVIL SERVICE RFC
North Midlands 2
Ground Address: Old Damson Lane, Elmdon, Solihull, West Midlands
Brief Directions: Opposite Birmingham Airport on A45
Club Secretary: R.G.Webb, 51 Ladbrooke Road, Solihull, West Midlands , B91 3RW.
Tel 0121 705 2812
Fixtures Secretary: Mark howard, 325 Alcester road, Burcot, Bromsgrove, Worcs. B60 1BQ
Tel: 015278 36584
Club Colours: Red and White shirts, blue socks and red socks

BIRMINGHAM EXILES
Midlands West 1
Ground Address: Catherine de Barnes Lane, Bickenhill, Solihull, West Midlands B92 0DX
Tel: 01675 442995
Brief Directions: Leave M42 at J.6 then leave A45 Coventry Road at Birmingham Airport junction and take Catherine de Barnes Lane exit.
Club Secretary: M. Whateley, 19 Wimbourne Road, Sutton Coldfield, West Midlands B76 2SU
Tel: 0121 687 5169 (W) 0121 378 3446 (H)
Fixtures Secretary: Julian Griffiths, 39 School Road, Moseley, Birmingham B13 9TF
Tel : 0121 233 2838 (W) 0121 449 2471
Club Colours: Blue and Red hoops, navy blue shorts

BISHOPS CASTLE & ONNY VALLEY RFC
North Midlands 2
Ground Address: Love Lane, Berillo Park, Bishops Castle, Shropshire
Tel: 01588 638816
Brief Directions: On Eastern edge of town adjacent to A488 Shrewsbury to Clun Road
Club Secretary: D. Bryan Jones, c/o Halls, Church Street, Bishops Castle, Shropshire
Fixtures Secretary: R. Jones, Hayford Farm, Westbury, Shrewsbury, Shropshire
Club Colours: Green and red stripes

BLOXWICH RFC
Staffordshire 1
Ground Address: Bloxwich Sports Club, Stafford Road, Bloxwich. WS3 3NJ
Tel: 01922 405891
Brief Directions: 0.25 mile outside Bloxwich town on A34 to Cannock, entrance between houses on left marked by black and white posts, 100yds past traffic lights
Club Secretary: Mr Anthony Allen, 16 Sorrel Close, Featherstone, Staffs. WV10 7TX
Tel: (H) 01902 739835 (W) 01902 864726
Fixtures Secretary: Robert Tittley, Burnham Cottage, 31 Wallington Heath, Bloxwich.
Tel: 01922 712519
Club Colours: Green with black and white chest hoops and black shorts

BOLSOVER
Notts Lincs & Derby 2
Ground Address: Oxcroft Miners Welfare, Clowne Road, Stanfree Derbyshire.
Club Secretary: F L Skinner, 17 Oxcroft Lane, Bolsover, Chesterfield, Derbyshire SS4 6DJ

BOSTON RFC
Notts, Lincs & Derby 2
Ground Address: Great Fen Road, Wyberton, Boston, Lincs. PE21 7PB Tel: 01205 362683
Brief Directions: 0.25 mile west of Boston on A1121 next to airfield
Club Secretary: Mrs Lynn Creasey, 48 Glen Drive, Boston, Lincs. PE21 7QB Tel: (H) 01205 356753
Fixtures Secretary: Mr T Bembridge Tel: (H) 01205 351973
Club Colours: Blue and white hoops, navy shorts, blue and white socks

BOOTS ATHLETIC RFC
Notts Lincs & Derby 1
Ground Address: Boots Athletic Ground, Holme Road, Lady Bay, West Bridgford, Notts
Tel: 01159 492388
Brief Directions: Follow signs to either Trent Bridge Cricket or Nottingham Forest, the Athletic Ground is on the south bank of the river Trent, next to Lady Bay bridge and Notts Forest
Club Secretary: Greg Haywood, Slaughterhouse Cottage, Main St., Epperstone, Nottingham. NG14 6AD
Tel: (H) 0115 9664629 (W) 0115 9712851
Fixtures Secretary: Andy Taylor, 43 Wellin Lane, Edwalton, Nottingham NG12 4ASTel: (H) 0115 945 2860 (W) 0115 9616 476 ext. 248
Club Colours: Dark blue and light blue quarters

BOURNE RUFC
Notts Lincs & Derby 3
Ground Address: Milking Nook Drive, Splading Road,Bourne, Lincs. Tel: 01778 393346
Brief Directions: Take the Spalding road out of Bourne and the ground is on the right after one and a half miles.
Club Secretary: Martin Hunter, 16 Rochester Court, Bourne, Lincs.
Tel No: 01778 423 259
Fixtures Secretary: As Secretary.
Club Colours: Navy Blue with broad gold band and navy blue shorts

BOURNVILLE RFC
North Midlands 2
Ground Address: Rowheath, Heath Road, Bournville, Birmingham. B30 Tel: 0121 475 0480
Brief Directions: A38 out of B'ham city centre, after approx 5 miles turn left into Oaktree Ln and follow signs for Cadbury World, turn right into Maryvale Rd, ground 0.5 mile on left
Club Secretary: Keith Smith, 1 Whitley Rd., Northfield, Birmingham B31 3BD Tel No: 0121 6801269
Fixtures Secretary: Michael Palmer
Tel: (H) 0121 475 0480 (M) 0802 935243
Club Colours: Blue, maroon and gold shirts, blue shorts

BRACKLEY RUFC
East Midlands & Leicester 2
Ground Address: Fine Lady Fields, Nightingale Close, Brackley, Northants. NN13 6PNTel: 01280 700685
Brief Directions: Find Halse Road, then left off second roundabout , right at next roundabout and ground is on left.
Club Secretary: Paul Harper, 16 Mixbury, Brackley, Northants NN13 5RR
Fixtures Secretary: Mike Harper, Horwell Farm, Baynards Green, Bicester, Oxon. OX6 9SQ
Tel: 01869 345821
Club Colours: Royal blue and white quarters, navy blue shorts

BREDON STAR RFC
North Midlands 3
Ground Address: Bredon Playing Fields, Kemerton Road, Bredon, Nr Tewkesbury, Glos
Tel: 01684 772831
Club Secretary: Carol Julie Malpass, 33 Plantation Crescent, Bredon, Nr Tewkesbury, Glos
Tel: (H) 01684 72831
Fixtures Secretary: Neil Evans
Tel: (H) 01684 772645 (W) 0973 171451
Club Colours: Red and black hoops

BRIDGNORTH RFC
Midlands West 2
Ground Address: The Bull, Bridge Street, Bridgnorth, Shropshire. WV15 5AA Tel: 01746 762796
Brief Directions: The clubhouse is adjacent to the bridge over the river in Lowtown
Club Secretary: Pete Shimmin, 7 Buck Cottage, Sheinton, Cressage, Shropshire. SY5 6DJ
Tel: (H) 01952 510604 (W) 01746 766488
Fixtures Secretary: Alun Stoll
Tel: (H & W) 01902 332025
Club Colours: Black shirts, black shorts

BRIXWORTH
East Midlands & Leicester 3
Ground Address: Northanptonshire Boys Grammer School, Pitsford, Northampton.
Club Secretary: M Pateman, 11 Oathill Close, Brixworth, Northampton
Tel: 01604 881008
Fixtures Secretary: Miss J Jones, 16 Oathill Close, Brixworth, Northampton NN6 9BE
Tel: 01604 882066
Club Colours: Red and Black Hoops

BROADSTREET RFC
Midlands 1
Ground Address: The Ivor Preece Field, Brandon Road, CoventryTel: 01203 453982 (Clubhouse), 01203 451706 (Caretaker).
Brief Directions: M6 Junction 2, take signs for Banbury, Stratford, Warwick. Along Coventry Eastern bypass. Ground entrance between TGI Fridays and Morrisons supermarket
Club Secretary: Mr C J McGinty, 14 Glendower Ave, Whoberley, Coventry. CV5 8BE
Tel: (H) 01203 679261 or 0035373 23155
Fixtures Secretary: Mr Dave Wilkinson
Tel: (H) 01203 543548
Club Colours: White shirts with red and green bands, green shorts

BROMSGROVE RFC
Midlands 2
Ground Address: Finstall Park, Finstall Road, Bromsgrove, Worcs. B60 3DH
Tel: 01527 874690
Brief Directions: Situated between Aston Fields and Finstall on Finstall Road (B4184), Bromsgrove
Club Secretary: Jon A Watson, 7 Bowmore Road, Bromsgrove, Worcs. B60 2HH
Tel: (H) 01527 875467 (W) 01926 484000
Fixtures Secretary: Ralph M Gordon., 66 Hanbury Road, Stoke Heath, Bromsgrove, Worcs.
Tel: (H & W) 01527 832003
Club Colours: White jerseys with red/black/red hoops, white shorts

BROMYARD RFC
North Midlands 1
Ground Address: The Clive Richards Sports Ground, Instone, Tenbury Road, Bromyard
Tel: 01885 483933
Brief Directions: From Bromyard, take the B4214 towards Tenbury Wells, the ground is on the right hand side, approx 0.5 mile from the town
Club Secretary: Deborah J Piggot, Upper Brockington, Bredewbury, Bromyard, Hereford, HR7 4TH. Tel: (H) 01885 483322
Fixtures Secretary: Simon Irwin, 2 Pinetree Cottages, Tedstone Wafre, Bromyard, Hereford, HR7 4QD. Tel: (H) 01885 488322
Club Colours: Green and gold

BUGBROOKE RUFC
East Midlands & Leicester 2
Ground Address: The Playing Fields, Pilgrims Lane, Bugbrooke, Northants
Tel: 01604 831137
Brief Directions: A45 from Northampton towards J16 M1 at Kislingbury R/about. Turn L. sign Rugbrook. Drive through village on same road almost out till other end. On L. signposted Bugbrooke Community Centre. Turn left in there.
Club Secretary: Mr John Gowen, 8 Middle Street, Nether Heyford, Northants. NN7 3LL
Tel: (H) 01327 342422 (W) 01604 758857
Fixtures Secretary: Mr Staff Hurlston, 97 Mount Pleasant, Harpole, Northants, NN7 4DL.
Tel: (H) 01604 831184
Club Colours: Bottle green and yellow quarters, green shorts, green and yellow hooped socks

BURNTWOOD RUFC
Staffs & Warwicks 1
Ground Address: The North Shore, Church Street, Chasetown, Staffordshire, WS7 8XE.
Tel: 01543 676651
Brief Directions: From A5 follow directions to Chasetown Clubhouse at end of Church St. Club is next to Chasetown Football Club.
Club Secretary: Kevin Cantrill, 39 Hunter Avenue, Burntwood, Staffs. WS79AQ
Tel: 01543 672737
Fixtures Secretary: Mark Bourne, 27 Willett Avenue, Burntwood, Staffordshire, WS7 8FJ.
Tel: 01543 675918
Club Colours: Scarlet & Emerald & white hoops , black shorts.

BURTON FC
Midlands 1
Ground Address: Peelcroft, Lichfield Street, Burton upon Trent, Staffordshire. DE14 3RH
Tel: 01283 564510
Brief Directions: Centre of Burton, adjacent to Safeways supermarket
Club Secretary: J D Lowe, 20 The Chevin, Stretton, Burton upon Trent, DE13 0XU
Tel/Fax: (H) 01283 534422
Fixtures Secretary: P E Richard, 20 Olton Road, Mickleover, Derby DE5 5PL
Tel: (H) 01332 516901
Club Colours: White jerseys with black diagonal stripe over right shoulder, white shorts, black socks

BURTON JOYCE RFC
Notts Lincs & Derby 3
Ground Address: The Poplars Playing Ground, Station road, Burton Joyce, Nottingham, NG14 2AN.
Brief Directions: Back of railway station at Burton Joyce A614 Nottingham to Southwell.
Club Secretary: Tony Hallam, 9 Copse Close, Burton Joyce, Nottingham, NG14 5DD
Fixtures Secretary: Mark Britton, 15 Main Street, Burton Joyce, Nottingham, NG14 5DX.
Club Colours: Red/Yellow/Blue

BUXTON RUFC
Midlands East 2
Ground Address: Fairfield Centre, Victoria Park Road, Buxton, Derbyshire
Tel: 01298 24081
Brief Directions: Follow A6 Stockport, up up Fairfield Rd. 1st R. Queens Rd becomes Bench Rd, left at T jcn with Victoria Park Rd, Centre on left after Royal Foresters
Club Secretary: David Robson, 20 Errwood Avenue, Buxton, Derbyshire. SK17 9BD
Tel: (H) 01298 22432 (W) 01298 26121 Ext 125
Fixtures Secretary: Lorraine Trevis Brown, 6 New Road, Whaley Bridge, Derbyshire, SK23 7JG. Tel: (H) 01663 73504 (W) 01298 23195
Club Colours: Blue, red and gold hoops, blue shorts

CAMP HILL RFC
Midlands 1
Ground Address: Haslucks Green Road, Shirley, Solihull, West Midlands Tel: 0121 7444175
Brief Directions: Haslucks Green Road is off Stratford Road (A34) - at city centre end of Shirley - Junction 4 of M42
Club Secretary: A.D.Muray, 40 Robin Hood Lane, Hall Green, Birmingham B28 OLN Tel; 0121 744 3804
Fixtures Secretary: Graham Scutt, 130 Longmore Road, Solihull, West Midlands
Tel: (H) 0121 7444495
Club Colours: Maroon and light blue

CANNOCK RUFC
Staffordshire 1
Ground Address: The Morgan Ground, Stafford Road, Huntingdon, Staffordshire. WS12 4NU Tel: 01543 467906
Club Secretary: Pauline Athersmith, 355 Cemetry Road, Cannock. WS11 2AY Tel: (H) 01543 574711
Fixtures Secretary: Phil Pearson Tel: (H) 01889 575 167 (W) 0121 544 2387
Club Colours: Blue and gold hoops

CASTLE DONINGTON RUFC
Notts Lincs & Derby 1
Ground Address: The Spital Pavilion, The Spital, Castle Donington, Derbyshire
Tel: 01332 812214 (pub)
Brief Directions: Travel into Donington from A6 turning right into the Spittal after the Tudor Inn, ground is situated 400yds on right
Club Secretary: A Hackett, The Old Bakery, Thringstone, Leicestershire. LE67 5AP
Tel: (H) 01530 223599 (W) 0831 675987
Fixtures Secretary: Alan Hampson, 77 Station Rd Castle Donington, Derby.
Tel: (H)01332 812314
Club Colours: Red and black quartered shirts, black shorts, red and black socks

CHADDESLEY CORBETT
North Midlands 3
Ground Address: Chaddesly Corbett Sports Club, Longmore, Fox Lane, Chaddesly Corbett
Brief Directions: On A448 between Kidderminster & Bromsgrove. Do not enter village, turning to ground is on sharp corner between The Fox P.H. and Rowberrys farm shop. Signed CCRFC - turn right from Kidderminster, left from Bromsgrove.
Club Secretary: N Evens, Cherry Tree House, Mustow Green, nr Kidderminster DY10 4LQ
Tel: 01562 777070
Fixtures Secretary: M Page, 8 The Green, Chaddesley Corbett DY10 4PZ
Tel: 01562 777070
Club Colours: Green & Blue Quarters/Blue/Green

CHESTERFIELD RUFC
Notts Lincs & Derby 2
Ground Address: The Rugby Field, Stonegravels, Sheffield Road, Chesterfield, Derbyshire.
Tel: 01246 232321
Brief Directions: M1 J29, follow signs to Chesterfield town centre A61 to Sheffield (old road, not bypass), ground is on left 1 mile from town centre
Club Secretary: D. J. Taylor, 7 Hallfields Rise, Shirland, Alfreton, Derbyshire, DE55 6DH.
Tel: 0115 9895223W - 01773 836138H
Fax: 0115 958 9113W - 01773 521778H
Fixtures Secretary: M Lord, 34 Pennine Way,Loundsley Green,Chesterfield, Derbyshire, S40 4ND
Tel: (H) 01246 274105
Club Colours: Red and white hoops, white shorts

CLAVERDON RFC
Staffs & Warwicks 1
Ground Address: Ossetts Hole Lane, Yarningale Common, Claverdon, Warwicks. CV35 8HN
Tel: 01926 843133
Brief Directions: Off A4189 Warwick to Henley in Arden.
Club Secretary: Basil Sayer, The White House, 45 Station Road, Balsall Common, Coventry. CV7 7FN
Tel: (H) 01676 532164 (W) 01933 303232
Fixtures Secretary: Lindsey Shaw, 23 Castle Close, Henley in Arden, Solihuiull, B95 5LR.
Tel: (H) 01564 795474 (W) 01789 41411 Ext 4598
Club Colours: Red and white

CLEE HILL RFC
North Midlands 3
Ground Address: 2 Lion Lane, Tenbury Road, Clee Hill, Ludlow, Shropshire.
Tel: 01584 890262
Brief Directions: Between Ludlow and Cleobury Mortimer on A4117. Take B4214 to Clee Hill (signposted Tenbury Wells). Ground approx. I mile on right hand side.
Club Secretary: Mrs. Penny Cooper, Studley Cottage, Clee Hill, Nr. Ludlow, Shropshire, SY8 3NP.
Tel: 01584 890990
Fixtures Secretary: Philip Edwards, Shop Farm, Dhustone Lane, Clee Hill, Ludlow, Shropshire, SY8 3PQ. Tel: 01584 890252
Club Colours: Maroon & Blue quarters, Blue shorts

CLEETHORPES RUFC
Notts Lincs & Derby 2
Ground Address: Wilton Road, Cleethorpes, N E Lincs Tel: 01472 812936
Brief Directions: Follow signs for Teaco suoerstore, ground is first tyrning right past Tesco.
Club Secretary: Peter Winn, 27 Grainsby Avenue, Cleethorps, N.E.Lincs ON35 PA .
Tel No: 01472 6953434
Fixtures Secretary: John Walsham
Tel: (H) 01472 699322
Club Colours: Blue & Gold hoops

CLEOBURY MORTIMER RFC
North Midlands 1
Ground Address: Cleobury Mortimer Sports & Social Club,, Love Lane, Cleobury Mortimer, Kidderminster, Worcs DY14 8PE Tel: 01299 271448
Brief Directions: To Cleobury along main street, then turn right just before the Three Horseshoes pub, left at mini roundabout, car park and ground 100 yards on left
Club Secretary: Mr P J Howman,2 Fryers Close, Cleobury Mortimer, Kidderminster, Worcs. DY14 8EB
Tel: (H & W) 01299 270462
Fixtures Secretary: MrT Wright, Candleford, 17 Larks Rise, Cleobury Mortimer, Kidderminster, Worcs. DY14 8JJ.
Tel: (H) 01299 271702
Club Colours: Red and green quarters, black shorts

COALVILLE RFC
Midlands East 2
Ground Address: Memorial Ground, Broomleys Road, Coalville, Leicester
Tel: (H) 01530 812090
Brief Directions: Leave M1 at Junction 22. Cooalville is signposted on A511.Go over four roundabouts and then turn left at fifth roundabout and Coalville RFC is 100 yards on right.
Club Secretary: Peter Smith, 50 Parkdale, Ibstock, Leics
Tel: (H) 01530 262113 (W) 01530 832085
Fixtures Secretary: Charles Coulson, 12 Broomley"s Road, Coalville, Leics.
Tel: (H) 01530 811280 (W) 01530 834079
Club Colours: Navy blue with amber stripe, Navy blue shorts

COLWORTH HOUSE RUFC

East Midlands & Leicester 3
Ground Address: Unilever Research, Colworth House, Sharnbrook, Bedford. MK44 1LQ
Tel: 01234 222221
Brief Directions: Frm sth: A6 to Sharnbr'k, turning left, thro' village to Colworth Hse sign, take sports field signs. Frm north: A6 to Souldrop, turning right, thro' S'drop to S'brook & C'wth Hse sign, as above
Club Secretary: Andrew Reynolds, 21 Alburgh Close, Bedford MK42 OHG
Tel: 01234 406113
Fixtures Secretary: D.Hebden, 54 Lilac Walk, Kempston, Beds MK42 7PH
Tel: 01234 300145
Club Colours: Emerald green, scarlet band, black shorts and socks

CORBY RFC

East Midlands & Leicester 2
Ground Address: Northen Park, Rockingham Triangle, Corby, Northants
Tel: 01536 204466
Brief Directions: Junction of A6003 & A6116 to the north of Corby, next to Corby Football & Athletics Club and Post House Hotel
Club Secretary: George A Ewen, 24 Charnwood Road, Corby, Northants. NN17 1XS
Tel: (H) 01536 504690 (W) 01536 265291
Fixtures Secretary: Charles Sanders, 21 Brunswick Gardens, Corby, Northants.
Tel: (H) 01536 745440 (W) 01536 534760
Club Colours: Red and white Quarters

COTGRAVE COLLIERY RUFC

Notts, Lincs & Derby 2
Ground Address: Cotgrave Community Centre, Woodview, Cotgrave, Nottingham
Tel: 0115 9892916
Brief Directions: Cotgrave lies in triangle boarded by A52 Nottingham/ Grantham rd, A46 Leicester/Newark rd & A606 N'ham-Melton Mowbray rd, Community Centre is opposite the Miners Welfare
Club Secretary: Nicholas Webb, 30 Marwood, Cotgrave, Nottingham NG12 3NS
Tel: 0115 989 3038
Fixtures Secretary: Anthony Hood, 14 Willowdene, Cotgrave, Nottingham, NG12 3ND
Tel: (H) 0115 9894518
Club Colours: Claret and blue quarters

COVENTRIANS RFC

Warwickshire
Ground Address: Black Pad, off Yelverton Road, Radford, Coventry. CV6 4NW
Tel: 01203 682885
Brief Directions: M6 J3 onto A444 to Coventry, right at 2nd roundabout to Holbrook, at next 2nd roundabout Yelverton Road is 50yds on right
Club Secretary: J S Daniell, 116 Mill Farm Park, Marston Jabbett, Nuneaton, Warks. CV12 9SF
Tel: 02476 373470
Fixtures Secretary: J S Daniell
Tel: (H) 01203 373470
Club Colours: Royal blue and white quarters

COVENTRY SARACENS

Warwickshire
Ground Address: Bredon Avenue, Binley, Coventry, CV6 2AR
Tel: 01203 453557
Brief Directions: From A46 (eastern bypass) take A428 to Coventry city centre for approx 1 mile, left into Bredon Ave, ground approx 200mtrs on left
Club Secretary: Brian Craner, 71 Westhill Road, Coundon, Coventry. CV6 2AD
Tel: (H) 01203 590280
Fixtures Secretary: Roger Hancox, 23 Rugby Lane, Stretton-on-Dunsmore, Rugby, CV23 9JW
Tel: (H) 01203 542252
Club Colours: Black

COVENTRY TECHNICAL R.F.C.

Warwickshire
Ground Address: Mitchell Avenue, Canley, Coventry
Tel: 01203 471733
Brief Directions: The club is only 5 mins from A45 Flethhampstead Highway, northbound take right turn into Charter Ave, southbound left at island by Canley fire and police station
Club Secretary: Stuart Kennedy, 48 Nutbrook Avenue, Tile Hill, Coventry.
Tel: 01203 461063
Fixtures Secretary: Neil Franklin
Tel: (H) 01203 335560
Club Colours: Green, gold and brown

COVENTRY WELSH RFC
Staffs & Warwicks 1
Ground Address: Burbages Lane, Longford, Coventry. CV6 6AY
Tel: 01203 360303
Brief Directions: M6 J3, take bypass road A444 to next roundabout and the right hand turn at roundabout is Burbages Lane
Club Secretary: Jean Williams, 173 Goodyers End Lane, Bedworth, Nuneaton. CV12 0HH.
Tel: (H) 01203 364596
Fixtures Secretary: Gary Greenway
Tel: (H) 01203 315403
Club Colours: Red shirts, black shorts

DAVENTRY RFC
East Midlands & Leicester 1
Ground Address: Stefen Hill, Western Avenue, Daventry, Northants. NN11 4ST
Tel: 01327 703802
Brief Directions: M1 J16, A45 west to Daventry, upon reaching Daventry, straight over roundabout heading for Daventry town centre, 3rd road on left and the ground is facing you
Club Secretary: Peter Weckerman, 3 Portland Close, Daventry, Northants, NN11 4SQ.
Tel: (H) 01327 311151
Fixtures Secretary: Graham Woodliffe, The Old Barne House, The Green,Badby, , Daventry, Northants, NN11 3AF
Tel: (H) 01327 703496 (W) 01327 305137
Club Colours: All black

DEEPINGS RUFC
East Midlands & Leicester 2
Ground Address: Linchfield Road, Deeping St James, Peterborough
Tel: 01778 345228
Brief Directions: R'bout Market Deeping (Jcn of A15/A16) take A16 towards Spalding, through town until sight footbridge, left at Xroads before bridge, immediate right thro' gates to ground
Club Secretary: Brian Kirby, 29 Tattershall Drive, Market Deeping, Peterborough. PE6 8BS
Tel: (H) 01778 343048 (W) 01733 556173
Fixtures Secretary: Colin Astley Tel No: 01778 342190
Club Colours: Green, black and gold hoops

DERBY RFC
Midlands 2
Ground Address: The Pavilion, Kedleston Road, Derby. DE22 2TF
Tel: 01332 344341
Brief Directions: Off A38 at Markeaton Park towards University of Derby campus - ground half a mile further on the left
Club Secretary: Mrs P.Dickens, 57 Wheeldon Avenue, Derby DE22 1HP
Tel: 01332 341546
Fixtures Secretary: John Dickens
Tel: (H) 01332 341546
Club Colours: Black and amber hoops, black shorts

DIXONIANS RFC
Midlands West 2
Ground Address: 31A Fountain Road, Edgbaston, Birmingham. B17 8NJ Tel: 0121 434 3313
Brief Directions: From Five Ways Biringham A456 direction Kidderminster in 1.5 miles turn right Fountain Road/Stanmore Road
Club Secretary: Vivian Shingler, Timberhonger House, Timberhonger, Bromsgrove, Worcestershire. B61 9ET
Tel: (H) 01527 861686
Fixtures Secretary: David Hall
Tel: (H) 0121 378 2839
Club Colours: Maroon, green and black jerseys, black shorts and green stockings

DROITWICH RUFC
North Midlands 1
Ground Address: Hanbury Road, Droitwich Spa, Worcs., WR9 8PR
Tel: 01905 771919
Brief Directions: M5 J5, A38 towards Droitwich, turn towards town centre. At traffic lights turn left into Hanbury Road, club 2 miles on left.
Club Secretary: Stuart Gosney, 33 Calder Close, Droitwich, Worcs WR9 8DU
Tel: 01905 796352 (H) 01905 772534 (W)
Fixtures Secretary: Richard Latham, 3 Tsaacs Way, Droitwich, Worcs., WR9 8UZ.
Tel: (H) 01905 794638 - (W) 0121 5853033
Club Colours: Black and gold hoops

DRONFIELD RUFC
Notts Lincs & Derby 1
Ground Address: Gosforth School, Carr Lane, Dronfield-Woodhouse, Dronfield.
Brief Directions: From north (Sheffield) into Dronfield, right at Coach & Horses, bear right under bridge, follow road at top of hill turn left (Stubley Drive), turn into school car park
Club Secretary: R.Nixon,114 Whirlowdale Road, Sheffield S7 2NJ
Tel: 01142257557
Fixtures Secretary: Mick Rodgers, 56 Ribblesdale Drive, Sheffield. S12 3XE.
Tel: (W) 0114 271 6716
Club Colours: Red shirts, black shorts

DUDLEY KINGSWINFORD RFC
Midlands 1
Ground Address: Heathbrook, Swindon Road, Wallheath, Kingswinford, West Midlands
Tel: 01384 287006
Brief Directions: Just off A449 at Wallheath, halfway between Kidderminster and Wolverhampton
Club Secretary: David Evans, 156 Common Road, Woybourne, West Midlands. WV5 0LT
Tel: (H) 01902 894463
Fixtures Secretary: Bill Jones
Tel: (H) 01902 682056 (W) 0121 6067777
Club Colours: Cambridge blue and navy hoops, black shorts

DUNLOP RFC
Staffs & Warwicks 1
Ground Address: Dunlop Sports and Social Club, Burnaby Road, Radford, Coventry
Tel: 01203 662394
Brief Directions: M6 J3, take 4th exit to Coventry, along bypass, over roundabout, right at 2nd roundabout, left at 3rd roundabout, turn right into Burnaby Rd, ground 0.5 mile on right
Club Secretary: Mrs Kim Challis, 24 Birchfield Road, Counden, Coventry. CV6 2BD
Tel: (H) 01203 337152
Fixtures Secretary: Mr John Ormsby, 5 Postbridge Road, Stuvechale, Coventry CV3 5AG
Tel: (H) 01203 410313
Club Colours: Black and amber hoops, black shorts

DUNSTABLIANS RUFC

Midlands East 1
Ground Address: Bidwell Park, Bedford Road, Houghton Regis, Dunstable, Beds. LU5 6JW
Tel: 01582 866555/864107
Brief Directions: North out of Dunstable on A5, turn right after roundabout to Thorn, at end of road, ground is opposite, or M1 J12 through Toddington, ground is 3 miles on left
Club Secretary: Paul Freeman, 10B Tabor Close, Harlington, nr Dunstable, Beds. LU5 6PF
Tel: (H) 01525 750852 or 0976 834932
Fixtures Secretary: Dai Gabriel, 19 Hillyfields, Dunstable, Beds. LU6 3NS
Tel: (H) 01582 606262
Club Colours: Red, black, silver

EARLSDON RFC

Staffs & Warwicks 1
Ground Address: Mitchell Avenue, Canley, Coventry. CV4 8DY Tel: 01203 464467
Brief Directions: Along A45 to Police and Fire Stations, follow signs to Canley & Warwick University
Club Secretary: J Ward, 18 Wainbody Avenue, Green Lane, Coventry. CV3 6DB Tel: (H) 01203 419729
Fixtures Secretary: R Price, 25 Montrose Drive, Nuneaton. CV10 7LX Tel: (H) 01203 346190
Club Colours: Red and white

EAST LEAKE RFC

Notts, Lincs & Derby 2
Ground Address: Costock Road Playing Fields, Costock Road, East Leake, Loughborough, Leicestershire
Brief Directions: A60 N'gham tow'ds L'boro, right at Costock tow'ds E. Leake, ground on right. M1 J24, A6 tow'ds L'boro, left onto A6006 tow'ds Rempstowe, left where signed, thro' village, club on right
Club Secretary: Mrs C. Daniels, 23 Repton Road, West Bridgford, Nottingham NG2 7EP
Tel No: 0115 9745613
Fixtures Secretary: Lee Dufty. Tel No: 01509 854239
Club Colours: Maroon and white hooped shirts, black shorts

EAST RETFORD RUFC

Notts Lincs & Derby 2
Ground Address: Ordsall Road, Retford, Nottinghamshire
Tel: 01777 703234
Brief Directions: From A1, join B620 from Worksop, past Ranby prison on left, through Babworth crossroads, right at mini roundabout, ground 0.5 mile on right
Club Secretary: E M Henderson, 51 Trent Street, Retford, Notts. DW22 6NG
Tel: (H) 01777 706987
Fixtures Secretary: I.McComb, 125 Ordsall Road, Retford, Nottinghamshire.
Tel No: 01777 701092
Club Colours: Emerald and amber hoops, navy blue shorts

ECCLESHALL RUFC

Staffs 2
Ground Address: Baden Hall Farm, Near Eccleshall
Brief Directions: From cetre of Eccleshall follow A519 (Newcastle), take right fork after leaving town, past Drake Hall then follow signs to Baden Hall on right
Club Secretary: K. E. Levitt, 46 Old Road, Stone, Staffs. ST15 8HR
Tel: (H) 01785 818234 Tel: (W) 01785 817211
Fixtures Secretary: I. Bradford, 1 Buckmaster Avenue, Clayton, Newcastle, Staffs. ST5 3AJ
Tel: (H) 01782 632256 Tel: (W) 01785 609867
Club Colours: Yellow with green & black band,black shorts.

EDWARDIAN FC

Midlands West 2
Ground Address: The Memorial Ground, Streetsbrook Road, Solihull, West Midlands. B90 3PE
Tel: 0121 744 6831
Brief Directions: 2 miles north west of Solihull town centre. Opposite the main entrance to The Robin Hood cemetary
Club Secretary: John L Forster, 16 Brookfield Way, Olton, Solihull, West Midlands, B92 7HA.
Tel:0121 6949172H/0121 7069524B/0121 7069525Fax/0410 032965M
Fixtures Secretary: Steve Abercrombie, 35 Green Lane, Shirley, Solihull West Midlands B90 1AP
Tel: 0121 4307508B/0121 6086195H
Club Colours: Old gold and claret hoops on navy, navy shorts

ERDINGTON RFC

North Midlands 1
Ground Address: Spring Lane Playing Fields, Kingsbury Road, Erdington, Birmingham 23
Tel: 0121 373 7597
Club Secretary: Derek Owen, 129 Bradbury Road, Solihull, West Midlands. B92 8AL
Tel: (H) 0121 706 4699 (W) 0121 654 4022
Fixtures Secretary: Keith Robinson
Tel: (H) 0121 351 2740
Club Colours: White shirts with single blue hoop

ESSINGTON RUFC (merged with **WULFRUN)**

North Midlands 3
Ground Address: High Hill Centre, High Hill, Essington, West Midlands. WV11 2DW
Tel No: 01922 492795
Club Secretary: M.R. Chandler, 32 Coppice RTd., Walsall Wood, Walsall, West MIdlands. WS9 9BL
Tel No: 01543 820611
Fixtures Secretary: G.Smith. 7 Oakwood Close, Essington, West Midlands WV11 2DQ
Tel No: 01922 400222
Club Colours: All black.

EVESHAM RFC

Midlands West 1
Ground Address: Evesham Sports Club, Albert Road, Evesham, Worcs
Tel: 01386 446469
Brief Directions: A435 south - over railway bridge, Albert Road is 2nd right off High Street, Evesham, go to end to Evesham Sports Club
Club Secretary: J P Hartley, Nightingale Hill, Bishampton, Pershore, Worcs. WR10 2NH
Tel: (H) 01386 462325 (B) 01527 873457
Fixtures Secretary: J. Nettels, 43 Prin cess Road, Evesham, Worcs., WR11 4GQ.
Tel: (H) 01386 45611 (B) 01386 496253
Club Colours: Navy and maroon hoops

FIVE WAYS OLD EDWARDIANS FC
North Midlands 1
Ground Address: Masshouse, Ash Lane, Hopwood, Birmingham
Tel: 0121 445 4909
Brief Directions: M42 J2, signpost to Birmingham reach roundabout to Birmingham, 100yds before garage on right turn right into Ash Lane, club on right at end of lane
Club Secretary: Richard Lisseter, 138 Chatsworth Road, Halesowen, West Midlands. B62 8TH
Tel: (H) 0121 559 6549 (W) 0121 550 1724
Fixtures Secretary: Paul Hipkiss
Tel: (H) 0121 550 4280
Club Colours: Navy blue and gold

FORD LEAMINGTON RFC
Warwickshire
Ground Address: Newbold Comyn, Newbold Terrace, Leamington Spa, Warwickshire
Brief Directions: Follow signs for Newbold Comyn from Leamington
Club Secretary: G.Teasdale, 5 Emerald way, Leamington Sp[a. CV34 3LD
Tel No: 01926 421729
Fixtures Secretary: Eric Newton Tel: (H) 01926 770624
Club Colours: Blue & white quarters with black collar.

GAINSBOROUGH RUFC
Notts Lincs & Derby 3
Ground Address: Castle Hills School, The Avenue, Gainsborough
Brief Directions: Follow signs for Leisure Centre, the school is next to it
Club Secretary: T Tanner, 11 Northolme, Gainsborough, Lincs. DN21 2QN
Tel: (H) 01427 610768 (W) 01246 451245
Fixtures Secretary: Howard Russel
Tel: (H) 01427 628265 (W) 01724 276221
Club Colours: 1st team: black shirt and shorts. 2nd team: black and yellow quarters

GEC ST LEONARDS RUFC
Staffordshire 1
Ground Address: GEC Protection and Control, GEC St Leonards Social Club, St Leonards Avenue, Stafford, Staffs
Tel: 01785 258070
Club Secretary: J A Waibley, 26 Hall Close, Stafford, Staffs. ST17 4JJ
Tel: (H & W) 01785 253201
Fixtures Secretary: Mr I McLeod
Tel: (H) 01889 579365 (W) 0860 694548
Club Colours: Black with a gold hoop

GLOSSOP RUFC
Midlands East 2
Ground Address: Hargate Hill Lane, Charlesworth, Glossop, SK13 5HG.
Tel: 01457 864553
Brief Directions: Through Glossop on A57, take A626 signposted Marple, ground is 1.5 miles on left
Club Secretary: Alastair May, 6 Kinder Grove, Romiley, Stockport. SK6 4EU
Tel: (H) 0161 427 5774
Fixtures Secretary: Phil Littlewood, Oakmount, 76 Dinting Road, Glossop.
Tel: 01457 867168
Club Colours: Royal blue shirts, black shorts

GNOSALL RUFC
Staffordshire 2
Ground Address: Gnosall Sports Club, Brookhouse Road, Gnosall, Stafford.
Tel No: 01785 823500
Brief Directions: A518 Newport Road to roundabout in village. From Stafford 2nd exit, from Newport 1st exit, onto Brookhouse Road. Turn left at children's playground.
Club Secretary: Mrs Anne Timmins, Norden Newport Road, Gnosall, Stafford. ST20 0BN
Tel No: 01785 823 431
Fixtures Secretary: Stuart Davies, 11 Waterside Court, Gnosall, Stafford. ST20 0AR
Tel No: 01785 822376
Club Colours: Green & Black quarters, black shorts.

GPT (COVENTRY) RFC
Staffs & Warwicks 1
Ground Address: GPT Sports Pavillion, Allard Way, coventry.
Tel: 01203 451157
Brief Directions: From M62 J2 join A46. After approx 2 miles rt at r'about. Left at next r'about. Rt at lights, rt at next lights, then left at 2nd set of lights. Ground 300 yds on the left.
Club Secretary: Richard Beddow, 26 Lilac Avenue, Coundon, Coventry CV6 1DE
Tel: (H) 01203 590 665
Fixtures Secretary: A Machin, 64 Stevenson Road, Kersley, Coventry. CV6 2JW.
Tel: 01203 338236
Club Colours: Red, green & blue hoops, black shorts.

GRIMSBY RUFC
Midlands East 2
Ground Address: The Pavillion, Springfield Road, Scartho, Grimsby, North East Lincolnshire. DN33 3JF
Tel: 01472 878594
Brief Directions: From M180/A180, take A1136, left at roundabout, right at Toothill roundabout, left at Bradley crossroads,right at Nuns corner, right fork, 1st right
Club Secretary: Mr T Horswood, 5 Ferriby Lane, Grimsby. DN34 3NU.
Tel: 01472 872416
Fixtures Secretary: Roger Davies
Tel: (H) 01472 812763
Club Colours: Royal Blue shirts and black shorts.

HANDSWORTH RUFC
Staffs & Warwicks 1
Ground Address: 450 Birmingham Road, Walsall
Tel: 0121 357 6427
Brief Directions: M6 J7, take A34 towards Walsall, ground at bottom of hill at end of dual carriageway on left
Club Secretary: Alec Hardy, 6 Freemount Square, Great Barr, Birmingham. B43 5QT
Tel: (H) 0121 358 6612 (W) 01902 422399
Fixtures Secretary: As Secretary
Club Colours: Red and white hooped shirts, black shorts, red socks

HARBORNE RFC

North Midlands 2
Ground Address: Playing Fields, Metchley, Park Road, Harborne, Birmingham
Tel: 0121 427 2690
Brief Directions: From Birmingham city Centre follow signs to Harborne (3 miles) Ground to south of High Street
Club Secretary: Richard Lunson, Bournehouse Cottage, Weeford, Lichfield, Staffs
Tel: 01543 480851
Fixtures Secretary: Simon Parker, 56 Farm Road, Rowley Regis, West Midlands
Tel: (H) 0121 532 4780
Club Colours: Green, red and black band

HARBURY RFC

Warwickshire
Ground Address: Waterloo Fields, Middle Road, Harbury, Warwickshire
Tel: 01926 613462
Brief Directions: From Fosse Way take sign for Harbury nearest to railway line. The club is three quarters of a mile on right.
Club Secretary: Peter Rollason, 27 Farm Street, Harbury, CV33 9LR.
Tel: 01926 613422
Fixtures Secretary: Jerry Birbeck, 22 Campion Terrace, Leamington Spa, Warks.
Tel: (H) 01926 424053
Club Colours: Red &White Hoops, Black Shorts

HEREFORD RFC

Midlands 1
Ground Address: Wyeside, Belvadere Lane, off Broomy Hill, Hereford HR4 9UT Tel: 01432 273410
Brief Directions: Follow ring road to Ross-On-Wye, turn right before bridge, over River Wye. 1st left after 'The Antelope' into Broomy Hill. 1st left, narrow lane clun is on riverside.
Club Secretary: Peter Greenow, Hackford House, Dinedor Cross, Hereford, HR2 6PD Tel: (H) 01432 870874
Fixtures Secretary: Mr. Fred Walsh, 32 Chandos Street, Whitecross, Hereford.Tel: (H) 01432 351560 (M) 07970 012544
Club Colours: Red and Black

HOPE VALLEY RUFC

Notts, Lincs & Derby 2
Ground Address: Castleton Playing Fields, Hollowford Road, Castleton, Derbyshire (No mail to this address)
Tel: (c/o The Peak Hotel) 01433 620247
Brief Directions: From Sheffield A625 through Hathersage and Hope to Castleton, 100 metres past Peak Hotel turn right into Back St, ground is 500 metres on right
Club Secretary: Ian Broad, 10 Farndale Road, Hillsborough, Sheffield. S6 1SH
Tel: (H) 0114 233 8264
Fixtures Secretary: Paul Johnson, Tel No: 01298 814158
Club Colours: Purple, green and white quarters, black shorts

HORNCASTLE

Notts, Lincs & Derby 3
Ground Address: Horncastle Playing Fields, The Wong, Horncastle, Lincolnshire.
Brief Directions: To centre of Horncastle traffic lights, take Boston direction 200yds turn right follow signs to playing field.
Club Secretary: Danny Kendle, 10a High Street, Horncastle, Lincs, LN9 5BL. Tel: (H) 01507 527156
Fixtures Secretary: J I Bentley, 1 Albert Cottages, Chapel Lane, Legbourne, Louth, Lincolnshire LN11 8LW Tel: (H) 01507 600318
Club Colours: Green and gold quarters black shorts

HUNTINGDON & DISTRICT RUFC

Midlands 2
Ground Address: Huntingbroke School, Brampton Road, Huntingdon, Cambs. PE18 6BN
Brief Directions: Heading into Huntingdon from A14 or A1, Hinchingbroke School is adjacent to Hinchingbroke Hospital on the left.
Club Secretary: Jonathon C S Buckingham, Teal House, Morris Close, Buckden, Cambs. PE18 9YU
Tel: (H) 01480 810006
Fixtures Secretary: David Harris, New Manor Farm, Woolley, Huntingdon, Cambs.
Tel: (H) 01480 896060
Club Colours: Green shirts, blue shorts, green and white socks

ILKESTON RUFC

Midlands East 1
Ground Address: The Stute, Hallam Fields Road, Ilkeston, Derbys. DE7 4AZ Tel: 0115 9323244
Brief Directions: M1 Exit 25, A52 to Nott'ham. Left at 2nd round't (A6007) Ilkeston Rd. At mini round't, A6007 now Stapleford Rd. Left at T jct to A609.Left at garage toThurman St/Corpor'n Rd,T jct left
Club Secretary: Michael Green, 62 Northen Drive, Trowell, Nottingham NG9 3QL
Tel No: 0115 9170740 (H) 0115 9064709 (W)
Fixtures Secretary: Colin Fox, 39 Nursery Hollow, Ilkeston, Derbys. DE7 4LO
Tel: (H) 0115 9308421 0802 714518 (M)
Club Colours: Blue, green and white hoops, white shorts

KEMPSTON RFC

East Midlands & Leicester 3
Ground Address: Sports Club,134 High Street, Kempston, Beds. MK42 7BN Tel NO: 01234 852499
Brief Directions: Head towards Kempston. Find Sainsburys, go down hill past Citroen Garage on right , stay on this road and club is on right before you go out of Kempston
Club Secretary: Rob Byrnage, 8 King Street, Kempston, Bedford MK42 8BN
Tel No: 01234 301477
Fixtures Secretary: Chris Pitts, 34 Park Road, Kempston, Beds.MK42 8NZ
Tel: 01234 840921
Club Colours: Red & Black Quarters

KENILWORTH RFC

Midlands 1
Ground Address: The Jack Davies Memorial Ground, Glasshouse Lane, Kenilworth. CV8 2AJ
Tel: 01926 853945
Brief Directions: A452 off A46 into Kenilworth, turn right off roundabout into Birches Lane, Ground about 0.5 mile on right
Club Secretary: W J Whitesmith, 4 Glasshouse Lane, Kenilworth. CV8 2AJ
Tel: (H) 01926 859465 (W) 01926 851113
Fixtures Secretary: Dai Davies Tel: (H) 01926 854824
Club Colours: Yellow and blue, dark blue shorts

KERESLEY RFC
Midlands West 1
Ground Address: The John Radford Fields, Burrow Hill Lane, Chorley, Nr Coventry. CV7 8BE
Tel: 01676 540082
Brief Directions: Situated off Bennetts Road North, just past Keresley village
Club Secretary: John Frawley, 37 The Crescent, Keresley, Coventry.
Tel: (H) 01203 337537
Fixtures Secretary: A.Atkins. Tel No: 01455 611256
Club Colours: Royal blue, scarlet and white hoops, navy blue shorts

KESTEVEN RUFC
Midlands East 2
Ground Address: Wood Nook, High Dyke, Grantham, Lincs.
Tel: 01476 564887
Brief Directions: A52 out of Grantham towards Spalding, past the R.A.F. camp then right at roundabout (B6403). Club on right about 400 yards.
Club Secretary: Bill Berridge, 60 Belton Grove, Grantham, Lincs. NG33 5AA
Tel: 01476 590561
Fixtures Secretary: Rob Cole.Tel No: 01476 401194
Club Colours: Black shirts, white shorts

KETTERING RUFC
Midlands 2
Ground Address: Waverley Road (off Pipers Hill Road), Kettering, Northants
Tel: 01536 485588
Brief Directions: A14 J10, turn onto A6 to Kettering, at second traffic lights turn right, first left and first left again into Waverley Road, Ground is at end of road
Club Secretary: Helen Bridgeman c/o club address
Fixtures Secretary: Rob Bowley, Messuage Farnmhouse, 10 lower Benefield, Peterborough PE8 5AF
Tel: (H) 01832 205382 (W) 01536 722181
Club Colours: Blue and white hoops, blue shorts

KEYWORTH RUFC
Notts Lincs & Derby 1
Ground Address: Willoughby Lane, Widmerpool, Nottingham. NG12 5BU
Brief Directions: Out of Nottingham on A606 Melton Rd, turn right taking signs for Widmerpool, on entering village turn left at T jctn, follow road to right, 1st left to Willoughby on the Wolds, ground on right
Club Secretary: Michael Waplington, Maythorn House, High Street, Stapleford, Lincolnshire. LN6 9LB
Tel: (H) 01522 789192
Fixtures Secretary: S.Richards, 52 The Elms, Colwick, Nottingham
Tel: 0115 847 1201
Club Colours: Black + two amber hoops, black shorts, black and gold socks

KIBWORTH RUFC
Midlands East 2
Ground Address: Northampton Road, Market Harborough, Leicestershire
Tel: 01858 464210
Brief Directions: From town centre, follow signs for Leisure Centre, club on right as you enter centre. From M1, M6, A14, follow A508 to Mkt Harborough, ground on left as entering town
Club Secretary: David R Coe, 4 Applegarth Close, Corby, Northamptonshire. NN18 8EU
Tel: (H) 01536 460052
Fixtures Secretary: As Secretary
Club Colours: All Black

KIDDERMINSTER CAROLIANS RFC
Midlands West 2
Ground Address: Marlpool Lane, Kidderminster, Worcs. DY11 4HP
Tel: 01562 740043
Brief Directions: Follow signs from Kidderminster ringroad to Bridgnorth, at end Proud Cross Ringway is Jackson pub, Marlpool Lane is to one side, ground 400m from pub
Club Secretary: Mr Keith Stooksbury, 122 Crestwood Avenue, Kidderminster, Worcs. DY11 6JS
Tel: (H) 01562 753916
Fixtures Secretary: Mr Tim Carder
Tel: (H) 01562 747910 (W) 01902 774217
Club Colours: Black with gold hoops

KINGS NORTON RFC
Midlands West 1
Ground Address: Ash Lane, Hopwood, Birmingham. B48 7BB Tel: 0121 445 3340
Brief Directions: Near exit 2 from the M42, take Birmingham road and turn down Ash Lane, ground on right
Club Secretary: G S C Maciver, 11 Chapel Walk, Kings Norton, Birmingham. B30 3LW
Tel: (H) 0121 459 2279
Fixtures Secretary: N.Osbotne.Tel No: 01564 822831
Club Colours: Red and gold hoops, black shorts, red socks

KYNOCH RFC
North Midlands 3
Ground Address: Holford Drive, Perry Barr, Birmingham. B42 2TU Tel: 0121 356 4369
Brief Directions: M6 J7 Take A34 (Walsall Rd) Towards B'ham, then take A453 (Aldridge Rd) followsigns for Holford. B'ham A-Z page 60 grid ref 1A
Club Secretary: Paul L. Sturch, 132 Brantley Rd., Witton, Birmingham B67 DP
Tel: 0121 6862648
Fixtures Secretary: Ray Jones, 23 Blounts Rd, Erdington, Birmingham, B23 7DE
Tel: (H) 0121 382 0310
Club Colours: Black and white hoops

LEAMINGTON RUFC
Midlands West 1
Ground Address: Moorefields, Kenilworth Road, Blackdown, Leamington Spa, Warwickshire. CV32 6RG
Tel/Fax: 01926 425584
Brief Directions: Join A46 Warwick bypass (from North M6, J2, from South M40, J15). Leave bypass at Leamington/Kenilworth junction. Take A452 towards Leamington 1 mile, ground on left
Club Secretary: John Lyons, 3 Denewood Way, Kenilworth, CV8 2NY.
Tel: 01926 855787
Fixtures Secretary: Tony Grimes, White Hall, Long Itchington, Rugby, CU23 8PU
Tel: (H) 01926 813501
Club Colours: Royal blue with single scarlet and gold hoop

LEDBURY RFC
North Midlands 1
Ground Address: Ross Road Playing Field, Ross Road, Ledbury, Herefordshire, HR8 2LP
Tel: 01531 633926
Brief Directions: M50 Junction 2 follow signs to Ledbury Left at lst Island 2nd L. at next, ground 200yds on right
Club Secretary: Mr W Rogers, 33 Jubilee Close, Deer Park, Ladbury, Hrerefordshire HR8 2XA
Tel No: 01531 634789
Fixtures Secretary: Keith Watkins. Tel NO: 01531 670223
Club Colours: Black and white hoops

LEEK RUFC
Midlands West 2
Ground Address: Birchall Playing Fields, Cheddleton Road, Leek (A520)
Tel: 01538 383697
Brief Directions: From M6 south, exit J14, A34 to Stone, A520 to Leek. From M6 north, exit J16, A500 exit Etruria roundabout, A53 to Leek, A520 right turn at lights
Club Secretary: Mike Clewes, 55 Westwood Park Drive, Leek. ST13 8NW
Tel: (H) 01538 382922
Fixtures Secretary: Daniel Hunt, 4 Southbank St., Leek, Staffs STT13 5LN
Tel no: 01538 388526
Club Colours: Blue and white hoops, blue shorts

LEESBROOK RUFC
Notts Lincs & Derby 2
Ground Address: Asterdale Sports Centre, Borrowash Road, Spondon, Derby. DE21 7PH
Tel: 01332 668656
Brief Directions: M1 J25, 3rd turn marked Spondon. From city centre take A52, take turning marked Spondon (Ntm Old Road)
Club Secretary: John Burns, 160 Cole Lane, Borrowash, Derby, DE72 3GP
Tel: (H) 01332 674216
Fixtures Secretary: Dave Wood, 18 Netherside Drive, Chellaston, Derby, DE73 1QU
Tel: (H) 01332 600112
Club Colours: Black, green, white and blue quarters, black shorts and socks

LEICESTER FOREST
Midlands East 2
Ground Address: Hinkley Road, Leicester Forest East, Leicester LE3 3PJ
Tel: 0116 2387136
Club Secretary: R Beason, The Laurels, Main Road, Claybrooke Magna, Lutterworth, Leics. LE17 5AJ
Tel: (H) 01455 202605 (W) 0116 2734700
Fixtures Secretary: J McGee, 16 Tudor Grove, Gorby, Leicestershire LE8 0YL
Tel: (H) 0116 2870031 (W) 0115 9860208

LEIGHTON BUZZARD
Midlands 2
Ground Address: Wright's Meadow, Leighton Buzzard, Stanbridge, Leighton Buzzard, Beds. LU7 9HR
Tel: 01525 371322
Brief Directions: North: M1 J13, A507 through Woburn, South: M1 J9, then A5 to Dunstable, A505 to Aylesbury, 2nd turn right, Club 1 mile on right
Club Secretary: J W McCormack, 15 Neptune Gardens, Leighton Buzzard, Beds. LU7 8NW
Tel: (H) 01525 378194 (W) 0181 427 4311
Fixtures Secretary: A. Perry, 22 The Coppins, Ampthill, Beds, MK45 2SN.
Tel: (H) 01525 379976 (W) 01462 851515
Club Colours: Navy blue & white regular hoops

LINCOLN RFC
Midlands 2
Ground Address: c/o Lindum Sports Association, St Giles Avenue, Wragby Road, Lincoln, Lincs
Tel: 01522 526592
Brief Directions: Close to the city centre , due east to the Carthedral
Club Secretary: R.M Swainson, 14 Lindum Road, Lincoln LN2 1NJ
Tel No: 01522 531433
Fixtures Secretary: C Buchanan-Smith
Tel: (H) 01522 827878
Club Colours: Red, white, green hooped shirts, green shorts

LINLEY & KIDSGROVE RUFC
Staffordshire 1
Ground Address: Ski Centre, Bathpool Park, West Morland Avenue, Kidsgrove, Stoke-on-Trent
Brief Directions: M6 J16, A500 towards Stoke-on-Trent, 2nd junction A34 Kidsgrove, follow signs for the Ski Centre
Club Secretary: Jason Swingewood, 48 Appledore Grove, Packmoor, Stoke-on-Trent. ST6 6XH
Tel: (H) 01782 816213 (W) 0151 9556835
Fixtures Secretary: Jason Swingewood, 48 Appledore Grove, Packmoor, Stoke-on-Trent. ST6 6XH
Tel: (H) 01782 816213 (W) 0151 9556835
Club Colours: Green and gold quarters

LONG BUCKBY RFC
Midlands East 1
Ground Address: Station Road, Long Buckby, Northamptonshire
Tel: 01327 842222
Brief Directions: 0.25 mile from market square, along Station Road towards Daventry
Club Secretary: P J Osborne, Ashthorne, Teeton Road, Ravensthorpe, Northampton
Tel: (H) 01604 770772 (W) 01327 705785
Fixtures Secretary: S Ruddlesden
Tel: (H) 01327 842933
Club Colours: Emerald green

LONG EATON RFC
Midlands East 2
Ground Address: West Park, Long Eaton, Nottingham. Tel: 0115 946 0907
Brief Directions: M1 Jct 25. Follow signs to Long Eaton. Right at mini roundabout and straight on at next roundabout.West Park Leisure Centre is on left.Clubhouse in changing rooms on the park
Club Secretary: Richard Ward, Long Eaton Rugby, P.O. Box 5830, Long eaton, notts NG10 1LX
Tel No: 0115 8491960
Fixtures Secretary: Chris Brookes . Tel No: 0115 9468485
Club Colours: Blue and white hoops, blue shorts.

LONGTON RFC
Midlands 1
Ground Address: Roughcote Lane, Caverswall, Nr Stoke on Trent, Staffs. ST11 9EG Tel: 01782 394449
Brief Directions: From South-Leave M6 at J14 take A34 North to Stone follow A520 Leek for approx 9 miles, turn right after Parkhall Country Park enterance on left. North- M6 J16 A500 to A50. A520 to Leek at Meir.
Club Secretary: M.Cantcay, Old School House, New Road, Dichorne, Nr Stoke-on-Trent, Staffs. Tel: (H) 01782 397046
Fixtures Secretary: Brent Rawlings, 20 Fernlea Grove, Weston Coyney, Stoke-on-Trent, Staffs, ST3 5HT. Tel: (H) 01782 335317
Club Colours: Black and amber

LOUGHBOROUGH RFC
Midlands East 2
Ground Address: The Clubhouse, Derby Road Playing Fields, Derby Road, Loughborough (not a postal address) Tel: 01509 216093
Brief Directions: M1: J23, left at second roundabout, then right at second roundabout-straight ahead at next roundabout then first left and follow signs for golf centre.
Club Secretary: Steve Hughes, 76 Braddon Road, Loughborough, Leicestershire LE11 5YZ
Tel: (H) 01509 646604
Fixtures Secretary: Nick Moore, 35 Mill Lane, Barrow on Soar, Leicestershire LE12 8LQ
Tel: (H) 01509 620703
Club Colours: Blue and old gold

LOUGHBOROUGH STUDENTS
East Midlands & Leicester 1
Ground Address: Loughborough University, Leics. LE11 3TU Tel: 01509 632009 (Athletic Union)
Brief Directions: M1 J21, head towards Loughborough along Ashly Rd, follow directions into university, 1st XV pitch immediately on left
Club Secretary: Steve Harrod
Fixtures Secretary: Glynn James
Tel: (H) 01780 51793
Club Colours: White and maroon

LUCTONIANS RFC
Midlands 2
Ground Address: Mortimer Park, Hereford Road, Kingsland, Leominster, Herefordshire
Tel: 01568 709080 (T/Fax)
Brief Directions: Opposite the Monument Inn, on the A4110 in the village of Kingsland, 4 miles north west of Leominster
Club Secretary: Huw Davies, The Bell House, Kingsland, Leominster, Herefordshire. HR6 9RU
Tel: (H) 01568 708450 (W) 01432 362130
Fixtures Secretary: Simon Green-Price, Luctonians RFC,Mortimer Park, Kingsland, Leominster, Herefordshire.
Tel: 01568 709080 (T/Fax)
Club Colours: Black and white shirts, black shorts.

LUDLOW RFC
Midlands West 2
Ground Address: The Linney, Ludlow. SY8 1EE
Tel: 01584 875762
Brief Directions: Approaching Ludlow town centre from north, turn right just after Honda Equipe, follow narrow road for 0.5 mile, club on right behind football pitch
Club Secretary: Colin Spanner, 58 Henley Orchards, Ludlow. SY8 1TN
Tel: (H) 01584 873107 (W) 01584 872333
Fixtures Secretary: Rob Flemons
Tel: (H) 01568 780334 (W) 01562 820505 Ext 2545
Club Colours: Red shirts, black shorts

LUTON RFC
Midlands East 1
Ground Address: Newlands Road, Luton, Beds
Tel: 01582 20355
Brief Directions: M1 J10, take spur to roundabout, turn right, 200m turn right again, ground 1km on left
Club Secretary: P J Wilson, 17 Burghley Close, Flitwick, Bedford. MK45 1TF
Tel: (H) 01525 713409 (W) 01480 52451 Ext 5232
Fixtures Secretary: Martin Alexander
Tel: (H) 01582 598581 (W) 01582 22333
Club Colours: Green with red and white hoops, black shorts

LUTTERWORTH RFC
Midlands East 1
Ground Address: Ashby Lane, Bitteswell, Nr Lutterworth, Leics LE17 4SQ. Tel: 01455 557329
Brief Directions: Approx 1.5 miles north off Lutterworth on A426 at cross roads take turn for Ashby Parva & Ullesthorpe. Ground at end of lane approx 1 mile.
Club Secretary: Colin Hudson, “Spring Bank”, Ashby Lane, Bitteswell, Lutterworth, LE17 4SQ. Tel: (H) 01455 553115 (W) 01788 534606
Fixtures Secretary: Chris Payne, Cawder Ghyll, Shawell, Nr. Lutterworth, Leics. Tel: (H) 01788 860442
Club Colours: Red, green and white hoops blue shorts

MALVERN
Midlands 2
Ground Address: Spring Lane, Malvern Link, Worcester. WR14 1AJ Tel: 01684 573728
Brief Directions: Turn left at Texaco garage on approaching Malvern from Worcester on A449. Ground is on right.
Club Secretary: Ray Gillard, Lygon Cottage, Beauchamp Lane, Callow End, Worcester. WR2 4UQ
Tel: (H & W) 01905 831777
Fixtures Secretary: W Pomeroy
Tel: (H) 01684 562279
Club Colours: Maroon, gold and light blue hoops, navy shorts

MANOR PARK RFC
Staffs & Warwicks 1
Ground Address: Griff & Coton Sports Club, Heath End Road, Stockingford, Nuneaton, Warks
Tel: 01203 386798
Brief Directions: M1-M6 J3, A444 Nuneaton, keep left at George Elliot hospital, into Heath End Road, turn into Griff & Coton Sports Ground on right
Club Secretary: W J Newcombe, 489 Heath End Road, Stockingford, Nuneaton, Warks. CV10 7HD
Tel: (H) 01203 374476
Fixtures Secretary: S Atkinson Tel: (H) 01203 730606
Club Colours: Red and black hooped jerseys, black shorts and hose

MANSFIELD RUFC

Midlands 2
Ground Address: Eakring Road, Mansfield, Notts, NU18 3EN Tel: 01623 649834
Brief Directions: From south: M1 J27 onto A608, left to town centre, right onto A617, left onto Oak Tree Lane, right onto Eakring Road. Club 1 mile on right
Club Secretary: A. McFarlane, 39 Forest Road, Mansfield, Notts, NG18 4BY. Tel: (H) 01623 656563
Fixtures Secretary: Kevin Swithenbank, 40 Summercourt Drive, Ravenshead, Notts, NG15 9FT
Club Colours: Royal blue and white hoops, navy shorts, blue socks

MARKET BOSWORTH RFC

Midlands East 2
Ground Address: Cadeby Lane, Cadeby, Market Bosworth, Nuneaton. CV13 0BE
Tel: 01455 291340
Brief Directions: Off the A447, Hinckley to Ibstock road, turn at signs for Cadeby and follow lane in direction of Market Bosworth
Club Secretary: G.Donnelly, 23 Norfolk Road, Desford, Leicester. LE9 9HR
Tel No: 01455 823522
Fixtures Secretary: M.Hill, 11 Powers Road, Barwell, Leicester, LE9 8DY
Tel No: 01455 842674
Club Colours: Blue, white and gold hoops, black shorts

MARKET DRAYTON

Staffordshire 2
Ground Address: Greenfields, Market Drayton, Shropshire, TF9.
Brief Directions: Turn into town centre from the Gingerbread Man. Greenfield is signposted 300m from the R/about on the R.hand side.
Club Secretary: R. S. Davies, 73 Longslow Road, Market Drayton, Shropshire, TF9 3BP.
Fixtures Secretary: D. Gould, 16 Pendral Close, Tern Hill, Market Drayton, Shropshire, TF9 2ET.
Club Colours: Black/Green trim

MARKET RASEN AND LOUTH RUFC

Notts Lincs & Derby 1
Ground Address: Willingham Road, Market Rasen
Tel: 01673 843162
Brief Directions: On entering Market Rasen, take A631 Louth road, on entering 40mph section ground is approx 100 yards on right
Club Secretary: B N Harper, Nongoby, Church Lane, Manby, Louth. LN11 8HL
Tel: (H & W) 01507 327318
Fixtures Secretary: P.Topper.Tel Nos: 01673 844850 (H) 01472 371245 (W)
Club Colours: Red and green hoops, white shorts.

MATLOCK RUFC

Midlands East 2
Ground Address: Cromford Meadows, Cromford, Matlock, Derbyshire Tel: 01629 822821
Brief Directions: Turn off A6 at Cromford towards Crich/Holloway, Ground 100yds on right
Club Secretary: C Baker, Badger House, Lumb Lane, Darley Dale, Matlock, Derbyshire. DE4 2HP
Tel: (H & W) 01629 735294
Fixtures Secretary: D Pearson
Tel: (H) 01629 55440
Club Colours: Royal blue, gold and grey quartered shirts, royal blue socks, navy blue shorts

MEDEN VALE RFC

Notts, Lincs & Derby 2
Ground Address: Welbeck Colliery Welfare, Elkersley Road, Meden Vale, Mansfield, Notts.
Tel: 01623 842267
Brief Directions: From A60 turn towards Meden Vale, follow road until petrol station then turn left up the hill, take 2nd left into car park
Club Secretary: Mike Heaton, 5 Budby Crescent, Meden Vale, Mansfield, Notts
Tel: (H) 01623 846076 (W) 0115 9476091
Fixtures Secretary: David Ellison, 7 Priory Gardens, Swanwick, Derbyshire DE55 1DU
Tel: (H) 01773 609040 (W) 01283 539211
Club Colours: Red with black collars

MELBOURNE RFC
Notts Lincs & Derby 1
Ground Address: Melbourne Recreation Ground, Cock Shut Lane, Melbourne, Derbyshire DE73 1DG
Tel: 01332 863674
Brief Directions: From M1, A453 to Melbourne. From Derby/Uttoxeter, A514 to Melbourne. Then B587 to Recreation Ground
Club Secretary: John James, 62 Potter St., Melbourne, Derby De73 1DW
Tel No: 01332 863130
Fixtures Secretary: Jo Cherry, 5 George Street, Melbourne, Derby.
Tel: (H) 01332 863930
Club Colours: Bottle green and white

MELLISH RFC
Notts Lincs & Derby 1
Ground Address: War Memorial Ground, Plains Road, Mapperley, Nottingham. NG3 5RT
Tel: 0115 926 6653
Brief Directions: Ground situated on west side of B684 opposite The Travellers Rest, 2 miles east of the turn off the A614 and 2 miles north of the Plains squash club (national grid ref: 605463)
Club Secretary: Knowles, 20 Spring Lane, Lambley, Nottingham, NG4 4PH.
Tel NO: 0115 931 2037
Fixtures Secretary: Syd Harris, 2 Tilstock Court, Watnall, Nottingham, NG16 1JZ
Tel: (H)0115 938 5456
Club Colours: Green, black, gold hooped jerseys, black shorts and socks

MELTON MOWBRAY RFC
East Midlands & Leicester 1
Ground Address: Burton Road, Melton Mowbray,Leics. LE13 1DR Tel: 01664 63342
Brief Directions: Leave Melton Mowbray via the A606 to Oakham . Access is on the left past King Edward VII upper school.
Club Secretary: Hugh Middleton, 10 New Road, Burton Lazars, Leics. LE14 2UU.
Tel No: 01664 563792
Fixtures Secretary: S,Kerr Tel No: 01664 850954
Club Colours: Maroon shirts and socks with white shorts

MICHELIN RUFC
Staffordshire 2
Ground Address: Michelin Athetic Club, Rosetree Avenue, Trent Vale, Stoke on Trent
Tel: 01782 402899
Brief Directions: M6 Junct. 13 straight across island towards Stoke, take slip road after 1 mile, left at roundabout, first left into Rosetree Avenue
Club Secretary: Ian Williams, 6 Ferndale Close, Blyth Bridge, Stoke on Trent ST11 9PQ
Tel: (H) 01782 395385
Fixtures Secretary: Brian Davies, 15 Stanley Grove, Baddeley Green, Stoke on Trent ST2 7SA
Tel: (H) 01782 545085
Club Colours: Navy Blue & Gold Hoops

MODERNS RUGBY FOOTBALL CLUB
Midlands 2
Ground Address: Main Road, Wilford Village, Nottingham Tel: 0115 981 1374
Brief Directions: Nottingham ring road until Clifton Bridge, leave at slip road taking B687 to traffic lights then left into main road Wilford, ground is at end of the road
Club Secretary: Steve Strickland, 124 Highfield Road, Nuthall, Nottingham. NG16 1BP
Tel: (H) 0115 913 5944 (W) 01623 421210
Fixtures Secretary: Alistair Clark
Tel: (H) 0115 981 9207
Club Colours: Red and white quartered shorts, red shorts

NEWARK RFC
Midlands East 1
Ground Address: Kelham Road, Newark, Nottinghamshire Tel: 01636 702355
Brief Directions: From A1, A46 Newark bypass, ground is on Kelham Road on the road marked to Kelham on the right. From A46, take Newark bypass, left at roundabout, ground on right
Club Secretary: J.E. Rimmer, Old Vicarage, Chapel Lane, Coddington, Newark NG24 0PW
Tel: 01636 640352
Fixtures Secretary: Owen Mathias, Rookery Nook, Main Street, Upton Newark Tel: 01636 814334
Club Colours: Blue & white hoops and blue shorts.

NEWCASTLE (STAFFS) RUFC
Midlands West 1
Ground Address: Pavilion Ground, Lilleshall Road, Clayton, Newcastle-under-Lyme, Staffordshire. ST5 3BX Tel: 01782 617042
Brief Directions: M6 J15 to Newcastle, turn L. at 1st R/about, straight over next R/about, R. at next R/about down Stafford Ave. 3rd Rd on L. Lilleshall Road - past Cricket Ground on R.
Club Secretary: Ian Haley Esq.
Tel: (H) 01782 634836 (W) 01782 634358
Fixtures Secretary: Kelvin Probert Esq. 19 Reeves Avenue, Newcastle, Staffs., ST5 9KG.
Tel: (H) 01782 662103 (W) 01782 232405 ext 2495
Club Colours: Maroon and white hoops, black shorts & socks.

NEWPORT (SALOP) RUFC
Midlands 2
Ground Address: The Old Showground, Forton Road, Newport, Shropshire Tel: 01952 810021
Brief Directions: From the bypass, take turning to Newport on the roundabout that also signs to Shrewsbury, the ground is on the right
Club Secretary: David W. H. Rees, Valhalla, 19 Granville Avenue, Newport, Shropshire TF16 7DX
Fixtures Secretary: David Vasilionka
Tel: (H) 01952 810755
Club Colours: Maroon and white hoops

NORTH KESTEVEN RUFC
Notts, Lincs & Derby 3
Ground Address: Pavilion Club (rear of Memorial Hall), Newark Road, North Hykeham, Lincoln
Brief Directions: From A46 south of Lincoln, take towards Lincoln, look for Memorial Hall sign on left opposite North Kesteven school and sports centre
Club Secretary: Adrian France, 5 Mareham Cls, Bracebridge Heath, Lincoln LN4 8AR
Tel: (H)01522 545026
Fixtures Secretary: Nigel Thomas, 192 Hykeham Rd, Lincoln LN6 8AR
Tel: (H) 01522 696666
Club Colours: Black jersey, white, red and green hoops, black shorts

Northampton Mens Own RFC, pictured after beating a Sant Boi XV (Barcelona), during their tour to Spain in April 1999

NORTHAMPTON BOYS BRIGADE OLD BOYS RUFC

East Midlands & Leicester 1
Ground Address: St Andrews Mill, St Andrews Road, Northampton. NN1 2PQ
Tel: 01604 632460
Brief Directions: M1 J15A, follow signs for town centre, left at 1st lights just past 'Saints' Northampton RFC, cross 3 sets of lights, left into St Andrews Rd, ground entrance by Texaco garage
Club Secretary: Mrs Helen Bolden, 15 Berry Lane, Wootton, Northampton. NN4 6JU Tel: (H) 01604 766949
Fixtures Secretary: Mr Peter Johnson
Tel: (H) 01604 586421
Club Colours: Light blue, dark blue and maroon hoops with black shorts

NORTHAMPTON CASUALS RFC

East Midlands & Leicester 1
Ground Address: Rushmills House, Bedford Road, Rushmills, Northampton Tel: 01604 36716
Brief Directions: At J15 of M1 take A508 to Northampton and then 4th slip road and take A428 to Bedford. At first roundabout go right round and back towards Northampton, then take first left.
Club Secretary: Martyn Dimmock, 44A Park Drive, Kings Heath, Northampton NN5 7JU
Tel: (H) 01604 457175
Fixtures Secretary: M D Askew
Tel: (H) 01604 821148
Club Colours: Black with amber band

NORTHAMPTON HEATHENS RFC

East Midlands & Leicester 3
Ground Address: The Racecourse, East Park Parade, Northampton. Tel: 01604 39250
Club Secretary: Martin Labrum, 101 Yoemans Meadow, Northampton NN4 9YX.
Tel: (H) 01604 765287
Fixtures Secretary: Derek Hodgkinson
Tel: (H) 01604 416442

NORTHAMPTON MENS OWN RFC

Midlands East 1
Ground Address: Stoke Road, Ashton, Northampton
Tel: 01604 862463
Brief Directions: M1 J15, take A508 to Milton Keynes for 2.5 miles, through Roade village, take next left turning at crossroads, after 1 mile, signed Ashton, ground 0.5 mile on right
Club Secretary: John Goold, 38 Millway, Duston, Northampton. NN5 6ES
Tel: (H) 01604 756297
Fixtures Secretary: Ernie Dalby
Tel: (H) 01604 870609 (W) 01332 252132/0802 765527
Club Colours: White shirts with blue hoops and black shorts.

NORTHAMPTON OLD SCOUTS RFC

Midlands East 1
Ground Address: Rushmere Road, Northampton.
Tel: 01604 33639
Club Secretary: M. Heath, 16 Sandringham Road, Abington, Northampton. Tel: (H) 01604 38331
Tel: (W) 01604 643699
Fixtures Secretary: Keith Shurville,
Tel: (H) 01604 494374 Tel: (W) 01908 690333 x 3406
Club Colours: Red, green, gold & navy hooped shirts, navy shorts.

NOTTINGHAM CASUALS RFC

Notts Lincs & Derby 1
Ground Address: Canal Side, Meadow Road, Beeston Rylands, Nottingham. NG9 1JG
Tel: 0115 925 0135
Brief Directions: M1 J25, A52 to Nottingham, after 2nd roundabout, right at 2nd lights, straight across 2 crossroads, continue till road makes sharp right, over bridge, turn left
Club Secretary: John Littlestone, 87 Main Street, Loudham, Nottingham.NG14 7BN

Tel: 0115 966 3869
Fixtures Secretary: Lech Kluk, 46 Springfiield Avenue,Sandiacre,Nottingham, NG10 5LZ
Tel: 0115 946 2846
Maroon and white hoops, navy shorts.
Club Colours: White with maroon hoops, black shorts

NOTTINGHAMIANS

Notts, Lincs & Derby 1
Ground Address: Adbolton Lane, West Bridgford, Nottingham
Tel: 0115 981 1372
Brief Directions: M1 jct 24, A453 to A52, the Nottingham ring road. Follow signs to Holme Pierrepont (National Water Sports centre)
Club Secretary: David Hampson, 36 Longleat Crescent, Chilwell, Nottingham, NG9 5EU
Tel: (H) 0115 9258395
Fixtures Secretary: Phil Quinn, 7 Eley Close, Ilkeston, Derbyshire.
Tel: (H) 0115 9329129
Club Colours: Black, white and purple hoops black shorts

NOTTS CONSTABULARY RFC

Notts, Lincs & Derby 2
Ground Address: Mellish RFC, War Memorial Ground, Plains Road, Mapperley, Nottingham
Tel: 0115 926 6655
Brief Directions: Situated on B684 approx 4 miles north of Nottingham city c
centre.
Club Secretary: G.M.Hind, 18 Westfield Drive, Ilkeston, Derbyshire DE7 9JR
Tel No: 0115 9305894
Fixtures Secretary: Martin Hewitt
Tel: (H) 0115 952 4186 9W) 0115 942 0999
Club Colours: Black all black with green socks.

NUNEATON OLD EDWARDIANS RFC

Midlands West 2
Ground Address: Weddington Road, Nuneaton, Warwickshire Tel: 01203 386778
Brief Directions: Off M6 J3: follow A444 into and through Nuneaton, on left leaving town. Off A5 at A444 junction: A444 into Nuneaton for 2 miles, ground on right
Club Secretary: K McBride, 40 Somerset Drive, Nuneaton. CV10 8DD Tel: (H) 01203 347370
Fixtures Secretary: J F Sparkes Tel: (H) 01203 326029 (W) 01203 216331
Club Colours: Red and white hoops, black shorts

OADBY WYGGESTONIAN RFC

Midlands East 1
Ground Address: Oval Park, Wigston Road, Oadby, Leicester Tel: 0116 2714848
Brief Directions: M1 J21, follow Leicester South and East for 4 miles to A50, turn right, left at roundabout, ground 0.5 mile on left
Club Secretary: Jim Kilgallen, 75 Leicester Road, Oadby, Leicester. LE2 4DP
Tel: (H) 0116 2713987 (W) 0116 285 8032
Fixtures Secretary: Tony Bayley, 27 Dover House, Dover St., Leicester.
Tel: (H & W) 0116 255 3787
Club Colours: Black, white and gold hoops, black shorts

OAKHAM RFC

East Midlands & Leicester 1
Ground Address: The Showground, Barleythorpe Road, Oakham
Tel: 01572 724206
Club Secretary: Peter Bateman, 26 Well Street, Langham, Oakham, Rutland. LE15 7JS Tel: (H) 01572 756143
Fixtures Secretary: Peter Bateman
Tel: (H) 01572 756143
Club Colours: Black shirts with single amber band

OLD COVENTRIANS RFC

Midlands West 1
Ground Address: Tile Hill Lane, Coventry. CV4 9DE
Tel: 01203 715273
Brief Directions: Junction of A45 and B4101
Club Secretary: Phil Gill, 27 Glebe Crescent, Kenilworth CV88 1JA
Tel No: 01926 858634
Fixtures Secretary: IRich Clarke, 63 Mary Herbert Street, Coventry. CV3 5EY
Club Colours: Black, red and gold

OLD GRIFFINIANS RFC

North Midlands 1
Ground Address: Billesley Common, Wheelers Lane, Kings Heath, Birmingham
Brief Directions: M42 J3, take A435 into B'ham, at Kings Heath turn right into Wheelers Lane and follow signs for Indoor Tennis Centre (B'ham A-Z page 106, grid ref C2)
Club Secretary: Rick Adie, 33 Middlemore Road, Northfield, Birmingham. B31 3UD
Tel: (H) 0121 624 7504
Fixtures Secretary: Bernard Malin, 59 Spiceland Road, Northfield, Birmingham B311NL
Tel: (H) 0121 475 3788
Club Colours: All Black

OLD HALESONIANS RFC

Midlands West 1
Ground Address: Wassell Grove, Hagley, Stourbridge. DY9 9JD
Tel: 01562 883036
Brief Directions: Wassell Grove is signposted on the A456, 4 miles from junction 3 of the M5 motorway
Club Secretary: Mr Simon J Hussey, 67 Carol Crescent, Halesowen, West Midlands. B63 3RR
Tel: (H) 0121 550 5725
Fixtures Secretary: Mr Ian Glendinning, 31 Middle Acre Rd.,Bartley Green, West Midlands.B32
Tel: 0121 603 5639
Club Colours: Royal Blue , amber and gold irregular hoops, blue shorts

OLD LAURENTIAN RFC

Midlands 2
Ground Address: Fenley Field, Limetree Avenue, Rugby. CV22 7QT
Tel: 01788 810855
Brief Directions: From A45 take A4071 from M6 through Rugby to Bilton Village
Club Secretary: Alan Willis, 45 Frobisher Road, Rugby. CV22 7HS
Tel: (H) 01788 813481
Fixtures Secretary: Ray Roberts
Tel: (H) 01788 810276
Club Colours: Maroon, green and gold hoops, green shorts

OLD LEAMINGTONIANS RFC
Midlands West 1
Ground Address: The Crofts, Bericote Road, Blackdown, Leamington Spa. CV32 6QP
Tel: 01926 424991
Brief Directions: From A46 take A452 towards Leamington Spa, after 600 yards take left fork towards Cubbington, ground 0.75 mile on right
Club Secretary: Dennis Fisher, 14 New Street, Cubbington, Leamington Spa. CV32 7LA
Tel: (H) 01926 422131
Fixtures Secretary: Martyn Rawbone
Tel: (H) 01926 497464 (not after 9pm) (W) 0121 698 4021
Club Colours: Blue and gold hoops, navy shorts & socks

OLD NEWTONIANS RFC
East Midlands & Leicester 1
Ground Address: Hinckley Road (A47), Leicester Forest East, Leicester
Tel: 0116 2392389
Brief Directions: Follow main A47 to Hinckley out of Leicester, pass Red Cow pub on right, ground 0.75 mile on right
Club Secretary: G A Clark, 250 Wigston Lane, Aylestone, Leicester. LE2 8DH
Tel: (H) 0116 2832309 (W) 0116 2785288
Fixtures Secretary: Peter Muggleton, 20 The Meadway, Birstall, Leicester, LE4 4NF. Tel: (H) 0116 2671725
Club Colours: Navy with white, red, green, white central band, navy shorts

OLD NORTHAMPTONIANS RFC
Midlands East 1
Ground Address: Sports Field, Billing Road, Northampton. Tel: 01604 634045
Brief Directions: Follow signs for Northants County Cricket Ground and District of Abington
Club Secretary: Michael Parsons, 65 Porlock Close, Northampton. NN5 6BS
Tel No: 01604 755887
Fixtures Secretary: Simon James , 7 Chipsey Avenue, Northampton. NN1 5SE
Tel No: 01604 639860
Club Colours: Cardinal red, navy, gold hoops navy shorts

OLD SALTLEIANS RFC
Midlands West 2
Ground Address: Watton Lane, Water Orton, Coleshill, Birmingham. B46 1PJ
Tel: 0121 748 3380
Brief Directions: Junction of Gilson Road/Watton Lane, off A446, near Coleshill
Club Secretary: Matthew Lukeman, 20 Church Way, Longdon, Nr Rugeley, Staffs. WS15 4PG
Tel: (H) 01543 490376 (W) 0121 323 2889
Fixtures Secretary: Kelvin Roberts
Tel: (H) 0121 351 1473
Club Colours: Red and yellow hooped shirts, navy shorts, red, yellow and blue socks

OLD WARWICKIAN RFC
Warwickshire
Ground Address: Sports Ground, Hampton Road, Warwick
Tel: 01926 496295
Brief Directions: Follow road out of Warwick towards Henley in Arden pass the Warwick Horse Race Stadium and ground is on the right after bypass
Club Secretary: Patrick Wing, 57 Broadeers Road, Knowle, Solihull, West Midlands. B93 9OG Tel: (H) 01564 779947
Fixtures Secretary: Andrew Marshall
Tel: (H) 01926 651750
Club Colours: Maroon and white hoops

OLD WHEATLEYANS RFC
Warwickshire
Ground Address: Norman Place Road, Coundon, Coventry
Tel: 01203 334888
Brief Directions: At J9 on Coventry ring road, take A4170 (Radford Rd), after 1.5 miles turn left into Norman Place Rd, entrance is at the far end of road, on left
Club Secretary: Andrew Hibberd, 59 Frilsham Way, Allesley Park, Coventry. CV5 9LJ
Tel: (H) 01203 711955 (W) 01203 563166
Fixtures Secretary: Graham Paine, 2 Craven Street, Earlsdon,Coventry
Tel: 01203 679864
Club Colours: Blue, maroon and gold

OLD YARDLEIANS RFC
Midlands West 2
Ground Address: Tilehouse Lane, Shirley, Solihull, West Midlands
Tel: 0121 744 3380
Brief Directions: From nth, M42 J4 - Stratford Rd-Dog Kennel Ln - Dickens Heath Rd - Tythebarn Ln - Tilehouse Ln, From sth, M42 J3 - Alcetter Ln - Station Rd - Lowbrook Ln - Tilehouse Ln
Club Secretary: Brian Hope, 'Silver Birches',93 Hazelwood Road, Birmingham B27 7XW
Tel: 0121 243 8765
Fixtures Secretary: Tlan wallace, Silver Birches, 93 Hazlewood Road, B'Ham, B27 7XW.
Tel no: 0121 243 8765
Club Colours: Old gold, maroon and green

OLLERTON RFC
Notts Lincs & Derby 3
Ground Address: Boughton Sports Field, Church Road, Boughton, Newark, Notts
Brief Directions: From A614 take A6075 through New Ollerton and Boughton, turn left on apex of right hand bend at Harrow Inn, 200 yds right at Church, follow lane to the back of houses of Church Lane
Club Secretary: Dave Price, Lathmill, Harrow Farm, Tuxford Road, Boughton, Newark, Notts. NG22 9JZ
Tel: (H) 01623 860871
Fixtures Secretary: D.Wilford . Tel No: 01623 824120
Club Colours: Yellow and black hoops Change Colours : Black

OUNDLE RFC
East Midlands & Leicester 2
Ground Address: Occupation Road, Oundle, Peterborough
Tel: 01832 273101
Brief Directions: From Peterborough, cross bridge, turn right by garage, turn right then right again down single track road
Club Secretary: Mr Duncan Hook, 12 Wyatt Way, Oundle, Peterborough, Cambs. PE8 4HE
Tel: (H) 01832 275407
Fixtures Secretary: Andrew Kendall.
Tel No: 01832 734 976
Club Colours: Red and white hoops on black

PAVIORS RFC
Midlands East 1
Ground Address: The Ron Rossin Ground, Burntstump Hill, Arnold, Nottingham. NG5 9PQ
Tel: 0115 9630384
Brief Directions: A614 from Nottingham to Doncaster, 2 miles north of city turn left onto Burntstump Hill, first left pass the school on left to Rugby Club
Club Secretary: Miss Ruth Marriott, 5 Kerrs Crescent, Marston, Grantham, Lincs. NG32 2HJ
Tel NO: 01400 251079
Fixtures Secretary: Len Hines, 6 Beverley Gardens, Gelding, Nottingham NG4 3LF
Tel: (H) 0115 9563379
Club Colours: Green with red bands green

PERSHORE RFC
Midlands West 2
Ground Address: Piddle Park, Mill Lane, Wyre Piddle, Pershore, Worcestershire
Tel: 01386 554105
Brief Directions: Between Worcester and Evesham on B4538, turn off main road in middle of village on the corner by the War Memorial, club 0.5 mile down the lane
Club Secretary: Sam Cook, 7 Allsebrook Gardens, Badsey, Evesham, Worcs. WR11 5HJ.
Tel: (H) 01386 831494
Fixtures Secretary: David Kelly. Tel No: 01386 554307
Club Colours: Black shirts with two scarlet hoops, black shorts

PETERBOROUGH RUFC
Midlands East 1
Ground Address: Second Drove, Fengate, Peterborough. PE1 5XA
Tel: 01733 69413
Club Secretary: B A Hedges, 85 Apsley Way, Longthorpe, Peterborough. PE3 9NZ
Tel: (H) 01733 332287
Fixtures Secretary: M Proud
Tel: (H) 01487 822951
Club Colours: Red, silver, gold

PINLEY RFC
Staffs & Warwicks 1
Ground Address: The Croft, Wyken Croft, Coventry
Tel: 01203 602059
Club Secretary: M D Brown,11 Minton Road,Minton Gardens,Coventry,CV2 2XH
Tel: (H) 01203 363353 (W) 01203 003991
Fixtures Secretary: B Lester
Tel: (H) 01203 443605
Club Colours: Red and black quarters

REDDITCH RFC
North Midlands 1
Ground Address: Bromsgrove Road, Redditch
Brief Directions: Bromsgrove Highway - Birchfield Road - Bromsgrove Road
Club Secretary: Brian Carr, 60 Wychbury Rd., Quarry Bank, Brierley Hill, West Midlands DY5 2XX
Tel: (H) 01384 79092 (W) 013884 422494
Fixtures Secretary: Paul Thurston, 18 Crendon Close, Stuclley, Warks.
Tel: (H) 01527 854802
Club Colours: Light and dark blue hoops, dark shorts

ROLLS ROYCE RFC
Notts, Lincs & Derby 2
Ground Address: Merrill Way, Allenton, Derby
Club Secretary: TC.Davies, 31 Mear Drive, Borrowash, Derby DE72 3QW
Terl No: 01332 820445
Fixtures Secretary: D.Miller, 37 Rosemary Drive, Alvaston,Derby De24 0TA
Tel:01332 246879
Club Colours: Maroon and sky blue quarters, black shorts, maroon socks

ROSS ON WYE RFC
North Midlands 2
Ground Address: Sports Centre, Wilton Rd, Ross-on-Wye. Tel: 01989 63256
Brief Directions: M50 south to end,A40 to Monmouth.Take Ross exit(1st from south, 2nd from north), A40 at Wilton roundabout, Sports Centre 1st right over bridge.
Club Secretary: Miss Sarah Bourne, 1 Prospect Terrace, Homs Road, Ross on Wye HR9 7DE
Tel: 01989 562081
Fixtures Secretary: Mr G Bourne, address as secretary.
Club Colours: Royal blue and white hoops

RUBERY OWEN
Staffordshire 1
Ground Address: High Hill Centre, High Hill, Essington, West Midlands. Wv11 2DW
Tel: 01922 492795
Brief Directions: M6 J11, A462 to Willenhall, 3 miles traffic lights turn right into Upper Sneyd Rd running into High Hill, club 0.5 mile on left
Club Secretary: Michael R Chandler, 32 Coppice Rd, Walsall Wood, Walsall. WS9 9BL
Tel: (H) 01543 370678 (W) 01384 400999
Fixtures Secretary: Graham Smith
Tel: (H) 01922 400222
Club Colours: Red

RUGBY ST ANDREWS RFC
Warwickshire
Ground Address: Hillmorton Grounds, Ashlawn Road, Rugby.
Tel: 01788 542786
Brief Directions: Ring Fixture Secretary
Club Secretary: Patricia Lee, 29 Faraday Road, Rugby CV22 5ND
Tel: (H) 01788 570 707
Fixtures Secretary: John Hunt, 14 Northcott Road, Rugby, Warks, CV21 2EJ.
Tel: (H) 01788 574496
Club Colours: Sky Blue & navy hoops. Navy shorts.

RUGELEY RUFC
Staffordshire 2
Ground Address: Hagley Park, Burnthill Lane, Rugeley, Staffs. Tel: 01889 582266
Brief Directions: M6 J11 - A460 towards Cannock to Hednesford then Rugeley. 3rd road on left 50metres on right - Rugeley Youth Centre.
Club Secretary: Ian McLeod, 17 St. Augustines Road, Rugeley, Staffs. WS15 1NF.
Tel: 01889 579365
Fixtures Secretary: Mr. P. McGann, 64 Springhill Terrace, Rugeley, WS15 1BW.
Tel: 01889 519297
Club Colours: Amber shirts and black shorts

RUSHDEN AND HIGHAM RUFC
East Midlands & Leicester 1
Ground Address: Manor Park, Bedford Road, Rushden, Northants Tel: 01933 312071
Brief Directions: On main A6 Bedford side of Rushden, on the left leaving Rushden and the right when approaching Rushden from Bedford
Club Secretary: Steve Miles, Kialanga, The Green, Orlingbury, Kettering, Kettering,Northants. NN14 1JA
Tel: 01933 400123 (H)
Fixtures Secretary: Terry Dancer, 4 Orwell Close, Raunds, Northants. NN9 6SG
Tel: (H) 01933 624889
Club Colours: Black and white hoops, black shorts, yellow & white socks

SCUNTHORPE RUFC
Midlands 1
Ground Address: Heslam Park, The Queensway, Scunthorpe, North Lincolnshire
Tel: 01724 843013
Brief Directions: From end M181, roundabout 3rd exit, next roundabout 3rd exit, next roundabout 3rd exit Ashby Road, 400 mtrs signposted Heslam Park
Club Secretary: Mr Andrew S Bagshaw, 51 Old Brumby Street, Scunthorpe, North Lincolnshire. DN16 2AJ
Tel: (H) 01724 849838 (W) 01652 652031 (FAX) 01652 659354
Fixtures Secretary: Mr Nigel Cleal, 18 Cheltenham Close,Bottesford, Nr Scunthorpe, Lincs.
Tel: (H) 01724 856801 (W) 01724 402763
Club Colours: Lincoln Greeb shirts with 2 white & 2 black bands,black shorts

SELLY OAK RFC
Midlands West 1
Ground Address: Holders Lane, Moseley, Birmingham
Brief Directions: From Edgbaston Cricket Ground turn right into Russell Road, proceed until right turn into Moor Green Lane, Holders Lane is 1st right
Club Secretary: Simon Walster, 52 Wheats Avenue, Harborne, Birmingham B17 0RJ
Fixtures Secretary: Barry Pearce
Tel: (H) 0121 358 4442 (W) 0121 360 8500
Club Colours: Blue and white hoops with red spangles

SHIPSTON ON STOUR RFC
Staffs & Warwicks 1
Ground Address: Mayo Road, Shipston on Stour, Warks Tel: 01608 662107
Brief Directions: From north, enter Shipston on A3400, turn right opposite hospital, 1st left then 1st right. From south enter on A3400, left opposite hospital, 1st left then 1st right
Club Secretary: Richard H Slatter, Woodhills Farm, Todenham, Moreton in Marsh, Gloucestershire. GL56 9PH Tel: (H) 01608 650453 (W) 01608 650453
Fixtures Secretary: Rob Hawkins
Tel: (H) 01608 682216
Club Colours: Black shirts, shorts and socks
Change: All yellow

SHOTTERY RFC
Warwickshire
Ground Address: Shottery Fields, Shottery Road, Shottery
Brief Directions: From A46 Stratford Northern Bypass, tuurn onto A422 Alcester Road. turn right into Community Sports Centre.
Club Secretary: Mr. C. Cond, Lane End House, Little Wolford, Shipston on Stour, Warwickshire, CV36 5LZ.
Tel: 01608 684613
Fixtures Secretary: Mr. S. Burford, 20 Valetta Way, Wellesbourne, Warwickshire.
Tel: 01789 842454
Club Colours: St. Andrew's blue & gold

SHREWSBURY RUFC
North Midlands 3
Ground Address: Sundorne Castle, Uffington, Shrewsbury. SY4 4RR
Tel: 01743 353380
Brief Directions: Follow M54/A5 extension from north or south to Shrewsbury, exit bypass at roundabout, marked B5062 Haughmond Abbey, ground 800 mtrs on left
Club Secretary: Graham S Jackson, 99 Highfields, Shrewsbury. SY2 5PJ
Tel: (H) 01743 361802
Fixtures Secretary: Glyn Jones, 10 Copthorne Park, Copthorne, Shrewsbury, Shropshire.
Tel NO: 01743 360194
Club Colours: Sky blue and navy blue narrow hooped shirts, navy shorts

SILHILLIANS RUFC
Midlands West 2
Ground Address: Warwick Road, Copt Heath, Knowle, Solihull, West Midlands
Tel: 01564 777680
Brief Directions: J5 M42, then towards Knowle, ground 50yds on left hand side
Club Secretary: G R Loader, 12 Stubbs Road, Penn, Wolverhampton, West Midlands. WV3 7DF
Tel: (H) 01902 338474 (W) 01902 774103
Fixtures Secretary: Andrew Wiles Tel No: 01564 730105
Club Colours: Maroon and blue shirts, blue shorts

SKEGNESS RFC
Notts, Lincs & Derby 2
Ground Address: Wainfleet Road Playing Fields, Skegness
Tel: 01754 765699
Brief Directions: A153 turn right for town centre, 0.5 mile turn right at Highwayman pub, ground across A52
Club Secretary: Alan Hawkes, Grunters Grange, East Keal, Spilsby. PE23 4AY
Tel: (H) 01790 752788 FAX:01790 754611
Fixtures Secretary: John Harris, 13 Jenkins Close, Beacon Park Estate, Skegness
Tel: (H) 01754 765797
Club Colours: Royal blue and white hoops, navy shorts

SLEAFORD RFC
Notts, Lincs & Derby 1
Ground Address: Sleaford RFC, East Road Ground, Ruskington Road, Sleaford, Lincs.
Tel: 01529 303335
Brief Directions: One mile north east of Sleaford on the A153 Skegness road, at the junction with the A17 Sleaford by-pass.
Club Secretary: J.S.West, 38 St John's Close, Leasingham, Sleaford , Linc. NG34 8LU .
Tel No: 01529 414327
Fixtures Secretary: George Marsh, 37 Meadow Field, Sleaford, Lincs Tel: (H) 01529 303859
Club Colours: Red and black hoops, black shorts., red socks

SOUTH LEICESTER RFC

Midlands East 1
Ground Address: Welford Road, Wigston, Leicester, LE18 1TE Tel: 011 2882066
Brief Directions: M1/M69 J21, head east on ringroad towards Oadby & Wigston, take A50 towards Northampton, ground at the final roundabout of the built up area of Wigston
Club Secretary: Richard Dowdall, 4 Bodmin Avenue, Wigston Magna, Leicester. LE18 2HB
Tel: (H) 0116 2885606
Fixtures Secretary: J. Pinnock Esq, 49 Monica Rd, Braunstone, Leicester
Club Colours: Green and white hoops

SOUTHAM

Midlands West 2
Ground Address: Kineton Road, Southam, nr Rugby, Warwickshire Tel: 01926 813674
Brief Directions: Take Leamington road (A425) off Southam by-pass(A423). Left at next roundabout, past ind.estate. Ground on right.
Club Secretary: Ivan Harvey, Rookery Nook, Priors Hardwick, nr Rugby, Warwickshire. CV23 8SL
Tel: (H) 01327 260709
Fixtures Secretary: Gary Gilks
Tel: (H) 01926 812370 (W) 0831 885150
Club Colours: Navy blue jerseys, white hoops

SOUTHWELL RUFC

Notts Lincs & Derby 1
Ground Address: Pentelowes, Park Lane, Southwell, Notts. NG25 0LA
Brief Directions: On entering into Southwell follow signs to the recreation centre. The rugby club is behind the recreation centre.
Club Secretary: Adam Platts, 59 Church Street, Southwell, Notts, NG25 0HQ.
Tel: (H) 01636 814818
Fixtures Secretary: Phil Gordon
Tel: (H) 01636 830485
Club Colours: Maroon and navy quarters

SPALDING RFC

Midlands East 1
Ground Address: Memorial Field, St Thomas' Road, Spalding, Lincs Tel: 01775 725191
Brief Directions: From north, south & east, exit bypass at town centre sign, 1st left over river, immediate right, left into St Thomas Rd, From west, in town, 1st right after railway crossing
Club Secretary: J F Constable, 100 Halmergate, Spalding, Lincs. PE11 2EL
Tel: (H) 01775 723790
Fixtures Secretary: Tim Davies, Ten Mile House, The Raceground, Spalding, Lincs.
Club Colours: Maroon and blue hoops

SPARTANS RUFC

Staffs & Warwicks 1
Ground Address: Coppice Lane, Middleton, Nr Tamworth, Staffordshire. B78 2BS
Tel: 0121 308 5857
Brief Directions: Club is situated by the junction of A446 and Coppice Lane, 0.25 mile on the Colehill side of the A453 at Bassetts Pole
Club Secretary: Miss Sarah McGrory, 33 Alexandra Mews, Victoria Road, Tamworth, Staffordshire. B79 7HT
Tel: (H) 01827 63132 or 01426 842795
Fixtures Secretary: Ben Billings, 16 Dickinson Drive, Sutton Coldfield, West Midlands B76 1FP
Tel: (H) 0121 378 0067 (W) 0976 281981
Club Colours: Black shirts and black shorts

ST IVES (CAMBS) RUFC

East Midlands & Leicester 1
Ground Address: Somersham Road, St Ives, Huntingdon, Cambs. PE17 4LY
Tel: 01480 464455
Brief Directions: From the St Ives bypass, follow the B1040 towards Somersham, the ground is on the left
Club Secretary: Michael Prince,Vine Cottage, Church St, Woodhurst, Hunt'don
Tel: 01487 822693
Fixtures Secretary: Nick Nicholson
Tel: (H) 01480 381693
Club Colours: Royal blue and black shorts

ST NEOTS RUFC

East Midlands & Leicester 2
Ground Address: The Common, St Neots. PE19 1HA
Tel: 01480 474285
Brief Directions: Follow signs for Little Paxton from town centre, ground on left as you leave St Neots (1 mile from Town centre)
Club Secretary: D.Young, 3 Constable Drive, Eaton Ford, St. Neots, Cambs. PE19 3RH
Fixtures Secretary: D.Warmington. Tel No: 01954 718153
Club Colours: Light blue with navy blue hoops.

STAFFORD RUFC

Midlands West 1
Ground Address: County Ground, Castlefields, Newport Road, Stafford. ST16 1BG
Tel: 01785 211241
Brief Directions: M6 J13, A449 to Stafford for 1.5 miles, turn on left marked Rowley Park Westway, continue to junction with Newport Rd, turn right, Club 500 yds on left
Club Secretary: P.L.Hill, 39 Rising Brook, Stafford. ST17 0PV
Tel: (H) 01785 259583
Fixtures Secretary: B Bowen, 6 Fallowfield, Wildwood, Stafford ST17 4QU
Tel: 01785 603961
Club Colours: Black and amber hooped jerseys, black shorts

STAMFORD COLLEGE OLD BOYS RFC

Notts Lincs & Derby 2
Ground Address: Stamford College, Drift Road, Stamford, Lincs
Brief Directions: Follow signs to Stamford College, ground behind Leisure Centre
Club Secretary: James Gerever, 77 Radcliffe Rd., Stamford,Lincs. PE91AU
Tel No: 01780 766849
Fixtures Secretary: Chris Mitchell,10 Sandringham Close, Stamford, Lincs. PE9 1HL
Tel No: 01780 757806
Club Colours: Red and green hoops

STAMFORD RUFC
Midlands East 2
Ground Address: Hambleton Road, Stamford, Lincolnshire PE9
Tel: 01780 52180
Brief Directions: Take the A606 into Stamford. Turn right at the Danish Invader inn. and the ground is then 200 yards on the left
Club Secretary: A W Jones, 45 Caledomian Road, Stamford, Lincs, PE9 2TG. Tel: (H&F) 01780 766680 (W) 01780 764782
Fixtures Secretary: Andrew Baker, 27 Queens Walk, Stamford, Lincs.
Tel: (H) 01780 756367
Club Colours: Purple, black and white shirts, black shorts

STANDARD RFC
Warwickshire
Ground Address: Tanners Lane off Tile Hill Lane, Canley, Coventry Cv4 9BD
Tel No 01203 675186
Brief Directions: A45 to Tile Hill Lane, straight to the bottom then into Tanners Lane . Ground 100 yds on left.
Club Secretary: Chris Hughes, 108 Earlsdon Avenue South, Coventry. CV5 8DN
Tel: (H) 01203 679552
Fixtures Secretary: Pete Horgan, 106 Grangemouth Rd., Radford, Coventry. CV6 3FE
Club Colours: Dark blue, sky blue and white hoops with blue shorts

STEWARTS & LLOYDS RFC
Midlands East 1
Ground Address: Occupation Road, Corby, Northants. NN17 1EH
Tel: 01536 400317
Brief Directions: From Kettering, A6003 towards Oakham, right at roundabout at top of Rockingham Hill, 0.75 mile, turn 1st right past Game Bird Pub into Occupation Rd, 1st right into ground
Club Secretary: J M Thompson, 5 Howe Crescent, Corby, Northants. NN17 2RY
Tel: (H) 01536 202433(M) 07970 783253 (Fax) 01536 202433
Fixtures Secretary: Alan Brooks. Tel No: 01536 266901 (H) 07977 825071 (M) and 01536266901 (Fax.)
Club Colours: Black shirts, black shorts with black & white socks.

STOCKWOOD PARK RFC
Midlands 2
Ground Address: Stockwood Park, London Road, Luton, Beds. LU1 4BH Tel: 01582 728044
Brief Directions: M1 J10, left at end of slip road, left at 1st set of traffic lights into Stockwood Park, Club on right
Club Secretary: Dave Joy, 89 Stanhope Crescent, Luton. LU3 2RJ
Fixtures Secretary: R A Poulter
Tel: (H) 01462 456634 (W) 01582 742366
Club Colours: Red with yellow hoop, navy shorts, red socks

STOKE OLD BOYS RFC
Midlands West 2
Ground Address: A G Gale Field, Brookvale Avenue, Binley, Coventry. CV3 2RF
Tel: 01203 453631
Brief Directions: Off Binley Road, closest landmark is Binley Fire Station, 40 yards out of town
Club Secretary: Mr Brian Jose, 33 Hothorpe Close, Binley, Coventry. CV3 2HX
Tel: (H) 01203 457127 (W) 01203 335121 Ext 245
Fixtures Secretary: Mr J Monaghan
Tel: (H) 01203 451198
Club Colours: Maroon and white

STOKE - ON - TRENT RUFC
Midlands 1
Ground Address: Hartwell Lane, Barlaston, Stoke on Trent, ST`15 8TL
Brief Directions: From M1: A38 to A50. Left at lights (A520) at town outskirts. Take Rd. to Barlaston after 3m.Club 1m on left.From M6 leaveJ15(A34 South).to Barlaston club on right
Club Secretary: Stephen Beck, 10 Hillside Close, Fulford, Stoke on Trent St11 9RU Tel: 0121 212 5406
Fixtures Secretary: Eric Hardistry, 29 Kingston Drive, Stone, Staffs ST15 OEJ
01785 813641(H) 01782 206672(W)
Club Colours: Dark Blue with Light Blue Hoops

STONE RUFC
Staffordshire 2
Ground Address: Bibby's Social Club, Tilling Drive, Walton, Stone.
Tel: 01785 810206
Brief Directions: From A34 take B5026 to Eccleshall. Take first L. `Tilling Drive', Ground is at end of Tilling Drive.
Club Secretary: Fiona Foster, 17 Granville Terrace, Stone, ST15 9DF.
Tel: 01785 615591
Fixtures Secretary: Matt Upton, 11 St. Michael's Mount, Stone, ST15 8PZ.
Tel: 01785 605598
Club Colours: Maroon & Green Quarters, Black shorts

STONEYGATE FC
Midlands East 1
Ground Address: Covert Lane, Scraptoft, Leics. LE7 9SP
Tel: 0116 2419188
Brief Directions: A47 east out of Leicester (Signposted Peterborough), left at lights (Coles Nurseries) into Station La, turn right at bottom onto Covert Lane.
Club Secretary: S Morris, 203 Evington Lane, Leicester. LE5 6DJ
Tel: (H) 0116 2628596/2735927 (W) 0116 2628596
Fixtures Secretary: M C Herbert
Tel: (H) 0116 271 4229 (W) 0116 255 2694
Club Colours: Cardinal red and white hoops, navy shorts

STOURPORT RFC
North Midlands 2
Ground Address: Starport Cricket and Rugby Club, Walshes Meadow, Dunley Road, Stourport-on-Severn, Worcestershire
Tel: 01299 822210
Brief Directions: From town centre follow signs for Great Witley, cross River Severn Bridge, turn left to Leisure Centre, ground straight ahead
Club Secretary: Dr. T.W. Harding, The Oaks, Wilden Top, Stourport-On-Severn, Worcs, DY13 9JQ
Fixtures Secretary: Pete Wall, 1 Lingfield Rd, Meadow Rise, Bewdley, Worcs.
Club Colours: Navy blue, gold V on chest

STRATFORD UPON AVON RFC
Midlands West 1
Ground Address: Pearcecroft Loxley Road, Stratford upon Avon
Tel: 01789 297796
Brief Directions: Central Stratford, off Tiddington Road, alongside river on southern bank
Club Secretary: Mr R J Grant, 4 St Gregory's Road, Stratford upon Avon. CV37 6UH
Tel: (H) 01789 266722 (W) 0121 502 7116
Fixtures Secretary: Mrs A Prentice
Tel: (H) 01789 269892
Club Colours: Black and white hooped jerseys, white shorts

SUTTON COLDFIELD RFC
Midlands 2
Ground Address: Walmley Road, Sutton Coldfield
Tel: 0121 351 5323
Brief Directions: M6 north J5 take A452 (Brownhills) to Bagot Arms pub, then right onto B4148, ground is 0.5 mile on right from Walmley village shops
Club Secretary: Ian Larsen, 29 Willmott Road, Four Oaks, Sutton Coldfield BT5 5NR
Tel: (H) 0121 308 6245
Fixtures Secretary: Dick Harris
Tel: (H) 0121 353 1806
Club Colours: Emerald green shirts, white shorts

SYSTON RUGBY FOOTBALL CLUB
Midlands 1
Ground Address: Barkby Road, Queniborough, Leicester
Tel: 0116 2601223
Brief Directions: Off A607 Melton Mowbray road (Ring secretary for map)
Club Secretary: Mr J D Newton, 62 Fosse Way, Syston, Leicester. LE7 1NE
Tel: (H) 0116 2694647
Fixtures Secretary: Mrs T Sturgess
Tel: (H) 0116 2694250
Club Colours: Navy and saxe (light blue) hooped shirts, navy shorts

TAMWORTH RUFC
Midlands West 2
Ground Address: Wigginton Lodge, Wigginton Park, Tamworth, Staffs
Tel: 01827 68794
Brief Directions: Head north out of town towards Burton, left turn into Thackeray Drive, right at T junction, 1st left, 1st left to park
Club Secretary: Michael Hobbs, 227 Hockley Road, Tamworth, Staffs
Tel: (H) 01827 288602
Fixtures Secretary: Gordon Penley
Tel: (H) 01827 285211
Club Colours: Maroon, black and white

TELFORD HORNETS RFC
Midlands West 1
Ground Address: Town Park, Hinnshay Road, Dawley, Telford. TF4 3NZ
Tel: 01952 505440
Brief Directions: M54, J4 for town centre, 2nd exit at roundabout, 1st exit next roundabout onto A442, continue to Cattlefield, 4th exit at roundabout to Dawley, 4th right, club 0.75 mile on left
Club Secretary: Mrs Linda Potts, 17 Ellesmere Court, Newport, Shropshire. TF10 7SD
Tel No: 01952 418801 (H & Fax.)
Fixtures Secretary: Mrs Pam Sherry, 185 Blakemore, 8 Rookside, Telford TF3 1PZ
Tel NO: 01952 275529
Club Colours: Black and gold chest band

TENBURY RFC
North Midlands 2
Ground Address: Penlu, Worcester Road, Tenbury Wells, Worcs. WR15 8AY
Tel: 01584 810456
Brief Directions: Nex to Tenbury Hospital
Club Secretary: Mr M Spicer, 19 Castle Close, Tenbury Wells, Worcestershire. WR15 8AY. Tel: (H) 01584 819541
Fixtures Secretary: Mark Morgan, Deepcroft Farmhouse, Newnham Bridge, Tenbury Wells, Worcs. Tel: (H) 01584 781412
Club Colours: Green and black Hoops

THORNEY RUFC
East Mids/Leics 3
Ground Address: Thorney Ex Servicemens Club, Station Road, Thorney, Cambs. PE6 0QE
Tel: 01733 270283
Brief Directions: A47 from Peterborough towards Wisbech, at traffic lights on crossroads turn towards Crowland, club house 150 metres from crossroad
Club Secretary: Mr L Depwancke, 7 Headlands Way, Whittlesey. PE7 1RL
Tel: (H) 01733 204893
Fixtures Secretary: Mr R Turner
Tel: (H) 01733 571259
Club Colours: Navy and gold quarters

TOWCESTRIANS RFC
Midlands East 1
Ground Address: Towcestrians RFC, Greens Norton Road, Towcester, Northamptonshire. NN12 8AW
Tel: 01327 350141
Brief Directions: From A43/A5 junction roundabout take exit for Greens Norton and Blakesley, ground situated approx 1/2 mile on right
Club Secretary: Richard Titmuss, 67 Clare Crescent, Towcester, Northants NN12 6QQ
Tel: 01327 358031
Fixtures Secretary: Geoff Hanson, 21 High Street, Creaton, Northants. Tel: (H) 01604 505491
Club Colours: Maroon with white edged amber band, black shorts, maroon socks

TRENTHAM RUFC
Staffs & Warwicks 1
Ground Address: Oaktree Road, Trentham, Stoke-on-Trent, Staffordshire
Tel: 01782 642320
Brief Directions: M6 J15, A500 towards Stoke-on-Trent, A34 south signs to Trentham, at Trentham Gardens roundabout left onto A5035, Oakhill Road 0.5 mile on right
Club Secretary: Mrs Jane Procter, Holly House, Barn Court Clayton, Newcastle, Satffs ST5 4NL
Tel: 01782 623292
Fixtures Secretary: Mr Michael Procter. Tel No: 01782 623292 (H)
Club Colours: Green and white hoops, black shorts

TRINITY GUILD RFC
Staffs & Warwicks 1
Ground Address: Rowley Road, Baginton, Coventry
Tel: 01203 305928
Brief Directions: From north, follow A45 west of Coventry, follow airport signs. From south, follow A45 from M45. From west, follow A46 to A45
Club Secretary: D H Williams, 122 Grange Road, Longford, Coventry. CV6 6DA
Tel: (H) 01203 360833 (W) 01203 666655 Ext 2420
Fixtures Secretary: K Lightowler
Tel: (H) 01203 598932
Club Colours: Maroon, old gold and dark navy stripes

TUPTON RUFC
Notts, Lincs & Derby 2
Ground Address: The Recreation Ground, North Side, Tupton, Chesterfield
Tel: (Tupton Social Club) 01246 862002
Brief Directions: From Chesterfield south A61 to Tupton, left at roundabout into Queen Victoria Road, then 2nd left into North Side
Club Secretary: Bob Curry, 190 Queen Victoria Road, Tupton, Chesterfield. S42 6DW 0976 538682 (M)
Tel: (H) 01246 862059
Fixtures Secretary: I. Bulloch.Tel NO: 01246 238920 (H) 07977 413389 (M)
Club Colours: Shirts-navy blue with 3 gold hoops, blue shorts and socks

UNIVERSITY OF DERBY MENS RUGBY CLUB
Notts, Lincs & Derby 3
Ground Address: Kedleston Campus, Kedleston Road. DE22 1GB
Tel: 01332 633333
Brief Directions: A38 to Markeaton roundabout and follow directions to University at Kedleston Road Campus
Club Secretary: c/o Jo Gill, Sports & Recreation Manager Sports & Recreation DEpt. UDSU, Keoleston Rd., Derby, DE22 1GB
Fixtures Secretary: David French, 73 Cedar Street, Derby, DE22 1GE. Tel: (H) 01332 340748
Club Colours: Green and white quarters

UPTON-UPON-SEVERN RFC
North Midlands 1
Ground Address: Collingshurst Meadow, Old Street, Upton-upon-Severn
Tel: 01684 594445
Brief Directions: Opposite Upton-upon-Severn Church in the main street of the town. 10 miles south of Worcester and 7 miles north of Tewkesbury on the A38 trunk road
Club Secretary: Stuart Clarke, Barston, Picken End, Hanley Swan, Worcs WR8 0DQ Tel No: 01684 310285
Fixtures Secretary: Nigel Banwell
Tel: (H) 01684 592046
Club Colours: Black and white quarters, black shorts

UTTOXETER RFC
Staffs & Warwicks 1
Ground Address: Oldfields Sports Centre, Springfield Road, Uttoxeter, Staffs. Tel: 01889 564347
Brief Directions: From the centre of Uttoxeter, take Stone Road, after 200 yards right into Springfield Road. After 50 yards turn right
Club Secretary: Simon Bailey, Stoneleigh Cottage, Gt. Cubley, Ashbourne, Derbyshire DE6 2EY Tel: (H) 01335 330306
Fixtures Secretary: Les Humphries, 14 Eaton Road, Rocester, Stafffs.
Tel: (H) 01889 590604 Tel: (W) 01889 593680
Club Colours: Blue with orange band

VAUXHALL MOTORS RUFC
East Midlands & Leicester 2
Ground Address: 20 Gypsy Lane, Luton, Beds
Tel: 01582 748240
Brief Directions: Off M1 at J10, across 1st roundabout, down dual carriageway, left at roundabout then left immediately at next roundabout, entrance 200 yds on left
Club Secretary: Mr S. MacLaughlan, Adelaide House, 51 Adelaide Street, Luton, Beds. LU1 5BD. Tel: 01582 400138. Fax: 01582 411685
Fixtures Secretary: M Neate
Tel: (H) 01525 716393 (W) 01582 420565
Club Colours: Royal blue and gold shirts, black shorts

VESEYANS RFC
North Midlands 1
Ground Address: Memorial Ground, Little Hardwick Road, Streetly, Sutton Coldfield, West Midlands
Tel: 0121 353 5388
Brief Directions: A452 to Brownhills. Turn left at the Hardwick pub and the ground is 1 mile further on the left.
Club Secretary: Mr Karl Ward, Claret Wood, Streetly Wood,, Sutton Coldfield. B74 4HJ.
Tel: (B) 07000 527592
Fixtures Secretary: Steve Smith, 206 Highbridge Road, Sutton Coldfield. B74 3DQ
Tel: (H) 0121 321 1797
Club Colours: Black and white hoops, black shorts

VIPERS RFC
Midlands East 2
Ground Address: Blaby Bypass, Whetstone, Leicester
Tel: 0116 2864777
Brief Directions: M1 J21, follow A46 to roundabout at Fosse Park, right onto B4114, straight over next roundabout, next roundabout left, next roundabout right, club on left at end of d/c
Club Secretary: Andrew Barraclough, 47 Kiplins Drive, Enderby, Leicester LE99 5QR
Tel No: 0116 2865164
Fixtures Secretary: Ian Reid, 52 Stanhope Road, Wigston, Leicester LE18 3SJ
Tel: (H) 0116 281 0472
Club Colours: Green with gold and black hoops

WARLEY RFC
Midlands West 2
Ground Address: St John's Recreation Grounds,St John's Road,Smethwick,Warley,West Midlands.
Brief Directions: From Jct2 on M5, follow A4123 to Birmingham.Turn left at Hen& Chicken Pub, continue to traffic lights, turn right into Warley then first left is St Johns Rd.
Club Secretary: Keiron Ward, 72 Oak Road, Oldbury, Warley. B68 0BD
Tel: (H) 0121 422 4639 (W) 0121-200-2120
Fixtures Secretary: Peter Davies
Tel: (H) 0121 420 3141
Club Colours: Red and white hoops, black shorts

WEDNESBURY RUFC

Staffs & Warwicks 1
Ground Address: Hydes Road Playing Fields, Hydes Road, Wednesbury
Tel: 0121 502 2477
Brief Directions: M6 J9, to Wednesbury, straight on at traffic lights, take 5th left after that, playing fields 0.75 mile on right
Club Secretary: Peter Hughes , 28 Alder Road, Wednesbury, West Midlands. WS10 9PX
Tel: (H) 0121 556 5005 (W) 0121687 6005
Fixtures Secretary: The Landlord, Jolly Sailor Public House, Oldbury Road, West Bromwich WS10 9PX.
Tel Nos: 0121 556 5005 (H) 0121 687 6005 (W)
Club Colours: Black and white hoops, black shorts

WELLINGBOROUGH OLD GRAMMARIANS RFC

East Midlands & Leicester 1
Ground Address: Wellingborough O.G. New Memorial Sports Field, Sywell Road, Wellingborough, Northants NN8 8BS
Tel: 01933 226188
Brief Directions: From Park Farm North go along Sywell Road, ground is on right.
Club Secretary: Ken Bernthal, 38 Torrington Road, Wellingborough ,Northants NN85AF
Tel: (H) 01933 679474 (W) 0171 887 5384
Fixtures Secretary: John Bernthal. Tel Nos: 01536 485474 (H) 0961 9682256 (M)
Club Colours: Claret and white hoops, black shorts

WELLINGBOROUGH RFC

Midlands 2
Ground Address: Cut Throat Lane, Great Doddington, Wellingborough, Northants. NN29 7TZ
Tel: 01933 222260
Brief Directions: Leave A45 at Earls Barton/Gt Doddington, turn left at end of exit road, left at small crossroads in approx 500mtr, clubhouse is at top of hill on right, approx 500 metres
Club Secretary: Bob Stevenson, 12 South Street, Wollaston, Northants. NN29 7RX
Tel: (H) 01933 664538 (W) 01933 226077
Fixtures Secretary: Ian Brown
Tel: (H & W) 01933 663622
Club Colours: White shirts with red hoop, navy shorts

WEST BRIDGFORD RFC

Midlands East 2
Ground Address: The Memorial Ground, Stamford Road, West Bridgford, Nottingham
Tel: 0115 9232506
Brief Directions: Enter West Bridgford on A52, just over Gamston Bridge turn left, 1st left onto Brockley Rd, left at T junction, 2nd left onto Rufford Way, club on next bend
Club Secretary: K Howells, 117 Mount Pleasant, Keyworth, Nottingham. NG12 5ES
Tel: (H) 0115 9374468
Fixtures Secretary: N Davies, 17 Chantrey Road, West Bridford, Nottingham.
Tel: 0115 981 4344
Club Colours: Black shirts with red and gold hoops, black shorts and socks

WESTLEIGH RFC

Midlands 1
Ground Address: Lutterwirth Road, Blaby, Leicester
Tel: 0116 2771010
Brief Directions: M1/M69 J21, take B4114 to Narborough, left at Foxhunter pub roundabout, right next roundabout, straight over next roundabout, left next roundabout, ground 150 yds on left
Club Secretary: A.B. Gilhooley, 86 Kirkby Road, Desford, Leicester. Tel: (H) 01455 823678
Fixtures Secretary: C.J. Barker, c/o 12 Talbot Lane, Leicester, LE1 4LR. Tel: (W) 01162 518139
Club Colours: Black and white hooped jerseys, black shorts

WESTWOOD RUFC

East Midlands & Leicester 3
Ground Address: Phorpres Club, London Road, Peterborough
Tel: 01733 343501
Club Secretary: Andy Sullivan, 15 Swallowfield, Werrington, Peterborough. PE4 5BN.
Fixtures Secretary: Darren Smith, 25 Westfield Rd Yaxley, Peterborouigh PE7 3LF
Club Colours: Red and white hoops, black shorts, red and white socks.

WHEATON ASTON RUFC

Staffordshire 1
Ground Address: Monckton Recreation Centre, Pinfold Lane, Penkridge, Staffordshire
Tel: 01785 712264
Brief Directions: M6 J12, A5 towards Telford, at 1st island take A449 to Stafford, when you enter Penkridge take 1st left past Ford dealership, club 800 yds on left
Club Secretary: Paul Donoghue, Clouds End,3 Sandy Lane,Brewood, Staffs.St19 9ET
Tel: 01902 851700
Fixtures Secretary: David Tipton, Hocklehill Farm, Brewood, Staffs. ST19 9BQ
Tel: (H & W & FAX) 01902 850386
Club Colours: Black shirts with gold collar and cuffs, black shorts

WHITTINGTON

Staffordshire 1
Ground Address: Whittington Barracks, Tarnworth Road, Whittington, Staffs
Brief Directions: Off A51, between Lichfield and Tamworth
Club Secretary: Mrs L Emery, 284 Whetstone Road, Aldridge, Walsall WS9 0RU
Tel: (H) 01922 863213
Fixtures Secretary: S Clark, 25 Wissage Lane, Lichfield WS13 6DQ
Tel: 01543 252894
Club Colours: Blue and White Hoops

WILLENHALL RFC

Midlands West 2
Ground Address: Bognor Road, Essington, Nr Wolverhampton, NV11 2BA
Tel: 01922 405694
Brief Directions: M6 M54 off at Junction 1, take road towards Wolverhampton, 1st left past traffic lights into Bognor Road, 1 mile towards Essington, club on right
Club Secretary: Elfyn Pugh, 9 Five-Fields Road, Willenhall, West Midlands. WV12 4NZ
Tel: (H) 01902 607747 (W) 0197 885 2141
Fixtures Secretary: D.Peach Tel: 01922 419188
Club Colours: Maroon with black shorts

WOLVERHAMPTON RUFC

Midlands 2
Ground Address: Rear of Castlecroft Hotel, Castlecroft Road, Wolverhampton. WV3 8NA
Tel: 01902 763900
Brief Directions: Wolverhampton ring road, take A454 Compton Rd/Bridgnorth Rd to traffic lights at Mermaid, turn left, 2nd right into Castlecroft Ave, ground straight ahead, behind hotel
Club Secretary: Dr D J Rutherford, Rose Cottage, 3 Woodland Cottages, Penn, Wolverhampton
Tel: (H) 01902 335926 (W) 01902 24847
Fixtures Secretary: Mr.R.N.Astbury 1 Hamble Grove, Perton , South Staffs.WV6 7QW
Tel: (H) 017902 741495
Club Colours: All Black

WOODRUSH RFC

Midlands West 1
Ground Address: Icknield St, Forhill, Birmingham. B38 0EL Tel: 01564 822878
Brief Directions: M42 J3, take A435 to Birmingham, left to Weatheroak, over crossroads, past Kings Norton Golf Club, left at T junction, 1st right, ground on right
Club Secretary: Peter Leahy, 8 Burns Close, Redditch, Worcs, B97 5BS
Tel: (H) 01527 543722
Fixtures Secretary: Wayne Morris, 6 School Drive, Wythall, Worcs, B47 6EJ Tel: (H) 01564 824177
Club Colours: Emerald green and white hoops, black shorts

WORKSOP RUFC

Notts Lincs & Derby 1
Ground Address: The Meadows, Stubbing Lane, Worksop, Notts. S80 1NF Tel: 01909 484247
Brief Directions: Get onto Worksop bypass at roundabout with Mill House pub, take road to town centre then take 1st left into Stubbing Lane, club and grounds at end of road
Club Secretary: Ken Thompson, 35 Common Road, Thorpe Salvin, Worksop, Notts. S80 3JJ
Tel No: 01909 771761
Fixtures Secretary: Ian Hawksworth, 7 Carling Avenue, Worksop, Notts. S80 1YF
Tel No: 01909 489137 (H) 01909 534133 (W)
Club Colours: Black and white hooped shirts and socks, black shorts

YARBOROUGH BEES RUFC

Notts, Lincs & Derby 3
Ground Address: Yarborough Sports Centre, Riseholme Road, Lincoln
Tel: 01522 524228
Brief Directions: Follow A46 to junction with A15 turn - signed Ermine, turn into Yarborough School 400 yards approx
Club Secretary: H Sampson, 7 Shannon Avenue, Lincoln. LN6 7JG
Tel: (H) 01522 691631
Fixtures Secretary: Tony Goude, 44 Rooklands, Scotter, Gainsborough, Lincs DN21 3TT
Tel: 01724 763825
Club Colours: Maroon , amber and black hoops.

YARDLEY & DISTRICT RFC

North Midlands 2
Ground Address: No 1 Cole Hall Lane, Stechford, Birmingham
Tel: 0121 789 8450
Brief Directions: B'ham outer ringroad A4040 to Stechford, at t/light jcn of A4040/ A47 take A47 Coleshill Rd, over 1st island, immediate right into H'way, 1st island right, over next island, ground left after bridge
Club Secretary: John Shaw, 3 Barbourne Close, Solihull, B91 3TL
Tel: (H) 0121 705 3292
Fixtures Secretary: Ron Knight
Tel: (H) 0973 204 534
Club Colours: Royal blue, old gold bands

LONDON & SOUTH EAST DIVISION

LONDON & SOUTH EAST	Officials & League Secretaries	568
LONDON ONE	League table & Fixture Grid	569
	Clubs	570
LONDON & SOUTH EAST	1998-99 League Tables	576
	1999-2000 Fixture Grids	580
	Clubs (in alphabetical order)	590

London & South East Division Structure 1999-2000

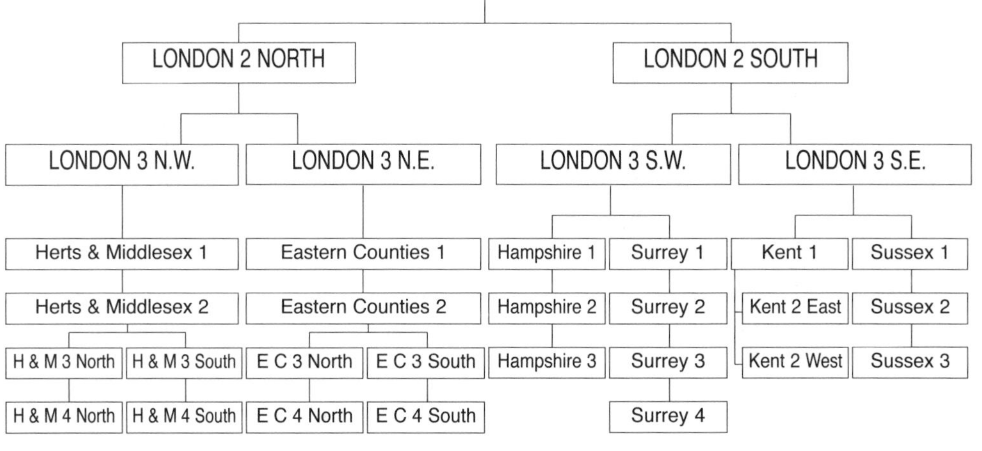

OFFICIALS
LONDON & SOUTH EAST DIVISION

Chairman
R Tennant, 57 Boveney Rd, Forest Hill London SE23 3 NL
Tel: 0181 699 9025 H/F

Secretary
M A Ward, English Clubs Championship PO Box12 Beccles Suffolk NR34 9HZ Tel: 01502 711343, 01502 710233 F

F A G Ford, "Fairhaven" 36 Haynes Rd., Hornchurch Essex RM11 2HT Tel: 01708 457807 H/F
EASTERN COUNTIES (London Competition Committee Member)

Lt Col D M Hathorn, 3 Broomacres Fleet, Aldershot Hants GU13 9UU Tel: 01252 621565 H 01276 65155 x 201
HANTS (London Competition Committee Member)

D J Williams, 7 Sadlers Way Hertford Herts SG14 2DZ
Tel: 01992 586744 H
HERTS (London Competition Committee Member)

D Attwood, 6 Somerset Gardens Lewisham London SE13 7SY 0181 692 2820 H
KENT (London Competition Committee Member)

P Astbury, 32 Kneller Gardens Isleworth Middlesex TW7 7NW Tel: 0181 898 5372 H
MIDDX (London Competition Committee Member)

H Brady, 16 Selwood Terrace London SW7 3QG
Tel: 0171 370 1078 H
SURREY (London Competition Committee Member)

B Vincent, 29 St Botolphs Rd Worthing, Sussex BN11 4JS
Tel: 01903 206516 H
SUSSEX (London Competition Committee Member)

I Reeve, The Croft, Romsey Rd Kings Somborne Hampshire SO20 6PP Tel: 01794 388064 H
Co-opted (L.E.A.F. Manager)

League Secretaries

F A G Ford — LONDON 1
"Fairhaven" 36 Haynes Rd Hornchurch Essex RM11 2HT
Tel: 01708 457807 H/F

D J Williams — LONDON 2 NORTH
7 Sadlers Way Hertford Herts SG14 2DZ
Tel: 01992 586744 H

B Vincent — SUSSEX ALL LEAGUES
29 St Botolphs Rd Worthing, Sussex BN11 4JS
Tel: 01903 206516 H

M J Stott — LONDON 3 N EAST
Brick Kiln Farm North Walsham Norfolk
Tel: 01692 403096 H/F

D Gerschlick — LONDON 3 N WEST
20a The Avenue Potters Bar Hertfordshire EN6 1EB
Tel: 01707 644433 H

D Attwood — LONDON 3 S EAST
6 Somerset Gardens Lewisham London SE13 7SY
Tel: 0181 692 2820 H

Lt Col D M Hathorn — LONDON 3 S WEST
3 Broomacres Fleet, Aldershot Hants GU13 9UU
Tel: 01252 621565 H 01276 65155 x 201

M Tuck — EASTERN COUNTIES 1 & 2
51 Highfield Rd Billericay Essex CM11 2PE
Tel: 01277 655483 H/F

R Hatch — EASTERN COUNTIES 3 SOUTH
99 Ernest Rd Wivenhoe Essex CO7 9LJ
Tel: 01206 823548 H

B H Rees — EASTERN COUNTIES 3 NORTH
161A Aldborough Rd South Ilford, Essex IG3 8HU
Tel: 0181 597 1158 H

R Wyatt — EASTERN COUNTIES 4 NORTH & SOUTH
Stone Cottage, The Green Beyton, Bury St Edmunds Suffolk IP30 9AF. Tel: 01359 270410 H

J Sneezum — HANTS ALL LEAGUES
Bursledon Lodge Salterns Lane, Old Bursledon Southampton SO3 8DH Tel: 01703 402286 H

R Willingale — HERTS/ MIDDX 1
Fairmile Farm Cottage Cobham Surrey KT11 1JY
Tel: 01932 866927 H

N Alway — HERTS/ MIDDX 2
20 Herndon Rd London SW18 2DG
Tel: 0181 870 6818 H

A Rabjohn — HERTS/ MIDDX 3
62 Central Avenue Hounslow Middlesex TW3 2QL
Tel: 0181 894 1850 H

J Gregory — HERTS/ MIDDX 4 NORTH
58 Luton Rd Redbourne Hertfordshire AL3 6PY
Tel: 01582 792798 H

B East — HERTS/ MIDDX 4 SOUTH
64 Station Rd Harpenden Herts AL5 4TL
Tel: 01582 762209 H/F

J Carley — KENT ALL LEAGUES
11 Vlissingen Drive Deal Kent CT14 6TZ
Tel: 01304 381273 H

R G Kirkwood — SURREY GENERAL
63 Shaftesbury Way Strawberry Hill, Twickenham Middx TW2 5RW. Tel: 0181 898 1767 H

J S Laidman — SURREY 1
2 West Dene, Park Lane Cheam, Sutton Surrey SM3 8BW
Tel: 0181 643 2919 H

M P Tanner — SURREY 2
1 Woodland Way Morden Surrey SM4 4DS
Tel: 0181 540 5784 H, 01923 214123 B

J Mason — SURREY 3
30 Ryefield Rd London SE19 3QU
Tel: 0181 771 5815 H

P Lovering — SURREY 4
Mynthurst Garden Leigh, Reigate, Surrey RH2 8RJ
Tel: 01293 862331 H

John Thompson — SUSSEX 2
Chennies London Road Watersfield Pulborough W. Sussex RH20 1ND

Andy Stephenson — SUSSEX 3
52 Camelot Close, Southwater Horsham W. Sussex RH13 7XP

LONDON ONE

1989-1999 LEAGUE TABLE

	P	W	D	L	PF	PA	PD	Pts	
Westcombe Park	16	15	0	1	706	201	505	30	
Staines	16	15	0	1	626	184	442	30	
Thanet Wanderers	16	12	0	4	389	284	105	24	
Sutton & Epsom	16	10	1	5	487	273	214	21	
Harlow	16	10	0	6	382	300	82	20	
Thurrock	16	9	2	5	355	322	33	20	
Old Colfeians	16	9	1	6	310	316	-6	19	
Basingstoke	16	8	0	8	423	280	143	16	
*Wimbledon	16	9	0	7	349	324	25	16	(-2)
Woodford	16	8	0	8	360	388	-28	16	
Guildford & Godalming	16	7	0	9	417	378	39	14	
Sudbury	16	6	0	10	365	299	66	12	
*Cheshunt	16	6	0	10	241	349	-108	10	(-2)
*Ruislip	16	5	0	11	270	295	-25	8	(-2)
Old Mid-Whitgiftian	16	3	1	12	247	498	-251	7	
Charlton Park	16	1	1	14	166	593	-427	3	
Southend	16	0	0	16	107	916	-809	0	

1999-2000 FIXTURE GRID

	Basingstoke	Cambridge	Cheshunt	Guildford & Goda.	Havant	Harlow	Old Colfeians	Old Midwhitgiftians	Ruislip	Staines	Sudbury	Sutton & Epsom	Thanet wands.	Thurrock	Wimbledon	Winchester	Woodford
Basingstoke		12.02	11.03			27.11	9.10				15.01	18.12	8.04			25.09	
Cambridge		x		8.01	11.12	26.02		29.01	9.10		11.09	25.03		20.11			
Cheshunt		23.10	x	29.01	8.01	25.03		26.02			2.10	11.09		11.12			
Guildford & Godalming	2.10			x	11.03		11.09		15.01	27.11				12.02	23.10		18.12
Havant	11.09				x		25.03		18.12	23.10				15.01	2.10	26.02	27.11
Harlow				9.10	25.09	x		20.11	11.03	15.01				8.04	18.12		12.02
Old Colfeians		15.01	12.02			23.10	x	2.10			15.12	27.11	11.03			8.04	
Old Mid-Whitgiftians	23.10			25.09	8.04			x	12.02	18.12				11.03	27.11		15.01
Ruislip	26.02		20.11				29.01		x	11.09			11.12		25.03	8.01	2.10
Staines	8.01	8.04	25.09				11.12			x	11.03		9.10		29.01	20.11	
Sudbury				11.12	20.11	29.01		8.01	25.09		x	26.02		9.10			8.04
Sutton & Epsom				20.11	9.10	8.01		11.12	8.04	12.02		x		25.09			11.03
Thanet Wanderers		27.11	18.12	26.02	29.01	11.09		25.03			23.10	2.10	x				
Thurrock	25.03						26.02		27.11	2.10			8.01	x	11.09	29.01	23.10
Wimbledon	11.12	11.03	8.04				20.11				12.02	15.01	25.09		x	9.10	
Winchester		18.12	15.01	25.03		2.10		11.09			27.11	23.10	12.02			x	
Woodford	29.01	25.09	9.10				8.01			25.03			20.11		26.02	11.12	x

BASINGSTOKE R.F.C.

Founded: 1948

President John Evans CBE, TD. Meadow View, Green Lane, Ellisfield RG25 2QP 01256 381470 (H)
Chairman Dr Stephen Tristram 5 Paddock View, Old Basing, Basingstoke RG24 0DB 01256 328327 (H) 0370 227312 (M)
Secretary Peter Allen 155 Pack Lane, Kempshott, Basingstoke RG22 5HN 01256 811466 (H)
Match/Fixture Sec. Kevin Barrett Burnt Oak, Silchester Road, Little London, Tadley, Hants. RG26 5EP
0118 970 0906 0118 970 1755 (Fax/Ansaphone)
Chairman of Playing John Byett 42 Byfleet Avenue, Old Basing, Basingstoke RG24 7HR 01256 323313 (H)
Director of Rugby Nigel Redman c/o club **Treasurer:** D R Hornblow 01635 298791 (H) 0118 981 9316(B) 0118 981 7958 (Fax)
Ground: Down Grange, Pack Lane, Kempshott, Basingstoke RG22 5HH Tel: 01256 323308 Fax: 01256 814390
Capacity: 2,000 approx 150 Covered Seats **Car Parking:** Spaces at ground + 2 nearby overflow car parks
Directions: M3 J7. Head towards town, turn left at 2nd r'about (1st - Sainsbury, 2nd Kempshott) into Heather Way, right at juntion (Kempshott Lane) & right at lights into Pack Lane. 250 yards on right turn into Coniston Rd - clubhouse on left
Nearest Railway Station: Basingstoke - 3 miles
Admission: Matchday - £2 league £3 cup, incl. programme
Clubhouse: Normal licensing hours. Meals available.Seats 150. Contact Ron/Sue Marchant 01256 323308
Club Shop: Open before & after 1st XV games & Sunday 10-12 am.
Colours: Blue & amber **Change colours:** All white **Training Nights:** Monday and Thursday (1st XV) - others Wed..
Programme Size: A5 Price: with admission Pages: 20 Editor: C Hibberd 01256 844340
Advertising Rates Spot Colour - £180+VATfull page, £100+VAT half page

CAMBRIDGE R.U.F.C.

Founded: 1923

Chairman	J Fear	10 Parkway, Shudy Camps, Cambridge CB1 6RQ 01799 584432
President	R Bishop	The Court House, Manor Farm Court, Cottenham CB4 4RD 01954 252055
Hon. Secretary	D Martin	45 York Street, Cambridge CB1 2PZ 01223 314705
Hon. Treasurer	G Hochmuth	47A Lambs Lane, Cottenham, Cambs. CB4 4TB 01954 200636

Ground Grantchester Road, Cambridge CB3 9ED Tel: 01223 312437 Web site: http://www.crufc.co.uk
Capacity: 3,750 250 Covered standing
Directions leave M11 at Exit 12 (A603) to Cambridge. Take 1st right into Granchester Road (opp. Wolfson College). Ground 300 yds on right, just past the last house.
Nearest Railway station: Cambridge Car Parking: Spaces for 350+ cars at ground.
Admission £3 league & cup matches only
Clubhouse: Open Tues & Thurs eve & Saturday & Sunday during season
Club Shop: Open sats & Suns during season
Programme Size: A5 Pages: 8 Price: £1 Editor: Sally Hunt, 48 High st., Over, Cambs. 01954 230764
Advertising: Contact Sarah Powell, 103 High St., Cottenham. 01954 250733
Colours: Blood and sand
Training Nights: Tuesday & Thursday 7.15pm

CHESHUNT R.F.C.

Founded: 1952

Secretary Tudor Roberts Archers Hall, Westmill, Buntingford, Herts. SG9 9LW
Tel: 01763 273827 (H) 01763 273994 (F)

Fixtures Secretary Maurice Phillips c/o Cheshunt RFC
Tel: 01992 440415 (H)

Ground Rosedale, Andrews Lane, Cheshunt, Herts. EN7 6TB Tel: 01992 623983
Directions M25, Junction 25, north on the A10, left at 1st roundabout, straight over next two roundabouts, 1st left into Andrews Lane and the club is 200 yards on the left.

Club colours Green and white

GUILDFORD & GODALMING R.F.C.

Founded: 1922

President Dr Des Carroll Portledge, The Drive, Wonersh Park, Guildford, Surrey 01483 892452
Chairman Mark Read 15 Hillside way, Godalming, Surrey GU7 2HN 01483 424946 (H) 01483 425710 (B)
Hon. Secretary David Gambold 10 Treebys Avenue, Jacobs Well, Guildford, Surrey GU4 7NT
01483 566304 (H) 01483 565771 (B) 01483 300168 (Fax)
Club Manager Dave Lambert 14 Wykeham Road, Merrow, Guildford, Surrey. 01483 424900
Fixture Secretary Len Bodill 4 Orchard Road, Burpham, Guildford, Surrey 01483 570580 (H)
Youth Brian Piper Lepe House, Minster Road, Godalming, Surrey. 01483 427534

Ground Address:Broadwater, Guildford Road, Godalming, Surrey GU7 3BU Tel: 01483 416199/424900
Web Site: http://www.ggrugby.co.uk Capacity: **Car Parking:** Extensive
Directions: A3100 from Guildford centre to Godalming - beside Broadwater lake, 1 mile before Godalming for A3 by-passing Guildford: B3000 thro' Compton - 3 miles - T junction - right to Godalming - 300 yards on right.
Nearest Railway Station: Farncombe
Admission:
Clubhouse: Open Saturdays & Tues & Thur eves during the season. Big screen for main matches/internationals
Club Shop: Open matchdays
Colours: Green & white bands **Training Nights:** Tuesday and Thursday **Nickname**: `Gees`
Programme Advertising Rates Contact Dave Lambert

HARLOW R.U.F.C.

Founded: 1955

Secretary David Enyon 12 Highfield, Harlow, Essex CM18 6HE
Tel: 01279 426389 (H)
Fixture Secretary John Pendleton 56 Priory Court, Harlow, Essex
Tel: 01729 439265 (H)
Treasurer A Webb 33 Peacocks, Harlow, Essex
Tel: 01279 830584 (H)

Ground Ram Gorse, Elizabeth way, Harlow, Essex CM20 2JQ Tel: 01279 426389
Directions Phone Fixtures Secretary

Club Colours: Red shirts, green trimmings and green shorts

HAVANT R.F.C.

Founded: 1951

President: Raymond Quinn 5 Holt Gardens, Rowlands Castle, Hants 01705 413931 (H), 01705 241122 (B), 01705 257596 (F)
Chairman: Richard Pearcey, Wisteria House, 34 Queens Rd., Waterlooville PO7 7SB
Tel: 0411 644525 (M), 01730 236236 (B), 01730 269596 (F)
Secretary: Stephen Lawrence 323 Havant Road, Farlington, Portsmouth PO6 1DD 01705 369492 (H), 01705 834699 (B)
1st XV Manager: Mick Chalk 16 Highclere Ave, Havant, Hants PO9 4RB01705 - 472239 (H) 723749 (B) 726455 (F)
Chair of Finance: Colin Sewell 01705 - 731705 (H) 421055 (F) **Chair of Rugby: Adam King** **Press Officer** Ray Quinn
Steward & Commercial Mgr Julian Davies 01705 473533 (H) **Match Secretary** Russ Godfrey 01243 371759 (H) 0802 389636 (M)
Ground: Hooks Lane, Fraser Rd, Bedhampton, Havant, Hants. PO9 3EJ Tel: 01705 477843 Fax: 01705 492311
Web: www.havant-rfc.co.uk **Capacity**: 2,700 **Seated**: 200 **Standing**: 2,500 **Car Parking:** 200 at ground, 200 nearby.
Directions: From the A3(M) take the B2177 to roundabout. Follow signs to Bedhampton - straight on over mini-roundabout. Straight across traffic lights then bear left at level crossing. Take second left (James Road) then turn into Fraser Road at T-junction. Clubhouse is 200 yards on the right. Nearest Railway Station: Bedhampton - go east - James Rd then as above
Admission: Season tickets - Standing Adults £60 Matchdays - Adult £3. Extra for seat £2.
Clubhouse: Normal licensing hours, snacks available Functions: Up to 100,contact Julian Davies 01705 492311
Club Shop: Open matchdays & Sun am. Contact J Davies 01705 477843
Colours: Blue, red & white/navy **Change colours:** Red/navy **Nickname**: Hav **Training Nights:** Tuesday and Thursday.
Programme Size: A5 Price: With entry Pages: 36 Advertising contact Julian Davies
Editor: Bill Sugden, 01243 372323 (H) 01243 371103 (F)

OLD COLFEIANS R.F.C.

Founded: 1928

President Moby Wale 65 Riverside Walk, The Alders, West Wickham, Kent BR4 9PZ 0181 325 0379 (H)
Chairman Nigel Glaister The Manor House, High St., Farningham, Kent DA4 0DG 01322 862000 (H) 0171 260 3178 (B)
Secretary Dai Andrew 80 Dallinger d., Lee, London SE12 0TH 00181 857 4036 (H) 0171 924 8252 (B)
Match Secretary John Nunn 27 Westmount Rd., Eltham, London SE9 1JB 0181 265 7447 (H)
Fixture Secretary Clive Corlett 1 Lasseter Place, Vanbrugh Hill, Blackheath, London SE3 7UX 0181 305 1261 (H)
Press Secretary 39 Holme Lacey Road, Lee, London SE12 0181 857 4049 (H)

Ground Address:Horn Park, Eltham Road, Lee, London SE12 Tel: 0181 852 1181
Capacity: **Car Parking:**
Directions: Ground is in Eltham Road opposite Weigal Road, on the A20, 600 metres in the direction of Lee, Lewisham and London from the intersection of the A20 & A205 roundabout.
Nearest Railway Station: Lee (BR) **Car Parking:**
Admission: Nil
Clubhouse: Normal Licensing hours **Club Shop:** Open on home league matches
Colours: Navy blue, burgundy, old gold & black bands/navy/navy
Training Nights: Tuesday and Thursday
Programme **Size**: A5 **Editor**: Clive Reffell 0181 853 1004 (H) 0171 306 2582 (B)

OLD MID-WHITGIFTIANS RFC

Founded: 1924

President: Mike Oliver, Oak Ridge, Wolfs Row, Limpsfield, Oxted, Surrey.
Chairman (General) : Terry McLaren, The Stables, Old Surrey Hall, East Grinstead, W.Sussex, RH19 3PR Tel: 01342 325197 (h)
Chairman (Playing) : Tim Edney, 47, Cherry Tree Walk, Beckenham, Kent BR3 3PE Tel: 0181 402 5695 (h)
Hon. Secretary : John Crate, 16, Mallard Way, Wallington, Surrey SM6 9LZ Tel: 0181 647 9081 (h&b)
e-mail: Johncrate@16mallard.freeserve.co.uk **Programme Editor:** Sean Lacey Contact via Hon. Sec. (above)
Hon. Fixture Sec.: Andy Hillburn 47a, Foxearth Rd, Selsdon, Surrey CR2 8EL Tel: 0181 657 1825 (h) 0171 817 8888 X4571 (b)
Marketing Manager: Aaron Pennington, 35, Hayden Road, Purley, Surrey CR8 4AG Tel: 0181 645 9216 (h)
Ground Address: Lime Meadow Avenue, Sanderstead, Surrey CR2 9AS Tel: 0181 657 2014
Capacity,1,000 standing uncovered
Directions: BY CAR: From Sanderstead roundabout travel 1 mile down Limpsfield Road. Opposite Sanderstead Methodist Church (blue sign) turn left into Sanderstead Court Avenue. After 100 yards turn right into Lime Meadow Ave. Ground is at end of the road. BY COACH: As above toSanderstead Court Avenue. After 100 yards, turn left, then first right into Blacksmiths Hill. Ground is on right at end of road. Nearest Railway Stn.: Sanderstead (approx.2 1/2 miles north of ground). Car Parking: 75 cars Free parking
Admission: Entry free. Spectators are requested to buy a match programme.
Clubhouse: Normal licensing hours. Good catering facilities. snacks and meals available all day on match days.
Programme: Size:A5 Pages: Varies weekly Price: £1 Editor: Sean Lacey (see above)
Advertising Rates vary from£100/quarter page to £750 for special positions. Contact Aaron Pennington (see above)
Colours: Navy Blue **Change Colours:** Green/blue **Nickname:** Midwives **Training:**Tuesday & Thursday eves.

RUISLIP R.F.C.

Founded: 1953

Chairman	Jim Brassett	7 Cornwall Court, Cornwall Road, Uxbridge Middx.	01895 258249
Treasurer	Christine Walker	88 Deane Croft Road, Eastcote, Middx.	0181 582 9640
Secretary	Michael Searls	16 Park Way, Rickmansworth, Herts	01923 773903
Rugby Manager	Chris Snowdon	7 Farthings Close, Eastcote, Middx.	0181 868 0144
Fixture Secretary	Steve Hazell	23 Hopfield Avenue, Byfleet, Surrey	01932 400361

Ground West End Road, Ruislip, Middx. HA4 6DR Tel: 01895 633102
Directions: M25, Junct 16 onto M40 towards London onto A40. After Northolt Airport T/L into West End Road A4180. Ground 3 miles on left beforeRuislip High Street.
Nearest Railway Station: Ruislip (London Underground) **Car Parking:** Plenty

Admission: Matchdays: By programme (£2) for league & cup games Season tickets: Not available
Programme: Size: A5 Pages: 24 Price: £2 (incl. entry)

Colours: Maroon & white hoops/white/maroon **Change colours:** All maroon
Training Nights: Tuesday & Thursday. Colts & Youth: Wednesday

STAINES R.F.C.

Founded: 1926

Web site: www.stainesrugby.co.uk

Club Secretary Kevin McMahon 23 Cherry Orchard, Staines, Middx, TW13 7NB
Tel: 01784 463220
Fixture Secretary E J de Voil 94 Groveley Road, Sunbury in Thames, Middx, TW16 7LB
Tel: 0181 8906643

Ground The Reeves, Feltham Hill Road, Hanworth, Middlesex, TW13 7NB
Tel 0181 8906643 e-mail: Dave@stainesrugby.c.uk
Capacity: All uncovered standing
Directions Take Lower Feltham exit from A316 turn left pass Unigate Dairy into Feltham Hill Road, Ground 400yds on left.
Nearest Railway Station: Feltham **Car Parking:** Yes

Club Shop Yes contact Pam
Training Nights Tuesday & Thursday **Club Colours:** Blue & Red Shirts/ White Shorts

SUDBURY R.U.F.C.

Founded: 1925

President	**Adrian Gilbert**	**26 Abbey Road, Sudbury, Suffolk CO10 6LA 01787 373470**
Chairman	**Brian Lorking**	**4 Pot Kilns, Great Cornard, Sudbury, Suffolk CO10 0DY 01787 310765**
Secretary	**Mike Maddocks**	**8 Nether Court, Halstead, Essex CO9 2HE 01787 473027**
Fixture/Match Sec.	**Greg Underwood**	**11 Bures Road, Great Cornard, Sudbury, Suffolk CO10 0EJ 01787 373045**

Ground **Moorsfield, Rugby Road, Great Cornard, Sudbury, Suffolk CO10 0JR Tel: 01787 377547**
Nearest Railway station: Sudbury Car Parking: Planty space available at the ground

Admission: Matchday: £3
Club Shop: Open matchdays and Sundays
Taining Nights: Tuesday & Thursday
Programme Size: A5 Price: with admission
Colours: Blue with wide white hoop Change colours: Maroon with blue hoop

SUTTON & EPSOM R.F.C.

Founded: 1881

President Pat O'Hagan c/o Sutton & Epsom RFC. 0181 256 0500 (B) 0181 661 0586 (H)
Secretary Bob Poole Well Cottage, Loxwood Rd, Wisborough Green, W. Sussex RH14 0DJ
0181 770 6441 (B) 01403 700594 (H)
Fixture Sec. Ian Frazer 111 Benhill Road, Sutton, Surrey SM1 3RR 0181 643 4835 (H) 0171 542 8549 (B)
Rugby Director Geoff Green 1 Central way, Carshalton, Surrey SM3 3NF 0181 286 2532 (H) 0181 390 1200 (B)
1st XV Manager Willie Moore 21 Windmill Lane, Ewell, Epson KT17 1HY 0181 394 0887 (H) 01372 722999 (B)
Press Officer John Ashton 0181 644 9664 (H) 0403 189661 (M)

Ground: Cuddington Court, Rugby Lane, West Drive, Cheam Surrey SM2 7NF Tel: 0181 642 0280
Capacity: 2,000 approx 300 Covered Seats **Car Parking:** 500 spaces at ground
Directions: M25, J8>A217>A240 Reigate road>A24 Ewell by-pass>A232 Cheam road>West Drive, club entrance at junction with Hays Walk. or M25, J10>A3 (London bound)>A240 Kingston road>A232 Cheam road, then as above.
Nearest Railway Station: Cheam BR
Admission: Matchday - £2.50 incl. programme. Season tickets not available
Clubhouse: Yes **Club Shop:** Open league matchdays, training nights & Sunday am.
Colours: Narrow black & white hoops **Change colours:** Peacock blue **Training Nights:** Mon & Thur (1st XV) - others Wed.
Programme Size: A5 Price: with admission Pages: 40 Editor: John Ashton
Advertising Rates Page £250, 1/2 £150, 1/4 £80, i/s cover £350

THANET WANDERERS RUFC

Founded: 1886

Secretary Peter Hawkins 51 Park Road, Ramsgate, Kent CT11 9TL Tel: 01483 593142
Fixture Secretary As above 01843 593142 (Home, Business & Fax)
Director of Rugby Andy Williamson 105 Minnis Road, Minnis Bay, Birchington, Kent CT7 9NY
Tel: 01483 845981 (H) 01843 591075 (B) 01843 851907 (Fax)

Ground: St Peters Recreation Ground, Callis Court Road, Broadstairs, Kent CT10 3AETel: 01843 866763
Capacity: 2000 uncovered standing
Directions: A2 M2, A299, A256 A255 From Broadstairs Broadway turn left at traffic lights into St Peters Park Road. Take the first right under the railway bridge and the ground is on the left after about 400 metres.
Nearest Railway Station: Broadstairs **Car Parking:** 50 spaces at the ground, others in the nearby streets.
Admission: Nil **Clubhouse**: Open during normal licensing hours. Food is available
For functions contact Bill May on 01843 604376 or 01304 611248 (B)
Club Shop: Open matchdays & Sun. am. Contact Mrs Penny Smith 01843 850904
Programme: Size: A5 Pages: 24 Price: £1.50 Editor: Peter Ruranski 01843 845895 (T & F)
Advertising: Full page £450 Half: £300 Quarter: £175
Colours: Blue black & gold hoops **Change colours:** Black & white
Nickname: Wanderers **Training**: Tuesday & Thursday

THURROCK R.F.C.

Founded: 1928

President B Godden 1 Laxtons, Stanford-le-Hope, Essex SS17 8AF 01375 676386
Chairman G Sansom 140 Long Lane, Grays, Essex 01375 375603
Secretary D H Evans 29 Mayfield, Connaught Ave., Grays RM16 2X
Treasurer B Howells 'Highlands', 6 Branksom Ave., Stanford-le-Hope, Essex. 01375 404280

Ground: 'Oakfield', Long Lane, Grays, Essex. 01375 374877
Capacity: Unlimited Seats: 100
Directions: M25 (N/S), Junction 30/31. take the A13 towards Southend. 2nd exit, A1012 towards Grays. 'Treaclemine' roundabout exit Stifford Clays. Continue to end.
Nearest Railway station: Grays Car Parking: spaces for 200 cars

Admission: Prices vary. Season tickets not available.
Clubhouse: Hall/Lounge/Squash/Gym/Sports injuries Clinic **Club Shop:** Yes
Programme Size: A4 Pages: Varies Price: £1 Editor: Mrs D Howells 01375 404280
Advertising: Contact the editor
Training Nights: Tuesday & Thursday **Nickname:** 'Tees'
Colours: Black with white hoops **Change colours:** All black

WIMBLEDON

Founded: 1865

Chairman	Mike Keane	17 Auriol Park Rd., Worcester Park, Surrey KT4 7DP Tel: 0181 337 6036 (H) 0171 261 3255 (B)
Treasurer	James Boetman	17 Montford Place, London SE11 5DE Tel: 0171 5820877 (H) 0171 629 7666 (B)
Coaching Director	Ian Pickup	99 Broadhurst, Ashstead, Surrey KT21 1QF Tel: 01372 273141 (H)
Secretary	David Dixon-Smith	42 Princes Rd., Wimbledon, London SW19 8RB Tel: 0181 542 3550 (B)

Ground: Beverley Meads, Barham Road, Copse Hill, Wimbledon, London SW20 0E
Tel: 0181 946 3156

Directions: By Car: Turn off the A3 onto Coombe Road. Turn up Copse Hill and then 1st left into Barham Road.
Nearest Railway Station: Ratnes Park **Car Parking**: at the end of Barham Road

Colours: Cambridge blue and maroon **Change colours:** White **Training Nights:** Tuesday & Thursday

WINCHESTER R.F.C.

Founded: 1929

Secretary	John H Prosser MBE	10 Princess Court, St Peter St., Winchester SO23 8DN Tel: 01962 863550 (H)
Fixture Secretary	James Jermain	7 Park Road, Winchester SO22 6AA Tel: 01962 620230
Treasurer	Miss E Harrison	c/o Winchester RFC Tel: 01962 867021 (B)

Ground: North Walls Park, off Nuns Road, Winchester SO23 7EF Tel: 01962 867021

Directions: M3, Junction 9, A34/A33 signed to Basingstoke. Left at Kingsworthy on B3047. After 1.7 miles turn left into Arthur Rd, right at the end, left into Nuns Rd and ground is 50 metres on left at end.

Colours: Black with amber band **Change colours:** All red

WOODFORD R.F.C.

Founded: 1924

President	R de Berry, 2 Lodge Villas, Woodford Green, Essex IG8 9DC 0181 505 7098 (H)
Chairman	D Shepherd, Randmoor Cottage, Robins Lane, Coppice Row, Theydon Bois, Essex CM16 7DS Tel/Fax: 01992 814903 (H)
Secretary	N A R Pearce 33 Forest Drive West, Leytonstone, London E11 1JZ 0181 539 8184 (H) 0181 925 1029 (Fax)
Director of Rugby	I Palmer 21 Forest Way, Woodford Green, Essex IG8 0QF 0181 504 3694 (H)
Fixture Secretary	M A Whiteley 62 Beresford Road, London E4 6EF 0181 524 2737 (H) 0171 865 5972 (B)
Publicity	H Colley 7 Fairlight Avenue, Woodford Green, Essex IG8 9JP 0181 505 7016 (H)

Ground Address:`Highams`, High Road, Woodford Green, Essex IG8 9LB Tel: 0181 504 6769
Capacity: 1,000 approx - uncovered standing **Car Parking:** Limited spaces at ground

Directions: A406 North Circular road to junction with A104. Take northbound exit signed to Woodford Green & Epping past the Napier Arms pub to trinagle. Entrance opposite green with signboard.
Nearest Railway Station: Woodford (Central Line, Underground) then 15 minute walk.

Admission: Nil

Clubhouse: Normal licensing hours, also available for private functions **Club Shop:** Open matchdays & Sun am.

Colours: Lavender, black & white **Change colours:** All red **Training Nights:** Tuesday and Thursday.

Programme Size: A5 Price: £2.00 Pages: Varies Editor: Harold Colley 0181 505 7016 (H)
Advertising Rates Colour - £90 per half page

LONDON & SOUTH EAST DIVISION FINAL TABLES 1998-99

LONDON TWO NORTH

	P	W	D	L	PF	PA	PD	Pts
Cambridge	16	14	1	1	652	118	534	29
Ipswich	16	13	2	1	563	144	419	28
Diss	16	12	1	3	451	179	272	25
Bishop's Stortford	16	11	1	4	422	289	133	23
Old Verulamians	16	11	0	5	452	229	223	22
Harpenden	16	10	0	6	427	307	120	20
Old Albanians	16	9	1	6	342	335	7	19
Welwyn*	16	9	1	6	226	299	-73	17
Finchley	16	7	1	8	290	244	46	15
Old Merch Taylors	16	5	1	10	258	398	-140	11
R'ford & Gidea Pk	16	5	1	10	159	428	-269	11
Braintree	16	5	0	11	200	422	-222	10
Brentwood*	16	6	0	10	143	378	-235	10
Lowestoft & Yar	16	4	1	11	265	312	-47	9
Barnet Elizabethans	16	4	1	11	279	371	-92	9
Colchester	16	2	0	14	185	517	-332	4
Chingford*	16	3	0	13	191	535	-344	4

LONDON THREE NORTH EAST

	P	W	D	L	PF	PA	PD	Pts
Chelmsford	16	13	2	1	349	115	234	28
Shelford	16	12	0	4	308	200	108	24
Basildon	16	11	0	5	527	288	239	22
Campion	16	10	1	5	402	225	177	21
Hadleigh	16	10	0	6	419	216	203	20
Rochford Hundred	16	9	2	5	343	211	132	20
West Norfolk	16	9	2	5	317	257	60	20
Canvey Island	16	8	1	7	271	375	-104	17
Bury St. Edmunds	16	8	0	8	308	204	104	16
Eton Manor	16	7	0	9	273	315	-42	14
Wymondham	16	6	1	9	170	270	-100	13
Maldon	16	6	1	9	233	343	-110	13
Newmarket	16	6	0	10	270	305	-35	12
Holt	16	5	0	11	210	463	-253	10
Woodbridge*	16	5	0	11	254	378	-124	8
Old Edwardians*	16	4	2	10	234	375	-141	8
Bancroft	16	1	0	15	143	491	-348	2

LONDON THREE NORTH WEST

	P	W	D	L	PF	PA	PD	Pts
London Nigerians	16	16	0	0	535	124	411	32
Hertford	16	13	0	3	404	200	204	26
Fullerians	16	11	1	4	344	178	166	23
Grasshoppers	16	10	1	5	355	242	113	21
Twickenham	16	10	1	5	341	288	53	21
Old Gaytonians	16	10	0	6	264	251	13	20
Hampstead	16	8	0	8	313	310	3	16
Kingsburians	16	8	0	8	245	285	-40	16
Old Millhillians	16	7	1	8	241	259	-18	15
Uxbridge	16	7	0	9	286	271	15	14
Ealing	16	7	0	9	264	256	8	14
Chiswick	16	6	0	10	189	270	-81	12
Tring	16	6	0	10	236	329	-93	12
Letchworth Gdn C	16	5	0	11	254	318	-64	10
St Albans	16	4	0	12	263	472	-209	8
Mill Hill	16	4	0	12	144	361	-217	8
Lensbury	16	2	0	14	155	419	-264	4

LONDON TWO SOUTH

	P	W	D	L	PF	PA	PD	Pts
Winchester	14	14	0	0	474	138	336	28
Sevenoaks	14	12	0	2	492	127	365	24
Haywards Heath	14	12	0	2	507	157	350	24
Gravesend	14	10	0	4	300	202	98	20
Lewes	14	9	0	5	385	265	120	18
Alton	14	9	0	5	236	218	18	18
Old Blues	14	8	0	6	243	216	27	16
Dorking	14	7	1	6	245	248	-3	15
Canterbury*	14	7	0	7	411	288	123	12
Old Wimbledonians	14	5	0	9	217	313	-96	10
Beckenham	14	3	1	10	218	368	-150	7
Warlingham	14	3	0	11	166	343	-177	6
Old Guildfordians	14	2	0	12	154	358	-204	4
Old Juddian*	14	3	0	11	147	579	-432	4
Askeans	14	0	0	14	86	461	-375	0

LONDON THREE SOUTH EAST

	P	W	D	L	PF	PA	PD	Pts
Maidstone	15	15	0	0	629	122	507	30
Brighton	15	11	1	3	352	199	153	23
East Grinstead	15	10	0	5	323	225	98	20
Eastbourne	15	10	0	5	289	208	81	20
Tunbridge Wells	15	10	0	5	285	275	10	20
Folkestone	15	9	1	5	286	177	109	19
Sidcup	15	9	0	6	384	207	177	18
Hthfield & Wald'n	15	8	1	6	222	218	4	17
Worthing	15	8	0	7	275	189	86	16
Cranbrook	15	7	0	8	227	247	-20	14
Crawley	15	5	1	9	251	304	-53	11
Park House	15	5	1	9	213	306	-93	11
Chichester	15	5	0	10	220	282	-62	10
Beccehamian	15	3	0	12	159	490	-331	6
Medway	15	1	1	13	136	381	-245	3
Uckfield	15	1	0	14	97	518	-421	2

Sheppey did not play Maidstone and are relegated

LONDON THREE SOUTH WEST

	P	W	D	L	PF	PA	PD	Pts
Eff'ham & L'head	17	16	0	1	508	140	368	32
Jersey	17	15	0	2	512	159	353	30
Gosport & F'ham	17	14	0	3	685	143	542	28
Portsmouth	17	13	0	4	445	209	236	26
Old Emanuel	17	13	0	4	503	294	209	26
Andover	17	11	0	6	422	182	240	22
Barnes	17	10	0	7	412	303	109	20
Purley John Fisher	17	10	0	7	332	284	48	20
Cranleigh	17	10	0	7	331	294	37	20
Old Whitgiftians	17	9	0	8	316	362	-46	18
Old Alleynian	17	7	0	10	296	312	-16	14
University Vandals	17	7	0	10	260	356	-96	14
Old Reedonians	17	6	0	11	320	379	-59	12
Southampton	17	6	0	11	350	432	-82	12
Esso (Fawley)	17	2	0	15	229	466	-237	4
Old Reigatian	17	2	0	15	178	657	-479	4
Farnborough	17	1	0	16	164	608	-444	2
Streatham-Croydon*	17	1	0	16	152	835	-683	0

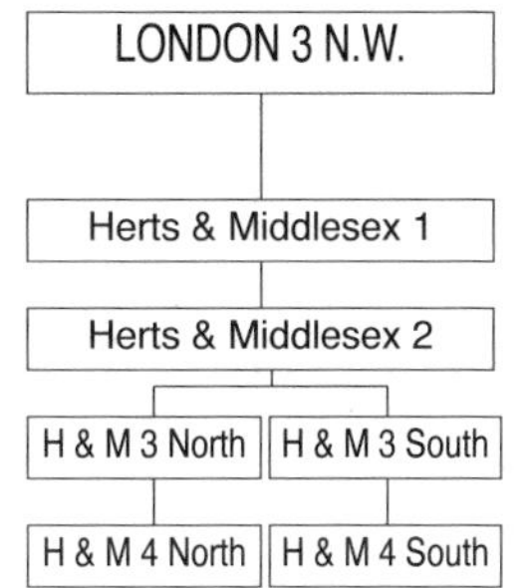

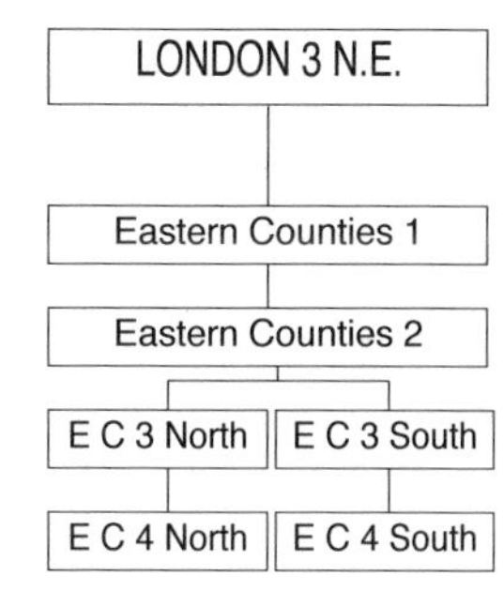

HERTS/MIDDLESEX ONE

	P	W	D	L	PF	PA	PD	Pts
Imperial Medicals	13	12	0	1	404	85	319	24
Hemel Hempstead	13	11	1	1	324	89	235	23
London N Zealand	13	9	0	4	282	189	93	18
Harrow	13	9	0	4	220	155	65	18
Feltham	13	8	1	4	241	200	41	17
U.C.S. Old Boys	13	7	1	5	241	224	17	15
Upper Clapton	13	6	0	7	212	265	-53	12
Civil Service	13	5	0	8	181	218	-37	10
Enfield Ignatians	13	4	1	8	195	221	-26	9
Stevenage Town	13	4	0	9	155	225	-70	8
Old Hamptonians	13	4	0	9	188	299	-111	8
Old Haberdashers	13	3	0	10	132	327	-195	6
H.A.C.*	13	5	0	8	284	303	-19	4
Haringey	13	2	0	11	128	387	-259	4

HERTS/MIDDLESEX TWO

	P	W	D	L	PF	PA	PD	Pts
Bank Of England	11	9	0	2	327	123	204	18
Hitchin	11	9	0	2	285	147	138	18
St Nicholas O.B.	11	8	0	3	268	117	151	16
London French	11	6	0	5	236	154	82	12
Datchworth	11	5	1	5	193	173	20	11
Old Actonians	11	5	0	6	216	191	25	10
Barclays Bank*	11	6	1	4	333	163	170	9
Old Abbotstonians	11	4	1	6	198	190	8	9
H'smith & Fulham	11	4	0	7	179	231	-52	8
Hendon*	11	4	1	6	112	286	-174	7
Roxeth Mnr OB*	11	4	0	7	143	276	-133	6
Wembley*	11	0	0	11	55	494	-439	-2

HERTS/MIDDLESEX THREE

	P	W	D	L	PF	PA	PD	Pts
Northolt	12	11	0	1	255	102	153	22
Southgate	12	9	0	3	204	109	95	18
Quintin	12	9	0	3	168	125	43	18
Old Tottonians	12	8	0	4	193	135	58	16
London Exiles*	12	8	1	3	366	90	276	15
Old Isleworthians	12	7	1	4	218	132	86	15
Old Streetonians	12	7	0	5	239	158	81	14
Old Ashmoleans	12	5	0	7	230	262	-32	10
Old Grammarians	12	5	0	7	135	170	-35	10
British Airways	12	3	0	9	114	264	-150	6
Millfield O.B.*	12	3	0	9	179	316	-137	4
Watford	12	1	1	10	85	226	-141	3
Royston*	12	0	1	11	119	416	-297	-1

EAST COUNTIES ONE

	P	W	D	L	PF	PA	PD	Pts
Thetford	18	17	0	1	504	148	356	34
Ely	18	13	1	4	508	190	318	27
Cantabrigian	18	10	1	7	315	259	56	21
Upminster	18	10	0	8	323	298	25	20
Saffron Walden	18	9	1	8	244	253	-9	19
Westcliff	18	8	0	10	195	322	-127	16
Felixstowe	18	7	0	11	251	306	-55	14
Met. Police, Chig.	18	6	1	11	195	400	-205	13
Ilford Wanderers	18	5	0	13	234	362	-128	10
Wanstead	18	3	0	15	182	413	-231	6

EAST COUNTIES TWO

	P	W	D	L	PF	PA	PD	Pts
Billericay	16	16	0	0	875	58	817	32
Old Cooperians	16	10	1	5	334	208	126	21
Mersea Island	16	10	0	6	364	214	150	20
South Woodham F	16	9	1	6	277	213	64	19
H'wich & D'court	16	8	0	8	246	351	-105	16
Beccles	16	6	1	9	174	464	-290	13
Thames	16	6	0	10	242	353	-111	12
Old Palmerians	16	4	0	12	166	371	-205	8
Southwold*	16	1	1	14	154	600	-446	1

EAST COUNTIES THREE NORTH

	P	W	D	L	PF	PA	PD	Pts
Wisbech	16	15	1	0	478	78	400	31
Crusaders	16	12	2	2	409	101	308	26
Ipswich Y.M.	16	11	1	4	315	124	191	23
Broadland	16	8	2	6	233	223	10	18
Swaffham	16	7	0	9	226	332	-106	14
Lakenham Hewett*	16	6	2	8	178	241	-63	12
Thurston	16	6	0	10	189	288	-99	12
Stowmarket	16	1	0	15	123	355	-232	2
March BRAZA*	16	2	0	14	113	522	-409	2

EAST COUNTIES THREE SOUTH

	P	W	D	L	PF	PA	PD	Pts
East London	14	13	0	1	480	105	375	26
Stanford Le Hope	14	11	1	2	485	124	361	23
Old Brentwoods	14	7	1	6	342	215	127	15
Ravens	14	6	2	6	198	263	-65	14
Ongar	14	5	2	7	201	310	-109	12
Sawston	14	4	1	9	173	302	-129	9
Burnham-Crouch	14	4	0	10	134	322	-188	8
Witham	14	2	1	11	174	546	-372	5

HERTS/MIDDLESEX FOUR NORTH

	P	W	D	L	PF	PA	PD	Pts
Chess Valley	10	9	0	1	259	104	155	18
Cuffley	10	8	1	1	335	62	273	17
Kilburn Cosmos	10	5	0	5	297	163	134	10
Belsize Park	10	4	1	5	138	176	-38	9
Q.E.II Hospital	10	1	0	9	60	295	-235	2
Hatfield*	10	2	0	8	62	351	-289	0

HERTS/MIDDLESEX FOUR SOUTH

	P	W	D	L	PF	PA	PD	Pts
London Tribes*	10	10	0	0	521	63	458	16
Pinner & Grams	10	8	0	2	369	136	233	16
Osterley	10	5	0	5	200	296	-96	10
G.W.R.*	10	4	0	6	209	272	-63	4
Orleans F.P.*	10	3	0	7	157	239	-82	4
Hayes	10	0	0	10	29	479	-450	0

EAST COUNTIES FOUR NORTH

	P	W	D	L	PF	PA	PD	Pts
Brightlingsea	8	8	0	0	233	75	158	16
Norwich Union	8	6	0	2	180	81	99	12
Clacton	8	4	0	4	208	101	107	8
Mistley	8	1	0	7	107	210	-103	2
RAF Lakenheath	8	1	0	7	38	299	-261	2

EAST COUNTIES FOUR SOUTH

	P	W	D	L	PF	PA	PD	Pts
Millwall Albion	12	10	0	2	481	103	378	20
May & Baker	12	8	0	4	247	135	112	16
Old Bealonians	12	7	0	5	219	194	25	14
Haverhill & District	12	6	0	6	220	142	78	12
Dagenham	12	5	0	7	226	316	-90	10
Rayleigh Wyverns	12	4	0	8	172	242	-70	8
Pegasus	12	2	0	10	108	541	-433	4

KENT ONE

	P	W	D	L	PF	PA	PD	Pts
Dartfordians	16	15	1	0	759	156	603	31
Guy's Hospital*	16	15	1	0	728	161	567	29
Ashford	16	11	0	5	303	220	83	22
Old Dunstonians*	16	11	0	5	387	240	147	20
O Shootershillians	16	9	0	7	255	269	-14	18
Brockleians	16	7	2	7	211	208	3	16
Lordswood	16	7	2	7	225	239	-14	16
Whitstable	16	8	0	8	277	296	-19	16
Gillingham Anch.	16	7	1	8	212	217	-5	15
Tonbridge	16	7	1	8	229	323	-94	15
Midland Bank	16	7	0	9	273	327	-54	14
Dover*	16	6	3	7	207	272	-65	13
Bromley	16	6	0	10	237	377	-140	12
Nat. West. Bank	16	5	1	10	234	362	-128	11
Betteshanger	16	4	1	11	163	427	-264	9
Sittingbourne*	16	3	0	13	162	405	-243	4
Met. Police, Hayes	16	1	1	14	163	526	-363	3

KENT TWO

	P	W	D	L	PF	PA	PD	Pts
New Ash Green	13	13	0	0	540	105	435	26
Old Elthamians	13	11	0	2	407	100	307	22
Aylesford	13	10	0	3	272	123	149	20
Erith	13	9	0	4	255	131	124	18
O Williamsonians*	13	8	1	4	221	161	60	15
Snowdown CW*	13	8	0	5	251	166	85	14
Old Gravesendians	13	6	0	7	196	318	-122	12
Foots Cray	13	4	2	7	175	223	-48	10
Bexley*	13	5	1	7	236	242	-6	9
Deal Wanderers*	13	5	1	7	185	214	-29	9
Old Olavians	13	4	1	8	149	234	-85	9
Faversham*	13	3	1	9	120	279	-159	5
Orpington	13	0	1	12	85	488	-403	1
Vigo*	13	1	0	12	73	381	-308	0

KENT THREE

	P	W	D	L	PF	PA	PD	Pts
Greenwich	6	5	1	0	154	21	133	11
Darenth Valley*	6	4	0	2	116	66	50	6
Greenwich Acad	6	1	2	3	59	157	-98	4
Edenbridge*	6	0	1	5	36	121	-85	-1

LONDON 3 S.E.

Kent 1 | Sussex 1

Kent 2 East | Sussex 2

Kent 2 West | Sussex 3

SUSSEX ONE

	P	W	D	L	PF	PA	PD	Pts
Hove	16	16	0	0	476	84	392	32
Crowborough	16	13	0	3	544	134	410	26
Bognor	16	11	1	4	635	177	458	23
Seaford	16	10	1	5	322	179	143	21
Royal Sun Allnce	16	8	0	8	205	269	-64	16
Hastings & Bexhill	16	6	1	9	344	292	52	13
Old Brightonians	16	4	0	12	256	460	-204	8
Ditchling*	16	2	0	14	124	877	-753	2
Burgess Hill	16	0	1	15	171	605	-434	1

SUSSEX TWO

	P	W	D	L	PF	PA	PD	Pts
Pulborough	14	11	1	2	472	136	336	23
Hellingly	14	11	0	3	419	168	251	22
Chichester IHE*	14	10	1	3	418	204	214	19
Newick	14	6	1	7	143	149	-6	13
B.A. Wingspan	14	6	0	8	224	286	-62	12
Shoreham	14	4	1	9	124	314	-190	9
St Francis*	14	5	0	9	245	261	-16	8
Robertsbridge*	14	1	0	13	61	588	-527	0

SUSSEX THREE

	P	W	D	L	PF	PA	PD	Pts
Plumpton	10	9	1	0	239	76	163	19
Sussex Police	10	6	1	3	200	197	3	13
Rye	10	6	0	4	258	70	188	12
Midhurst	10	4	0	6	149	254	-105	8
Arun	10	3	0	7	120	172	-52	6
Barns Green	10	1	0	9	65	262	-197	2

LONDON 3 S.W.

Hampshire 1 | Surrey 1

Hampshire 2 | Surrey 2

Hampshire 3 | Surrey 3

Surrey 4

HAMPSHIRE ONE

	P	W	D	L	PF	PA	PD	Pts
Tottonians	18	16	0	2	536	170	366	32
Trojans	18	12	0	6	453	288	165	24
Utd Serv, Portsmth	18	11	1	6	408	261	147	23
Ventnor	18	11	0	7	369	196	173	22
Petersfield	18	11	0	7	349	213	136	22
Millbrook	18	11	0	7	401	367	34	22
Isle Of Wight*	18	9	1	8	332	329	3	17
Guernsey*	18	5	0	13	303	428	-125	8
Eastleigh	18	3	0	15	176	540	-364	6
Overton	18	0	0	18	180	715	-535	0

HAMPSHIRE TWO

	P	W	D	L	PF	PA	PD	Pts
Romsey	14	11	1	2	281	172	109	23
N Milton & Dist	14	9	1	4	370	186	184	19
Sthampton Inst*	14	7	4	3	372	247	125	14
Fareham Heathens	14	6	0	8	196	169	27	12
Hamble	14	6	0	8	227	246	-19	12
Nomads	14	5	1	8	212	298	-86	11
S'down & Shanklin	14	4	1	9	189	313	-124	9
Fordingbridge	14	4	0	10	162	378	-216	8

*Points deducted

HAMPSHIRE THREE

	P	W	D	L	PF	PA	PD	Pts
A.C. Delco*	16	15	0	1	521	95	426	28
Chineham	16	12	0	4	501	222	279	24
Alresford	16	12	0	4	396	150	246	24
Fleet	16	11	0	5	456	154	302	22
Kingsclere	16	7	0	9	322	290	32	14
Univ of Portsmth*	16	7	1	8	506	265	241	13
Ell'ham & R'wood	16	5	0	11	194	363	-169	
Waterlooville*	16	2	1	13	150	445	-295	1
Brockenhurst	16	0	0	16	56	1118	-1062	0

SURREY ONE

	P	W	D	L	PF	PA	PD	Pts
Cobham	12	12	0	0	369	106	263	24
Chobham	12	10	0	2	368	144	224	20
Woking	12	9	0	3	317	143	174	18
Old Cranleighans	12	8	0	4	254	165	89	16
Farnham	12	8	0	4	259	185	74	16
Old Walcountians	12	6	1	5	191	234	-43	13
Raynes Park	12	4	2	6	148	215	-67	10
K.C.S. Old Boys	12	4	1	7	211	221	-10	9
Old Paulines	12	4	0	8	175	207	-32	8
Old Caterhamians	12	3	2	7	144	249	-105	8
Merton	12	2	2	8	95	258	-163	6
Chipstead	12	2	1	9	104	315	-211	5
Wandsworthians	12	0	3	9	143	336	-193	3

SURREY TWO

	P	W	D	L	PF	PA	PD	Pts
Old Tiffinians	12	11	0	1	397	149	248	22
Kingston	12	9	0	3	317	134	183	18
Battersea Ironsides	12	9	0	3	251	130	121	18
Teddington	12	8	0	4	241	206	35	16
Old Rutlishians	12	7	1	4	232	124	108	15
O Wellingtonians	12	7	1	4	260	211	49	15
Law Society	12	7	0	5	301	268	33	14
London Media	12	6	0	6	192	271	-79	12
Old Haileyburians	12	4	1	7	156	211	-55	9
Shirley Wanderers	12	3	0	9	114	194	-80	6
London Fire Brig	12	2	1	9	95	245	-150	5
Reigate & Redhill	12	2	1	9	119	377	-258	5
London Cornish	12	0	1	11	161	316	-155	1

SURREY THREE

	P	W	D	L	PF	PA	PD	Pts
Haslemere	10	9	0	1	393	101	292	18
Mitcham	10	9	0	1	244	111	133	18
Old Freemans	10	7	0	3	228	98	130	14
Lightwater*	10	5	0	5	179	142	37	8
Egham	10	4	0	6	111	166	-55	8
Croydon	10	3	1	6	83	236	-153	7
Kings Coll. Hosp*	10	4	0	6	130	148	-18	6
Bec Old Boys*	10	5	0	5	163	223	-60	6
Worth Old Boys*	10	4	0	6	166	251	-85	4
Univ of Surrey*	10	2	1	7	161	254	-93	3
Old Suttonians*	10	2	0	8	127	255	-128	2

SURREY FOUR

	P	W	D	L	PF	PA	PD	Pts
Old Bevonians*	4	4	0	0	106	33	73	6
Old Johnians*	4	2	0	2	74	70	4	0
Economicals	4	0	0	4	37	114	-77	0

Surrey Police Withdrawn - all results and fixtures removed.

LONDON TWO NORTH

	Barnet Eliz	Bishops Stort	Braintree	Brentwood	Chelmsford	Diss	Finchley	Harpenden	Ipswich	London Nig.	Lowestoft & Y	Olad Albanians	Old Merch T	Old Verulamians	Romford & GP	Southend	Welwyn
Barnet Eliz		15.1		11.9	2.10	12.2					25.3	23.10			27.11		18.12
Bishops Stortford			11.12	26.2	25.3					8.1	29.1	11.9			2.10		23.10
Braintree	29.1					8.1	2.10	11.9	27.11				25.3	26.2		23.10	
Brentwood			11.3				18.12	27.11	12.2	8.4	25.9		23.10			15.1	
Chelmsford			8.4	20.11			15.1	18.12	11.3	25.9	9.10					12.2	
Diss		18.12		25.3	11.9					29.1	26.2	2.10			23.10		27.11
Finchley	20.11	25.9				9.10		29.1					8.1	11.12	11.3		8.4
Harpenden	9.10	8.4				25.9						15.1	11.12	20.11	12.1		11.3
Ipswich	8.1	20.11				11.12	11.9	25.3					26.2	29.1		2.10	
London Nigerian	26.2		15.1				23.10	2.10	18.12				11.9	25.3		27.11	
Lowestoft & Yar			12.2				27.11	23.10	15.1	11.3			2.10	11.9		18.12	
Old Albanians			25.9	11.12	8.1		12.2		8.4	9.10	20.11					11.3	
Old Merch Taylors	25.9	11.3			27.11	8.4						18.12		9.10	15.1		12.2
Old Verulamians	8.4	12.2		2.10	23.10	11.3						27.11			18.12		15.1
Romford & GP			9.10	8.1	29.1				25.9	20.11	11.12	26.2				8.4	
Southend	11.12	9.10				20.11	25.3	26.2					29.1	8.1			25.9
Welwyn			20.11	29.1	26.2				9.10	11.12	8.1	25.3			11.9		

LONDON THREE NORTH EAST

	Basildon	Bury St Ed	Campion	Canvey Island	Chingford	Colchester	Ely	Eton Manor	Hadleigh	Holt	Maldon	Newmarket	Rochford	Shelford	Thetford	West Norfolk	Wymondham
Basildon				23.11	15.1				25.3		2.10	12.2	11.9		23.10		18.12
Bury St. Edmunds	11.12		26.2		9.10		25.3	8.1				20.11				29.1	25.9
Campion	9.1			12.2	8.4			20.11				25.9			15.1	11.12	11.3
Canvey Island		8.4				25.9			11.12	9.10	29.10		8.1	20.11	29.2		
Chingford				2.10					29.1	11.12	25.3		26.2	8.1	11.9		23.10
Colchester	8.1	2.10	25.3		20.11		11.9	29.1				11.12				26.2	
Ely	20.11		29.1	11.3	25.9			11.12				9.1				8.1	8.4
Eton Manor	8.4			18.12	12.2						23.10	11.3	2.1		27.11		15.1
Hadleigh		18.2	23.10			15.1	27.11	11.9		12.2				11.3		2.10	
Holt	29.1	23.10	11.9			27.11	2.10	26.2				8.1				25.3	
Maldon		12.2	18.2			11.3	15.1		9.10	8.4			20.11	25.9			
Newmarket				23.1	18.12				26.2		11.9		25.3	29.1	2.10		27.10
Rochford		15.1	27.11			12.2	18.2		25.9	11.3				8.4		23.10	
Shelford	26.2	27.11	2.10			18.12	23.10	25.3		15.1						11.9	
Thetford		11.3				8.4	12.2		20.11	25.9	8.1		11.2	9.10			
West Norfolk	25.9			15.1	11.3			9.10			27.11	8.4			18.12		12.2
Wymondham				11.9		9.10			8.1	20.1	26.2		29.1	11.12	25.3		

EASTERN COUNTIES ONE

	Bancroft	Billericay	Cantabrigians	Felixstowe	Old Cooperians	Old Edwardians	Saffron Walden	Upminster	Westcliff	Woodbridge
Bancroft		9.10	11.9	26.2	29.1	20.11	8.4	8.1	11.12	25.9
Billericay	12.2		2.10	23.10	8.1	11.12	11.3	8.4	11.9	20.11
Cantabrigians	25.3	26.2		25.9	9.10	29.1	11.2	20.11	8.1	8.4
Felixstowe	2.1	29.1	11.3		20.11	8.1	11.9	11.12	8.4	9.10
Old Cooperians	23.10	27.11	12.2	15.1		8.4	2.1	11.9	11.3	11.9
Old Edwardians	15.1	15.4	23.10	27.11	18.2		12.2	11.3	2.10	25.3
Safrfron Walden	18.12	25.9	15.4	25.3	26.2	9.10		29.1	20.11	8.1
Upminster	27.11	18.12	15.1	15.4	25.3	25.4	23.10		12.2	26.2
Westcliff	15.4	25.3	27.11	18.10	25.9	26.2	15.1	9.1		29.1
Woodbridge	11.3	15.1	18.12	12.2	15.4	11.9	27.11	2.10	23.10	

EASTERN COUNTIES TWO

	Beccles	East London	Harwich & Dov	Ilford Wndrs	Mersea Island	Met Pol. Chig	Thames	S Woodham F	Wanstead	Wisbech
Beccles		23.10	25.3	27.11	15.1	11.3	2.10	15.4	12.2	18.12
East London	29.1		8.4	25.9	25.3	20.11	8.1	26.2	11.12	9.10
Harwich & Dover	11.9	18.12		12.2	11.3	2.10	23.10	15.1	27.11	15.4
Ilford Wanderers	8.1	11.3	9.10		2.10	11.12	8.4	29.1	11.9	20.11
Mersea Island	20.11	11.9	25.9	26.2		8.1	11.12	9.10	8.4	29.11
Met. Police, Chigwell	25.9	15.1	26.2	15.4	27.11		12.2	18.2	23.10	25.3
Thames	26.2	27.11	29.1	18.12	15.4	9.10		25.3	15.1	25.9
S. Woodham Ferrers	11.12	2.10	20.11	23.10	12.2	8.4	11.9		11.3	8.1
Wanstead	9.1	15.4	8.1	25.3	18.12	29.1	20.11	25.9		26.2
Wisbech	8.4	12.2	11.12	15.1	23.10	11.9	11.3	27.11	2.10	

EASTERN COUNTIES THREE NORTH

	Broadland	Crusaders	Ipswich YM	Lakenham H	Norwich Union	Sawston	Southwold	Swaffham	Thurston
Broadland		15.1	15.4	2.10	11.3	23.10	11.9	27.11	12.2
Crusaders	20.11		8.1	8.4	12.2	11.9	11.12	11.3	23.10
Ipswich YM	11.2	27.11		11.9	23.10	11.3	8.4	2.10	15.1
Lakenham Hewett	26.2	18.12	25.3		27.11	12.2	25.9	23.10	15.4
Norwich Union	25.9	9.10	29.1	831		11.12	20.11	8.4	26.2
Sawston	29.1	25.3	25.9	9.10	15.4		26.2	15.1	18.12
Southwold	25.3	15.4	18.12	11.3	15.1	2.1		12.2	27.11
Swaffham	8.1	25.9	26.2	29.1	18.12	20.11	9.10		25.3
Thurston	9.10	29.1	20.11	11.12	2.10	8.4	8.1	11.9	

EASTERN COUNTIES THREE SOUTH

	Brightlingsea	Burnham on C	May & Baker	Millwall Albion	Old Brentwoods	Old Palmerians	Ongar	Ravens	Stanford le H
Brightlingsea		8.4	11.9	20.11	2.10	9.10	29.1	11.12	8.1
Burnham-on -Crouch	18.2		15.1	25.9	15.4	29.1	25.3	9.10	26.2
May & Baker	25.3	20.11		26.2	18.12	8.1	25.9	29.1	9.10
Millwall Albion	15.1	11.3	2.10		23.10	11.12	27.11	11.9	8.4
Old Brentwoods	26.2	11.12	8.4	29.1		25.9	9.10	8.1	20.11
Old Palmerians	12.2	23.10	27.11	15.4	11.3		15.1	2.10	11.9
Ongar	23.10	11.9	11.3	8.1	12.2	20.11		8.4	11.12
Ravens	15.4	12.2	23.10	25.3	27.11	26.2	18.2		25.9
Stanford Le Hope	27.11	2.10	12.2	18.12	15.11	25.3	15.4	11.3	

EASTERN COUNTIES FOUR NORTH

	American Ex	Clacton	Eccles	Haverhill	March	Mistley	Stowmarket
American Exiles		27.11	11.3	12.2	18.2	83.4	2.10
Clacton	26.2		25.9	25.3	29.12	20.11	11.12
Eccles	11.12	15.12		8.1	20.11	26.12	25.3
Haverhill	20.11	18.12	8.4		25.9	29.12	26.2
March	25.3	2.10	12.2	15.12		11.12	8.12
Mistley	8.12	12.2	27.11	2.10	11.3		15.12
Stowmarket	29.12	11.3	18.12	27.11	8.4	25.9	

EASTERN COUNTIES FOUR SOUTH

	Dagenham	Loughton	Old Bealonians	Pegasus	Rayleigh	Witham
Dagenham		2.10	12.2	27.11	11.3	15.1
Loughton	29.1		11.3	25.9	27.11	20.11
Old Bealonians	20.11	11.12		29.1	15.1	26.2
Pegasus	26.2	15.1	2.10		12.2	11.12
Rayleigh	11.12	26.2	25.9	20.11		29.1
Witham	25.9	12.2	27.11	11.3	2.10	

LONDON THREE NORTH WEST

	Chiswick	Ealing	Fullerians	Grasshoppers	Hampstead	Hemel Hemp.	Hertford	Imperial Meds	Kingsburians	Letchworth	Mill Hill	Old Gaytonians	Old Millhillians	St Albans	Tring	Twickenham	Uxbridge
Chiswick		11.9	18.12	2.10		25.3			27.11		15.1				23.10	26.2	
Ealing					11.3	9.10	15.1					27.11	18.12	8.4		25.9	12.2
Fullerians		26.2		25.3	20.11	29.1			2.10					11.12	11.9	8.1	
Grasshoppers		11.12			8.4	20.11	12.2						15.1	25.9		9.10	11.3
Hampstead	8.1						2.10	29.1		26.2	11.12	25.3	11.9				23.10
Hemel Hempstead					12.2		18.12			2.10		23.10	27.10	11.3		8.4	15.1
Hertford	20.11		25.9					11.12	8.4	8.1	9.10	29.1	26.2				
Imperial Medicals	11.3	2.10	15.1	23.10		11.9			18.12		12.2				27.11		
KIngsburians		29.1		26.2	9.10	8.1								20.11	25.3	11.12	25.9
Letchworth	8.4	23.10	12.2	27.11				25.9	15.1		11.3				18.12		
Mill Hill		25.3	27.11	11.9		26.2			23.10					8.1	2.10	29.1	
Old Gaytonians	25.9		11.3	18.12				9.10	12.2	20.11	8.4				15.1		
Old Millhillians	9.1		8.4					20.11	11.3	11.12	25.9	8.1			12.2		
St. Albans	29.1				18.12		23.10	26.2		25.3		11.9	2.10				27.11
Tring		8.1		29.1	25.9	11.12	11.3							9.10		20.11	8.4
Twickenham					15.1		27.11	25.3		11.9		2.10	23.10	12.2			18.12
Uxbridge	11.12		9.10				11.9	8.1		29.1	20.11	26.2	25.3				

HERTS/ MIDDLESEX ONE

	Bank of England	Civil Service	Enfield Ignatian	Feltham	Hackney	Haringey	Harrow	Hitchin	Lensbury	London NZ	O Haberdashers	Old Hamptons	Stevenage	UCS Old Boys	Upper Clapton
Bank of England		23.10	15.1			18.12	27.11			25.3		26.2		25.9	
Civil Service				11.3	2.10			8.4		11.12	12.2	20.11		8.1	
Enfield Ignation		25.9			8.1	27.11	23.10			26.2		29.1		25.3	
Feltham	11.12		20.11			2.10			8.1		25.3		26.2		29.1
Hackney	29.1			27.11				18.12	26.2		23.10		25.9		25.3
Haringey		25.3			11.122		25.9	20.11		29.1		8.1		26.2	
Harrow		26.2		8.4	20.11			2.10		8.1		11.12		29.1	
Hitchin	8.1		11.12	23.10					29.1		25.9		25.3		26.2
Lensbury	11.3	27.11	12.2			15.1	18.12			25.9				23.10	
London NewZealand				15.11	11.3			12.2			18.12	8.4	27.11		23.10
Old Haberdashers	20.11		2.10			8.4	11.3		11.12				29.1		8.1
Old Hamptonians				18.12	12.2			15.1	25.3		27.11		23.10		25.9
Stevenage	2.10	15.1	8.4			11.3	12.2		20.11						11.12
UCS Old Boys				12.2	8.4			11.3		20.11	15.1	2.10	18.12		
Upper Clapton	8.4	18.12	11.3			12.2	15.1		2.10					27.11	

HERTS/ MIDDLESEX TWO

	Barclays Bank	Datchworth	Hammersmith	Hendon	London French	Northolt	O Abbotstonian	Old Actonians	Old Tottonians	Quinton	Roxeth Manor	St Nicholas OB	Southgate	Wembley
Barclays Bank			11.3		27.11		12.2		18.12		15.1			2.10
Datchworth	11.12		20.11				25.9	8.1	12.2		11.3			
Hammersmith & Fulham					2.10	26.2	15.1		27.10		18.12		12.2	25.3
Hendon	29.1	25.3	8.1				11.2	26.2		2.10			27.11	
London French		15.1		11.3		20.11				12.2		25.9		11.12
Northholt	25.3	27.11		15.1				2.10		18.12		12.2	11.3	
Old Abbotstonian					25.3	29.1			2.10		27.11	8.1	18.12	26.2
Old Actonians	20.11		25.9		18.12		11.3		15.1		12.2			
Old Tottonians				25.9	29.1	11.12				11.3		20.11		8.1
Quinton	8.1	26.2	11.12				20.11	29.1			25.9			
Roxeth Manor Old Boys				20.11	26.2	8.1			25.3			11.2	2.10	29.1
St. Nicholas Old Boys	26.2	2.10	29.1	18.12				25.3		27.11			15.1	
Southgate	25.9	29.1			8.1			11.12	26.2	25.3				20.11
Wembley		18.12		12.2		25.9		27.11		15.1		11.3		

HERTS/ MIDDLESEX THREE NORTH

	Cuffley	Hackney	Old Ashmolean	O Grammarian	Old Streetonian	Royston	Watford
Cuffley		25.9	29.1	20.11	26.2	11.12	25.3
Hackney	15.1		20.11	26.2	11.12	25.3	8.1
Old Ashmolean	2.10	12.2		11.12	25.3	8.1	15.1
Old Grammarian	12.2	27.11	11.3		8.1	15.1	2.10
Old Streetonian	27.11	11.3	18.12	8.4		2.10	12.2
Royston	11.3	18.12	8.4	25.9	29.1		27.11
Watford	18.12	8.4	25.9	29.1	20.1	26.2	

HERTS/ MIDDLESEX THREE SOUTH

	British Air	Chess Valley	London Ex	London T	Millfield OB	Old Isleworth	Pinner & G
British Airways		25.9	29.1	20.11	26.2	11.12	25.3
Chess Valley	15.1		20.11	26.2	11.12	25.3	8.1
London Exiles	2.10	12.2		11.12	25.3	8.1	15.1
London Tribes	12.2	27.11	11.3		8.1	15.1	2.10
Millfield Old Boys	27.11	11.3	18.12	8.4		2.10	12.2
Old Isleworthians	11.3	18.2	8.4	25.9	29.1		27.11
Pinner & Grammarians	18.2	8.4	25.9	29.1	20.11	26.2	

HERTS/ MIDDLESEX FOUR NORTH

	Belsize Park	Hatfield	Kilburn C	Q E Hosp	Sudbury C	Ware
Belsize Park		15.1	2.10	12.2	27.11	11.3
Hatfield	25.9		12.2	27.11	11.3	2.10
Kilburn Cosmos	29.1	20.11		11.3	25.9	27.11
Queen Elizabeth Hospital	20.11	26.2	11.12		29.1	15.1
Sudbury Court	26.2	11.12	15.1	2.10		12.2
Ware	11.2	29.1	26.2	25.9	20.11	

HERTS/ MIDDLESEX FOUR SOUTH

	Centaurs	GWR	Hayes	Orleans FP	Osterley	Thamesians
Centaurs		15.1	2.10	12.2	27.11	11.3
G.W.R.	25.9		12.2	27.11	11.3	2.10
Hayes	29.1	20.11		11.3	25.9	27.11
Orleans F.P.	20.11	26.2	11.12		29.1	15.1
Osterley	26.2	11.12	15.1	2.10		12.2
Thamesians	11.2	29.1	26.2	25.9	20.11	

LONDON TWO SOUTH

	Alton	Askeans	Beckenham	Canterbury	Charlton Pk	Dorking	Effingham	Gravesend	Haywards H	Lewes	Maidstone	Old Blues	Old Guild	Old Juddian	Old Wimble.	Sevenoaks	Warlingham
Alton		25.3	8.1		9.10								11.9	28.2	29.1	20.11	11.12
Askeans			20.11	12.2	8.4			11.3						8.1	11.12	25.9	9.10
Beckenham				27.11	15.1		11.9	18.12		2.10		23.10				12.2	11.3
Canterbury	8.4					25.9	11.2		9.10	8.1	20.11	29.1	11.3				
Charlton Park				11.9		20.11	29.11	2.10	11.12	28.2	8.1	25.3					
Dorking	23.10	11.9	29.1										2.10	25.3	28.2	11.12	8.1
Effingham	15.1	27.11				12.2			11.3		8.4		18.12	23.10	2.10		
Gravesend	25.9			25.3		9.10	8.1		20.11	29.1	11.12	28.2					
Haywards Heath	27.11	2.10	28.2			18.12							23.10	11.9	25.3		29.1
Lewes	12.2	18.2				11.3	9.10		8.4		25.9		15.1	27.11			
Maidstone	18.2	23.10	25.3			15.1			12.2				27.11	2.10	11.9		
Old Blues	11.3	15.1				8.4	20.11		25.9	11.12	93.10		12.2				
Old Guildfordian		28.2	11.12		25.9			8.4						29.1	8.1	9.10	20.11
Old Juddian			9.10	15.1	11.3			12.2				18.12			20.11	8.4	25.9
Old Wimbledonian			25.9	18.12	12.2			15.1		23.10		27.11				11.3	8.4
Sevenoaks				2.10	27.11		28.2	23.10	8.1	25.3	29.1	11.9					
Warlingham				23.10	18.12		25.3	27.11		11.9	26.2	2.10				15.1	

LONDON THREE SOUTH WEST

	Andover	Barnes	Cobham	Cranleigh	Esso Fawley	Gosport & F	Jersey	Old Alleynian	Old Emanuel	Old Reedonians	Old Reigatian	Old Whitgiftians	Portsmouth	Purley John F	Southampton	Tottonians	Univ Vandals
Andover		25.9			9.10			11.3	8.1			8.4	29.1		11.12		20.11
Barnes			8.1	26.2		29.1			2.10	11.12	11.9	23.10				25.3	
Cobham	23.10						27.11		11.9	15.1			2.10	18.12	25.3		26.2
Cranleigh	18.12		8.4			25.9	15.1		23.10	11.3			27.11	12.2			
Esso Fawley		18.2	29.1	25.3		26.2		23.10			2.10	27.11				11.9	
Gosport & Fareham	27.11		11.3				18.2	2.10		12.2			23.10	15.1	11.9		
Jersey	25.3	9.10			20.15				29.1			25.9	26.2		8.1		11.12
Old Alleynian			20.11	8.1		11.12	8.4			9.10	26.2			25.9		29.1	
Old Emanuel		11.3			8.4			15.1			18.12	12.2			9.10	27.11	25.9
Old Reedonians	2.10				8.1		23.10		25.3				11.9	27.11	26.2		29.1
Old Reigatian	12.2		9.10	11.12		20.11	21.3			25.9				8.4		8.1	
Old Whitgiftians			11.12	29.1		8.1		11.9		20.11	25.3			9.10		26.2	
Portsmouth		8.4			25.9			12.2	11.12		15.1	11.3			20.11		9.10
Purley John Fisher	11.9	20.11			11.12		2.10		26.2				25.3		29.1		8.1
Southhampton		12.2		2.10	11.3			18.12			27.11	15.1				23.10	8.4
Tottonians	15.1		25.9	20.11		9.10	12.2			8.4			18.12	11.3			
University Vandals		15.1		11.9	12.2	25.3		27.11			23.10	18.12				2.10	

HAMPSHIRE ONE

	Farnborough	Guernsey	Isle of Wight	Millbrook	New Milton	Petersfield	Romsey	Trojans	US Portsmouth	Ventnor
Farnborough		11.9	15.4	11.3	15.1	27.11	12.2	18.12	2.10	23.10
Guernsey	25.3		18.2	15.1	15.4	12.2	27.11	23.10	11.3	2.10
Isle of Wight	11.12	8.4		23.10	27.11	2.10	15.1	12.2	11.9	11.3
Millbrook	25.9	20.11	29.1		9.10	8.4	26.2	11.9	8.11	11.12
New Milton	20.11	11.12	8.1	12.2		11.3	23.10	2.10	8.4	11.9
Petersfield	8.1	9.10	26.2	18.12	25.9		25.3	15.4	29.1	20.11
Romsey	9.10	8.1	20.11	2.10	29.1	11.9		11.3	11.12	8.4
Trojans	8.4	29.1	9.10	25.3	26.2	11.12	25.9		20.11	8.1
U.S. Portsmouth	26.2	25.9	25.3	27.11	18.12	23.10	15.4	15.1		12.2
Ventnor	29.1	26.2	25.9	15.4	25.3	15.1	18.12	27.11	9.10	

HAMPSHIRE TWO

	AC Delco	Chineham	Eastleigh	Fareham H	Hamble	Nomads	Overton	Sandown & S	Soton Institute
A.C. Delco		26.2	18.12	9.10	25.3	29.1	25.9	8.1	20.11
Chineham	2.10		23.10	8.4	15.1	11.9	27.11	11.12	11.3
Eastleigh	8.4	29.1		20.11	26.2	8.1	9.10	25.9	11.12
Fareham Heathens	15.2	18.12	15.1		27.11	11.12	15.4	25.3	2.10
Hamble	11.9	20.11	2.10	8.1		11.12	29.1	9.10	8.4
Nomads	23.10	25.3	27.11	25.9	15.4		18.12	26.2	12.2
Overton	11.3	8.1	12.2	11.12	23.10	8.4		20.11	11.9
Sandown & Shanklin	27.11	15.4	11.3	11.9	12.2	2.10	15.1		23.10
Soton Institute	15.1	25.9	15.4	26.2	18.12	9.10	25.3	29.1	

HAMPSHIRE THREE

	Alresford	Brockenhurst	Ellingham & R	Fleet	Fordingbridge	Hants Police	Kingsclere	Portsmouth	Waterlooville
Alresford		27.11	15.1	23.10	11.9	2.10	12.2	15.4	11.3
Brockenhurst	8.1		25.9	20.11	9.10	29.1	25.3	26.2	18.12
Ellingham & Ringwood	20.11	11.3		11.9	11.12	8.4	23.10	8.1	12.2
Fleet	29.1	15.1	25.3		26.2	9.10	18.12	25.9	15.4
Fordingbridge	25.3	12.2	15.4	2.10		11.3	27.11	18.12	15.1
Hants. Police	26.2	23.10	18.12	12.2	25.9		15.4	25.3	27.11
Kingsclere	9.10	11.9	29.1	8.4	8.1	11.12		20.11	2.10
Portsmouth	11.12	2.10	27.10	11.3	8.4	15.9	15.1		23.10
Waterlooville	25.9	8.4	9.10	11.12	20.11	8.1	26.2	29.1	

SURREY ONE

	Chobham	Farnham	KCS Old Boys	Kingston	Merton	Old Caterham	Old Cranleigh	Old Paulines	Old Tiffinians	Old Walcourt	Raynes Park	Streatham & C	Working
Chobham		25.9				12.2		27.11	18.2		15.1		11.3
Farnham						15.1	25.3	2.10	27.11		18.12		12.2
K.C.S. Old Boys	25.3	26.2		15.1	27.11					2.10		18.12	
Kingston	26.2	29.1			2.10					25.3		27.11	8.1
Merton	8.1	11.12				25.9				29.1	11.3		20.11
Old Caterhamian			8.1	11.2			29.1	26.2	25.3		2.10		
Old Cranleighan	2.10		11.3	12.2	18.12					27.11		15.1	
Old Paulines			25.6	11.3	15.1		20.11			18.12		12.2	
Old Tiffinians			20.11	25.9	12.2		11.12	8.1				11.3	
Old Walcountian	11.12	20.11				11.3			15.1		12.2		25.9
Raynes Park			11.12	20.11			8.1	29.1	26.2			25.9	
Streatham & Croydon	29.1	8.1			25.3	20.11				26.2			11.12
Working			29.1			18.12	26.2	25.3	2.10		27.11		

SURREY TWO

	Battersea Iron	Chipstead	Haslemere	Law Society	London Fire	London Media	Mitcham	Old Hailey	Old Rutlishian	Old Wellington	Shirley Wndrs	Teddington	Wandsworthian
Battersea Iron			15.1		25.9			11.3	20.11	12.2	11.12		
Chipstead	26.2				11.12			20.11	8.1		29.1	25.1	
Haslemere		11.3		20.11		8.1	11.12					12.2	25.9
Law Society	2.10	18.12							26.2		25.3	27.11	15.1
London Fire Brigade			2.10	29.1		25.3	26.2	18.12		27.11			
London Media	18.12	12.2		25.9			20.11					15.1	11.3
Mitcham	27.11	15.1		11.3							2.10	18.12	12.2
Old Haileyburians			25.3	8.1		26.2	29.1			2.10			11.12
Old Rutlishian			27.11		12.2	2.10	25.3	15.11		18.12			
Old Wellingtonian		25.9	26.2	11.12		29.1	8.1						20.11
Shirley Wanderers			18.12		11.3	27.11		12.2	25.9	15.1			
Teddington	29.1				20.11			25.9	11.12	11.3	8.1		
Wandsworthian	25.3	27.11			8.1				29.1		26.2	2.10	

SURREY THREE

	Bec Old Boys	Croydon	Egham	Kings Coll H	Lightwater	London Corn	Old Bevonians	Old Freemans	Old Suttonians	Reigate & R	Surrey Univ	Worth Old B
Bec Old Boys					15.1		27.11	2.10	11.3	12.2		
Croydon	25.9					2.10	12.2			11.3	27.11	15.1
Egham	26.2	11.12		29.1			25.9			20.11		11.3
Kings College Hospital	11.2	20.11					11.3			25.9	15.1	12.2
Lightwater		26.2	15.1	25.3				27.11		29.1		
London Cornish	20.11		2.10	27.11	11.3			12.2	25.9			
Old Bevonians					11.2	26.2			29.1		25.3	2.10
Old Freemans		29.1	25.3	26.2			20.11			11.12		
Old Suttonians		25.3	27.11	2.10	12.2			15.1				
Reigate & Redhill						25.3	15.1		26.2		2.10	27.11
Surrey University	29.1		12.2		25.9	11.2		11.3	20.11			
Worth Old Boys	25.3				20.11	29.1		25.9	11.12		26.2	

SURREY FOUR

	Economicals	Kings Cross S.	Old Abingdonian	Old johnian	Racal Decca	Royal Holloway	St. Georges Hosp.
Economicals		20.11	18.12	26.02	29.01	*25.09*	*08.04*
Kings Cross Strs.	12.02		27.11	02.10	08.04	*18.12*	*11.03*
Old Abingdonain	25.03	26.02		11.12	20.11	*29.01*	*25.09*
Old Johnian	27.11	29.01	11.03		25.09	*08.04*	*18.12*
Racal Decca	02.10	08.01	12.02	15.01		*11.03*	*27.11*
Royal Hollway C	*15.01*	*25.03*	*02.10*	*08.01*	*11.12*		*12.02*
St. Georges Hosp.	*08.01*	*11.12*	*15.01*	*25.03*	*26.02*	*20.11*	

Fixtures in normal type are official League Fixtures whilst those in italics are included in an Unofficial League

LONDON THREE SOUTH EAST

	Beccehamians	Brighton	Chichester	Cranbrook	Crawley	Dartfordians	Eastbourne	EGrinstead	Folkestone	Heathfield	Horsham	Hove	Medway	Park House	Sidcup	Tunbridge W	Worthing
Beccehamians		11.12		25.9	8.1	20.11		9.10	8.4		29.1				26.2		
Brighton				15.1		11.3	11.9	12.2	18.12			23.10		2.10		27.11	
Chichester	11.9	8.1		9.10	29.1	11.12		20.1			26.2				25.3		
Cranbrook							29.1		2.10	11.12		25.3	8.1	26.2		11.9	20.11
Crawley		25.9		12.2		8.4		11.3	15.1			27.11		23.10		18.12	
Dartfordians				18.12			25.3	15.1	27.11			2.10	26.2	11.9		23.10	
Eastbourne	18.12		15.1		2.10					11.3	23.10		8.4		27.11		12.2
East Grinstead				27.11			26.2		23.10	8.1		11.9	29.1	25.3		2.10	
Folkstone			25.9				8.1			20.11		26.2	11.12	29.1		25.3	9.10
Heathfield & Waldron	23.10	26.2	22.11		25.3	29.1					11.9				2.10		18.12
Horsham		9.10		11.3	20.11	25.9		8.4	12.2			18.12				15.1	
Hove	12.2		11.3				20.11			25.9			9.10	11.12	15.1		8.4
Medway	27.11	25.3	18.12		11.9					12.2	2.10				23.10		15.1
Park House	15.1		12.2				9.10			8.4	27.11		25.9		18.12		11.3
Sidcup		20.11		8.4	11.12	2.10		25.9	11.3		8.1					12.2	
Tunbridge Wells	11.3		8.4				11.12			9.10		29.1	20.11	8.1			25.9
Worthing	2.10	29.10	20.10		26.2	8.1		11.12			25.3				11.9		

KENT ONE

	Ashford	Betteshanger	Brockleians	Bromley	Dover	Gillingham A	Guy's Hosp	HSBC	Lordswood	Nat West	New Ash G	Old Dunst	Old Eltham	Old Shooter	Sheppey	Whitstable
Ashford		11.12					25.3	2.10			8.1	29.1	20.11	12.2	9.10	
Betteshanger			27.11			26.2		12.2	25.3	23.10			15.1		18.12	2.10
Brockleians	25.9			20.11	9.10	11.12		25.3	8.1	26.2						29.1
Bromley	27.11	29.1			18.12		23.10	15.1			26.2	25.3		2.10		
Dover	23.10	8.1					2.10	27.11			29.1	12.2	11.12	25.3		
Gillingham Anchorians	18.12			12.2	15.1		27.11				25.3	2.10		23.10		
Guy's Hospital		20.11	11.3					12.2			11.12	8.1	9.10	29.1	25.9	
H.S.B.C.						11.3			9.10	29.1	25.9	20.11		8.1		11.12
Lordswood	15.1			11.3	12.2	25.9	18.12					23.10		27.11		
NatWest Bank	11.3			9.10	25.9	20.11	12.2		11.12							8.1
New Ash Green		11.3	18.12						2.10	27.11			12.2		15.1	23.10
Old Dunstonian		25.9	15.1							18.12	9.10		11.3		12.2	27.11
Old Elthamians			23.10	8.1		29.1		18.12	11.2	2.10					27.11	25.3
Old Shootershillians		9.10	12.2		20.11					15.1	20.11	11.12	25.9		11.3	
Sheppey			2.10	11.12		8.1		23.10	29.1	25.3						12.2
Whitstable	12.2			25.9	11.3	9.10	15.1		20.11					18.12		

KENT TWO EAST

	Aylesford	Deal Wndrs	Edenbridge	Faversham	Old Gravesend	Old Williams	Sittingbourne	Snowdonw CW	Vigo
Aylesford		11.9	11.3	2.10	12.2	23.10	15.1	27.11	15.4
Deal Wanderers	25.3		15.1	11.3	27.11	2.10	15.4	12.2	18.12
Edenbridge	25.9	20.11		8.1	26.2	11.12	9.10	8.4	29.1
Faversham	26.2	25.9	27.11		15.4	12.2	18.12	23.10	25.3
Old Gravesendians	9.10	8.1	2.10	11.12		8.4	29.7	11.9	20.11
Old Williamsonians	29.1	26.2	15.4	9.10	18.12		25.3	15.1	25.9
Sittingbourne	20.11	11.12	12.2	8.4	23.10	11.9		11.3	8.1
Snowdown C.W.	8.1	9.10	18.12	29.1	25.3	20.11	25.9		26.2
Vigo	11.12	8.4	23.10	11.9	15.1	11.3	27.11	2.10	

KENT TWO WEST

	Bexley	Darenth Valley	Erith	Footscray	Greenwich	Greenwich A	Met Police, H	Old Olavians	Orpington
Bexley		11.9	11.3	2.10	12.2	23.10	15.1	27.11	15.4
Darenth Valley	25.3		15.1	11.3	27.11	2.10	15.4	12.2	18.12
Erith	25.9	20.11		8.1	28.2	11.12	9.10	8.4	29.1
Footscray	28.2	25.9	27.11		15.4	12.2	18.12	23.10	25.3
Greenwich	9.10	8.1	2.10	11.12		8.4	29.1	11.9	20.11
Greenwich Academicals	29.1	26.2	15.4	9.10	18.12		25.3	15.1	25.9
Met. Police, Hayes	20.11	11.12	12.2	8.4	23.10	11.9		11.3	8.1
Old Olavians	8.1	9.10	18312	29.1	25.3	20.11	25.9		26.2
Orpington	11.12	8.4	23.10	11.9	15.1	1.3	27.11	2.10	

SUSSEX ONE

	Bognor	Crowborough	Hastings & B	Hellingly	Old Brighton	Pulborough	Royal Sun A	Seaford	Uckfield
Bognor		27.11	1.3	15.4	12.2	2.10	18.12	25.3	15.1
Crowborough	8.1		11.12	29.1	11.9	8.4	20.11	9.10	2.10
Hastings & Bexhill	25.9	15.4		18.12	23.10	12.2	25.3	26.2	27.11
Hellingly	11.12	23.10	8.4		11.3	11.9	8.1	20.11	12.2
Old Brightonians	9.10	25.3	29.1	25.9		20.11	26.2	8.1	18.12
Pulborough	26.2	18.2	9.10	25.3	15.1		25.9	29.1	15.4
Royal Sun Alliance	8.4	15.1	11.9	27.11	2.10	11.3		11.2	23.10
Seaford	11.9	12.2	2.1.0	15.1	27.11	23.10	15.4		11.3
Uckfield	20.11	26.2	8.1	9.10	8.4	11.12	29.12	25.9	

SUSSEX TWO

	BA Wingspan	Burgess Hill	Chichester	Ditching	Newick	Plumpton	Shoreham	Sussex Police
B.A. Wingspan		25.9	29.1	9.10	26.2	20.11	25.3	11.12
Burgess Hill	15.1		9.10	26.2	20.11	25.11	11.12	29.1
Chichester	2.10	12.2		20.11	25.3	11.12	15.1	23.10
Ditching	12.2	23.10	11.3		11.12	15.1	2.10	25.3
Newick	23.10	11.3	27.11	8.4		2.10	12.2	25.9
Plumpton	11.3	27.11	8.4	25.9	29.1		23.10	12.2
Shoreham	27.11	8.4	25.9	29.1	9.10	26.2		20.11
Sussex Police	8.4	2.10	26.2	27.11	15.1	9.10	11.3	

SUSSEX THREE

	Arun	Barnes Green	Midhurst	Norfolk Arms	Robersbridge	Rye	St Francis	Sussex Univ
Arun		25.9	29.1	9.10	26.2	20.11	25.3	11.12
Barnes Green	15.1		9.10	26.2	20.11	25.3	11.12	29.1
Midhurst	2.10	12.2		20.11	25.3	11.13	15.1	23.10
Norfolk Arms	12.2	23.10	11.3		11.12	15.1	2.10	25.3
Robertsbridge	23.10	11.3	27.11	8.4		2.10	12.2	25.9
Rye	11.3	27.11	8.4	25.9	29.1		23.10	12.2
St. Francis	27.11	8.4	25.9	29.1	9.10	26.2		20.11
Sussex University	8.4	2.10	26.2	27.11	15.1	9.10	11.3	

London & South East Division Clubs

AC DELCO RFC
Hampshire 2
Ground Address: AC Delco (Southampton) Sports and Social Club, Sports Ground, Stoneham Lane, Eastleigh, Southampton, Hants
Tel: 01703 613334
Brief Directions: M27 Jct 5. Stoneham Lane Northbound. Ground on left just after Concorde club on right.
Club Secretary: Sandra Franks, 286 Middle Road, Sholing, Southampton SO19 8NX
Tel No: 01703 422802 or 02380 422802
Fixtures Secretary: John Hunter. Tel No: 01703 396688 or 02380 396688
Club Colours: Navy blue and red quarters or navy blue and light blue hoops

ALRESFORD RFC
Hampshire 3
Ground Address: Bighton Cricket Club, Brighton, Nr Alresford
Brief Directions: Contact Club House (Horse & Groom 01962 734809)
Club Secretary: Mark Elliott, c/o Horse & Groom, Broad Street, Alresford, Hampshire
Tel: (H) 01962 734809
Fixtures Secretary: P. Budge, Horse and Crown P.H., Broad Street, Alresford, Hampshire, SO24 9ET.
Club Colours: Gold, green and black

ALTON RFC
London 2 South
Ground Address: Anstey Park, Anstey Road, Alton, Hampshire. GU34 2RL
Tel: 01420 82076
Brief Directions: From A31 take A339 towards Alton Town. After approx half a mile ground on right.
Club Secretary: Keith Page, 31 Nursery Rd, Alresford, Hampshire. SO24 9JW
Tel: (H) 01962 734302 (W) 01483 573727
Fixtures Secretary: Martin Simpson, 10 Gauvain Cl, Alton, Hampshire. GU34 2SB
Tel: (H) 01420 86880
Club Colours: Red & black irregular hoops, black shorts

AMERICAN EXILES
Eastern Counties 4 North

CLACTON RUFC
Ground Address: Clacton Rugby Clubhouse, Recreation Ground, Valley Road, Clacton-on-Sea, Essex. CO15 4NA
Tel: 01255 421602
Club Secretary: David Jaffray, 30 Craigfield Avenue, Clacton-on-Sea, Essex. CO15 4HS
Tel: (H) 01255 429762 (W) 01255 678793
Fixtures Secretary: Damian Williams
Tel: (H) 01255 222823
Club Colours: Maroon jersey, navy shorts, maroon socks with white tops

ANDOVER RFC
London 3 South West
Ground Address: The Goodship Ground, Foxcotte Park, Hatherden Road, Andover, Hants
Tel: 01264 339518
Brief Directions: From town centre take ring road to Portway Ind Estate, turn into Goch Way, right onto Hatherden Rd, follow road for 0.75 mile to roundabout, turn into Sports Centre
Club Secretary: Tony Holden, Saddlers Cottage, Monxton, Andover, Hants. SP11 8AW
Tel: (H) 01264 710322 (Fax) 01264 710319
Fixtures Secretary: Paul Turnner Tel No: 01264 353114
Club Colours: Black. Change strip Green

ARUN RUFC
Sussex 3
Ground Address: The Littlehampton School, Hill Road, Littlehampton, West Sussex Tel: 01903 713944
Brief Directions: Off Horsham Road, Littlehampton
Club Secretary: S White, 66 Holmes Lane, Rustington, West Sussex. BN16 3PU Tel: (H) 01903 774434
Fixtures Secretary: P Best Tel: (H) 01903 723969
Club Colours: Red, white and navy quarters

ASHFORD (KENT) RFC LTD
Kent 1
Ground Address: Kinneys Field, Canterbury Road, Bybrook, Ashford, Kent
Brief Directions: A28 from Ashford to Canterbury, 400 yards after crossing M20 motorway, the ground narrow entrance is on right directly opposite the Fire Station
Club Secretary: Jenny Lake, 6 Wellesley Villas, Wellesley Road, Ashford, Kent
Tel: (H) 01233 624795
Fixtures Secretary: Simon Hall, 2 Patterson Cottages, Aldington, Kent
Tel: (H) 01233 720174
Club Colours: Red, gold and black hooped shirts & socks with black shorts

ASKEAN R.F.C.
London 2 South
Ground Address: 60A Broad Walk, Kidbrooke, London. SER3 8NB Tel: 0181
Brief Directions: A2 from London, Broad Walk is first left off Rochester way, which is reached by following signs for local traffic at Kidbrooke turn off
Club Secretary: Graham Terry, Endwaye, Brookhurst Gardens, Tunbridge Wells, Kent TN4 0UA
Tel: (H & FAX) 01892 528996
Fixtures Secretary: Mike Sidgwick
Tel: 01689 857436
Club Colours: White with blue and white bands

AYLESFORD RFC
Kent 2 East
Ground Address: Ferry Fields Ground, Hall Road, Aylesford, Kent, ME20 7DS.
Tel: 01622 790380
Brief Directions: Leave M20 at J5. Head westwards on A20. Turn R. at the second set of traffic lights (Hall Road). Turn R. into Ground after motorway bridge.
Club Secretary: Kevin Burbridge, 77 Holborough Road, Snodland, Kent, ME6 5PA. Tel: (H) 01634 242147

Fixtures Secretary: Dave Enston, 47 Hornbeam Close, Larkfield, Aylelsford, Kent, ME20 6LZ.
Tel: (H) 01732 842666
Club Colours: Red and navy hoops thin silver/grey line between

BANCROFT RFC
Eastern Counties 1
Ground Address: Buckhurst Way, Buckhurst Hill, Essex. IG9 6JD Tel: 0181 504 0429
Brief Directions: M11/A406 to 'Waterworks' junction, exit & take A104 to Woodford, at Castle pub turn right (Broadmead Rd), left at 2nd traffic lights, ground 1mile on right before railway bridge
Club Secretary: S B Thirsk, 4 Bentley Way, Woodford Green, Essex. IG8 0SE
Tel: (H) 0181 504 1468 (W) 01279 441111
Fixtures Secretary: M. Correa, 77 Braxted Park, Streatham, SW16 3AV
Tel No: (H) 0207 395 9305 (W) 0208 679 9703
Club Colours: Blue, black, light blue, claret hoops

BANK OF ENGLAND RFC
Hertfordshire & Middlesex 1
Ground Address: Priory Lane, Roehampton, London. SW15 5JQ
Tel: 0181 876 8417
Brief Directions: A205 (Upper Richmond Rd) towards Richmond, past junction with Roehampton Lane and Rocks Lane then left into Priory Lane
Club Secretary: Mike Anderson, 4 Charles Street, Barnes, London, SW13 0NZ
Tel: (H) 0181 781341 (W) 0171 4919600
Fixtures Secretary: Mike Anderson
Club Colours: Old gold, blue and white hoops

BARCLAYS BANK RFC
Hertfordshire & Middlesex 2
Ground Address: Park View Road, Ealing, London. W5 2JF Tel: 0181 998 4904
Brief Directions: Piccadilly Line to North Ealing Station, Central Line to Ealing Broadway. By car to Hanger Lane, turn into Woodville Gardens and then into Park View Road
Club Secretary: S C Payne, Barclays Acquisition Finance, 1st Floor, 54 Lombard Street, London, EC3 3AH. Tel: 0171 699 3520
Fixtures Secretary: D M Bevan-Jones
Tel: (H) 0181 898 4107 (W) 0171 699 3732
Club Colours: Maroon jersey with silver edged gold band

BARNES RFC
London 3 South West
Ground Address: Barnes Harrodians Sports Club, Barn Elms, Queen Elizabeth Walk, Barnes, London SW13 8DG. Tel: 0181 876 7685
Brief Directions: From Hammersmith and Kensington cross Hammersmith Bridge, down Castlenau for 3/4 mile, left into Quenn Elizabeth Walk at Red Lion PH, Ground at end of road 1/2 mile long. (Plenty parking).
Club Secretary: Paul Kirby, 53 Stanhope Gardens, London SW7 5RF. Tel: (H) 0171 373 9120 Tel: (W) 0171 602 5678
Fixtures Secretary: Andy Long: Tel: (H) 0181 948 3809 (W) 01784 474746
Club Colours: Green and gold shirts, green shorts.

BARNET ELIZABETHANS
London 2 North
Ground Address: Byng Road, Barnet, Hertfordshire
Tel: 0181 449 0040
Brief Directions: From M25(Jct 23) on A1081 to Barnet. At pedestrian crossing,right into Alston Rd.,through restriction, third right (Wentworth Road, then left (Byng Road) ,ground at end.
Club Secretary: Peter Yates, Woodlands, 19 Hornefield Road, Ware, Herts. SG12 7NG
Tel: (H)01920 484382 (W) 01992 503304
Fixtures Secretary: Peter Glenister
Tel: (H) 01438 820692
Club Colours: Navy blue and claret quarters

BARNS GREEN RFC
Sussex 3
Ground Address: Christ's Hospital School, Horsham, West sussex.
Club Secretary: Miss Sue Blanchard, 42 Finians Field,Barns Green, West Sussex RH13 7PW.
Tel: (H) 01403 731652
Fixtures Secretary: Mr P A Bailey,
Tel: (H) 01403 730058 Tel: (W) 0181 667 5504
Club Colours: Gold & green quarters.

BASILDON RFC
London 3 North East
Ground Address: Gardiners Close, Basildon, Essex. SS14 2AW Tel: 01268 533136
Brief Directions: Frm wst: A127 London/S'thend arterial rd, past 1st signs for B'don, rt A132, rt at 2nd r'bout A1235, rt at 1st lights (not Zebra) Gardiners Lans south is first left-ground at end.
Club Secretary: T.Ramsbottom, 12 Stafford Green, Basildon SS16 6DY
Tel: 01268 492558
Fixtures Secretary: B. Reynolds, 102 Elder Avenue, Wickford, Essex SS12 0LT Tel: 01268 475532
Club Colours: Bottle green with two white hoops, white shorts

BATTERSEA IRONSIDES RFC
Surrey 2
Ground Address: Garret Green, Burntwood Lane, Earlsfield, London. SW17 Tel: 0181 879 9913
Brief Directions: From south: turn left at Tooting Broadway towards Wandsworth, after 2nd r'bout Burntwood Ln is 1st main road on right, Garret Green is 500m on right, club a further 300m on left
Club Secretary: Martin Paul Tanner, 1 Woodland Way, Morden, Surrey. SM4 4DS Tel: (H) 0181 540 5784 (W) 0585 778712
Fixtures Secretary: Tony Szulc Tel: (H) 0171 622 7694
Club Colours: Green jerseys with white band, white shorts, red socks

BEC OLD BOYS
Surrey 3
Ground Address: Sutton Manor Sports & Social Club, Northey Avenue, Cheam, Surrey. SM2 7HJ
Tel: 0181 642 3423
Brief Directions: Right off of A217 into Northey Avenue
Club Secretary: Mr Nick Ryan, 201 Lennard Road, Beckenham, Bromley. BR3 1QN
Tel: (H) 0181 778 9984 (W) 0171 247 7441
Fixtures Secretary: Mr Rick Mayhew
Tel: (H) 0181 286 2463
Club Colours: Blue, old gold and white hoop

BECCEHAMIAN RFC
London 3 South East
Ground Address: Sparrows Den, Corkscrew Hill, West Wickham, Kent
Tel: 0181 777 8105
Brief Directions: Corner of Corkscrew Hill and Addington Road (A2022)
Club Secretary: Alan Pitt, 3 Kent Road, West Wickham, Kent
Tel: (H) 0181 289 6629 (W) 01923 817537
Fixtures Secretary: C Putmer
Tel: (H) 0181 777 6307
Club Colours: Maroon, black and silver hoops

BECCLES RUFC
Eastern Counties 2
Ground Address: Beef Meadow, Common Lane, Beccles
Tel: 01502 712016
Brief Directions: Into Beccles from Safeway roundabout, over mini roundabout, follow road left over railway, 1st left is Common Lane
Club Secretary: Amanda Sutton, 4 The Bridles, Worlingham, Beccles, Suffolk NR34 7RQ
Fixtures Secretary: Rob Sutton, 4 The Bridles, Worlingham, Beccles, Suffolk NR34 7RQ
Club Colours: Green and black quarters

BECKENHAM RFC
London 2 South
Ground Address: Balmoral Avenue, Elmers End, Beckenham, Kent. BR3 3RD
Tel: 0181 650 7176
Brief Directions: Entrance in Balmoral Ave which runs between Eden Park Ave & Upper Elmers End Rd (A214). From bottom of Beckenham High St take Croydon Rd (A222), left into Eden Pk
Club Secretary: Mr M L Parker, c/o H & V Controls Ltd, Orchard Business Centre 2, Kangley Bridge Road, Sydenham. SE26 5AQ Tel: (W) 0181 776 7272
Fixtures Secretary: Mr J M Arger
Tel: (H) 01580 891550
Club Colours: Royal blue and old gold hoops

BELSIZE PARK RFC
Hertfordshire & Middlesex 4 North
Ground Address: c/o Hendon RFC, Copthall Stadium, Hendon, Middlesex
Brief Directions: As for Hendon RFC
Club Secretary: Sebastian Colquhoun, 9 Regency Lawn, Croftdown Road. NW5 1HF
Tel: (H) 0171 485 5767 (W) 0171 355 0219
Fixtures Secretary: Hugh Reeve-Tucker
Tel: (H) 0181 874 5907 (W) 0171 234 4822
Club Colours: Lavender and black

BETTESHANGER CW RFC
Kent 1
Ground Address: Welfare Ground, Cavill Square, Deal, Kent. Clubhouse: Welfare Club 1st floor, Condray Square, Deal, Kent Tel: 01304 365090
Brief Directions: A258 to Walmer, 3rd left Church St, right at T junction Court Rd, left at T junction St Richards Rd, past water tower turn right Mill Hill, 2nd left, 2nd left Cavell Sq, 1st left to ground & changing
Club Secretary: Simon Rickatson, 40 Mongeham Road, Great Mongeham, Deal, Kent. CT14 9PQ
Tel: (H) 01304 361178
Fixtures Secretary: Bob Pinnick
Tel: (H) 01227 750530 (W) 01843 822686
Club Colours: Red and white hoops

BEXLEY RFC
Kent 2 West
Ground Address: Hall Place Park, Bourne Road, Bexley, Kent
Club Secretary: Peter Butler, 194 Claremont Road, Hextable, Kent. BR8 7QU
Tel: (H) 01322 664389
Fixtures Secretary: Paul Herbert
Tel: (H) 01322 555556
Club Colours: Royal blue and white hooped shirts, blue shorts, blue socks with white tops

BILLERICAY RFC
Eastern Counties 1
Ground Address: Willowbrook Sports & Social Club, Stock Road, Billericay, Essex
Club Secretary: Neil Jarvis, Brenenden, North Road, Crays Hill, Billericay, Essex. CM11 2XD
Tel: (H) 01268 289481 (W) 0171 797 8000
Fixtures Secretary: Sean Norris
Tel: (H) 01277 654952
Club Colours: Black with gold band, black shorts, black and gold socks

BISHOPS STORTFORD RFC
London 2 North
Ground Address: Silver Leys, Hadham Road, Bishops Stortford, Herts. CM23 2QE
Tel: 01279 652092
Brief Directions: From north/south, M11 J8, A120 signed Puckeridge. From east/west, A120 to Tesco roundabout, Tesco on right, ground 400m left
Club Secretary: Jim Smith, 16 Hillcroft, Bishops Stortford, Herts. CM23 2BP.
Tel: 01279 831667
Fixtures Secretary: Terry Ellis, Flat 2, 72 South Street, Bishop's Stortford, Herts. CM23 3AZ
Tel No: 01279 461186
Club Colours: Royal blue and white hoops

BOGNOR RFC
Sussex 1
Ground Address: The Clubhouse, Hampshire Avenue, Bognor Regis, West Sussex. PO21 5JY
Tel: 01243 824000
Brief Directions: Proceed along main A259 Bognor to Chichester road, turn south into Hampshire Avenue, ground is 100mtrs on left
Club Secretary: John Donoghue, 62 Victoria Drive, Bognor Regis PO21 2TG.
Tel No: 01243 823287 (H) 07971 052857 (M)
Fixtures Secretary: Ian Misselbrook. Tel NO: 01243 866354.
Club Colours: Purple, green and white hoops, black shorts, green socks

BRAINTREE RUFC
London 2 North
Ground Address: the Clubhouse, Beckers Green Road, Braintree, essex CM7 6PR. Tel: 01376 311181
Brief Directions: From Braintree bypass A120 exit at Galleys Corner roundabout to Braintree East (B1018 Cressing Road), 300 metres turn right into Beckers Green Road, Ground at end of road.
Club Secretary: Mrs C Wadford, 8 Chelmer Road, Braintree, Essex CM7 3PY. Tel: (H) 01376 341642
Fixtures Secretary: Mrs D Nightingale, Tel: (H) 01371 850013
Club Colours: Black and amber hoops.

BRENTWOOD RFC
London 2 North
Ground Address: King Georges Playing Fields, Ingrave Road, Brentwood, Essex. CM13 2AQ
Tel: 01277 210267
Club Secretary: Mr Paul Kehoe, 11 Clifton Way, Hutton, Brentwood, Essex. CM13 2QR Tel: (H)01277 215821
Fixtures Secretary: Nick Priddle, Foxhurst, Coxes Farm Rd, Billericay. CM11 2UA
Tel: (H) 01277 656685
Club Colours: Claret, grey and white hoops, black shorts

BRIGHTLINGSEA RFC
Eastern Counties 3 South
Ground Address: Strangers Corner, Brightlingsea, Essex
Tel: 01206 303274
Brief Directions: Take the B1029 into Brightlingsea. Sports Centre is on left as you enter town.
Club Secretary: Roger Kemble, 8 Tabor Close, Brightlingsea, Essex. CO7 0QS
Tel: (H) 01206 302432
Fixtures Secretary: Graham Williams, 4 St Andrews Place, Brighlingsea CO7 ORH Tel: 01206 304667
Club Colours: Scarlet, black socks and shorts

BRIGHTON FOOTBALL CLUB (RFC)
London 3 South East
Ground Address: Waterhall Playing Fields, Waterhall Road, Brighton, East Sussex. BN1 8YR
Tel: 01273 562729
Brief Directions: From London A23 to Patcham roundabout, round roundabout, turn into Hill Rd, underneath Railway arch, 1st right, under road arch, 1st left, straight up to clubhouse
Club Secretary: Miss Gaelle Thompson, 34 West Hill Street, Brighton, E. Sussex BN1 3RR
Tel: (H) 01273 321425
Fixtures Secretary: R Greenwood, 11 Lyminster Ave, Brighton
Tel: (H) 01273 502898
Club Colours: Royal Blue shirts, dark blue shorts and red socks

BRITISH AIRWAYS RFC
Hertfordshire & Middlesex 3 South
Ground Address: Cherry Lane Playing Fields, Cherry Lane, Langley Green, Crawley
Brief Directions: From A23 turn North onto London Road at Holiday Inn roundabout, at lights turn left into Martyrs Avenue and then right into Cherry Lane
Club Secretary: James McCormick, 14 Brisbane Close, Langley Green, Crawley, Sussex RH11 7UE
Tel: (H) 01293 523035
Fixtures Secretary: Paddy Minnis, 25 Leatherhead Road, Ashtead, Surrey KT21 2TP
Tel: (H/W) 01372 275132
Club Colours: Red, white and blue quarters, white shorts

BRITISH AIRWAYS WINGSPAN RUFC
Sussex 2
Ground Address: Bewbush Leisure Centre, Coachmans Drive, Bewbush, Crawley
Tel: 01293 546477
Brief Directions: Turn west off A23 at Cheals roundabout, signed Horsham, on A264, 3rd exit at 2nd roundabout (Breezehurst Drive), sports centre is 0.5 mile on left
Club Secretary: Mike Duff, 10 Brooklands Road, Tollgate Hill, Crawley, Sussex. RH11 9QQ
Tel: (H) 01293 409908 (W) 01293 662258
Fixtures Secretary: Harry Townsend
Tel: (H & W) 01342 322508
Club Colours: Red, white and blue

BROCKENHURST RFC
Hampshire 3
Ground Address: Brockenhurst College, Lymington Road, Brockenhurst, Hants.
Brief Directions: M27 to exit 1 signs to Lyndhurst signs to Brockenhurst turn L. just prior to Rose & Crown Pub. Ground on Left.
Club Secretary: Peter White, Water Splash House, The Rise, Brockenhurst, Hants. SO42 7SJ Tel: 01590 623203 (H) 0171 208 4209 (B)
Fixtures Secretary: Chris Edwards, Nyewoods, Collyers Road, Brockenhurst, Hants, SO42 7SE.
Tel: 01590 622713
Club Colours: Black & white quarters

BROCKLEIANS RFC
Kent 1
Ground Address: Eltham Palace Road, Eltham, London. SE9 5LX
Tel: 0181 8508650
Brief Directions: A20 to junction with South Circular, turn into Eltham Palace Road at World of Leather.
Club Secretary: Paul Parish, 38 Cobden Road, South Norwood, London SE25 5NX
Tel: (H) 0181 656 0790
Fixtures Secretary: George Wright
Tel: (H) 01622 738396
Club Colours: Chocolate, emerald and old gold

BROMLEY RFC
Kent 1
Ground Address: Warman Sports TrustBarnet Wood Road, Hayes, Kent
Tel: 0181 462 3430
Brief Directions: From Bromley take B265 to Hayes village. After village turn left into Five Elms Road and immediately left into Barnet Wood Road. Club is next to Baston school.
Club Secretary: Alec Lauder, 32 Turnpike Drive, Pratts Bottom, Orpington, Kent BR6 7SJ
Tel: 01689 855004
Fixtures Secretary: Alex Mackintosh
Tel: (H) 0181 460 8049
Club Colours: Black jerseys & thin amber hoops, black shorts and sockssock

BURGESS HILL RFC
Sussex 2
Ground Address: Poveys Close, Burgess Hill, West Sussex Tel: 01444 232221
Brief Directions: Royal George Road turn into Southway at Weald public house right intoPoveys Close - ground at end.
Club Secretary: Mike Bushell, 4 Kirdford Close, Burgess Hill, West Sussex. RH15 0BW
Tel: (H) 01444 246795
Fixtures Secretary: Tony Balsdon, 102 Marlborough Drive, Burgess Hill, West Sussex. RH15 0EU.
Tel: (H) 01444 246170 (W) 01273 273234
Club Colours: All black

BURNHAM-ON-CROUCH RUFC

Eastern Counties 3 South
Ground Address: Dengie Hundred Sports Centre, Millfields, Station Rd, Burnham-on-Crouch, Essex. CM0 8HS
Tel: 01621 784633 (Office) 01621 784656 (Bar)
Brief Directions: From all main routes continue east (north of River Crouch), pick up B1010 into B.-0-Crouch, right at T jctn, over rail bridge into town centre, library on right, entrance to ground immediate right
Club Secretary: Mr Antony Marchetto, 95 Maple Way, Burnham on Crouch, Essex CM0 8DN
Tel 01621 782907 (H) 01708 774318 (W)
Fixtures Secretary: Mr Warwick H Bridge
Tel: (H) 01621 783807
Club Colours: Navy blue and amber 2" hooped jerseys, navy shorts

BURY ST EDMONDS RFC

London 3 North East
Ground Address: The Haberden, Southgate Green, Bury St Edmonds Tel: 01284 753920
Brief Directions: Leave A14 on A134 (B.S.E. east & Sudbury), ground is 400 yards on right, next to Mobil Petrol Station
Club Secretary: Mrs C.Palombo, 41 Oakes Road, Buury St Edmunds. IP31 6PX
Tel No: 01284 761871 (H)
Fixtures Secretary: Mr S Lord
Tel: (H) 01284 769722 (W) 0171 720 2188
Club Colours: Green and yellow quarters

CAMPION RFC

London 3 North East
Ground Address: Cottons Park, Cottons Approach, Romford, Essex. RM7 7AA Tel: 01708 753209
Brief Directions: Frm W. exit A12 at lights after Moby Dick pub, rt -Mawney Rd, before T junction rt -Marks Rd, ground 1st left. Frm E., A12 thro' 3 lights after Gallows Crnr, lt-Hawney Rd-as above
Club Secretary: P O'Brien, 68 Lancaster Drive, Elm Park, Hornchurch, Essex. RM12 5ST
Tel: (H) 01708 446980 (W) 01708 342453
Fixtures Secretary: K O'Neill, 26 Priests Field, Ingrave, Brentwoon, CM13 3Q
Tel: 01277 812605
Club Colours: Red and black hoops

CANTABRIGIAN RFC

Eastern Counties 1
Ground Address: Sedley Taylor Road, Cambridge. CB2 2PW Tel: 01223 516061
Brief Directions: Leave M11 exit 11(A1309) to Cambridge. Right at 2nd traffic lioghts into Long Rd.,. Left after railway bridge into Sedley Taylor Rd.Ground down narrow entrance immediately on left.
Club Secretary: R L Ladds, 4 Flamstead Road, Cambridge. CB1 3QU Tel: (H) 01223 249008
Fixtures Secretary: J Edmonds
Tel: (H) 01223 563256 (W) 01223506606
Club Colours: Navy blue and white hoops

CANTERBURY CHRISTCHURCH COLLEGE "Wild Geese" RUFC

Kent 3
Ground Address: Canterbury Christchurch College S.U., North Holm Road, Canterbury, Kent CT1 1QU
Brief Directions: Stodmash playing field, Stodmash Lane, Canterbury, off A257 Littlebourne Road.
Club Secretary: James Knight, Canterbury Christchurch College S.U., North Holm Road, Canterbury, Kent CT1 1QU
Fixtures Secretary: Niel Chamberlain, Canterbury Christchurch College S.U., North Holm Road, Canterbury, Kent CT1 1QU
Club Colours: Burgandy sky blue hoops

CANTERBURY EXILES

Kent 3
Ground Address: The University of Kent, Canterbury, Kent
Brief Directions: Follow the signs into Canterbury from the A2. Head for St. Thomas Hill (Westgate) and follow signs to University
Club Secretary: Stephen Gile, Trapham Farmhouse, Wingham Green, Canterbury, Kent CT3 1NL
Fixtures Secretary: Mr Tony Allan, St Andrews, Upper Street, Tilmanstone, Deal, Kent CT14 oJW
Club Colours: Red, black and amber hoops.

CANTERBURY RFC

London 2 South
Ground Address: Merton Lane (North), Nackington Road, Canterbury, Kent Tel: 01227 768958
Brief Directions: Exit A2 for Canterbury, at 4th roundabout take 3rd exit, proceed over traffic lights, turn right after cricket ground on B2068, 9-10 miles turn right to ground
Club Secretary: T D O Hall, Whiteacre Farmhouse, Whiteacre Lane, Waltham, Canterbury. CT4 5SR
Tel: (H) 01227 700344 (W) 01227 767557 X 167
Fixtures Secretary: P. Coakley Esq, Cedarhill, Lee Priory, Littlebourne, Canterbury, CT3 1UR.
Tel: (H) 01227 721230 (W) 01227 463529
Club Colours: Black and amber

CANVEY ISLAND RUFC

London 3 North East
Ground Address: Trewkes Creek, Dovervelt Road, Canvey Island, Essex Tel: 01268 681881
Brief Directions: A130 to Canvey Island, straight across 2 roundabouts, turn left at 3rd Climmen Road, follow road, club on left
Club Secretary: Mr Stephen Clarke, 26 Thelma Avenue, Canvey Island, Essex. SS8 9DT
Tel: (H) 01268 699858 (W) 0171 473 1144
Fixtures Secretary: G M Henderson, 3 Brindles, Canvey Island. Tel: (H) 01268 681121 (M) 0802 700886
Club Colours: Red and blue

CENTAURS RFC

Hertfordshire & Middlesex 4 South
Ground Address: Gower Road, Syon Lane, Osterley, Middlesex. TW7 5PY
Tel: 0181 560 4500
Brief Directions: A4 to Gilette Corner, take Syon Lane, north past Tescos, Gower Road is next right
Club Secretary: M W Root, 116 Uxbridge Road, Hatch End, Middlesex. HA5 4DS
Tel: (H & W) 0181 421 5988
Fixtures Secretary: Jerry Goldie Tel: (H) 0181 568 7240
Club Colours: Light blue and dark blue quarters

CHARLTON PARK RFC

London 2 South
Ground Address: Pippenhall Sports Ground, Avery Hill Park, Footscray Road, Eltham SE9
Brief Directions: From A2 to A20 follow signs for Eltham High Street, turn into Southend Crescent or Footscray Road, Entrance at junction Southend Crescent and Footscray road.

Club Secretary: Andy Potts, 37 Beechhill Road, Eltham, London SE9 1HJ
0181 859 8775
Fixtures Secretary: Please contact Secretary
Club Colours: Red and White Hooped shirts, blue shorts and red socks.

CHELMSFORD RFC
London 2 North
Ground Address: Coronation Park, Timsons Lane, Springfield, Chelmsford, Essex. CM2 6AF
Tel: 01245 261159
Brief Directions: A12 - take Boreham/North Springfield turning, head for Chelmsford, over 1st roundabout, 2nd roundabout 3rd exit, over roundabout, 1st turning after Plough pub Timsons Lane
Club Secretary: Lawrence Crispin, 33 Jenner Mead, Chelmer Village, Chelmsford , Essex CM2 6SJ
Tel: 01245 465021
Fixtures Secretary: Clare St. John Coleman, 139 Pollards Gren, Chelmsford, Essex CM2 6UX Tel : 01245 602239
Club Colours: Navy Blue shirts and shorrts, navy blue & white hooped socks

CHESS VALLEY
Hertfordshire & Middlesex 3 South
Ground Address: Rickmansworth Sports Club, Park road, Rickmnsworth, Herts WD3 1HU . Tel: 01923 445440
Club Secretary: Jerry GReen, The Briars House, Sarratt, Herts WO3 6AU
Tel: 01923 263047 (H) 01923 291322 (W)
Fixtures Secretary: Iain Campbell, 15 The Highlands, Rickmansworth, Herts WD3 2EW. Tel: 01923 7735266 (H) 0171 816 1899 (W)
Club Colours: Bottle green shirts with pink collars, black , green & black

CHICHESTER INSTITUTE
Sussex 2
Ground Address: Bishop Otter Cottage, College Lane, Chichester, West Sussex PO19 4PE
Tel: 01243 816 043.
Secretary: I Davies, Ch. I.H.E., Bishop Otter Campus, New Hall, College Lane, Chichester PO19 4PE
Tel: 01243 787314 (H) 01243 816043 (B) 01243 816080 (F).
Fixture Secretary: I Davies, Ch. I.H.E., Bishop Otter Campus, New Hall, College Lane, Chichester PO19 4PE Tel: 01243 787314 (H) 01243 816043 (B) 01243 816080 (F).

CHICHESTER RFC
London 3 South East
Ground Address: Oaklands Park, Wellington Road, Chichester, West Sussex
Tel: 01243 779820
Brief Directions: Oaklands Park is near The Festival Theatre.
Club Secretary: Simon Hill, St Ronans, 8 Clayton Ave, Selsey, West Sussex. PO20 4OB
Tel: (H) 01243 602598 (W) 01243 781000
Fixtures Secretary: F. Corby, Caretakers Cottage, School Lane, Selsey, West Sussex, PO20 9EH
Club Colours: Dark blue and light blue hoops

CHINEHAM
Hampshire 2

CHINGFORD RFC
London 3 North East
Ground Address: Lea Valley Playing Fields, Waltham Way, Chingford, London. E4 8AQ
Tel: 0181 529 4879
Brief Directions: M11 to A406 westbound,approx 3miles to Cook's ferry junction. Signs to Chingford, around roundabout,under viaduct and led into 1009.over mini roundabout then 1 mile on left.
Club Secretary: Howard Hartley, 127A The Ridgeway, Chingford, E4 6QU
Tel: 0181 559 5774
Fixtures Secretary: David Butler
Tel: (H) 0181 529 3412 (W) 0181 529 4879
Club Colours: Black jerseys with royal blue and white hoops

CHIPSTEAD RFC
Surrey 2
Ground Address: The Meads, High Road, Chipstead, Surrey
Tel: 01737 553035
Brief Directions: From London via Coulsdon thence Portnalls Road and Coulsdon Lane into High Road. Ground is on left behind the pond and village hall.
Club Secretary: Tony Greig, 8 Yew Tree Close, Chipstead, Surrey CR5 3LH Tel: (W) 0171 327 3415 Tel: (H) 01737 552396
Fixtures Secretary: R. W. Adair, 56 Woodcrest Road, Purley, Surrey CR8 4JB
Tel: (H) 0181 668 3428 (W) 0181 686 8911
Club Colours: Gold and royal blue

CHISWICK RFC (FORMERLY KNOWN AS **OLD MEADONIANS)**
London 3 North West
Ground Address: Riverside Lands, Chiswick. W4
Tel: 0181 995 6956
Brief Directions: A316 to Chiswick bridge, turn left along Riverside Lands
Club Secretary: Adrian Lewis, 21 Paxton Road, Chiswick, London. W4 2QT
Tel: (H) 0181 995 0927 (W) 0171 378 5510
Fixtures Secretary: Roger Willmgale
Tel: (H) 01932 866927
Club Colours: Sky blue and maroon

CHOBHAM RFC
Surrey 1
Ground Address: Fowlers Wells, Windsor Road, Chobham, Woking, Surrey. GU24 8NA
Tel: 01276 858616
Brief Directions: Take road to Sunningdale out of village centre (B383), ground is 500 yards on right behind Cobham Working Mens Club
Club Secretary: Mrs Pam Squire, Cobbitts, Guildford Road, Chobham, Woking, Surrey. GU24 8EA
Tel: (H) 01276 858438
Fixtures Secretary: Duncan Souster, The Jarrow, Ivy Dene, KNaphill, Surrey GU2 12TA
Tel NO: 01483 832104
Club Colours: Navy Blue with Scarlet and gold hoops

CHRISTCHURCH COLLEGE
Kent 3

CIVIL SERVICE FC (RU)

Hertfordshire & Middlesex 1
Ground Address: Dukes Meadows, Riverside Drive, Chiswick. W4
Tel: 0181 994 1202
Brief Directions: By road: From Hogarth Roundabout (A4) take A316 towards Richmond.After 1/2 mile turn left at traffic lights into Riverside Drive.By Train: Waterloo to Barnes Bridge, over bridge on right
Club Secretary: N G Alway, 20 Herndon Road, London. SW18 2DG
Tel: (H) 0181 8706818 (W) 0171 583 5333
Fixtures Secretary: R Hulme
Tel: (H) 01438 832 054
Club Colours: White shirts

COBHAM RFC

London 3 South West
Ground Address: The Memorial Ground, Fairmile Lane, Cobham, Surrey Tel: 01932 863245
Brief Directions: Ground situated on junction of Fairmile Lane and the Portsmouth road (A307) approx 3 miles from Esher, 1 mile from Cobham opposite Fairmile Hotel
Club Secretary: Andrew Harburn, 21 The Avenue, Surbiton, Surrey, KT5 8JW/
Tel: 0181 8482738
Fixtures Secretary: Ian Johnson, 209 Portsmouth Road, Cobham, Surrey, KT11 1JR.
Tel: (H) 01932 862694 (W) 0181 942 1033
Club Colours: Blue, maroon and gold quarters

COLCHESTER RFC

London 3 North East
Ground Address: Mill Road, Colchester. CO4 5JF
Tel: 01206 851610
Brief Directions: Turn off A12 onto A1232, right at roundabout into business park, right at next roundabout, straight over next roundabout into Mill Road, ground is 400yds on right
Club Secretary: Ron Hatch, 99 Ernest Road, Wivenhoe. CO7 9LJ
Tel: (H) 01206 823548
Fixtures Secretary: Jon Roberts
Tel: (H) 01621 854043
Club Colours: Black

CRANBROOK RFC

London 3 South East
Ground Address: Tomlin Ground, Angley Road, Cranbrook, Kent. TN17 3LB Tel: 01580 712777
Brief Directions: Off A229 Hastings road, 14 miles south of Maidstone, 4 miles north of Hawkhurst at junction of Cranbrook bypass with Whitewell Lane
Club Secretary: David Davies, Beeches, Station Road, Staplehurst, Kent. TN12 0QG
Tel: (H) 01580 891448 (W) 01580 891448
Fixtures Secretary: Alan Shorter, 2 Thornden Cottages, Rolvenden Layne, Cranbrook. TN17 4PS Tel: (H) 01580 241409 (W) 01580 890095
Club Colours: Magenta and white

CRANLEIGH RFC

London 3 South West
Ground Address: Wildwood Lane, Alfold, Cranleigh, Surrey Tel: 01483 275843
Brief Directions: From Guildford A281 towards Horsham, left turn after Bookers Lea Farm, signed Cranleigh Brickworks. From Cranleigh High St, via Knowle Lane turn right at Wildwood Lane
Club Secretary: Mrs Christine Williams, 36 Sylvaways Close, Cranleigh, Surrey. GU6 7HG
Tel: (H) 01483 276928
Fixtures Secretary: Mr N Spong. Tel No: 01483 272700
Club Colours: Red and navy blue quarters, red socks, blue shorts

CRAWLEY RFC

London 3 South East
Ground Address: Willoughby Fields, 1 Field Avenue, Cranley Tel: 01293 533995
Brief Directions: Off A23 Crawley bypass from north take M23 J10 onto A23 bypass, 1.5 miles pass Sainsburys, right at next roundabout into Field Ave towards Charlwood, ground approx 0,75 mile on right
Club Secretary: Paul Chapman, 19 Longwood View, Furnace Green, Crawley, West Sussex.
Tel No: 01293 446961
Fixtures Secretary: Lee McDonough. Tel No: 01293 552114
Club Colours: Maroon and blue hoops

CROWBOROUGH RFC

Sussex 1
Ground Address: Steel Cross, Crowborough, East Sussex Tel: 01892 654832
Brief Directions: South on A26 from Tunbridge Wells, Club signposted at roundabout after village of Boarshead
Club Secretary: Gavin Tyler, 3 Wallis Close, Crowborough, East Sussex. TN6 2YA
Tel: (H) 01892 665153 (W) 01892 506155
Fixtures Secretary: Carol Stevenson, 4 Howard Place, Alexandra Road, Uckfield, TN22 5QQ.
Tel: 01825 760963
Club Colours: Red with graduated white hoops, blue shorts

CROYDON RFC

Surrey 3
Ground Address: Layhams Road (junction with King Henry's Drive), Keston, Bromley, Kent
Tel: 01959 573409
Brief Directions: A2022 to Addington Village, at r'bout 200yds beyond Gravel Hill, fork south to New Addington as signed up Lodge Ln, left at next r'bout into King Henry's Drive, left at end into Layhams Rd
Club Secretary: Trevor Davies, 62 Coulsdon Road, Coulsdon, Surrey. CR5 2LB
Tel: (H) 0181 668 4864 (W) 0171 976 0066
Fixtures Secretary: Alan Doe, 16 Cherry Hill Gardens, Waddan, Croydon, CR0 4QL Tel: (H) 0181 581 0793
Club Colours: Black, magenta & white hoops. Black shorts and red socks.

CRUSADERS RUFC

Eastern Counties 3 North
Ground Address: Beck Hythe, Little Melton, Nr Norwich, Norfolk Tel: 01603 811157
Brief Directions: Situated in Little Melton, S.E. of Norwich. From southern bypass take Watton Rd (B1108), turn left past the garden centre, thro' village, pass village inn, next left, 1st right, club 400yds right
Club Secretary: John Alton Jones, Norwich Food Co, 19 Alston Road, Hellesden Park, Norwich
Tel: (W) 01603 486666
Fixtures Secretary: Michael Bridgman
Tel: (H) 01603 250926
Club Colours: Gold and emerald green hoops, black shorts, green socks

CUFFLEY RFC
Hertfordshire & Middlesex 3 North
Ground Address: Cheshunt School, College Road, Cheshunt, Herts. EN7 9LY
Brief Directions: Approx 2 miles north of J25 on M25 on the A10, turn left by 1st set of traffic lights, school 50 yards on left opposite Crocodile public house
Club Secretary: C A Palmer, 10 Connaught Road, Harpenden, Herts. AL5 4HF
Tel: (H) 01582 768152 (W) 0171 895 1515
Fixtures Secretary: P Cushing
Tel: (H) 01455 5557568 (W) 01582 470605
Club Colours: Red with black hoop

DAGENHAM RFC
Eastern Counties 4 South
Ground Address: Central Park Pavilion, Central Park, Rainham Road North, Dagenham, Essex. RM10
Tel: 0181 593 8302
Club Secretary: R J Moreton, 21 Central Park Avenue, Dagenham, Essex. RM10 7DA
Tel: (H) 0181 984 8444
Fixtures Secretary: R J Moreton
Tel: (H) 0181 984 8444
Club Colours: Red and white quarters

DARENTH VALLEY RFC
Kent 2 West
Ground Address: The Leigh Clubhouse, Leigh City Technical College, Green Street, Dartford, Kent
Tel: 01322 290801
Brief Directions: M25 J1, take road towards Dartford (across M25), 1st left at roundabout (past petrol garage) and 1st right onto College campus
Club Secretary: Mrs. Christine Murray, c/o Greengarth Borough, Green Road, Ightam, Sevenoaks, Kent TN15 9HS
Tel No: 0802 704724
Fixtures Secretary: Mr. Will Willetts, The Billiards House, Summerhill, Headcorn, Kent, TN27 9NX. Tel: (H) 01622 891866
Club Colours: Black with white V

DARTFORDIANS RUFC
London 3 South East
Ground Address: Bourne Road, Bexley, Kent
Tel: 01322 524176
Club Secretary: Jack Morris, 7 Irving Way, Swanley, Kent. BR8 7EP
Tel: (H) 01322 669817
Fixtures Secretary: D Rapley
Tel: (H) 0181 857 6198
Club Colours: Maroon and old gold.

DATCHWORTH RFC
Hertfordshire & Middlesex 2
Ground Address: Datchworth Green, Datchworth, Herts. SG3 6TL
Tel: 01438 812490
Brief Directions: Leave A1(M) at J6 (Welwyn) on B197 north towards Stevenage, at Woolmer Green turn right towards Datchworth, pitches and clubhouse behind tennis courts
Club Secretary: Mrs L D Wyatt, 7 Hazeldell, Watton-at-Stone, Hertford. SG14 3SL
Tel: (H) 01920 830407
Fixtures Secretary: (Pre-season) Mr P Nightingale Tel: (H) 01438 820500 (During season) Mr T Johnson Tel: (H) 01438 814460
Club Colours: Green shirts and socks, black shorts

DEAL WANDERERS RUFC
Kent 2 East
Ground Address: Clubhouse, Western Road, Deal, Kent. Tel:01304 365892
Brief Directions: The ground is located at the junction of West Street and Western Avenue to the North West of the town centre
Club Secretary: Chris Rook, 2 Wesleyan House, Union Road, DEal Kent Ct14 6EA
Tel No: 01304 379136
Fixtures Secretary: Andy Bodman. Tel No: 01304 375750
Club Colours: Yellow & Blue Hoops

DISS RFC
London 2 North
Ground Address: Mackenders, Bellrope Lane, Roydon, Diss, Norfolk
Tel: 01379 642891
Brief Directions: 1 mile west of Diss on A1066 through Roydon village, at end of 40mph limit turn into Bellrope Lane opposite White Hart pub, club 150 yards on left
Club Secretary: N P Kingsley, Diss RFC, c/o Unit 18, Diss Business Centre, Frenze, Diss, Norfolk. IP21 4EY
Tel: (H) 01379 641717 (Fax) 01379 651177
Fixtures Secretary: J Green
Tel: (H) 01379 741705
Club Colours: Royal blue and white

DITCHLING RFC
Sussex 2
Ground Address: The Playing Fields, Lewes Road, Ditchling, East Sussex
Tel: 01273 843423
Brief Directions: From the village crossroads, head east on the Lewes Road and the ground is approx 0.25 mile down on the left
Club Secretary: Robert Boswell, 60 Kings Way, Burgess Hill, WEst Sussex.
Fixtures Secretary: Chris Atkinson, 170 Leylands Road, Burgess Hill, West Sussex
Tel: (H) 01444 416174 (W) 0181 681 5500
Club Colours: Myrtle green shirts, white shorts

DORKING RFC
London 2 South
Ground Address: The Pavilion, The Big Field, Kiln Lane, Brockham, Betchworth, Surrey. RH3 7LZ
Tel: 01737 843928
Brief Directions: From Dorking take A25 to Reigate after 2 miles turn right towards Brockham, then first left into Kiln Lane
Club Secretary: Mr Mark Gardner, 30 The Borough, Brockham, Betchworth,
Surrey. RH3 7NB
Tel: (H) 0173 784 4258 (W) 01372 378 788
Fixtures Secretary: Geoff Taylor, 27 Dodds Park Road, Reigate, surrey, RH2 0PZ
Tel: 01737 244142
Club Colours: Red and white hoops, Blue shorts

DOVER RFC

Kent 1

Ground Address: Crabble Athletic Ground, Crabble Road, River, Dover, Kent Tel: 01304 210296

Brief Directions: From M2/A2, at Esso garage take River exit, left at mini r'bout, sharp right at lights, 300m on left. From M20/A20 leave Dover to Canterbury, fork left at lights on Crabble Hill, 300m on left

Club Secretary: J D Thomas, Karma, Minnis Lane, River, Dover. CT17 0PT Tel: (H) 01304 822169

Fixtures Secretary: P.Batty-Smith, 46 Lower Road, River, Dover CT17 0QY Tel No: 01304 823163

Club Colours: Light and dark blue hoops

EALING

London 3 North West

Ground Address: Berkeley Avenue, Greenford, Middlesex. UB6 0NZ Tel: 0181 422 0868

Brief Directions: Take A40 - Western Ave to Greenford Rd fly over, turn north onto A4127 (Greenford Rd), Berkeley Ave 1 mile up on right just past canal bridge, opposite Glaxo offices

Club Secretary: Mr. M. Carroll, 132 Byron Way, Northolt, Middx Tel: (H) 0181 723 1908

Fixtures Secretary: Paul Monteith
Tel: (H) 01572 757021 (W) 0171 204 2932

Club Colours: White shorts, green and white stripes

EAST GRINSTEAD RFC

London 3 South East

Ground Address: Saint Hill Green, East Grinstead, West Sussex. RH19 4JU Tel: 01342 322338

Brief Directions: On Minor Road to Horsted Keynes off B2110 Turners Hill Road

Club Secretary: Mrs Carol Chandler, Rushbrook, Little Frenches Farm, Snowhill, Copthorne, Surrey. RH10 3EG Tel: (H) 01342 718933

Fixtures Secretary: R P Russell
Tel: (H) 01342 834648

Club Colours: White with varied blue hoops.

EAST LONDON RUFC

Eastern Counties 2

Ground Address: Holland Road, West Ham, London. E15 3BP Tel: 0171 476 5526

Brief Directions: From Canning Town roundabout proceed down Manor Road, turn right before West Ham tube station follow road round and turn right at Holland Road

Club Secretary: Ian Bessant, 111Croydon Road, Plaistow, London E13 8EP
Tel: (H) 0171 474 3770 (W) 0171 9767213

Fixtures Secretary: Rob Williams
Tel: (H) 0181 558 8651 (W) 0181 5563322

Club Colours: Maroon and navy hoops

EASTBOURNE RFC

London 3 South East

Ground Address: Park Avenue, Hampden Park, Eastbourne, East Sussex. BN22 9QN
Tel: 01323 503076

Brief Directions: 500yds north of Eastbourne District General Hospital, clearly signposted.

Club Secretary: Hugh Graham, 17A Pashley Road, Eastbourne, East Sussex. BN20 8DU
Tel: (H) 01323 646600

Fixtures Secretary: David Hone, 43 Kings Avenue, Eastbourne Tel: 01323 738986

Club Colours: Navy blue and gold

ECCLES RFC

Eastern Counties 4 North

Ground Address: Gorton Street, Peel Green, Eccles, M30 7LZ Tel: 0161 789 2613

Brief Directions: M63 J2 towards Eccles, Gorton Street 2nd on left

Club Secretary: A C Brunt, 12 Woodstock Drive, Worsley, Manchester. M28 2WW
Tel: (H) 0161 794 4114

Fixtures Secretary: A E Chettoe, 16 Sandalwood, Westhoughton, Bolton, BL5 2RQ.
Tel: (H) 0161 794 5642 (W) 0161 790 7711

Club Colours: Navy blue and white hoops, white shorts

EASTLEIGH RFC

Hampshire 2

Ground Address: Bishopstoke Playing Fields, Bishopstoke Road, Eastleigh Tel: 01703 641312

Brief Directions: From Eastleigh Railway station take turning over railway bridge to Fair Oak and ground is approx 600 yards up on the left

Club Secretary: M.B.Jones, 15 Corvette Avenue, Warsash, Southampton SO31 9AN Tel: 01439 579493.

Fixtures Secretary: Dr J S Sneezum Tel: (H) 01703 402286

Club Colours: Red, amber and black hoops

ECONOMICALS RUFC
Surrey 4
Ground Address: LSE Sports Ground, Windsor Avenue, New Malden, Surrey
Tel: 0181 942 1229
Brief Directions: A3 southbound, right at New Malden roundabout, 3rd left into Presbury Rd leads into Windsor Ave. A3 north, left into South Lane, 2nd left Thetford Rd leads into Windsor Ave
Club Secretary: Steve Bowen, 60 South Eden Park Road, Beckenham, Kent, BR3 3BG.
Tel: 0181 7762953
Fixtures Secretary: Steve Bowen
Tel: (H) 0181 7762953
Club Colours: Black with a Gren and Gold Band

EDENBRIDGE RFC
Kent 2 East
Ground Address: The Pavilion, Lingfield Road Recreation Ground, Lingfield Road, Edenbridge, Kent. TN8
Tel: 01732 862435
Brief Directions: From Edenbridge High Street travelling south, turn right into Stangrove Road, left into Crouch House Road, right into Lingfield Road.
Club Secretary: N. A. Dearmer, 13 Court Drive, Sutton, Surrey, SM1 3RG.
Tel: (H) 0181 6437791 (W) 01707 662662
Fixtures Secretary: John Martin, Little Acre, Swan Lane, Edenbridge, Kent, TN8 6AJ.
Tel: (H) 01732 862761
Club Colours: Black and yellow hoops

EFFINGHAM & LEATHERHEAD RFC
London 2 South
Ground Address: King George V Playing Fields, Browns Lane, Effingham, Surrey, KT24 5ND.
Tel: 07070 704136.
`Web Site' http;//www.eaglesrugby.co.uk.
E-mail Eagles@eaglesrugby.co.uk.
Brief Directions: M25 J.10. Effingham signpost left on slip road south bound from M25 to A3, follow road until Lord Howard pub on R. go R. then L. forward until lights, then L. and 1st L.
Club Secretary: Alistair Aird, 32c Upper Bridge Road, Redhill Surrey, RH1 6DD
Tel No: 01737 289283. E-mail: aliaird@breathemail.net
Fixtures Secretary: Ed Newton, 42 Milner Road, Kingston upon Thames, Surrey, KT1 2AU. E-mail: ed@42milnerrd.freeserve.co.uk
Tel: (H) 0181 549 8213 - (W)0171 6283700
Club Colours: Emerald green and amber hoops, black shorts

EGHAM RUFC
Surrey 3
Ground Address: Sports Field, Kings Lane, Englefield Green, Egham TW20
Brief Directions: Arrive St. Judes Road, Englefield Green, turn into Bond Street, follow into Kings Lane, entrance 75 yards on left
Club Secretary: David Evans, 42 Armetrong Road, Englefield Green, Egham TW20 0RW
Tel: (H) 01784 432915
Fixtures Secretary: Paul Ellis, 14 Rydal Way, Egham, Surry TW20 8JH
Tel: (H) 01784 094000 (email) ellis@btinternet.com
Club Colours: Mid blue with gold hoop

ELLINGHAM & RINGWOOD RFC
Hampshire 3
Ground Address: Picket Post, Ringwood, Hants
Tel: 01425 476668
Club Secretary: Douglas Middleton, 56 Eastfield Lane, Ringwood, Hants. BH24 1UP
Tel: (H) 01425 475521 (W) 01202 893000
Fixtures Secretary: Philip Lambert
Tel: (H) 01425 476643
Club Colours: Blue and amber

ELY RUFC
London 3 North East
Ground Address: Downham Road Playing Fields, Ely, Cambs Tel: 01353 662363
Brief Directions: Just North of Ely. L.H.S. of A10 bypass which is signed Downham Market, King's Lynn.
Club Secretary: Christopher Ormerod, 14, Ponts Hill, Littleport, Cambs.
Tel/FAX: 01353 863425 Mobile: 0467 248056
Fixtures Secretary: Martin Hammond, Hillcrest House, 110 Bexwell Road, Downham Market, Norfolk, PE388 9LH.
Tel: (H) 01366 384990 Fax: 01366 385739
Club Colours: Gold and black hoops, black shorts

ENFIELD IGNATIANS RFC
Hertfordshire & Middlesex 1
Ground Address: Queen Elisabeth Stadium, Donkey Lane, Enfield, Middlesex
Tel: 0187 363 2877
Brief Directions: M25 J25 south on A10 to Carterhatch Lane, follow signs
Club Secretary: Glyn Jones, 45 Halifax Road, Enfield, Middlesex
Tel: (H) 0181 366 3207 (W) 0181 967 9474
Fixtures Secretary: Pete Tiernan
Tel: (H) 0181 529 8130
Club Colours: Blue and gold

ERITH RFC
Kent 2 West
Ground Address: Sussex Road, Northumberland Heath Playing Fields, Northumberland Heath, Erith, Kent Tel: 01322 432295
Brief Directions: A2 towards London, Blackprince turn off towards Erith, turn left into Brook St and left into Sussex Road
Club Secretary: R W Shepherd, 24 Lesney Park, Erith, Kent. DA8 3DN
Tel: (H) 01322 341073 (W) 0181 285 7082
Fixtures Secretary: S Button
Tel: (H) 01322 387689
Club Colours: Light and dark blue hoops, blue shorts

ESSO (FAWLEY) RFC
London 3 South West
Ground Address: Esso Recreation Ground, 179-181 Long Lane, Holbury, Southampton.
Tel: 01703 893750
Brief Directions: From M27 J2 follow A326 to Fawley for approx 8 miles. Ground on right after Haraley Roundabout.
Club Secretary: Gordon Powell, 7 Charnwood Way, Blackfield, Southampton, SO45 1ZL. Tel: (H) 01703 891133
Fixtures Secretary: Ray Lewis, 2 Sherwood Way, Blackfield, Southampton. SO45 1ZQ . Tel No: 01703 898391
Club Colours: Red shirts, Navy blue shorts, red socks

ETON MANOR RFC
London 3 North East
Ground Address: Eastway Sports Centre, Quartermile Lane, London. E10
Tel: 0181 555 2670
Club Secretary: Mr John Ayling, 44 Lytton Road, Leytonstone, London. E11 1JH
Tel: (H) 0181 558 1800 (W) 0171 831 3666
Fixtures Secretary: Martin Scott
Tel: (H) 0181 530 4451
Club Colours: Dark blue with light blue hoops dark blue shorts

FAREHAM HEATHENS RFC
Hampshire 2
Ground Address: Cams Alders Sports Centre, Highfield Avenue, Fareham
Tel: 01329 221793
Brief Directions: From Fareham centre A27 west signed S'hampton, at Firestation r'bout stay on A27 for 100m, rt at lights Redlands Ln, rt at next j'tion by pub/church, Sports C'tre next left
Club Secretary: R Townsend, 9 Daisy Lane, Locksheath, Southampton. SO31 6RA
Tel: (H) 01489 574945
Fixtures Secretary: Pete Mitchell, 2 Chilworth Gardens, Clanfield, Portsmouth, PO8 0LD.
Tel: 01705 348744
Club Colours: Red and black quarters

FARNBOROUGH RUFC
Hampshire 1
Ground Address: Tile Barn Close, Cove, Farnborough, Hampshire. GU14 8LS
Tel: 01252 542750
Brief Directions: M3 J4, follow road signs to A325 Farnborough, at 1st set of lights, follow direction signs to Rugby Club
Club Secretary: JPaul Davies, 33 Wentworth Crescent, Ash Vale, Aldershot.
Tel No: 01252 674421
Fixtures Secretary: Barry Mackay, 43 The Grove, Farnborough, GU14 6QS
Tel: (H) 01252 512363
Club Colours: Dark and light blue hoops

FARNHAM RUFC
Surrey 1
Ground Address: Westfield Lane, Wreulesham, Farnham, Surrey. GU10 4QP
Tel: 01252 721138
Brief Directions: Take A325 to Petersfield from A31 Farnham bypass, after 0.75 mile pass Bear & Ragged Staff pub on right turn next right into Riverdale, 1st left onto recreation ground
Club Secretary: Derek R Wall, 22 Hope Lane, Farnham, Surrey. GU9 0HZ
Tel: (H) 01252 710476
Fixtures Secretary: Bob Smith, 21 Riverside Close, Farnborough, Hants GU14 8Q5
Tel: 01252 650719 (H) 01256 484185 (W)
Club Colours: Black & yellow with one white hoop

FAVERSHAM RUFC
Kent 2 East
Ground Address: Faversham Recreation Ground Lodge, Faversham, Kent. ME13 8HA
Tel: 01795 530651
Club Secretary: Pat Rowan, 14 Abbey Street, Faversham, Kent. ME13 7BE
Tel: (H) 01795 530651
Fixtures Secretary: Pat Rowan
Tel: (H) 01795 530651
Club Colours: Sky blue and white squares

FELIXSTOWE RUFC
Eastern Counties 1
Ground Address: Coronation Sports Ground, Mill Lane, Felixstowe, Suffolk. IP11 8LN
Tel: 01394 270150
Brief Directions: Follow A14 to Felixstowe, at roundabout take right to dock, 1st slip road come off, left at bottom, right at mini roundabout, next mini roundabout turn right
Club Secretary: Danny Cain,16 Berners Rd., Felixstowe, Suffolk. 1P11 7LF
Tel: (H) 01394 278112
Fixtures Secretary: Wayne Bagley, 8Hyldon Court, Wolsey Gardens, Felixstowe, Suffolk. 1P 11 7NR
Tel: 01394 273038 (H) 0410 442396 (Mobile)
Club Colours: Black and white hooped shirts, black shorts

FELTHAM RFC
Hertfordshire & Middlesex 1
Ground Address: Park Road, Hanworth, Middlesex
Tel: 0181 894 3609
Brief Directions: Hanworth Road (located near the air park)
Club Secretary: S C Griffiths, 27 Fosse Way, Ealing, London. W13 0BZ
Tel: (H) 0181 997 6153 (W) 0181 861 1313
Fixtures Secretary: W.Orrell, 52 Ormond Drive, Hampton, TW12 2TN
Club Colours: Dark blue, light blue and gold

FINCHLEY RFC
London 2 North
Ground Address: Summers Lane, Finchley, London. N12 0PD
Tel: 0181 445 3746
Brief Directions: From North Circular Rd (A406) take A1000 north towards Barnet/N Finchley, past Leisure centre on right, turn right at lights into Summers Ln, ground 100yds on right
Club Secretary: D G Wedderburn Esq, 41 Oxford Gardens, Whetstone, London. N20 9AG
Tel: (H) 0181 446 2430 (W) 0171 378 9988
Fixtures Secretary: Leo Gibbons.
Tel No: 0208 368 7253
Club Colours: Scarlet and white hoops

FLEET RUFC
Hampshire 3
Ground Address: Wavell-Cody School, Lynchford Road, Farnborough, Hants. GU14 6BH
Brief Directions: M3 J4 follow signs for A331, turn right at first roundabout (Lynchford Road), ground is on left just past Fire station and opposite Forte Post House Hotel on A325
Club Secretary: Merrik Knight, 31 Osborne Road, Farnborough, Hants. GU14 6AE Tel: (H) 01252 654818 (M) 0802 976691
Fixtures Secretary: Lauren Wadehn,22 Twisell Thorne, Church Crookham, Fleet GU13 0YT
Tel: 01252 623701
Club Colours: Red and Royal Blue hoops blue shorts and red socks.

FOLKESTONE RFC
London 3 South East
Ground Address: New Burlington Field, Bargrove, Newington, Folkestone, Kent. CT18 8BH
Tel: (H) 01303 266887
Brief Directions: Take the Hythe Road (B2065) from the A20 (Ashford to Folkestone road), 1 m on left. From London M20 Exit J12 (Cheriton).Follow A20 for 1m then B2065 to Hythe.1/4m on Rt.
Club Secretary: Barry Keating, Carbery, Church Hill, Hythe, Kent. CT21 5DW
Tel: (H) 01303 264604
Fixtures Secretary: A D Ruddock
Tel: (H) 01303 276530
Club Colours: Green and white hooped shirts, white shorts, green and white socks

FOOTSCRAY RUFC
Kent 2 West
Ground Address: 239A Foots Cray Road, New Eltham, London. SE9 2EL
Club Secretary: Rob Wara, 7 Eastview Avenue, Plumstead, London SE18 2HU
Tel: (H) 981 854 6747
Fixtures Secretary: Tony Codd, 74 Felthampton Road, New Eltham, London SE9 3NX
Tel: (H) 0181 857 6040
Club Colours: Royal Blue and gold hoops, blue shorts

FORXINGBRIDGE RFC
Hampshire 3
Ground Address: Recreation Ground, Fordingbridge, Hants Tel: 01425 652047
Brief Directions: Off A338 (12 miles south of Salisbury and 15 miles north of Bournemouth) alongside by-pass, western side adjacent to river .
Club Secretary: Mr K.A.Young, 1 Elmwood Avenue, Fordingbridge, Hants. SP6 1DL
Tel No: 01425 652681
Fixtures Secretary: John Trim, Trees, Fryern Court Road, Fordingbridge, Hants SP6 1NG
Tel: (H) 01425 655156 (W) 01202 664781
Club Colours: Sky blue , black shorts, sky blue or black hooped socks

FULLERIANS RFC
London 3 North West
Ground Address: Watford Grammar School, New Field, Coningesby Drive (end of Parkside Dr), Watford, Herts Tel: 01923 237974
Brief Directions: From Hunton Bridge Roundabout on A41 (J13 M25) follow Hempstead Rd towards Watford town centre. Turn rt.at lights into Langley Way then turn right at end into Coningesby Drive
Club Secretary: Chris Windsor, 5 Nascot Road, Watford, Herts WD1 3RD
Tel: (H) 01923 442355 (W) 0171 393 6169
Fixtures Secretary: N.Thomas, 11 Ashridge Close, Bovingdon, Herts.
Tel: 01442 834 226
Club Colours: Red, green and black hooped shirts & stocks, black shorts

GILLINGHAM ANCHORIANS RFC
Kent 1
Ground Address: Watling Street Playing Fields, off Darland Avenue, Gillingham, Kent
Tel: 01634 851495
Brief Directions: Leave M2 by A278, turn left at terminal roundabout (signed A2 Gillingham), across new roundabout, left at 2nd traffic lights at Darland Ave, ground 200 yards on left
Club Secretary: I.C. Price, 78 Broadview Avenue, Rainham, Gillingham, Kent. ME8 9DE
Fixtures Secretary: Mr Doug Chidley, 67 Parkfield Road, Rainham, Gillingham, Kent ME8 7TA
Tel: (H) 01634 376891
Club Colours: Purple, black and white hoops

GOSPORT AND FAREHAM RFC
London 3 South West
Ground Address: Gosport Park, Dolphin Crescent, Gosport, Hants. PO12 2HE Tel: 01705 353235
Brief Directions: M27 J11, A32 Gosport at dble r'bout, lft at 2nd r'bout, past HMS Sultan lft at r'bout, r.h. lane after Kellys Hotel & immediate left, 5th rt (Molesw'th Rd), turn right & left over bridge
Club Secretary: Ian Rackham, 265 Hawthorn Crescent, Cosham ,Portsmouth PO6 2TL
Tel: (H) 01705 796625
Fixtures Secretary: Mr P Tomlinson
Tel: (H) 01705 617673
Club Colours: Royal blue and old gold

GRASSHOPPERS RFC
London 3 North West
Ground Address: Macfarla, Middlesex Tel: 0181 568 0010ne Sports Field, Macfarlane Lane, off Syon Lane, Osterley Tel: 0181 568 0010
Brief Directions: Train: to Syon stn, lft out of stn to major Xroads, straight on across Gt Wst Rd (A4), ground 0.5 mile on right after Tescos. Road: Frm L'don on A4, rt into Syon Ln at Gillette Cnr
Club Secretary: Mr. A Dean, 29 Albert Road, Twickenham, Middlesex TW1 4HU
Fixtures Secretary: Andy Brown
Tel: (H) 0181 560 4844 (W) 0181 560 2583
Club Colours: Green, gold and black hoops, black shorts and socks

GRAVESEND RFC
London 2 South
Ground Address: The Rectory Field, Milton Road, Gravesend, Kent. DA12 2PP
Brief Directions: M25 A2 intersection, head towards Dover, leave A2 at Gravesend East (Valley Drive), follow 1.75 mile to end, right at roundabout, 1st left, ground 0.75 miles on left
Club Secretary: John Moore, 375A Singlewell Road, Gravesend, Kent. DA11 7RL
Tel: (H) 01474 362998
Fixtures Secretary: Bobby Wright
Tel: (H) 01474 327303
Club Colours: Four inch black and white hoops

GREAT WESTERN RAILWAY RFC
Hertfordshire & Middlesex 4 South
Ground Address: G. W. Railway (London) RFC, Castle Bar Park, Vallis Way, West Ealing W13. Tel: 0181 998 7928
Brief Directions: By train to Ealing Broadway, then to Castle Bar Park Halt via E1, E2 or E9 buses.
Club Secretary: Peter Allsop, 41 Lyncroft Avenue, Pinner, Middlesex HA5 1JU. Tel: (H) 0181 866 0532
Fixtures Secretary: Roy Sullivan, Tel: (H) 0181 575 6074
Club Colours: Cardinal and black jerseys.

GREENWICH ACADEMICALS RFC
Kent 2 West
Ground Address: Poly Sports and Social Club, Kidbrooke Lane, Eltham, London. SE9 6TA
Tel: 0181 850 0210
Brief Directions: Kidbrooke Lane is a turning off the South Circular - called Westhorne Ave at this point - and is 300 yards from the intersection of the A2 and the South Circular
Club Secretary: Huw Davies, 29 Cumberland Avenue, Welling ,Kent DA16 2PT
Tel No: 0181 301 5531
Fixtures Secretary: Danny Hogan. Tel No: 0181 310 6980
Club Colours: Green with gold and red bands

GREENWICH RFC
Kent 2 West
Ground Address: The Pavilion, Old Mill Road, Plumstead, London SE18. Tel: 0181 854 8637
Brief Directions: Off Plumstead Common opposite Old Mill public house.
Club Secretary: Nick Wallden,277 Wickham Lane, Abbey Wood, London SE2 0NX
Tel: 0181 854 0092
Fixtures Secretary: George Dorton c/o secretaries address
Tel: 0181 687 5235
Club Colours: Red and black quarters, black shorts.

GUERNSEY RUFC
Hampshire 1
Ground Address: Footes Lane, St Peter Port, Guernsey Tel: 01481 54590
Club Secretary: B J Mildon, P O Box 181, St Peter Port, Guernsey
Tel: (H) 01481 65493 (W) 01481 715055
Fixtures Secretary: Greg Ahme, La Chanson, Route de L'Ancresse, Vale, Guernsey.
Tel: 01481 45090
Club Colours: Green and white

GUYS HOSPITAL RFC
Kent 1
Ground Address: Honor Oak Park, London. SE23 1NW Tel: 0181 690 1612
Brief Directions: South Circular A205 onto B218 (Brockley Rise), crossroads B238 turn right 200 yards club on right
Club Secretary: Richard Clinton, 385 Southwark Park Road, Bermondsey. SE16
Tel: (H) 0171 237 0522 (W) 0171 955 5000 Ext 5430
Fixtures Secretary: Graham Cawtom
Tel: (H) 0171 735 3857 (W) 0171 955 4255
Club Colours: Blue and gold hoops

HACKNEY RFC
Hertfordshire & Middlesex 3 North
Ground Address: Spring Hill, Clapton, London. E5
Tel: 0181 806 5289
Club Secretary: David Clarke, 31 Cowley Road, Wanstead, London. E11 2HA
Tel: (H) 0181 926 2310 (W) 0181 262 5000
Fixtures Secretary: G.Noga , 11 Hookstone Way, Woodford Green, Essex IG8 7LF
Tel: (H) 0181 304 2577 (W) 0181 985 2349
Club Colours: Gold, blue and green quarters

HADLEIGH RUFC
London 3 North East
Ground Address: Layham Road Sports Ground, Hadleigh, Ipswich, Suffolk. IP7 5NE
Tel: 01473 824217
Brief Directions: From Hadleigh High St turn into Layham Rd (flanked by library and chemist), over bridge and go on round bends, ground is on the left
Club Secretary: Jane Stannard, 21 Kersey Close, Stowmarket, Suffolk IP14 2BG Tel no: 01449 77496o
Fixtures Secretary: Mike Harris,24 Heath Est., Gt. Waldringfield, Sudbury CO10 0TZ
Tel: 01787 312685
Club Colours: Maroon and gold

HAMBLE
Hampshire 2
Ground Address: Hamble School, Satchell Lane, Hamble, Southampton
Brief Directions: Take Jct 8 off M27, Satchell Lane is a left off Hamble lane Approx. 2 miles from jct 8
Club Secretary: Helen Adams, 48 Woolwich Close, Bursledon, Southampton. SO31 8GE
Tel: ((H) 01703 406465
Fixtures Secretary: Peter Woolcock, Ferndale, The High Street, Hamble le Rice, Southampton SO31 5JP
Tel: (H) 01703 452117
Club Colours: Blue, light blue and white quarters

HAMMERSMITH & FULHAM RFC
Hertfordshire & Middlesex 2
Ground Address: Hurlingham Park, Hurlingham Road, London. SW6 Tel: 0171 736 5186
Brief Directions: From Putney Bridge (southside) turn right into New Kings Rd (A308) and right again under rail bridge into Hurlingham Rd, Hurlingham Park is 300m on right
Club Secretary: Chris Cuthbertson, 17 Wheatsheaf Lane, London. SW6 6LS Tel: (H) 0171 381 5064
Fixtures Secretary: Lyndon Walters
Tel: (H) 0171 790 1233
Club Colours: Red with navy and white bands

HAMPSHIRE CONSTABULARY
Hampshire 2
Ground Address: Police Training School, Netley, Southampton, Hants
Brief Directions: Junction 8 off M27 . Follow signs to Hamble, turn right after hump back bridge.
Club Secretary: Contact Insprector Glenn Cairns, Cosham Polive Station.
Tel : 01705 891593
Fixtures Secretary: Chris Small, c /o Police Station Totton Tel: 01703 867911
Club Colours: Red and Black hoops. Change: Canary Yellow

HAMPSTEAD RFC
London 3 North West
Ground Address: Hampstead Heath Extension, Hampstead Way, London. NW11
Tel: 0181 458 4548/0181 731 7183
Brief Directions: North End Rd (between Jack Straws & Golden Green) opposite Solders Hill Park turn into Hampstead Way, changing rooms are in middle of Heath Extension
Club Secretary: Mark Spilsbury, 39 Lanebourne Avenue, Holly Lodge, Highgate, London N6 6PS
Tel No: 0181 347 7178
Fixtures Secretary: Ian Munroe. Tel No: (H0 0181 452 0842 (W) 0171 465 3815
Club Colours: Maroon and gold halves separated by a white band

HARINGEY RFC

Hertfordshire & Middlesex 1
Ground Address: New River Sports Centre, White Hart Lane, Wood Green. N22 5QW
Brief Directions: By tube to Wood Green, then W3 bus to White Hart Lane. By road: New River Sports Centre is positioned towards the Wood Green end of White Hart Lane
Club Secretary: Peter A. Wilson, 13 Chambers Gardens, East Finchley, London N2 9AL
Tel: (H) 0181 883 7974
Fixtures Secretary: Colin Field, 6 Inglefield, Potters Bar, Herts. EN6 1HD
Tel: (H) 01707 857297
Club Colours: Green, scarlet and white

HARPENDEN RFC

London 2 North
Ground Address: Redbourn Lane, Harpenden, Herts. AL5 2BA
Tel: 01582 460711
Brief Directions: Take B487 off A1081 (was A6) on south side of Harpenden Ground is 400 metres past entrance to Golf Club
Club Secretary: Donald Fraser, 12 Browning Road, Harpenden, Herts. AL5 4TR
Tel No: (W) 0171 831 7393
Fixtures Secretary: Paul Thompson, 7 Kirkdale Road, Harpenden, Herts AL5 2PT
Tel: (H) 01582 763786 (W) 0171 895 8600
Club Colours: T.B.C.

HARROW RFC

Hertfordshire & Middlesex 1
Ground Address: Grove Field, Wood Lane, Stanmore, Middlesex. HA7 4LF Tel: 0181 954 2615
Brief Directions: Nearest tube station is Stanmore (Jubilee line). 142 bus up Stanmore Hill, alight at `Vine' PH. Ground is 5 mins walk along Wood Lane.
Club Secretary: Mrs Lesley Wyatt, 17 Rucklands Drive, Stanmere, Middlesex
Tel: (H) 0181 9071191 (M) 0860 887066
Fixtures Secretary: Peter Pope, 16 Kenilworth Drive, Croxley Green, Watford. WD3 3NW.
Tel: (H) 01923 241504
Club Colours: Navy blue with white hoops

HARWICH AND DOVERCOURT RUFC

Eastern Counties 2
Ground Address: Swimming Pool Road, Wick Lane, Dovercourt, Harwich, Essex. CO12 3TS
Tel: 01255 240225
Brief Directions: A120 to Ramsey roundabout, 3rd exit, right at War Memorial into Fronks Rd, 2nd right into Hall Lane, left into Wick Lane, right towards swimming pool, clubhouse past pool
Club Secretary: Keiran Coyles, 4 Acorn Close, Dovercourt, Harwich, Essex. CO12 4XF
Tel: (H) 01255 504432 (W) 01255 224822
Fixtures Secretary: Barry Male, 28 Maves Lane, Dovercourt, Harwich, Essex
Tel: (H) 01255 886165 (W) 01255 244813
Club Colours: Black shirts with one white hoop, black shorts, black socks with white top

HASLEMERE RUFC

Surrey 2
Ground Address: The Pavilion, Woolmer Hill Sports Ground, Haslemere, Surrey Tel: 01428 643072
Brief Directions: Off A3 turn down Sandy Lane at Bramshott Chase towards Hammer Vale, turn left to Woolmer Hill and then left to Woolmer Hill Sports Ground and school
Club Secretary: Martin Coakley, 3 St Mary's Terrace, Mill Lane, Guildford, Surry GU7 3T2
Tel: 01483 562434 Fax: 01483 562433
Fixtures Secretary: R,Davies ,6 Heath Rd., Hammor, Haslemere,Surrey GV27 3 QN
Club Colours: Light blue and white hoops

HASTINGS AND BEXHILL RFC

Sussex 1
Ground Address: William Parker School Site, Park Avenue, hastings, East Sussex. Tel 01424 444255
Brief Directions: Take London road out of Hstings town centre and then into St Helens Road adjacent to Alexander Park and follow signs to Rugby Club.
Club Secretary: L.Bolton.180 Harrow Road, St Leonards on-Sea, East Sussex TN 34 2JW
Tel No: 01424 755612
Fixtures Secretary: Ken Nichols, 189 St. Helens Road, Hastings, East Sussux
Tel: 01424 423614
Club Colours: Blue and white hoops.

HATFIELD RFC

Hertfordshire & Middlesex 4 North
Ground Address: Roe Hill Hall, Briars Lane, Hatfield, Hertfordshire Tel: 01707 269814
Brief Directions: Take exit for Briars Lane from roundabout by swimming pool and Asda in town centre. Up hill 1st left and ground is on the right.
Club Secretary: Ian Cranforth, 15 Little Thistle, Welwyn Garden City, Herts. Tel: (H) 01707 334258 (W) 01462 489211
Fixtures Secretary: Mr G Waddingham, 9 Stable Mews, Brookmans Park, Herts, AL9 6NX
Tel: (H) 01707 663659 (W) 01707 666013
Club Colours: Green, white, brown and gold

HAVERHILL & DISTRICT RFC

Eastern Counties 4 North
Ground Address: Castle Playing Fields, School Lane, Haverhill, Suffolk. CB9 9DE Tel: 01440 702871
Brief Directions: Take Haverhill bypass. Junction signed Clements Estate. Take 2nd left up School Lane.
Club Secretary: Mr Ian Stewart, 7 Minster Road, Haverhill, Suffolk, CB9 0DR.
Tel: (H) 01440 706076 (W) 01279 442611
Fixtures Secretary: Gordon Anderson, 2 Arundel Walk, Haverhill, Suffolk, CB9 9BE.
Tel: 01440 763555
Club Colours: Maroon and blue checks, black shorts and socks

HAYES RFC

Hertfordshire & Middlesex 4 South
Ground Address: Grosvenor Playing Fields, Kingshill Avenue, Hayes, Middlesex Tel: 0181 845 4963
Brief Directions: From A40, off at "Target" roundabout head south, at next roundabout (White Hart) take Yeading Lane, at 1st major set of lights turn right into Kingshill Ave, ground is 1 mile on right
Club Secretary: Gary Peacock, 13 Ivy Cottages, Uxbridge Road, Hillingdon. UB10 09J
Tel: (H) 01895 232079 (W) 0956 937883
Fixtures Secretary: Alun Davies
Tel: (H) 0181 248 7640 (W) 0956 304909
Club Colours: Navy blue and yellow quarters

HAYWARDS HEATH RFC
London 2 South
Ground Address: The Clubhouse, Whitemans Green, Cuckfield, Haywards Heath, West Sussex
Tel: 01444 413950
Brief Directions: On B2114 about 0.5 mile west of Cuckfield
Club Secretary: M K Cook, Tinkers, Summerhill Lane, Haywards Heath, West Sussex. RH16 1RL
Tel: (H) 01444 452327 (W) 0171 753 1972 (M) 0468 658355
Fixtures Secretary: B.Killick, 106 Royal George Road, Burgess Hill, West Sussex RH15 9SL
Tel: 01444 233361
Club Colours: Red and black quarters, black shorts

HEATHFIELD & WALDRON RFC
London 3 South East
Ground Address: Hardy Roberts Recreation Ground, Cross in Hand, Heathfield, East Sussex
Tel: 01435 868747
Brief Directions: Adjacent to Cross in Hand public house in centre of village opposite Esso garage
Club Secretary: Peter R Mercer, Mapsedge, Cross in Hand, Heathfield, East Sussex. TN21 0TA
Tel: (H) 01435 863396
Fixtures Secretary: Phil Bell, Hedge Nest, Willingford Lane, Burwash Weald, East Sussex TN19 7HR
Tel: (H) 01435 882871
Club Colours: Green and white hoops, green shorts

HELLINGLY RFC
Sussex 1
Ground Address: Horsebridge Sports Clubs, Horsebridge, Hailsham, East Sussex
Brief Directions: Turn east off A22 onto A271, ground half mile on right opposite White Hart pub and before Kings Head.
Club Secretary: Peter Stotesbury, 10 Hawkswood Drive, Hailsham, East Sussex. BN27 2RB
Tel: (H) 01323843835
Fixtures Secretary: James Bedford. Tel No 01323 845660
Club Colours: Amber and black

HEMEL HEMPSTEAD (CAMELOT) RUFC
London 3 North West
Ground Address: Club House, Chaulden Lane, Hemel Hempstead, Herts., HP1 2BS
Tel: 01442 230353/213408
Brief Directions: Kodak R/about take Station Road exit (left off Kodak Tower) 2nd right into St. Johns Road through Boxmoor Village into Northridge Way, Club 250 yds on left at Chaulden Lane.
Club Secretary: John Clapham, 49 Brook Court, Watling Street, Radlett. WD7 7JA
Tel: 01923 542104
Fixtures Secretary: Bob Skinner, 137 Fern Drive, Hemel Hempstead, Herts. Tel: 01442 246586
Club Colours: Royal Blue and white quarters

HENDON RFC
Hertfordshire & Middlesex 2
Ground Address: Copthall Playing Fields, Great North Way, Hendon. NW4
Tel: 0181 203 1737
Brief Directions: From north - M1 J2, ground 200 yards on left behind garage. Elsewhere - follow signs to Barnet Copthall stadium. Half mile south on A1 of junction(five ways corner) with A41.
Club Secretary: T Brownsell, 9 Winscombe Way, Stanmore, Middlesex. HA7 3AX
Tel: (H) 0181 954 7060 FAX: 0181 954 2845
Fixtures Secretary: C Silver
Tel: (H) 0181 952 0806
Club Colours: Bottle green, white, black unequal horizontal stripes

HERTFORD RFC
London 3 North West
Ground Address: Highfields, Hoe Lane, Ware, Hearts. SG12 9NZ
Tal: 01920 462975
Brief Directions: Leave A10, Direction A414 Heartford, Immediatley take B1502 direction Great Amwell. Hoe Lane is first left then ground is 300 yds on left.
Club Secretary: Nigel Dawes, 2 Grasmere Road, Ware, Herts. SG12 7NP
Tel: (H) 07000 473265
Fixtures Secretary: John Atkinson, 86 Winterscroft Road, Huddesdon, Herts. EN11 8PS
Tel: (H) 01992 462206
Club Colours: Black, royal blue and gold shirts, black shorts

HITCHIN RFC
Hertfordshire & Middlesex 1
Ground Address: King George V Recreation Ground, Old Hale Way, Hitchin, Herts
Tel: 01462 432679
Brief Directions: At Angel Reply pub turn into Bearton Road, take 2nd left into Old Hale Way, turn into ground by phone box
Club Secretary: G Morgan, 209 Cambridge Road, Hitchin, Herts. SG4 0JP
Tel: (H) 01462 635197 (W)01462 444622
Fixtures Secretary: Roger Hood. Tel No: 01438 820534
Club Colours: Maroon shirts, white shorts, maroon socks.

HOLT RFC
London 3 North East
Ground Address: Bridge Road, High Kelling, Holt, Norfolk. NR25 6QT
Tel: 01263 712191
Brief Directions: Take Crome Road (A148) from Holt, after approx 1 mile turn left into Bridge Road (signposted Holt RFC)
Club Secretary: Jimmy Lockhart, April Cottage, The Rosary, Millbarton, Norwich. NR14 8AL
Tel: (H) 01508 570835 (W) 01603 628251 (FAX) 01603 762194
Fixtures Secretary: As Secretary
Club Colours: All black

HORSHAM RUFC
London 3 South East
Ground Address: Hammer Pond Road, Coolhurst, Horsham, West Sussex. RH13 6PJ
Tel: 01403 265027
Brief Directions: From Horsham town centre take Brighton road (A281), 1 mile from town centre turn left by the St Leonards Arms - St Leonards Rd, Hammerpond Rd 0.5 mile on right
Club Secretary: Peter Robbins, 4 Holming End, Horsham RH12 4UW
Tel: (H) 01403 270715 (W) 01483 862019
Fixtures Secretary: Nick Brown, 21 Crawley Rd., Horsham, RH12 4DS
Tel: (H) 01403 250892 (W) 01403 234449
Club Colours: Green and white

HOVE RFC
London 3 South East
Ground Address: Hove Park, Goldstone Crescent, Hove, East Sussex. Tel: 01273 505103
Brief Directions: Adjacent to Brighton and Hove FC on A27 Coast Road.
Club Secretary: James Angus, 28 Lyndhurst Road, hove, Sussex, BN3 6FA. Tel: (H) 01273 726309
Fixtures Secretary: Mike Richardson T6, Wayside, Westdene, Brightion, BN1 5HL
Club Colours: Maroon and sky blue hoops.

HSBC RFC
Kent 1
Ground Address: Lennard Road, Beckenham, Kent Tel: 0181 778 7784
Club Secretary: C Rouse, 59 Crantock Road, London. SE6 Tel: (H) 0181 698 4527
Fixtures Secretary: J R D Hayhow
Tel: (H) 0181 467 3314 (W) 0171 623 9333
Club Colours: Green shirts, blue shorts

ILFORD WANDERERS RFC
Eastern Counties 2
Ground Address: The Club House, Forest Road, Barkingside, Ilford, Essex. IG6 3HJ
Tel: 0181 500 4622
Brief Directions: By road: A12 to Gants Hill r'bout take Cranbrook Rd to Barkingside High St, into Forest Rd at Fulwell Cross R/A Fairlop Oak pub, ground 1 mile left, signposted
Club Secretary: J.S.Haines, 11 Nyth Close, Upminster Essex RM14 1RB
Tel No: 01708 226717 (H) 01708 640 645 (FAX)
Fixtures Secretary: Beiron Rees, 161a Aldborough Road, Seven Kings, Ilford, Essex IG3 8HU
Tel: (H) 0181 5971158
Club Colours: Red, green and white hoops

IMPERIAL MEDICAL
London 3 North West
Ground Address: St Mary's Hospital Athletic Ground, Udney Park Road, Teddington, Middlesex
Brief Directions: Teddington Station (SW Network). Exit to (East, Garden Centre) Station Road. Turn right and then take the third left.
Club Secretary: Ral Young FRCS, West Middlesex Hospital, Twickenham Road, Isleworth. TW7 6AF
Tel: (H) 0181 891 063 (W) 0181 565 5768 (Fax) 01812872778
Fixtures Secretary: Professor P S Sever, Dept. Clinical Pharmacology, St Mary's Hospital, Praed St. , Pa 0171 886 6145 (FAX)ddington, London. W2 1NY.
Tel: (W) 0171 725 1117
Club Colours: Blue shirt with a white, green & red hoop.

IPSWICH RUFC
London 2 North
Ground Address: Humber Doucy Lane, Ipswich. IP4 3PZ Tel: 01473 724072 Fax: 710439
Brief Directions: A12 ToysRus r'bout straight over towards Ipswich at 3rd traffic light garage on L&R Turn L. go over 2 sets lights. 2 r'bouts. Over bridge turn L. at end T.Junction
Club Secretary: Mrs Lisa Greetham, 159 Woodbridge Road, Ipswich IP4 2PE
Tel: (H) 01473 233731 (W) 01473 724072
Fixtures Secretary: Mrs Lisa Greetham
Tel: (H) 01473 233731 (W) 01473 724072 Fax: 01473 710439
Club Colours: Black with gold chevron

IPSWICH YM RUFC
Eastern Counties 3 North
Ground Address: The Street, Rushmere, Ipswich, Suffolk Tel: 01473 713807
Brief Directions: From A14 west, exit on A1156 (Ipswich W & N), 1st exit at r'bout tow'ds town centre, under r/w bridge, left at dbl mini r'bout, over lights, left at 4th r'bout Rushmere Rd, past church, ground on rt
Club Secretary: Mr R Daniels, 85 Western Avenue, Felixstowe, Suffolk. IP11 9NT
Tel: (H) 01394 283907 (W) 01473 553149
Fixtures Secretary: Mr R Hullis, 2 Godbold Close, Kesgrave, Ipswich IP5 7SE
Tel: (H) 01473 625027 (W) 01473 622701
Club Colours: Maroon and amber hoops

ISLE OF WIGHT RFC
Hampshire 1
Ground Address: The Clubhouse, Wootton Recreation Ground, Wootton, Isle of Wight. PO33 4NQ
Tel: 01983 883240
Brief Directions: Right at the Cedars, Wootton, into Church Road, left into Footways, left onto Recreation Ground
Club Secretary: Mrs Sue Bradshaw, 16 Upton Road, Ryde, Isle of Wight, PO33 3DX Tel: 01983 566649
Fixtures Secretary: Mr Dave Metcalfe
Tel: (H) 01983 755339
Club Colours: Navy, gold hoops

JERSEY RFC
London 3 South West
Ground Address: Ruedes Landes, St Peter, Jersey C I. JE3 7BG Tel: 01534 499929
Brief Directions: Opposite airport
Club Secretary: Mr.R.Shambrook, Maufont Lodge, Jardin de la Fontaine, St. Saviour, Jersey. Channel Islands Tel: 01534 855645
Fixtures Secretary: Mr C Chipperfield
Tel: 01534 811961
Club Colours: Red shirts, white shorts

K.C.S. OLD BOYS RFC
Surrey 1
Ground Address: Arthur Road, Motspur Park, New Malden, Surrey. KT3 6LX Tel: 0181 336 2512
Brief Directions: 10 mins walk from Motspur Park station. From A3 at New Malden underpass, south along A2043, approx 400m left into Motspur Park (Rd), cto Arthur Rd, 2nd right after level crossing
Club Secretary: Noel M Crockford, 78 Claygate Lane, Hinchley Wood, Esher, Surrey. KT10 0BJ
Tel: (H) 0181 398 7474 (W) 0181 398 6499
Fixtures Secretary: Andy Todd
Tel: (H) 0181 942 0048 (W) 0181 395 3808
Club Colours: Red, blue and old gold hoops

KILBURN COSMOS RFC
Hertfordshire & Middlesex 4 North
Ground Address: Brondesbury (Fields) Park, on Aylestone Avenue, NW6
(Changing facilities at South Ham pstead Cricket Club, entrance Milverton Road, NW6.
Brief Directions: A40 to Wood Lane. Go towards Harrow Road.1st Left is Wrothashey Road. Go over R/about onto All Souls Avenue. Turn Left Sidmouth Road then Right into Milverton Road.
Club Secretary: Maurice Scott, 44 Montrose Avenue, Garden Flat, Queen's Park, London, NW6 6OB.
Fixtures Secretary: Owen Sanders, 146 Fleetwood Road, Willesden, London, NW10.
Club Colours: Yellow, Black, Blue & Jade Quarters

KINGS COLLEGE HOSPITAL RFC

Surrey 3

Ground Address: The Griffin Sports Ground, 12 Dulwich Village, Dulwich, London, SE21 7AL.

Brief Directions: South Circular to Herne Hill. Follow signs for Dulwich village.

Club Secretary: Christopher Barber, 40 Hollingbourne Road, Herne Hill, London, SE24 9ND. Tel: (H) 0171 274 4379

Fixtures Secretary: Nick Bunker, 24 Maxted Road, Peckham, London, SE15 4LL. Tel: (H) 0171 277 6919 (W) 0171 737 4000 ext 4050/4051 (F) 0171 733 0210

Club Colours: Maroon, Navy & Sky Blue Hoops

KINGSBURIANS RFC

London 3 North West

Ground Address: Northwick Park Pavilion, Northwick Park Open Space, The Fairway, North Wembley, Middlesex Tel: 0181 904 4414

Brief Directions: Frm nth: To Harrow, Watford Rd at N'wick r'bout (A404), left - Norval Rd, 1st left - Fairway. Frm S. & W.: M40/A40 - Gr'nford Rd, north - J. Lyon r'bout, left - Watford Rd

Club Secretary: Neil Keeler, 25 Lansdown Road, Stanmore, Middlesex. HA7 2RX
Tel: (H) 0181 954 7211 (W) 01442 844342

Fixtures Secretary: Bruce Bland
Tel: (H) 0181 868 5244 (W) 0181 204 4442

Club Colours: Black and amber hooped shirts, black shorts

KINGSCLERE

Hampshire 3

Ground Address: The Field Gate Centre, Fieldgate Drive, Kingsclere, Newbury, Berkshire.
Tel: 01635 298???

Brief Directions: From A339 follow signs to village centre then follow signs to the Field Gate Centre.

Club Secretary: Chris Smith, 30 Oakfield Close, Ecchinswell, Newbury, Berkshire. Tel:(H) 01635 298006

Fixtures Secretary: D.Barton. Tel No: 01256 782383

Club Colours: Red and white hoops or All Black

KINGSTON RFC

Surrey 1

Ground Address: King Edward Recreation Ground, Hook Road, Chessington, Surrey. KT9 1PL Tel: 0181 397 8385

Brief Directions: Leave A3 at Hook roundabout, follow sign for A243 Chessington, entrance approx 200 yards on the right

Club Secretary: J. Scrimshaw, 66 Drake Road, Chessington, Surrey, KT9 1LW.

Fixtures Secretary: C. Holden, 14 Bramshott Court, Southbank, Surbiton. Surrey, KT6 6DD.

Club Colours: Maroon and white hoops, blue shorts

LAKENHAM - HEWETT RFC

Eastern Counties 3 North

Ground Address: Hilltops, Norwich Road, Swardeston, Norwich, Norfolk Tel: 01508 578826

Brief Directions: Approach Norwich on the Southern bypass, leave on the Norwich/Ipswich exit (A140), head towards Norwich, turn 1st left (B1113), ground is on right about 1.25 miles

Club Secretary: Phil Boyce, 2 Branksome Road, Norwich. NR4 6SN Tel: (H) 01603 454208

Fixtures Secretary: Bruce Ridgeway
Tel: (H) 01603 897771 (W) 01603 628333 Ext 271

Club Colours: Red

LAW SOCIETY RFC

Surrey 2

Ground Address: C /O Wimbledon RFC, Beverly Meads, Barham Road, Copse Hill, Wimbledon. Sw20
Tel: 0181 946 3156

Brief Directions: A3 from London to Coombe Lane and A238 Junction to Raynes Park. Left into Barham Road and take left fork at end.

Club Secretary: Peter Watts, c/o 16 Bedford St., Covent Garden, London WC2 E9HF
Tel No: 0171 395 3102 (W) 0171 376 8563 (H)

Fixtures Secretary: Simon Lee, 57 Upper Culver Road,St. Albans, Herts. AL1 4EE
Tel: 01727 830601 (H) 0468 384 731 (M)

Club Colours: Black,Purple and White Hoops.

LENSBURY RFC

Hertfordshire & Middlesex 1
Ground Address: Broom Road, Teddington, Middlesex. TW11 9NU
Tel: 0181 977 8821
Brief Directions: By rail: Teddington Station, through High St towards river, over traffic lights into Broom Road
Club Secretary: Andy Brampton, 79 Stanley Garden Road, Teddington, Middlesex. Tw11 8 SF
Fixtures Secretary: Ross Cardew, 11 Westfield Road, Surbiton, Surrey KT6 4EZ Tel: (H) 0181 339 9563 (W) 0181 332 3751
Club Colours: Blackshirts and shorts, black, gold and purple socks

LETCHWORTH GARDEN CITY RUFC

London 3 North West
Ground Address: Baldock Road, Letchworth, Herts
Tel: 01462 682554
Brief Directions: Turn off A1 to Letchworth, turn right at A505 towards Baldock, turn right at mini roundabout. Ground situated behind North Herts Laisure Centre.
Club Secretary: Kevin McMahon, Whitecroft, 3 Purcell Close, Teniin Wood, Welwyn AL6 0NN
Fixtures Secretary: R G Steele
Tel: (H) 01462 676985
Club Colours: Black and amber hoops

LEWES RFC

London 2 South
Ground Address: Stanley Turner Ground, Kingston Road, Lewes, East Sussex
Tel: 01273 473732
Brief Directions: From railway station take old road to Newhaven, passing Swan Inn on right, cross bypass bridge and entrance is on the left
Club Secretary: A J Page, 13 Greater Paddock, Ringmer, Lewes, East Sussex. BN8 5LH
Tel: (H) 01273 813419
Fixtures Secretary: S Rhodes, 12 Harrow Close, Seaford BN25 3PE
Tel: (H) 01323 492462
Club Colours: Blue and white hoops

LIGHTWATER RFC

Surrey 3
Ground Address: The Sports Centre, The Avenue, Lightwater, Surrey. GU18 5RQ
Tel: 01276 472664
Brief Directions: Take Junction 3 off M3 towards Guildford. turn right 100yds down A322 into Lightwater and follow signs to Country Park.
Club Secretary: Tony Sharp, 65 Cedar Close, Bagshot, Surrey. GU19 5AB
Tel: (H) 01276 472994
Fixtures Secretary: Dave Forsaith, 87 Wordsworth Avenue, Yateley, Hants GU46 6YP
Tel: (H) 01252 665387
Club Colours: Green and white hoops, black shorts

LONDON CORNISH RFC

Surrey 3
Ground Address: Richardson Evans Memorial Ground, Roehampton Lane, Kingston, Surrey
Tel: 0181 788 3628
Brief Directions: On main A3, 200 yards north of Robin Hood roundabout
Club Secretary: Dave Fletcher, 27 Riverbank, Laceham Road, Staines, Middlesex. TW18 2QE
Tel: (H) 01784 461927 (W) 0181 813 9494
Fixtures Secretary: Angus Milne, 13 Durand Gardens, London SW9 0PS
Tel: (H) 0171 735 5100 (W) 0171 716 6645
Club Colours: Black with narrow gold hoops

LONDON EXILES RUFC

Hertfordshire & Middlesex 3 South
Ground Address: Barn Elms Sports Ground, Queen Elizabeth Walk, Barnes, London. SW13 0DG
Brief Directions: A205 (S. Circular) to Junction with A306 turn towards Barnes Village. Q. Elizabeth Walk is a small turning on R. at second set of Traffic Lights by the Red Lion Public House.
Club Secretary: Tim Edghill, 11 Martindale Road, London, SW12 9PW.
Fixtures Secretary: Tim Edghill, As above
Club Colours: Claret, navy and white hoops, white shorts, claret, white and navy socks

LONDON FIRE BRIGADE RFC

Surrey 2
Ground Address: Priest Hill Sports Ground, Banstead Road, Ewell, Surrey. KT17 3HG
Tel: 0181 394 1946
Brief Directions: Junction of Cheam Road and Banstead Road, Ewell, next to Ewell East railway station
Club Secretary: Charlie Gilbert, 15 Park Road, Banstead, Surrey. SM7 3BY
Tel: (H) 01737 362191
Fixtures Secretary: Chris Drummond
Tel No: 0181 669 5225
Club Colours: Flame, ember, charcoal

LONDON FRENCH RFC

Hertfordshire & Middlesex 2
Ground Address: Barn Elms, Rocks Lane, Barnes, London. SW20
Club Secretary: Jeremy O'Dwyer, 117 Sugden Road, London. SW11 5ED
Tel: (H) 0171 223 2274 (W) 0171 814 2166
Fixtures Secretary: Chris Hutton
Tel: (H) 0181 287 9892 (W) 0181 490 1538
Club Colours: French blue shirt, white shorts, red socks

LONDON MEDIA RUFC

Surrey 2
Ground Address: Battersea Park, London
Brief Directions: Albert Bridge Road entrance to Battersea Park (near Albert Bridge)
Club Secretary: Nick Field, 315a Cavendish Road, Balham, London. SW12 0PQ
Tel: (H) 0181 673 3809 (W) 0171 734 5358
Club Colours: Black and white quarters

LONDON NEW ZEALAND RFC

Hertfordshire & Middlesex 1
Ground Address: c/o Osterley Sports & Social Club, Tentelow Lane, Osterley, Middlesex
Tel: 0181 574 3774
Club Secretary: Tudor Davies, 46 Lamorna Grove, Stanmore, Middlesex. HA7 1PQ
Tel: (H) 0181 952 6822 (W) 0171 723 0022
Fixtures Secretary: Richard Peacock
Tel: (H) 0181 952 6822 (W) 0171 723 0022
Club Colours: All black

LONDON NIGERIAN RFC
London 2 North
Ground Address: Copthall Playing Fields, Great North Way, Hendon, London. NW4
Tel: 0181 203 1737
Brief Directions: Frm Hendon Cntral: Watford Way north at Page St turn, cross to sthbnd lane, take lft fork (to Gt Nth Way), ground 500yds by NorthWays Tyres. Frm north: M1 J2, ground 200 yds
Club Secretary: John Orchard, 43 Portland Place, London. W1N AG
Tel: (H) 0831 304 126 (W) 0171 636 9386
Fixtures Secretary: Babs Kehinde
Tel: (H) 0171 366 7036
Club Colours: Green and white quarters

LONDON TRIBES
Hertfordshire & Middlesex 3 South

LORDSWOOD RUFC
Kent 1
Ground Address: Lordswood Sports & Social Club, Martin Grove, North Dane Way, Lordswood, Chatham, Kent Tel: 01634 669 138
Brief Directions: M2 J3, A229 t'wd Chatham, 3rd exit at 3rd r'bout (Walderslade), over 1st r'bout, 3rd exit at 2nd r'bout (Lordswood Lane), 3rd exit at r'bout (Albermarle Rd), left at end, clubhouse 500yds on right
Club Secretary: Sam Wellings, 167 Ballens Rd,. Lordswood, Kent ME5 8PG
Tel No: 01634 861924
Fixtures Secretary: Martin Hunt.Tel No: 01634 869871
Club Colours: Black with gold collar

LOUGHTON RFC
Eastern Counties 4 South
Ground Address: Squirrels Lane, Hornbeam Road, Buckhurst Hill, Essex. Tel: 0171 504 0065
Brief Directions: A11 out of NE London to Woodford Green, turn right following police station into Monkhams Lane, follow to end and straight over crossroads into Chesnut Avenue, continue onto Squirrels Lane.
Club Secretary: Craig Clark, 15 Herenard Green, Coughton, Essex. Tel: (H) 0181 502 4854
Fixtures Secretary: Brian Westley, Tel: (H) 01689 819365 Tel: (W) 0171 777 2883
Club Colours: White with green hoop between black hoops.

LOWESTOFT & YARMOUTH RUFC
London 2 North
Ground Address: Gunton Park, off Corton Long Lane, Old Lane, Corton, Nr Lowestoft, Suffolk
Brief Directions: Frm L'toft A12 to Gt Yarm'th, at start of d. c'way (past Pleasure wood Hills) turn right into Corton Long Ln, 200yds right to Old Ln, ground at end. Frm Gt Yarm'th left at end of d. c'way off A12
Club Secretary: George Redpath, 6 Priors Close, Lowestoft. NR32 4NT
Tel: 01502 569304
Fixtures Secretary: Tex Colby. Tel No: 01502 585924
Club Colours: Blue and white hoops

MAIDSTONE FC
London 2 South
Ground Address: The William Day Memorial Ground, The Mote, Willow Way, Maidstone, Kent. ME16 0RN
Tel: 01622 754159
Brief Directions: From M20 J.7 Proceed 1-2 miles on A249 towards Maidstone at R/about keep L. onto A20. 100 yds to traffic lights turn R to Square Hill turn L at mini R/about into Mote Avenue
Club Secretary: Eva Howson, Rose Lodge, Sandbourne Drive, Maidstone, Kent ME14 2JA.
Tel: 01622 692364
Fixtures Secretary: Tony Kelleher, 5 Conway Road, Maidstone, ME16 0HD
Tel: (H & W) 01622 754872
Club Colours: Red, white and black hoops

MALDON RUFC
London 3 North East
Ground Address: Drapers Farm Sports Club, Drapers Chase, Heybridge, Maldon, Essex. Tel: 01621 852152
Brief Directions: A414 to Maldon. Then northern by-pass to Heybridge.Follow signs to Goldhanger. Half a mile up Goldhanger road on left.
Club Secretary: Mark Taylor, 5 Hall Road, Tollesbury, Maldon, Essex CM9 8QF
Fixtures Secretary: Mr. Nick Foss, 23 Ramsey Close, Heybridge, Maldon
Club Colours: Royal blue and white hoops

MARCH BRAZA RUFC
Eastern Counties 4 North
Ground Address: Braza Sports Pavilion, Elm Road, March, Cambridgeshire. Tel: 01354 59741
Brief Directions: Follow signs for HMP Whitemoor Sportsfield, on junction off side road to prison.
Club Secretary: Miss Andria Mills, 2 Broad Alder Farm, Mount Pleasant, Chatteris. PE16 6XL
Tel NO: 01354 694901
Fixtures Secretary: Colin Buck. Tel No: 01354 650074
Club Colours: Maroon and white hoops.Change: Green with single gold band.

MAY AND BAKER
Eastern Counties 3 South
Ground Address: Dagenham Road, Dagenham, Essex. Tel: 0181 919 3156
Brief Directions: A13 to oprds, from London ,left at McDonalds to roundabout. First exit past Dagenham East Station to traffic lights. Right and right again at mini roundabout into Sports ground.
Club Secretary: Terry Simmons, 105 Albion Road, Dagenham Essex RM10 8DE. Tel: (H) 0181 593 2630 Tel: (W) 0181 919 2579
Fixtures Secretary: Mike Parnell, Tel: (H & W) 01245 231302
Club Colours: Black with single red band., black shorts and red socks.

MEDWAY RFC
London 3 South East
Ground Address: Priestfield, Rochester, Kent ME1 3AD
Brief Directions: M2 J3, follow A249 to Chatham, at Bridgewood roundabout left (Maidstone/Rochester road), past Comet on right, take left turn signed B, ground 200m on left
Club Secretary: Michael Burford, 20 Wouldham oad, Borstal , Rochester, Kent Tel: 01634 319013
Fixtures Secretary: Tony Bourne, 65 Hawthorn Avenue, Gillingham, Kent ME8 6TSTel: 01634 375947
Club Colours: Yellow and red

MEOPHAM
Kent 3
Ground Address: New ground being built, using school ground near King's Arms.
Club Secretary: P. Cornell, The Kings Arms, Meopham Green, Meopham, Kent. DA13 0QB.
Tel: (H) 01474 813323
Fixtures Secretary: Shaun Ellis
Tel: (H)01474 812650
Club Colours: Navy Blue with 2 white hoops

MERSEA ISLAND RFC
Eastern Counties 2
Ground Address: E.C.C. Youth Camp, East Road, East Mersea, Colchester
Brief Directions: From Colchester - over Causeway, turn left East Road, 3rd turning right, lane to Youth Camp
Club Secretary: Tony Eves, Dormy House, Lower Road, Peldon, Colchester, Essex. CO5 7QR
Tel: (H & W & Fax) 01206 735537
Fixtures Secretary: Graham Woods
Tel: (H) 01206 383525
Club Colours: Blue and white

MERTON RFC
Surrey 1
Ground Address: Morden Recreation Ground, Faversham Road, Morden, Surrey
Tel: 0181 646 5192
Brief Directions: From Rose Hill roundabout take St Helier Ave (A297), 1st left into Middleton Rd, then 4th exit from roundabout into Faversham Rd, entrance to ground is 100 yards on left
Club Secretary: Robert Smith, SCCS, Charrington Street, London. NW1 1RG
Tel: (W) 0171 387 0126
Fixtures Secretary: Paul Webster
Tel: (H) 0171 736 0149 (W) 0181 874 8182
Club Colours: Gold, black and white quarters

MET POLICE CHIGWELL RFC
Eastern Counties 2
Ground Address: Metropolitan Police Sports Ground, Chigwell Hall, High Road, Chigwell, Essex
Tel: 500 2735
Brief Directions: From A406 north circular road, take A113 Chigwell road, pass under M11 up hill, take left fork (A113) straight on 1st & 2nd mini roundabouts, ground 100 yds on left
Club Secretary: Malcolm Bartlett, 11 Fairfield Rd, Ongar, Essex. CM5 9HJ
Tel: (H) 01277 364206 (W) 01426 241278
Fixtures Secretary: James Handing
Tel: (H) 0181 501 3981 (W) 01975 709578
Club Colours: Blue shirts, black shorts

METROPOLITAN POLICE (HAYES) RFC
Kent 2 West
Ground Address: The Warren Sports & Social Club, Hayes Common Road, Hayes, Kent
Tel: 0181 462 1266
Brief Directions: A232 Hayes Common, from M25 J4 north on A21 then east on A232
Club Secretary: Gary D Morant, 57 Orchard Way, Shirley, Croydon.
Tel: 0181 777 3700
Fixtures Secretary: K.Carvalho, Willow, 3 The mead, West Wickham, Kent
Tel: 0181 289 1761
Club Colours: Navy and Royal Blue Quarters

MIDHURST RFC
Sussex 3
Ground Address: Cowdray Ruins, Cowdray Park, Midhurst, West Sussex
Tel: 01730 816658
Brief Directions: At mini roundabout junction of A286 and A272 take entrance to Cowdray Park, turn left 200 yards along drive
Club Secretary: Simon Flint, Broadoak, Chichester Road, Midhurst, West Sussex. GU29 9PF
Tel: (H) 01730 816465 (W) 0181 390 1144
Fixtures Secretary: Simon Fay
Tel: (H) 01730 813357
Club Colours: Gold with royal blue hoop.

MILL HILL RUFC
London 3 North West
Ground Address: Mill Hill RFC, Page Street, London. NW7 2EJ
Tel: 0181 203 0685
Brief Directions: Next to J2 of M1, follow signs for Barnet Copthall and club is next to school just off Page St on entrance to stadium
Club Secretary: Mr. Ian Webster, 76 Grants Close, Mill Hill, London NW7 1DE
Tel: (H) 0181 346 8136
Fixtures Secretary: Mr. Ken Reed, 10 Rushden Gardens, Mill Hill, London NW7 2NY
Tel: (H) 0181 906 2395
Club Colours: Chocolate and gold hoops

MILLBROOK RUFC
Hampshire 1
Ground Address: Lordshill Outdoor Recreation Centre, Redbridge Lane, Lordshill, Southampton
Tel: 01703 739759
Brief Directions: M27 J3 to M271 to J1, A3051, 1st left into Redbridge Lane, 1 mile on right
Club Secretary: Mrs J Ings, 27 Gemini Close, Lordshill, Southampton
Tel: (H)01703 345559
Fixtures Secretary: Wayne Renwick
Tel: (H) 01489 892231
Club Colours: Emerald and scarlet hoops

MILLFIELD OLD BOYS RFC
Hertfordshire & Middlesex 3 South
Ground Address: Harrow RFC, Wood Lane, Stanmore, Middlesex
Tel: 0181 954 2615
Club Secretary: Angela Lesly, Westmill Fisheries, PO Box 24, Ware, Herts. SG12 0YN
Tel: (H) 01920 486534
Fixtures Secretary: Alan Burns
Tel: (H) 01920 486534
Club Colours: Red, green and blue hoops, white shorts

MILLWALL ALBION
Eastern Counties 3 South
Ground Address: Mellend Stadium, Rhodeswell Road, London E14. Tel: 0181 980 18??
Club Secretary: B Lancaster, 14 Reef house, Manchester Road, London E14. Tel: 0171 538 0453
Fixtures Secretary: Mr Gareth Batley, c/o B Lancaster as above.
Club Colours: Black and white quarters with red collars.

MISTLEY RFC

Eastern Counties 4 North
Ground Address: Mistley Parish Playing Fields, Shrubland Rd., Furzehill, Mistley, Manningtree, Essex. CO11 2QL
Brief Directions: %Take B1352 from Manningtree towards Harwich through Mistley. Over railway bridge, past Anchor Inn, turn right into Shrubland Road at corner of next left hand bend.
Club Secretary: Mark Hexley, 29 Silver Leys, Bentley, Ipswich, Suffolk IP9 2BS
Tel No: 01473 310711
Fixtures Secretary: Horace Downey, 3 Thorn Mews, The Green, Mistley, Manningtree, Essex CO11 1EY
Tel: 01206 392454
Club Colours: Red and purple quarters, black shorts

MITCHAM RUFC

Surrey 2
Ground Address: Potter Park, Bishopsford Road, Peterborough Road, Carshalton, Surrey
Brief Directions: The ground can only be entered from Bishopsford Road.
Club Secretary: Damian Brady, Flat 7, Laburnham Court, St James Road, Sutton, Surry
Tel: 0181 643 8170
Fixtures Secretary: Tony Antoniou
Tel: (H) 0181 679 5644
Club Colours: Lavender and green hoops

NATIONAL WESTMINSTER BANK RFC

Kent 1
Ground Address: Copers Cope Road, Beckenham, Kent. BR3 1NZ Tel: 0181 650 4559/650 9217
Brief Directions: Freq trains to Charing X and London Bridge to Lower Sydenham. Out of Station on down side. Turn right at bottom into Worsley Bridge Rd. 1st Right (100yds) into Coopers Cope Rd, on right.
Club Secretary: Nigel Adam, 40 Montana Gardens, London SE26 5BF. Tel No: 0181 461 4056 (H) 0171 462 2003 (W)
Fixtures Secretary: L. A. Giblin, 656 Davidson Road, Croydon, Surrey CR0 6DJ
Tel: (H) 0181 654 1884
Club Colours: Light and dark blue hoops

NEW ASH GREEN RFC

Kent 1
Ground Address: Punch Croft, New Ash Green, Kent. Tel: 01474 874660
Club Secretary: Tracy Shopland, 57 Wellington Street, Gravesend, Kent DA12 1JQ.
Tel: (H) 01474 567263
Fixtures Secretary: Paul Martin, Tel: (H) 01474 874513
Club Colours: Dark green and black quarters, black shorts.

NEW MILTON RFC

Hampshire 1
Ground Address: The Sports Ground, Ashley Road, Ashley, New Milton, Hants Tel: 01425 610401
Brief Directions: From centre of town, to Ashley Ground next to Junior School and behind Ashley Hotel
Club Secretary: N E Hanmer, Walsingham, Andrew Lane, Ashley, New Milton, Hants
Tel: (H) 01425 612613
Fixtures Secretary: A Williams, 57 Oakwood Avenue, New Milton, Hants. Tel No: 01425 628428
Club Colours: Green with band of blue, gold,blue.

NEWICK RFC

Sussex 2
Ground Address: King George V Playing Fields, Allington Road, Newick, East Sussex.
Brief Directions: A272 from Haywards Heath, right at village green, 2nd right, playing field Allington Road, on first bend, left into field
Club Secretary: Mrs. Diane Thomas, Pinecroft, Allington Rd., Newick, East Sussex BN8 4NA
Tel: (H) 01825 723824
Fixtures Secretary: Martin Barling, Cairn Cottage,41 Western Road, Newick.
Tel: 01825 724054
Club Colours: Dark blue and maroon hooped jerseys and socks.White shorts

NEWMARKET RUFC

London 3 North East
Ground Address: Sports Pavilion, Scaltback Middle School, Elizabeth Avenue, Newmarket, Suffolk. CB8 0JJ
Tel: 01638 663082
Brief Directions: A14 (Newmkt bypass), A142 towards Newmkt, right at Tesco r'bout, left at T junction, past 3 factories on right, turn right into Elizabeth Ave, clubhouse at rear of school
Club Secretary: Robert Voss, 58 King Edward VII Road, Newmarket, Suffolk. CB8 0EU
Tel: (H) 01638 669596 (W) 01763 264629
Fixtures Secretary: John Taylor
Tel: (H) 01638 507483 (W) 01638 507483
Club Colours: Emerald green and black hoops

NOMADS RFC

Hampshire 2
Ground Address: Farlington's Recreation Ground, Eastern Road, Portsmouth, Hampshire.
Tel: 01705 691574
Brief Directions: North side of A27, behind Hilton International Hotel.
Club Secretary: Ken Walker, 38 Warblington Road, Emsworth, Hampshire. PO10 7HQ.
Tel: (H) 01243 375263 Tel: (W) 01705 671969
Fixtures Secretary: Ken Walker, as above.
Club Colours: Red and black irregular hoops.

NORFOLK ARMS

Sussex 3

NORWICH UNION RFC

Eastern Counties 3 North
Ground Address: Pinebanks Sports and Leisure Club, White Farm Lane, off Harvey Lane, Norwich, Norfolk
Tel: 01603 433752
Brief Directions: Approach city from S.E. A47 bypass, at end enter city towards Thorpe St Andrew, right into Pound Ln, immediate left before lights onto B1150, 1st left at r'bout Harvey, 4th left, club at end
Club Secretary: Adam Fox, 56 Cremorne Lane, Norwich, Norfolk. NR1 1YW
Tel: (H) 01603 767150 (W) 01603 681303
Fixtures Secretary: Mark Howell
Tel: (H) 01603 501503 (W) 01603 622200
Club Colours: Green and white quarters, white shorts, green socks

OLD ABBOTSTONIANS RFC

Hertfordshire & Middlesex 2
Ground Address: Pole Hill Open Spaces, Raeburn Road, Hayes, Middlesex
Tel: 0181 845 1452

Brief Directions: A40 exit for Hillingdon Long Lane towards Uxbridge Rd, left at BP station, left into Pole Hill Rd (Midland Bank at corner),round bend, 1st left after bus stop, club at end
Club Secretary: Mr Denis Halloran, 8 Swallow Drive, Northolt, Middlesex. UB5 6UH
Tel: (H) 0181 842 2154 (W) 0171 707 2203
Fixtures Secretary: Mr Mark Nettleton
Tel: (H) 01895 440714
Club Colours: Blue and red

OLD ACTONIANS RFC
Hertfordshire & Middlesex 2
Ground Address: Gunnersbury Drive (off Paper Lane), London. W5
Tel: 0181 567 4556
Brief Directions: Coming west from Acton Town tube station, cross North Circular Rd, take 1st right (opposite Gunnersbury Park main entrance), ground 50yds on left of G'sbury Drive
Club Secretary: Mr. Wostek Swistak, 16 Buxton Gardens, London W3 9LQ
Tel: (H) 0181 992 5870
Fixtures Secretary: Mr. Kim Karpeta, 11 Grove House, 95 Addison Road, London W14 8DB
Tel: (H) 0956 581692
Club Colours: Royal blue, white hoops, red collar

OLD ALBANIAN RFC
London 2 North
Ground Address: Beech Bottom, Old Harpenden Road, St Albans, Herts
Tel: 01727 864476
Brief Directions: Approx 1 mile from centre of St Albans on A1081 towards Luton, 150 yards from Ancient Briton public house
Club Secretary: Peter Lipscomb, 35 Gurney Court Road, St Albans, Herts. AL1 4QU
Tel: (H) 01727 760466 (W) 0181 784 5924
Fixtures Secretary: Mr David Verdon
Tel: (H) 0171 538 0184 (W) 0171 712 8947
Club Colours: Red, blue and gold hooped shirts, blue shorts

OLD ALLEYNIAN FC
London 3 South West
Ground Address: Dulwich Common, Dulwich, London. SE21 7HA
Tel: 0181 693 2402
Brief Directions: On the south side of the South Circular (A205), 0.5 mile east of Dulwich College one mile from Dulwich Village.By train to West Dulwich (10 minutes walk) passing school on south circular.
Club Secretary: Jason Daniels, Flat 3, 1 Park Hill Road, Bromley, Kent. BR2 0JX
Tel:0181 466 0115
Fixtures Secretary: Alastair N Capon, 182 Hayes Lane, Bromley, Kent. BR2 9EL.
Tel: 0181 462 0886
Club Colours: Dark blue, light blue and black hoops

OLD ASHMOLEANS RFC
Hertfordshire & Middlesex 3 North
Ground Address: Ashmole School, Burleigh Gardens, Southgate, London. N14
Brief Directions: At Southgate underground station roundabout, turn into Ashfield Parade, bear right into Burleigh Gardens, school entrance 250 metres on left
Club Secretary: Chris Fussell, 22 Holtwhites Hill, Enfield, Middlesex EN2 0RP
Tel No: 0181 372 3924
Fixtures Secretary: Mr S Stamp
Tel: (H) 0181 364 3212 (W) 0171 494 2785
Club Colours: Scarlet and emerald hoops, black shorts

OLD BEALONIANS
Eastern Counties 4 South

OLD BEVONIANS RFC
Surrey 3
Ground Address: Ballard Coombe, Robin Hood Way, London. SW15 3QF
Tel: 0181 942 2907
Brief Directions: Along A3, London bound side between New Malden & Robin Hood R'about.
Club Secretary: Mrs A. Lefeure, 100 Longfellow Road, Worcester Park, Surrey. KT4 8BR Tel: 0181 3302278 or 0181 286 9674
Fixtures Secretary: Peter Hunt,Flat 1, Pinewold, 20 Oatlands Chase, Weybridge, Surrey KT113 9SD
Tel No: 01932 246241
Club Colours: Black, amber and green hoops, black shorts

OLD BLUES RFC
London 2 South
Ground Address: Dornan Fields, Arthur Road, Motspur Park, Nr New Malden, Surrey
Tel: 0181 336 2566
Brief Directions: From London A3, along Kingston bypass, take sliproad signed Worcester Pk & Cheam, 1st left after pillarbox into Motspur Pk, over levelcrossing into W. Barnes Ln, 2nd right
Club Secretary: Giles Simons, 66B Gowrie Road, London, SW11 5NR. Tel: (H) 0171 2070010 (W) 0171 6282441
Fixtures Secretary: Alistair Burns, 47 Becmead Avenue, London, SW16 0UJ. Tel:
(H) 0181 769 7045 (B) 0421 380315
Club Colours: French Navy, cardinal & old gold

OLD BRENTWOODS
Eastern Counties 3 South
Ground Address: Old Brentwoods Clubhouse, Ashwells Road,Bentley, Brentwood, Essex CM15 9SE
Tel: 01277 374070
Brief Directions: Take the Onger road from Brentwood and after 2 1/'2 miles turn right at the end of the "straight mile" intop Ashwells Road. GRound 1/4 mile on left.
Club Secretary: T.J.Faiers, I Woodway, Shenfield, Essex CM15 8ILP
tel: 01277 214503 (H) 0181 270 4545 (W)
Fixtures Secretary: Roger Seaman, 5 The Knoll , Rayleigh, Essex SS6 7HD
Tel: 01268 774113 (H) 01268 560040 (W)
Club Colours: Dark Blue and Light Blue Hoops.

OLD BRIGHTONIAN RFC
Sussex 1
Ground Address: Share with Brighton FC (RFU). Waterhall Playing Fields, Mill Road, Patcham, Brighton
Tel: 01273 562729
Brief Directions: From London & north- A23 turn right at 1st roundabout entering Brighton, past garage under railway bridge, 100 metres sign post, turn right
Club Secretary: C D Loadsman, 20 Meadow Close, Hove, Sussex
Tel: (H) 01273 552988 (W) 01273 736000
Fixtures Secretary: P Rumney Tel: (H) 01273 504981
Club Colours: Light blue and magenta hoops on navy

OLD CATERHAMIANS RFC
Surrey 1
Ground Address: Park Avenue, Caterham, Surrey. CR3 6AH Tel: 01883 343488
Brief Directions: From Caterham Station up Church Hill, 1st left into Stansted Road, Park Avenue 1st on right
Club Secretary: Mrs L Myland, Ash Trees, 15 Portley Lane, Caterham, Surrey. CR3 5JR Tel: (H&B 01883 343319
Fixtures Secretary: M Rowland
Tel: (H) 01342 842115 (W) 01737 775160
Club Colours: Black, amber, silver, mauve, black shorts

OLD COOPERIANS RUFC
Eastern Counties 1
Ground Address: Wanstead Sports Ground, Nutter Lane, Wanstead, London E11
Brief Directions: The club is now ground sharing with Eton Manor Rugby Club please check their details or phone their clubhouse (0181 555 2670).
Club Secretary: John C Green, Greenlow House, Melbourn, Herts. SG8 6OG
Tel: (H) 01763 260624
Fixtures Secretary: Chris Nicholls
Tel: (H & Fax) 0181 592 9450
Club Colours: Dark blue with thin gold and light blue hoops

OLD CRANLEIGHAN RFC
Surrey 1
Ground Address: Old Portsmouth Road, Thames Ditton, Surrey. KT7 0HB
Tel: 0181 398 3092
Club Secretary: Mark Lubbock, 52 Sarsfield Road, London. SW12 8HN
Tel: (H) 0181 398 3092
Fixtures Secretary: Tony Price
Tel: (H) 0181 949 1194 (W) 0181 533 7588
Club Colours: Blue white and gold hoops

OLD DUNSTONIAN RFC
Kent 1
Ground Address: St Dunstan's Lane, Langley Park, Beckenham, Kent. BR3 3SS
Tel: 0181 650 1779
Brief Directions: Frm Bromley Sth station, rt at lights Westmoreland Rd, rt at next lights Hayes Ln, 2nd lft Brabourne Rs, at the bottom entrance to St D'stans Ln is almost opp. between no's 114/6 Wickham Way
Club Secretary: Mike Rogers, Aboyne, Pickhurst Lane, West Wickham, Kent. BR4 0HN
Tel: (H) 0181 462 3064 (W) 0171 447 2238
Fixtures Secretary: Philip France
Tel: (H) 0181 776 2335
Club Colours: Navy and white circlet

OLD EDWARDIANS RFC
Eastern Counties 1
Ground Address: Westlands Playing Fields, London Road, Romford, Essex
Brief Directions: On A118 towards London from Romford (known locally as London Road)
Club Secretary: P. Hensher, c/o 45 Durban Lane, Noak Bridge, Essex SS15 4JU
Tel No: 01268 440199
Fixtures Secretary: B.Robinson. Tel No: 0181 491 9262 (H) 0171 414 5575 (W)
Club Colours: Navy blue shirts, white shorts or red and white hoops.9Change)

OLD ELTHAMIANS RFC
Kent 1
Ground Address: Old Elthamiansl Sports Ground, Foxbury Avenue,Chislehurst, Kent
Tel: 0181 4671296
Brief Directions: From M25 take A20 towards London,take second exit (A222) to Bromley and then second right is Foxbury Avenue.
Club Secretary: Ian McKinnon, 25 The Gardens, Beckenham, Kent. BR3 2PH
Tel: (H) 0181 650 1936
Fixtures Secretary: David Organ
Tel: (H) 0181 464 2542
Club Colours: Royal blue and gold hoops

OLD EMANUEL RFC
London 3 South West
Ground Address: Blagdons, Blagdon Lane, New Malden, Surrey
Tel: 0181 942 3857
Brief Directions: Using London A-Z locate where Burlington Rd crosses A3 at New Malden. Using north bound slip road to London ground is situated 200 yards on left
Club Secretary: I A Blair, 28 Hunters Road, Chessington, Surrey. KT9 1RV
Tel: (H) 0181 397 1272 (W) 0171 872 3349
Fixtures Secretary: J Monkhouse
Tel: (H) 01483 827323 (W) 01483 764114
Club Colours: White

OLD FREEMANS RFC
Surrey 3
Ground Address: City of London Freemen's School, Ashtead Park, Ashtead, Surrey. KT21 1ET
Tel: 01372 274158
Brief Directions: From Epsom Leatherhead A24 road turn into Park Lane Epsom end of Ashstead take 1st left through gates into park. Entrance to school ground 400 yards on right.
Club Secretary: Peter Ling, 74 Woodlands Road, Bookham, Surrey. KT24 4HH.
Tel: 01372 459172.
Fixtures Secretary: M J Bailey, 123 Overdale, Ashstead, Surrey. KT21 1PZ.
Tel: (H) 01372 278505 (W) 0181 642 3419
Club Colours: Dark blue, maroon & gold shirts, dark blue shorts

OLD GAYTONIANS RFC
London 3 North West
Ground Address: South Vale, Harrow, Middlesex HA1 3PN. Tel: 0181 423 4133
Brief Directions: A40 leaving London for Greenford fly over exit. turn right into A4127. Southvale is first turning on left after Sudbury Hill B.R.station.
Club Secretary: D A Garvey, 17 Lowlands Road, Eastcote, Pinner, Middlesex HA5 1TP. Tel: (H) 0181 866 5850
Fixtures Secretary: B A C Kennet, Tel: 0181 998 2879
Club Colours: White with thin chocolate, green and blue bands.

OLD GRAMMARIANS RFC
Hertfordshire & Middlesex 3 North
Ground Address: The Sports Field, Corner of Worlds End Lane/Green Dragon Lane, Enfield.
Brief Directions: M25 J24 (Potters Bar), A1005 towards Enfield, after about 3 miles right down Slades Hill, 4th left into Bincote Rd to Worlds End Ln, L turn to Green Dragon Ln entrance 80yds on left.

Club Secretary: Brian Calderwood, 17 Birch Crescent, Aylesford, Kent. ME20 7QE
Tel: (H) 01622 718350 (W) 01622 710811
Fixtures Secretary: Mike Holt, 60 Chandos Road, East Finchley, London.
Tel: (H) 0181 883 4016
Club Colours: Navy, red and light blue band

OLD GRAVESENDIANS RFC
Kent 2 East
Ground Address: Fleetway Sports Ground, Bronte View, Parrock Road, Gravesend, Kent DA12 1PX. Tel: 01474 365503
Brief Directions: A2 to Gravesend (not Gravesend East), take A227 (Tolgate) towards town.Turn right at lights at 2nd road junction. First turning at roundabout into Parrock Rd.. Ground 800 yds right
Club Secretary: Jeremy Strike, 33 Portland Road, Gravesend, Kent.
Tel No: 01474 321962
Fixtures Secretary: Stuart Hedge , 61 Parock Aveneue.Gravesend, Kent. DA12 1ZG
Club Colours: Light blue and dark blue hoops

OLD GUILDFORDIANS RFC
London 2 South
Ground Address: Stoke Park, London Road, Guildford, Surrey Tel: 01483 300752
Brief Directions: A3 turn off to Burpham, follow signs for Guildford town centre, Stoke Park on right after large roundabout, club house at northern end of Stoke Park
Club Secretary: David Bedford, 23 Brodie Road, Guildford, Surrey. GU1 3KZ
Tel: 01483 502023 (W) 0171 240 0074
Fixtures Secretary: Terry Maguire
Tel: (H) 01483 36514 (W) 0181 788 4351
Club Colours: Green with red and white hoops, green shorts

OLD HABERDASHERS
Hertfordshire & Middlesex 1
Ground Address: Old Haberdashers' Sports Ground, Croxdale Road, Theobald Street, Boreham Wood, Hertfordshire WD6 4PY. Tel: 0181 9531987
Club Secretary: M S Baker, Rookwood, Hedsor Road, Bourne End, Bucks, SL8 5EE. Tel: 0181 5876399
Fixtures Secretary: A Gray. Tel: 01494 778127
Club Colours: Blue, white and magenta.

OLD HAILEYBURIANS
Surrey 2
Ground Address: 27 Ruxley Lane, Kingston Road, Ewell, Surrey. KT19 0JB Tel: 0181 393 3901
Brief Directions: Reached from London by Portsmouth Rd (A3), take left filter to Epsom about 200 yds from Tolworth underpass along Kingston Rd, after 1 mile right into Ruxley Lane, 100 yards on left
Club Secretary: Roderick Sheen, 29 Kenilworth Avenue, London. SW19 7LN
Tel: (H) 0181 879 7851 (W) 0171 782 0990
Fixtures Secretary: Peter Blackmore 19 St, Andrews Street, Hertford, Herts. SG14 1HZ
Tel: 01992 553900
Club Colours: Magenta and white hoops

OLD HAMPTONIANS RFC
Hertfordshire & Middlesex 1
Ground Address: The Pavilion, Dean Road, Hampton, Middlesex. TW12 1AQ Tel: 0181 979 2784
Brief Directions: Leave A316 (London to M3) at signs for A316 Hampton proceed on Uxbridge Road for half mile. R. into Hanworth Road pass 3 schools on R. before turning R into Dean Road
Club Secretary: Sean Dalton, 18 Cromwell Road, Teddington, Middlesex TW11 9EW
Fixtures Secretary: Subhash Kamath, 267 Uxbridge, Middlesex TW12 1AR
Tel No: 0181 979 4339
Club Colours: Gold, silver and black hoops

OLD ISLEWORTHIANS RFC
Hertfordshire & Middlesex 3 South
Ground Address: Memorial Ground, Wood Lane, Isleworth, Middlesex
Tel: 0181 560 7949
Brief Directions: A4 (Great West Road) or London Road to Isleworth
Club Secretary: Huw Davies, 230 Whitton Dene, Isleworth, Middlesex. TW7 7LU
Tel: (H) 0181 8985929 (W) 01344 662958
Fixtures Secretary: Robert Davis, 4 York Road, Camberley, Surrey, GU15 4HR.
Tel: (H)01276 676242 (W) 01483 798712
Club Colours: Blue jersey with a horizontal red band and grey stripe

OLD JOHNIAN RFC
Surrey 4
Ground Address: Oaken Lane, Hinchley Wood, Surrey Tel: 0181 398 0535
Club Secretary: Mike Stuttard, 8 Woodside Avenue, Esher, Surrey. KT10 8JQ
Tel: (H) 0181 398 9417 (W) 01372 379011
Fixtures Secretary: David Robinson
Tel: (H) 01243 775901 (W) 01243 770374
Club Colours: Bottle green and white hoops

OLD JUDDIANS RFC
London 2 South
Ground Address: Tonbridge Sports Ground, The Slade, Tonbridge, Kent. TN9 1HR
Tel: 01732 358548
Brief Directions: From Tonbridge High St turn into Castle St signed Swimming Pool, bear right, left, then right again through bend, next right into The Slade, fork right at end into car park
Club Secretary: Justin C Hams, 33 Sullivan road, Tonbridge, Kent TN10 4DD
Tel: 01732 350220 (H) 0171 920 5993 (W)
Fixtures Secretary: Tony Russell, 28 Whistler Road, Tonbridge, Kent
Tel: (H) 01732 355582
Club Colours: Claret and light blue hoops, navy blue shorts

OLD MERCHANT TAYLORS' FC
London 2 North
Ground Address: Durrants, Lincoln Way, Croxley Green, Herts. WD3 3ND
Tel: 01923 773014
Brief Directions: M25 Jct 18.to Rick'worth. A412 to Croxley Grn.1st exit to C.G. at SportsmanPH.T.Jct rt to BaldwinsLn, left Manor Way at mini round't.Rt. Kenilw'th Drive,left Roch'ter Way. Durrants ahead.
Club Secretary: M G Foster, 199 Uxbridge Road, Rickmansworth, Herts. WD3 2DP
Tel: (H) 01923 771552 (W) 0973 657412
Fixtures Secretary: G W Shilling, The Lodge, Wellingrove, Woodcock Hill, Rickmansworth, Herts. WD3 1TP
Tel: (H) 01923 774506 (W) 01923 774506
Club Colours: Black shirts, black shorts

OLD MILLHILLIANS RFC
London 3 North West
Ground Address: Pinner Park, Headstone Lane, Middlesex. HA2 6BR Tel: 0181 428 2281
Brief Directions: Entrance to ground 20 yds to left of Headstone Lane station, exit on opposite side, 5 minutes walk from station
Club Secretary: P.R.Amlot, 369 Nether Street, London N3 1JN Tel No: 0181 346 1199
Fixtures Secretary: D.G.A. Penson, 43 Wesley Square, London W11 1TS
Tel: 0171 243 3544 (H)
Club Colours: Chocolate and white hoops

OLD OLAVIANS RUFC
Kent 2 West
Ground Address: St Olaves School, Goddington Lane, Orpington, Kent Tel: 01689 830744
Brief Directions: Join A224, either from A20 at Crittals Corner or M25 at Jinction 4. Follow signs to Orpington and Goddington Lane is near Volvo BP Garage.
Club Secretary: C.Hudson, 18 St., Leonards Rise, Orpington, Kent BR6 9NB
Fixtures Secretary: L.Fairhurst, 27 Cookson Road, Erith, Kent, DA8 1YE
Tel: 01322 430766
Club Colours: Purple, black and white hoops

OLD PALMERIANS RFC
Eastern Counties 3 South
Ground Address: Palmers Cottage, Chadwell Road, Grays, Essex Tel: 01375 370121
Brief Directions: A13 take A1012 towards Grays, at next roundabout take B149 to Palmers College (follow signposts Palmers College)
Club Secretary: Carwyn Owen, 1b Rose Cottage, Mill Lane, Grays, Essex. RM20 4YD
Tel: (H) 01375 378668
Fixtures Secretary: Andy Cresswell. Tel Nos: 01394 274252 (H) 01375 487920 (W)
Club Colours: Light blue and dark blue hoops .
Change Colours: Black

OLD PAULINE FC
Surrey 1
Ground Address: St Nicholas Road, off Speer Road, Thames Ditton, Surrey. KT7 0PW
Tel: 0181 398 1858
Brief Directions: From r'bout in Hampton Court Way (A309) turn east, 400m to Thames Ditton Station, after railway arch 1st left into Speer Rd, 2nd right into St Nicholas Rd
Club Secretary: John Howard, 93A Richmond Park Road, Kingston, Syrrey. KT2 6AF
Tel: (H) 0181 541 3817 (W) 01372 464470 (FX) 0171 982 2258
Fixtures Secretary: John Howard
Tel: (H) 0181 541 3817 (W) 01372 464470
Club Colours: Red, white and black hoops

OLD REEDONIANS
London 3 South West
Ground Address: North Avenue, Whiteley Village, Walton-on-Thames, Surrey. KT12 4DX
Tel: 01932 849616
Brief Directions: From A3/A245 junction towards Woking. After 1/4 mile turn right on B365 (Seven Hills Road). At 1st r'about turn right into Burwood Rd. Enter village & ground is 1/4 mile on right.
Club Secretary: John B Rogers, 8 Model Cottages, East Sheen, London. SW14 7PH.
Tel: (H & W) 0181 876 1512
Fixtures Secretary: David Nash, 41 Kennel Road, Fetcham, Surrey. KT12 2JR.
Tel: (H) 01372 452601 (W) 0181 560 4111.
Club Colours: Dark blue, light blue, red and white hoops.

OLD REIGATIAN RFC
London 3 South West
Ground Address: Park Lane, Reigate, Surrey RH2 9DL. Tel: 01737 245634
Brief Directions: Park Lane on A25 Reigate 3/4 mile on RHS
Club Secretary: D Forsyth, 76 Station Street, Redhill, Surrey RH1 1PL
Tel: (H) 01737 773533
Fixtures Secretary: D Payton, The Croft, Babylon Lane, Lower Kingswood, Surrey KT20 6UU
Club Colours: Green and blue hoops.

OLD RUTLISHIANS RFC
Surrey 2
Ground Address: Old Rutlishians Association, Poplar Road, Merton Park. SW19
Tel: 0181 542 3678
Brief Directions: Kingston Rd Merton to Dorset Rd by Merton Park level crossing, proceed along Dorset Rd to Melrose Ave, take left fork for Poplar Road
Club Secretary: Philip Rumbelow, 5A Moreton Road, Worcester Park, Surrey. KT4 8EY
Tel No: 0181 330 5586
Fixtures Secretary: John Petrides
Tel: (H) 0181 657 7750
Club Colours: Gold, silver, azure and black

OLD SHOOTERSHILLIAN S RFC
Kent 1
Ground Address: 123/125 Mayday Gardens, Kidbrooke, London. SE3
Tel: 0181 856 1511
Brief Directions: Frm Well Hall r'bout take signs for Woolwich & Ferry, over lights at top of hill, next left Broadwalk, over 4 humps, left Mayday Gdns, follow road to green on left, entrance to ground in corner
Club Secretary: B.A.C. Kennett, 18 Elmwood Drive, Bexley, Kent DA5 3PT
Tel: 0181 304 4982
Fixtures Secretary: N.Sharpe. Tel No: 01322 408333
Club Colours: Red, blue, green and yellow

OLD STANDFORDIANS RFC
Hertfordshire & Middlesex 3 North
Ground Address: Old Kents Lane, Standon, Herts
Brief Directions: At the junction between A10/A120 at Puckeridge, take A120 towards Bishops Stortford, pitch on right after 0.5 mile opposite Heron public house
Club Secretary: Ted Modoy, 522 Hatfield Road, St Albans, Herts
Tel: (H) 01727 834413
Fixtures Secretary: Adrian Watson
Tel: (H) 01763 271139
Club Colours: Black with pink hoop

OLD SUTTONIANS RFC
Surrey 3
Ground Address: Sutton Grammar School Playing Fields, Northey Avenue,, Cheam, Sutton, Surrey.
Brief Directions: On A232 between Cheam & Ewell take exit on St Pauls church roundabout into Northey Avenue. Ground is 1/4 mileon the right.
Club Secretary: S J Udall, 16 Kingsdown Road,

Cheam, Surrey. SM3 8NY
Tel: (H) 0181 644 7259 (W) 0585 681212
Fixtures Secretary: I M Connell
Tel: (H) 0181 642 8915 (W) 0181 224 6696
Club Colours: Red, white and black hoops

OLD TIFFINIAN RFC

Surrey 1
Ground Address: Grist Memorial Ground, Summer Road, off Hampton Court Way, East Molesey, Surrey
Tel: 0181 398 1391
Brief Directions: Hampton Court roundabout along Hampton Court way (A309).To turn into Summer Road you have to go to roundabout and come back , it is then first left.
Club Secretary: Andy Green, 2 Caroline Court, 25 Lovelace Road, Surbiton, Surrey
Tel: (H) 0181 399 9223 (W) 0181 330 8877
Fixtures Secretary: Greer Kirkwood, 63 Shaftesbury Way, Strawberry Hill, Twickenham, Middlesex, TW2 5RW.
Tel: (H) 0181 898 1767
Club Colours: Violet, white & navy blue hoops, shirts & socks, navy shorts

OLD TOTTONIANS RFC

Hertfordshire & Middlesex 2
Ground Address: Churchfields Playing Fields, Great Cambridge Road/Harrow Drive, Edmonton, London. N9
Tel: 0181 364 3099
Brief Directions: "Churuhfields" is located on the main A10 (Southbound) at Enfield between the Bury Street and Church Street junctions.
Club Secretary: Trevor De La Salle, 55 Welsummer Way, Le Motte Chase, Cheshunt, Herts. EN8 0UG
Tel: (H) 01992 638492 (W) 01494 444811
Fixtures Secretary: John Cockrill, 7 Sutherland Way, Cuffley, Herts, EN6 4EG
Tel: (H) 01707 872507 (W) 0171 421 2039
Club Colours: Blue & amber hooped shirts, blue shorts

OLD VERULAMIAN RFC

London 2 North
Ground Address: Cotlandswick, London Colney, nr St Albans, Hertfordshire. AL2 1DW Tel: 01727 822929
Brief Directions: Just off North Orbital Road (A414) ground opposite nursery
Club Secretary: Barry Smith, 58 Kings Road, St Albans, Herts AL3 4TG
Fixtures Secretary: Mrs V Halford , 35 The Ridgeway, St.Albans ,Herts. Tel: (H) 01727 830732
Club Colours: Royal blue with gold 'V', white shorts

OLD WALCOUNTIANS RFC

Surrey 1
Ground Address: Clockhouse, Carshalton Road, Woodmansterne, Banstead, Surrey. SM7 3HU
Tel: 01737 354348
Brief Directions: Carshalton Rd is approx 2 miles from A217, off Croydon Lane, the clubhouse is approx 0.5 mile along Carshalton Rd on the left
Club Secretary: Michael Swettenham, 4 Blakehall Rd., Carshalton, Surrey SM5 3EZ
Fixtures Secretary: Mr R McDowell
Tel: (H) 0181 669 6801
Club Colours: Black, blue and gold

OLD WELLINGTONIAN RFC

Surrey 2
Ground Address: 27 Ruxley Lane, Kingston Road, Ewell, Surrey (Shared with Old Haileyburians RFC)
Tel: 0181 393 3901
Brief Directions: East off the A3 from Tolworth Roundabout.
Club Secretary: Nick Dennis, 24 Coleford Road, London SW18 1AD.
Tel: (H) 0181 874 8486 (B) 0171 600 2801
Fixtures Secretary: Nick Prichard, 86a Iffley Road, London. W6 0PF.
Tel: (H) 0181 748 4002 (B) 01784 452600
Club Colours: Black with orange, light blue & yellow stripes

OLD WHITGIFTIAN RFC

London 3 South West
Ground Address: Croham Manor Road, South Croydon, Surrey. CR2 7BG
Tel: 0181 686 2127 (office) 0181 688 3248 (bar)
Brief Directions: 1 mile south of Central Croydon on A235, fork left at The Swan & Sugarloaf pub into Selsdon Rd, 300 yds mini r'bout 2nd exit into Croham Rd, ground 0.5 mile on right
Club Secretary: Huntley Norman, ' St. Dorothys', 52 Croham Manor Rd., South Croydon, Surrey CR2 7BE
Tel NBo.: (H&W) 0181 688 7199
Fixtures Secretary: Geoff Austin, 97 Clifton Road, Kingston-upon-Thames, Surrey. KT2 6PL
Tel: (H) 0181 549 3757 (W) 0171 926 5400 (M) 0850068409
Club Colours: Red, black and blue hooped shirts, white shorts

OLD WILLIAMSONIAN RFC

Kent 2 East
Ground Address: Maidstone Road, Rochester, Kent.
Tel: 01634 842883
Club Secretary: Mark Ian Smith, 26 Chalkenden avenue, Gillingham Kent. ME8 6AQ
Tel: (H) 01634 235 094
Fixtures Secretary: Dean Painter Tel: (H) 01634 260892
Club Colours: Navy blue, single gold hoop

OLD WIMBLEDONIANS RFC

London 2 South
Ground Address: 143 Coombe Lane, London, SW20 0NQ.Tel: 0181 879 0700
Brief Directions: From Raynes Park station follow Coombe Lane towards Kingston. Cross traffic lights at WEST barnes Lane junction, ground approx 800 yds on lefthand side.
Club Secretary: Mrs Margaret Parsons, Hawth, Glaziers Lane, Normandy, Guildford, Surrey. GU3 2EA
Tel: (H) 01483 811103
Fixtures Secretary: Mr Des Hawken, 23 Southway, Carshalton, Surrey, SW5 4HP.
Tel & Fax: (H) 0181 643 2833
Club Colours: Green, maroon and gold hoops

ONGAR RFC

Eastern Counties 3 South
Ground Address: Love Lane, Ongar, Essex
Tel: 01277 363838
Brief Directions: To Ongar from Brentwood A128, turn right into town, proceed along High St, before tube station on left turn right into Love Lane, ground 300 metres
Club Secretary: Nigel Doubleday, 105 Roundhill, Waltham Abbey, Essex. BN9 1TF
Tel: (H) 01992 768950 (W) 0802 284346
Fixtures Secretary: Peter Hodgson
Tel: (H) 01277 354404 (W) 0468 277258
Club Colours: Blue with amber band

ORLEANS F.P. RFC
Hertfordshire & Middlesex 4 South
Ground Address: Orleans Park, off Richmond Road, Twickenham Tel: 0181 892 5743
Brief Directions: Off Richmond Road, between Crown pub and Orleans Park School
Club Secretary: Steve Frost, 13 Langham Place, Chiswick, London. W4 2QL
Tel: (H) 0181 747 5026 (W) 0181 943 5331
Fixtures Secretary: Graham Todd
Tel: (H) 0181 898 4982
Club Colours: Gold, maroon and white

ORPINGTON RFC
Kent 2 West
Ground Address: Hoblingwell Wood, Leesons Way, St Pauls Cray, Orpington, Kent. BR5 2QB
Tel: 01689 823913
Brief Directions: From M25 Jct 3, take A20 towards London. Take first exit, A224 Orpington, then first right, third left and third right into Leesons Way.
Club Secretary: Chris Evens c/o PO Box 145, Orpington, Kent BR5 2ZY
Tel: (H) 01689 896709 (W) 01959 514152
Fixtures Secretary: Dave Corry c/o PO Box 145, Orpington, Kent BR5 2ZY
Tel: (H) 01689 811396
Club Colours: Black and yellow hoops Change Colours: All Black

OSTERLEY RFC
Hertfordshire & Middlesex 4 South
Ground Address: Tentelow Lane, Norwood Green, Southall, Middlesex Tel: 0181 574 3774
Brief Directions: From A4 Great West Road: north from Gilette Corner up Windmill Lane
Club Secretary: Richard Evans, 111 Rowlands Avenue, Pinner, Middlesex. HA5 4AW
Tel: (H) 0181 428 5797
Fixtures Secretary: John Green
Tel: (H) 0181 568 5557
Club Colours: Black and white hoops

OVERTON RFC
Hampshire 2
Ground Address: The Old Cricket Ground, Laverstoke Park, Watch Lane, Laverstoke, Hampshire
Brief Directions: From Witchurch take B3400 to Basingstoke. After Watership Down Pub take 2nd left into watch lane, follow signs to Rigby Club
Club Secretary: David Overall, Dagnam, 7 Belmont Heights, Hatchwarren, Basingstoke, Hampshire PG22 4RW Tel: (H) 01256 843974
Fixtures Secretary: Alec Coles, 15 Rochford Road, Basingstoke, Hants RG21 9TQ
Tel: (H) 01256 410836
Club Colours: Royal blue

OXTED RFC
Surrey 4
Ground Address: Holland Fields, Holland Road, Hurst Green, Oxted, Surrey Tel: 01883 717468
Brief Directions: M25 J6, follow sign to Oxted, turn left onto A25, right into Woodhurst Lane (under railway viaduct), follow for 2 miles, club on right
Club Secretary: Mick Berry, 12 Coldshot Lane, Hurst Green, Oxted, Surrey Tel: (H) 01883 717261
Fixtures Secretary: Steve Taylor
Tel: (H) 01883 716899
Club Colours: Red hoop on blue shirt, blue shorts, red socks

PARK HOUSE FC
London 3 South East
Ground Address: Barnet Wood Road, Hayes, Kent. BR2 7AA
Tel: 0181 462 7318
Brief Directions: A21 to Bromley (or from M25 J4), turn off on A233 (Oakleigh Rd) towards Biggin Hill, Barnet Wood Road is a turning on the right
Club Secretary: Robert D Elves, 47 Ramillies Road, Sidcup, Kent. DA15 9JA
Tel: (H) 0181 304 9170 (W) 01474 853731
Fixtures Secretary: G Bunnage, 48 Southborough Road, Bickley, Kent BR1 2EL
Tel: (H) 0181 467 1447 (W) 0181 401 0111
Club Colours: Black shirts with red circlet, black shorts

PEGASUS
Eastern Counties 4 South

PETERSFIELD RFC
Hampshire 1
Ground Address: Penns Place, Petersfield, Hants. GU31 4EP
Tel: 01730 264588
Brief Directions: East edge of town, co-located with East Hants District Council offices and Taro Sports Centre as signed
Club Secretary: Geoff Litchfield, 13 Copse Close, Petersfield. GU31 4DL
Tel: (H) 01730 265072 (W) 01483 300636
Fixtures Secretary: Albert Winterbottom. Tel No: 01730 261860 (W) 01730 234271
Club Colours: Red with white hoop

PINNER & GRAMMARIANS RFC
Hertfordshire & Middlesex 3 South
Ground Address: Shaftesbury Playing Fields, Grimsdyke Road, Hatchend Pinner, Middlesex
Tel: 0181 428 3136
Brief Directions: By rail: Hatchford (NSG & B'loo), west A410 Uxbrge Rd to Hatch End B'way Shps, rt G'sdyke Rd, 2nd rt H'view, 1st lt C'burn Ave, club lt. Road: frm E. same, frm W. A410 Uxbrg Rd, lt G'dyke Rd
Club Secretary: David Hiles, 31 Lulworth Close, South Harrow, Middlesex. HA2 9NR
Tel: (H & Fax) 0181 864 0787
Fixtures Secretary: Phil Kojcinovic.
Tel No: 01895 621680 (H) 01923 231 936 (W) 0956 679824 (M)
Club Colours: Navy and 1" scarlet hoops

PLUMPTON RFC
Sussex 2
Ground Address: The Racecourse, Plumpton Green, East Sussex
Brief Directions: Plumpton Racecourse opposite railway station in village of Plumpton Green
Club Secretary: Chris Woodward, 2 Monks Way, Lewes, East Sussex. BN7 2EX
Tel: (H) 01273 476219
Fixtures Secretary: Graham Glendenning, 55/56 Surrey Street, Brighton, BN1 3PB
Tel: (H) 01273 328931
Club Colours: Maroon and amber hoops

PORTSMOUTH RFC
Hampshire 2
Ground Address: Norway Road, Hilsea, Portsmouth
Tel: 01705 660610

Club Secretary: Roger T Hollis, 69 Blackbrook Road, Fareham, Hampshire. PO15 5DE.
Tel: 01329 236506
Fixtures Secretary: Mr W. Arnold, 61 Chetwynd Road, Southsea, Hampshire.
Tel: (H) 01705 821109 (W) 01705 819125
Club Colours: Black with 3 white & gold hoops

PULBOROUGH RFC

Sussex 1
Ground Address: Sports & Social Club, Rectory Lane, Pulborough, West Sussex Tel: 01798 873020
Brief Directions: Approach by Rectory Lane branching north off east end of Lower Street opposite Arundale School
Club Secretary: Chris Brazier, 2 Heather Farm Cottages, Chobham Rd., Horsell Common, Woking, Surrey GU21 4XY Tel: (W) 01798 812345
Fixtures Secretary: Michael Ford, 14 Ravenscroft, Sturrington, West Essex
Tel: (H) 01903 745697
Club Colours: Black and white hoops

PURLEY RFC

London 3 South West
Ground Address: Parsons Pightle, Coulsdon Road, Old Coulsdon, Surrey. CR5 1EE
Tel: 01737 553042
Brief Directions: M25 J7 - M23-A23, turn right in Coulsdon to Marl Pit Lane, to end turn right, Coulsdon Road, ground 0.5 mile on right
Club Secretary: Simon Witham, 2 Kingswood Avenue, Sanderstead, Surrey. CR2 9DQ
Tel: (H) 0181 657 2089 (W) 0171 247 4466
Fixtures Secretary: Martin Bazley
Tel: (H) 0181 660 2157 (W) 0171 377 5423
Club Colours: Black and white

QUEEN ELIZABETH II RFC

Hertfordshire & Middlesex 4 North
Ground Address: Hatfield Hyde Sports Club, King George V Playing Fields, Beehive Lane, Welwyn Garden City, Hertfordshire. Al7 4BP
Tel: 01707 326700
Brief Directions: From A1 take WGC exit, follow signs to QE II Hospital, when in the road "Howlands" turn into Beehive Lane, turn left past Beehive public house
Club Secretary: Steve Murray, 73 Howicks Green, Welwyn Garden City, Hertfordshire. AL7 4RJ
Tel: (H) 01707 887324
Fixtures Secretary: Rod Ibbinson, 29 The Moors, Welwyn Garden City, Herts .
Tel: 01707 331341
Club Colours: Myrtle green and amber

QUINTIN RFC

Hertfordshire & Middlesex 2
Ground Address: Quintin Hogg Memorial ground, Cavendish Road, Grove Park, London W4 . Tel: 0181 994 0467
Brief Directions: Go north from Chiswick Bridge 1st L. Hartington Rd (Pitches on L.) continue turn 1st R. Cavendish Rd for entry to Pavilion on right side of road.
Club Secretary: Nigel Smith, 4 Australia Avenue, Maidenhead, Berks. SL6 7DJ
Tel: (H) 01628 675899 (W) 01895 279919
Fixtures Secretary: Jon Adcock, 2 Meadowbank Road, Lightwater, Surrey GU18 5SX Trl: (H) 01276 475305
Club Colours: Scarlet and green hoops, blue shorts

RACAL DECCA RFC

Surrey 4
Ground Address: Decca Sports and Social Club, Kingston Road, Tolworth, Surrey
Tel: 0181 337 9190
Brief Directions: A3 from Guildford/London, turn off at Tolworth junction then A240 towards Ewell, approx 200 yards turn left at traffic lights, ground on left
Club Secretary: Andrew Howard, Flat 7, 18-24 Warwick Way, Pimlico, London. SW1V 1RX Tel: (H) 0171 8345956 (W) 0171 4124607
Fixtures Secretary: Andrew Howard - As above
Club Colours: Blue and white hoops

RAF LAKENHEATH

Eastern Counties 4 North
Club Secretary: D Rees, c/o Rugby Club RAF Lakenheath, Mildenhall, Suffolk. Tel: (H) 01638 751552 Fax: 01638 542118
Fixtures Secretary: D Rees, as above.
Club Colours: Navy and amber quarters.

RAVENS RFC
Eastern Counties 3 South
Ground Address: Ford Sports and Social Club, Aldborough Road South, Newbury Park, Ilford, Essex. Tel: 0181 590 3797.
Brief Directions: From North M11 then A406 (North Circular Road) to junction with A12 and Eastbound along A12 past Newbury Park Underground then right at lights. Ground on left.
Club Secretary: Gary Bishop, c/o BACB Ltd, 30 Gresham Street, London, EC2V 7LP.
Tel: (H) 0181 788 7962
Fixtures Secretary: A C Guest, 57 Shaftsbury Road, Forest Gate, London, E7 8PD
Tel:(H) 0181 471 7571
Club Colours: Navy blue and gold hoops

RAYLEIGH WYVERNS RFC
Eastern Counties 4 South
Ground Address: John Fisher Playing Fields, Little Wheatleys Chase, Rayleigh, Essex
Brief Directions: From A127 take A130 towards Chelmsford, next roundabout turn right, towards Rayleigh (A129), take 1st right Little Wheatleys Chase, ground 500 yds on right after school
Club Secretary: S J Earl, 22 The Fairway, Leigh-on-Sea, Essex. SS9 4QL
Tel: (H) 01702 524111
Fixtures Secretary: N. McQuire, 6 Copper Beeches, Thundersley, Essex SS7 3UA
Tel: 01268 772835
Club Colours: Scarlet and emerald quarters, black shorts

RAYNES PARK RFC
Surrey 1
Ground Address: Raynes Park Sports Ground, Taunton Avenue, Raynes Park, London. SW20
Brief Directions: Shannon Corner exit A3 to Raynes Park, last turning left (Camberley Ave) before Coombe Lane/West Barnes Lane traffic lights
Club Secretary: Russell Price, 101 Belmont Avenue, New Malden, Surrey. KT3 6QE
Tel: (H) 0181 949 2448 (W) 0171 299 5082
Fixtures Secretary: As for Secretary
Club Colours: Blue and gold quarters, blue shorts and socks

REIGATE & REDHILL RFC
Surrey 3
Ground Address: Eric Hodgkins Memorial Ground, Colley Lane, Reigate, Surrey
Tel: 01737 221110
Brief Directions: M25 J8 south on Reigate Hill, turn right before level crossing, to end of road turn right then keep left into Colley Lane, club 200m on right
Club Secretary: Norman Phillips, 28 Hurstleigh Drive, Redhill, Surrey. RH1 2AA
Tel: (H) 01737 212912
Fixtures Secretary: Nick Weddon. Tel No: 01737 277 243
Club Colours: Royal blue with white hoops

ROBERTSBRIDGE RUFC
Sussex 3
Ground Address: Robertsbridge Community College, Knelle Road, Robertsbridge, East Sussex. TN32 5EA
Brief Directions: From the village follow signs to the railway station, go over the level crossing, take the 2nd right then go straight up to the college
Club Secretary: Bernard Davies , 12 Ridgeway, Hurst Green, East Sussex TN19 7PJ
Tel: 01580 860325
Fixtures Secretary: James MacDonald, 2 Victoria Cottages, The Moor, Hawkhurst, Kent, TN18 4NY. Tel: (H) 01580 753853
Club Colours: Blue and Black Quarters

ROCHFORD HUNDRED RFC
London 3 North East
Ground Address: The Clubhouse, Magnolia Road, Hankwell, Essex. SS4 3AD
Tel: 01702 544021
Club Secretary: Mr R Simon Wakefield, 54 Parklands Drive, Springfield, Chelmsford, Essex. CM1 7SP
Tel: (H) 01245 266158 (W) 01702 541581
Fixtures Secretary: Mr Colin Chandler
Tel: (H) 01277 766748
Club Colours: Black shirt and shorts, black socks with white tops

ROMFORD & GIDEA PARK RFC
London 2 North
Ground Address: Crowlands, Crow Lane, Romford, Essex. RM7 0EP
Tel: 01708 760068
Brief Directions: A12 to Moby Dick pub, from London right, from east left,into Whalebone Ln Nth,at lights left Londn Rd, 0.5 mile right Jutsums Ln,under bridge,left Crow Ln,ground 100m right
Club Secretary: D G E Davies, 25 Stanley Avenue, Gidea Park, Romford, Essex. RM2 5DL
Tel: (H) 01708 724870 (W) 0181 270 4544
Fixtures Secretary: G Finch
Tel: (H) 01277 229817
Club Colours: Black, purple and white hoops

ROMSEY RUFC
Hampshire 1
Ground Address: Romsey Sports Centre, Lower Southampton Road, Romsey, Hampshire. SO51 8AF
Tel: 01794 519400
Brief Directions: M27 J3, follow signs to Romsey, straight over 1st roundabout, left at 2nd roundabout, at end of long wall turn left into Sports Centre
Club Secretary: Andrew Mott, 3 South Close, Romsey, Hampshire. SO51 7UP
Tel: (H) 01794 515295
Fixtures Secretary: Malcolm Pain, 2 Nursery Road, Bitterne Park, Southampton. SO2 4NS Tel: 01703 557972
Club Colours: Royal blue with gold hoops

ROXETH MANOR OLD BOYS RFC
Hertfordshire & Middlesex 2
Ground Address: Queensmead School, Queens Walk off Victoria Road, Ruislip, Middlesex
Tel: 0181 845 6010
Club Secretary: Mr D Peacham, 26 Yeading Avenue, Harrow, Middlesex. HA2 9RN
Tel: (H) 0181 868 1799
Fixtures Secretary: Mr P Noot
Tel: (H) 01753 888775
Club Colours: Black

ROYAL & SUN ALLIANCE
Sussex 1
Ground Address: Royal & Sun Alliance Club, North Heath Lane, Horsham, West Sussex RH12 4PJ
Brief Directions: A264 leave at roundabout for Ruffey, 3rd exit at next roundabout, go half mile and turn left

into North Heath Lane at mini roundabout, ground is half mile on LHS.
Club Secretary: K.J.Reed, 38 Red Admiral Street, North Heath Lane, Horsham, West Sussex RH12 5YJ
Fixtures Secretary: S West
Tel:(H) 01403 269838 (W) 01403 234285
Club Colours: Navy Blue with yellow, Green,and White chevron

ROYSTON RUFC
Hertfordshire & Middlesex 3 North
Ground Address: Heath Sports Club, Baldock Road, Royston. SG8
Tel: 01763 243613
Brief Directions: A10 north or south to roundabout by cinema, turn west through town centre, past golf club on left, A505 from Baldock turn right at Little Chef, club on right
Club Secretary: Mrs Anne McGarry, 7 Huttles Green, 7 Huttles Green, Shepreth, Royston, Herts S98 6PR
Fixtures Secretary: Godfrey Everett, 24 Clarkes Way,Bassingbourne, Royston, Herts. SG8 5LT
Tel: (H) 01763 243846
Club Colours: Black and white hoops, black shorts, black socks

RYE RFC
Sussex 3
Ground Address: Rye RFC, New Road, Rye, East Sussex Tel: 01797 224867
Brief Directions: Situated east of main town on the A259 coast road
Club Secretary: Jason Bowen, 15 Southundercliff, Rye, East Sussex. TN31 7HN
Tel: (H) 01797 226597 (W) 0468 453671
Fixtures Secretary: Graham Nunn
Tel: (H) 01797 280517
Club Colours: Red and white quarters, black shorts, black socks

SAFFRON WALDEN RFC
Eastern Counties 1
Ground Address: Springate, Henham, Nr Bishops Stortford
Tel: 01279 850791
Club Secretary: B Peachey, 2 Gloucester Place, Clare, Suffolk. CO10 8QR
Tel: (H) 01787 278464 (W) 01277 260600
Fixtures Secretary: D. Cassells, 25 Cambridge Crescent, Bassingbourn, Royston SG8 5LP
Tel: (H) 01763 243978 (W) 01223 203704
Club Colours: Myrtle green

SANDOWN & SHANKLIN RUFC
Hampshire 2
Ground Address: The Clubhouse, Station approach, The Fairway Lake, Sandown, Isle of Wight. PO36 9ES
Tel: 01983 404707
Brief Directions: By rail - Pitch is adjacent to Sandown Station (50 yards). By road - Follow main Sandown Shanklin road to Lake, take `The Fairway' - Pitch on right opposite high school.
Club Secretary: Kevin Squibb, The Acorns, Alverstone Road, Queen Bower, Sandown, Isle Of Wight, PO36 0LB.
Tel: 01983 405682
Fixtures Secretary: Colin Bond, Basement Flat, rear of18 High Street, Sandown, Isle of wight, PO36 8DE.
Tel: (H) 01983 402374
Club Colours: Dark Blue with Red, White and Blue

SAWSTON RFC
Eastern Counties 3 North
Ground Address: Sawston Village College, New Road, Sawston, Cambs. CB2 4BP
Tel: 01223 836615
Brief Directions: M11 J10, take A505 to Sawston, next roundabout take A1301 marked Sawston/Cambridge, after 1 mile turn right to Sawston then 1st left New Road, College on left
Club Secretary: Paul Clerke, 1 Crossways, Linton, Cambridge. CB1 6NQ
Tel: (H) 01223 843985 (W) 01223 834555 Ext 3575
Fixtures Secretary: Philip Mason
Tel: (H) 01279 812545 (W) 0171 377 6161 Ext 289
Club Colours: Black, navy and white quarters

SEAFORD RFC
Sussex 1
Ground Address: The Salts Recreation Ground, The Esplanade, Seaford Tel: 01323 892355
Brief Directions: Situated on the sea front just off the A259
Club Secretary: A.Smith, 11 Chichester Road, Seaford, Sussex BN25 4DJ. Tel No: 01323 490993
Fixtures Secretary: P Ungoed Tel: (H) 01323 893688
Club Colours: Scarlet

SEVENOAKS RUFC
London 2 South
Ground Address: Knole Paddock, Plymouth Drive, Sevenoaks, Kent. TN13 3RP
Tel: 01732 452027
Brief Directions: J.5 M25. Follow signs to Sevenoaks. At Riverhead R/about turn R. up Amhersa Hill. L. after BR station R. at top then L. around Cricket Ground - Plymouth Drive on right.
Club Secretary: John Maslin, 198 Chesterfield Drive, Sevenoaks, Kent. TN13 2EH Tel: 01732 460910 H
Fixtures Secretary: Howard Pearl, Nearly Corner, Heaverham, Kew, Sevenoaks, Kent, TN15 6NQ.
Tel: 01732 763431H
Club Colours: Navy & Gold

SHELFORD RUFC
London 3 North East
Ground Address: Davey Field, Cambridge Road, Gt Shelford, Cambridge
Tel: 01223 843357
Brief Directions: M11 J11 heading into Cambridge, right at traffic lights into Shelford Rd, continue for 1 mile, club is on the right opposite Scotsdale Garden Centre
Club Secretary: Lydia D Langenheim, 22 London Road, Gt. Shelford, Cambridge. CB2 5DD
Tel: (H) 01223 503644
Fixtures Secretary: Ian Coupe, 95 Tamarin Gardens, Cherry Hinton, Cambridge. CB1 9GQ
Club Colours: Maroon and white hoops, blue shorts

SHEPPEY FOOTBALL CLUB LTD
Kent 1
Ground Address: The Clubhouse, Scocles Field, Lower Road, Minster, Sheerness, Kent ME12
Tel: 01795 872082
Brief Directions: A249 to Sheppey, from M2 or M20 on Sheppey, at 1st roundabout take
Club Secretary: Mrs Linda Neal, 16 New Road, Minster, Sherness, Kent.
Tel No: 01795 873983 (H) 01795 439409 (W)
Fixtures Secretary: As Secretary.
Club Colours: White with single red hoop, black shorts

SHIRLEY WANDERERS RUFC

Surrey 2
Ground Address: Kent Gate, Addington Road, West Wickham, Kent
Tel: 0181 777 5298
Club Secretary: Martin Stone, 251 Quentin Court, Regency Walk, Shirley, Croydon, Surrey
Tel: (H) 0181 777 6712
Fixtures Secretary: Geoff Jeffcoat
Tel: (H) 0181 777 5174 (W) 0181 761 3000
Club Colours: All white

SHOREHAM RFC

Sussex 2
Ground Address: Kings Manor School, Kingston Lane, Shoreham-by-Sea, West Sussex
Tel: 01273 597625
Brief Directions: Take A27 to Shoreham (Old Shoreham road) westward Kingston Lane is on left at traffic lights before Holmbush shopping centre r'bout, Kings Manor School 0.5 mile on right
Club Secretary: Simon Edgar, 17 Newtimber Gardens, Shoreham-by-Sea, West Sussex BN43 5GQ.
Tel: (H) 01273 701618 (W) 0831 236918
Fixtures Secretary: Mrs Sandy Beal
Tel: (H) 01273 884827
Club Colours: Amber and bottle green quarters

SIDCUP FC (RFU)

London 3 South East
Ground Address: Crescent Farm, Sydney Road, Sidcup, Kent. DA14 6RA
Tel: 0181 3002336
Brief Directions: A20-A222 towards Sidcup (Chislehurst Rd), proceed to 1st traffic lights (Police Station), left into Main Road, left just past fire station into Sydney Rd, ground 200mtrs on left
Club Secretary: Allan Jones, 53 Goodwin Drive, Sidcup, Kent. DA14 4NX
Tel: 0208 302 2382
Fixtures Secretary: Malcolm Leamon
Tel: 0208 859 5598
Club Colours: White shirts with navy blue collar and cufs. Maroon Shorts

SITTINGBOURNE RUFC

Kent 2 East
Ground Address: Gore Court Sports Club, The Grove, Key Street, Sittingbourne, Kent. ME10 1YT
Tel: 01795 423813
Brief Directions: From M2 eastbound, A249 to Sittingbourne & Sheerness, after 2 miles take A2 towards Sittingbourne, after 0.5 mile turn left just after Sports ground, left again into club car park
Club Secretary: Steve Smith, 34 Crouch Hill Court, Lower Halstow, Sittingbourne, Kent. ME9 7EJ
Tel: (H) 01795 843356
Fixtures Secretary: Denise Smith as above.
Tel: (H) 01795 843356
Club Colours: Blue and gold hoops

SNOWDON COLLIERY WELFARE RFC

Kent 2 East
Ground Address: Welfare Ground, Aylesham, Canterbury, Kent
Tel: 01304 840278
Brief Directions: Take A2, 8 miles south of Canterbury, take Aylesham turn off, ground 2 miles further along this road
Club Secretary: Eddie Sullivan, 4 Burgess Road, Aylesham, Canterbury, Kent. CT3 3AU
Tel: (H) 01304 840052
Fixtures Secretary: Alan Booth
Tel: (H) 01304 840619
Club Colours: Red and blue hoops

SOUTH WOODHAM FERRERS RFC

Eastern Counties 2
Ground Address: Saltcoats Playing Fields, Saltcoats Pavilion, South Woodham Ferrers, Essex
Tel: 01245 320041
Club Secretary: David Parkinson, 43 Cklements Green Lane, South Woodham Ferrers, Essex. Tel No: 01245 321376
Fixtures Secretary: Paul Gregory, 1 Maydene, South Woodham Ferrers, Essex
Tel No: 01245 328930
Club Colours: All black

SOUTHAMPTON INSTITUTE

Hampshire 2
Ground Address: Hardmoor Playing Fields, Stoneham Lane, Eastleigh. So5 3HT
Tel: 01703 617574
Brief Directions: Exit junction 5 on M27 (Airport turn off)
Club Secretary: D H Prout, 38 Chessel Avenue, Bitterne, Southampton. SO2 4DX
Tel: (H) 01703 394795 (W) 01703 319343
Fixtures Secretary: Martin Hughes , Southampton Institute, East Park Terrace
Southampton
Club Colours: Maroon and white

SOUTHAMPTON RFC

London 3 South West
Ground Address: Test Park Playing Fields, Lower Brownhill Road, Millbrook, Southampton, Hants
Tel: 01703 737777
Brief Directions: M27 onto M271, take 1st slip road, 1st exit off roundabout towards Lordshill, after 150 yds turn right into Lower Brownhill Road
Club Secretary: Paul Raine, Tanglewood, Winchester Rd., Boorley Green , Southampton SO32 2DH
Tel: (H) 01489 788460
Fixtures Secretary: Rob Swain .Tel No: 01703 367140
Club Colours: Red and white hoops

SOUTHEND RFC

London 2 North
Ground Address: Warners Bridge Park, Sumpters Way, Southend on Sea SS2 5RR Tel: 01702 546682
Brief Directions: From London A127 to Southend, continue past park and large garage, left at roundabout into Sutton Rd, 0.5 mile left at mini roundabout, ground at bottom through ind. est.
Club Secretary: David Dilley, 106 Woodside, Leigh on Sea, Essex. SS9 4RB Tel: (H) 01702 75075
Fixtures Secretary: David Dilley, 106 Woodside, Leigh on Sea, Essex SS94RB
Tel: 01702 523553
Club Colours: Brown and white

SOUTHGATE RFC

Hertfordshire & Middlesex 2
Ground Address: Nortel Ltd, Oakleigh Road South, New Southgate, London. N11 1HB
Tel: 0181 945 2655/2181
Brief Directions: A406 frm E., exit for Arnos Grove, pass Arnos Grve stn to r'bout, 2nd exit for Oakl'gh Rd Sth. A406 frm W., left for New Southgate stn, right at Turrets pub, 1st exit r'bout for Oakl'gh Rd Sth

Club Secretary: David Hockey, 5 The Vineries, Enfield, Middlesex. EN1 3DQ
Tel: (H) 0181 342 0202 (W) 0171 270 3874
Fixtures Secretary: Simon Shuttler
Tel: (H) 0181 368 5025 (W) 0181 446 8324
Club Colours: Dark blue, light blue and gold irregular hoops

SOUTHWOLD RFC
Eastern Counties 3 North
Ground Address: The Pavilion, The Common, Southwold, Suffolk
Brief Directions: First right at Kings Head Hotel and proceed towards water tower
Club Secretary: Amanda Pywell, Cymru, The Street, Rumburgh, Halesworth, Suffolk. IP!9 0NN
Tel: 01986 785418
Fixtures Secretary: John Winter, Stream House, Chediston, Halesworth, Suffolk
Tel: (H) 01986 875994
Club Colours: Black with Gold hoop.

ST ALBANS RFC
London 3 North West
Ground Address: Boggey Mead Spring, Oaklands Lane, Smallford, St Albans, Herts. AL4 0HR
Tel: 01727 869945
Club Secretary: N J Millar, 39 Watford Road, St Albans, Herts. AL1 2AE
Tel: (H) 01727 830169 (W) 01582 794007
Fixtures Secretary: Mr. Tim Andrews, 77 Batchwood Drive, St. Albuns, Herts. Tel: (H) 01727 857440
Club Colours: Royal blue and gold hoops, navy shorts

ST FRANCIS RFC
Sussex 3
Ground Address: Southgate Playing Fields, Southgate Avenue, Crawley, West Sussex. Tel No: 01293 616941
Brief Directions: M23 J11, take A23 to Crawley, right at roundabout into Southgate Ave, ground approx 1 mile on right hand side
Club Secretary: IMark Eastman, 182 Buckswood Drive, Gossops Green, Crawley, West Sussex RH11 8PS
Tel No: 01293 529414 (H) 0171 391 7030
Fixtures Secretary: Vince McGahan
Tel: (H) 01293 547194 (W) 01293 503389
Club Colours: Black with blue and two white hoops

ST NICHOLAS OLD BOYS RFC
Hertfordshire & Middlesex 2
Ground Address: c/o Ickenham Cricket Club, Oak Avenue, Ickenham, Middlesex Tel: 01895 639366
Brief Directions: From Hillingdon turn off A40, follow signs to Ickenham and Ruislip, turn left after 2nd petrol station into Oak Avenue
Club Secretary: Cliffird Lewis, 98 Hartherleigh Road, Ruislip, Middx HA4 6AV
Tel: (H) 01895 622746
Fixtures Secretary: Bob Maynard, 117 SWakeleys Road, Ickenham, Middlesex UB10 8DF
Tel NO: 0973 503 530
Club Colours: Red shirts, white shorts

STANFORD LE HOPE RFC
Eastern Counties 3 South
Ground Address: Stanford Recreation Ground, Corringham Rd.,Stanford-le Hope. Tel: 01375 640957
Brief Directions: A13 to Stanford-le-Hope then turn off at A1014. Right at roundabout into Corringham Rd. First left Rainbow Lane, First Right Billet Lane. Clubhouse at far end on right.
Club Secretary: Darren Watkins, 169 London Road, Grays, Essex RM17 5YP. Tel: (H) 01375 374776
Fixtures Secretary: Kyran M SS17 7BQcDonald, 3 St. James Avenue East, Stanford-le-Hope Essex
Tel: (H) 01375 403520
Club Colours: Red, White and Black Hoops .

STEVENAGE TOWN RFC
Hertfordshire & Middlesex 1
Ground Address: North Road, Stevenage, Herts. SG1 4BB Tel: 01438 359788
Brief Directions: Take A1M Stevenage North Jcn 7, take road towards Graveley, 1st right (past garden centre) towards St'age, ground 400yds on right, parking on access road by pitches
Club Secretary: Richard Stephens, 18 Russell Close, Stevenage, Herts. SG2 8PB
Tel: (H) 01438 351971 (answerphone) (W) 01438 355751
Fixtures Secretary: Fred McCarthy, 69 Stirling Close, Stevenage SG2 2LN
Tel: (H) 01438 811590 (W) 01438 767231
Club Colours: Black shirts with green hoop, black shorts, green socks

STOWMARKET RUFC
Eastern Counties 4 North
Ground Address: Chilton Fields Sports Club, Chilton Way, Stowmarket, Suffolk
Tel: 01449 613181
Brief Directions: From Bury St Edmonds direction along A14, take exit marked Stowmarket, 2nd exit at roundabout, left onto housing estate, follow road, last road on the right
Club Secretary: Mrs Sharon Crowe, 1 Lime Tree Place, Stowmarket. IP14 1BU
Fixtures Secretary: Mr Darryl Chapman
Tel: (H) 01449 672787
Club Colours: Navy blue, white and red

STREATHAM-CROYDON RUFC
Surrey 1
Ground Address: Rosevale, 159 Brigstock Road, Thornton Heath, Surrey. CR7 7JP
Tel: 0181 684 1502
Brief Directions: A23 turn off at Thornton Heath Pond, 1st left is Brigstock Road, club 400 yards on right
Club Secretary: Ian Stevenson, 18 Crown Woods Way, Eltham, London. SE9 2NN
Tel: (H) 0181 850 9061
Fixtures Secretary: R V Towers
Tel: (H) 0181 658 2333 (W) 0181 698 8911
Club Colours: Maroon shirts, white shorts

SUDBURY COURT RFC
Hertfordshire & Middlesex 4 North
Ground Address: East Lane Pavilion, East Lane, North Wembley, Middlesex Tel: 0181 904 8485
Brief Directions: By road: at junction of Watford Road and East Lane turn into East Lane, ground 400 yards on right. By train: To North Wembley station turn left ground 600yds on left.
Club Secretary: Derek Gray, 33 Northwick Park Road, Harrow, Middlesex. HA1 2NY
Tel: (H) 0181 427 4155
Fixtures Secretary: David Keeling, 17 Nunnery Lane, Luton, Bed. Tel: 01582 652417
Club Colours: Red and white on dark blue shirts, navy shorts, red socks with white tops

SUSSEX POLICE RFC
Sussex 2
Ground Address: Brighton Rugby Club, Patcham, Waterhall, Brighton, Sussex
Tel: 01273 562729
Brief Directions: A23 London to Brighton road, turn right at Patcham along Mill Road, then left into Waterhall ground
Club Secretary: P Johnson, Police Station, Kingsham Road, Chichester, Sussex
Tel: (H) 01243 825408 (W) 01243 520230
Fixtures Secretary: C Gale
Tel: (H) 01444 458482 (W) 01444 451555
Club Colours: Blue and gold quarters, blue shorts, blue socks

SUSSEX UNIVERSITY
Sussex 3

SWAFFHAM RUFC
Eastern Counties 3 North
Ground Address: North Pickenham Road, Swaffham, Norfolk
Tel: 01760 724829
Brief Directions: Into town centre, at traffic lights take A47 towards E. Dereham, turn right at Gradys Hotel along North Pickenham Road, ground 400 metres on right
Club Secretary: Hugh Green, Gemini Cottage, Weasenham St Peter, Kings Lynn, Norfolk. PE32 2TD
Tel: (H) 01328 838269
Fixtures Secretary: Eric Nye, 7 Warstade Way, Swaffham, Norfolk PE37 7NX
Tel: 01760 723377
Club Colours: Amber shirts, black shorts

TEDDINGTON R.F.C.(Previously Antlers R.F.C.)
Surrey 2
Ground Address: Bushy Park, Teddington, Middlesex
Tel: 0181 977 4989
Brief Directions: Ground adjacent to Teddington Cricket Club in Bushy Park, at the rear of N.P.L.
Club Secretary: Peter Woolgar, 114 Elgin Avenue, Ashford, Middlesex. TW15 1QG
Tel: (H) 01784 259734 (
Fixtures Secretary: Rod Bromfield, 104 Station road, Hampton, Middlesex
Tel: (H) 0181 979 5635
Club Colours: Dark blue

THAMES RUFC
Eastern Counties 2
Ground Address: St Cedds Playing Field, Garron Lane, Aveley, South Ockendon, Essex
Brief Directions: Turn off Tunnel Junction, down Ship Lane, right at T junction, second off roundabout. First left, second left.
Club Secretary: David Northfield, 179 Blackshots Lane, Grays, Essex. RM16 2LL
Tel: (H) 01375 407043 (W) 01268 402239
Fixtures Secretary: Tony Lincoln, 65 Victoria Avenue, Grays, RM16 2RN.
Tel: 01375 391404.
Club Colours: Emerald Green and black hoops

THAMESIANS RFC
Hertfordshire & Middlesex 4 South
Ground Address: Marble Hill Park, off Richmond Road, Twickenham, Middlesex. TW1 2NL
Tel No: 0181 892 1900
Brief Directions: Entrance to ground is on Richmond Road (A305) with dressing rooms adjacent to car park.
Club Secretary: E J Burrows, 133 Cranleigh Road, Lower Feltham, Middlesex. TW13 4QA
Tel: (H & W) 0181 890 7162
Fixtures Secretary: Keith Wills, 42 Overdale Road, London, W5 4TTTel: (H) 0181 840 0297
Club Colours: Maroon and green

THETFORD RFC
London 3 North East
Ground Address: Two Mile Bottom, Mundford Road, Thetford
Tel: 01842 755176
Brief Directions: From A11 take the A134 Kings Lynn/Mundford road, travel for 1 mile and take the first turning on the right
Club Secretary: Velda Luckhurst, Stanley House, 77 Vicarage Road, Thetford, Norfolk. IP24 2LW
Tel No: 01842 750240
Fixtures Secretary: Terry Ellans. Tel No: 01842 753506
Club Colours: Red and white hoped shirts, white shorts, red & white socks.

THURSTON RUFC
Eastern Counties 3 North
Ground Address: Robinson Field, Ixworth Road, Thurston, Suffolk
Tel: 01359 232450
Brief Directions: Exit A14 Thurston and follow Thurston signs, along Thurston Rd past Cracknells garage on right, under railway bridge, head out of village (school on left), ground 200 yards on right
Club Secretary: Jeremy Kendall, 137 Southgate Street, Bury St Edmunds, Suffolk IP332AF
Tel: 01284 703043
Fixtures Secretary: Declan Gallagher.
Tel No: 01284 725229
Club Colours: Navy blue shirts with red collar & cuffs, blue shorts, stockings

TOTTONIANS RFC
London 3 South West
Ground Address: Water Lane, Totton, Hampshire.
Tel: 01703 663810
Brief Directions: From centre of Totton follow directions to Totton College/Recreation Centre. The club is located next door.
Club Secretary: Mr G Searle, Meadow End, Romsey Road, Kings Somborne, Hampshire.
Tel: (H) 01794 388779 (W) 01256 482572
Fixtures Secretary: Chris Edwards, 22 Ash Road, Ashurst, Southampton, SO40 7AT.
Tel: 01703 293294
Club Colours: Green, black and white hoops

TRING RUFC
London 3 North West
Ground Address: Pendley Sports Centre, Cow Lane, Tring, Herts., HP23 Tel: 01442 825710
Brief Directions: M25 to A41 towards Aylesbury . At Tring turn off, go back under dual carriageway - right towards Berkhamsted, Cow Lane is 100 yds on right. Club at bottom of Cow Lane.
Club Secretary: Paul Lamberth, 10 Long Field Gardens, Tring, Herts., HP23 4DN.
Tel: 01442 824288
Fixtures Secretary: Malcolm Rose, 25 Grenadine Way, Tring, Herts., HP23 5EA.
Tel: 01442 381110
Club Colours: Black and gold hoops

TROJANS RFC
Hampshire 1
Ground Address: Stoneham Park, Stoneham Lane, Eastleigh, Hants. SO50 9HT
Tel: 01703 612400/613068
Brief Directions: M27 J5, proceed south signed Southampton on A335 to 1st lights, right into Bassett Green Rd, right at next lights into Stoneham Ln, under motorway and immediate left
Club Secretary: J W J Mist, Westbury House, 14 Bellevue Road, Southampton. SO15 2AY
Tel: (H) 01703 583450 (W) 01703 332844
Fixtures Secretary: C G Holt
Tel: (W) 01703 771195
Club Colours: Blue with narrow red hoops

TUNBRIDGE WELLS RFC
London 3 South East
Ground Address: St Marks Recreation Ground, Frant Road, Tunbridge Wells
Tel: 01892 527448
Brief Directions: Southern outskirts of town, 0.5 miles along the a267 (Frant Road) left hand side at brow of hill
Club Secretary: Barry Kench, 63 Frant Rd., Tunbridge Wells, Kent TN2 SL4
Tel No: 01892 617121
Fixtures Secretary: Steve Webb, 31 Old Wardsdown, Union Street, Flimwell, East Sussex TN5 7NX
Tel: (H) 01580 879712
Club Colours: Navy blue and white quarters

TWICKENHAM RFC
London 3 North West
Ground Address: Park Fields, South Road, Hampton, Middlesex
Tel: 0181 979 2427
Brief Directions: A316 to Unigate Dairy, take road to Hampton, turn right into Oak Ave, South Rd on right by Royal Oak public house
Club Secretary: J. N. Francis, 50 Hatherop Road, Hampton, Middlesex, TW12 2RF.
Tel: (H) 0181 9410877 (W) 0181 5808094
Fixtures Secretary: Tony Kaye, 29 Geange Road, Twickenham, Middlesex TW2 5TW
Tel: (H & W) 0181 898 7210
Club Colours: Red and black hoops

UCKFIELD RFC
Sussex 1
Ground Address: Hempsted Playing Fields, Nevill Road, Manor Park, Uckfield
Tel: 01825 768956
Brief Directions: The Manor Park Estate is on northern outskirts of the town, turn into Browns Ln entrance & take 2nd road on left, the ground is at the end of the 3rd road on the right
Club Secretary: A.Bell, 24 Harcourt Close, Uckfield. TN22 5DT
Tel: 01825 765984
Fixtures Secretary: Mrs Maureen Poole, Pentlands, 9 Keld Avenue, Uckfield TN22 5BN
Tel: (H) 01825 761151
Club Colours: Amber with purple and white hoops

UCS OLD BOYS RFC
Hertfordshire & Middlesex 1
Ground Address: Farm Avenue, London. NW2
Tel: 0181 452 4337
Club Secretary: Paul Gee, 63 Blackhorse Lane, South Mimms, Herts. EN6 3PS
Tel: (H) 01707 662 748 (M) 0402 803961 (W) 01707 871702
Fixtures Secretary: Frank Butterworth, 33 Algernon Rd., London NW4 3TA
Tel: (H) 0181 2033369 (W)01189 735 003
Club Colours: Maroon, black and white

UNITED SERVICES PORTSMOUTH RFC
Hampshire 1
Ground Address: United Services Sports Club, Burnaby Road, Portsmouth, Hampshire.
Tel: 01705 830125
Brief Directions: Enter Portsmouth via M275, follow signs to Isle of Wight Car Ferries, ground on right under railway bridge
Club Secretary: Mr.R.McAree, 146 Manners Road, Portsmouth, PO4 0BG. Tel: (H) 01705 792818 (W) 01705 841411
Fixtures Secretary: Bob Gray, 11 Chatham Drive, Old Portsmouth.
Tel: (H) 01705 341375 (B) 01705 726610
Club Colours: Navy blue & red hoops, navy blue shorts

UNIVERSITY OF SURREY RFC
Surrey 3
Ground Address: Varsity Centre Sports Pavilion, Egerton, Guildford, Surrey Tel: 01483 259242
Club Secretary: B.R McCauley, University of Surrey Students Union, University of Surrey, Guildford, Surrey GU2 5XH
Tel: 01483 259393
Fixtures Secretary: A.Langley, University of Surrey Students Union, Sports office, University of Surrey, Guildford, Surrey Gu2 5XH
Tel: 01483 259393
Club Colours: Blue and Gold

UNIVERSITY VANDALS RFC
London 3 South West
Ground Address: Brownacres, The Towing Path, Walton-on-Thames, Surrey Tel: 01932 227659
Club Secretary: A Williams, 7 Clarence Close, Walton-on-Thames, Surrey. KT12 5JX
Tel: (H) 01932 229727 (W) 0171 259 6633
Fixtures Secretary: C J Cockrean
Tel: (H) 01932 226837
Club Colours: Black, purple and emerald green

UPMINSTER RFC
Eastern Counties 1
Ground Address: Hall Lane Playing Fields, Hall Lane, Upminster, Essex Tel: 01708 220320
Brief Directions: From M25 take A127 towards Romford, take Upminster turn off, ground 0.5 mile on left over mini roundabout
Club Secretary: M Eve, 142 Cranson Park Avenue, Upminster, Essex. RM14 3XJ
Tel: (H) 01708 225383 (W) 01708 858935
Fixtures Secretary: Shaun Neale
Tel: (H) 01708 445423
Club Colours: Yellow and blue hoops

UPPER CLAPTON FOOTBALL CLUB
Hertfordshire & Middlesex 1
Ground Address: Upland Road, Thornwood Common, Epping, Essex. CM16 6NL Tel: 01992 572588
Brief Directions: M11 north, jct 7.Follow signs to B1393 to Epping. Upland Rd. on right after 500yds after Rooky Garage.
Club Secretary: David Miller, 13 Rushfield, Sawbridgeworth, Herts. CM21 9NE
Tel: 01279 724131 (H) 0181 309 6398 (W) 0181 300 6922 (Fax) 0860 427651 (Mobile)
Fixtures Secretary: Damien Bateman, 53 The Lindens, Loughton, essex. IG10 3HS
Tel: 0181 521 6182(H) 0171 242 9777(W)
Club Colours: Red and white 7inch hoops, white shorts, red & white socks

UXBRIDGE RFC
London 3 North West
Ground Address: Uxbridge Cricket Club, Gatting Way, Park Road, Uxbridge, Middlesex. UB10 0SL
Tel: 01895 237571
Brief Directions: From A40 Swakeleys Rouundabout, take Uxbridge exit (B467) Park Road. Approx 1/4 mile, turn left into Gatting Way then left to cricket club.
Club Secretary: N.Rushton, 50 Ash Grove, Harefield, Middlesex. UB9 6EY
Tel No: 01895474 638 (H) 0171 2467602 (W)
Fixtures Secretary: R McPherson
Tel: (H) 01895 233273
Club Colours: Black, red, white hooped shirts and socks, black shorts

VENTNOR RUGBY FOOTBALL CLUB
Hampshire 1
Ground Address: The New Pavilion, Watcombe Bottom, Whitwell Road, Upper Ventnor, Isle of Wight
Tel: 01983 834155
Brief Directions: Just outside Ventnor on the Whitwell road
Club Secretary: Tony Flower, 2 Stonebowe Gardens, Niton. PO38 2AH
Tel No: 01983 730567
Fixtures Secretary: John Adams, B1-1K Avenue Rd., Wroxall, Isle of Wight
Tel No: 01983 854201
Club Colours: Navy and white hoop.

VIGO RFC
Kent 2 East
Ground Address: Swanswood Field, Vigo Village, Havvel Road, Vigo, Kent
Tel: 01732 823830
Club Secretary: N W Simpson, Pitfield House, Meopham Green, Meopham, Kent. DA13 0PZ
Tel: (H) 01474 812407 (W) 0181 8541331
Fixtures Secretary: John Taylor
Tel: (H) 01322 227363 (W) 0171 488 0733
Club Colours: Red shirts, black shorts

WANDSWORTHIANS RFC
Surrey 2
Ground Address: Kings College Sports Ground, Windsor Avenue, New Malden, Surrey. KT3 5HA
Tel: 0181942 0495
Club Secretary: Ian Maclean, 45 More Lane, Esher, Surrey
Tel: (H) 01372 463121
Fixtures Secretary: Gary Kirkwood
Tel: (H) 0181 640 0263 (W) 0181 665 3756
Club Colours: Maroon, white and gold hoops

WANSTEAD RFC
Eastern Counties 2
Ground Address: Roding Lane North, Woodford Bridge, Essex
Club Secretary: Neil Joyce, 21 Grosvenor Road, Leyton, London E10 6LG. Tel: (H) 0181 556 9125
Fixtures Secretary: Terry Elliot, Tel: (H) 0181 599 2743
Club Colours: Blue and white hoops.

WARE
Hertfordshire & Middlesex 4 North

WARLINGHAM RFC
London 2 South
Ground Address: Limpsfield Road, Hamsey Green, Warlingham, Surrey. CR6 9RB
Tel: 01883 62 2825
Brief Directions: Frm A235 Sth Croydon, B269 - Hamsey Green, on leaving H. Green ground on rt after H.G. Gardens. Frm M25 J6, A22 4 miles, rt on B270, 1st lft, right at T jcn, ground on right
Club Secretary: Peter Wrightson, 2 Markville Gardens, Caterham, Surrey CR3 6RJ
Fixtures Secretary: Paul Fettes, 63 Mitchley Hill, Sanderstead, Surrey.
Tel: (H) 0181 657 7628
Club Colours: Royal blue and white hoops, navy shorts

WATERLOOVILLE RFC

Hampshire 3
Ground Address: Jubilee Park, Rowlands Avenue, Waterlooville, Hants
Brief Directions: From A3M take B2150 J3 into Waterlooville, over 1st roundabout up to Waterlooville. Next roundabout turn right, turn left into Rowlands Avenue.
Club Secretary: Ray Mowatt, 9 Holst Way, Waterlooville, Hants. PO7 5SJ
Tel: (H) 01705 269275
Fixtures Secretary: Ian Day, Body Work, 270a London Road, Waterlooville, Hants.
Tel: (H) 01705 264080
Club Colours: Sky blue and red halves

WATFORD RFC

Hertfordshire & Middlesex 3 North
Ground Address: Knutsford Playing Fields, Radlett Road, Watford, Herts
Tel: 01923 243292
Brief Directions: From A41 (M1 J5) take Watford/ town centre link road, right at 1st roundabout, over bridge, car park on left, ground on right.
Club Secretary: Brian De-Honri 12 Stripling way, Moorview, Watford, Herts. WD1 8QT
Tel No: 01923 801727
Fixtures Secretary: Liam Dalmon, 10 Derwent Road, Leverstock Green.
Tel: (H) 01442 219350
Club Colours: Red, white and blue hoops

WELWYN RUGBY CLUB

London 2 North
Ground Address: Hobbs Way, Colgrove, Welwyn Garden City, Herts
Tel: 01707 329116
Brief Directions: A1(M) J4, follow signs to Gosline sports park, bear left into Parkway, left at next r'bout into Turmore Dale, 1st left into Colgrove, 30 yds right into Hobbs Way
Club Secretary: J M Sargeant, 67 Woodhall Lane, Welwyn Garden City, Herts. AL7 3TG
Tel: (H) 01707 331186
Fixtures Secretary: K Smith, 20 Rookwood Drive, Stevenage, Herts.
Tel: (H & W) 01438 351807 (Fax) 01438 249129
Club Colours: Maroon and white hoops, blue shorts, maroon socks

WEMBLEY & KODAK RFC

Hertfordshire & Middlesex 2
Ground Address: Roger Bannisters Playing Fields, Uxbridge Road, Harrow Weald, Middlesex
Tel: 0181 420 1789
Brief Directions: From Harrow on Hill take Harrow View to roundabout, ground on right. From Watford take Oxley Lane, ground on left
Club Secretary: J. Williams, 37 Chestnut Drive, Pinner, Middlesex HA5 1LX
Tel: (H) 0181 8686300
Fixtures Secretary: Mr. P. McKeown, 16 Brinsley Road, Harrow Weald, Middlesex, HA3 5ND. Tel: (H) 0181 4270900
Club Colours: Black & white quarters

WEST NORFOLK RUFC

London 3 North East
Ground Address: Gatehouse Lane, North Wootton, Kings Lynn
Tel: 01553 631307
Brief Directions: A149 to K. Lynn to Hunstanton bypass A148 to K. Lynn r'bout at top of hill, right at lights in Castle Rising Rd, left at T junction to North Wootton, through village to green, left at Gatehouse Lane
Club Secretary: JDr R.T. Hewson, Grange Meadows, Manor Road, North Wootton, King's Lynn PE30 3PZ
Tel No: 01553 631660
Fixtures Secretary: M.H.Ballman. Tel No: 01362 668935
Club Colours: French grey with cerise band, navy shorts

WESTCLIFF RFC

Eastern Counties 1
Ground Address: The Gables, Aviation Way, Southend-on-Sea, Essex. SS2 6UN
Tel: 01702 541499
Brief Directions: A127 turn left at Perrys Ford Garage at Kent Elms corner about .5 mile from Southend. After 200yds turn R. in to Snakes Lane go to end turn R and L at 4th r'about to Aviation Way . Ground 600yds.
Club Secretary: T J Eastwell, 21 Dawlish Drive, Leigh-on-Sea, Essex. SS9 1QX
Tel: (H) 01702 714850
Fixtures Secretary: Tony Pendry, 71A Burdett Avenue, Westcliff-on-Sea, Essex, SS0 7JN.
Tel: 01702 334872
Club Colours: Maroon and old gold hoops

WHITSTABLE RFC

Kent 1
Ground Address: Reeves Way, Chestfield, Whitstable, Kent. CT5 3QS
Tel: 01227 794343
Brief Directions: A299 Thanet Way to Whitstable, by Chestfield roundabout. The ground is opposite Chestfield & Swalecliffe Railway Station
Club Secretary: Colin James, 71 Swalecliffe Court Drive, Whitstable, Kent. CT5 2NF
Tel: (H) 01227 793031
Fixtures Secretary: Roger Dengate, 70 Regent St. Whitstable, Kent. CT5 1JQ.
Tel: (H) 01227 264604
Club Colours: Blue and white.

WISBECH RUFC

Eastern Counties 2
Ground Address: Chapel Road, Harecroft Road, Wisbech, Cambridgeshire. PE1 1RG
Tel: 01945 481500
Brief Directions: Along South Brink, (from A47) proceed to Old Market Place, turn left, ground approx 200 yards on right next to garage
Club Secretary: J R C Pallant,139 Lynn Road, Wisbech, Cambs. PE13 3DH
Tel: 01945 588147
Fixtures Secretary: David Dobson, 5 Buckingham Walk, Wisbech, Cambridgeshire, PE13.
Tel: (H) 01945 461223
Club Colours: Red shirts, blue shorts

WITHAM RUFC

Eastern Counties 4 South
Ground Address: Spa Road, Witham, Essex. CM8 1UN
Tel: 01376 511066
Brief Directions: Frm A12 Col'ter: Witham turn, right at 4th lights, right at end, left under rail bridge. Frm A12 Chelmsf'd: Witham turn, left at 1st lights, right at end, left under bridge. Frm B1018 B'tree: over r'bouts to centre, right at lights, right at next lights, right at end
Club Secretary: Mrs Pam Whelan, 34 Highfields Road, Witham, Essex.
Tel No: 01376 575871
Fixtures Secretary: Angus Downes. Tel No: 01621 857593
Club Colours: Brown and white hoops, black shorts

WOKING RFC

Surrey 1
Ground Address: Byfleet Recreation Ground, Stream Close, off Rectory Lane, Byfleet, Surrey
Tel: 01932 343693
Brief Directions: Leave A3 at Painshill (Cobham & Byfleet) junction A245 to Byfleet, over 3 main roundabouts, turn left at 4th into High Rd and then right into Rectory Lane
Club Secretary: Andrew Jones, 66 Kings Rd, New Haw, Surrey KT15 3BQ Tel: (H) 01932 880936 (W) 0181 214 2525
Fixtures Secretary: Mr Ian Vousden Tel: (H) 01483 836817
Club Colours: Blue and gold hoops, black shorts

WOODBRIDGE RUFC

Eastern Counties 1
Ground Address: Hatchley Barn, Bromeswell, Woodbridge, Suffolk. IP12 2PP
Tel: 01394 466630
Brief Directions: From A12 take B1084 to Orford, after passing junction to Eyke, entrance is approx 600 yards on right
Club Secretary: K J Blow, 43 Hasketon Road, Woodbridge, Suffolk. IP12 4LE
Tel: (H) 01394 384642 (W) 01473 643417
Fixtures Secretary: Dacid Neal, Sequoia House, Rendham, Saxmundham, Suffolk IP17 2AQ
Tel: 01728 663208 (H) 01449 612215 (W)
Club Colours: Blue

WORTH OLD BOYS SOCIETY RFC

Surrey 3
Ground Address: North Avenue, Whiteley Village, Walton On Thames.
Club Secretary: Mark Madsen, Little Friars, Great Chart, Nr Ashford, Kent
Tel: (H) 01233 625441 (W) 0171 629 8863
Fixtures Secretary: Jim Little, 9 Rainville Road, London, W6 9HA.
Tel: (H) 0171 381 8475 (W) 01252 718 999
Club Colours: Blue and gold quarters

WORTHING RFC

London 3 South East
Ground Address: The Rugby Park, Roundstone Lane, Angmering, West Sussex BN16 4AX.
Tel/Fax: 01903 784706
Brief Directions: A27 Worthing to Arundel Road, leave at Clapham follow signs to Angmering and A259 Worthing to Littlehampton Road, Turn north at Roundstone Pub R/about, quarter mile on right.
Club Secretary: Brian Vincent, 29 St. Botolph's Rd., Worthing, W. Sussex. BN11 4JS.
Tel: (H) 01903 206516 (B) 01903 821981
Fixtures Secretary: Nigel Lyons, 48 Brook Barn Way, Goring-by-Sea, Worthing, West Sussex, BN12 4DW.
Tel: 01903 506880
Club Colours: Blue, chocolate and gold hoops

WYMONDHAM RUFC

London 3 North East
Ground Address: Foster Harrison Memorial Ground, Tuttles Lane, Wymondham, Norfolk
Tel: 01953 607332
Brief Directions: To Wymonham on A11, onto the Wy'ham bypass until slip road marked Wy'ham & E. Dereham B1135, past Somerfield on left, thro' next r'bout, ground 0.25 mile right
Club Secretary: Martin Warren, 14 Newark Close, Thorpe St Andrew, Norwich. NR7 0YJ
Tel: (H) 01603 437805 (W) 01603 616112
Fixtures Secretary: Adrian Anema, 41 Lakeland Way, Hethersett, Norwich,. NR9 3QA
Club Colours: Red and black hooped shirts, black shorts and socks

OLD MERCHANT TAYLORS' FC 1st Xv Squad 1999

WATFORD RFC

BRIGHTLINGSEA RUGBY CLUB
Undefetaed League Champions Eastern Counties Division 4 North

SOUTH WEST DIVISION

SOUTH WEST DIVISION	Officials & League Secretaries	630
SOUTH WEST ONE	League table & Fixture Grid	631
	Clubs	632
SOUTH WEST DIVISION	1998-99 League Tables	636
	1999-2000 Fixture Grids	639
	Clubs (in alphabetical order)	647

South West Division Structure 1999-2000

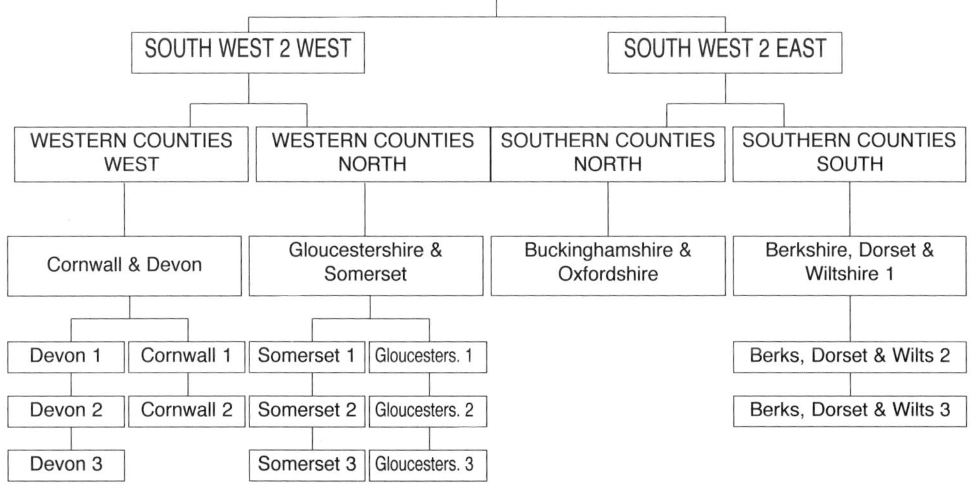

OFFICIALS
SOUTH WEST DIVISION

Chairman of Competition Sub-Committee
Dr C V Phillips
"Barlowena" Alexandra Rd, Illogan, Cornwall TR16 4EN
01209 842660 H 01209 842892 F
01209 714866 B 01209 716977 F

Deputy Chairman Competition Sub Committee
A Boyer, 11 Christopher Court, Boundary Rd, Newbury, Berks RG14 7PQ 01635 40574 H

League Co-ordinating Secretary
M Gee, Lowenna, 70 Halsetown, St Ives, Cornwall TR26 3LZ 01736 797777 (H & F) E mail: SWRFU@lineout.net

Deputy League Co-ordinating Secretary
B Flanders, The Penthouse, The Old Mill, Mill Street, Wantage, Oxon OX12 9AB 01235 769945 (H & F)
E mail: Brian.Flanders@RFU.btinternet. com

League Secretaries

South West 1 Secretary
J D Wooldridge, 16 Grange Drive, Durleigh, Bridgwater, Somerset TA6 7LL 01278 422009 H/F

Deputy Secretary
M Gee, Lowenna, 70 Halsetown, St Ives, Cornwall TR26 3LZ 01736 797777 (H & F) E mail: SWRFU@lineout.net

South West 2 West Secretary
J Lipscomb, 16 Main Road, Weston Zoyland, Bridgwater, Somerset TA6 7LL 01278 691345 H & F

Deputy Secretary
J D Wooldridge, 16 Grange Drive, Durleigh, Bridgwater, Somerset TA6 7LL 01278 422009 H/F

South West 2 East &
Bucks/Oxon 1/2 Secretary
B Flanders, The Penthouse, The Old Mill, Mill Street, Wantage, Oxon OX12 9AB 01235 769945 (H & F)
E mail: Brian.Flanders@RFU.btinternet.com

Deputy Secretary
J D Wooldridge, 16 Grange Drive, Durleigh, Bridgwater, Somerset TA6 7LL 01278 422009 H/F

Deputy Secretary
H Pocock10 Laceys Drive, Hazelmere, High Wycombe, Bucks HP15 7JY 01494 713879 H 0181 575 4572 B 0181 575 4885 F

Berks/Dorset & Wilts 1 & 2 Secretary
D McAteer, 1 Rowlands Close, Mortimer West End, Reading RG7 3US 0118 9701245 H/F

Deputy Secretary
K Jones, 13 Stratfield Road, Basingstoke, Hants RG21 5RS 01256 410461 H 0118 982 6750 B

Berks/Dorset & Wilts 3 Secretary
P Richell, 26 Durweston, Blandford Forum, Dorset DT11 0QE 01258 452918 H 01258 472652 B

Deputy Secretary
A Bott, Kew House, Anchor Rd., Calne, Wiltshire SN11 8DI 01249 821448 H/F 0410 017478 B/M

Cornwall/Devon League Secretary
B Davis, 8 Penrose Rd, Helston, Cornwall TR13 8TP 01326 563744 H/F 01209 215620 B

Deputy Secretary
G Simpson, 108 Pattinson Drive, Mainstone, Plymouth, Devon PL6 8RU 01752 206662 E mail:gks49@hot mail.com

Cornwall 1 & 2 Secretary
N J Barber, 2 The Crescent, Alexandra Rd, St Ives, Cornwall TR13 8TP 01209 796861 H/F 01752 665951 B

Deputy Secretary
D Jenkins, Albaston Post Office, Albaston, Gunnislake, Cornwall PL18 9AL 01822 832785 H/F

Devon 1 & 2 Secretary
G Simpson, 108 Pattinson Drive, Mainstone, Plymouth, Devon PL6 8RU 01752 206662 E mail: gks49@hotmail.com

Deputy Secretary.
J D Irvine, 1 Great Rea Road, Brixham Devon TQ5 9SW 01803 882219

Devon 3 Deputy Secretary
J D Irvine (see above)

Deputy Secretary
G Simpson, 108 Pattinson Drive, Mainstone, Plymouth, Devon PL6 8RU 01752 206662 E mail: gks49@hotmail.com

Gloucester/Somerset & Gloucester 1 Secretary
A Townshend, St Kenelm, 2 Kencourt Close, Kenilworth Ave, Gloucester GL2 0QL 01452 522721 H/F

Deputy Secretary
A Barnes, 18 Podsmead Place, Tuffley, Gloucester GL1 5PD 01452 525530 H

Gloucester 1, 2 & 3 Secretary
C Ravenhill, 18 Merevale Rd, Longlevens, Gloucester GL2 0QY 01452 304317 H/F

Deputy Secretary
A Townshend, St Kenelm, 2 Kencourt Close, Kenilworth Ave, Gloucester GL2 0QL 01452 522721 H/F 01452 414403 B

Southern Counties North Secretary
M Wild, 14 Stanton Way, Langley, Slough
SL3 7LB 01753 770870 (b) 01628 604311 (h) E Mail: Sales@shephard.co.uk

Deputy Secretary
H Pocock, 10 Laceys Drive, Hazelmere, High Wycombe Bucks HP15 7JY 01494 713879 (H & F) 0208 575 4572 (F)
e mail: humphrey.pocock@taywood.co.uk

Southern Counties South Secretary
A Bott, Kew House, Anchor Rd, Calne, Wiltshire SN11 8DI 01249 821448 H/F 0410 017478 B/M

Deputy Secretary
N Stafford, Veryan, 46 Bulkington, Devizes, Wiltshire SN10 SL 01380 828264 H

Somerset 1 2 & 3 Secretary
C MacDonald, 8 Sycamore Drive, Crewkerne, Somerset TA18 7BT 01460 76136 H/F

Deputy Secretary
R Fisher, 20 Rookery Road, Knowle, Bristol BS4 2DS 0117 983 6325 H

Western Counties North Secretary
W Bishop, "Hellvellyn", 1 Wiltshire Place, Kingswood, Bristol BS15 4XA. 0117 9575729 H 0117 9352017 B 0117 9401290 F
e-mail: BillBishop1@compuserve.com

Deputy Secretary
R Fisher, 20 Rookery Road, Knowle, Bristol BS4 2DS 0117 983 6325 H

Western Counties West Secretary
D Jenkins, Albaston Post Office, Albaston, Gunnislake, Cornwall PL18 9AL 01822 832785 H/F

Deputy Secretary
A Higgs, Roseleigh, Hollis Road, Cheltenham, Gloucs GL51 6JG 01242 230104 H

SOUTH WEST ONE

1989-1999 LEAGUE TABLE

	P	W	D	L	F	A	PD	Pts	-
Penzance/Newlyn	22	20	0	2	1083	245	838	40	
Launceston	22	20	0	2	1021	228	793	40	
Barnstaple	21	18	0	3	529	260	269	36	
Maidenhead	22	14	0	8	576	383	193	28	
Matson	21	12	0	9	465	456	9	24	
Keynsham	21	10	1	10	383	540	-157	21	
Gloucester Old Boys	21	7	1	13	353	490	-137	15	
Stroud	22	7	0	15	363	574	-211	14	
Old Patesians	22	6	1	15	320	506	-186	13	
Berry Hill	22	6	0	16	265	697	-432	12	
Torquay Athletic	22	4	1	17	250	847	-597	9	
Salisbury	22	4	0	18	305	687	-382	8	

1999-2000 FIXTURE GRID

	Barnstaple	Berry Hill	Cinderford	Dorchester	Gloucester OB	Keynsham	Launceston	Maidenhead	Matson	Old Patesians	Stroud	Torquay Ath.
Barnstaple		25.03	08.01	11.03	02.10	20.11	12.02	23.10	22.01	11.09	11.12	08.04
Berry Hill	04.09		12.02	11.09	20.11	11.12	11.03	08.01	02.10	22.01	08.04	23.10
Cinderford	27.11	09.10		29.01	04.09	25.09	06.11	18.03	15.01	08.04	26.02	11.12
Dorchester	25.09	18.03	23.10		08.01	08.04	02.10	11.12	12.02	20.11	04.09	22.01
Gloucester Old Boys	26.02	15.01	25.03	27.11		29.01	15.04	09.10	18.12	11.03	06.11	11.09
Keynsham	15.01	15.04	11.03	18.12	23.10		25.03	22.01	11.09	12.02	27.11	02.10
Launceston	09.10	25.09	22.01	26.02	11.12	04.09		08.04	23.10	08.01	18.03	20.11
Maidenhead	29.01	27.11	11.09	15.04	12.02	06.11	18.12		25.03	02.10	15.01	11.03
Matson	06.11	26.02	20.11	09.10	08.04	18.03	29.01	04.09		11.12	25.09	08.01
Old Patesians	18.03	06.11	18.12	15.01	25.09	09.10	27.11	26.02	15.04		29.01	25.03
Stroud	15.04	18.12	02.10	25.03	22.01	08.01	11.09	20.11	11.03	23.10		12.02
Torquay Athletic	18.12	29.01	15.04	06.11	18.03	26.02	15.01	25.09	27.11	04.09	09.10	

BARNSTAPLE R.F.C.

Founded: 1877

President	M Oerton	c/o
Chairman	E Gubb	Barnstaple R.F.C.
Secretary	D Pettifer	Pottington Road, Barnstaple EX31 1JH
Fixture Secretary	M Hughes	Tel: 01271 345627

Ground **Address:** Pottington Road, Barnstaple, EX31 1JH **Tel:** 01271 345627

Capacity: 3,000 Covered Seats: 500 Uncovered Standing: 2,500

Directions Take the A361 from Banstaple to Ilfracombe, left at 2nd traffic lights after Rolle Quay Bridge in Barnstaple.

Nearest Railway Station: Barnstaple **Car Parking:** Plenty at the ground

Admission: Matchday: £3.00 OAPs £1.50 Children Free Season tickets: Not available.

Clubhouse: Yes **Club Shop:** Yes **Colours**: Red/white/red **Change colours:** Black/white/red

Nickname: Barum **Training Nights:** Tuesday & Thursday 7pm

Programme **Size**: A5 **Pages**: 32 **Price**: Free **Editor**: D Pettifer **Advertising**: Contact Secretary

BERRY HILL R.F.C.

Founded:

Secretary David Pitaway, Ty Mai, Crow Ash Road, berry Hill, Coleford, Glos. GL16 7RB
Tel: 01594 836372 (H)

Fixture Secretary G R Goddard, 71a Cheltenham Road, Gloucester. GL2 0JG
Tel: 01452 306749 (W)

Ground: Lakers Road, berry Hill, Coleford, Glos. GL16 7YL Tel: 01594 833295

Directions: From M4 Severn Bridge, M48 to Chepstow, B422B to Coleford, follow signs to Berry Hill.
From M50 to Ross, A40 to Monmouth then A4136 to Berry Hill.

Colours: Black and amber quarters

CINDERFORD R.F.C.

Founded: 1886

President	Doug Hunt	
Chairman	Rob Worgan	
Treasurer	Barry Holmes	
Club Administrator	Dennis Hargreaves	Tel/Fax: 01594 825503
Director of Rugby	Dennis Hargreaves	
Press Officer	Nigel Wilce	25, The Oakfield, Cinderford, Glos. GL14 2DA 01594 824017

c/o Cinderford RFC
Dockham Road
Cinderford
Glos. GL14 2AQ
Tel: 01594 822673 Fax: 01594 822400

Ground **Address:** The Recreation Ground, Dockham Rd., Cinderford, Glos. GL14 2AQ
Tel: 01594 822673 **Fax:** 01594 822400
Capacity: 2,000 Covered Seats: 300 Uncovered Standing: 2,700

Directions From the A48 or A40 follow signs for Cinderford. In town centre, at mini-r'about, turn into Dockham Road, towards the County Store supermarket & the ground is just past the car park on the left.
Car Parking: 100 free spaces at the ground **Admission**: Matchday: £3.00

Clubhouse: Open 7-11pm weekdays & 12-11pm weekends **Club Shop:** open clubhouse hours
Colours: Red, black & amber **Change colours:** White with red, black & amber ecntre stripes.
Training Nights: Monday, Tuesday & Thursday evenings
Programme **Size**: A5 **Pages**: 26 **Price**: With admission **Advertising**: Contact Club Administrator

CINDERFORD SQUAD 98-99

DORCHESTER R.F.C.

Founded: 1934

President	Harry Brewer	Stallen Cottage, Nether Compton, Sherborne, Dorset DT9 4PZ 01935 812815
Chairman	Don Brierley	3 Sutton Close, Sutton Poyntz, Weymouth DT3 6LJ 01305 833244
Secretary	Graham Aspley	5 Nappers Court, Charles St., Dorchester DT1 1EE 01305 269944
Treasurer	John Palmer	45 Ackerman Rd., Dorchester DT1 1NZ 01305 262929
Fixtures Sec.	Tony Foot	1 Cutsome Close, Dorchester DT1 2SN 01305 250137

Ground Coburg Road, Dorchester, Dorset Tel: 01305 265692
Capacity: Ample - all uncovered standing **Car Parking**: 100 spaces beside clubhouse
Directions: From the by-pass follow signs to "West Dorset Leisure Centre"
Nearest Railway station: Dorchester South & Dorchester West

Admission Matchday: £3 Season tickets not available
Clubhouse Open Tues & Thur evenings, & all day Saturday
Club Shop No, but club ties & blazers are available
Programme Size: A5 Pages: 40 Price: With admission Editor: David Biddlecombe (Clubhouse Manager)
Advertising: Contact editor at clubhouse
Colours: Green & white hoops/navy blue **Change colours:** All red **Training Nights:** Tuesday & Thursday

GLOUCESTER OLD BOYS R.F.C.

Founded: 1903

President	N P Partridge	17 Armscroft Place, Gloucester	01452 527658
Chairman	D Brown	Robinswood Hill Farm, Reservoir Rd., Gloucester	01452 308732
Secretary	R Ellis	15 Armscroft Way, Gloucester	01452 525375
Fixture Secretary	S Turner	19 St Mark's Street, Gloucester	01452 422973
Press Officer	G R Wilce	Mitre farm, Corse Lawn, Glos.	01684 292492

Ground **Address:** Armscroft way, Gloucester GL2 0ST **Tel:** 01452 302390
Capacity: 2,000 - all uncovered standing
Directions: Leave M5 at Junction 11A. Follow sgns to city centre. Take 3rd exit from roundabout adjacent to Walls Ice Cream factory, then 2nd left into Horton Road.
Nearest Railway Station: Gloucester **Car Parking:** 150 spaces at clubhouse

Admission: Matchday: By programme £2 Season tickets: Not available.
Clubhouse: **Club Shop:** Open on matchdays
Colours: Claret, gold and navy **Change colours:** All navy blue
Training Nights: Tuesday & Thursday **Nickname**: B's
Programme **Size**: A5 **Pages**: 28 **Price**: £2

KEYNSHAM R.F.C.

Founded: 1923

President Dennis Coackbaine 'Somercourt', Homefield Rd., Saltford, Bristol 01225 873118
Chairman Ian Crossman 13 St. Keyna rd., Keynsham, Bristol BS31 2UD 0117 986 8009 (H) 0117 986 1573 (B)
Hon. Secretary Gill Wilson 3 Wellsway, Keynsham, Bristol BS31 1HS 0117 909 2643 (H) 0117 972 1165 (B)
Hon. Treasurer Graeme Wilson 3 Wellsway, Keynsham, Bristol BS31 1HS 0117 909 2643 (H) 0117 972 1165 (B)
Hon. Coach Pete Blackett Flat 2, Kingshead square, Bath 0467 622343 (M)
Fixture Secretary David Veal 118 Harrington Rd., Stockwood, Bristol BS14 8JR 01275 543416

Ground **Address:** Crown Fields, Bristol Rd., Keynsham BS31 2BE **Tel:** 0117 987 2520
Capacity: All uncovered standing
Directions Follow A4 from Bristol city centre, follow signs for Keynsham & Keynsham town centre. As you enter Keynsham the rugby club is on the right hand side.
Nearest Railway Station: Keynsham, 10 mins walk **Car Parking:** Unlimited
Admission: Matchday: £2.00, incl programme. Season tickets: Not available.
Clubhouse: Open lunch & evening every day. Available for hire, contact Liz Way at the club.
Club Shop: open matchdays & sun. am
Colours: Amber & black **Change colours:** Black **Training Nights:** Tuesday & Thursday
Programme **Size**: A5 **Pages**: 10 **Price**: With admission **Editor**: Contact club
Advertising: Contact Jim Brooks 01761 470229

LAUNCESTON R.F.C.

Founded: 1948

President Les Baker Victoria House, St Catherines Hill, Launceston PL15 7EJ 01566 772821
Secretary Bill Gladwell 5 Hendra tor View, Five Lanes, Launceston PL15 7RG
Tel: 01566 86864 (H) 01208 77287 (B) Fax: 01208 73744 e-Mail: Baggins@lrfc53.freeserve.co.uk
Fixture Secretary Mervyn Yeo Whiterow Farm, Lewdown, Okehampton, Devon EX20 4QL 01566 783230
Treasurer Dave Baker Heightleigh, Tavistock Road, Launceston PL15 9HB 01566 773070
Ground **Address:** Polson Bridge, Launceston, Cornwall PL15 9QU
Tel: 01566 773406 e-mail: baggins@lrfc53.freeserve.co.uk
Capacity: 2,000 - all uncovered standing
Directions M5 to Exeter, then A30 to Launceston. After 45 minutes look for big sign on left "Tavistock, Polson, Lifton" - turn left to T junction, left again, down hill to river Tamar, ground on the left.
Nearest Railway Station: Exeter 1hr, Plymouth 45 mins **Car Parking:** Plenty at the ground

Admission: Matchday: £3.00 Season tickets: £35
Clubhouse: **Club Shop:** Yes, selling replica kits
Colours: All black **Change colours:** Red/white/green
Training Nights: Monday & Wednesday **Nickname:** Cornish All Blacks
Programme **Size**: A5 **Pages**: Several **Price**: Free **Editor**: Hon. Sec.
Advertising: Contact John Dunn 01822 870300

MAIDENHEAD R.U.F.C.

Founded: 1921

President K J Lawton 3 Manor Lane, Maidenhead, Berks. 01628 629688
Chief Executive G R Fisher `Bramleigh`, Shopenhangars Road, Maidenhead SL6 2PZ 01628 625555
Hon. Secretary R M Brown 49 Bannard Road, Maidenhead, Berks. SL6 4NP 01628 670586
Finace Director R Keeping 2 Willow Drive, Ascot Road, Bray, Berks. 01628 635987
Club Coach S Edwards `Highfield House`, High Road, Cookham, Berks. 01628 521125

Ground Address Braywick Park, Braywick Road, Maidenhead, Berks. Tel: 01628 629633 Fax: 01628 635452
Capacity: 1,750 Covered Seats: 250 Uncovered Standing: 1,500
Directions From M4 junct 8/9 follow signs A308(M) Maidenhead Town Centre. A308(M) to r'about, left on A308 towards Maidenhead. After 1/4 mile filter right across dual carriageway & club is directly opposite.
Nearest Railway Station: Maidenhead - 800 yds from clubhouse.
Car Parking: 100 spaces at clubhouse plus 150 at overflow park, 100 yds away
Admission: Matchday: £2 + £1 transfer to stand Season tickets: Not available.
Clubhouse: Open Tues, Thur, Sat & Suns. Food available matchdays. Available for functions - contact Mike Dance 01628 629663
Club Shop: Currently open Sat & Suns. **Colours**: Magenta, violet & black **Change colours:** Green, violet & white
Nickname: `Maids` **Training Nights:** Tuesday & Thursday 7.15 for 7.30 sharp
Programme: **Size**: A5 **Pages**: 32 **Price**: with admission **Editor**: Contact club
Advertising: Contact Club Steward - Mike Dance 01628 629663

MATSON R.F.C.

Founded: 1957

Chairman John Windley 74 Mandara Grove, Abbeydale, Gloucester. Tel 01452 534747
Secretary Ron Etheridge 63 Hawk Close, Abbeydale, Gloucester, GL4 4NE.
Tel 01452 539114(H) 01452 335652(W)
Colours Black Shirts, white shorts, black/white socks **Change Colours:** Green Shirts
Ground Matson RFC, Redwell Road, Matson, Gloucester, GL4 6JG. Tel 01452 528963 Fax 01452 414713
Directions 3 miles south of City Centre on B4073. Turn towards Ski Slope. 1st left into Matson Avenue, 3rd right into Redwell Road. Nearest Railway Station: Gloucester
Admission £1 by programme
Clubhouse Best in South West at Junior Level. **Training Nights:** Tuesday & Thursday

OLD PATESIANS R.F.C.

Founded: 1913

President Taff Powell RJGI, Western Rd., Cheltenham 01242 514980
Chairman Colin Smith 7 Oxford St., Cheltenham GL52 6DT 01242 526379
Treasurer James Luxton 6 Littledown Rd., Cheltenham GL53 9LP 01242
Fixture Secretary Mark Knight 14b Canterbury Walk, Cheltenham GL53 5HC 01242 698756
Secretary Steve Webley 56 Mead Rd., Cheltenham GL53 7DT 01242 244865

Ground **Address:** Everest Rd., Leckhampton, Cheltenham. **Tel:** 01242 524633
Capacity: 500 all uncovered standing
Directions From town centre follow signs to Leckhampton, carry on up Leckhampton road, turn left at Honda garage, carry straight on over crossroads, clubhouse at end of Everest Road.
Nearest Railway Station: Cheltenham, 2 miles **Car Parking:** 60 spaces at the ground
Admission: Matchday: £2.00. Season tickets: Not available.
Clubhouse: Open lunch & evening every day. Food available. Available for hire, contact club. **Club Shop:** No
Colours: magenta, navy & silver hoops **Change colours:** Black & yellow hoops
Training Nights: Tuesday & Thursday **Nickname**: Ols Pats
Programme **Size**: A5 **Pages**: 16 **Price**: With admission **Editor**: Contact club
Advertising: Contact Ryan Farrell 01242 518486

STROUD R.F.C.

Founded: 1873

President W J Silverthorne
Chairman C Skey, Byways, Cirencester Road, Minchinhampton, GL6 9EQ. Tel: 01453 731243
Hon Secretary M Jenkins 31 Rowley, Cam, Dursley, GL11 5NT. Tel: 01453 547085
Hon Treasurer Mrs. L. Gomer 46 Oxmoor, Abbeydale, Gloucester, GL4 5XW Tel: 01452 415867
Registration Officer J Kennedy 26 Pauls Rise, N. Woodchester, Stroud, GL5 5PN Tel: 0973 697910.
Club Coaches J Breeze & J Gadd
Fixture Secretary R J Hillier (1st XV - 01453 764381) G Woodmason (Nomads & Goths - 01452 724525)
Colours: Royal Blue & White **Change Colours:** Red & White
Ground Fromehall Park, Stroud, Glos, GL5 3HS. Tel: 01453 763019.
Fax: 01453 758799 (Office Hours Only) **e-mail:** srfe@spring.co.uk
Directions Off A46 Bath Road, opposite Great Mills - well sign-posted.
Nearest Railway Station Stroud 3/4 mile
Admission Matchday £3.00
Clubhouse 7.30pm - 11.00pm daily. 12noon to 11.00pm Saturdays.
Training Nights: Tuesdays & Thursdays 7.30pm prompt **Programme:** Size A5 - Pages 20 - Price Incl.

TORQUAY ATHLETIC R.F.C.

Secretary J Stuart Bradshaw, 6 All Hallows Road, Preston. Paignton TQ3 1EB
Tel: 01803 521848 (H) 01392 204134 (B) 01392 204159 (Fax)
Fixture Secretary Dave Thompson, 44 Bidwell Brook Drive, Paignton.
Tel: 01803 845115 (H) 01803 858271 (B)
Ground: Seafront Recreation Ground, Seafront, Torquay. Tel: 01803 293842
Directions: Head for the seafront, ground on the main seafront road, adjacent to the railway station.
Colours: Black and white

SOUTH WEST DIVISION FINAL LEAGUE TABLES 1998-99

SOUTH WEST TWO WEST

	P	W	D	L	PF	PA	PD	Pts
Cinderford	22	19	2	1	621	181	440	40
Dings Crusaders	22	17	0	5	466	222	244	34
Brixham	22	14	0	8	355	268	87	28
Clevedon	22	12	0	10	371	348	23	24
Camborne	22	11	1	10	440	404	36	23
Tiverton	22	10	0	12	504	411	93	20
Taunton	22	10	0	12	392	379	13	20
St Mary's OB*	22	10	1	11	296	352	-56	19
St Austell	22	9	0	13	417	511	-94	18
Spartans*	22	9	1	12	377	368	9	17
Penryn	22	7	1	14	321	496	-175	15
St Ives (SW)*	22	1	0	21	185	805	-620	-2

SOUTH WEST TWO EAST

	P	W	D	L	PF	PA	PD	Pts
Dorchester	22	20	1	1	573	207	366	41
Swanage & W'ham	22	20	0	2	636	250	386	40
Marlow	22	15	0	7	452	340	112	30
A'sham & Chiltern	22	13	3	6	439	299	140	29
Chinnor	22	12	2	8	381	372	9	26
Abbey	22	9	2	11	318	329	-11	20
Aylesbury	22	8	1	13	264	387	-123	17
High Wycombe	22	8	0	14	392	469	-77	16
Stow-on-the-Wold	22	5	3	14	253	376	-123	13
Slough	22	6	1	15	249	438	-189	13
Wimborne	22	6	1	15	287	548	-261	13
Bournemouth	22	3	0	19	307	536	-229	6

WESTERN COUNTIES NORTH

	P	W	D	L	PF	PA	PD	Pts
Hornets	16	15	0	1	558	119	439	30
Coney Hill	16	12	0	4	392	177	215	24
Old Redcliffians	16	11	2	3	302	178	124	24
Cheltenham North	16	10	0	6	355	267	88	20
Drybrook	16	10	0	6	326	263	63	20
North Bristol	16	9	1	6	300	247	53	19
St Bernadettes OB	16	9	1	6	282	260	22	19
Whitehall	16	9	1	6	283	274	9	19
Cleve	16	8	1	7	269	245	24	17
Old Richians	16	7	0	9	269	292	-23	14
Wiveliscombe	16	7	0	9	225	323	-98	14
Bristol Harlequins	16	6	1	9	231	269	-38	13
Gordon League	16	6	0	10	248	342	-94	12
Oldfield Old Boys	16	6	0	10	212	360	-148	12
Cirencester	16	4	1	11	217	324	-107	9
Thornbury	16	3	0	13	206	414	-208	6
Avonmouth	16	0	0	16	88	409	-321	0

WESTERN COUNTIES WEST

	P	W	D	L	PF	PA	PD	Pts
Truro	18	13	0	5	432	155	277	26
Ivybridge	18	10	2	6	389	297	92	22
Crediton	18	9	1	8	367	259	108	19
South Molton	18	9	0	9	260	217	43	18
Paignton	18	9	0	9	320	333	-13	18
Hayle	18	8	0	10	273	350	-77	16
Okehampton	18	8	0	10	264	361	-97	16
Wellington	18	7	1	10	239	279	-40	15
Devonport Serv	18	7	1	10	307	379	-72	15
Kingsbridge	18	7	1	10	211	432	-221	15

SOUTHERN COUNTIES SOUTH

	P	W	D	L	PF	PA	PD	Pts
Chippenham	18	15	2	1	506	141	365	32
Wootton Bassett	18	14	1	3	370	157	213	29
Windsor	18	12	3	3	368	230	138	27
Tadley	18	10	1	7	407	240	167	21
Devizes	18	10	1	7	367	206	161	21
Sherborne	18	9	1	8	335	195	140	19
Redingensians	18	8	0	10	398	340	58	16
Swindon*	18	4	0	14	229	336	-107	6
North Dorset	18	2	1	15	161	725	-564	5
Blandford*	18	1	0	17	114	685	-571	0

SOUTHERN COUNTIES NORTH

	P	W	D	L	PF	PA	PD	Pts
Olney	18	18	0	0	621	186	435	36
Bicester	18	12	0	6	444	316	128	24
Chipping Norton	18	12	0	6	345	322	23	24
Beaconsfield	18	9	0	9	345	332	13	18
Oxford H'quins*	18	8	4	6	349	296	53	16
Wallingford	18	6	3	9	286	359	-73	15
Oxford	18	7	0	11	376	376	0	14
Buckingham	18	6	2	10	318	413	-95	14
Bletchley*	18	7	1	10	282	316	-34	13
Pennanians*	18	0	0	18	162	612	-450	-2

GLOUCESTER/SOMERSET

	P	W	D	L	PF	PA	PD	Pts
Barton Hill	16	15	0	1	503	128	375	30
Chew Valley	16	13	0	3	378	181	197	26
Yatton	16	13	0	3	341	150	191	26
Walcot Old Boys	16	12	0	4	368	213	155	24
Longlevens	16	11	0	5	325	257	68	22
Midsomer Norton	16	10	0	6	316	170	146	20
Combe Down	16	10	0	6	379	254	125	20
Old Centralians	16	8	1	7	346	352	-6	17
Gordano	16	7	1	8	244	278	-34	15
O Culverhaysians	16	7	0	9	296	212	84	14
Bream	16	6	1	9	244	297	-53	13
Tor	16	5	1	10	282	312	-30	11
Brockworth	16	5	1	10	245	428	-183	11
Bristol Saracens	16	4	1	11	183	397	-214	9
Frampton Cotterell	16	4	0	12	240	424	-184	8
Chard	16	2	0	14	205	453	-248	4
Old Sulians	16	1	0	15	72	461	-389	2

GLOUCESTER ONE

	P	W	D	L	PF	PA	PD	Pts
Chipping Sodbury	11	10	0	1	194	93	101	20
Hucclecote	11	9	1	1	262	90	172	19
Cheltenham Civ S	11	7	1	3	221	124	97	15
Aretians	11	6	0	5	220	143	77	12
Old Bristolians	11	6	0	5	252	179	73	12
Painswick	11	5	1	5	148	119	29	11
Ashley Down OB	11	5	1	5	160	136	24	11
Southmead	11	5	1	5	162	212	-50	11
Chelt. Saracens	11	5	0	6	160	157	3	10
Chosen Hill F. P.*	11	3	2	6	192	182	10	6
Old Cryptians	11	0	2	9	99	344	-245	2
Cainscross*	11	0	1	10	57	348	-291	-3

Tredworth have withdrawn from the league.

GLOUCESTER TWO

	P	W	D	L	PF	PA	PD	Pts
Westbury on Sev.	11	11	0	0	220	89	131	22
Tetbury	11	10	0	1	275	117	158	20
Tewkesbury	11	7	0	4	226	81	145	14
Smiths (Industries)	11	7	0	4	232	133	99	14
Glos All Blues	11	7	0	4	186	148	38	14
Kingswood	11	7	0	4	139	163	-24	14
Bishopston	11	5	0	6	166	194	-28	10
Dursley	11	4	0	7	154	169	-15	8
Minchinhampton	11	2	0	9	125	205	-80	4
Old Elizabethans	11	2	0	9	119	223	-104	4
Bristol T'phones*	11	2	0	9	132	378	-246	2
Cotham Park*	11	2	0	9	121	195	-74	0

Widden Old Boys have withdrawn from the league.

GLOUCESTER THREE

	P	W	D	L	PF	PA	PD	Pts
Gloucester Civ S	7	7	0	0	168	48	120	14
Old Colstonians	7	6	0	1	202	36	166	12
Bristol Aero Co	7	5	0	2	104	74	30	10
Dowty	7	3	0	4	122	117	5	6
Newent*	7	3	0	4	102	82	20	4
Wotton-under-Edge	7	1	0	6	63	143	-80	2
St Brendans OB*	7	2	1	4	100	171	-71	1
Pilning	7	0	1	6	34	224	-190	1

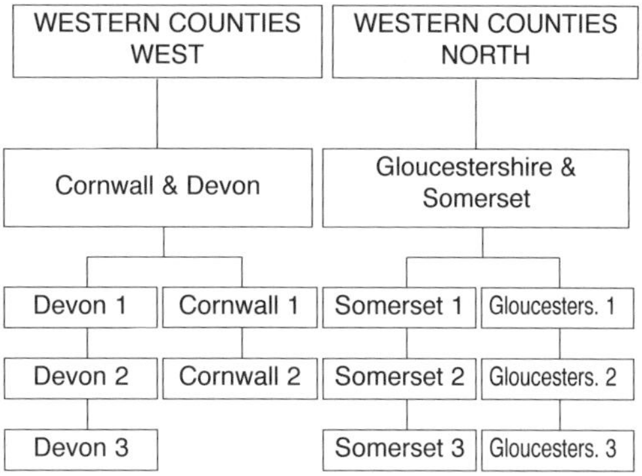

WESTERN COUNTIES WEST
WESTERN COUNTIES NORTH
Cornwall & Devon
Gloucestershire & Somerset
Devon 1 | Cornwall 1 | Somerset 1 | Gloucesters. 1
Devon 2 | Cornwall 2 | Somerset 2 | Gloucesters. 2
Devon 3 | Somerset 3 | Gloucesters. 3

SOMERSET ONE

	P	W	D	L	PF	PA	PD	Pts
Avon	18	17	0	1	520	148	372	34
North Petherton	18	13	0	5	409	203	206	26
Frome	18	13	0	5	350	197	153	26
Wells	18	12	0	6	340	230	110	24
Nailsea & Backwell	18	8	1	9	336	268	68	17
Imperial	18	6	2	10	216	323	-107	14
Stothert & Pitt	18	7	0	11	244	363	-119	14
Old Ashtonians	18	6	0	12	198	300	-102	12
Minehead Barb's	18	4	0	14	236	285	-49	8
Winscombe	18	2	1	15	104	636	-532	5

SOMERSET TWO

	P	W	D	L	PF	PA	PD	Pts
Broad Plain	14	13	1	0	348	104	244	27
Bristol Barbarians	14	10	0	4	221	120	101	20
Avonvale*	14	9	2	3	310	133	177	18
Blagdon*	14	9	0	5	289	127	162	16
Burnham on Sea	14	5	0	9	235	271	-36	10
Bath Saracens*	14	5	1	8	185	245	-60	9
Bath Old Eds*	14	2	0	12	111	300	-189	
Cheddar Valley*	14	1	0	13	74	473	-399	-12

SOMERSET THREE

	P	W	D	L	PF	PA	PD	Pts
Castle Cary	8	8	0	0	304	43	261	16
Crewkerne	8	6	0	2	272	75	197	12
Martock	8	3	0	5	86	135	-49	6
Wincanton	8	3	0	5	71	275	-204	6
Morganians	8	0	0	8	67	272	-205	0

CORNWALL/DEVON

	P	W	D	L	PF	PA	PD	Pts
Newton Abbot	18	15	0	3	495	165	330	30
Withycombe	18	14	0	4	370	213	157	28
Sidmouth	18	13	0	5	433	237	196	26
Bude	18	8	1	9	230	282	-52	17
Exmouth	18	8	0	10	304	247	57	16
Newquay Hornets	18	8	0	10	265	299	-34	16
Bideford	18	8	0	10	175	235	-60	16
Teignmouth	18	7	1	10	281	356	-75	15
Old Plym & Mann*	18	8	0	10	254	313	-59	6
Falmouth*	18	0	0	18	117	577	-460	-6

SOUTHERN COUNTIES NORTH

SOUTHERN COUNTIES SOUTH

Buckinghamshire & Oxfordshire

Berkshire, Dorset & Wiltshire 1

Berks, Dorset & Wilts 2

Berks, Dorset & Wilts 3

CORNWALL ONE

	P	W	D	L	PF	PA	PD	Pts
St Just	16	15	1	0	409	74	335	31
Saltash	16	14	0	2	553	109	444	28
Bodmin	16	10	0	6	342	188	154	20
Perranporth	16	9	1	6	230	189	41	19
W'bridge Camels	16	6	0	10	322	245	77	12
Illogan Park*	16	7	0	9	190	431	-241	12
Helston*	16	6	0	10	297	267	30	10
Redruth Albany*	16	3	0	13	114	375	-261	4
Veor*	16	1	0	15	100	679	-579	-2

CORNWALL TWO

	P	W	D	L	PF	PA	PD	Pts
St Agnes	11	10	0	1	333	117	216	20
St Day	12	8	0	4	299	127	172	16
Liskeard-Looe	12	8	0	4	266	151	115	16
Callington	12	6	0	6	188	196	-8	12
Camborne S o M	11	5	0	6	219	171	48	10
Roseland*	12	4	0	8	129	256	-127	6
Lankelly Fowey*	12	0	0	12	75	491	-416	-2

DEVON ONE

	P	W	D	L	PF	PA	PD	Pts
Wessex	18	17	0	1	398	158	240	34
Tavistock	18	13	0	5	376	256	120	26
Old Technicians*	18	13	0	5	381	179	202	24
Honiton	18	12	0	6	431	246	185	24
Torrington	18	8	1	9	411	289	122	17
Cullompton	18	7	1	10	379	346	33	15
Plymouth Civ Serv	18	7	1	10	310	292	18	15
Ilfracombe	18	6	0	12	260	462	-202	12
Old Public Oaks	18	3	2	13	138	371	-233	8
Topsham	18	1	1	16	131	616	-485	3

DEVON TWO

	P	W	D	L	PF	PA	PD	Pts
Totnes	18	17	1	0	545	172	373	35
Tamar Saracens	18	14	0	4	347	118	229	28
Exeter Saracens*	18	14	0	4	371	214	157	26
Dartmouth	18	11	0	7	282	250	32	22
Marjons*	18	9	2	7	327	280	47	18
North Tawton	18	8	0	10	247	282	-35	16
Plymouth Argaum	18	6	0	12	217	382	-165	12
Plymstock*	18	4	0	14	177	412	-235	6
Devonport HSOB	18	2	1	15	169	362	-193	5
Prince Rock*	18	3	0	15	79	289	-210	-6

Salcombe have withdrawn.

DEVON THREE

	P	W	D	L	PF	PA	PD	Pts
Plymouth YMCA	10	7	1	2	146	104	42	15
Buckfastleigh	10	6	2	2	187	88	99	14
Bovey Tracey	10	4	3	3	95	93	2	11
Plympton Victoria	10	5	0	5	140	89	51	10
St Col & Torpoint	10	2	1	7	56	198	-142	5
Woodland Fort*	10	2	1	7	92	144	-52	3

* Points deducted

BERKS/DORSET/WILTS ONE

	P	W	D	L	PF	PA	PD	Pts
Ivel Barbarians	18	15	1	2	701	146	555	31
Swindon College	18	14	0	4	478	278	200	28
Westbury	18	13	0	5	340	207	133	26
Calne	18	10	1	7	241	240	1	21
Trowbridge	18	9	1	8	319	261	58	19
Melksham	18	7	1	10	267	259	8	15
Corsham	18	7	1	10	241	347	-106	15
Thatcham	18	5	0	13	204	568	-364	10
Portcastrians	18	4	0	14	181	467	-286	8
Weymouth	18	3	1	14	229	428	-199	7

BERKS/DORSET/WILTS TWO

	P	W	D	L	PF	PA	PD	Pts
Minety	16	13	0	3	278	150	128	26
Bridport*	16	12	0	4	482	174	308	22
Oakmeadians	16	11	0	5	401	200	201	22
Colerne	16	10	0	6	289	255	34	20
Lytchett Minster	16	9	0	7	260	173	87	18
Aldermaston	16	7	0	9	214	311	-97	14
Marlborough*	16	6	0	10	248	316	-68	10
Puddletown	16	4	0	12	219	473	-254	8
Hungerford	16	0	0	16	108	447	-339	0

Christchurch have withdrawn from the league.

BERKS/DORSET/WILTS THREE

	P	W	D	L	PF	PA	PD	Pts
Bradford on Avon	12	11	0	1	431	74	357	22
Berks Shire Hall	12	10	0	2	286	101	185	20
Pewsey Vale	12	6	0	6	194	166	28	12
Warminster*	12	6	0	6	199	141	58	10
Supermarine*	12	6	0	6	130	198	-68	10
Poole*	12	3	0	9	199	298	-99	4
Verwood*	12	0	0	12	31	492	-461	-4

BUCKS/OXON ONE

	P	W	D	L	PF	PA	PD	Pts
Witney	12	10	0	2	360	113	247	20
Drifters	12	9	0	3	272	101	171	18
Littlemore	12	7	1	4	217	184	33	15
Phoenix	12	7	0	5	187	178	9	14
Milton Keynes	12	5	1	6	157	171	-14	11
Chesham	12	3	0	9	119	206	-87	6
Abingdon*	12	0	0	12	69	428	-359	-2

BUCKS/OXON TWO

	P	W	D	L	PF	PA	PD	Pts
Wheatley	10	9	1	0	329	83	246	19
Didcot	10	6	0	4	136	115	21	12
Grove*	10	7	1	2	196	67	129	11
Harwell	10	3	1	6	75	201	-126	7
Gosford All Blacks	10	2	1	7	82	165	-83	5
Winslow	10	1	0	9	64	251	-187	2

SOUTH WEST DIVISION - 1999-2000 FIXTURE GRIDS

SOUTH WEST TWO WEST

	Brixham	Camborne	Clevedon	Dings Crusaders	Hornets	Penryn	Spartans	St Austell	St Mary's OB	Taunton	Tiverton	Truro
Brixham		25.09	06.11	15.01	18.03	15.04	18.12	26.02	09.10	29.01	25.03	27.11
Camborne	11.03		15.01	27.11	26.02	18.12	25.03	09.10	29.01	06.11	11.09	15.04
Clevedon	22.01	20.11		11.09	04.09	02.10	12.02	08.01	11.12	08.04	23.10	11.03
Dings Crusaders	20.11	08.01	18.03		25.09	12.02	23.10	11.12	08.04	04.09	22.01	02.10
Hornets	11.09	02.10	25.03	11.03		22.01	08.01	23.10	20.11	11.12	08.04	12.02
Penryn	11.12	08.04	26.02	09.10	06.11		20.11	04.09	18.03	25.09	08.01	29.01
Spartans	08.04	04.09	09.10	29.01	27.11	15.01		18.03	25.09	26.02	11.12	06.11
St Austell	02.10	12.02	27.11	15.04	29.01	25.03	11.09		06.11	15.01	11.03	18.12
St Mary's O.B. (SW)	12.02	23.10	15.04	18.12	15.01	11.09	11.03	22.01		27.11	02.10	25.03
Taunton	23.10	22.01	18.12	25.03	15.04	11.03	02.10	20.11	08.01		12.02	11.09
Tiverton	04.09	18.03	29.01	06.11	18.12	27.11	15.04	25.09	26.02	09.10		15.01
Truro	08.01	11.12	25.09	26.02	09.10	23.10	22.01	08.04	04.09	18.03	20.11	

WESTERN COUNTIES WEST

	Crediton	Hayle	Ivybridge	Newton Abbot	Okehampton	Paignton	South Molton	St Ives (SW)	Wellington	Withycombe
Crediton		25.09	12.02	11.03	06.11	15.01	27.11	09.10	25.03	18.12
Hayle	26.02		20.11	08.01	29.01	15.04	23.10	02.10	11.03	11.12
Ivybridge	02.10	18.12		26.02	25.03	09.10	11.09	27.11	06.11	15.01
Newton Abbot	11.09	06.11	25.09		27.11	12.02	25.03	18.12	15.01	09.10
Okehampton	08.01	09.10	11.12	15.04		11.03	20.11	15.01	12.02	25.09
Paignton	23.10	27.11	29.01	02.10	11.09		26.02	25.03	18.12	06.11
South Molton	15.04	15.01	11.03	11.12	18.12	25.09		06.11	09.10	12.02
St Ives (SW)	29.01	12.02	15.04	20.11	23.10	11.12	08.01		25.09	11.03
Wellington	11.12	11.09	08.01	23.10	02.10	20.11	29.01	26.02		15.04
Withycombe	20.11	25.03	23.10	29.01	26.02	08.01	02.10	11.09	27.11	

CORNWALL & DEVON

	Bideford	Bude	Devonport Serv.	Exmouth	Kingsbridge	Newquay H.	Sidmouth	St Just	Teignmouth	Wessex
Bideford		02.10	27.11	26.02	11.09	18.12	15.01	09.10	25.03	06.11
Bude	12.02		09.10	11.03	27.11	25.09	18.12	15.01	06.11	25.03
Devonport Services	15.04	29.01		20.11	08.01	12.02	11.03	11.12	23.10	25.09
Exmouth	25.09	11.09	18.12		25.03	06.11	09.10	12.02	27.11	15.01
Kingsbridge	11.03	15.04	06.11	11.12		15.01	12.02	25.09	18.12	09.10
Newquay Hornets	20.11	26.02	02.10	08.01	23.10		11.12	15.04	29.01	11.03
Sidmouth	23.10	20.11	11.09	29.01	02.10	25.03		08.01	26.02	27.11
St Just	29.01	23.10	25.03	02.10	26.02	27.11	06.11		11.09	18.12
Teignmouth	11.12	08.01	15.01	15.04	20.11	09.10	25.09	11.03		12.02
Wessex	08.01	11.12	26.02	23.10	29.01	11.09	15.04	20.11	02.10	

DEVON ONE

	Cullompton	Honiton	Ilfracombe	Old Plymothians	Old Technicians	Plymouth Civil	Tamar Saracens	Tavistock	Torrington	Totnes
Cullompton		23.10	26.02	27.11	29.01	18.12	11.09	25.03	06.11	02.10
Honiton	15.01		27.11	25.09	12.02	25.03	06.11	09.10	18.12	11.03
Ilfracombe	25.09	15.04		15.01	11.03	09.10	18.12	06.11	12.02	11.12
Old Plymothian &	15.04	26.02	23.10		20.11	11.03	29.01	02.10	11.12	08.01
Old Technicians	09.10	02.10	11.09	18.12		06.11	25.03	27.11	15.01	26.02
Plymouth Civil	20.11	11.12	29.01	11.09	08.01		02.10	26.02	15.04	23.10
Tamar Saracens	11.03	08.01	20.11	09.10	11.12	12.02		15.01	25.09	15.04
Tavistock	11.12	29.01	08.01	12.02	15.04	25.09	23.10		11.03	20.11
Torrington	08.01	20.11	02.10	25.03	23.10	27.11	26.02	11.09		29.01
Totnes	12.02	11.09	25.03	06.11	25.09	15.01	27.11	18.12	09.10	

DEVON TWO

	Buckfastleigh	Dartmouth	Exeter Saracens	Marjons	North Tawton	Old Public Oaks	Plymouth Arg.	P'mouth YMCA	Plymstock	Topsham
Buckfastleigh		11.03	25.09	12.02	09.10	15.01	06.11	18.12	27.11	25.03
Dartmouth	11.09		06.11	25.09	18.12	12.02	27.11	09.10	25.03	15.01
Exeter Saracens	26.02	08.01		20.11	02.10	15.04	29.01	11.12	23.10	11.03
Marjons	02.10	26.02	18.12		27.11	09.10	25.03	15.01	11.09	06.11
North Tawton	29.01	20.11	12.02	15.04		11.12	23.10	11.03	08.01	25.09
Old Public Oaks	23.10	02.10	27.11	29.01	25.03		11.09	06.11	26.02	18.12
Plymouth Argaum	08.01	15.04	09.10	11.12	15.01	11.03		25.09	20.11	12.02
Plymouth YMCA	20.11	29.01	25.03	23.10	11.09	08.01	26.02		02.10	27.11
Plymstock	15.04	11.12	15.01	11.03	06.11	25.09	18.12	12.02		09.10
Topsham	11.12	23.10	11.09	08.01	26.02	20.11	02.10	15.04	29.01	

DEVON THREE

	Bovey Tracey	Devonport	Plympton Vic	Prince Rock	Rolle Rats	Salcombe	St Columbe	University of
Bovey Tracey		08.01	02.10	29.01	23.10	11.12	20.11	11.03
Devonport HSOB	25.09		20.11	15.01	11.03	12.02	09.10	11.12
Plympton Victoria	15.01	26.02		27.11	29.01	25.09	25.03	23.10
Prince Rock (WF)	09.10	02.10	11.03		11.12	20.11	12.02	04.03
Rolle Rats	12.02	27.11	09.10	25.03		15.01	25.09	26.02
Salcombe	25.03	23.10	08.01	26.02	02.10		27.11	29.01
St Columba &	26.02	29.01	11.12	23.10	08.01	11.03		02.10
University of Plymouth	27.11	25.03	12.02	06.11	20.11	09.10	15.01	

CORNWALL ONE

	Bodmin	Falmouth	Helston	Illogan Park	Perranporth	Saltash	St Agnes	St Day	Wadebridge C.
Bodmin		12.02	11.03	25.09	15.01	09.10	27.11	18.12	06.11
Falmouth	02.10		26.02	18.12	09.10	27.11	11.09	15.01	25.03
Helston	11.09	25.09		06.11	12.02	18.12	25.03	09.10	27.11
Illogan Park	26.02	20.11	08.01		15.04	02.10	23.10	11.12	29.01
Perranporth	23.10	29.01	02.10	27.11		25.03	26.02	06.11	11.09
Saltash	29.01	15.04	20.11	12.02	11.12		08.01	11.03	23.10
St Agnes	15.04	11.03	11.12	15.01	25.09	06.11		12.02	18.12
St Day	20.11	23.10	29.01	25.03	08.01	11.09	02.10		26.02
Wadebridge Camels	08.01	11.12	15.04	09.10	11.03	15.01	20.11	25.09	

CORNWALL TWO

	Callington	Camborne S oM	Lankelly Fowey	Liskeard-Looe	Redruth Albany	Roseland	Stithians	Veor
Callington		08.01	02.10	29.01	11.03	23.10	11.12	20.11
Camborne S o M	25.09		20.11	15.01	11.12	11.03	12.02	09.10
Lankelly Fowey	15.01	26.02		27.11	23.10	29.01	25.09	25.03
Liskeard-Looe	09.10	02.10	11.03		08.01	11.12	20.11	12.02
Redruth Albany	27.11	25.03	12.02	25.09		20.11	09.10	15.01
Roseland	12.02	27.11	09.10	25.03	26.02		15.01	25.09
Stithians	25.03	23.10	08.01	26.02	29.01	02.10		27.11
Veor	26.02	29.01	11.12	23.10	02.10	08.01	11.03	

WESTERN COUNTIES NORTH

	Barton Hill	Bristol H'quins	Cheltenham N	Chew Valley	Cirencester	Cleve	Coney Hill	Drybrook	Gordon League	North Bristol	Old Redcliffians	Old Richians	Oldfield OB	St Bernadettes	Thornbury	Whitehall	Wiveliscombe
Barton Hill					09.10		25.09	06.11	27.11			25.03	29.01	08.01	26.02		
Bristol Harlequins	11.09		09.10	27.11		13.11				08.01	29.01					25.03	26.02
Cheltenham North	02.10			08.01		27.11	23.10			29.01	26.02					11.09	25.03
Chew Valley	20.11				15.01		11.12	12.02		25.03	11.09					23.10	02.10
Cirencester		23.10	20.11					08.01	29.01			02.10	25.03	26.02	11.09		
Cleve	23.10			29.01	11.12		20.11			26.02	25.03					02.10	11.09
Coney Hill		02.10			06.11			27.11	08.01			11.09	26.02	29.01	25.03		
Drybrook		20.11	11.12			15.01			26.02			23.10	11.09	25.03	02.10		
Gordon League		11.12	15.01	11.03		12.02						20.11	02.10	11.09	23.10		
North Bristol	11.12				12.02		15.01	11.03	08.04		02.10					20.11	23.10
Old Redcliffians	15.01				11.03		12.02	08.04	25.09					09.10		11.12	20.11
Old Richians		08.04	25.09	06.11		09.10				27.11	08.01					26.02	29.01
Oldfield Old Boys		12.02	11.03	25.09		08.04				09.10	06.11	15.01			11.12		
St Bernadettes Old		15.01	12.02	08.04		11.03				25.09		11.12	23.10		20.11		
Thornbury		11.03	08.04	09.10		25.09				06.11	27.11	12.02					08.01
Whitehall	11.03				25.09		08.04	09.10	06.11				08.01	27.11	29.01		
Wiveliscombe	12.02				08.04		11.03	25.09	09.10				27.11	06.11		15.01	

GLOS & SOMERSET

	Avon	Avonmouth OB	Bream	Bristol Saracens	Brockworth	Chard	Chipping S'bury	Combe Down	Frampton Cott.	Gordano	Longlevens	Midsomer N.	Old Centralians	Old Culver'sians	Tor	Walcot O B	Yatton
Avon					25.09	27.11	08.01		09.10		30.10		25.03	26.02	29.01		
Avonmouth OB	15.01				12.02	25.09	09.10		11.03		08.04					20.11	11.12
Bream	11.09	29.01		09.10				08.01		06.11		27.11				26.02	25.03
Bristol Saracens	02.10	26.02			23.10			29.01		27.11		08.01				25.03	11.09
Brockworth			02.10			08.01	29.01		06.11		27.11		11.09	25.03	26.02		
Chard			11.12	15.01			11.09			12.02		11.03	20.11	23.10	02.10		
Chipping Sodbury			15.01	12.02				25.09		11.03		08.04	11.12	20.11	23.10		
Combe Down	11.12	02.10			15.01	08.04			12.02		11.03					23.10	20.11
Frampton Cotterell			23.10	20.11		29.01	26.02				08.01		02.10	11.09	25.03		
Gordano	23.10	25.03			20.11			26.02	11.12			29.01				11.09	02.10
Longlevens			20.11	11.12		26.02	25.03			15.01			23.10	02.10	11.09		
Midsomer Norton	20.11	11.09			11.12			25.03	15.01		12.02					02.10	23.10
Old Centralians		08.01	08.04	25.09				27.11		09.10		06.11				29.01	26.02
Old Culverhaysians		27.11	11.03	08.04				06.11		25.09		09.10	12.02			08.01	
Tor		06.11	12.02	11.03				09.10		08.04		25.09	15.01	11.12			
Walcot Old Boys	12.02				11.03	09.10	06.11		08.04		25.09				27.11		15.01
Yatton	11.03				08.04	30.10	27.11		25.09		09.10			29.01	08.01		

SOMERSET ONE

	Bristol Barb.	Broad Plain	Frome	Imperial	Nailsea & Back.	Nth Petherton	Old Ashtonians	Old Sulians	Stothert & Pitt	Wells
Bristol Barbarians		15.01	12.02	09.10	06.11	18.12	25.09	25.03	27.11	11.03
Broad Plain	23.10		29.01	25.03	11.09	06.11	27.11	18.12	26.02	02.10
Frome	02.10	09.10		27.11	25.03	15.01	18.12	06.11	11.09	26.02
Imperial	29.01	11.12	15.04		23.10	11.03	12.02	25.09	08.01	20.11
Nailsea & Backwell	08.01	11.03	11.12	15.01		25.09	09.10	12.02	20.11	15.04
North Petherton	20.11	08.01	23.10	11.09	26.02		25.03	27.11	02.10	29.01
Old Ashtonians	26.02	15.04	20.11	02.10	29.01	11.12		11.03	23.10	08.01
Old Sulians	11.12	20.11	08.01	26.02	02.10	15.04	11.09		29.01	23.10
Stothert & Pitt	15.04	25.09	11.03	30.10	18.12	12.02	15.01	09.10		11.12
Wells	11.09	12.02	25.09	18.12	27.11	09.10	06.11	15.01	25.03	

SOMERSET TWO

	Avonvale	Bath Saracens	Blagdon	Burnham on Sea	Castle Cary	Crewkerne	Minehead	Winscombe
Avonvale		11.03	11.12	29.01	23.10	08.01	02.10	20.11
Bath Saracens	27.11		09.10	25.09	20.11	25.03	12.02	15.01
Blagdon	25.03	29.01		26.02	02.10	23.10	08.01	27.11
Burnham on Sea	09.10	08.01	20.11		11.12	02.10	11.03	12.02
Castle Cary	12.02	26.02	15.01	25.03		27.11	09.10	25.09
Crewkerne	25.09	11.12	12.02	15.01	11.03		20.11	09.10
Minehead	15.01	23.10	25.09	27.11	29.01	26.02		25.03
Winscombe	26.02	02.10	11.03	23.10	08.01	29.01	11.12	

SOMERSET THREE

	Bath Old Ed	Cheddar Valley	Martock	Morgonians	Wincanton
Bath Old Edwardians		11.03	11.12	20.11	29.01
Cheddar Valley	27.11		08.01	25.03	20.11
Martock	25.03	02.10		29.01	11.03
Morganians	12.02	11.12	23.10		08.01
Wincanton	23.10	12.02	27.11	02.10	

GLOUCESTER ONE

	Aretians	Ashley Down O	Cainscross	Cheltenham Civ.	Cheltenham	Chosen Hill FP	Hucclecote	Old Bristolians	Old Cryptians	Painswick	Southmead	Tetbury	Westbury on S.
Aretians		23.10		15.01			12.02		27.11			11.03	02.10
Ashley Down Old			20.11		11.12			15.01	09.10	12.02	11.03		
Cainscross	08.01				12.02	27.11		11.03		02.10	23.10		
Cheltenham Civil		27.11	29.01				11.03		08.01			02.10	23.10
Cheltenham	29.01			26.02		08.01		02.10		23.10	27.11		
Chosen Hill F. P.	20.11	02.10		11.12			15.01					12.02	11.03
Hucclecote		08.01	26.02		25.03				29.01			23.10	27.11
Old Bristolians	26.02			25.03		29.01	09.10			27.11	08.01		
Old Cryptians			11.12		15.01	23.10		12.02		11.03	02.10		
Painswick	25.03			09.10		26.02	20.11				29.01	11.12	
Southmead	09.10			20.11		25.03	11.12					15.01	12.02
Tetbury		29.01	25.03		09.10			20.11	26.02				08.01
Westbury on Severn		26.02	09.10		20.11			11.12	25.03	15.01			

GLOUCESTER TWO

	Bishopston	Bristol Tele.	Cotham Park	Dursley	Gloucester A B	Gloucester Civil	Kingswood	Minchinhampton	Old Colstonians	O Elizabethans	Smiths (Ind)	Tewkesbury
Bishopston				11.12	23.10	02.10		15.01			12.02	
Bristol Telephones	09.10			20.11		11.03		11.12			15.01	
Cotham Park	27.11	23.10					15.01		11.03	12.02		02.10
Dursley			08.01		27.11	23.10		12.02			11.03	
Gloucester All Blues		02.10	20.11				11.12		12.02	15.01		11.03
Gloucester Civil			09.10		25.03		20.11		15.01	11.12		12.02
Kingswood	08.01	27.11		29.01					02.10	11.03		23.10
Minchinhampton			29.01		08.01	27.11	26.02				02.10	
Old Colstonians	26.02	29.01		25.03				09.10			20.11	08.01
Old Elizabethans	29.01	08.01		26.02				25.03	23.10			27.11
Smiths (Industries)			26.02		29.01	08.01	25.03			09.10		
Tewkesbury	25.03	26.02		09.10				20.11			11.12	

GLOUCESTER THREE

	Bristol Aero Co	Dowty	Newent	Pilning	St Brendans Old	Tredworth	Widden OB	Wotton u Edge
Bristol Aeroplane Co		08.01	02.10	29.01	23.10	20.11	11.03	11.12
Dowty	25.09		20.11	15.01	11.03	09.10	11.12	12.02
Newent	15.01	26.02		27.11	29.01	25.03	23.10	25.09
Pilning	09.10	02.10	11.03		11.12	12.02	08.01	20.11
St Brendans Old	12.02	27.11	09.10	25.03		25.09	26.02	15.01
Tredworth	26.02	29.01	11.12	23.10	08.01		02.10	11.03
Widden Old Boys	27.11	25.03	12.02	25.09	20.11	15.01		09.10
Wotton-under-Edge	25.03	23.10	08.01	26.02	02.10	27.11	29.01	

SOUTH WEST TWO EAST

	Abbey	Amersham	Aylesbury	Chinnor	Chippenham	High Wycombe	Marlow	Olney	Salisbury	Slough	Stow on the W	Swanage
Abbey		25.09	18.03	08.01	20.11	08.04	12.02	11.12	23.10	02.10	22.01	04.09
Amersham &	11.03		25.03	02.10	11.09	20.11	22.01	23.10	08.01	12.02	08.04	11.12
Aylesbury	11.09	04.09		20.11	22.01	11.12	02.10	08.01	12.02	11.03	23.10	08.04
Chinnor	27.11	26.02	15.01		11.03	29.01	18.12	09.10	25.03	15.04	11.09	06.11
Chippenham	15.01	18.03	06.11	25.09		09.10	15.04	26.02	18.12	27.11	25.03	29.01
High Wycombe	18.12	15.01	15.04	23.10	12.02		11.09	22.01	11.03	25.03	02.10	27.11
Marlow	09.10	06.11	26.02	08.04	11.12	18.03		04.09	20.11	29.01	08.01	25.09
Olney	15.04	29.01	27.11	12.02	02.10	06.11	25.03		11.09	18.12	11.03	15.01
Salisbury	29.01	27.11	09.10	04.09	08.04	25.09	15.01	18.03		06.11	11.12	26.02
Slough	26.02	09.10	25.09	11.12	08.01	04.09	23.10	08.04	22.01		20.11	18.03
Stow-on-the-Wold	06.11	18.12	29.01	18.03	04.09	26.02	27.11	25.09	15.04	15.01		09.10
Swanage &	25.03	15.04	18.12	22.01	23.10	08.01	11.03	20.11	02.10	11.09	12.02	

SOUTHERN COUNTIES NORTH

	Beaconsfield	Bicester	Bletchley	Buckingham	Chipping Nort.	Drifters	Oxford	Oxford H'quins	Wallingford	Witney
Beaconsfield		02.10	26.02	18.12	11.09	09.10	15.01	25.03	27.11	06.11
Bicester	12.02		11.03	25.09	27.11	15.01	18.12	06.11	09.10	25.03
Bletchley	25.09	11.09		06.11	25.03	12.02	09.10	27.11	18.12	15.01
Buckingham	20.11	26.02	08.01		23.10	15.04	11.12	29.01	02.10	11.03
Chipping Norton	11.03	15.04	11.12	15.01		25.09	12.02	18.12	06.11	09.10
Drifters	29.01	23.10	02.10	27.11	26.02		06.11	11.09	25.03	18.12
Oxford	23.10	20.11	29.01	25.03	02.10	08.01		26.02	11.09	27.11
Oxford Harlequins	11.12	08.01	15.04	09.10	20.11	11.03	25.09		15.01	12.02
Wallingford	15.04	29.01	20.11	12.02	08.01	11.12	11.03	23.10		25.09
Witney	08.01	11.12	23.10	11.09	29.01	20.11	15.04	02.10	26.02	

BUCKS & OXON

	Abingdon	Chesham	Didcot	Gosford A B	Grove	Harwell	Littlemore	Milton Keynes	Pennanians	Phoenix	Wheatley	Winslow
Abingdon		25.03	11.09	11.03	02.10	12.02	23.10	22.01	20.11	08.01	11.12	08.04
Chesham	04.09		22.01	11.09	20.11	11.03	08.01	02.10	11.12	12.02	08.04	23.10
Didcot	18.03	06.11		15.01	25.09	27.11	26.02	15.04	09.10	18.12	29.01	25.03
Gosford All Blacks	25.09	18.03	20.11		08.01	02.10	11.12	12.02	08.04	23.10	04.09	22.01
Grove	26.02	15.01	11.03	27.11		15.04	09.10	18.12	29.01	25.03	06.11	11.09
Harwell	09.10	25.09	08.01	26.02	11.12		08.04	23.10	04.09	22.01	18.03	20.11
Littlemore	29.01	27.11	02.10	15.04	12.02	18.12		25.03	06.11	11.09	15.01	11.03
Milton Keynes	06.11	26.02	11.12	09.10	08.04	29.01	04.09		18.03	20.11	25.09	08.01
Pennanians	15.01	15.04	12.02	18.12	23.10	25.03	22.01	11.09		11.03	27.11	02.10
Phoenix	27.11	09.10	08.04	29.01	04.09	06.11	18.03	15.01	25.09		26.02	11.12
Wheatley	15.04	18.12	23.10	25.03	22.01	11.09	20.11	11.03	08.01	02.10		12.02
Winslow	18.12	29.01	04.09	06.11	18.03	15.01	25.09	27.11	26.02	15.04	09.10	

SOUTHERN COUNTIES SOUTH

	Bournemouth	Devizes	Ivel Barbarians	Redingensians	Sherborne	Swindon Coll.	Tadley	Wimborne	Windsor	Wootton Bass.
Bournemouth		25.09	11.09	27.11	25.03	12.02	09.10	06.11	18.12	15.01
Devizes	26.02		02.10	25.03	11.09	09.10	15.01	18.12	27.11	06.11
Ivel Barbarians	11.03	12.02		06.11	27.11	15.01	18.12	25.09	09.10	25.03
Redingensians	15.04	11.12	08.01		20.11	11.03	25.09	09.10	15.01	12.02
Sherborne	11.12	11.03	15.04	18.12		25.09	12.02	15.01	06.11	09.10
Swindon College	02.10	29.01	23.10	11.09	26.02		06.11	27.11	25.03	18.12
Tadley	29.01	23.10	20.11	26.02	02.10	08.01		25.03	11.09	27.11
Wimborne	08.01	20.11	26.02	29.01	23.10	15.04	11.12		02.10	11.03
Windsor	20.11	15.04	29.01	23.10	08.01	11.12	11.03	12.02		25.09
Wootton Bassett	23.10	08.01	11.12	02.10	29.01	20.11	15.04	11.09	26.02	
Westbury										

BERKS/DORSET/WILTS ONE

	Blandford	Bridport	Calne	Cooper Avon T.	Corsham	Minety	North Dorset	Swindon	Trowbridge	Westbury
Blandford		02.10	18.12	27.11	26.02	06.11	25.03	11.09	15.01	09.10
Bridport	12.02		25.09	09.10	11.03	25.03	06.11	27.11	18.12	15.01
Calne	20.11	26.02		02.10	08.01	11.03	29.01	23.10	11.12	15.04
Cooper Avon Tyres	15.04	29.01	12.02		20.11	25.09	23.10	08.01	11.03	11.12
Corsham	25.09	11.09	06.11	18.12		15.01	27.11	25.03	09.10	12.02
Minety	08.01	11.12	11.09	26.02	23.10		02.10	29.01	15.04	20.11
North Dorset	11.12	08.01	09.10	15.01	15.04	12.02		20.11	25.09	11.03
Swindon	11.03	15.04	15.01	06.11	11.12	09.10	18.12		12.02	25.09
Trowbridge	23.10	20.11	25.03	11.09	29.01	27.11	26.02	02.10		08.01
Westbury	29.01	23.10	27.11	25.03	02.10	18.12	11.09	26.02	06.11	

BERKS/ DORSET/WILTS TWO

	Aldermaston	Berks Shire Hall	Bradford on A	Colerne	Lytchett Minster	Marlborough	Oakmeadians	Portcastrians	Thatcham	Weymouth
Aldermaston		11.03	12.02	25.09	09.10	25.03	15.01	18.12	06.11	27.11
Berkshire Shire Hall	11.09		25.09	06.11	18.12	15.01	12.02	09.10	27.11	25.03
Bradford on Avon	02.10	26.02		18.12	27.11	06.11	09.10	15.01	25.03	11.09
Colerne	26.02	08.01	20.11		02.10	11.03	15.04	11.12	29.01	23.10
Lytchett Minster	29.01	20.11	15.04	12.02		25.09	11.12	11.03	23.10	08.01
Marlborough	11.12	23.10	08.01	11.09	26.02		20.11	15.04	02.10	29.01
Oakmeadians	23.10	02.10	29.01	27.11	25.03	18.12		06.11	11.09	26.02
Portcastrians	20.11	29.01	23.10	25.03	11.09	27.11	08.01		26.02	02.10
Thatcham	08.01	15.04	11.12	09.10	15.01	12.02	11.03	25.09		20.11
Weymouth	15.04	11.12	11.03	15.01	06.11	09.10	25.09	12.02	18.12	

BERKS/ DORSET/WILTS THREE

	Hungerford	Pewsey Vale	Poole	Puddletown	Supermarine	Verwood	Warminster
Hungerford		26.02	29.01	25.09	25.03	27.11	23.10
Pewsey Vale	20.11		11.03	12.02	09.10	15.01	11.12
Poole	09.10	27.11		15.01	25.09	25.03	26.02
Puddletown	08.01	23.10	02.10		27.11	26.02	29.01
Supermarine	11.12	29.01	08.01	11.03		23.10	02.10
Verwood	11.03	02.10	11.12	20.11	12.02		08.01
Warminster	12.02	25.03	20.11	09.10	15.01	25.09	

DRIFTERS (Southern Counties North). **Back Row:** D Barker, V Rawson, M Hughes, J Flower, C Ashton, P Nice, D Hancock. **Front Row:** M Albertini, G Miller, N Gates, C Pritchard, A Thomas, P Spellman. **Very Front:** P Pappenheim, S James.

South West Division Clubs

ABBEY RFC
South West 2 East
Ground Address: Rosehill, Peppard Road, Emmer Green, Reading, Berkshire. RG4 8XA
Tel: 01734 722881
Brief Directions: On B481 from Reading through Caversham & Emmer Green to Peppard & Nettlebed, after leaving Borough Boundary, 2 sharp bends later, Abbey on the left
Club Secretary: Eric Moyse, 9 Lancaster Close, Reading, Berkshire RG1 5HB
Tel: 0118 9751216
Fixtures Secretary: Mrs Lynne Lee, Cotswold, Behoes Lane, Woodcote, Nr. Reading RG8 0PP
Tel: (H) 01491 680102
Club Colours: Navy blue with green and white hoops

ABINGDON RUFC
Bucks & Oxon 1
Ground Address: Southern Sports Park, Lambrick Way, Abingdon. OX14 5TJ Tel: 01235 553810
Brief Directions: Exit Abingdon on the B4017, Drayton Road, Just prior to leaving the town limits, take left into Preston Road. Lambrick Way is 3rd turning on the right.
Club Secretary: T. J. Davies, Stonehill Cottage, Oday Hill, Abingdon OX14 4AA
Tel: (H) 01235 527973
Fixtures Secretary: M.Hedges. Tel No: 01235 202796
Club Colours: Green and gold hooped shirts & socks, black shorts

ALDERMASTON RFC
Berks, Dorset & Wilts 2
Ground Address: Aldermaston Recreational Society Sports Ground, Tadley, Hants Tel: 01189 817233
Brief Directions: From Basingstoke follow directions for Tadley on A340, then for Awe Aldermaston, then for Recreational Society.
Club Secretary: Kevin Jones, 13 Stratford Road, Basingstoke, Hants. RG21 5RS Tel: (H) 01256 410461 (W) 01189 826750
Fixtures Secretary: David Jenkins Tel: (H) 01189 813078 (W) 01189 837487
Club Colours: Scarlet shirts, black shorts

AMERSHAM & CHILTERN RFC
South West 2 East
Ground Address: Ash Grove, Weedon Lane, Amersham, Bucks. HP6 5QU
Tel: 01494 725161
Brief Directions: From Amersham/Chesham road, take Copperkings Lane (signed Hyde Heath), Weedon Lane is 2nd left
Club Secretary: I McKenzie Esq, 17 Highover Park, Amersham, Bucks. HP7 0BN
Tel: (H) 01494 431966
Fixtures Secretary: R Cook, 120 Chestnut Lane, Amersham, Bucks, HP6 6DZ.
Tel: (H) 01494 433144
Club Colours: Maroon & White

ARETIANS RFC
Gloucestershire 1
Ground Address: Station Road, Little Stoke, Bristol. BS12 6HW
Tel: 01454 888069
Brief Directions: M5 J16, A38 into Bristol, at flyover turn left signed Yate (Gypsy Patch Ln), along road to railway bridge, directly left past bridge, ground approx 600yds on right on Station Rd
Club Secretary: Andy Vaughan, 42 Elm Close, Little Stoke, Bristol
Tel: (H) 0117 9756513 (W) 0117 9557767
Fixtures Secretary: Andy Williams
Tel: (H) 01454 886179 (W) 0117 9797187
Club Colours: Black

ASHLEY DOWN OLD BOYS RFC
Gloucestershire 1
Ground Address: Lockleaze Combination Ground, Bonnington Walk, Lockleaze, Bristol
Tel: 0117 9312642
Brief Directions: From Filton Avenue, into Bonnington Walk, left at railway bridge, 0.25 mile along lane
Club Secretary: Peter Heath, 28 Carisbrook Close, Enfield, Middx EN1 3NB Tel: 0181 245 5105
Fixtures Secretary: R Johnson Tel: (H) 0117 9691581
Club Colours: Purple and white

AVON RFC
Gloucestershire & Somerset
Ground Address: Hicks Field, London Road East, Bath, Somerset
Tel: 01225 852446
Brief Directions: On A4 towards Batheaston approx 0.5 mile from A46/A4 junction, entrance on right hand side
Club Secretary: Mr David Loader, 114 Southdown Road, Southdown, Bath, Somerset. BA2 1JJ Tel: (H)01225 316864 (W)01225 331116
Fixtures Secretary: Mr C Nicholson, 116 Free View Road, Twerton, Bath. BA2 1DZ
Tel: (H) 01225 401623
Club Colours: Black and amber hoops

AVONMOUTH OLD BOYS RFC
Gloucestershire & Somerset
Ground Address: Barracks Lane, Shirehampton, Bristol
Tel: 0117 982 9093
Brief Directions: Exit M5 J.19 following motorway signs to Bristol. At first R/about take 1st L. continue to second turning L. 300yds down road.
Club Secretary: R.K. Kennett, 41 Woodland Grove, Westbury-on-Trym, Bristol, BS9 2BD.
Tel: 0117 9683598
Fixtures Secretary: A Woodruff, 69 Priory Road, Shirehampton, Bristol, BS11 9TF.
Tel: (H) 0117 983 3066 (W) 0117 936 2173
Club Colours: Red / Black

AVONVALE RFC

Somerset 2
Ground Address: Bathford Playing Fields, Crown Field, Bathford, Bath, Avon
Tel: 01225 858295
Brief Directions: A4 out of Bath, through Batheaston, right at next roundabout, under railway bridge and next left, clubhouse is along a track next to phone box 200yds up Bathford Hill
Club Secretary: Paul Beaxer, 1 Tropenell Close, Corsham, Wilts.
Tel No: 01249 716135 (H) 01225 733220 (W)
Fixtures Secretary: Steve Vowles, 77 Lockswood Road, Lower Weston, Bath BA1 3ES
Tel: (H) 01225 333852 (W) 01225 766451
Club Colours: Blue shirts with a white band

AYLESBURY RFC

South West 2 East
Ground Address: Ostlers Field, Brook End, Weston Turville, Aylesbury, Bucks. HP22 5RN
Tel: 01296 612556
Brief Directions: A413 from Wendover to Aylesbury. 2 miles rt to B4544 - thro. - ground is on left Weston Turville. Or A41 fromAylesbury, turn rt after 3 miles before Aston cl;inton ,the club is then on right.
Club Secretary: Graham N Roberts, Burghley, 2 Wheelwrights, Weston Turville, Bucks. HP22 5QS
Tel: (H) 01296 612925
Fixtures Secretary: James P Williams, Tumbleweed, Winslow Rd., Granborough, Bucks MK18 3NJ
Tel: (H) 01296 670798
Club Colours: Black and magenta hooped shirts, black shorts and socks

BARTON HILL OLD BOYS RFC

Western Counties North
Ground Address: Argyle Road Playing Fields, Duncombe Lane, Speedwell, Bristol.
Tel: 0117 987 2895
Brief Directions: Follow roads to Lodge Causeway, Fishponds. At lights half way up Causeway turn right opposite St. Josephs and take second left into Duncombe Lane.
Club Secretary: Don Blackmore, 31 Battens Lane, St. George, Bristol. BS5 8TG.
Tel: (H) 0117 961 1754 (B) 0117 9365310
Fixtures Secretary: Rob Porter, 72A Regent Street, Kingswood, Bristol.
Tel: 07775 690291
Club Colours: White with a cherry band

BATH OLD EDWARDIANS RFC

Somerset 3
Ground Address: King Edward School Sports Ground, Bathampton, Bath
Tel: 01225 462354
Brief Directions: M4 J18, A46 to Bath, London Rd towards Batheaston, turn right over Tollbridge to Bathampton, ground next to canal
Club Secretary: C.P. Weeks, 74 Third Avenue, Oldfield Park, Bath BA2 3NZ
Tel: (H) 01225 429027
Fixtures Secretary: Rob Mitchell
Tel: (H) 01225 310989 (W) 01373 463333 (F) 01373 451299
Club Colours: Gold, maroon and blue hoops

BATH SARACENS RFC

Somerset 2
Ground Address: Civil Service Sports Ground, Claverton Down, Bath, Avon. Tel: 01225 832403
Brief Directions: From Bath take A367 to Frys Garage mini roundabout.Take first left, then straight on for 2 miles and turn right immediately after Ralph Allen School.
Club Secretary: Mike York, 2 Unden Gardens, Bath, BA1 2YB Tel: (H) 01225 424613
Fixtures Secretary: S. Jewell, 27 Liddington Way, Trowbridge, BA14 0UBTel: (H) 01225 353709
Club Colours: Blue with red and gold hoops.

BEACONSFIELD RFC

Southern Counties North
Ground Address: Oak Lodge Meadow, Windsor End, Beaconsfield, Buckinghamshire
Tel: 01494 673783
Brief Directions: A40 to Beaconsfield, Saracens Head roundabout turn south down Windsor End, ground and club house 400 yards on left
Club Secretary: Mike Eagle, 12 South Park View, Gerrards Cross, Bucks SL9 8HN
Tel: 01753 887809
Fixtures Secretary: P.Miles. Tel No: 01494 875461
Club Colours: Green and gold hoops, green shorts, hooped socks

BERKSHIRE SHIRE HALL RUFC

Berks, Dorset & Wilts 2
Ground Address: Royal County of Berkshire Sports & Social Club, Sonning Lane, Sonning, Reading
Tel: 01734 691340
Brief Directions: From Reading head towards A4 up Sheppards House Hill, pass Mobil garage on right, take left Sonning Lane, 2nd turning on the right
Club Secretary: Simon Negus, 20 Merrifield Close, Lower Early, Reading, RG6 4BN
Tel: (H) 0118 9751241
Fixtures Secretary: Steve Bentey
Tel: (H) 118 954 2030
Club Colours: Royal Blue & gold.

BICESTER RUFC

Southern Counties North
Ground Address: Oxford Road, Bicester, Oxon. OX6 8AB
Tel: 01869 241000
Brief Directions: As you approach Bicester from south on A34, the ground is on the right on the edge of town just past Tescos
Club Secretary: Mrs Jane Feist , 37 Moor Pond Close, Bicester, Oxon.
Fixtures Secretary: G Davies
Tel: (H & W) 01869 241993
Club Colours: Amber, red and brown hooped shirts, navy shorts

BIDEFORD RFC

Cornwall & Devon
Ground Address: King Georges Field, Riverside, Bank End, Bideford, Devon Tel: 01237 474049
Brief Directions: N.D. link road, left end of Bideford New Bridge, into town until reach river, immediate left at Charles Kingsley statue, proceed River Bank Road to Bideford RFC car park

Club Secretary: Bernard A Ridd, The Firs, Glen Gardens, Bideford, Devon. EX39 3PH
Tel: (H) 01237 475180 (B) 01271 388617
Fixtures Secretary: C.Balsdon, 15 Middleton Road, Bideford, Devon EX39 3LU
Tel: 01237 472166
Club Colours: Red and white hooped shirts, white shorts, red socks

BISHOPSTON RFC
Gloucestershire 2
Ground Address: Bonnington Walk, Lockleaze, Bristol
Tel: 0117 969 1916
Brief Directions: From Almondsbury M'way interchange, A38 to Bristol, left at lights at end of Toronto Rd, cross lights at Filton Ave into B'nington Wk, ground on left straight after rail bridge
Club Secretary: Jim Hockley, 21 Pinewood Close, Westbury-on-Trym, Bristol. BS9 4AJ
Tel: (H) 0117 962 3509 (W) 0117 929 1031 Ext 2390
Fixtures Secretary: Stuart Brain
Tel: (H) 0117 958 5560
Club Colours: Red with black hoop edged in centenary gold

BLAGDON RFC
Somerset 2
Ground Address: The Mead, Blagdon Village
Tel: 01761 463196
Brief Directions: Turn left off the A38 at Churchill traffic lights and follow road for approx 3 miles into Blagdon
Club Secretary: John Thompson, Nadams PPaddock, High Street, Chew Magna, North Somerset.
Tel No: 07808 578807
Fixtures Secretary: Steve Clarke, Tudor Barn, South W iacombe, East Harptree,Bristol BS40 6BL
Tel: 01761 221619
Club Colours: Green , Black and white hoops

BLANDFORD RFC
Berks, Dorset & Wilts 1
Ground Address: Milldown Leisure Centre, Milldown Road, Blandford.
Brief Directions: From town centre, follow signs to Sturminster Newton, Pitches situated at Melldown Leisure Centre opposite hospital.
Club Secretary: Simon Heart, Swingletree, 1 Wares Close, Winterborne Kingston, Blandford Forum, Dorset DT11 9BS
Tel: (H) 01929 472274
Fixtures Secretary: Dave Stringer
Tel: (H) 01258 456954
Club Colours: Red, Yellow & Brown

BLETCHLEY RUFC
Southern Counties North
Ground Address: Manor Fields, Bletchley, Milton Keynes, Bucks Tel: 01908 372298
Brief Directions: On B488 from Leighton Buzzard, fork right at 'The Plough', from this fork take 3rd right - Manor Road, proceed down road over bridge to ground
Club Secretary: C W Spence, 17 Milesmere, Two Mile Ash, Milton Keynes. MK8 8QP
Tel: (H) 01908 561876 (W) 0171 374 3051
Fixtures Secretary: I Punter
Tel: (H) 01908 642994
Club Colours: Burgundy and white hoops

BODMIN RFC
Cornwall 1
Ground Address: Clifton Park, Carminnow Cross, Bodmin, Cornwall
Tel: 01208 74629
Brief Directions: Off A38 before Flyover at A30 take B Road signed Lanhydrock 400yds turn right down private drive.
Club Secretary: Keith Richardson, " Yoomes Dew", Westheath Road, Bodmin, PL 11QG
Tel: 01208 77643 (H) 0421 442825 (Mobile)
Fixtures Secretary: Mike Roberts, 3 Castle Drive, Bodmin, PL31 2RE
Tel: 01208 74861 (H) 0410 0166770 (Mobile)
Club Colours: Light Blue/ with Dark Blue Hoops edged with white.

BOURNEMOUTH RFC
Southern Counties South
Ground Address: Bournemouth Sports Club, Chapel Gate, Bast Parley, Christchurch, Dorset. BH23 6BD
Tel: 01202 581933
Brief Directions: Take Bournemouth spur road (A338 Ringwood-Bournemouth). Follow signs to Hurn Airport. Ground is just to the west of the airport.
Club Secretary: Cliff Deane, 3 Blake Hill Avenue, Poole, Dorset, BH14 8QA.
Tel: (H) 01202 709901
Fixtures Secretary: Andy Cumming, 106 Avon Road, Charminster, Bournemouth, BH8 8SF
Tel: (H) 01202 393012
Club Colours: Sable and gold

BOVEY TRACEY RFC
Devon 3
Ground Address: Bullands, Monks Way, Bovey Tracey, Devon
Brief Directions: Follow signs to Moreton Hampstead through Bovey Tracey, ground is on right hand side as you leave the town
Club Secretary: Carolyn Leigh, 34 East Street, Bovey Tracey, Devon. TQ13 9EJ
Tel: (H) 01626 834432
Fixtures Secretary: Martin Evans. Tel No: 01626 832535
Club Colours: Navy and white hoops

BRADFORD ON AVON
Berks, Dorset & Wilts 2
Ground Address: St Lawrence School, Ashly Road, Bradford on Avon, Wiltshire BA15 1DZ
Club Secretary: J. S. Pendrey, 6 Fitzmaurice Close, Bradford on Avon, Wiltshire BA15 1UE
Tel: (H/W) 01225 864186
Fixtures Secretary: A. Gerrish, 14 Huntingdon Street, Bradford on Avon, Wiltshire BA15 1RF
Tel: (H) 01225 864165

COLERNE RFC
Ground Address: Higgins Field, Bath Road, Colerne, Wiltshire
Brief Directions: Under water tower on main road past village
Club Secretary: Mrs Karen Sayers, 8 Cleaves Avenue, Colerne, Wiltshire. SN14 8BX
Tel: (H) 01225 744355
Fixtures Secretary: Mark Gratton, 6 Westminster Gardens, Chippenham, SN14 0DFTel: 01249 658586
Club Colours: Black

BREAM RFC
Gloucestershire & Somerset
Ground Address: High Street, Bream, Nr Lydney, Glos. GL15 6JG
Tel: 01594 562320
Brief Directions: Approx 3 miles off main A48 Gloucester to Chepstow road, turn right after Westbury Homes Site on right hand side
Club Secretary: Colin Henderson, 12 Maypole Road, Bream, Lydney, Glos, GL15 6XN
Tel: (H) 01594 562430
Fixtures Secretary: Colin Henderson, 12 Maypole Road, Bream, Lydney, Glos, GL15 6XN
Tel: (H) 01594 562430
Club Colours: Red and black

BRIDPORT RFC
Berks, Dorset & Wilts 1
Ground Address: Bridport Leisure Centre, Skilling Hill Road, Bridport, Dorset. DT6 3LN Tel: 01308 420555
Brief Directions: Take A35 Bridport By-Pass, at R'bout south of Town turn R. (North). After 300yds turn L. at Traffic Lights opp. Safeway store.
Club Secretary: Richard Salt, 21 South Street, Bridport, Dorset. DT6 3NR Tel: (H) 01308 458347 (W) 01308 422236
Fixtures Secretary: John Greig Tel: (H) 01308 456692 (W) 01308 424600
Club Colours: Dark blue

BRISTOL AEROPLANE COMPANY RFC
Gloucestershire 3
Ground Address: Bristol Aerospace Welfare Association Sports Ground, 589 Southmead Road, Filton, Bristol. BS12 7DG Tel: 0117 9768066
Brief Directions: Travel south along A38, right at the roundabout at top of Filton Hill into Southmead Road, ground on the right
Club Secretary: Clive Prewitt, 64/66 West street, Oldland Common, Bristol BS30 9WS
Tel: (W) 0117 9794567 (H) 0117 9323677
Fixtures Secretary: Julian Mason-Fluke,
Tel: (W) 0117 9790827 (H) 0117 9442132
Club Colours: Red, white and blue hoops

BRISTOL HARLEQUINS RFC
Western Counties North
Ground Address: Valhalla, Broomhill Road, Brislington, Bristol. BS4
Tel: 0117 972 1650
Club Secretary: Mr P Broome, 1 Ketch Road, Lower Knowle, Bristol
Tel: (H) 0117 940 7929 (W) 0117 972 1261
Fixtures Secretary: Mr E Morrison
Tel: (H) 01275 832580
Club Colours: Blue, black and white hoops

BRISTOL SARACENS RFC
Gloucestershire & Somerset
Ground Address: Bakewell Memorial Ground, Station Road, Cribbs Causeway, Henbury, Bristol
Tel: 0117 9500037
Brief Directions: M5 J17 towards Bristol city centre, approx 1000 metres at 2nd roundabout on right
Club Secretary: A E Swash, 6 Downs Road, Westbury-on-Trym, Bristol. BS9 3TX
Tel: (H) 01179 629047
Fixtures Secretary: C J Matthews
Tel: (H) 01179 243696
Club Colours: Myrtle green and white hooped shirts, black shorts

BRISTOL TELEPHONE AREA RFC
Gloucestershire 2
Ground Address: B.T.R.A. Sports Ground, Stockwood Lane, Stockwood, Bristol. BS14
Tel: 01275 891776
Brief Directions: Take A37 (Wells Road) for approx 4 miles from city centre, left at Black Lion pub at Whitchurch, ground approx 1 mile on right
Club Secretary: Mark Morgan, 21 Durville Road, Headley Park, Bristol BS13 7PS
Tel: 01179 642331
Fixtures Secretary: Chris Watts, 22 Ladman road, Stockwood, Bristol
Tel: (H) 01275 543208
Club Colours: Blue with red & white V neck.

BRIXHAM RFC
South West 2 West
Ground Address: Astley Park, Rea Barn Road, Brixham
Tel: 01803 882162
Brief Directions: M5, then A380 to Torbay, follow signs for Brixham
Club Secretary: R B Houston, St Cloud, Cliff Park Road, Paignton
Tel: (H) 01803 550427 (W) 01548 855000
Fixtures Secretary: J D Irvine B.E.M., ! Great Rea Rd., Brixham, TQ5 9SW
Tel: (H) 01803 882219
Club Colours: Black with 6" white band

BROAD PLAIN RFC
Somerset 1
Ground Address: Hengrove School, Patherton Rd., Hengrove, Bristol
Brief Directions: Adjacent to Wells Road out of Bristol. Contact Secretary for directions
Club Secretary: Don Collins, 77 Lake Road, Henleaze, Bristol. BS10 5JE
Tel: (H) 0117 9622094 (W) 0117 9248051
Fixtures Secretary: Ivan Gregory
Tel: (H) 0117 9393713 (W) 0117 9552866
Club Colours: Blue, maroon and gold hoops

BROCKWORTH RFC
Gloucestershire & Somerset
Ground Address: Badgers Mount, Mill Lane, Brockworth. Tel: 01452 862556
Brief Directions: From south: M5 turn off at junct. 11A, follow signs to Gloucester, 1st left to Blockworth at roundabout, straight over next, past Du-Pont, left at lights into Vicarage Lane, straight over small roundabout, 1st right into Mill Lane, 400 metres on LHS.
Club Secretary: Andrew Yarworth, 22 Speedwell Close, Abbeymead, Gloucester, GL4 4GQ Tel No: 01452 614902 (H) 01452 333111 (W) 01452 333121 (F)
Fixtures Secretary: Andy Cook. Tel No: 01452 619278 (H) 07808 479821 (M)
Club Colours: Black shirts with white 'V'

BUCKFASTLEIGH
Devon 2
Ground Address: The Cricket Club, Buckfastleigh, Devon Tel: 01364 643895
Club Secretary: Mrs A Lawton, 10 Russell Road, Buckfastleigh, Devon TQ11 0DD Tel: (H) 01364 642608 Tel: (W) 01364 643750
Fixtures Secretary: N Godwin, Tel: (H) 01364 642306
Club Colours: Black and yellow quarters.

BUCKINGHAM RUFC
Southern Counties North
Ground Address: Floyd Field, Moreton Road, Maids Moreton, Buckingham
Tel: 01280 815474
Brief Directions: From Buckingham town centre, take A413 to Towcester, after approx 0.5 mile ground is on the left
Club Secretary: Finlay Gemmell, 22 Elmfields Gate, Winslow, Bucks. MK18 3JG
Tel: (H) 01296 714640 (W) 01628 893772
Fixtures Secretary: Anthony Smith
Tel: (H) 01280 815634
Club Colours: Green and white hoops, black shorts, green socks

BUDE RFC
Cornwall & Devon
Ground Address: Bencoolen Meadow (off Kings Hill), Bude, Cornwall. EX23 8DG
Tel: 01288 354795
Club Secretary: Mr F B Sykes, 65 Kings Hill, Bude, Cornwall. EX23 8QL
Tel: (H) 01288 354210
Fixtures Secretary: Mr J A Boundy
Tel: (H) 01288 381296 (W) 01288 353766
Club Colours: Maroon and sky blue hoops

BURNHAM ON SEA RFC
Somerset 2
Ground Address: B.A.S.C. Ground, Stoddens Road, Burnham on Sea, Somerset. TA8 2DE
Tel: 01278 788355
Brief Directions: Signposted from M5, J22.
Club Secretary: Lucy Harris, 106 Burnham Road, Highbridge. Somerset, TA9 3EQ. Tel: 01278 781673
Fixtures Secretary: Andy Marsh, 217 Berrow Road, Burnham on Sea, Somerset TA8 2JG
Club Colours: Blue and white hoops

CAINSCROSS RFC
Gloucestershire 1
Ground Address: Victory Park,Caincross, Ebley, Stroud, Glos
Tel: 01453 766707
Brief Directions: Take second exit from Horse Trough Roundabout. Westward round Ebley into Church Road (on left just before Imo carwash). When travelling from M5
Club Secretary: Dave Roberts, 41 Boakes Drive, Bristol Rd., Stonehopuse, Glos. GL10 3QW
Fixtures Secretary: Richard Stonebridge: 01453 758659
Club Colours: Amber and blue

CALLINGTON RFC
Cornwall 2
Ground Address: Duchy College Ground, Stoke Climsland, Callington, Cornwall.
Brief Directions: Callington to Launceston Road, turn off at Kelly Brayy to Stoke Climsland. At Stoke Climsland follow signs to Ventodon then Duchy College.
Club Secretary: Michelle Campbell, Heartland House, 11 Church Street, Callington, Cornwall, PL17 7BL.
Tel: 01579 382875
Fixtures Secretary: Mr. John N. N. Pritchard, 2 Drakewalls Terrace, St. Ann Chapel, Gunnislake, Cornwall.
Tel: 01822 833371
Club Colours: Red & Black Quarters, Black Shorts

CALNE RFC
Berks, Dorset & Wilts 1
Ground Address: The Recreation Ground, Anchor Road, Calne, Wiltshire. SN11 8DX Tel: 01249 812206
Brief Directions: Turn into Bank Row opposite Lansdowne Strand Hotel, past Somerfields into Mill St, follow road uphill into Anchor Rd, car park on left after 500 yards
Club Secretary: Leigh Martin, 12 brewer Mead, Chippenham, wilts. SN 15 3FB
Tel: 01249 443284
Fixtures Secretary: Ian West, 23 Tern Close, Calne, Wilts.
(H) 01249 813737
Club Colours: Blue with red and white hoop

CAMBORNE RFC
South West 2 West
Ground Address: The Recreation Ground, Camborne, Cornwall
Tel: 01209 713227
Brief Directions: Leave the A30 Camborne/Redruth bypass at junction for Camborne West following signs for the recreation ground
Club Secretary: W J C Dunstan, The Retreat, 11 Station Hill, Praze-an-Beeble, Camborne, Cornwall. TR24 0JT
Tel: (H) 01209 831373 (W) 01736 795456
Fixtures Secretary: David Smith
Tel: (H)01209 716992
Club Colours: Cherry and white

CAMBORNE SCHOOL OF MINES RFC
Cornwall 2
Ground Address: The Memorial Ground, Boundervean Lane, Penponds, Camborne (not a postal delivery address)
Tel: 01209 612959 - Clubhouse Tel: 01209 711935
Brief Directions: Off Pendraves Road, Camborne, B3303 to Helson, turn right into Boundervean Lane. Before railway bridge, ground is 250m on right.
Club Secretary: Dr C V Phillips, Barlowena, Alexandra Road, Illogan, Redruth. Cornwall, TR16 4EN
Tel: (H) 01209 842660 (W) 01209 714866
Fixtures Secretary: N. R. Clarke, 2 Tremayne Close, Devoran, Truro, TR3 6QE.
Tel: (H) 01872 863139 (W) 01209 717724
Club Colours: Navy, gold and silver hoops

CASTLE CARY RUFC
Somerset 2
Ground Address: Brookhouse Field, Sutton, Ditcheat, Shepton Mallet, Somerset
Tel: 01963 351178
Brief Directions: A361 to Castle Cary from Shepton Mallet, turn right at Brookhouse Inn, 2nd on right
Club Secretary: Mr A J Bailey, 2 Enfield Terrace, Weymouth Road, Evercreech, Somerset
Tel: (H) 01749 830268
Fixtures Secretary: J. Franklin, 17 cothier Meadows, Castle Cary, Somerset..
Tel No: 01963 351193
Club Colours: Red and black hoops. Change Colours: All Blue.

CHARD RFC
Gloucestershire & Somerset
Ground Address: The Park, Essex Close, Chard, Somerset
Tel: 01460 62495
Brief Directions: Bottom of Chard High Street (by Cerdic DIY shop), 100 yards up Essex Close
Club Secretary: Mr N J Urch, 2 South View, Listers Hill, Ilminster, Somerset
Tel: (H) 01460 57864 (W) 01935 702913
Fixtures Secretary: Mr R Stuckey, 9 Cerdic Close, Chard, Somerset
Tel: (H) 01460 63579 (W) 01460 63781
Club Colours: Black, red and gold

CHEDDAR VALLEY RFC
Somerset 3
Ground Address: Sharpham Road Playing Fields, Cheddar, Somerset
Tel: 01934 743623
Club Secretary: Ceri Davies, 16 Round Oak Grove, Cheddar, Somerset. BS27 3BW
Tel: (H) 01934 744167
Fixtures Secretary: Callum Mackenzie
Tel: (H) 01934 744277
Club Colours: Sky blue and scarlet hoops

CHELTENHAM CIVIL SERVICE RFC
Gloucestershire 1
Ground Address: Civil Service Sports Ground, Tewkesbury Road, Uckington, Cheltenham
Tel: 01242 680424
Brief Directions: 2 miles from Cheltenham on the main road to Tewkesbury (A4019)
Club Secretary: Brian Didlick, 15 Stoneville Street, Cheltenham. GL51 8PH
Tel: (H) 01242 519285
Fixtures Secretary: Mrs Julie Mortlock, 15, Edendale Rd., Golden Valley, Cheltenham Glos. GL51 0TX
Tel No: 01242 582945
Club Colours: Navy Blue Change Colours: Lght Blue or red

CHELTENHAM NORTH RFC
Western Counties North
Ground Address: Stoke Orchard Road, Bishops Cleeve, Nr Cheltenham Tel: 01292 675968
Brief Directions: Junction 10 or 11 Cheltenham, head out of Cheltenham past racecourse on A435 towards Bishops Cleeve, turn toward Stoke Orchard village, 500 yards on left
Club Secretary: Andrew David Page, Baytrees, Chargrove Lane, Up Hatherley, Cheltenham
Tel: (H) 01242 510932
Fixtures Secretary: Neil Carpenter
Tel: 01242 570048
Club Colours: Black with red band, black shorts, and black socks with red tops.

CHELTENHAM SARACENS RFC
Gloucestershire 1
Ground Address: King George V Playing Fields, Brooklyn Road, St Marks, Cheltenham, Glos
Brief Directions: From Gloucester & M5 follow dual carriageway to main GCHQ roundabout take 1st exit then right at square junction.
Club Secretary: Mrs E Clapham, Hillside Cottage, Gambles Lane, Woodmancote, Cheltenham. Glos.
Tel No: 01242 673550
Fixtures Secretary: J.Knight.Tel No: 01242 522408
Club Colours: Royal Blue with black and gold hoops

CHESHAM RUFC
Bucks & Oxon 1
Ground Address: Chesham Park Community College, Chartridge Lane, Chesham, Bucks. HP5 2RG Tel: 01494 793827
Brief Directions: Chartridge Lane of St. Marys Way in central Chesham. Club is 400 metres on L. Furthest College gate is entrance
Club Secretary: M M Hogg, 37 Lye Green Road, Chesham, Bucks. HP5 3LS
Tel: (H) 01494 771576 (W) 01494 791656 FAX: 01494 791649
Fixtures Secretary: Dick King, 75 Dravell Drive, Chesham, Bucks HP5 2QN
Tel: (H) 01494 780056
Club Colours: Blue and claret hoops

CHEW VALLEY OLD BOYS RFC
Western Counties North
Ground Address: Lobbingtons, Chew Lane, Chew Stoke, Bristol
Brief Directions: Through Chew Magna, on to Chew Stoke, next to the school
Club Secretary: Jim Gethin, April Cottage, Top Sutton, Bishop sutton, Bristol BS39 5UW
Tel: 01275 332080
Fixtures Secretary: Bob Martin, 66 Meadowside Drive, Whitchurch, Bristol BS14 0NS
Tel: (H) 01275 832547
Club Colours: Green and white hoops

CHINNOR RFC
South West 2 East
Ground Address: The Pavilion, Kingsey Road, Thame, Oxon. OX9 3PB
Tel: 01844 213735/213907
Brief Directions: Situated on the Thame Western bypass at the junction with the a4129 Thame-Princes Risborough road
Club Secretary: Doug Humphries, 2 Naseby Close, Thame, Oxon OX9 3WA
Tel: 01844 215205
Fixtures Secretary: Keith Cannock, 31 Cowleaze, Chinnor, Oxon. OX9 4TB
Tel: 01844 353181
Club Colours: Wide black and narrow white hooped jersey, black shorts, black and white hooped socks

CHIPPENHAM RFC
South West 2 East
Ground Address: Allington Field, Frogwell, Chippenham. SN14 0YZ
Tel: 01249 446997
Brief Directions: A420 twoards Bristol. Turn left by Allington Farm shop for Corsham & Sheldon Manor. After 600 yards turn sharp left, entrance on left. NB Now no entrance from Frogwell.
Club Secretary: J.S.Murrow, 34, Park Lane, Chippenham, Wiltshire.SN!5 1LN
Tel No: 01249 6657720 (H) 01249 442125
Fixtures Secretary: A Lloyd, 27 Lords Mead, Chippenham.
Tel: (H) 01249 656793
Club Colours: Black & white irregular hoops Change Colours: Red

CHIPPING NORTON RUFC
Southern Counties North
Ground Address: Greystones, Burford Road, Chipping Norton, Oxon. OX7 5UZ
Tel: 01608 643968 Tel. & Fax.
Brief Directions: Follow A361 to Burford out of Chipping Norton
Club Secretary: Vincent Murphy,Finsbury House, New St., Chipping Norton OX7 5LS
Tel No: 01608 641041
Fixtures Secretary: Mr T Cripps, 4 Portland Place, Chipping Norton, Oxon Tel: (H) 01608 641182
Club Colours: Black and red hoops

CHIPPING SODBURY RFC
Gloucestershire & Somerset
Ground Address: The Ridings, Wickwar Road, Chipping Sodbury, South Gloucestershire
Tel: 01454 312852
Brief Directions: 2nd turning on the right on Wickwar Road out of Chipping Sodbury
Club Secretary: Joan Coadfy, 14 Brookfield Close, Chipping Sodbury, Bristol
Tel NO; 01454 313958
Fixtures Secretary: Tony Windsor
Tel: (H) 01454 313959
Club Colours: Black

CHOSEN HILL FP RFC
Gloucestershire 1
Ground Address: Brookfield Road, Churchdown, Gloucester Tel: 01452 712384
Brief Directions: Equi-distant between Cheltenham/Gloucester on edge of village towards Cheltenham
Club Secretary: Dave Harries, 5 Cherston Court, Barnwood, Gloucester GL4 3LE
Tel No: 01452 371529
Fixtures Secretary: Bob Newton. Tel Nos: 01452 857046 (H) 01452 335367 (W)
Club Colours: Myrtle green and white

CIRENCESTER RFC
Western Counties North
Ground Address: The Whiteway, Cirencester, Glos
Tel: 01285 654434
Brief Directions: Positioned at traffic lights on main Gloucester to Swindon A419 road, approx 1 mile from town centre
Club Secretary: R H Evans, 66 Rose Way, Cirencester, Glos. GL7 1PS
Tel: (H) 01285 640954
Fixtures Secretary: J Lawrence Esq
Tel: (H) 01285 821435
Club Colours: Red and black hoops, black shorts

CLEVE RFC
Western Counties North
Ground Address: The Hayfields, Cosham Street, Mangotsfield, Bristol
Brief Directions: M4 onto M32, M32 J1, carry straight through traffic lights to next roundabout, follow directions to Downend, then to Mangotsfield, turn into Cosasham St. Ground 300yds on Rt.
Club Secretary: Ron Pocock, 44 Spring Hill, Kingswood, Bristol
Tel: (H) 0117 9611079
Fixtures Secretary: S.Williams, 15 Lincombe Road, Downend, Bristol
Tel: 0117 9402159
Club Colours: Maroon

CLEVEDON RFC
South West 2 West
Ground Address: Coleridge Vale Playing Fields, Southey Road, Clevedon, North Somerset. BS21 6PF
Tel: 01275 877772
Brief Directions: M5 J20, 1st roundabout take 12 o'clock exit, mini roundabout take 12 o'clock exit, left at traffic lights, 1st left by garage Binding & Payne which is signed for Clevedon RFC
Club Secretary: Robert G Legge, 2 Kingston Avenue, Clevedon, North Somerset. BS21 6DS Tel: (H) 01275 341491 - (M) 07899 067072
Fixtures Secretary: John Evans Tel: (H) 01275 871443
Club Colours: Old Gold & Royal blue

COMBE DOWN RFC
Gloucestershire & Somerset
Ground Address: Holly's Corner, North Road, Combe Down, Bath. BA2 5DE
Tel: 01225 832075
Brief Directions: Follow A3062 out of Bath to Combe Down
Club Secretary: David Hall, 52 Ivy Avenue, Oldfield Park, Bath, BA2
Tel: (H) 01225 401 803
Fixtures Secretary: Paul Ashman. Tel No: 01225 427958
Club Colours: Black and amber

CONEY HILL RFC
Western Counties North
Ground Address: Metz Way, Coney Hill, Gloucester
Tel: 01452 306238
Brief Directions: Gloucester ring road (Eastern Ave) to Texas DIY store, turn into Metz Way, club 0.25 mile on left
Club Secretary: D C Veale, 13 Stanway Road, Coney Hill, Gloucester. GL4 4RE
Tel: (H) 01452 306510
Fixtures Secretary: Len Hayward, 14 Latymer Croft, Churchdown Glos. GL3 2QW
Tel: (H) 01452 855769
Club Colours: Black,amber,white

COOPER AVON TYRES (MELKSHAM) RFC
Berks, Dorset & Wilts 1
Ground Address: Cooper Avon Sports & Social Club, Melksham, Wiltshire Sn12
Tel: 01225 704982
Club Secretary: Mr A C Butcher, 14 Lowbourne, Melksham, Wilts. 7SN12 7DZ
Tel: 01225 707426 (H), 01225 702400 (W) 01225 702011 (Fax)
Fixtures Secretary: Mrs V. Holtom, 63 Foresters Park Road, Melksham, Wilts. SN 12 7 RW
Club Colours: Blue and sky blue hoops

CORSHAM RFC
Berks, Dorset & Wilts 1
Ground Address: Lacock Road, Corsham
Brief Directions: Off A4 at the Hare & Hounds, keep straight down Pickwick Rd 0.5 mile past War Memorial on Lacock Rd
Club Secretary: J G Wiltshire, 84 Springfield Close, Rudloe, Corsham, Wilts. SN13 0JR
Tel: (H) 01225 810800
Fixtures Secretary: R Slade, 49 Paul Street, Corsham, Wilts
Tel: (H) 01249 712683
Club Colours: Red and white hoops

COTHAM PARK RFC
Gloucestershire 2
Ground Address: Beegar Bush Lane, Failand, Bristol
Tel: 01275 392501
Brief Directions: M5 J19, A369 towards Bristol, left on A3129 (Beegar Bush Lane)
Club Secretary: Frank Nesbitt, 94 Kenn Road, Clevedon, North Somerset. BS21 6EX
Tel: (H) 01275 342334
Fixtures Secretary: Mike Gill
Tel: (H) 0117 9076387 (W) 0117 9306200
Club Colours: Black and white hoops

CREDITON RFC
Western Counties West
Ground Address: Blagdon, Exhibition Road, Crediton. EX17 1BY Tel: 01363 772784
Brief Directions: M5 to Exeter, A377 to Crediton then A3072 towards Tiverton, club on left hand side of road
Club Secretary: Mrs Marilyn Daw, Clotworth, Coldridge, Crediton, Devon EX17 6AR
Tel: (H) 01363 877238 Tel: (W) 01363 83448
Fixtures Secretary: Mr Mick Leyman, 6 Exeter Road, Crediton, Devon EX17 3BH
Tel: (H) 01363 775419
Club Colours: Black and amber

CREWKERNE RFC
Somerset 2
Ground Address: Henhayes, Main Car Park, South Street, Crewkerne, Somerset. TA18 7JJ. Tel: 01460 76422
Brief Directions: Head towards town centre, look for signs to Crewkerne Aqua Centre and follow to main car park.
Club Secretary: Jeanette Collings, 59 Seycamore Close, Holway, Taunton, Somerset TA1 2QJ.
Tel: (H) 01823 279837
Fixtures Secretary: Trevor Boyer, 8 St James, Beaminster, Dorset DT8 3PW
Tel: 01308 863169
Club Colours: Scarlet and black hoops.

CULLOMPTON RFC
Devon 1
Ground Address: Stafford Park, Knowle Lane, Cullompton, Devon. EX15 1PZ Tel: 01884 32480
Brief Directions: M5 J28 town centre, turn right by Manor Hotel, past fire station turn left to Langlands Rd, turn right at end of road, club at top of lane
Club Secretary: Dave Jewell, 34 Higher Street, Cullompton, Devon
Tel: (H) 01884 35371
Fixtures Secretary: D J Keeling
Tel: (H) 01823 660199
Club Colours: Scarlet and black hoops

DARTMOUTH RFC
Devon 2
Ground Address: Clubhouse: Roseville Pavilion, Roseville Street, Dartmouth, TQ6 9QH
Brief Directions: Milton Lane: Enter Dartmouth from Totnes. First right,past Park& Ride , Dartmouth School and Community College
Club Secretary: Dr. P.S. Jackson, High & Over, 140 Above Town, Dartmouth TQ6 9RH
Tel: 01803 833101
Fixtures Secretary: Mr S Atkins, 125 Victoria Road, Dartmouth, TQ6 9DY
Tel: (H) 01803 832381
Club Colours: Green and red hoops

DEVIZES RFC
Southern Counties South
Ground Address: Chivers Ground, Sports Club, London Road, Devizes, Wiltshire
Tel: 01380 723763
Brief Directions: Beside the Wiltshire Constabulary H.Q. on the A361 in Devizes town centre.
Club Secretary: Ron Perkins, Hill Barn, The Fairway, Devizes, Wilts.
Tel: (H) 01380 726112 (W) 01380 729550
Fixtures Secretary: Clive Meaney, 10 Park Road, Market Lavington, Devizes, Wilts.
Club Colours: Black shirts with broad white band, white shorts

DEVONPORT HIGH SCHOOL OLD BOYS RFC
Devon 3
Ground Address: Devonport High School for Boys, Paradise Road, Millbridge, Plymouth, Devon. PL1 5QP
Tel: 01752 564682
Brief Directions: A38 to Home P"k,along Outland Rd,to Mllehouse traffic lights. Into Mllehouse Rd ,left at top of hill ights into Molesworth Rd. Right at bottom of hill lights then top of hill left to DHS
Club Secretary: Mr G K Simpson, 108 Pattinson Drive, Mainstone, Plymouth, Devon. PL6 8RU
Tel: (H) 01752 206662
Fixtures Secretary: Mr C N Hill
Tel: (H) 01752 776792
Club Colours: Green & white hoops, black shorts and socks.

DEVONPORT SERVICES RFC
Cornwall & Devon
Ground Address: The Rectory, 2nd Avenue, Devonport, Plymouth. PL1 5QE. Tel: 01752 50559
Brief Directions: Maps are issued to visiting clubs
Club Secretary: Allan Berry, 36 Beechwood Avenue, Plymouth , Devon
PL4 6PW
Tel: 01752 662443
Fixtures Secretary: G Kelly, 24 Youldon Way, Morrabridge, Yelverton, Devon. PL20 7SN
Tel: 01822 854251
Club Colours: Navy shirts, blue shorts, scarlet socks

DIDCOT RUFC
Bucks & Oxon 1
Ground Address: Edmonds Park, Park Road, Didcot
Brief Directions: From roundabout at Georgetown filling station/Wallingford Arms, take road to West Hagbourne, ground is about 0.5 mile on left
Club Secretary: Mrs Jane Llewellyn, 54 Loyd Road, Didcot, Oxon. OX11 8JT
Tel: (H) 01235 813634 (W) 01235 512902
Fixtures Secretary: Mark Maidment, Sprat Public House, Hagbourne Road, Didcot, Oxon Tel: 01235 812224
Club Colours: Red and white hoops

DINGS CRUSADERS RFC
South West 2 West
Ground Address: Shaftesbury Crusade, Landseer Avenue, Lockleaze, Bristol. BS7
Tel: 0117 9691367
Brief Directions: Take J2 off M32 go towards Horfield and turn right at second set of traffic lights (before bridge)After about one mile turn left into Hogarth Waslk and right at the end into Landseer Avenue.
Club Secretary: Rob Stevens , 4 Fonthill Way, B itton,

Bristol BS15 6JT
Tel: (H) 0117 9329138
Fixtures Secretary: Terry Webb, 50 Monks Park Avenue, Horfield, Bristol B57OKH
Tel: (H) 0117 9830273
Club Colours: Royal blue and black

DOWTY RFC
Gloucestershire 3
Ground Address: ports & Social, Down Hatherley Lane , Staverton, Gloucester
Tel: 01452 714567
Brief Directions: M5 J11 head for Gloucester, Elmbridge Court r'bout exit 4 - Churchdown, straight through 2 sets of lights, 1st left after golf course - down Hatherley, 1st right after factory
Club Secretary: Mrs G Blackwell, 6 Kaybourne Crescent, Churchdown, Gloucester. GL3 2HL
Tel: (H) 01452 859388
Fixtures Secretary: Mr G. Worrall, 24 Theresa Street, Gloster GL1 5PC
Tel No: 01452 416854
Club Colours: Blue and white hoops

DRIFTERS RFC
Southern Counties North
Ground Address: Farnham Common Sports Club, One Pin Lane, Farnham Common, Bucks
Tel: 01753 644190
Brief Directions: From M40 J2, or M4 J6 take A355 `One Pin Lane' half mile north of Farnham Common.
Club Secretary: Dave Hancock, 19 Thurston Road, Slough, Berks, SL1 3JW.
Tel: 01753 576512
Fixtures Secretary: Alan Pearce, 9 Stevenson Road, Hedgerley, Bucks.
Tel: 01753 645973
Club Colours: Black with magenta and gold chest band

DRYBROOK RFC
Western Counties North
Ground Address: Mannings Ground, High Street, Drybrook, Glos
Tel: 01594 542595
Brief Directions: Gloucester to Mitcheldean via Huntley, ground is on outskirts of village on Mitcheldean Road
Club Secretary: Glyn Tingle, 16 Woodland Road, Drybrook, Glos. GL17 9HE
Tel: (H) 01594 544334 01594 542769 (W)
Fixtures Secretary: Derek Trigg
Tel: (H) 01594 542258
Club Colours: Green with black on white band

DURSLEY RFC
Gloucestershire 2
Ground Address: Stinchcombe Stragglers, Hounds Green, The Avenue, Stinchcombe, Dursley, Glos. GL11 6AJ
Tel: 01453 543693
Brief Directions: On the Dursley to Wotton-under-Edge road (B4060), on right just before entering Stinchcombe village
Club Secretary: Simon Bilous, 8 Ferney, Dursley, Glos. GL11 5AB
Tel: (H) 01453 545493 (B) 0117 908 8369
Fixtures Secretary: Andy Webb, 2 Elmleigh Cottages, Bristol Road, Cambridge, Glos. GL2 7BG
Tel: (H) 01453 890536
Club Colours: Maroon and amber

EXETER SARACENS RFC
Devon 2
Ground Address: Exhibition Fields, Summer Lane, Whipton, Exeter, Devon Tel: 01392 462651
Brief Directions: From M5 follow signs for Exeter Arena or from other direction follow Whipton signs then Exeter Arena signs
Club Secretary: David Mortimore, 39 Lonsdale Road, Heavitree, Exeter, EX1 3DP
Tel: 01392 433305
Fixtures Secretary: Mr A Martin, 63 Parkers Cross Lane, Pinhoe, Exeter,
Tel: (H) 01392 464288
Club Colours: Red shirts, black shorts

EXMOUTH RFC
Cornwall & Devon
Ground Address: Imperial Recreation Ground, Royal Avenue, Exmouth. EX8 1DG Tel: 01395 263665
Brief Directions: M5 to Sandy Gate-Exeter, exit here, follow Exmouth signs 8 miles, enter Exmouth on town bypass from which ground can be seen adjacent to River Exe
Club Secretary: Mr B L Cornall, Hillside Court, 65 The Marles, Exmouth. EX8 4NE
Tel: (H) 01395 275332
Fixtures Secretary: Mr. G. Williams, 40 Bapton Close, Exmouth, EX8 3LQ.
Tel: 01395 271373
Club Colours: Heliotrope, white hoops, white shorts

FALMOUTH
Cornwall 1
Ground Address: Teh Recreation Ground, Dracaena Avenue, Falmouth, Cornwall Tel: 01326 311304/316924
Brief Directions: Straight along Dracaena Avenue, visible from main road. Ground at junction of Tregenver and Killigrew roads.
Club Secretary: F.H.Murton, c/o 9 Highfield Road, Falmouth, Cornwall. Tel No: 01326 317031
Fixtures Secretary: G V Wilkes
Tel: (H) 01872 277249
Club Colours: Black and white

FRAMPTON COTTERELL RFC
Gloucestershire & Somerset
Ground Address: School Road, Frampton Cotterell, Bristol Tel: 01454 772947
Brief Directions: Off B3058 Winterbourne to Chipping Sodbury road
Club Secretary: Nigel Smith, 18 Tyning Close, Yate, Bristol BS37 5PN
Tel No: 01454 887860
Fixtures Secretary: Nathan Cole. Tel No: 01454 778875 (H) o797 1616287 (M)
Club Colours: Green, black and gold

FROME RFC
Somerset 1
Ground Address: Gypsy Lane, Frome, Somerset. BA11 2NA Tel: 01373 462506
Brief Directions: Follow signs for Leisure Centre, Frome RFC is signposted from the Bath Road/Princess Anne Road traffic lights
Club Secretary: Ray Harding, 93 Dakfield Road, Frome, Somerset BA11 4JH
Tel NO: 01373 461638 (H) 01373 456410 (W)
Fixtures Secretary: Symon Crouch 7Alder Walk, Frome, Ssomerset Tel: 01373 465600
Club Colours: Red, black & white hoops. Change Colours: Black

GLOUCESTER ALL BLUES RFC

Gloucestershire 2
Ground Address: The Oxleaze, Westgate Bridge, Westgate Street, Gloucester Tel: 01452 306984
Brief Directions: Bottom end of Westgate St over bridge, turn immediately left and club is about 100yards.
Club Secretary: Mr G R Selwyn, Millbank, Chessgrove Lane, Longhope, Gloucester. GL17 0LE.
Tel: (H) 01452 831215
Fixtures Secretary: Mr M Heath, 35 Dimore Close, Hardwicke, Glos.
Tel: (H) 01452 728159
Club Colours: Navy blue shirts, shorts and socks,Change: Navy & Sky Blue

GLOUCESTER CIVIL SERVICE TIGERS RFC

Gloucestershire 2
Ground Address: CSSA, Estcourt Road, Gloucester. GL1 3LG Tel: 01452 528317
Brief Directions: M5 J11, A40 to Gloucester, continue on A40 to Longford roundabout, left at Longford Inn (Beefeater), left at next roundabout, ground is on immediate right
Club Secretary: R.W. Shepherd, 95 Lavington Drive, Longlevens, Gloucester GL2 0HR
Fixtures Secretary: Mr B Humphries, 283 Bristol Road, Quedgley, Gloucester, Gloucestershire GL2 6QP
Tel: (H) 01452 728024
Club Colours: Red and blue hoops whit trim, white shorts, red socks

GORDANO RFC

Gloucestershire & Somerset
Ground Address: The National Stadium, Caswell Lane, Portbury, Nr Bristol BS20 9TH. Tel: 01275 373486
Brief Directions: Take A369, head into village of Portbury and bear left at the village green.
Club Secretary: Mrs R Pike, 10 Burtford Close, Portis Head, Nr Bristol. Tel: (H) 01275 847957
Fixtures Secretary: A Stanton, Tel: (H) 01275 877103
Club Colours: Red and black shirts, black shorts.

GORDON LEAGUE RFC

Western Counties North
Ground Address: Hempsted Lane, Gloucester. GL2 6JN Tel: 01452 303434 Office/Fax 01452 507475
Brief Directions: Into Hempsted Lane past Colin Campbell pub, 500 yards on left
Club Secretary: Karl Gwilliam, Thornycroft, Tibberton, Glouster, GL2 8EB Tel: (H) 01452 310090
Fixtures Secretary: Mark Hayward, 17 Leonard Road, Tredworth, Gloucester, GL1 4PQ
Tel: (H) 01452 536012
Club Colours: White, red sash, black socks

GOSFORD ALL BLACKS RFC

Bucks & Oxon 1
Ground Address: Stratford Brake Sports Ground, Langford Lane, Kidlington, Oxon
Tel: 01865 373994
Brief Directions: Take A44 Evesham road from Oxford, follow signs to Oxford Airport, club is opposite airport
Club Secretary: Mr C. Tipler, 88 Maple Avenue, Kidlington, Oxon, OX5 1HW. Tel: (H) 01865 376263 (W) 01865 277037
Fixtures Secretary: Mr D. Duthie, 10 Lovell Close, Duckington, Witney, Oxon, OX8 7YQ
Tel: (H) 01993 702261
Club Colours: All Black

GROVE RFC

Bucks & Oxon 1
Ground Address: Recreation Ground, Cane Lane, Grove, Wantage, Oxfordshire
Tel: 01235 762750
Brief Directions: Frm Oxford (A338), turn right into village, rt at r'bout, lft at r'bout (Brereton Dv), lft at end to Cane Ln. Frm sth enter vlge at lights, lft at r'bout into D'worth Rd, follow as above
Club Secretary: Mrs S Morrison, 19 HardwellClose, Grove, Oxon.
Tel No: 01235 223903
Fixtures Secretary: Kevin Sanders
Tel: (H) 01235 771549
Club Colours: Red, white and blue hoops

HARWELL RUFC (50TH ANNIVERSARY SEASON)

Bucks & Oxon 1
Ground Address: Central Sports Field, Aere Harwell Laboratory, Nr Didcot, Oxon
Brief Directions: To the left of main gate at Harwell Laboratory on old Newbury-Abingdon road
Club Secretary: Colin Bartlett, 66 Upthorpe Drive, Wantage, Oxon. OX12 7DG
Tel: (H) 01235 767596
Fixtures Secretary: Jenny Bosley
Tel: (H) 01235 833688
Club Colours: Royal blue, light blue and white hoops

HAYLE RUGBY CLUB

Western Counties West
Ground Address: Memorial Park, Marsh Lane, Hayle, Cornwall, TR27 4PS.
Brief Directions: Take A30 to first roundabout, ground immediately in front
Club Secretary: Rod Porter, c/o Haytle RFC
Tel No: (H) 01736 757203
Fixtures Secretary: Mike Gee, Sunhail, 7 Hellesvean Close, St. Ives, Cornwall.
Tel: (H) 01736 797168
Club Colours: Green, black and white

HELSTON RFC

Cornwall 1
Ground Address: King George V Memorial Playing Fields, Clodgey Lane, Helston
Tel: 01326 573742
Brief Directions: A394 into north of town past Tesco superstore, 0.25 mile on right, before Flambards Theme Park
Club Secretary: Mrs A.M.Dodd, 78 Bulwark Road, Helston, Cornnwall TR13 8JG
Tel No: 01326 564785
Fixtures Secretary: Mrs Bev Davis
Tel: (H) 01326 563744
Club Colours: Navy and white hoops

HIGH WYCOMBE RUFC

South West 2 East
Ground Address: Kingsmead Road, High Wycombe, Bucks. HP11 1JB.
Tel: 01494 524407
Brief Directions: M40, J4 to A404 (Amersham) into town centre. A40 ((Beaconsfield). After 3rd mini r'about

right into Abbey Barn Rd. After 800 yds sharp left into Kingsmead Rd.
Club Secretary: Don Dickerson, 3 Talbot Ave., High Wycombe, Bucks. HP13 5HZ.
Tel: (H) 01494 532024 (B) 01494 479722
Fixtures Secretary: George Brown, Deerleap, Primrose Hill, Widmerend, High Wycombe, Bucks. HP15 6NU.
Tel: (H) 01494 716700
Club Colours: Green with narrow black & white hoops

HONITON RFC

Devon 1
Ground Address: Allhallows Playing Fields, Northcote Lane, Honiton Tel: 01404 41239
Brief Directions: From traffic lights in High St, turn into Dowell St, continue for 0.5 mile, turn right at the Fire station into Northcote Lane, follow road around to the Sports Centre
Club Secretary: Mick Huslins, The Old Post Office, Dalwood, Honiton, Devon EX13 7 EH
Tel No: 01404 881860
Fixtures Secretary: Roy Freemantle
Tel: (H) 01404 41888
Club Colours: Red, amber and black hoops Change Colours: BLack

HORNETS RFC

South West 2 West
Ground Address: Hutton Moor Park, Hutton Moor Road, Weston-Super-Mare, North Somerset. BS22 8LY
Tel: 01934 621433
Brief Directions: J.21 M5 dual carriage way to traffic lights. Turn R. ground is opposite Sports Centre.
Club Secretary: Tony Baker, 145 Earlham Grove, Weston Super Mare, Somerset, BS23 3LQ.
Tel: 01934 614223
Fixtures Secretary: John Wilson, Correspondance to the Club
Tel: 01934 513543H - 01179 293211W
Club Colours: Black and Amber

HUCCLECOTE RFC

Gloucestershire 1
Ground Address: The old School field, Churchdown Lane, Hucclecote, Glos .GL3 3QH
Brief Directions: Exit M5 (north) Jct 11A, To Glos take left at Zoons Ct round't to Glos Trading Estate roundabout. Rt. to Hucclecote.Rt. at lights to Churchdown Lane. Club on right past school.
Club Secretary: John Ring, 9 Conway Road, Hucclecote, Glos. GL3 3PD
Tel: (H) 01452 618920
Fixtures Secretary: Colin Bevan
Tel: (H) 01452 863689
Club Colours: Black and amber

HUNGERFORD RFC

Berks, Dorset & Wilts 3
Ground Address: The Cricket Pavilion, Hungerford Common, Hungerford, Berks
Tel: 01488 682663
Club Secretary: Angus Russel, 39 Chilton Way, Hungerford, Berks. RG17 0JR
Tel: (H) 01488 683993 (W) 01635 506297
Fixtures Secretary: Peter Goodwin
Tel: (H) 01635 45887 (W) 01635 48222
Club Colours: Claret and porter

ILFRACOMBE RFC

Devon 1
Ground Address: Brimlands, Hillsborough Road, Ilfracombe, North Devon
Tel: 01271 864249
Brief Directions: From town centre take road to east signed Combe Martin, look out for swimming pool, club on left close by
Club Secretary: Ian Roberts, Lower Court Barn,Shortacombe, East Down, Barnstable, North Devon. EX31 4NT
Tel: (H) 01271 850542
Fixtures Secretary: Stuart Swanson, 5 Church Cottages, Swimbridge, Barnstaple
Tel: (H) 01271 850514
Club Colours: Blue and white hoops

ILLOGAN PARK RFC

Cornwall 1
Ground Address: Illogan Park, New Inn, Park Bottom, Redruth, Cornwall
Brief Directions: Redruth to Illogan road, turn left before Pynter Lane End
Club Secretary: Mr G R Tonkins, 20 Lower Pengegon, Camborne, Cornwall. TR14 8RX
Tel: (H) 712395 (W) 218785
Fixtures Secretary: R J McLellan
Tel: (H) 01872 572696 (W) 712712
Club Colours: Yellow and black

IMPERIAL RFC
Somerset 1
Ground Address: Bristol Imperial Sports Ground, West Town Lane, Knowle, Bristol
Tel: 01275 546000
Brief Directions: From Wells road (A37) and Bath road (A4), turn into West Town Lane
Club Secretary: Stuart Eld, 43 Avonleigh Road, Bedminster, Bristol. B53 3HS
Tel: (H) 0117 9631 688
Fixtures Secretary: Jack Gommo
Tel: (H) 01275544811
Club Colours: Myrtle and amber shirts, blue shorts, myrtle and amber socks

IVEL BARBARIANS RFC
Southern Counties South
Ground Address: Johnson Park, Yeovil, Somerset
Tel: 01935 411636 (club) 01935 74433 (ground)
Brief Directions: A37 from Ilchester, on seeing built up area right at roundabout then left at mini roundabout, ground on right opposite garden centre
Club Secretary: V J Jenkins, 7 Chestnut Drive, Yeovil, Somerset. BA20 2NL
Tel: (H & W) 01935 29770
Fixtures Secretary: K. Smith, 39 Welbeck Road, Yeovil, Somerset, BA21 5BH. Tel: (H) 01935 420206
Club Colours: Black and white quarters

IVYBRIDGE RFC
Western Counties West
Ground Address: Cross-in Hand, Exeter Road, Ivybridge
Tel: 01752 894392
Brief Directions: From A38 Exeter/Plymouth main road, follow the `Park & Ride' signs. The ground is almost opposite the station entrance.
Club Secretary: S.Arthurs, 28 Woolms Meadow, Ivybridge, Devon. PL21 9UF
Tel: 01752 691236
Fixtures Secretary: Gary Aldridge, 99 Cleve Drive, Ivybridge.
Tel: (H) 01752 893773 (W) 01752 668351
Club Colours: Green and black . Change: Blue shirts, black shorts

KINGSBRIDGE RFC
Cornwall & Devon
Ground Address: High House, Kingsbridge, Devon. TQ7 1JL
Tel: 01548 852051
Brief Directions: From centre of Kingsbridge take Dartmouth road alongside estuary, take 1st left and 1st right to the top of the hill
Club Secretary: Martin Newman, Fourwinds, 46 Saffron Park, Kingsbridge, Devon. TQ7 1RL
Tel: (H) 01548 853976
Fixtures Secretary: Derrick Marshall, 5 Welle House Gardens, Kingsbridge, Devon.
Tel: 01548 852618
Club Colours: Blue and white hoops.

KINGSWOOD RFC
Gloucestershire 2
Ground Address: The Pavilion, Deanery Road Playing Field, Grimsbury Road, Kingswood, Bristol. BS15
Tel: 0117 9675001
Brief Directions: Bristol on A420, turn right into Grimsbury Rd immediately before Tennis Court pub, ground is 1st left
Club Secretary: Miss Hannah Carey, 119 Orchard Road, Kingswood, bristol BS15 9TZ Tel No: 0117 9601432
Fixtures Secretary: Mark McGarrigle. Tel No:0117 9478145
Club Colours: Sky blue and chocolate brown

LANKELLY FOWEY RFC
Cornwall 2
Ground Address: Lankelly Farm, Lankelly Lane, Lankelly, Fowey, Cornwall
Brief Directions: On entering Fowey, turn right into Lankelly Lane, follow road until T junction, turn left, ground is 100yds on right
Club Secretary: G.Rew, 123 Creak-A-Vose, St Stephen, St Austell. PL26 7NB
Tel: 01726 821471
Fixtures Secretary: R Sainsbury, 13 Greenbank, Polruan, Fowey PL23 1QP
Tel: (H) 01726 870830 (W) 01726 862228
Club Colours: Navy blue and white hoops

LISKEARD - LOOE RFC
Cornwall 2
Ground Address: Lux Park, Coldstyle Road, Liskeard, Cornwall Tel: 01579 342665
Brief Directions: Ask for the Leisure Centre, near town centre
Club Secretary: K. Coburn, Bryally Cottage,, Tredinnick,Nr Duloe, Liskeard, Cornwall
Tel No : 01503 262865 FAX: 01503 265386
Fixtures Secretary: Peter Pascoe
Tel: (H) 01579 342956
Club Colours: Red and black hoops

LITTLEMORE RFC
Bucks & Oxon 1
Ground Address: Peers School, Sandy Lane West, Littlemoor, Oxon. OX4 5JY
Tel: 01865 715776
Brief Directions: Oxford ring road to Cowley (eastern bypass A4142), past the Rover plant on left, left turn and signpost to Peers School
Club Secretary: Mr M Boyle, 40 Tallis Lane, Browns Wood, Milton Keynes. MK7 8OZ
Tel: (H) 01908 645949 (W) 01908 853723
Fixtures Secretary: C Wright
Tel: (H) 01865 374420
Club Colours: White shirts, white shorts, royal blue socks

LONGLEVENS RFC
Gloucestershire & Somerset
Ground Address: Longford Lane, Longlevens, Gloucester Tel: 01452 306880
Brief Directions: M5 J11 Golden Valley bypass towards Gloucester, right at 2nd lights into Old Cheltenham Rd, Church Rd then Longford Ln. Or A38 T'kesbury rd turn right into Longford Ln past Queens Head
Club Secretary: Colin Dunford, 66 Estcourt Road, Gloucester. GL1 3LG
Tel: (H) 01452 522795 (W) 01452 529751
Fixtures Secretary: Greg Thomas, 21 Rodney Close, Longlevens, Gloucester GL2 9DG
Tel: (H) 01452 526352
Club Colours: Red

LYTCHETT MINSTER RFC
Berks, Dorset & Wilts 2
Ground Address: South Manor Drive, Lytchett Minster, Poole
Brief Directions: Follow A35 Poole to Dorchester, at

end of dual carriageway follow signs to village, changing accommodation next to church
Club Secretary: D H Smurthwaite, Staddlestones, Cheselbourne, Dorchester. DT2 7NJ Tel: (H) 01258 837796 (W) 01202 622413
Fixtures Secretary: M Hobson Tel: (H) 01202 623287
Club Colours: Red and blue hoops, white shorts

MARJONS
Devon 2
Ground Address: The College of St Mark and St John, Driviford Road, Plymouth.
Club Secretary: Mr Simon Adams, 5 Dickenwall Lane, Honicknowle, Plymouth, Devon PL3 5NW. Tel: (H) 01752 7681411
Fixtures Secretary: As above.
Club Colours: Red and black quarters.

MARLBOROUGH
Berks, Dorset & Wilts 2
Ground Address: Rugby Club House, Frees Avenue, The Common, Marlboroughg, Wilts
Tel: 01672 514717
Brief Directions: Take Swindon road out of Marlborough, left at Common and right into Frees Ave.
Club Secretary: Mrs Joyce Adams, 10 Ailesbury Way, Burbage, Marlborough, Wilts. SN8 3TD
Tel: (H) 01672 810718
Fixtures Secretary: Mr Alec Thomas
Tel: (H) 01672 512296
Club Colours: Black and amber hoops, black shorts

MARLOW RUFC
South West 2 East
Ground Address: Riverwoods Drive, Marlow, Bucks
Tel: 016284 77054/83911
Club Secretary: Graham Cutts, 6 Eastern Dene, Hazlemere, Bucks. HP15 7BT
Tel: (H) 01494 711391 (W) 01494 431717
Fixtures Secretary: Graham Cutts
Tel: (H) 01494 711391 (W) 01494 431717
Club Colours: Black and white hoops, black shorts

MARTOCK RFC
Somerset 3
Ground Address: Martock Recreation Ground, Stoke Road, Martock
Brief Directions: Take Martock exit from A303 at Percombe Hill, left at T junction to join Stoke Road, ground on left after 1 mile
Club Secretary: Philip Jackson, Church Lodge Cottage, Church Street, Martock, Somerset. TA12 6JL
Tel: (H) 01935 823514
Fixtures Secretary: Kevin King. Tel No: 079 7954 3491
Club Colours: Green and black quarters

MIDSOMER NORTON RFC
Gloucestershire & Somerset
Ground Address: Norton Down Playing Fields, Stratton-on-the-Fosse, Somerset. BA3 4RD
Tel: 01761 412827
Brief Directions: From centre of Midsomer Norton follow Shepton Mallet road (B3355) for approx 800 yards
Club Secretary: John Presley, 73 Welton Grove, Midsomer Norton, Somerset. BA3 2TT
Tel: (H) 01761 416089 (W) 01749 682267
Fixtures Secretary: Brian Wilcox
Tel: (H) 01761 241477
Club Colours: Red and white hoops, black shorts

MILTON KEYNES RUFC
Bucks & Oxon 1
Ground Address: Sam Coster Pavilion, Field Lane, Greenleys, Wolverton, Milton Keynes, Bucks. MK12 6AZ
Tel: 01908 313858
Brief Directions: Travel from Stony Stratford town centre towards Wolverton, rt at double r'bout into Gt Monics St (V5), proceed across r'bout, rt into Field Ln, rt at T j'tion, next left to clubhouse
Club Secretary: Gary Spinks, Harley House, Bow Brickhill, Bucks. MK17 9LH
Tel No: 01908 277138
Fixtures Secretary: David Eales. Tel No: 01296 714422
Club Colours: Black and white hoops, black shorts

MINCHINHAMPTON RFC
Gloucestershire 2
Ground Address: Minchinhampton Sports & Social Club, Tobacconist Road, Minchinhampton, Glos
Tel: 01453 88
Brief Directions: From centre of village take Tetbury road (Tetbury Street), 1st left, clubhouse straight ahead
Club Secretary: Rob Edmonds, Woodlands Cottage, 205 Slad Road, Stroud, Glos
Tel: (H) 01453 766662 (W) 01452 308989
Fixtures Secretary: Pete Weaving
Tel: (H) 01453 755561
Club Colours: Green, white and black hoops

MINEHEAD BARBARIANS RFC
Somerset 2
Ground Address: Tom Stewart Field, Ellicombe, Minehead, Somerset. TA24 6TR
Tel: 01643 707155
Brief Directions: A39 to Minehead from Taunton/Bridgwater, left at roundabout signed Ellicombe, ground 100 metres
Club Secretary: Nick Demirtges, 34 St Georges Street, Dunster, Minehead, Somerset. TA24 6RS
Tel: (H) 01643 821349
Fixtures Secretary: Mr Cameron Ford, 13 Sampford Brett, Taunton, TA4 4LA
Tel: (H) 01984 633237 or Clubhouse
Club Colours: Black and white hoops

MINETY RUGBY FOOTBALL CLUB
Berks, Dorset & Wilts 1
Ground Address: The Playing Fields, Minety, Nr Malmesbury, Wiltshire Tel: 01666 860 680
Brief Directions: From Swindon take A419 to Cirencester, turn off at Cricklade, through Cricklade to Minety, right at Q8 garage (Minety Motors) to the playing fields
Club Secretary: Kevin Vancil, 12 Essex Walk, Walcot, Swindon. SN3 3EY
Tel: (H) 01793 525898 (W) 01793 504945
Fixtures Secretary: Mark Turner, 11 Cantors Way, Minety, Malesbury, SN16 9QZ
Tel: (H) 01666 860680 or
Dominic Rice, Maincroft, York Lane, Brinkworth, Chippenham, SN15 5AN
Tel: (H) 01666 510797
Club Colours: Green and purple hoops

MORGANIANS RFC

Somerset 3
Ground Address: Chedzoy Lane, Bridgwater, Somerset
Tel: 01278 423434
Brief Directions: On A39 Bridgwater to Glastonbury road, over M5 motorway, 1st right into Chedzoy Lane opposite Mole Valley Farms
Club Secretary: Peter Donnachie, 9 Duncombe Close, Bridgwater, SOmerset. TA6 4UT
Fixtures Secretary: Kevin Palfrey. 1 Oakley Close, Weston Zoyland, Somerset, TA7 0LL
Club Colours: Navy shirts with gold and red hoops

NAILSEA & BACKWELL RFC

Somerset 1
Ground Address: West End Park, West End Lane, Nailsea
Tel: 01278 810818
Brief Directions: Directions signed from Town Centre
Club Secretary: Anita Heappey, Wareham Lodge, Whitesfield Road, Nailsea BS48 4JE
Tel: 01275 851478 - 0973 499779M
Fixtures Secretary: Nigel Crawley, 78 Westway, Nailsea, BS48
Tel: 01275 854439
Club Colours: Black/White

NEWENT RFC

Gloucestershire 3
Ground Address: Recreation Ground, Watery Lane, Newent, Glos (Correspondence to: George Hotel, Newent) Tel: 01531 820203
Brief Directions: Drive into centre of town, turn right into Watery Lane by the library/health centre, ground is on the right about 400 metres along Watery Lane
Club Secretary: G,Hall,Teh Red Lion, 2 Broad Street, Newent. GL18 1Q
Tel No: 01531 820215
Fixtures Secretary: N. Hine, 21 Coopers Way, Newent, Glos, GL18 1TJ
Tel: (H) 01531 820 519
Club Colours: Green and gold

NEWQUAY HORNETS RFC

Cornwall & Devon
Ground Address: Newquay Sports Centre, Tretherras Road, Newquay, Cornwall
Tel: 01637 875533
Brief Directions: Newquay via A3058, lft Chester Rd, 2nd lft Whitegate Rd, lft at T jcn, club 50 yds lft. Frm Redruth, N'quay via A392, across mini r'bouts into Edgcumbe Ave, rt Hilgrove Rd, 1st rt, club at end
Club Secretary: Glenn Biddle, 1 Veor Road, Newquay, Cornwall TR7 3BX
Fixtures Secretary: Reg Roberts
Tel: (H) 01637 874568
Club Colours: Green and white hoops with black shorts

NEWTON ABBOT RFC

Western Counties West
Ground Address: Rackerhayes, Newton Road, Kingsteignton, Newton Abbot, Devon. TQ12 3AD
Tel: 01626 354150
Brief Directions: Follow signs for Racecourse, ground is opposite the course behind Fairway Furniture
Club Secretary: Maurice Young, 51 Lime Tree Walk, Milber, Newton Abbot, Devon, TQ12 4LF
Tel: (H) 01626 354287
Fixtures Secretary: Mr Gordon Hooper, 39 Wilton Way, Abbotskerswell, Newton Abbot, Devon, TQ12 5PG
Tel: (H) 01626 369791 (W) 01626 332160
Club Colours: All white

NORTH BRISTOL RFC

Western Counties North
Ground Address: Oaklands, Gloucester Road, Almondsbury, Bristol. BS32 4AG
Tel: 01454 612740
Brief Directions: M5 J16 onto A38, then to Gloucester, entrance 150 yards from Motorway behind motorway police station.
Club Secretary: C H Hill, 7 Keinton Walk, Henbury, Bristol. BS10 7EE
Tel: (H) 0117 9508123
Fixtures Secretary: M Cottle
Tel: (H) 0117 9506182
Club Colours: Red and light blue hoops.

NORTH DORSET RFC

Berks, Dorset & Wilts 1
Ground Address: Slaughtergate, Longbury Hill Lane, Gillingham, Dorset
Tel: 01747 822748
Brief Directions: Take Wincanton Road (B3081) from town centre, Longbury Hill Lane is on right about 1 mile from the town, 300 yds after the end of 30mph zone
Club Secretary: J.Evans, Kopstone, East Knole, Salisbury, Wilts SP3 6AL
Tel: 01747 830339
Fixtures Secretary: Clive Drake, Folly's End, Wyke, Gillingham, Dorset SP8 4NA
Tel: 01747 825856
Club Colours: Emerald Green and navy

NORTH PETHERTON RFC

Somerset 1
Ground Address: Beggars Brook, North Petherton, Nr Bridgwater, Somerset Tel: 01278 663028
Brief Directions: M5 J24, A38 Taunton, through North Petherton, layby on left at exit of North Petherton
Club Secretary: Phil Ham, 45 Tudor Way, Bridgwater, Somerset TA6 6UE
Tel: 01278429528
Fixtures Secretary: Mr M House, 2 Hardings Close, North Petherton, Somerset Tel: (H) 01278 663118
Club Colours: Black and white hoops / Black / Red, white and blue hoops

NORTH TAWTON RFC

Devon 2
Ground Address: Taw Meadows, Fore Street, North Tawton, Devon Tel No: 01837 82907
Brief Directions: On entering the town from De Bathe Cross, take the 1st turning right before reaching the square
Club Secretary: Mr C C Fear,York House,16 High St., North Tawton, Devon. EX20 2HG
Tel: (H) 01837 82553(H) 01837 55868 (B)
Fixtures Secretary: Mr Colin Sharp
Tel: (H) 01837 82869
Club Colours: Black and amber shirts, black shorts

OAKMEADIANS RUFC
Berks, Dorset & Wilts 2
Ground Address: Meyrick Park Pavilion, Bournemouth. BH2 6LJ
Tel: 01202 789497
Brief Directions: Bournemouth town centre then head for Meyrick Park Golf Club, approx 0.5 mile from town centre
Club Secretary: Mrs Rachel Griffin, 115 Viscount Walk, Bearwood, Bournmouth, Dorset BH11 9TH
Tel: (H) 01202 581798
Fixtures Secretary: Jenny Phillips, 47 Headswell Avenue, Bournmouth, Dorset BH10 6JX
Tel: (H) 01202 525311
Club Colours: Blue and white hoops with black shorts

OKEHAMPTON RUFC
Western Counties West
Ground Address: Oaklands Park Showfield, Oaklands, Okehampton
Tel: 01837 52508
Brief Directions: Off the Hatherleigh road, 250m from town centre
Club Secretary: Max Sansom, Moorcroft, Stoney Park Lane, Okehampton, EX20 1SF
Tel: 01837 53387
Fixtures Secretary: Andy Ewen, Brightley Farm, Okehampton, EX20 1RP.
Tel: 01837 54019
Club Colours: Maroon and amber unequal hoops

OLD ASHTONIANS RFC
Somerset 1
Ground Address: Ashton Park School, Blackmoors Lane, Bower Ashton, Bristol
Tel: c/o 0117 9877796
Brief Directions: From city follow signs for Portishead, school is indicated at 1st roundabout (turn left)
Club Secretary: Ian Reed, 42 Stockwood Crescent, Knowle, Bristol. BS4 1AW
Tel: (H) 0117 9833942
Fixtures Secretary: Tony Excell, 18 Perrycroft Rd., Bishopsworth, Bristol. BS13 7RY.
Tel: (H) 0117 9642352
Club Colours: Blue shirt, yellow, green and white band, black shorts, yellow socks

OLD BRISTOLIANS
Gloucestershire 1
Ground Address: Memorial Playing Field, Longwood Lane, Failand, Nr Bristol. Tel: 01275 392137
Brief Directions: M5 junction 19 head for Bristol, turn right at main lights onto B3129 for Failand, turn left after country club into Longwood Lane.
Club Secretary: Mr John Sisman, Flat 1, 39 Sydenham Hill, Cotham, Bristol. Tel: (H) 01179 232261 Tel: (W) 01179 885230
Fixtures Secretary: Mr Don Furze. Tel: (H) 01179 243182 Tel: (W) 01275 836077
Club Colours: Maroon, gold and green hoops.

OLD CENTRALIANS RFC
Gloucestershire & Somerset
Ground Address: Saintbridge Sports Centre, Painswick Road, Gloucester. GL4 9QX
Tel: 01452 303768
Club Secretary: Phil Niland, 12 Berry Lawn, Abbeydale, Gloucester. GL4 5YE.
Tel: (H) 01452 387264 (M) 0802 760434
Fixtures Secretary: Andy Knight, 54 Bittern Ave., Abbeydale, Gloucester. GL4 8NB.
Tel: (H) 01452 533744
Club Colours: Navy blue, royal blue and gold

OLD COLSTONIANS RFC
Gloucestershire 2
Ground Address: New Road, Stoke Gifford, Bristol
Tel: 0117 9690009
Brief Directions: Near Parkway Railway Station, next to Filton High School
Club Secretary: David Parker, 37 Ratcliffe Drive, Stoke Gifford, Bristol. BS12 6TX
Tel: (H) 0117 9697438 (W) 01275 555437
Fixtures Secretary: Steve Back, 9 Welsford Avenue, Stapleton, Bristol BS16 1BW
Tel: 0117 9390456
Club Colours: Black, blue and gold hoops

OLD CRYPTIANS RFC
Gloucestershire 1
Ground Address: Memorial Ground, Tuffley Avenue, Gloucester. GL1 5NS
Tel: 532002
Brief Directions: Off Bristol Road to Tuffley Avenue, ground 1 mile on right before Stroud Road
Club Secretary: Gordon Hill, 244 Stroud Road, Gloucester. GL4 0AU
Tel: (H) 01452 521651 (W) 01454 260681 Ext 295/337
Fixtures Secretary: Derek Howell, 255C Stroud Road, Gloucester, GL1 5JZ
Tel: (H) 01452 414010 (W) 01452 425611
Club Colours: Gold, maroon and navy blue

OLD CULVERHAYSIANS RFC
Gloucestershire & Somerset
Ground Address: The Glasshouse, Bradford Road, Combe Down, Bath. (Clubhouse: Old Fosse Road, Bath)
Brief Directions: Take Wells road out of Bath.Approx 1 mile, turn left at roundabout opposite Red Lion pub, across next junction, 200 yards on right
Club Secretary: Mike Harding, 6 Gages Close, KIngswood, Bristol. BS15 9UH
Tel: (H) 0117 947 5862 (W) 01453 835431
Fixtures Secretary: Martin Lynch, 2 Lyme Road, Newbbidge, Bath.
Club Colours: Black

OLD ELIZABETHANS RFC
Gloucestershire 2
Ground Address: Severn Road, Hallen, Bristol. BS10 7RZ
Tel: 0117 959 1072
Brief Directions: M5 J17, turn towards Pelning at roundabout then 1st left, continue for 2-3 miles until junction with King William IV pub on right, turn right, club 200 yards on left
Club Secretary: David Perkins, 855 Filton Avenue,Filton, Bristol
Tel: 0117 9692545
Fixtures Secretary: Ian Kembery .Tel No: 01179 575395
Club Colours: Blue, white and old gold hoops

OLD PLYMOTHIAN & MANNAMEADIAN RFC

Devon 1
Ground Address: King George V Playing Fields, Elburton, Plymouth, Devon
Brief Directions: A38 take 1st Plymouth junction to Marsh Mills roundabout, follow signs for Kingsb'dge for 3-4 miles, at r'bout (Plympton signed to left) 1st left, ground 0.25 mile on right
Club Secretary: Mr Ernie Bolster, 22 Carlton Close, Lower Compton, Plymouth, Devon
Tel: (H) 01752 223908 (W) 01752 673626
Fixtures Secretary: Mr Simon Matthews
Tel: (H) 01752 730114 (W) 01392 382222
Club Colours: Claret and blue quarters

OLD PUBLIC OAKS RFC

Devon 2
Ground Address: King George V Playing Fields, Elburton
Brief Directions: On leaving A38 at Marsh Mills roundabout, take A374 towards city, turn left onto A379 Billacombe Rd, left at 3rd roundabout into Haye Rd, ground on right
Club Secretary: Mr G H Mathews, 25 Colwill Road, Mainstone, Plymouth
Tel: (H) 01752 707363
Fixtures Secretary: Mr R Boyle
Tel: (H) 01752 336502
Club Colours: Green and gold hoops

OLD REDCLIFFIANS RFC

Western Counties North
Ground Address: Stockwood Lane, Brislington, Bristol
Tel: 0117 9778501
Brief Directions: A34 from Bristol, turn right at McDonalds/Park & Ride, travel for 0.25 mile, ground on right hand side
Club Secretary: Richard Yandell, 11 Imperial Walk, Knowle, Bristol. BS14 9AD
Tel: (H) 0117 9777657 (W) 0117 9873636
Fixtures Secretary: Russell Yandell
Tel: (H) 01275 373444 (W) 01275 836077
Club Colours: Red and black hoops. Change Colours: Blue

OLD RICHIANS RFC

Western Counties North
Ground Address: Sandleaze, Longlevens, Gloucester. GL2 0PU
Tel: 01452 524649
Brief Directions: Turn into Nine Elms Road from Cheltenham Road and follow to Sir Thomas Rich's School
Club Secretary: Paul Toleman, 4 Upper Rea, Hempsted, Gloucester. GL2 5LR
Tel: (H) 01452 422274 (Fax) 01452 416138
Fixtures Secretary: Steve Collier, 5 Foxleigh Crescent, Longlevens, Gloucester, GL2 0XW
Tel: (H) 01452 386808
Club Colours: Royal blue and gold hoops

OLD SULIANS RFC

Somerset 1
Ground Address: Lansdown Road, Bath
Tel: 01225 310201
Brief Directions: Follow Lansdown Road from city centre, ground is on left 400 m past MOD site
Club Secretary: Terry Haines, 24 Rockcliffe Avenue, Bath. BA2 6QP
Tel: (H) 01225 465107
Fixtures Secretary: Tony Slee, 8 Heathfield Close, Weston, Bath BA1 4NW
Tel: 01225 317256
Club Colours: Blue with red band

OLD TECHNICIANS RFC

Devon 1
Ground Address: Weston Mill Oak Villa, Ferndale Road, Weston Mill, Plymouth, Devon
Tel: 01752 363352
Brief Directions: A38 turn off onto B3396 to Devonport, left at 1st traffic lights, club approx 100 yards on left
Club Secretary: Tom Ozanne, 3 Victoria Cottages, Eggbuckland, Plymouth, PL6 5RH
Tel: (H) 01752 562832 (W) 01752 553834
Fixtures Secretary: Terry Chinner, 37 Underlane, Plymouth, PL7 1QX
Tel: (H) 01752 341979
Club Colours: Black with white circlet

OLDFIELD OLD BOYS
Western Counties North?
Ground Address: Shaft Road, Combe Down, Bath. Tel: 01225 834135
Brief Directions: Into Bath, follow signs for University, follow on towards Combe Down, turn down Shaft Road.
Club Secretary: Steve Godwin, 12 Lime Grove Gardens, Bath, Somerset BA2 4HE Tel: (H) 01225 318012 Tel (W) 01258 451441
Fixtures Secretary: Leon Book, 45 The Brow, Twerton, Bath. Tel: 01225 480234l
Club Colours: Maroon and gold.

OLNEY RFC
South West 2 East
Ground Address: Recreation Ground, East Street, Olney, Bucks
Tel: 01234 71288
Brief Directions: From Newport Pagnell & Milton Keynes take A509, on entering Olney past church & right at market place, left into East St, ground 300 yards on right
Club Secretary: Stuart Parkin, West View Farm, Olney, Bucks. MK46 5EX
Tel: (H) 01234 713165 (W) 01234 711792
Fixtures Secretary: Alec Tebby
Tel: (H) 01933 663385 (W) 0850 560660
Club Colours: Cerise and french grey

OXFORD HARLEQUINS RFC
Southern Counties North
Ground Address: * Horspath Rd Rec., Cowley, Oxford. Tel: 01865 775765
Marston Ferry Road, Oxford. Tel: 01865 552813
Brief Directions: * Off the Eastern ring road sign-posted to Horspath
By the Rover Car works
Club Secretary: A W G Barson, 97 Oxford Road, Garsington, Oxford OX44 9AD.
Tel: (H) 01865 361540
Fixtures Secretary: Peter Cox, 43 Oxford Road, Garsington, Oxford.
Tel: 01865 361267
Club Colours: Amber, dark blue, white and maroon quarters

OXFORD RFC
Southern Counties North
Ground Address: Southern by pass, North Hinksey Village, Oxford
Tel: 01865 243984
Brief Directions: Ground can only be approached from A34 going south, turn left off A34, sign posted
Club Secretary: Mrs Mary Bagnall, 3 Appleford Rd., Sutton Courtney, Oxon OX14 4NG
Tel: (H) 01235 848444 FAX 01235 848212
Fixtures Secretary: Roger Mountford, 28 Crecy Walk, Woodstock, Oxford OX20 1US
Tel: (H) 01993 812389
Club Colours: Green, black and silver hoops

PAIGNTON RFC
Western Counties West
Ground Address: Queens Park, Queens Road, Paignton, Devon
Tel: 01803 557715
Brief Directions: Into Paignton town centre, over railway track towards beach, next right turn into Queens Road.
Club Secretary: David Siddal, 37 Dartmouth Road, Paignton Tel: 01803 664691
Fixtures Secretary: Mr Gary Castleton, 18 New Street, Paignton, Devon, Tel: (H) 01803 525254 (W) 01803 556618
Club Colours: Red and white hoops

PAINSWICK RFC
Gloucestershire 1
Ground Address: Broadham Fields, Stroud Road, Painswick, Nr Stroud, Glos
Tel: 01452 813735
Brief Directions: Situated adjoining the A46 on the southern edge of the village on the Stroud side of Painswick
Club Secretary: P.M. Sharpe, Longacre, Slad, Stroud, Glos., GL6 7QF.
Tel: 01452 813651
Fixtures Secretary: I. Hogg, 146 Fieldcourt Gardens, Quedgeley, Gloucester
Tel: (H & W) 01452 725457
Club Colours: Cherry and white hoops, navy shorts

PENNANIANS RUFC
Bucks & Oxon 1
Ground Address: Farnham Park, Beaconsfield Road, Farnham Royal, Buckinghamshire. SL2 3BU
Tel: 01753 646252
Club Secretary: Mrs E. James, 47 Pearl Gardens, Slough, Berks, SL1 2YX
Tel: (H) 01753 734910 (W) 01344 28821
Fixtures Secretary: Richard Kearney
Tel: (H) 01753 581963
Club Colours: Black shirt with 2 white hoops

PENRYN RFC
South West 2 West
Ground Address: The Memorial Ground, Kernick Road, Penryn
Tel: 01326 372239
Brief Directions: From Exeter A38 to Plym'th Head twds L'keard, follow signs for Truro. From Truro A39 to Falm'th, continue to the Distribitor Rd, at r'bout turn to ind. est. (Asda), ground 2nd left
Club Secretary: Peter Webber, Avallen, West End, Penryn, Cornwall TR10 8HE FAX &Tel No: 01326 376613 Mobile: 07775 615774
Fixtures Secretary: Mr P Webber
Tel: (H & FAX) 01326 376613 (M) 07775 615774
Club Colours: Red and black hoops

PERRANPORTH RC
Cornwall 1
Ground Address: Ponsmere Valley, Perranporth, Cornwall, TR6 0DB
Brief Directions: From Newquay turn right at Goonhavern roundabouts, continue approx 2 miles, past Golf Club on right, down steep hill, 1st turning left
Club Secretary: T.Goodman, 18 Berveth Close, Threemilestone, Truro,Cornwall TR3 6DS
Tel: 01872 270642
Fixtures Secretary: S.Arthur, Oakridge farm, Goomhaven, Truro, cornwall
Tel: 01872 540590
Club Colours: Green and gold

PEWSEY VALE RFC

Berks, Dorset & Wilts 3
Ground Address: Pensey Vale Comprehensive School, Wilcot Road, Pewsey, Wiltshire
Brief Directions: A345 to Pewsey, into Wilcot Road, 2nd left into Pewsey Vale School car park, change at the adjacent Sports Centre, pitches are to the back of the school
Club Secretary: Mr David Steven Aroskin, 20a Rawlins Road, Pewsey, Wiltshire. SN9 5EB
Tel: (H & W) 01672 562218 (W) 0976 882103
Fixtures Secretary: Mr Kevin Robinson
Tel: (H) 01672 562989
Club Colours: Red, white, royal blue and black quarters

PHOENIX RFC

Bucks & Oxon 1
Ground Address: The Sports Ground, Institute Road, Taplow, Bucks. SL6 0NS Tel: 01628 664319
Brief Directions: M4 J7, take A4 towards Maidenhead, after Sainsburys superstore take next right (0.5 mile) then 1st left after the bridge is Institute Road
Club Secretary: Neil Bennett, 29 Belgrave Road, Slough, Berks SL1 3RG
Tel: 01753 570341 01753 615612 (W)
Fixtures Secretary: S.K.Turner, 20 Balmoral Close, Cippenham, Slough SL1 6JP
Tel: 01628 661660 (H) 01344 746052 (W)
Club Colours: Red & Black Quarters, black shorts, black socks with red trim

PILNING RFC

Gloucestershire 3
Ground Address: The Pitch, Beach Road, Severn Beach, South Glos. BS12 Tel: 01454 653549
Brief Directions: Head for visitor's centre at second Severn crossing, turn into Beach Ave, Beach Road on right
Club Secretary: John Cox, Oregon, Ableton Lane, Severn Beach, Bristol BS 35 4PP
Tel No: 01454 632762
Fixtures Secretary: Sean Hinksman, 16 Station Road, Pilning, Bristol BS35 4JP8
Club Colours: Blue and white hoops, blue shorts

PLYMOUTH ARGAUM RFC

Devon 2
Ground Address: The Clubhouse, Bickleigh Down Road, Roborough, Plymouth. PL6 7AD
Tel: 01752 772156
Brief Directions: At Roborough village turn down Bickleigh Down Rd, pass Medlands and carry on down lane, clubhouse on the right
Club Secretary: Mrs J L Davey, 3 Hazeldene Close, Lee Mill, Ivybridge, Devon. PL21 9EL
Tel: (H) 01752 894453 (W) 01752 636000
Fixtures Secretary: Mrs T Truscott, 55 Trevose Way, Monorfields, Efford, Plymouth, PL3 6PE
Tel: (H) 01752 707621
Club Colours: Black, bottle green, white

PLYMOUTH CIVIL SERVICE RFC

Devon 1
Ground Address: Civil Service Sports Ground, Recreation Road, Beacon Down, Plymouth PL2 3HA.
Tel: 01752 702303
Brief Directions: Ground directly behind Plymouth Albion's ground at Beacon Park. Top of Ham Drive.
Club Secretary: Danny Avery, 25 Weston Mill Hill, Weston Mill, Plymouth PL5 2AR
Tel: (H) 01752 206928 Tel: (W) 01752 553639
Fixtures Secretary: Paul Routley, 1 Chaddlewood Close, Plympton. PL7 2HR.
Tel: 01752 338575
Club Colours: Red & white shirts, black shorts., red socks

PLYMOUTH YMCA RFC

Devon 2
Ground Address: Suttons Field, John Kitto Community College, Burrington Way, Honicknowle, Plymouth Tel: 011752 268169
Brief Directions: Turn off A38 at Manadon flyover, left onto Tavistock Road, right at lights, right at lights onto Honicknowle Road.
Club Secretary: Mr. M. J. Wilson, 8 Hilton Avenue, Manadon, Plymouth, Devon PL5 3HS
Tel No: 01752 514579
Fixtures Secretary: S.Kalas Tel No: 01752 707073
Club Colours: Black with red hooped shirts.

PLYMPTON VICTORIA RFC

Devon 3
Ground Address: King George V Playing Fields, Elburton, Plymstock, Plymouth, Devon.
Club Secretary: A.R.Dibble, 8 Wolrige Way, Plympton,Plymouth PL7 2RU
Tel: 01752 347 981
Fixtures Secretary: C.G.Mayne, 12 Canhaye Close, Plympton,Plymouth PL7
01752 335594
Club Colours: Black.

PLYMSTOCK RFC

Devon 2
Ground Address: Staddiscombe Playing Fields, Staddiscombe Road, Staddiscombe, Plymouth
Tel: 402751
Brief Directions: Leave Plymouth on A379 and follow signs to HMS Cambridge Playing Fields at top of Goosewell Road
Club Secretary: Lynda Stewart, Laburnam House, 4 Woodland Avenue, Elburton. PL9 8JE
Tel: (H) 402751
Fixtures Secretary: Angela Duffg
Tel No: 01752 782163
Club Colours: Blue

POOLE RFC

Berks, Dorset & Wilts 3
Ground Address: Hamworthy Rec., Turlin Moor , Blandford Road, Hamworthy, Poole, Dorset
Brief Directions: From Poole quay, follow directions for Hamworthy, over the lifting bridge and continue for 2 miles.
Club Secretary: Mrs Tessa Ingle-Finch, 6 Mansfield Avenue, Parkstone, Poole, Dorset. BH14 0DQ
Tel: (H) 01202 241993
Fixtures Secretary: Jon Evans, 15 Old Road, Winborne BH21 1EJ
Tel: (H) 01020 887338 (W) 01202 782836 (emaiil) jon.evans@poole.siemens.co.uk
Club Colours: Blue and amber

PORTCASTRIAN RFC

Berks, Dorset & Wilts 2
Ground Address: Iford Lane Playing Fields, Iford Lane, Southbourne, Bournemouth, Dorset. BH6 5NF
Tel: 01202 434565
Brief Directions: Turn towards Southbourne off A228 (Wessex Way) into Iford Lane, past Bournemouth

Hospital to Iford Lane, playing fields on left
Club Secretary: Martin Davis, 9 GRange Court, Gervis Road, BOurnemouth, Dorfset. BH1 3EF
Tel Nos : (H) 01202 466616 (W) 01202 291483
Fixtures Secretary: Stuart Holt.
Tel No : 07970 635031 (Mobile)
Club Colours: Royal blue, yellow and red hoops

PRINCE ROCK (WOODLAND ORT) RFC
Devon 3
Ground Address: Bull Point, St. Budeaux, Devon
Brief Directions: Leave A38 at St. Budeaux/Ernesettle exit. Take 2nd exit off R/about to St. Budeaux. Follow Victoria Road to end. At oneway system go straight on. Take 1st R. follow sing to Bull Point. Talke 2nd L. (Bourne Rd). Turn L. at end. Changing Rms are about 200m on right.
Club Secretary: Steve Aris, 14 Fernhill Close, Iveybridge, Devon, PL21 9JE.
Tel: 01752 893360
Fixtures Secretary: Les Fowden 1 Hayes Rd., Oreston, Plymouth, Devon. PL9 7QA.
Tel: 01752 405018
Club Colours: Green and Amber quarters

PUDDLETOWN
Berks, Dorset & Wilts 3
Ground Address: Greenfields, Puddletown, Dorchester, Dorset. Tel: 01305 848808
Brief Directions: Leave Dorchester on A35 east, after 1/4 mile turn left on B3143, 3 miles on RHS, old army camp club.
Club Secretary: Mr David Smith, Providence House, 39 Dorchester Road, Maiden Newton, Dorset DT2 0BZ.
Tel: (H) 01300 320209 Tel: (W) 01305 251111
Fixtures Secretary: Mr P Smeeth, Tel: (H) 01300 348310
Club Colours: Red shirts, black shorts, red socks

REDINGENSIANS RFC
Southern Counties South
Ground Address: Old Bath Road, Sonning, Nr., Reading
Tel: 0118 9695259
Brief Directions: On the A4 east of Reading, next to Sonning Golf Club
Club Secretary: J H Cook, 95 Century Court, Grove End Rd, London. NW8 9LD
Tel: (H) 0171 289 1887 (W) 0171 551 0220
Fixtures Secretary: G F Nattriss, 64 Broadwater Rd, Twyford, Berks. RG10 0EU
Tel: (H) 0118 9340685 (W) 01753 774 379
Club Colours: Dark blue, light blue and white hoops

REDRUTH ALBANY RFC
Cornwall 2
Ground Address: Trewirgie Hill, Redruth, Cornwall.(Post to Clubhouse , 2 Station Hill , Redruth , Cornwall,. TR15 2PP) Tel: 01209 216945
Brief Directions: Adjacent to Redruth Cricket Club behind Trewirgie School, Falmouth Rd, Redruth, 0.5 mile from train station. Or ring club house for directions.
Club Secretary: M.Stevens, 32 Bellevue, Redruth, Cornwall. TR15 1LF.
Tel No: 01209 215904
Fixtures Secretary: W. J. Rogers, Pencoys, Roskear, Camborne, TR14 8DN.
Tel: (H) 01209 714102
Club Colours: Royal blue shirts, black shorts, blue and white socks

ROSELAND RFC
Cornwall 2
Ground Address: Philleigh, Truro, Cornwall. TR2 5ET
Brief Directions: 15 miles from Truro on the Roseland Peninsula, signposted via Tregony and Towary, St Mawes.
Club Secretary: C R Thomas, Parton Vrane, Gerrans, Portscatho, Truro, Cornwall. TR2 5ET
Tel: (H) 01872 580495
Fixtures Secretary: C J Trerise
Tel: (H) 01872 560248
Club Colours: Navy and scarlet

SALCOMBE RFC
Devon 3
Ground Address: Twomeads, Camperdown Road, Salcombe, Devon Tel: 01548 842639
Brief Directions: On entering Salcombe take 1st left, 1st right, 2nd left
Club Secretary: Graham Jacobs, Cornerways, Bohaventure Road, Salcombe
Tel: (H) 01548 842521
Fixtures Secretary: Carl Stenning. Tel No: 01548 844483
Club Colours: Red shirts, white shorts, white shorts, red and white socks

SALISBURY RFC
South West 2 East
Ground Address: Castle Road, Salisbury
Tel: 01722 325317
Brief Directions: On A345 Salisbury to Amesbury Road, just to the south of Old Sarum
Club Secretary: Dr G W Jack, 14 Windlesham Road, Salisbury, Wiltshire. SP1 3PY
Tel: (H) 01722 335542
Fixtures Secretary: Mr. M. Plimsoll , Longways, Southampton Road, Whaddon, Sailsbury, Wilts. Tel: (H) 01722 710718
Club Colours: Green and white

SALTASH RFC
Cornwall 1
Ground Address: Moorlands Lane, Saltash, Cornwall
Tel: 01752 847227
Brief Directions: From A38 westward over Tamar Bridge, through tunnel, left at 1st roundabout, right at lights, then 2nd right into Moorlands Lane, clubhouse at end of lane
Club Secretary: Mr D R Jenkins, Albaston Post Office, Albaston, Gunnislake, Cornwall. PL18 9AL
Tel: (H) 01822 832785 (W) 01822 832284
Fixtures Secretary: Mr J Westaway, 18 Orchard Close, Tideford
Tel: (H) 01752 851727
Club Colours: Black, gold and red hoops

SHERBORNE RFC
Southern Counties South
Ground Address: The Terrace, Sherborne, Dorset.
Tel: 01935 812478
Brief Directions: The ground is on the A352, half a mile south of the town centre going towards Dorchester.
Club Secretary: Rod Liddiard, 6 Vincents Close, Alweston, Sherborne, Dorset. DT9 5JH
Tel: (H) 01963 23402
Fixtures Secretary: Mrs V Rushton
Tel: (H) 01258 820195
Club Colours: All black

SIDMOUTH RFC
Cornwall & Devon
Ground Address: Blackmore Ground, Heydons Lane, Sidmouth
Tel: 01395 516816
Brief Directions: (Via footpath), behind Sidmouth/Victoria Cottage Hospital.(Follow signs to Hospital)
Club Secretary: P.H.H. Rossiter, "Gulls", Kings Lane, Sidmouth, Devon, EX10 8DU
Tel: (H) 01395 516414
Fixtures Secretary: T O'Brien, 2 Rivulet Cottages, Sidford, Sidmouth, Devon, EX10 0RT
Tel: (H) 01395 577403
Club Colours: Green, white shorts

SLOUGH RFC
South West 2 East
Ground Address: Tamblyn Fields, Upton Court Park, Upton Court Road, Langley, Slough, Berkshire. SL3 7LT
Tel: 01753 522107/692115
Brief Directions: M4 J5 towards Slough on A4 (London Rd), left at 2nd traffic lights into Upton Court Rd, club entrance approx 500 metres on left, 200 metres down Dedicated Drive
Club Secretary: Mike Wild, 4 Stanton Way, Slough Sl3 7LB
Tel: 7 Fax: 01753 770870
Fixtures Secretary: Clive Blackman
Tel: (H) 01753 684403 (W) 01895 836579
Club Colours: Sage green jersey with single white hoop,green green socks

SMITHS (INDUSTRIES) RFC
Gloucestershire 2
Ground Address: The Newlands, Evesham Road, Bishops Cleeve, Cheltenham, Glos
Tel: 01242 672752
Brief Directions: 2 miles due north of Cheltenham on A465
Club Secretary: Gerald Owen, 79 Station Road, Bishops Cleeve, Cheltenham, Glos
Tel: (H) 01242 676345 (W) 01242 673333 Ext 2912
Fixtures Secretary: Adrian Tedstone
Tel: (H) 01242 570674
Club Colours: Royal blue and white

SOUTH MOLTON RFC
Western Counties West
Ground Address: Pathfields, Station Road, South Molton, Devon
Tel: 01769 572024
Brief Directions: Taking Pathfields exit on the North Devon link road when reading signs for South Molton, take first right then first left
Club Secretary: Mrs Annie White, 8 Duke Street, South Molton, Devon. EX36 3AL
Tel: (H) 01769 573741 (W) 01769 573204
Fixtures Secretary: Denis Cronk
Tel: (H) 01769 550402
Club Colours: All Black

SOUTHMEAD RFC
Gloucestershire 1
Ground Address: Greenway Sports Centre, Greystoke Avenue, Southmead, Bristol
Tel: 0117 9593060
Brief Directions: A38 to Filton, Southmead Road into Doncaster Road, Southmead
Club Secretary: Mr Mike Davies, 90 Twenty Acres, Brentry, Bristol. BS10 6PR
Tel: (H) 0117 9497017
Fixtures Secretary: Mr Mike Haddow
Tel: (H) 01454 614019
Club Colours: Blue shirt with emerald green hoop

SPARTANS RFC
South West 2 West
Ground Address: Archdeacon Meadow, Cattle Market Complex, St Oswald Road, Gloucester
Tel: 01452 410552
Brief Directions: M5 J12 for Gloucester, into Glos, take signs for docks, past docks, veer right just before Esso g'ge, take l/h lane, under railbridge, 1st left at Bell & Gavel, down as far as can go
Club Secretary: David Badham, 102 Deans Way, Gloucester. GL1 2QD
Tel: (H) 01452 524252 (W) 01452 521521 Ext 2701
Fixtures Secretary: Paul Smith
Tel: (H) 01452 533027
Club Colours: Red and black

ST AGNES RFC
Cornwall 1
Ground Address: Enys Park, Trevaunance Road, St Agnes Tel: 01872 553673
Brief Directions: Turn left opposite church, turn right after 800 yards, Enys Park is 200 yards on right
Club Secretary: Tim Barnes, c/o T & JB Produce Ltd, Gover Farm, Gover Hill, Mt Hawke, Truro. TR4 8BQ
Tel: (H) 01209 890 218 (W) 01872 553311
Fixtures Secretary: Bob Howard, Lamorna Cottage, Mount Hawke, Truro.
Tel No: 01209 891571
Club Colours: Black and red hoops

ST AUSTELL RFC
South West 2 West
Ground Address: Tregorrick Park, Tregorrick Lane, St Austell, Cornwall. PL26 7AG
Tel: 01726 76430
Brief Directions: Located on the road behind Asda superstore and next to Mount Edgecumbe Hospice. From St Austell By-Pass take turning to Penrice Hopital.First right before Hospital.
Club Secretary: Brian Perkins, 28 Duporth Bay, St.Austell.PL26 6AF
Fixtures Secretary: Mr Howard Roberts
Tel: (H) 01726 812065
Club Colours: Red and white hoops

ST BERNADETTE RFC
Western Counties North
Ground Address: Hengrove Park, Bamfield, Whitchurch, Bristol Tel: 01275 891500
Brief Directions: A37 out of town, turn right at Airport Rd traffic lights, turn left 0.5 mile by The Happy Cock pub, club is 0.25 mile on right
Club Secretary: Barry Taylor, 39 Woodleigh Gardens, Whitchurch, Bristol. BS14 9JA
Tel: (H) 01275 831880
Fixtures Secretary: Tony Aldridge
Tel: (H) 0117 9770075
Club Colours: Green and blue hoops

ST BRENDANS OLD BOYS RFC
Gloucestershire 3
Ground Address: Combination Ground, Northway, Bristol. BS12 7QG Tel: 0117 9692 793
Brief Directions: On the A38, opposite the main runway

Club Secretary: Richard A Kolanko, 91 Church Road, Horfield, Bristol. BS7 8SD
Tel: (H) 0117 9241390 (W) 0117 9666861
Fixtures Secretary: Frank Probert
Tel: (H) 0117 964779
Club Colours: Maroon and old gold hoops

ST COLUMBA TORPOINT RFC

Devon 3
Ground Address: Defiance Field, Torpoint, Cornwall
Brief Directions: Torpoint Ferry, keep on main Liskeard road, in 2 miles ground on left
Club Secretary: P C Summers, 112 Rochford Crescent, Ernesettle, Plymouth. PL5 2QD
Tel: (H) 01752 362785
Fixtures Secretary: P C Summers
Tel: (H) 01752 362785
Club Colours: Scarlet with thin royal blue hoops

ST DAY RFC

Cornwall 1
Ground Address: The Playing Field, St Day, Redruth, Cornwall
Brief Directions: Leave A30 at Scorrier exit, left past Cross Roads Hotel, at crossroads go straight across, ground just less than 1 mile on left
Club Secretary: P C Newcombe, 21 Martinvale Parc, Mount Ambrose, Redruth
Tel: (H) 01209 212834
Fixtures Secretary: T Dunstan
Tel: (H) 01209 314353
Club Colours: White with cherry hoop.

ST IVES RFC

Western Counties West
Ground Address: Alexandra Road, St Ives, Cornwall. TR26 1ER
Tel: 01736 795346
Brief Directions: M5/A30 to Hayle A3074 then B3311 coach rout to St Ives, Alexandra Road is second left after Fire Station
Club Secretary: N.J.Barber, 2 The Crescent, Alexandra Rd., St Ives. TR26 1BY.
Tel NO: (H & F) 01736 796861 (W) 01752 665951
Fixtures Secretary: Mike Gee,Lowenna, 70 Halsetown, St Ives, Cornwall TR26 3LZ
Tel: (H & F) 01736 797777
Club Colours: Navy blue, and white

ST JUST RFC

Cornwall & Devon
Ground Address: St Just RFC, Tregeseal, St Just-in-Penwith, Cornwall. TR19 7PF
Tel: 01736 788593
Club Secretary: R W Bassett, 31 Boscathnoe Way, Heamdor, Penzance, Cornwall. TR18 3JS
Tel: (H) 01736 62311 (W) 01736 62341
Fixtures Secretary: P Whitman
Tel: (H) 01736 788150
Club Colours: All black

STITHIANS RFC

Cornwall 2
Ground Address: Playing Field, Stithians, Truro, Cornwall
Tel: 01209 860148
Brief Directions: Opposite the church in the centre of the village. The village lies in the centre of the triangle formed by Redruth, Falmouth and Helston.
Club Secretary: T J Knight, 6 Chainwalk Drive, Kenwyn, Truro, Cornwall. TR1 3ST
Tel: (H) 01872 270849 (W) 01872 276116
Fixtures Secretary: C Burley, 54 Collins Park, Stithians, Truro, Cornwall.
Tel: (H) 01209 860148
Club Colours: Maroon

STOTHERT & PITT RFC

Somerset 1
Ground Address: Adamsfield, Corston, Bath. BA1 9AY
Tel: 01225 874802
Brief Directions: On A4 road, Bristol side of Bath
Club Secretary: R V Garraway, 2 Westfield Park South, Lower Weston, Bath. BA1 3HT
Tel: (H) 01225 316863
Fixtures Secretary: Carlos Orzabal, 74 Clarance Street, Walcot, Bath Somerset BA1 5NS
Tel: 01225 314845
Club Colours: Blue, black and amber

STOW-ON-THE-WOLD & DISTRICT RFC

South West 2 East
Ground Address: Oddington Road, Stow-on-the-Wold, Cheltenham, Glos (No post box)
Tel: 01451 830887
Brief Directions: From 'Unicorn' traffic lights in Stow take Oddington/Chipping Norton Road, ground is 1.5 miles on right
Club Secretary: N Drury, 2 Chestnut Corner, White Hart Lane, Stow-on-the-Wold, Cheltenham, Glos
Tel: (H) 01451 831686 (W) 01608 650428
Fixtures Secretary: A Jones
Tel: (H) 01993 842757
Club Colours: Black and white hoops

SUPERMARINE RFC

Berks, Dorset & Wilts 3
Ground Address: Supermarine Sports and Social Club, Highworth Road, South Marston, Nr Swindon, Wiltshire
Tel: 01793 824828
Brief Directions: Take A419 M4 to Cirencester Rd, turn off at north or south 'Honda' junction, follow A361 signed Highworth, club entrance off roundabout for industrial estate
Club Secretary: Geoff Bath, 2 Folly Drive, Highworth, Wiltshire
Tel: (H) 01793 861619
Fixtures Secretary: Ian Frizzle, 277 Windrush, Highworth ,Wilts.
Tel: (H) 01793 763135
Club Colours: Sky Blue and dark blue quarters

SWANAGE & WAREHAM RFC

South West 2 East
Ground Address: Bestwall, Wareham, Dorset
Tel: 01929 552224
Brief Directions: Traffic lights at town centre, take Bestwall to end, turn left into ground
Club Secretary: Mr Kevin Large, 20 Gannetts Park, Swanage, Dorset
Tel: (H) 01929 426523 (W) 01929 425818
Fixtures Secretary: Mr John Hopkins
Tel: (H) 01202 886804
Club Colours: Maroon shirts and socks, white shorts

SWINDON COLLEGE OL BOYS RFC

Southern Counties South
Ground Address: Nationwide Sports Social Club, Pipers Way, Swindon, Wilts Tel No: 01793 513513
Brief Directions: M4 J15.Take A419 and turn left at first roundabout into Marlborough Road. After one mile turn left into Pipers Way and ground is on left after 800 yards
Club Secretary: Mark Lea, 152 Albion Street, Swindon SN1 5LP
Tel No: 01793 522834
Fixtures Secretary: Phil Tyler. Tel No: 01367 241337 (H) 0585 874 961 (M)
Club Colours: Black shirt with red stripe on sleeves, blackshorts.

SWINDON RFC

Berks, Dorset & Wilts 1
Ground Address: Greenbridge Road, Swindon, Wilts. SN3 3LA Tel: 01793 521148
Brief Directions: M4 Jct 15. Follow A419 towards Cirencester. Off at Oxford Junction follow signs to Swindon. Left at major roundabout and 100 metres right at next roundabout.Ground 100 metres on left
Club Secretary: Mike Scott, 9 West View, Nythe, Swindon. SN3 3NG
Tel NO: 01793 481505
Fixtures Secretary: Kevin Logan, 40 Nindum Road, Colview, Swindon. SN3 4BA
Tel: 01793 831398
Club Colours: Blue and amber hoops, white shorts Change: Green & Black

TADLEY RUGBY CLUB RFC

Southern Counties South
Ground Address: Red Lane, Aldermaston, Reading, Berks Tel: 0118 970072
Brief Directions: Frm M3: A340 Basingstoke into Tadley. Road to Burghfield, left into Red Ln. Frm M4: Jct 14 Theale A4 to Newbury, turn left A340 to Tadley, left into Aldermaston and Red Lane to Tadley
Club Secretary: R W Mears, 22 Winchfield Gardens, Tadley, Hants. RG26 3TX
Tel: (H) 0118 9811648
Fixtures Secretary: A,Boyer, 11 Christopher Court, Boundary road, Newbury RG14 7PQ
Tel No: 01635 40574
Club Colours: Black with amber hoop. Change: French Blue.

TAMAR SARACENS RFC

Devon 1
Ground Address: Parkway Sports Club, Ernesettle Lane, Ernesettle, Plymouth, Devon
Tel: 01752 363080
Brief Directions: A38 to St Budeaux, turn off then towards Ernesettle
Club Secretary: Joe Jones, 18 Montacute Avenue, Honicknoule, Plymouth, Devon.
Fixtures Secretary: John Bentley
Tel: (H) 01752 345020
Club Colours: Red , white and Green

TAUNTON RFC

South West 2 West
Ground Address: Priory Park, Priory Bridge Road, Taunton, Somerset Tel: 01823 275670
Brief Directions: From M5 exit 25 follow signs to town centre,then county cricket ground and ground on right after roundabout by Great Mills store.
Club Secretary: George Wilson, 10 Obridge Road, Taunton. TA2 7PX
Tel: (H) 01823 282495
Fixtures Secretary: Rodney Reed
Tel: (H) 01823 276354 (W) 01823 337900 Ext 3375
Club Colours: Crimson, black and white hoops

TAVISTOCK RFC

Devon 1
Ground Address: Sandy Park, Trelawney Road, Tavistock, Devon, PL19 8ET
Tel: 01822 618275
Brief Directions: From town centre take Brentor Road, under railway viaduct, 2nd right
Club Secretary: John Goodspeed, 21 Long Park Drive, Plymouth, Devon PL6 7QE
Fixtures Secretary: Martin Griffiths, 23 St.Maryhaye, Tavistock, Devon PL19 8LR
Tel: (H) 01822 613030
Club Colours: Black and red hoops

TEIGNMOUTH RFC

Cornwall & Devon
Ground Address: Bitton Sports Ground, Bitton Park Road, Teignmouth Tel: 01626 774714
Brief Directions: Adjacent to Shaldon Bridge, off main Teignmouth to Newton Abbot road
Club Secretary: Robert Lovendge, 59 Second Avenue, Teignmouth, Devon. TQ14 9DN
Tel: (H) 01626 775891
Fixtures Secretary: Brian Abraham, 10 Gloucester Road, Teignmouth, Devon.
Tel No: 01626 776346
Club Colours: Red, white and black hoops

TETBURY RFC

Gloucestershire 1
Ground Address: Recreation Ground, Hampton Street, Tetbury, Glos Tel: 01666 505052
Brief Directions: On the B4014 (Hampton St.) out of Tetbury towards Avening, the ground is situated on the right behind the betting shop.
Club Secretary: Mrs Tracey Wright,67 Charlton Road, Tetbury, GLos. GL8 8DX
Tel No: 01666 503098
Fixtures Secretary: Wayne Hillman, 2 Bartley Croft, Coygar Park, Tetbury, Glos. GL8 8ER
Tel: (H) 01666 502903
Club Colours: Black and gold

TEWKESBURY RFC

Gloucestershire 2
Ground Address: The Moats, Lankett Lane, Tewkesbury, Glos., Tel: 01684 294364
Brief Directions: Behind Tewkesbury Abbey
Club Secretary: Claire Bowes, 31 Gould Drive, Northway, Tewkesbury, Glos.,
Tel: (H) 01684 850093
Fixtures Secretary: Paul Cole, 7 East Street, Tewkesbury, Glos. GL20 5NR
Tel: (H) 01684 295932
Club Colours: Black and amber hoops

THATCHAM RFC
Berks, Dorset & Wilts 2
Ground Address: Henwick Worth Playing Fields,Henwick Lane, Thatcham, Berkshire.
Brief Directions: Henwick Playing Fields are on the north side of the A4 which runs from Newbury through Thatcham to Reading. The entrance in Henwick Lane is on the eastern side of Thatcham.
Club Secretary: Mr R B Morris, 182 Bath Road, Thatcham, Berkshire. RG18 3HJ
Tel: (H) 01635 826985 (W) 0118 9817474
Fixtures Secretary: Mrs Kathi Surtees
Tel: (H) 01635 868285 (W) 0171 2101387
Club Colours: Red and blue quarters

THE TOR RFC
Gloucestershire & Somerset
Ground Address: Lowerside Park, Lowerside Lane, Glastonbury, Somerset
Tel: 01458 832236
Brief Directions: Adjacent to and signposted off A39 Glastonbury bypass
Club Secretary: Ms Carol Plenty, 26 Sheldon Drive, Wells, Somerset
Tel: (H) 01749 676754 (W)01458 860264
Fixtures Secretary: Mr Keith Elver
Tel: (H) 01458 447284 (W) 01749 673199
Club Colours: Maroon tops blue shorts

THORNBURY RFC
Western Counties North ?
Ground Address: Lower Morton, Thornbury, Bristol. BS12 1LG
Tel: 01454 412096
Brief Directions: From Thornbury: at Royal George pub take Gloucester rd out of town, after Anchor pub take 2nd left (ignore turn directly next to pub), club is down this lane approx 0.5 mile on the right
Club Secretary: Howard Roy Bowker, 2 Broncksea Road, Filton Park, Bristol. BS7 0SE
Tel: (H) 0117 969 8744
Fixtures Secretary: Maurice Carling
Tel: (H) 01454 885353
Club Colours: Black and amber hoops

TIVERTON RFC
South West 2 West
Ground Address: Coronation Field, Bolham Road, Tiverton, Devon. EX16 7RD
Tel: 01884 252271
Brief Directions: M5 J27 north towards Tiverton, 7 miles roundabout at end of d/carriageway left to Tiverton, ground 250mtrs on right just before footbridge over road
Club Secretary: Geoff Bulley, 2 Besley Close, Tiverton, Devon, EX16 4JF
Tel: (H) 01884 259316
Fixtures Secretary: Mark Green, 11 Smallacombe Road, Tiverton, Devon, EX16 5BA
Tel: (H) 01884 256573
Club Colours: Light and dark blue

TOPSHAM RFC
Devon 2
Ground Address: The Bonfire Field, Exeter Road, Topsham. EX3 0LY
Tel: 01392 873651
Brief Directions: From M5 follow signs to Topsham, club on left hand side
Club Secretary: Ron Murray, 7 Higer Shapter St., Topsham, Exeter, Devon. Tel No:01392 873484
Fixtures Secretary: Lily Neal, 42 Ashford Road, Topsham, Exeter, Devon.
Club Colours: Light blue and dark blue hoops

TORRINGTON RUFC
Devon 1
Ground Address: Donnacroft, Torrington. Tel: 01805 622055
Brief Directions: Situated on B3227 South Molton Road.
Club Secretary: Daren Nudds, 4 South Street, Torrington, Devon.
Tel: 01805 624899
Fixtures Secretary: David Hickman, Tel: (H) 01769 560131
Club Colours: Green black and white hoops

TOTNES RFC
Devon 1
Ground Address: The Clubhouse, Borough Park, Totnes, Devon. TQ9 5XX
Tel: 01803 867796
Brief Directions: Pitch on public park adjacent to British Rail station
Club Secretary: Mrs J V Guy, 50 Punchards Down, Follaton, Totnes, Devon. TQ9 5FD
Tel: (H) 01803 864581 (Fax) 01803 867050
Fixtures Secretary: A Bourne
Tel: (H) 01803 864462
Club Colours: Royal blue and white

TREDWORTH RUFC
Gloucestershire 3
Ground Address: The Llannet Playing Fields, King Edwards Avenue, Lindon, Gloucester
Tel: 01452 525465
Brief Directions: Along A38 towards Glos turn right into Tuffley Ave, then 5th into the OVAL which then leads to ground on right hand side
Club Secretary: Ken Broady, 25 Stonechat Avenue, Abbeydale, Gloucester, GL4 4XD.
Tel: 01452 500361
Fixtures Secretary: Danny Smith, 138 Melbourne Street East, Tredworth, Gloucester.
Tel: 01452 536723
Club Colours: Black and green quarters

TROWBRIDGE RFC
Berks, Dorset & Wilts 1
Ground Address: Green Lane, Trowbridge, Wiltshire. BA14 7DH
Tel: 01225 761389
Brief Directions: Head for West Ashton from County Way
Club Secretary: Bryn Parfitt, 60 Paxcroft Way, Trowbridge, Wiltshire. BA14 7DJ
Tel: (H) 01225 351044
Fixtures Secretary: Mickey Milton, 13 Blair Road, Trowbridge, Wilts.
Tel: 01225 767204
Club Colours: Dark blue, light blue and gold hoops

TRURO RFC

South West 2 West
Ground Address: St Clements Hill, Truro, Cornwall, TR1 1NY. Tel: 01872 274750
Brief Directions: A30, leave signpost for Trispen, to Truro at large roundabout, enter St Clements Hill next to Police station, ground on right at top of hill
Club Secretary: John Collier, 1 Bishop Temple Road, Truro.
Tel No: 01872 261624
Fixtures Secretary: Chris Gill, 34 Cornubia Close, Truro.
Tel No: 01872 262724
Club Colours: Amber and royal blue

UNIVERSITY OF PLYMOUTH

Devon 3
Ground Address: Polytechnic Sports Ground, Ernesettle Lane, Plymouth Tel: 01752 365071
Club Secretary: Richard Mogford, Students Union, University of Plymouth, Drakes Circus, Plymouth PL4 8AA Tel: 01752 663337
Club Colours: Black and amber hoops, black shorts

VEOR RFC

Cornwall 2
Ground Address: Wheal Gerry, Cliff View Road, Canborne, Cornwall
Brief Directions: Turn off A30 signed Canborne & Pool, right at traffic lights down hill, right again before pedestrian crossing, 0.5 mile right again after TA centre, ground 100 yds on right
Club Secretary: Mrs Claire Vincent, 7 Wheal Cerry, Eastern Lane, Camborne, Cornwall TR14 7EE
Tel: (H) 01209 711749
Fixtures Secretary: Colin Pascoe
Tel: (H) 01209 716172
Club Colours: Black and Gold

VERWOOD

Berks, Dorset & Wilts 3
Ground Address: Potterne Park, Potterne Way, Verwood, Dorset
Club Secretary: M Cockram, 145 Ringwood Road, Verwood, Dorset BH31 7AE Tel: (M) 0402 034238 (W) 01202 821111 (F) 01202 813455
Fixtures Secretary: Robin Oliver Peirce, c/o 145 Ringwood Road, Verwood, Dorset BH31 7AE Tel: (H) 01202 826372 (W) 01483 750814 (F) 01483 295140
Club Colours: Red and white quarters

WADEBRIDGE CAMELS RFC

Cornwall 1
Ground Address: Molesworth Field, Egloshayle, Wadebridge Tel: 01208 815311
Brief Directions: Opposite Egloshayle Church
Club Secretary: M Richards, Perlees Farm, Wadebridge
Tel: (H) 01208 812848 (W) 01726 860308
Fixtures Secretary: Chris Taylor
Tel: (H) 01208 813919
Club Colours: Chocolate and gold

WALCOT OLD BOYS RFC

Gloucestershire & Somerset
Ground Address: Albert Field, Lansdown, Bath
Tel: 01225 330199
Brief Directions: Follow signs from city centre to Lansdown, proceed along top to racecourse/golf club, halfway on right is ground opposite Bath car park & ride sign
Club Secretary: D J Bishop, 9 Sheridan Road, Twerton, Bath. BA2 1QY
Tel: (H) 01225 428942 (W) 01225 477540
Fixtures Secretary: S Sharp
Tel: (H) 01225 215821
Club Colours: Black and white hoops

WALLINGFORD RFC

Southern Counties North
Ground Address: Hithercroft Road, Wallingford, Oxon
Tel: 01491 835044
Brief Directions: Situated on Wallingford bypass on west side of town, bypass signposted on all approaches to Wallingford
Club Secretary: T N Harding, 24 Roding Way, Didcot, Oxon. OX11 7RQ
Tel: (H) 01235 510602 (W) 0860 154217
Fixtures Secretary: M Porter
Tel: (H) 01734 410946
Club Colours: Amber and black

WARMINSTER RFC

Berks, Dorset & Wilts 3
Ground Address: Warminster Cricket Club, Sambourne Road, Warminster, Wiltshire
Tel: 01985 219039
Brief Directions: From by-pass take A36/A350 junction into Deverill Rd.Left into Fore St. and 2nd left at roundabout into Thornhill Rd.Then 1st left into Folly Lane. Club at top of lane on right.
Club Secretary: Eve Jenkins, 15 Were Close, Warminster, Wilts. BA12 8TB.
tel No: 01985 212261
Fixtures Secretary: Steve Evans
Tel: (H) 01985 212750
Club Colours: Royal blue and gold hoops. Change: Red & black hoops.

WELLINGTON RFC

Western Counties West
Ground Address: The Athletic Ground, Corams Lane, Wellington, Somerset. TA21 8LL
Tel: 01823 663758
Brief Directions: Leave M5 J25 or from A38 from Taunton, right at central traffic lights into North St, left at Sportsman Inn, enter via sports centre car park
Club Secretary: N.Robins, 37 Bircham Road, Taunton, Somerset. TA2 8EX.
Fixtures Secretary: G R Vickery, 7 Seymour Street, Wellington, Somerset TA21 8JT
Tel: (H) 01823 664695 (W) 01823 335166
Club Colours: Red and black hoops.

WELLS RFC

Somerset 1
Ground Address: Charter Way, off Portway, Wells
Tel: 01749 672823
Brief Directions: Off the Portway A371 or follow signs to the Leisure Centre (which is next door)
Club Secretary: Mr Anthony C Cox, 10 Mount Pleasant Avenue, Wells, Somerset. BA5 2SQ
Tel: (H) 01749 673407
Fixtures Secretary: Mike Clements, Sunrise, Easton, Somerset Tel: 01249 870561
Club Colours: Black and white hoops

WESSEX RFC
Cornwall & DEvon
Ground Address: Flowerpot Field, Exwick, Exeter
Brief Directions: From J31 M5 to A30 follow signs to Exeter then Exwick, along Buddle Lane turn right into Oakhampton Road, turn left onto Western Road
Club Secretary: Phil Langford, 7 Kinnerton Way, Exwick, Exeter EX4 2BL
Tel: (H) 01392 211959 (W) 01395 873781 Ext 4304
Fixtures Secretary: T.G.Turner, April House, Sandford, Nr. Crediton, Devon. Tel Nos: 01363 772044 (H)01392 210344 (W) 01392 204069(F)
Club Colours: Bottle green and amber collars, white shorts

WESTBURY RFC
Berks, Dorset & Wilts 1
Ground Address: Leighton Sports Ground, Wellhead Lane, Westbury, Wiltshire Tel: 01373 826438
Brief Directions: Warminster Road (A350), opposite Cedar Hotel turn into Welland Lane, ground 300 metres on left
Club Secretary: Mr. R. D. Jones, 36 Westbury Road, Yarnbrook, Trowbridge, Wiltshire, BA14 6AG.
Tel: 01225 766647
Fixtures Secretary: Mr Mark Knott, Slate Cottage, 30 Fore Street, Warminster, Wilts,
Tel: (H) 01985 215054
Club Colours: Irregular Green and black hoops

WESTBURY-ON-SEVERN RFC
Gloucestershire 1
Ground Address: Westbury-on-Severn Parish Grounds, Westbury-on-Severn, Glos
Tel: 01452 760359
Brief Directions: A48 from Gloucester to Chepstow, Parish Ground on left hand side before Westbury-on-Severn village
Club Secretary: Phil Bleathman, The Hollies, Elton, Westbury-on-Severn, Glos. GL14 1JJ
Tel (H & W) 01452 760751 also Fax.
Fixtures Secretary: A Hyett, 1 Moyshill Villas, Strand Lane, Westbury-on-SEvern. GL14 1PG.
Tel: 01452 760495
Club Colours: Royal blue and white hoops

WEYMOUTH RFC
Berks, Dorset & Wilts 2
Ground Address: Monmouth Avenue, Weymouth, Dorset Tel: 01305 778889
Brief Directions: 3rd turn left after passing Safeways supermarket
Club Secretary: Mrs G Llewellyn, 2 Goulds Hill Close, Upwey, Weymouth Tel: (H) 01305 812415
Fixtures Secretary: Dick Foyle Tel: (H) 01305 266144
Club Colours: Light blue, dark blue circle, black shorts

WHEATLEY RUFC
Bucks & Oxon 1
Ground Address: Playing Fields, Holton, Wheatley, Oxford Tel: 01865 873476
Brief Directions: Leave A40 at Wheatley signs in Oxford towards London, turn left at T junction and ground is on left about 500 yards from the turn
Club Secretary: Bryan Davies, 31 Anxey Way, Haddenham, Bucks, HP17 8DJ.
Tel: (H) 01844 292846
Fixtures Secretary: Stuart West, 39 Kelham Hall Drive, Wheatley, Oxford, OX33 1SL
Tel: (H) 01865 872850
Club Colours: Purple, white & black bands, black shorts

WHITEHALL RFC
Western Counties North
Ground Address: Foundry Lane, Speedwell, Bristol
Tel: 0117 9659636
Brief Directions: Off B4465 Whitehall Road at Crofts End, turn right into Deep Pit Rd, take 2nd left. From M32 J2 follow sign post up Muller Rd, left at ro'about
Club Secretary: c/o Chris Brown, 41 Royate Hill, Upper Eastville, Bristol. BS5 6LP
Tel No: 07971 729067
Fixtures Secretary: Alex Ferguson, 8 Stoneleigh Road, Knowle, Bristol BS24 2RJ
Tel: 0117 9772898
Club Colours: Myrtle green and gold

WIDDEN OLD BOYS RFC
Gloucestershire 3
Ground Address: Memorial Ground, Tuffley Avenue, Gloucester Tel: 01452 304080
Brief Directions: M5 north J12, right at 1st roundabout at end of bypass, left at next roundabout into Stroud Rd, approx 150 metres left into Tuffley Avenue
Club Secretary: Stuart McWalter, 52 The Causeway, Quedgeley, Gloucester GL2 4LD
Tel: 01452 724739
Fixtures Secretary: Andy Alder, 42 Darrell Close, Quedgeley, Gloucester GL2 4YR
Tel: (H) 01452 721050
Club Colours: Green shirts with red band & white hoops

WIMBORNE RFC
Southern Counties South
Ground Address: Leigh Park, Wimborne, Dorset
Tel: 01202 882602
Brief Directions: A31, take B3073 to Wimborne, approx 1.5 miles turn left into Gordan Rd, Leigh Park immediately ahead, approx 400yds
Club Secretary: Michael Moysey, 42 Lacy Drive, Wimborne, Dorset. BH21 1DG
Tel: (H) 01202 841478
Fixtures Secretary: Debbie Noyce, 24 Walters Drive, PImperne, Blandford,Dorset DT71 8UX.
Tel No: 01258 451608
Club Colours: All black

WINCANTON RUFC
Somerset 3
Ground Address: Wincanton Sports Ground, Balsam Fields, Wincanton, Somerset
Brief Directions: Into Wincanton from A303, after Fire station turn right down Moor Lane 0.5 mile
Club Secretary: Mr. J. Bastable, Church Farm, Charlton Musgrove, Wincanton, Somerset. BA9 8ES.
Fixtures Secretary: Mr Glen Ware, c/o Dolphin Hotel, High Street, Wincanton, Somerset. BA9 9JF.
Club Colours: Black and amber

WINDSOR RFC
Southern Counties South
Ground Address: Home Park, Datchet Road, Windsor, Berkshire Tel: 01753 860807
Brief Directions: Off M4, signed Windsor, follow d/carriageway to 1st slip road off left, left at roundabout, left at next roundabout, keep left past railway station, next left into Home Park
Club Secretary: Sean Leone, 35 Bell View, Windsor, Berks. SL4 4ET
Tel: (H) 01753 863713 (W) 0181 848 8881
Fixtures Secretary: Peter Davison
Tel: (H) 01753 840559
Club Colours: Black, green, gold and maroon quarters

WINSCOMBE RFC
Somerset 2
Ground Address: Longfield Recreation Ground, Winscombe, North Somerset Tel: 01934 842720
Brief Directions: Turn off A38 into Winscombe, turn left at right hand bend to ground.
Club Secretary: Alun George, 3 Landseer Close, Worle, Weston-Super-Mare. BS22 9NL
Tel: (H) 01934 518270
Fixtures Secretary: Geoff George. Tel No: 01275 472819
Club Colours: Black with white hoops

WINSLOW RUFC
Bucks & Oxon 1
Ground Address: The Winslow Centre, Park Road, Winslow, Buckingham. MK18
Brief Directions: A413 through Winslow, 0.5 mile towards Buckingham from town centre, turn left into Avenue Road, 1st right into Park Road
Club Secretary: Simon Drakeford, 31 Green Way, Newton Longville, Bucks. MK17 OAP
Tel: (H) 01908 644239
Fixtures Secretary: Colin Brown, Gardeners Cottage, 27 Horn Street, Winslow. MK18 3AP
Tel: (H) 01296 714312
Club Colours: Blue and gold hoops

WINSLOW RUFC
Bucks & Oxon 1
Ground Address: The Winslow Centre, Park Road, Winslow, Buckingham. MK18
Brief Directions: A413 through Winslow, 0.5 mile towards Buckingham from town centre, turn left into Avenue Road, 1st right into Park Road
Club Secretary: Simon Drakeford, 31 Green Way, Newton Longville, Bucks. MK17 OAP
Tel: (H) 01908 644239
Fixtures Secretary: Colin Brown, Gardeners Cottage, 27 Horn Street, Winslow. MK18 3AP
Tel: (H) 01296 714312
Club Colours: Blue and gold hoops

WITHYCOMBE RUGBY & RECREATION CLUB RFC
Western Counties (West)
Ground Address: Raleigh Park, 36 Hulham Road, Exmouth, Devon. EX8 3HSTel: 01395 266762
Brief Directions: M5 south J30, take A376 to Exmouth, at Box Junction before traffic lights turn left into Hulham Rd, ground 200 yards on right
Club Secretary: David M Josey, 2 Larch Close, Marley Gardens, Exmouth, Devon. EX8 5NQ
Tel: (H) 01395 275038
Fixtures Secretary: M J Norman 2 Claremont Lane, Exmouth Devon. ES8 2LE.
Tel: (H) 01395 270644
Club Colours: Emerald green and black hoops

WITNEY RFC
Southern Counties North
Ground Address: The Clubhouse, Hailey Road, Witney, Oxon. OX8 5UH
Tel: 01993 771043 Fax: 01993 779985
Brief Directions: Leave Witney centre by Bridge St, towards Oxford & Bicester, left at mini roundabout, keep along main road passing garage on right, ground on left after about 1 mile
Club Secretary: Chris Tucker, 19 Stanton Harcourt Road, Witney, Oxon. OX8 6LE
Tel: 01993 700323 (W) 0589 444655
Fixtures Secretary: Pete Holliday
Tel: (H) 01993 705327 (W) 01527 498259
Club Colours: Black hoops on sky blue

WIVELISCOMBE RFCC
Western Counties North
Ground Address: Recreation Ground, West Road, Wiveliscombe, Nr Taunton, Somerset. TA4 2TB
Tel: 01984 623897
Brief Directions: Take B3227 from Taunton to Barnstaple, ground is on left towards end of town
Club Secretary: G.Mabley, 3 Manor Park, Norton Fitzwarren, Taunton, Somerset
Tel: 01823 270002
Fixtures Secretary: C Mann
Tel: (H) 01823 400673 (Fax) 01823 400139
Club Colours: Navy blue with red sash

WOOTTON BASSETT RFC
Southern Counties South
Ground Address: Rylands Field, Stoneover Lane, Wootton Bassett, Wiltshire
Tel: 01793 851425
Brief Directions: M4 J16, past Sally Pussey's and Churchill House pubs, turn left along Stoneover Lane, Rugby ground is 200yds along on left
Club Secretary: John Ricketts, Foxleigh, Calne Road, Lyneham, Wilts. SN15 4PC
Tel: (H) 01249 890293
Fixtures Secretary: Jim Brierley, 25 Broad Town Road, Wooton Bassett, Wilts. SN4 7RB
Tel: (H) 01793 731780
Club Colours: Black

WOTTON-UNDER-EDGE RFC
Gloucestershire 3
Ground Address: K L B School Ground, Kingswood Road, Wotton-under-Edge
Tel: 01453 842138 (Falcon Hotel)
Brief Directions: Take b4058 towards M5 out of Wotton, Ground on Left at foot of hill.
Club Secretary: Adam Henshaw, 21 Wortley Terrace, Wotton-under-Edge Glos. GL12 7JY
Tel: (H) 01453 844530
Fixtures Secretary: Chris Hull, 56 Bradley Road, Wotton-under-Edge Glos. GL12 7DT
Tel: (H) 01453 844958
Club Colours: Black and amber hoops

YATTON RFC
Gloucestershire & Somerset
Ground Address: The Park, North End, Yatton, Avon
Tel: 01934 832085
Brief Directions: From centre of village, travel towards Clevedon, club is on right 300 yards after Railway bridge
Club Secretary: J G Crabtree, 11 Old Park Road, Clevedon, Avon
Tel: (H) 01275 876954 (W) 0117 943 2399
Fixtures Secretary: Nick Williams, Karibuni, Station Road, Congreibury, Somerset
Tel: (H) 01934 877250
Club Colours: Amber and black

TETLEY'S
BITTER
CUP

TETLEY'S
BITTER
COUNTY
CHAMPIONSHIP

TETLEY'S
BITTER
VASE

TETLEY'S
BITTER
NATIONAL U20
CHAMPIONSHIP

OTHER RFU AFFILIATED CLUBS 676

STUDENT RUGBY FOOTBALL UNION 693

ASSOCIATE MEMBERS 700

AEI (Rugby) - 1917 - Secretary: R I Stephens, 10 Northampton Lane, Dunchurch, Rugby, Warwickshire CV22 6QA (01788 817518 (H) 01788 563324 (B) 01788 563763 (Fax)). Fix Sec: A G Chronnell, 24 Kirkby Close, Brownsover, Rugby, Warwickshire CV21 1TT (01788 551781 (H) 01788 563484 (B) (F)). Ground: Hillmorton Road, Rugby, Warwickshire CV22 4AR Tel: 01788 576921.

ANZ Group - 1926 - Secretary: R A Baker, Dunvarra, 7 Robinscroft Mews, Blackheath Hill, London SE10 8DN (0181 692 9003 (H)).

Aesculapians - 1986 - Secretary: S D W Payne FRCS LLM, 28 Emanuel Avenue, Acton, London W3 6JJ (0181 992 1880 (H) 0181 967 5403(B) 0181 967 5311(Fax)). Fix Sec: J E T Payne, 28 Emanuel Avenue, Acton, London W3 6JJ (0181 992 1880 (H)). Treasurer: S D W Payne FRCS LLM, 28 Emanuel Avenue, Acton, London W3 6JJ (0181 992 1880 (H) 0181 967 5403(B) 0181 967 5311(Fax)). Ground: The Rugby Club, 49 Hallam Street, London W1 Tel: 0171 580 7917.

Aldbourne Dabchicks - 1992 - Secretary: A Woodrow, 61 Whitley Road, Aldbourne, Marlborough, Wilts. Fix Sec: C Flett, 71 Cottage Road, Aldbourne, Marlborough SN8 2EB (01672 541233 (H)). Treasurer: N Kennedy, 8 The Butts, Aldbourne, Marlborough, Wiltshire SN8 2DE (01672 540592 (H)). Ground: Ewins Hill, Aldbourne, Wiltshire.

Alderholt - 1977 - Secretary: Miss C Marshall, 24 Churchill Close, Alderholt, Fordingbridge, Hampshire SP6 3BG (01425 655861 (H)). Treasurer: P C Kimber, 30 Broomfield Drive, Alderholt, Fordingbridge, Hampshire SP6 3HY (01425 652825 (H) 01722 410055 Ext 222 (B) 01722 410088 (Fax)). Ground: Recreation Ground, Ringwood Road, Fordingbridge, Hampshire.

Andersen - 1990 - Secretary: A McQuarrie, c/o Arthur Andersen, 3rd Floor, 20 Old Bailey, London EC2M 7AN (0171 438 5130 (B) 0171 438 2984 (F)). Ground: 1 Surrey St, London WC2R 2PS Tel: 0171 438 3000.

Anglia (Cambridge) - 1990 - See University of East England Ground: c/o The Gymnasium, Anglia Polytechnic University, East Road, Cambridge CB1 1PT.

Avon & Somerset Constabulary - 1935 - Secretary: N Holland, 39 Blackdown View, Norton Fitzwarren, Taunton, Somerset TA2 6RP (01823 333202 (H) 01823 363653 (B) 01823 363651 (F)). Fix Sec: R Tully, Police Station, Northgate, Bridgewater, Somerset (01823 363319 (B)). Treasurer: R Brown, Police Station, Shuttern, Taunton, Somerset (01823 337911 (B)). Ground: Taunton School, Staplegrove Road, Taunton, Somerset TA2 6AD Tel: 01823 349200.

Aylesbury Athletic - Fix Sec: D Evans, HM Young Offender Inst, Bierton Road, Aylesbury, Bucks HP20 1EH (01296 424435 x318 (B) 01296 434139 (F)). Ground: HM Prison, Bierton Road, Aylesbury HP20 1EH Tel: 01296 424435 x318.

BAe Warton - 1992 - Fix Sec: M Jagger, 6 Hazel Coppice, Lea, Preston, Lancashire PR2 1XG (01772 511240 (H) 01772 854834 (B)). Treasurer: G Griffiths, 2nd Floor Flat, 15 Clifton Drive, Lytham St Annes FY8 5QY (01253 794402 (H) 01772 858130 (B)). Ground: Bank Lane Playing Fields, Bank Lane, Warton, Preston PR4 1AX Tel: 01772 856354/852788.

Bacchanalians - 1980 - Secretary: J P C H Broadway, 27 Greenhill Close, Winchester, Hampshire SO22 5DZ (01962 620039 (H) 01489 892256 (B) 01489 891453 (F)). Fix Sec: J P C H Broadway, 27 Greenhill Close, Winchester, Hampshire SO22 5DZ (01962 620039 (H) 01489 892256 (B) 01489 891453 (F)). Treasurer: S M Foster, Walnut Grove, 3 Starboard View, South Woodham Ferrers, Chelmsford, Essex CM3 5GR (01245 327162 (H) 0808 555666 (B)). Ground: Winchester RFC, Northwalls Park, Nuns Road, Winchester SO23 7EF Tel: 01962 867021.

Barclays Bank Birmingham District - 1955 - Secretary: K R Patterson, 42 Pennymore Close, Trentham, Stoke on Trent, Staffordshire ST4 8YQ (01782 642474 (H) 01606 312151 (B) 01606 312156 (F)). Fix Sec: K R Patterson, 42 Pennymore Close, Trentham, Stoke on Trent, Staffordshire ST4 8YQ (01782 642474 (H) 01606 312151 (B) 01606 312156 (F)). Treasurer: K R Patterson, 42 Pennymore Close, Trentham, Stoke on Trent, Staffordshire ST4 8YQ (01782 642474 (H) 01606 312151 (B) 01606 312156 (F)). Ground: Sunnybank Avenue, Perry Common, Birmingham B44 0HP Tel: none.

Basildon (Berkshire) - 1978 - Secretary: A Greener, Old Barn, Manor Road, Whitchurch-on-Thames, Oxon RG8 7EW (0118 984 5208 (H) 0118 956 1248 (B) 0118 958 9005 (F)). Fix Sec: J Hayes, 53 Willowtree Glade, Calcot, Reading (0118 967 8792 (H)). Treasurer: D Butler, 8 Gratwicke Road, Tilehurst, Reading, Berkshire RG30 4TT (0118 942 0151 (H)). Ground: The Recreation Ground, Bethesda Street, Upper Basildon, Berkshire.

Bath Harlequins - 1895 - Secretary: S Cleverly, 33 Haycombe Drive, Twerton, Bath (01225 400351 (H) 01225 425357 01225319850). Fix Sec: Keith Abrahams, 62 Kelston View, Bath BA2 1NB (01225 400398 01373 452231). Treasurer: P A Fiddes, 51 Fairfield Park Road, Fairfield Park, Bath BA1 6JP (01225 420748 (H) 01225 467550 (B)). Ground: Avon RFC, Hicks Field, Batheasten Tel: 01225 852446.

Bedford School - 1870 - Ground: Burnaby Road, Bedford Tel: 01234 362200.

Bedfordshire County Union - 1970 - Secretary: A W Perrey, 22 The Choppins, Ampthill, Bedfordshire MK45 2SN (01525 403812 (H) 01767 631100 (B) 01525 750877 (Fax)). Fix Sec: A W Perrey, 22 The Choppins, Ampthill, Bedfordshire MK45 2SN (01525 403812 (H) 01767 631100 (B) 01525 750877 (Fax)). Treasurer: K Green, 9 How End Road, Houghton, Conquest,, Bedfordshire MK45 3JT (01525 402921 (H) 01525 861990 (B)).

Bedfordshire Police - 1953 - Secretary: T Mulvaney, Peelers Lodge, Park Lane, Blunham, Bedfordshire MK44 3NJ (01767 640915 (H) 01234 275115 (B) 01234 275005 (F)). Fix Sec: M Nicholson, Bedford Police Station, Greyfriars, Bedford (01234 342011 (H) 01234 275229 (B)). Treasurer: A McKay, 37 Harrington Drive, Putnoe, Bedford MK41 8DB (01234 270606 (H) 01234 271212 (B)). Ground: Police Headquarters, Woburn Road, Kempston, Bedford Tel: 01234 841212.

Belgravia - Secretary: S O'Neill, 6 Priory Close, Sunbury on Thames, Middx TW16 5AB (0171 3216762 (B) 0171 321 6836). Fix Sec: S O'Neill, 6 Priory Close, Sunbury on Thames, Middx TW16 5AB (0171 3216762 (B) 0171 321 6836). Treasurer: M Potts, c/o Belgravia Police Station, 202-206 Buckingham Palace Rd, London SW1W 9SX (0797 092 2146 (H) 0171 321 6721 (B)). Ground: Imber Court, Ember Court Rd, East Molesey, Surrey Tel: 0181 398 1267.

Benton - 1964 - Secretary: C Reid, 114 Northumberland Street, Wallsend, Newcastle-upon-Tyne NE28 7PX (0191 262 4913 (H) 0191 218 7542 (B)). Fix Sec: R Jones, 46 Rosedale Court, West Denton, Newcastle upon Thames (0191 243 1602 (H)). Treasurer: P Summers, 2 Cambridge Avenue, Forest Hall, Tyne and Wear (0191 266 3096 (H) 0191 225 9895 (B)). Ground: Civil Service Sports Ground, (Darsley Pk), Old Whitley Road, Newcastle-upon-Tyne Tel: 0191 215 1929.

Berkshire Press - 1974 - Secretary: S Taylor, 9 Dorset Road, Windsor, Berkshire SL4 3BA (01753 867664 (H)). Fix Sec: S Walters, Lime Tree House, Brook Street, Dedham, Essex CO7 6AD (01206 323129 (H)). Treasurer: E Scragg, 5 Bar Close Avenue, Caversham, Reading, Berkshire (01189 474533 (H)). Ground: Civil Service Ground, Dukes Meadow, Chiswick Tel: 0181 994 1202.

Berwick - 1968 - Secretary: J H Greenwood, Ava Lodge, Castle Terrace, Berwick upon Tweed TD15 1NP (01289 382270 (H) 01289 302463 (B) 01289 330306 (Fax)). Fix Sec: C Budzynski, 17 Springfield Park, East Ord, Berwick Upon Tweed TD15 2FD (01289 305303 (H) 01289 330044 (B) 01289 330540 (Fax)). Treasurer: A Patterson, Denebank, Mordington, Berwick upon Tweed TD15 1UF (01289 386394 (H) 01289 306688 (B) 01289 307189 (Fax)). Ground: Scremerston, Berwick-upon-Tweed TD15 2QY Tel: 01289 306416.

Bicton College of Agriculture - 1947 - Secretary: R A Dunn, Bicton College of Agriculture, East Budleigh, Budleigh Salterton, Devon EX9 7BY (01395 562396 (H) 01395 562396 (B) 01395 567502 (Fax)). Fix Sec: P Massey, Bicton College of Agriculture, East Budleigh, Budleigh Salterton, Devon EX9 7BY (01395 568353 (B) 01395 567502 (F)). Treasurer: P Massey, Bicton College of Agriculture, East Budleigh, Budleigh Salterton, Devon EX9 7BY (01395 568353 (B) 01395 567502 (F)). Ground: Bicton College of Agriculture, East Budleigh, Budleigh Salterton EX9 7BY Tel: 01395 562335.

Birkenhead School - Ground: 11 Kingsmead Road South, Birkenhead, Merseyside L43 6TA Tel: 0151 652 4014.

Bishop's Stortford - 1920 - Fix Sec: J Swanson, Roselea, 14 Kingsbridge Road, Bishops Stortford, Hertfordshire CM23 (01279 651618 (H) 0171 579 6390 (B)). Treasurer: J Miller, 2 Chesfield Close, Bishops Stortford, Hertfordshire CM23 3PS (01279 656223 (H)). Ground: Silver Leys, Hadham Road, Bishops Stortford, Hertfordshire CM23 2QE Tel: 01279 652092.

Black Baa Baas - 1994 - Secretary: Julian Samuel, 23A Varna Road, Fulham, London SW6 (0171 385 1967 0171 265 0071/327 3208). Treasurer: Ben Thomson, 22 Stephendale Road, Fulham, London SW6 2PE (0171 371 0699 0181 567 3530). Fix Sec: R Leslie, 15 Sedlescombe Rd, Fulham, London SW6 1RE (0171 610 0787 0171 436 2100). Ground: c/o St Nicholas Road, off Speer Road, Thames Ditton, Surrey.

Black Horse - 1977 - Secretary: C R Daniels, 9 Currie Street, Hertford, Hertfordshire SG13 7DA (01992 421486 (H) 01920 466588 (B)). Fix Sec: S Martin, 25 Gladstone Road, Ware, Hertfordshire SG12 0AG (01920 424073 (H)). Treasurer: S Hibbert, 95 West Street, Hertford, Herts SG13 8EZ (01992 330312 (H) 0181 2586002 01992 81160). Ground: Balls Park, Mangrove Road, Hertford, Hertfordshire SG13 8AJ.

Blackpool Police - 1968 - Secretary: D Crocombe, 53 Kendal Avenue, High Furlong, Blackpool, Lancashire FY3 7LG (01253 395279 (H) 01253 293933 (B)). Fix Sec: C Farrow, 10 Newton Road, St Annes on Sea, Lancashire FY8 3JW (01253 723264 (H) 01253 293933 (B) 01253 293933 Ext 4200 (Fax)). Treasurer: M Kelsall, 1 Bramble Court, Marsh Road, Thornton, Lancs (01253 855918 (H)). Ground: c/o Blackpool RUFC, Fleetwood Road, Blackpool, Lancashire FY5 1RN Tel: 01253 853308.

Blue Boar - 1977 - Secretary: B Kentish, Old Farmhouse, Longworth, Abingdon, Oxfordshire OX13 5ET (01865 820711 (H) 01865 820711 (B)). Fix Sec: B Kentish, Old Farmhouse, Longworth, Abingdon, Oxfordshire OX13 5ET (01865 820711 (H) 01865 820711 (B)). Treasurer: P Anderson, Hill View, Hanney Road, Southmoor, Abingdon, Oxfordshire OX13 5HT (01865 820209 (H)). Ground: Cokethorpe School, Ducklington, Nr Witney OX8 7PU Tel: 01993 703921.

Blundell's School - 1868 - Ground: Tiverton, Devon EX16 4DN Tel: 01884 252543.

Border Park - 1961 - Secretary: C Earsman, Gladstone House, Stannersburn, Falstone, Hexham, Northumberland NE48 1DD (01434 240425 (H) 01434 603248 (B)). Fix Sec: W.J Turnbull, The Old Manse, Otterburn Rd,Bellingham, Hexham, Northunberland (01434 220860). Treasurer: S Robinson, Low Newton Farm Cottage, Newton Farm, Tarset, Hexham NE48 1PD (01434 240289 01434 602342). Ground: Symons Park, Butteryhaugh, Kielder, Hexham NE48 1HG.

Blundell's Squirrels - 1930 - Secretary: E R Crowe, 46 Higher Town, Sampford Peverell, Tiverton, Devon EX16 7BR (01884 820308 (H)). Fix Sec: A L C Ward, Well Common Cottage, Todber, Sturminster Newton, Dorset DT10 1JB (01747 838434 (H)). Treasurer: A L C Ward, Well Common Cottage, Todber, Sturminster Newton, Dorset DT10 1JB (01747 838434 (H)). Ground: Blundells School, Tiverton, Devon EX14 4DX Tel: 01884 252232.

Bourtonians - 1992 - Secretary: P Sherwood, 8 Southgate Court, Little Rissington, Cheltenham, Gloucestershire GL54 2LY (01451 810368 (H) 01451 820082 (B)). Fix Sec: J Moy, Rose Cottage, Sherborne, Cheltenham, Gloucs GL54 3DW (01451 844458). Treasurer: M Webb, 20 Southgate Court, Little Rissington, Cheltenham, Gloucestershire GL54 2LY (01451 822011 (H)). Ground: The Cotswold School, Bourton-on-the-Water, Cheltenham Gloucs Tel: 01451 844458.

Bristol Junior R F Combination - 1924 - Secretary: R J Batterbury, Windways, 1 Emmett Wood, Whitchurch, Bristol BS14 0JG (01275 837523 (H)). Fix Sec: John Randall, 25 Court Farm Road, Whitchurch, Bristo BS14 OEH (01275 839472 (H)). Treasurer: Laurie Peachey, 3 Knapp Road, Thornbury, South Glos. BS35 2HE (01454 417013 (H)).

British Maritime Technology - 1992 - Secretary: R Danns, 210 Lower Bristol Road, Bath, Avon BA2 3DQ (01225 425014 (H) 01225 473672 (B) 01225 448714 (Fax)). Fix Sec: D Connoly, 210 Lower Bristol Road, Bath, Avon BA2 3DU (01225 852548 (H) 01225 473626 (B)).

British Police - 1920 - Secretary: A Wathan, 9 Heol Castell, Coety, Litchard, Bridgend, Mid Glamorgan CF31 1PU (01656 660749 (H) 01639 850229 (B) 01656 660749 (Fax)). Treasurer: K Turner, Police Headquarters, PO Box 99, LLangunnor,, Carmarthen, Dyfed SA31 2PF (01269 851327 (H) 01267 222020 (B) 01267 222185 (Fax)).

British Telecom HQ - Secretary: D R Jones, 31 Powder Mill Lane, Twickenham TW2 6EF (0181 898 8754 (H) 01802 229666 (B)). Fix Sec: C Lenthal, 92 The Avenue, Sunbury on Thames, Middlesex TW16 58X (01932 765461 (H)). Treasurer: P W Sones, 52 Harwood Road, Marlow, Buckinghamshire SL7 2AS (01628 487116 (H) 0958 551968 (B)).

British Transport Police - 1980 - Secretary: Detective Inspector N Bracken, 2 Pett Close, Hornchurch, Essex RM11 1FF (01708 478558 (H) 0171 830 8835 (B) 0171 830 8944 (F)). Ground: East London RFC, The Memorial Ground, Holland Road, London E15 3BP Tel: 0171 474 6761.

British Steel - 1953 - Secretary: B Hunton, 54 Lingbeck Park, Seaton, Workington, Cumbria CA14 1JQ (01900 64120 (H)). Fix Sec: M Messenger, 68 Newlands Lane, Workington, Cumbria CA14 3NH (01900 62882 (H)). Treasurer: J Moore, 4 Abbey Close, Workington, Cumbria CA14 3PB (01900 62413 (H)). Ground: Mossbay Works, Mossbay, Workington, Cumbria Tel: 01900 603570.

British Universities Sports Association - 1919 - Secretary: G Gregory-Jones, BUSA, 8 Union Street, London SE1 1SZ (0171 357 8555 (B) 0171 403 0127 (Fax)). Fix Sec: G Jenkins, BUSA, 8 Union Street, London SE1 1SZ (0171 357 8555 (B) 0171 403 0127 (Fax)). Treasurer: D Morgan, B.U.S.A, 8 Union Street, London SE1 1SZ. Ground: 8 Union Street, London SE1 1SZ Tel: 0171 357 8555.

Bromsgrove School - Ground: Bromsgrove, Worcestershire B16 7DU Tel: 01527 32863.

Burtonwood - 1964 - Secretary: Mrs E Southern, 25 Knight Road, Burtonwood, Warrington WA5 4QQ (01925 227611 (H)). Fix Sec: J Harper, 8 Camborne Road, Burtonwood, Warrington WA5 (01925 221559 (H)). Treasurer: T Reynolds, 55 Clay Lane, Burtonwood, Warrington, Cheshire WA5 4JH (01925 229376 (H)). Ground: Burtonwood Community Centre, Fir Tree Lane, Burtonwood, Warrington Tel: 01925 224480/225584.

Burwell - 1988 - Secretary: C J Humphreys, 27 Cawburn Lane, Burwell, Cambridgeshire CB5 0ED (01638 741918 (H)). Fix Sec: B Mitchell, 15 Jubilee Close, Waterbeach, Cambridge CB5 9NY (01223 440091 (H)). Treasurer: A Thorpe, 147 George Lambton Avenue, Newmarket, Suffolk (01638 664174 (H)). Ground: Fen Edge, The Recreation Grnd, Hythe Lane, Burwell, Cambridge.

Butleigh Amateur - 1976 - Secretary: H C Harding, 23 Fairfield Gardens, Glastonbury, Somerset BA6 9NH (01458 834376 (H) 01458 442291 (B) 01458 834376 (Fax)). Fix Sec: D Roberts, The Stables, Northload Bridge, Glastonbury, Somerset BA6 9LF (01458 833088 (H&F) 01278 458631 (B)). Treasurer: A J C Berkeley, Badgers Holt, 20 Plough Close, Brookfield Road, Street, Somerset BA16 (01458 447115 (H)). Ground: Kingweston Park, Somerton, Somerset Tel: none.

CUACO - 1926 - Secretary: A P Wells, 3rd Floor, CU House, 69 Park Lane, Croydon, Surrey CR9 1BG (0171 283 7500 (B) 0171 662 1000 (Fax)). Ground: Cuaco Club, Copers Cope Road, Beckenham, Kent BR3 1RJ Tel: 0181 650 9902.

Camborne Colts - 1948 - Secretary: W J C Dunstan, The Retreat, 11 Station Hill, Praze-an-Beeble, Camborne, Cornwall TR14 0JT (01209 831373 (H) 01736 795456 (B) 01736 797075 (F)). Fix Sec: D Smith, 65 Hughville Street, Camborne, Cornwall TR14 8TS (01209 716992 (H) 01736 752207 (B)). Treasurer: G Chinn, 24 Trevenson Street, Camborne, Cornwall TR14 8JB (01209 717035 (H)). Ground: Recreation Ground, Camborne Tel: 01209 713227.

Cambridge University - 1872 - Secretary: A W Jessop, Leys School, Cambridge CB2 2AD (01223 508984 (H) 01223 508905 (B) 01223 508984 (F)). Fix Sec: Dr F J Clough, Cherry Tree Cottage, 4 Glaston Park, Spring Lane,, Glaston, Leics LE15 9BW (01572 821351 (H) 0116 2551551 ext 8429 (B) 0116 2757692 (F)). Treasurer: I G Peck, College Farm, Stoneley, Huntingdon, Cambridgeshire PE18 0EG (01480 860424(H)01480 861711(F) 01223 841841(B) 01480 840294(F)). Ground: Univ. Football Ground, Grange Road, Cambridge CB3 9BN Tel: 01223 354131 (355301 Fax).

Christ's College - Secretary: D Till, College Rugby Club, Christ's College, Cambridge CB2 3BU (01223 332900 (P'Lodge) 01223 334973 (F)). Fix Sec: D Till, College Rugby Club, Christ's College, Cambridge CB2 3BU (01223 332900 (P'Lodge) 01223 334973 (F)). Treasurer: D C Barker, College Rugby Club, Christ's College, Cambridge CB2 3BU (01223 334900 (P'Lodge) 01223 334973 (F)). Ground: College Sports Ground, 162a Huntingdon Road, Cambridge Tel: 01223 276218.

Churchill College - 1961 - Secretary: M Doherty, College Rugby Club, Churchill College, Cambridge CB3 0DS. Fix Sec: D Parry, Churchill College, Cambridge CB3 0DS (01223 336000 (B)). Treasurer: M Doherty, College Rugby Club, Churchill College, Cambridge CB3 0DS. Ground: Churchill College, Cambridge CB3 0DS Tel: 01223 336000.

Clare College - 1908 - Secretary: H M Vann, Clare College, Cambridge CB2 1TL. Ground: Clare College Sports Ground, Bentley Rd, Cambridge.

Corpus Christi - Secretary: Hon Secretary, College Rugby Club, Corpus Christi, Cambridge CB2 1RH. Ground: Leckhampton, Cranmere Road, Cambridge CB3 9BL Tel: 01223 353231.

Darwin College - Secretary: Hon Sec RFC, College Rugby Club, Darwin College, Cambridge CB3 9EU (01223 335660 (B)).

Downing College - Secretary: Hon Sec, College Rugby Club, Downing College, Cambridge CB3 9EU (01223 334800 (B)). Ground: Long Road, Cambridge.

Emmanuel College - Ground: Wilberforce Road, Cambridge CB3 0EQ Tel: 01223 353961.

Fitzwilliam College - 1966 - Hon Sec: A Cockburn, Fitzwilliam College, Cambridge CB3 ODG (01223 477223). Fix Sec: A Coote, Fitzwilliam College,, Cambridge CB3 ODG (01223 477307). Treasurer: R Rawstron, Fitwilliam College,, Cambridge CB3 ODG (01223 477328). Ground: 93 Oxford Road, Cambridge CB4 3PH Tel: 01223 353382.

Girton College - Secretary: Hon Sec, College Rugby Club, Girton College, Cambridge CB3 0JG. Treasurer: E Cystor, Girton College, Cambridge CB3 0JG (01223 276848 (H)). Ground: Huntingdon Road, Cambridge CB3 0JG.

Gonville & Caius College - Secretary: Hon Sec, College Rugby Club, Gonville & Caius College, Cambridge CB2 1TA. Ground: Gonville & Caius College, Cambridge CB2 1TA Tel: 01223 332400.

Homerton College - Secretary: A S Dinatar, College Rugby Club, Homerton College, Cambridge CB2 2PH (01223 507235/6 (B) 01223 507140 (F)). Ground: Hills Road, Cambridge CB2 2PH Tel: 01223 507235/6.

Hughes Hall - Secretary: Hon Sec, College Rugby Club, Hughes Hall, Cambridge CB1 2EW (01223 334893 (B)).

Jesus College - Secretary: Hon Sec, College Rugby Club, Jesus College, Cambridge CB5 8BL. Ground: Jesus College, Cambridge CB5 8BL Tel: 01223 339339.

King's College - Secretary: Hon Sec, College Rugby Club, King's college, Cambridge CB2 1ST (01223 350411 (B)).

Magdalene College - Secretary: Hon Secretary, College Rugby Club, Magdalene College, Cambridge CB3 0AG. Ground: St John's Sports Field, Queens Road, Cambridge Tel: 01223 357362.

Pembroke College - Secretary: R Macfarlane, College Rugby Club, Pembroke College, Cambridge CB2 1RF (01636 812583 (H) 01223 338100 (B)). Ground: Pembroke College, Cambridge CB2 1RF Tel: 01223 359543.

Peterhouse - Secretary: C Da Cunha, College Rugby club, Peterhouse College, Cambridge CB2 1RD (01223 338200 (B)). Ground: Bentley Road, Cambridge CB2 1RD Tel: 01223 356045.

Queens' College - Secretary: M Costello, College Rugby Club, Queen's College, Cambridge CB3 9ET. Treasurer: A Freestone, Queen's College, Cambridge CB3 9ET. Ground: Queens College Playing Grounds, Barton Road, Cambridge Tel: 01223 335604.

Robinson College - Secretary: Hon Sec, College Rugby Club, Robinson College, Cambridge CB3 9AN (01223 311431 (B)). Ground: Cambridge CB3 9AN.

Selwyn College - 1882 - Ground: Fulbrooke Road, Cambridge CB3 14G Tel: 01223 354642.

Sidney Sussex College - Secretary: M Petevinos, College Rugby Club, Sidney Sussex College, Cambridge CB2 3HU (01223 33800 (B)). Ground: CB2 3HU.

St Catharine's College - Secretary: Hon Sec, College Rugby Club, St Catharine's College, Cambridge CB2 1RL. Ground: Grantchester Meadows, South Green Road, Cambridge Tel: 01223 352474.

St Edmund's College - Secretary: Hon Sec, College Rugby Clube, St Edmund's College, Cambridge CB2 0BN (01223 336250 (B)).

St John's College - 1867 - Secretary: D P Langford, College Rugby Club, St John's College, Cambridge CB2 1TP. Fix Sec: I A De Weymarn, College Rugby Club, St John's College, Cambridge CB2 1TP (01223 338600 (H) 01223 338502 (F)). Treasurer: I A De Weymarn, College Rugby Club, St John's College, Cambridge CB2 1TP (01223 338600 (H) 01223 338502 (F)). Ground: St John's College, Cambridge CB2 1TP Tel: 01223 338600.

Trinity College - 1872 - Ground: Trinity Old Field, Grange Rd, Cambridge CB2 1TQ Tel: 01223 359566.

Trinity Hall - Secretary: T Greenwood, College Rugby Club, Trinity Hall, Cambridge CB2 1TJ. Treasurer: P Coomber, Trinity Hall, Cambridge CB2 1TJ (01223 332500 (H) 01223 332500 (B)). Ground: Cambridge CB2 1TJ Tel: 01223 332500.

Wolfson College - Secretary: Hon Sec, College Rugby Club, Wolfson College, Cambridge CB3 9BB (01223 335900 01223 335937). Ground: Cambridge CB3 9BB Tel: 01223335900.

Cambridgeshire - 1946 - Secretary: K L Walker, 7 Lucketts Close, Histon, Cambridge CB4 4HG (01223 561754 (H) 0181 214 2024 (B) 0181 214 2325 (Fax)). Fix Sec: K L Walker, 7 Lucketts Close, Histon, Cambridge CB4 4HG (01223 561754 (H) 0181 214 2024 (B) 0181 214 2325 (Fax)). Treasurer: M Curtis, New Barn Farm, Lindsell, Great Dunmow CM6 3QH (01371 870461 (H) 01371 870461 (B) 01371 870008 (F)).

Capenhurst - 1952 - Hon Sec: T Roberts, 8 Chichester Street,, Chester, Cheshire CH1 4AD (01244 378789). Fix Sec: J Lewis, 52 Kingsmede, Upton, Chester CH2 1EF (01244 380320 (H) 0151 347 2326 (B)). Treasurer: T G Grundy, 43 Cumberland Avenue, Prenton, Merseyside L43 0RY (0151 608 6790 (H) 0151 347 3768 (B)). Ground: Capenhurst Sports Field, Chester CH1 6ER Tel: 0151 339 2389.

Castle College - 1966 - Secretary: A Cook, 47 Bishop Hill, Woodhouse, Sheffield S13 7EN (0114 269 6596 (H) 0114 296 9696 (B)). Fix Sec: P Howard, 24 Birchen Close, Dronfield Woodhouse, Sheffield S18 5ZD (01246 411818 (H)). Treasurer: P Cholerton, 43 Firbeck Road, Sheffield S8 0NF (0114 255 3307 (H)). Ground: Meadowhead School, Dyche Lane, Sheffield S8.

Castletown - 1991 - Secretary: P D Martin, 16 Queen's Terrace, Douglas, Isle of Man IM1 4BZ (01624 622080 (H) 01624 824772 (B)). Fix Sec: J Quayle, 41 Campion Way RFC, Abbeyfieldsk, Doulglas, Isle of Man IM2 7DT (01624 612040 (H)). Treasurer: S Fuller, 24 Terence Avenue, Douglas, Isle of Man IM2 5BN (01624 672505 (H)). Ground: Castletown RFU, Poulsom Park.

Centurions Sth Kent Police SC - 1984 - Secretary: R Thomas, 196 Canterbury Road, Folkestone, Kent CT19 5PF (01303 850262). Treasurer: Joe Feeney, 21 Castle Road, Sandgate, Folkstone, Kent (01303 249904). Ground: New Burlington Field, Bargrove, Newington, Folkestone, Kent CT18 8BH Tel: 01303 266887.

Channings Wood - 1982 - Secretary: P J Gillard, H M prison, Channings Wood RFC, Denbury, Newton Abbot, Devon TQ12 6DW (01803 812361 Ext 333 (B) 01803 813175 (F)). Fix Sec: P J Gillard, H M prison, Channings Wood RFC, Denbury, Newton Abbot, Devon TQ12 6DW (01803 812361 Ext 333 (B) 01803 813175 (F)). Ground: HMP Channings Wood, Denbury, Newton Abbot, Devon TQ12 6DW Tel: 01803 812361.

Cheltenham College - 1844 - Ground: Cheltenham, Gloucestershire GL53 7LD Tel: 01242 513540.

Chevron - 1989 - Secretary: P Lynch, 2 Portman Street, London W1H 0AN (0171 487 8742 (B)). Fix Sec: S Claisse, 43-45 Portman Square, London W1H OAN (0171 487 8205 (B)). Treasurer: J O'Brien, 93 Wigmore Street, London W1H 9AA (0171 286 2077 (H) 0171 487 8069 (B) 0171 487 8212 (F)). Ground: Park Avenue, Caterham, Surrey CR3 6AH Tel: 01883 343488.

Chiswick Police - 1989 - Secretary: Sgt N Baillie, Chiswick Police Station, 209 High Rd, Chiswick, London W4 2DU (01306 886147 (H) 0181 247 6415 (B)). Fix Sec: Sgt N Baillie, Chiswick Police Station, 209 High Rd, Chiswick, London W4 2DU (01306 886147 (H) 0181 247 6415 (B)). Treasurer: P Rowntree, 13 Dunsdon Avenue, Guildford, Surrey GU2 5NX (0181 577 1212 (B)). Ground: c/o Grasshoppers RFC, McFarlane Lane, Syon Lane, Osterley.

Christ's Hospital School - 1553 - Secretary: J Barker, Christ's Hospital School, Wragby Road, Lincoln, Lincolnshire LN2 4PN (01522 682162 (H) 01522 881144 (B) 01522 881145 (F)). Fix Sec: J Barker, Lincoln Christs Hospital Schoo, Wragby Road, Lincoln LN2 4PN (01522 682162 (H) 01522 881144 (B) 01522 881145 (F)). Ground: Wragby Road, Lincoln LN2 4PN Tel: 01522 881144.

Citizens - 1929 - Secretary: C R Southgate, Sunny Bank, Kingsland, Nr Leominster, Herefordshire HR6 9SE (01568 708010 (H) 01568 708050 (B) 01568 708010 (F)). Fix Sec: P Upton, 68 Addington Road, West Wickham, Kent BR4 9BJ (0181 462 3520 (H)). Treasurer: R Lewis, 22 Eastnor Road, London SE9 2BG (0181 859 1094 (H) 0181 850 8170 (B)). Ground: Old Dunstonians Sports Ground, St Dunstans Lane, Langley Park, Beckenham, Kent BR3 3SS Tel: 0181 650 1779.

Civil Service Union - 1922 - Secretary: G R Finch, 20 Villiers Avenue, Surbiton, Surrey KT5 8BD (0181 399 3049 (H) 0171 865 3282 (B)). Fix Sec: J Whipp, HM Treasury Chambers, London SW1 (0171 270 5307 (B)). Treasurer: V Jones, 83 Melton Rd, Tollerton, Nottinghamshire NG12 4EN (0115 937 6916 (H) 0115 924 2299 (B) 0115 950 9468 (Fax)). Ground: Civil Service Sports Ground, Dukes Meadow, Riverside Drive, Chiswick W4 Tel: 0181 994 1202.

Clapham - 1982 - Secretary: D R Tough, Millbrook House, 109 High Street, Riseley, Bedfordshire MK44 1DF (01234 708453 (H) 01438 314281 (B) 01438 318674 (Fax)). Fix Sec: M Baker, 82 High Street, Oakley, Bedfordshire MK43 7RH (01234 824092 (H)). Treasurer: I Randall, 16 Wells Close, Kempston, Bedfordshire MK42 8TS (01234 857818 (H)). Ground: Twinwoods Road, Clapham, Bedfordshire Tel: 01234 353633.

Cleveland Constabulary - 1968 - Secretary: PC 848 Barfield, c/o ARV Unit, Police HQ, PO Box 70, Ladgate Lane, Middlesborough TS8 9EH (01642 301454 (B) 01642 301453 (F)). Fix Sec: PC 848 Barfield, c/o ARV Unit, Police HQ, PO Box 70, Ladgate Lane, Middlesborough TS8 9EH (01642 301454 (B) 01642 301453 (F)). Ground: Middlesbrough RUFC, Acklam Park, Green Lane, Middlesbrough TS5 7SL Tel: 01642 818567.

Clifton College - Secretary: Ian Williams, School House, College Road, Clifton, Bristol BS8 3HY (0117 973 7625 (H) 0117 973 7625 (W) 0117 946 6826 (F)). Fix Sec: Ian Williams, School House, College Road, Clifton, Bristol BS8 3HY (0117 973 7625 (H) 0117 973 7625 (W) 0117 946 6826 (F)). Treasurer: Ian Williams, School House, College Road, Clifton, Bristol BS8 3HY (0117 973 7625 (H) 0117 973 7625 (W) 0117 946 6826 (F)). Ground: 32 College Road, Clifton, Bristol BS8 3JH Tel: 0117 973 9187.

Combined London Old Boys - 1971 - Secretary: M S Baker, Rookwood, Hedsor Road, Bourne End, Buckinghamshire SL8 5EE (01628 529952 (H) 0181 587 6399 (B)). Fix Sec: A Washer, 119 Westleigh Avenue, Coulsdon, Surrey CR5 3AE (01737 553373 (H) 0181 668 8241 (B)). Treasurer: A Sexton, 138 Addiscombe Road, Croydon, Surrey CR0 7LA (0181 654 4491 (H)).

Cornwall Colts - 1951 - Secretary: F G Williams, 23 Woodland Avenue, Penryn, Cornwall TR10 8PG (01326 375876 (H)). Fix Sec: F G Williams, 23 Woodland Avenue, Penryn, Cornwall TR10 8PG (01326 375876 (H)).

Cornwall Combination - 1987 - Secretary: C J Trerise, Omega, West End, Blackwater, Truro, Cornwall TR4 8EX (01872 560248 (H) 01872 560248 (B)). Fix Sec: Mrs B Davis, 8 Penrose Road, Helston, Cornwall TR13 8TP (01326 563744 (H)). Treasurer: R Grove, Touchdown, Penlee Crescent, Tregony, Truro, Cornwall (01872 53267 (H)).

Coventry and Mid-Warwickshire - 1884 - Secretary: C J McGinty, 14 Glendower Avenue, Whoberley, Coventry CV5 8BE (01203 679261 (H) 00353 732 3155 (H)). Fix Sec: B Lester, 7 Tiverton Road, Wyken, Coventry CV2 3DN (01203 456144 (H)). Treasurer: S Mathews, 8 Randle Street, Coundon, Coventry CV6 1LW (01203 596419 (H)). Ground: c/o Coventry FC, Barkers Butts Lane, Coventry CV6 1DU Tel: 01203 591274.

Customs and Excise - 1903 - Secretary: S B Jenner, 23 Meadowfield, Bradford upon Avon, Wiltshire BA15 1PL (01225 866238 (H) 01179 002146 (B) 01179 002094 (F)). Treasurer: M Croft, c/o Custom houseill West, Clayton St, Avonmouth BS11 9DX (0117 984 3400 (B) 0117 984 3527 (Fax)). Ground: c/o Civil Service Sports Gnd, Chiswick.

Cricklade - 1992 - Secretary: D Kent, Whitegates, 33 Restrop View, Purton, Wiltshire SN5 9DG (01793 771405 (H) 01628 438830 (B) 01628 438894 (F)). Fix Sec: T Handy, 10 The Pry, Pry Holdings, Purton Swindon, Wiltshire SN5 9JS (01793 772491(H)). Treasurer: I Smith, Home Farm, Down Ampney (01793 750268 (H)). Ground: Hatchets, Cricklade, Wiltshire.

Cumbria Constabulary - 1953 - Secretary: P D Hutton, 24 Landsdown Close, Kendal, Cumbria LA9 7SB (01539 722092 (H) 01229 583311 (B)). Fix Sec: Mike Woolaghan, Police HQ, Carleton Hall, Penrith CA10 2AU (01768 891999 ext. 7320). Treasurer: S Clarkson, 6 Green Lane, Houghton, Carlisle CA3 0NT (01228 592674 (H) 01906 602422 (B)). Ground: Winters Park, Penrith, Cumbria CA11 8RG Tel: 01768 863151.

Darlington Railway Athletic - 1925 - Secretary: T P Sanderson, School House, Chapel Street, Middleton-St-George, Darlington DL2 1DA (01325 332986 (H)). Fix Sec: T P Sanderson, School House, Chapel Street, Middleton-St-George, Darlington DL2 1DA (01325 332986 (H)). Treasurer: P Kennedy, 114 Pendleton Road, Darlington, County Durham (01325 487525 (H)). Ground: Brinkburn Road, Darlington Tel: 01325 468125.

Derbyshire Constabulary - 1926 - Secretary: I T Roe, 10 Otterburn Drive, Kedlaston Grange, Allestree, Derby DE22 2TJ (01332 551476 (H) 01332 222060 (B) 01332 551476 (F)). Fix Sec: I T Roe, 10 Otterburn Drive, Kedlaston Grange, Allestree, Derby DE22 2TJ (01332 551476 (H) 01332 222060 (B) 01332 551476 (F)). Ground: Force Headquarters, Butterley Hall, Ripley, Derbyshire DE5 3RS Tel: 01773 570100.

Dereham - 1974 - Secretary: Ms B Endresen, 1 Bayfield Ave, Dereham, Norfolk NR19 1PH (01362 691487 (H)). Fix Sec: M Brown (01362 697 931). Ground: Moorgate Road, Dereham, Norfolk.

Devon & Cornwall Constabulary (No 1 District) - 1967 - Secretary: S J Bassett, 2 Police House, Yelverton, Devon PL20 6EF (01822 854510 (H)). Fix Sec: N Jones, Brixham Police Station, Brixham, Devon (01803 555702 (H) 01803 882231 (B)). Treasurer: J Lamsin, 57 Kingsway Avenue, Whiterock, Paignton (01803 844583 (H)). Ground: Police Headquarters, Middlemoor, Exeter Devon TR4 8NG Tel: 01392 52101.

Dorset Police - 1978 - Secretary: Det Con P Morgan, 17 Halstock Crescent, Canford Heath, Poole, Dorset BH17 9BO (01202 697987 (H) 01305 223797 (B)). Fix Sec: Det Con C Jenkins, Bournemouth Police Station, Madeira Road, Bournemouth, Dorset (01202 222117 (B)). Treasurer: Det Con M Perrott, Bournemouth Police Station, Madeira Road, Bournemouth, Dorset (01202 222117 (B)). Ground: Dorset Police Headquarters, Winfrith, Dorchester, Dorset Tel: 01305 223797.

Dover College - 1870 - Ground: Effingham Crescent, Dover, Kent CT17 9RX Tel: 01304 205969.

Dover Customs - 1972 - Secretary: R McCarthy, `Minimus', Cherry Lane, Gt Mongeham, Deal, Kent CT14 0HG (01304 364374 (H) 01304 224276 (B) 01304 224279 (F)). Fix Sec: R Spain, 3 Mounts Close, Deal, Kent CT14 9SL (01304 360171 (H)). Treasurer: P Norley, 87 Lower Road, River, Dover, Kent CT17 0QY (01304 821322 (H)). Ground: Dover Rugby Club, Crabble, Dover Tel: 01304 210296.

Dulwich College - 1859 - Ground: Dulwich Common, London SE21 7LD Tel: 0181 299 9211.

Durham Constabulary - Secretary: P Davis, 22 Rickleton Avenue,, Chester-Le-Street, co Durham DH3 4AE (0191 3890848 (H) 0191 3752295 (B) 0191 3752290 (F)). Fix Sec: P Davis, 22 Rickleton Avenue,, Chester-Le-Street, co Durham DH3 4AE (0191 3890848 (H) 0191 3752295 (B) 0191 3752290 (F)).

Durham School - 1850 - Fix Sec: P Gerrard, Durham School, Quarryheads Lane, Durham City DH1 4SZ (0191 286 3133 (H) 0191 386 4783 (B) 0191 383 1025 (F)). Treasurer: P Gerrard, Durham School, Quarryheads Lane, Durham City DH1 4SZ (0191 286 3133 (H) 0191 386 4783 (B) 0191 383 1025 (F)). Ground: Quarryheads Lane, Durham City DH1 4SZ Tel: 0191 386 4783.

EGOR - 1978 - Secretary: B Minor, 45 Gorton Street, Peel Green, Eccles, Lancashire M30 7LZ (0161 288 5324 (H) 0161 877 2650 (B)). Fix Sec: K Punshon, 24 Newcombe Road, Holcombe Brook, Bury, Lancashire (01706 82 499(H)). Treasurer: Mrs G C Kennedy, 55 Hayeswater Road, Davyhulme, Manchester M41 7AS (0161 748 4783 (H) 0161 748 4783 (B)). Ground: Old Salians RFC, Clarendon Road, Sale, Manchester Tel: 0161 973 7250.

Eastbourne College - 1900 - Ground: Old Wish Road, East Sussex Tel: 01323 21528.

East Kent Colts - 1980 - Secretary: J G Scurr, Sunnyhill Cottage, 45 Sunny Hill Road, Herne Bay, Kent CT6 8LU (01227 373393 (H)). Treasurer: G Hanlon, 28 Willow Drive, Ham Street, Ashford, Kent (01233 2684 (H)).

East Northants - 1986 - Secretary: S J Watkins, 82 Croyland Road, Wellingborough, Northamptonshire NN8 2AU (01604 753312 (B)). Fix Sec: V J Edwards, 24 Jubilee Crescent, Wellingborough, Northamptonshire NN8 2PE (01933 274125 (H) 01933 440077 (B) 01933 227599 (F)). Treasurer: S J Watkins, 82 Croyland Road, Wellingborough, Northamptonshire NN8 2AU (01604 753312 (B)). Ground: Stewarts & Lloyds, Occupation Road, Corby.

East Peckham - 1977 - Secretary: A Fyfe, 'Failte', 8 Linden Close, Paddock Wood, Kent TN12 6LH (01892 837006 (H) 0171 922 4438 (B) 0171 922 4493 (F)). Treasurer: R Cserjen, 52 Church Road, Paddock Wood, Kent TN12 6HE (01892 835947 (H) 0181 319 6481 (B)). Ground: Putlands Sport & Leisure Ctr, Mascalls Court Road, Paddock Wood, Kent TN12 Tel: 01892 838290.

Emanuel School - 1910 - Ground: Battersea Rise, London SW11 1HS Tel: 0181 874 4601.

England Fire Service - 1970 - Secretary: G Walsh, 32 Halsey Crescent, West Derby, Liverpool L12 7HW (0151 2262878 (H) 0151 5491330 (B)). Fix Sec: G Walsh, 32 Halsey Crescent, West Derby, Liverpool L12 7HW (0151 2262878 (H) 0151 5491330 (B)). Treasurer: C Large, 2 Keats Road, Flitwick, Beds MK45 1QD (01525 713371 (H) 01582 875201 (B)).

Entertainers - 1963 - Secretary: C R Nicholas, 13 Woodbury Street, London SW17 9RP (0181 767 5841 (H) 0171 434 3536 (B) 0171 434 3429 (F)). Fix Sec: M Plummer, 227 Frien Road, London SE22 (0181 299 3740 (H) 0171 375 5807 (B)). Treasurer: A Benson, 15 Sutherland Grove, Teddington TW11 87R (0181 943 5146 (H) 0181 607 4084 (B)). Ground: c/o Wimbledon RFC, Barham Road, London SW20 0ET Tel: 0181 946 3156.

Epsom College - 1870 - Ground: Epsom, Surrey KT17 4JQ Tel: 013727 24810.

Erlestoke - 1985 - Secretary: J Spencer, HMP Erlestoke, Near Devizes, Wiltshire SN10 5TU (01380 813475 (B)). Fix Sec: J Spencer, HMP Erlestoke, Near Devizes, Wiltshire SN10 5TU (01380 813475 (B)). Treasurer: J Spencer, HMP Erlestoke, Near Devizes, Wiltshire SN10 5TU (01380 813475 (B)). Ground: HMP Erlestoke, Devizes, Wiltshire SN10 5TU Tel: 01380 813475 Ext 333.

Ernst and Young - 1970 - Secretary: W Heywood, Ernst & Young, Rolls House, 7 Rolls Building, Fetter Lane, London EC4A 1NH (0181 960 7631 (H) 0171 931 1847 (B) 0171 405 2147 (F)).

Essex County - 1954 - Secretary: M Drinkwater, 64 Woodlands Road, Hockley, Essex SS5 4PY (01702 203045 (H) 01702 203045 (B) 01702 203045 (F)). Fix Sec: L Hymans, 32 Devon Way, Canvey Island, Essex SS8 9YD (01268 693899 (H)). Treasurer: R Oakley, 1 Gouldswell Cottages, Orsett Road, Orsett, Essex RM16 3BE (01375 891636 (H)).

Essex Police - Secretary: E Zagger, c/o Sports Secretary, Police, HQ, Springfield, Chelmsford, Essex CM2 1DA (01245 491491 (H)). Fix Sec: P Daly, c/o Sports Secretary, Police, HQ, Springfield, Chelmsford, Essex CM2 1DA (01245 491491). Treasurer: P Daly, c/o Sports Secretary, Police, HQ, Springfield, Chelmsford, Essex CM2 1DA (01245 491491). Ground: Coronation Park, Timson's Lane, Chelmsford, Essex Tel: 01245 452922.

Everthorpe - 1961 - Secretary: H Potts, 29 Nutwell Lane, Armthorpe, Doncaster DN3 3JH (01302 300319 (H) 01430 422471 Ext 240 (B) 01430 421351 (F)). Ground: HMP Everthorpe, Brough, North Humberside HU15 1RB Tel: 01430 422471.

Exeter Gentlemens - 1987 - Secretary: C Gibbs, 17 Irving Road, London W14 0JT (0171 602 1274 (H) 0171 528 4363 (B)). Ground: Barn Elms, Barnes, London.

Fakenham - 1982 - Secretary: D J Swift, 19 North Park, Fakenham, Norfolk NR21 9RG (01328 863991 (H)). Fix Sec: C Evans, 64 Boyd Avenue, Toftwood, East Dereham, Norfolk NR19 1ND (01362 694537 (H)). Treasurer: C Evans, 64 Boyd Avenue, Toftwood, East Dereham, Norfolk NR19 1ND (01362 694537 (H)). Ground: Old Wells Road, Fakenham, Norfolk NR21 0BJ Tel: 01328 851007.

Falmouth Colts - 1931 - Secretary: P Rawlings, Polventon, 2 Killigrew Villas, Falmouth, Cornwall TR11 3PY (01326 311195 (H)). Fix Sec: G V Wilkes, 33 Carrine Road, Truro, Cornwall TR1 3XB (01872 277249 (H) 01209 885605 (B) 01209 885699 (F)). Treasurer: Mrs C Barnett, Shandolyn, Kimberely Park Road, Falmouth, Cornwall TR11 2DQ (01326 315422 (H)). Ground: Falmouth Recreation Ground, Dracaena Avenue, Falmouth TR11 2EQ Tel: 01326 311304.

Feltham Phoenix - 1974 - Secretary: G Workman, 70 Clifton Road, Kingston-on-Thames, Surrey KT2 6PS (0181 541 5782 (H) 0181 890 0061 Ext 333). Fix Sec: R Hudson, 6 Redford Close, Bedfont Gate, Feltham Middlesex TW13 4TJ (0181 890 0061 ext 333 (B) 0181 844 1551 (F)). Treasurer: G Workman, 70 Clifton Road, Kingston-on-Thames, Surrey KT2 6PS (0181 541 5782 (H) 0181 890 0061 Ext 333). Ground: HMYCC Feltham, Bedfont Road, Feltham, Middlesex TW13 4ND Tel: 0181 890 0061 Ext 333.

Fermain Tavern - 1981 - Secretary: A A Coulson, Jabulami, Les Petites Capelles, St Sampson, Guernsey GY2 4GX (01481 42782 (H) 01481 719000 (B)). Fix Sec: M T P Cahill, Le Marecage, Le Marais, L'eree G77 9LD (01481 64035 (H)). Treasurer: A A Coulson, Jabulami, Les Petites Capelles, St Sampson, Guernsey GY2 4GX (01481 42782 (H) 01481 719000 (B)). Ground: Footes Lane, St Peter Port, Guernsey Tel: 01481 54590.

Five Horseshoes - 1982 - Secretary: G Cromack, 4 Milton Close, Henley on Thames, Oxon RG9 1UJ (01491 575014 (H) 01491 641282 (B) 01491 641086 (Fax)). Fix Sec: G Cromack, 4 Milton Close, Henley on Thames, Oxon RG9 1UJ (01491 575014 (H) 01491 641282 (B) 01491 641086 (Fax)). Treasurer: A Hearn, Loddam House, 81 St Marks Road, Henley on Thames, Oxon (01491 572814 (H)). Ground: Dry Leas, Marlow Road, Henley on Thames, Oxfordshire Tel: 01491 574499/641282.

Forest Old Boys - 1990 - Secretary: T Walters, Azalea Cottage, Merryhill Green Lane, Winnersh, Wokingham, Berks (01189 785383). Fix Sec: T Walters, Azalea Cottage, Merryhill Green Lane, Winnersh, Wokingham, Berks (01189 785383). Treasurer: S McGillivray, 55 Crail Close, Wokingham, Berkshire RG11 2PZ (01189 774824 (H) 01189 751508 (B)). Ground: Redingensians, Old Bath Road, Sonning, Reading, Berkshire Tel: 01189 695259.

Gatwick Handling - 1993 - Secretary: D Jacques, c/o Gatwick Handling, 7th Floor, Norfolk House, Gatwick Airport, Sussex.

Glen Parva Pirates - 1977 - Secretary: PEO G Markham, HMY01 Glen Parva, Tigers Road, Wigston, Leicestershire LE18 4TN (0116 277 2022 Ext 2221 (B)). Fix Sec: PEO G Markham, HMY01 Glen Parva, Tigers Road, Wigston, Leicestershire LE18 4TN (0116 277 2022 Ext 2221 (B)). Ground: PE Department, HMYOI, Glen Parva, Tigers Road, Wiston, Leicester LE18 4TN Tel: 0116 277 2022.

Gloucestershire Constabulary - 1948 - Secretary: A M Drummond, The Orchard, Green Lane, Churchdown, Gloucester GL3 2LB (01242 276246 (B)). Fix Sec: P Haines, Savannah, Church Road, Caincross, Stroud GL5 4JE (01453 765003 (H) 01242 528282 (B)). Treasurer: P Smithson, c/o Talbot House, Lansdown Road, Cheltenham (01242 276127). Ground: Dowty Rotol RFC, Down Hatherley Lane, Gloucester GL2 9QD Tel: 01452 714567.

Greater Manchester Fire Service - 1965 - Secretary: M E Higgins, 1 Langside Drive, Ladybridge, Bolton BL3 4US (01204 417667 (H) 0161 736 5866 (B) 0161 743 1777 (F)). Treasurer: M E Higgins, 1 Langside Drive, Ladybridge, Bolton BL3 4US (01204 417667 (H) 0161 736 5866 (B) 0161 743 1777 (F)).

Greater Manchester Police - 1974 - Secretary: Sgt M Sutton, GMP Rugby Section, Mottram Police Station, Atherton Grove, Mottram, Hyde SK14 6JE (0161 856 9435 (B)). Ground: Police Club, Hough End Centre, Mauldeth Road West, Manchester M21 1SX Tel: 0161
856 1798.

Greyhound - 1977 - Secretary: A Braithwaite, 1 Marlbrook Road, Redhill, Hereford HR2 7PU (01432 272921 (H)). Fix Sec: Nigel Greening, 9 Old School Lane, Hereford HR1 1EU (01432 356579). Treasurer: Martin Ackley, 27 Thomas Close, Lower Bullingham, Hereford HR2 6RF (01432 351688). Ground: City Sports Ground, Grandstand Rd, Hereford HR2 7RL Tel: 01432 272921.

HM Prison Service - 1976 - Secretary: S N Sporcic, HMP Birmingham, Winson Green Rd, Birmingham B18 4AS (0121 554 3838 (B)). Fix Sec: R Sawbridge, c/o H M Prison Leicester, Welford Rd,, Leicester (01162 546911 01162 471753). Treasurer: M Steel, 86 Onley Park, Willoughby, Rugby, Warwickshire CV23 8AP (01788 814 432 01788 522022 (B) 01788 522260 (Fax)). Ground: HM Prison Service College, Newbold Revel, Nr Rugby, Warwickshire Tel: 01788 832666.

HMP Acklington - Secretary: P Sanderson, 10 Foxhill Close, Fallowfield Estate, Ashington, Northumberland (01670 521475 (H) 01670 760411 Ext 333 (B) 01670 761361 (Fax)). Fix Sec: B Taylor, HMP Acklington, Morpeth, Northumberland (01670 760411 Ext 333 (B) 01670 761361 (Fax)). Ground: HM Prison Acklington, Morpeth, Northumberland NE65 9XF Tel: 01670 760411 Ext 333.

HMP Featherstone - 1985 - Secretary: A Scott, The Gymnasium, New Road, Featherstone, Near Wolverhampton WV10 7PU (01902 790991 ext 322 (B)). Fix Sec: A Scott, The Gymnasium, New Road, Featherstone, Near Wolverhampton WV10 7PU (01902 790991 ext 322 (B)). Treasurer: A Scott, The Gymnasium, New Road, Featherstone, Near Wolverhampton WV10 7PU (01902 790991 ext 322 (B)). Ground: New Road, Featherstone, Wolverhampton WV10 7PU Tel: 01902 790991 x332.

HMP Garth - 1989 - Secretary: T Probert, H M Prison Garth, Ulnes Walton Lane, Leyland, Preston PR5 3NE (01772 465218 (H) 01772 622722 Ext 465 (B) 01772 622276 (F)). Fix Sec: T Probert, H M Prison Garth, Ulnes Walton Lane, Leyland, Preston PR5 3NE (01772 465218 (H) 01772 622722 Ext 465 (B) 01772 622276 (F)). Treasurer: C Pawsey, Ulnes Walton Lane, Leyland, Preston PR5 3NE (01772 622722 ext 465 (B) 01772 622276 (F)). Ground: H.M.Prison Garth, Ulnes Walton Lane, Leyland, Preston PR5 3NE Tel: 01772 622722.

HMP Lincoln - 1989 - Secretary: C K Lewis, PE Dept, HMP Lincoln, Greetwell Road, Lincoln LN2 4BD (01522 560834 (H) 01522 533633 Ext 401 (B)). Fix Sec: C K Lewis, PE Dept, HMP Lincoln, Greetwell Road, Lincoln LN2 4BD (01522 560834 (H) 01522 533633 Ext 401 (B)). Treasurer: C K Lewis, PE Dept, HMP Lincoln, Greetwell Road, Lincoln LN2 4BD (01522 560834 (H) 01522 533633 Ext 401 (B)). Ground: HMP Lincoln, Greetwell Road, Lincoln LN2 4BD Tel: 01522 533633 Ext 401.

Haileybury - 1863 - Secretary: Master I/C Rugby, Haileybury College, Hertford (01992 464983 (H) 01992 444535 (B) 01992 467603 (Fax)). Ground: Hertford Heath, Hertford SG13 7NU Tel: 01992 462352.

Hartpury College - 1970 - Secretary: Mrs M Davis, Hartpury College, Hartpury House, Nr Gloucester GL19 3BE (01452 702102 (B) 01452 700629 (F)). Fix Sec: Sports Warden, Hartpury College, Hartpury House, Gloucester GL19 3BE (01452 700283 01452 700629). Treasurer: J Perry, Hartpury College, Hartpury House, Gloucester GL19 3BE. Ground: Hartpury College,, Hartpury House, Nr Gloucester GL19 3BE Tel: 01452 700283(T) 700629 (F).

Harrodians - 1912 - Secretary: P Kirby, 53 Stanhope Gardens, London SW7 5RF (0171 373 0120 (H) 0171 602 5678 (B) 0171 603 8680 (Fax)). Fix Sec: P Kirby, 53 Stanhope Gardens, London SW7 5RF (0171 373 0120 (H) 0171 602 5678 (B) 0171 603 8680 (Fax)). Treasurer: P Kirby, 53 Stanhope Gardens, London SW7 5RF (0171 373 0120 (H) 0171 602 5678 (B) 0171 603 8680 (Fax)). Ground: Barn Elms, Queen Elizabeth Wlk, Barnes, London SW13 9SA Tel: 0181 876 7685.

Hayle Colts - 1946 - Secretary: J Trevaskis, c/o Hayle RFC, Memorial Park, Hayle, Cornwall TR27 4PS. Ground: Marsh Lane, Hayle, Cornwall Tel: 01736 753320.

Heathrow Airport - 1974 - Secretary: Mrs C Burton, 236 Beavers Lane, Hounslow, Middlesex TW4 6HQ (0181 5725849 (H) 01932 825093 (B) 0181 5725849 (F)). Fix Sec: Mrs C Burton, 236 Beavers Lane, Hounslow, Middlesex TW4 6HQ (0181 5725849 (H) 01932 825093 (B) 0181 5725849 (F)). Treasurer: A M Rabjohn, 2 Brockenhurst Road, Martins Heron, Bracknell, Berkshire RG12 6FJ (01344 426523 (H) 0956 253616 (B) 01344 426523 (Fax)). Ground: BAA Heathrow Club, Printinghouse Lane, Hayes, Middlesex Tel: 0181 8136811.

Hertfordshire Fire & Rescue Service - 1974 - Secretary: J Horastead, 61 Acme Road, Watford, Herts WD2 5HQ (01923 496788 (H) 01923 211 991(B) 01923 211 994(F)). Fix Sec: C Strickland, HFRS HQ, Old London Road, Hertford SG13 7LD (01462 491906 (H) 01992 507514 (B) 01992 550242 (F)). Treasurer: J Horastead, 61 Acme Road, Watford, Herts WD2 5HQ (01923 496788 (H) 01923 211 991(B) 01923 211 994(F)). Ground: Hertford RFC, Hoe Lane, Ware, Hertfordshire SG12 9NZ.

Hertfordshire Police - 1949 - Secretary: R Larter, County Police Station, Lytton Way, Stevenage, Hertfordshire (01438 757011 (B) 01438 757009 (Fax)). Fix Sec: S Gibbs, County Police Station, High Street, Baldock, Hertfordshire (01438 757009 (F)). Treasurer: J Caldwell, County Police HQ, Standborough, Lane, Welwyn Garden City, Hertfordshire (01707 757000). Ground: Police HQ, Stanborough Road, Welwyn Garden City AL8 6XF Tel: 01707 757000.

Hillingdon Police - 1991 - Secretary: N Fretwell, 15 Sandgate House, Queens Walk, Ealing, London W5 1TN (0181 723 9786(H) 0956 304 909 (B)). Treasurer: Alun Davies, 102 fairview Road, Taplow, Maidenhead, Berkshire SL6 0NQ (01628 668997 0171 2304144). Ground: c/o Hayes RFC, Grosvenor Playing Fields, Kingshill Avenue, Hayes Tel: 0181 845 4963.

Hoddesdon White Swanarians - 1991 - Secretary: S Stagg, 10 Briscoe Rd, Hoddesdon, Herts EN11 9DQ (01992 468712 01992 463411 01992 461981). Fix Sec: P Reast, 15 Stafford Drive, Broxbourne, Herts EN10 7JT (01992 465725 01707 352804). Treasurer: N Wright, 22 Barley Ponds Road, Ware, Herts SG12 7EZ (01920 463809 (H) 01992 822988 (B) 01992 470271 (F)). Ground: King George v Playing Fields, Wormley, Hertfordshire EN11 8TN.

Honda - 1990 - Secretary: T Lee, c/o Honda Engineering Europe, Highworth Road, South Marston, Swindon, Wiltshire SN3 4TZ (01793 695448 (H) 01793 416500/416533 (B) 01793 458363 (F)). Fix Sec: N Harper, 385 Cricklade Road, Goarse Hill, Swindon SN2 2AQ (01793 538135 (H) 01793 831183 Ext 3003 (B) none). Treasurer: J Brown, 11 County Road, Swindon, Wiltshire SN1 2EG (01793 693172 (H) 01793 831183 Ext 8607 (B)). Ground: Supermarine Sport/Social Club, Highworth Rd, South Marston, Swindon, Wiltshire SN3 4TZ Tel: 01793 824828.

Hong Kong Bank Group - 1887 - Secretary: R Long, HSBC Asset M'Ment Europe Ltd, 6 Bevis Marks, London EC3A 7QP (0171 336 5813 (H)). Ground: Lennard Road, New Beckenham, Kent Tel: 0181 778 7434.

Humberside Fire Brigade - 1990 - Secretary: G Lester, The Stables, 17 Carr Lane, Willerby, East Yorkshire HU10 6JP (01482 659475 (H) 01482 354255 (B) 01482 573051 (F)). Fix Sec: A Martin, 28 The Meadows, South Cave, Hull HU15 2HR (01430 422242 (H) 01482 565333 (B) 01482 508635 (F)). Treasurer: P Stockton, 32 Manor Drive, Elloughton, Brough, East Yorkshire HU15 1JA (01482 665497 (H) 01405 768373 (B) 01405). Ground: Brantingham Park, Brantingham Grove, Elloughton,, Brough, East Yorkshire HU15 1HX Tel: 01482 667342.

Humberside Police - 1961 - Secretary: J Harris, 3 Stewart Garth, Cottingham, East Yorkshire HU16 5YQ (01482 326111 Ext3341(B) 01482 220337). Fix Sec: P Snowden, c/o Humberside Police, F.I.B, Queens G'dens Police St, Hull (01482 220274 01482 220337). Treasurer: P Finch, c/o Humberside Police, F.I.B , Queens Gardens Police, Station, Hull (01482 220274 (B)). Ground: Inglemire Lane Police Club, Inglemire Lane, Hull, East Yorks Tel: 01482 856954.

Huntingdon and Peterborough County Union - 1967 - Secretary: Mrs B A Hedges, 11 Westbrooke Park Road, Peterborough, Cambs PE2 9JG (01733 894854 (H)). Treasurer: Mrs B A Hedges, 11 Westbrooke Park Road, Peterborough, Cambs PE2 9JG (01733 894854 (H)).

IBM - 1969 - Secretary: Miss S Brown, 113c St Andrew's Road, Southsea, Portsmouth, Hampshire PO5 1ES (01705 828079 (H) 0990 440055 (B) 01705 492222 (F)). Fix Sec: J Richards, 27 Hamilton Court, Ashby Place, Southsea, Portsmouth, Hampshire PO5 3NP (01705 816948 (H) 01705 565286 (B)). Treasurer: G McMillan, 7 St David's Road, Southsea, Portsmouth, Hampshire PO5 1QH (01705 293541 (H) 01705 254753 (B)). Ground: Havant RFC, Hooks Lane, Fraser Rd, Bedhampton, Havant, Hants PO9 3EJ Tel: 01705 492311.

Imber Court - 1947 - Secretary: J Bailey, 84 Brightside Avenue, Staines, Middlesex TW18 1NQ (01784 459236 (H)). Fix Sec: J Bowens (01923 720478 (H)). Ground: Imber Court Sports Club, Ember Lane, East Molesey, Surrey KT8 0BT Tel: 0181 398 1267/6609.

Inland Revenue - 1924 - Secretary: Vivian Jones, The Croft, 83 Melton Road, Tollerton, Nottinghamshire NG12 4EN (01159 376916 (H) 01159 741857 (B) 01159 741851 (Fax)). Fix Sec: Vivian Jones, The Croft, 83 Melton Road, Tollerton, Nottinghamshire NG12 4EN (01159 376916 (H) 01159 741857 (B) 01159 741851 (Fax)). Treasurer: J Doyle, Kaloma, 9 Furrows Close, Oakwood, Derby DE21 2XP (01332 675053 (H) 01159 741201 (B) 01159 741300 (F)). Ground: Civil Service Sports Ground, Dukes Meadows, Chiswick, London Tel: 0181 994 1202.

Insurance Offices - 1927 - Secretary: P C Richardson, Panorama, Trenance, Mawgan Porth, Cornwall TR8 4BY (01637 860106 (H)). Fix Sec: P Roberts, 10 Park Lane, Thatcham RG18 4BJ (0345 573644). Treasurer: M Winn, 52 Lynton Park Avenue, East Grinstead, Surrey RH19 3XB (01342 323001 (H)).

Jersey Police - 1998 - Secretary: D A Joshua, Rouge Bouillon Police Station, St Helier, Jersey, Channel Islands JE4 8ZZ (01534 612612 (B) 01534 612613 (F)). Fix Sec: S Cross, Rouge Bouillon Police Station, St Helier, Jersey, Channel Islands JE4 8ZZ (01534 612612 (B) 01534 612613 (F)). Ground: Granville, St Saviour, Jersey JE2 7LG Tel: 01534 34350.

Jersey United Banks - 1969 - Secretary: S C Young, PO Box 236, First Island House, Peter Street, St Helier, Jersey JE4 8SG (01534 39797 (H) 01534 880088 (B) 01534 880099 (F)). Fix Sec: A Cotton, c/o Geest Limited, 31 The Parade, St Helier, Jersey JE2 3QQ (01534 888080 (B) 01534 616788 (F)). Treasurer: N Sangan, c/o Hambros (CI) Trust Corp., 7 The Esplanade, St Helier JE4 8RT (01534 887700 (B) 01534 887710 (F)). Ground: Grainville Playing Fields, St Saviour's Hill, St Saviour, Jersey JE2 7LG Tel: 01534 34350.

Jones Lang Wootton - 1970 - Secretary: M N Saper, 22 Hanover Square, London W1A 2BN (01753 647216 (H) 0171 493 6040 (B) 0171 4992592 (F)). Fix Sec: T Edgehill, 22 Hanover Square, London W1A 2BN (0171 493 6040 (B) 0171 408 0220 (F)). Treasurer: G Lambert, 22 Hanover Square, London W1A 2BN (0171 386 0260 (H) 0171 457 3914 (B) 0171 499 2592 (F)). Ground: Polytechnic of Central London, Cavendish Road, Chiswick, London Tel: 0181 994 1554.

Kent County Constabulary - 1963 - Secretary: PC S Rose, 29 Sutton Road, Maidstone, Kent ME15 9AE (01622 661979 (H) 01622 654766 (B) 01622 654769 (F)). Fix Sec: PC S Rose, 29 Sutton Road, Maidstone, Kent ME15 9AE (01622 661979 (H) 01622 654766 (B) 01622 654769 (F)). Treasurer: PC C Bramwell, 2 Greensand Road, Bearsted, Kent (01622 637465 (H) 01622 690055 (B)). Ground: Kent Police HQ, Sutton Road, Maidstone ME15 9DW Tel: 01622 690690.

Kew Occasionals - 1988 - Secretary: R Clark, 5 Maze Road, Kew, Richmond, Surrey TW9 3DA (0171 240 5024 (B) 0171 379 8030 (F)). Ground: Westminster Univ Sports Ground, Cavendish Road(off Hartington), Chiswick, London W4 3UH Tel: 0181 994 1554.

King Edward's School, Birmingham - 1875 - Ground: Edgbaston Park Road, Birmingham B15 2UA Tel: 0121 472 1147.

Kings Cross Steelers - 1999 - Ground: Beverly Hill, Barham Road,, Wimbledon SW20 OET.

LFB Southern Command (Moosehead) - 1986 - Secretary: J T Scudder, 11 Brookmead Avenue, Bromley, Kent BR1 2SX (0181 467 4997 (H) 0171 587 4524 (B)). Treasurer: B C Kemp, Fire Station, Sunbury St, Woolwich, London SE18 5LU (0171 587 4524 (H)). Ground: Fire Station, Sunbury Street, London SE18 5LU.

Lancashire Constabulary - 1954 - Secretary: K R Boyce, Riversmead, Tolsey Drive, Hutton, Preston, Lancashire PR4 55H (01772 613095 (H)). Fix Sec: A Edwards, County Police Office, Preston (01772 451293 (H) 01772 203203 (B)). Treasurer: A Edwards, County Police Office, Preston (01772 451293 (H) 01772 203203 (B)). Ground: County Police Headquarters, Hutton, Preston, Lancashire Tel: 01772 614444.

Leger - 1986 - Secretary: The Hon Secretary, c/o HM Prison Lindholme, Bawtry Rd, Hatfield Woodhouse, Doncaster, S Yorks. Ground: PE Department, HM Prison, Lindholme, Doncaster, South Yorkshire DN7 6EE Tel: 01302 846600 Ext 241.

Leicestershire Constabulary - 1951 - Secretary: T Perridge, 4 Copse Close, Leicester Forest East, Leicester LE3 3NZ (0116 248 2702 (B) 0116 248 2703 (F)). Fix Sec: C Cary, 10 Laundon Close, Groby, Leicester LE6 0YZ (0116 2482706 (B) 0116 2482703 (F)). Treasurer: G Jones, HQ Operations Planning, Leicestershire Constabulary, St.Johns, Marborough,Leics LE9 5BX (0116 248 2317 (B) 0116 248 2321 (F)). Ground: c/o Syston RFC, Barkby Road, Queniborough, Leicester LE7 3FE Tel: 0116 260 1223.

Leicestershire Fire & Rescue Service - 1971 - Secretary: P Crane, 15 Skye Way, 15 Skye Way, Countesthorpe, Leicester LE8 5TY (0116 2776782 (H) 0116 287 2241 (B)). Fix Sec: M Elliott, 7 Tynedale Road, Loughborough, Leicester LE11 3TA (01509 211747 (H) 0116 232 4524 (B)). Treasurer: S Kellock, 12 Woodhouse Road, Narborough, Leicester LE9 5ZA (0116 286 1384 (H) 0116 232 4540 (B)). Ground: c/o Lancaster Road Fire Statio, Lancaster Road, Leicester Tel: 0116 245 3230.

Leyhill - 1988 - Secretary: A.E Fleming, P.E Dept., H N P. Leyhill, Woston-U-Edge, Glos GL12 8BT (01454 260681). Secretary: A.E Fleming, P.E Dept., H N P. Leyhill, Woston-U-Edge, Glos GL12 8BT (01454 260681). Ground: HMP Leyhill, Wotton-under-Edge, Gloucester GL12 8BT Tel: 01454 260681 Ext 332.

Leys High School - 1875 - Ground: Woodrow Drive, Redditch, Worcestershire Tel: 01527 23088.

Limehouse - 1989 - Secretary: S H Adams, Dhekelia, Albert Road, Bulphan, Essex RM14 3SB (01375 891057 (H) 0171 488 6500 (B) 0181 983 1042 (Fax)). Ground: Chigwell Police Club, Chigwell, Essex Tel: 0181 500 2735.

Lincolnshire Police - 1958 - Secretary: C Moon, 5 Manor Lane, Welton, Lincoln LN2 3JQ (01673 861873 (H) 01522 532222 (B)). Fix Sec: S Verrills, 58 Hine Avenue, Beacon Heights, Newark, Nottinghamshire NG24 2LH (01636 673748 (H) 01522 532222 (B)). Treasurer: A Gibb, 26 Eve Gardens, Washingborough, Lincoln (01522 794837 (H)). Ground: Police HQ, Deep Dale Lane, Nettleham, Lincoln LN5 7PH Tel: 01522 532222.

Littlehey - 1988 - Secretary: A P Curtis, 6 Riverside Way, Islip, Kettering, Northamptonshire NN14 3LF (01832 733311 (H) 01480 812202 Ext 248 (B) 01480 812151 (B)). Fix Sec: A P Curtis, 6 Riverside Way, Islip, Kettering, Northamptonshire NN14 3LF (01832 733311 (H) 01480 812202 Ext 248 (B) 01480 812151 (B)). Treasurer: A P Curtis, 6 Riverside Way, Islip, Kettering, Northamptonshire NN14 3LF (01832 733311 (H) 01480 812202 Ext 248 (B) 01480 812151 (B)). Ground: HMP Littlehey, Perry, Huntingdon, Cambridgeshire PE18 0SR Tel: 01480 812202 Ext 248/249.

Lloyds TSB - 1913 - Secretary: B Brazier, 2 Crushes Close, Hutton, Brentwood, Essex CM13 1PB (01277 213626 (H) 01702 361245 (B) 01702 354147 (F)). Fix Sec: G Howells, 59 Lorne Gardens, Shirley, Croydon CR0 7RZ (0181 656 3901 (H) 0171 922 3884 (B)). Treasurer: K White, 173 Petts Wood Road, Petts Wood, Orpington, Kent BR5 1JY (01689 813228 (H) 0171 265 5801(B) 0171 488 2823). Ground: Lloyds T.S.B.Sports Club, 59 Lorne Gardens, Shirley, Croydon CR0 7RZ Tel: 0181 656 3901.

Loggerheads - 1976 - Secretary: R Macken, 1 Lexden Gardens, Belle Vue Road, Shrewsbury SY3 7NL (01743 248370 (H)). Fix Sec: R Macken, 1 Lexden Gardens, Belle Vue Road, Shrewsbury SY3 7NL (01743 248370 (H)). Ground: Sundorne Castle Ground, Shrewsbury Tel: 01743 53380.

London Fire Brigade NW Area - 1989 - Secretary: K A Heymer, 57 Manor Way, North Harrow, Middlesex HA2 6BZ (0181 248 8037 (H) 0171 587 2375 (B)). Fix Sec: K A Heymer, 57 Manor Way, North Harrow, Middlesex HA2 6BZ (0181 248 8037 (H) 0171 587 2375 (B)). Treasurer: K A Heymer, 57 Manor Way, North Harrow, Middlesex HA2 6BZ (0181 248 8037 (H) 0171 587 2375 (B)). Ground: Northolt RFC, Cayton Green Park, Cayton Road, Greenford, Middlesex UB6 8BJ Tel: 0181 813 1701.

London Goodenough Trust - 1992 - Secretary: A H Mellows, London House, Mecklenburgh Square, London WC1N 2AB (0171 837 8888 (H) 0171 837 8888 (B) 0171 837 9321 (Fax)). Treasurer: J McCready, London House, Mecklrnburgh Square, London WC1N 2AB (0171 837 8888 (H) 0171 837 8888 (B)).

London Manx - 1987 - Secretary: C J P Haslam, Pennine Lodge, 24 Gerard Avenue, Thorley, Bishops Stortford, Herts CM23 4DU (01279 659030 (H) 01480 224000 (B)) 01480 224066 (F)). Fix Sec: R White, Trees, Wycke Lane, Tollesbury, Maldon, Essex (01621 869252 (H)). Ground: Westminster Lodge, St Albans, Hertfordshire.

Long Lartin - 1977 - Secretary: A Madge, HM Prison, Long Lartin, South Littleton, Evesham, Worcestershire WR11 5TZ (01386 830101 x332 (B) 01386 832834 (Fax)). Fix Sec: A Madge, HM Prison, Long Lartin, South Littleton, Evesham, Worcestershire WR11 5TZ (01386 830101 x332 (B) 01386 832834 (Fax)). Ground: HM Prison, Long Lartin, South Littleton, Evesham, Worcestershire WR11 5TZ Tel: 01386 830101 Ext 332.

Manchester YMCA - 1903 - Secretary: M Kennedy, 14 Beeston Close, Sharples, Bolton BL1 7RT (01204 597891 (H) 0467 232634 (B) 01204 598585 (F)). Fix Sec: P Watson, 7 Vickers Close, Clifton, Swinton M27 2QE (0161 793 9212 (H)). Treasurer: B Reece, 24 Westdale Gardens, Burnage, Manchester M19 1JD (0161 432 6256 (H)). Ground: The Hollies, Mersey Meadows,, Mersey Road, Didsbury, Manchester M20 2GB.

Marlborough College - 1861 - Fix Sec: J E Patching, Elmhurst Boarding House, Bath Road, Marlborough SN8 1PA (01672 892260 (H) 01672 892260 (B) 01672 892267 (F)). Ground: Marlborough, Wiltshire SN8 1PA Tel: 01672 515511.

Menwith Hill - 1982 - Secretary: Steven Wilhelm, RAF Menwith Hill, Box 494, North Yorkshire HG3 2RF (01423 536281 01423 846202). Fix Sec: Jan Swenson, Sports and Fittness Centre, RAF Menwith Hill, North Yorkshire HG3 2RF (01423 777781). Treasurer: Shawn Eion Smith, Barnhill, Glasshouses HG3 5DH (01423 712225 01423 846561). Ground: Menwith Hill Station, Harrogate, North Yorkshire HG3 2RF Tel: 01423 777788.

Merchant Taylors' School (Crosby) - 1871 - Ground: Crosby, Liverpool, Merseyside L23 0QP Tel: 0151 928 3618.

Merchant Taylors' School (London) - 1859 - Ground: Sandy Lodge Lane, Northwood, Middlesex HA6 2HT.

Merseyside Fire Brigade - Secretary: S Smith, 4a The Parade, Wood Rd, Halewood, Liverpool L26 1UZ. Ground: Newbrigton RUFC, Reeds Lane, New Brighton Wirral L46 3RH Tel: 0151 677 1873.

Mill Hill School - Ground: The Ridgeway, Mill Hill, London NW7 Tel: 0181 959 4207.

Ministry of Defence - 1990 - Secretary: P Piper, 7 Phoenix Close, West Wickham, Kent BR4 0TA (0171 218 0192 (B)). Ground: CSSG Chiswick, Dukes Meadows, London W4 Tel: 0181 994 1202.

NESCOT - 1971 - Secretary: A Powell, Acting Recreation Officer, NESCOT Sports Hall, Reigate Rd, Ewell, Surrey KT17 3DS (0181 394 3133 (B) 0181 394 3030 (F)). Fix Sec: A Powell, Acting Recreation Officer, NESCOT Sports Hall, Reigate Rd, Ewell, Surrey KT17 3DS (0181 394 3133 (B) 0181 394 3030 (F)). Treasurer: P Cherubin, Finance Department, Reigate Road, Ewell, Surrey KT17 3DS (0181 3941731 (B)). Ground: Reigate Road, Epsom, Surrey KT17 3DS Tel: 0181 394 3133.

New Parks - 1968 - Secretary: T Smith, 10 The Birds Nest Avenue, New Parks Estate, Leicester LE3 9NB (0116 2911687 (H)). Fix Sec: R Brooks, 44 Bateman Road, New Parks Estate, Leicester LE3 9HD (0116 2332536 (H)). Treasurer: B Harrott, The Good Neighbours, Aikman Avenue, Leicester. Ground: New Parks Community College, St Oswalds Road, New Parks, Leicester Tel: 0116 287 2115.

Newland Park/Bucks College - 1955 - Secretary: Miss M Tremlin, Newlands Park,Gorelands Lane, Chalfont St Giles, Bucks HP8 4AD (01494 871225 (B) 01494 873699 (F)). Fix Sec: Miss M Tremlin, Newlands Park,Gorelands Lane, Chalfont St Giles, Bucks HP8 4AD (01494 871225 (B) 01494 873699 (F)). Ground: Gorelands Lane, Chalfont St Giles, Buckinghamshire HP8 4AD Tel: 01494 603084.

Newport - 1874 - Secretary: T Brown, Newport RUFC Ltd, Rodney Road, Newport, South Wales NP19 0UU (01633 670690/670691 (B) 01633 670696 (F)). Fix Sec: R W Atkins, 644 Chepstow Road, Newport, South Wales NP9 9EY (01633 275222 (H)). Treasurer: R Eady, 29 Seymour Avenue, Penhow,, Newport, South Wales NP26 3AG (01633 400767 (H) 01633 670690 (B) 01633 670696 (F)). Ground: Rodney Parade, Newport, Gwent NP9 0UU Tel: 01633 258193.

Nikko Securities - 1988 - Ground: 55 Victoria Street, London SW1H 0EU Tel: 0171 799 2222.

Norfolk - 1951 - Secretary: J Hipperson, Homefield, Homefield Paddock, Beccles NR34 9NE (01502 714380 (H) 01603 437 358 01603 702046 (F)). Fix Sec: N Trett, 7 Holkham Avenue, Cley Road, Swaffham PE37 7RX (01760 721998 (H) 01366 383301 (B) 01366 383301 (F)). Treasurer: J Martin, The Old Rectory, Costesser Road, Taverham, Norwich NR8 6TA (01603 868823 (H) 01603 663300 (B) 01603 663300 (F)).

North Midlands Colts - 1956 - Secretary: M S Evans, 44 Turlshill Road, Sedgley, Dudley DY3 1HG (01902 671085 (H) 01743 450501 (B) 01743 440904 (F)). Fix Sec: M S Evans, 44 Turlshill Road, Sedgley, Dudley DY3 1HG (01902 671085 (H) 01743 450501 (B) 01743 440904 (F)). Treasurer: I R Wallace, 93 Hazlewood Road, Acocks Green, Birmingham (0121 200 2211 (B)). Ground: Moseley FC, Reddings Road, Moseley, Birmingham Tel: 0121 449 2149.

North Yorkshire Police - 1974 - Secretary: S Smith, 7 Whitehouse Dale, Pulleyn Drive, York YO2 2EB (01904 645420 (H) 01904 631321 (B)). Fix Sec: S Smith, 7 Whitehouse Dale, Pulleyn Drive, York YO2 2EB (01904 645420 (H) 01904 631321 (B)). Ground: c/o York Railway Inst RUFC, New Lane, Acomb, York Tel: 01904 798930.

Northamptonshire Police - 1966 - Secretary: Sgt A M Collins, Northamptonshire Police, Traffics Ops, Mere Way, Northampton NN4 8BH (01604 703440 (B) 01604 703427 (Fax)). Fix Sec: PC P Holloway, Northamptonshire Police, Northampton Area, Campbell Square, Northampton NN1 3EL (01604 700700 (B)). Treasurer: Inspector A Street, Northants Police,, Northern Area, London Road, Kettering, Northamptonshire (01536 411411 (B)). Ground: NCC Sports & Social Club, Wootton Hall Park, Mereway, Northampton Tel: 01604 700934.

Northants & District Rugby Alliance - 1922 - Secretary: A J Snedker, 550 Obelisk Rise, Kingsthorpe, Northampton NN2 8SY (01604 847101 (H) 01604 644433 (B) 01604 492644 (Fax)). Fix Sec: D G Hodgkinson, 5 Pine Trees, Weston Favell, Northampton NN3 3ET (01604 416442 (H) 0973 417259 (B)). Treasurer: R Jeffery, 218 Eastern Avenue, Northampton NN2 7AT (01604 717947 (H) 01604 752311 (B).

Northumbria Police - Secretary: Sgt 1204 J Chappell, Cedar House, 61A Dunsgreen, Ponteland, Newcastle-Upon-Tyne NE20 9EJ (01661 821 432 (H) 0191 214 6555 Ext 63131). Fix Sec: A Park, 7 Axwell Park Road,, Blaydon, Tyne & Wear NE21 5NR (0191 499 0218 (H) 0191 214 6555 ext 65240). Treasurer: Sgt 1204 J Chappell, Cedar House, 61A Dunsgreen, Ponteland, Newcastle-Upon-Tyne NE20 9EJ (01661 821 432 (H) 0191 214 6555 Ext 63131). Ground: North Road, Ponteland, Northumberland Tel: 01661 72555 Ext 4306.

Nottinghamshire Fire & Rescue - 1990 - Secretary: K Elliott, 16 Sherwood Avenue, Edwinstone, Mansfield, Notts NG21 9NE (01623 822743 (H) 01623 836195 (F)). Fix Sec: K Elliott, 16 Sherwood Avenue, Edwinstone, Mansfield, Notts NG21 9NE (01623 822743 (H) 01623 836195 (F)). Treasurer: A Shepherd, 27 Acton Road, Arnold, Notts. NG5 7AB (0115 9528119 (H) 0115 9799803 (F)). Ground: c/o Mansfield RUFC, Eakring Road, Mansfield NG18 3EW Tel: 01623 649834.

Notts Lincs & Derby Colts - 1960 - Secretary: J W Bee, 273 Bostock Lane, Sandiacre, Nottingham NG10 5ND (0115 972 8720 (H) 0115 938 2535 (B) 0115 945 9618 (Fax)). Fix Sec: Doug Dearden, 18 Winchester Crescent, Upper Fulwood, Sheffield S10 4ED (0114 230 2920 (H & Fax) 0860 719844 (Mobile)).

Oaklands College - 1921 - Secretary: L Brown, Oaklands College, Oaklands Campus, Hatfield Rd, St Albans, Herts AL4 0JA (01727 737000 (B) 01727 847987 (Fax)). Fix Sec: L Brown, Oaklands College, Oaklands Campus, Hatfield Rd, St Albans, Herts AL4 0JA (01727 737000 (B) 01727 847987 (Fax)). Treasurer: Debbie Leech, Oaklands Campus, Hatfield Rd, St Albans AL4 0JB (01727 737000 01727 737759). Ground: Oaklands Campus, Hatfield Road, St Albans, Hertfordshire AL4 0JA Tel: 01727 737000.

Old Amplefordians - 1985 - Secretary: T L Judd, 25 Rusham Road, Balham, London SW12 8TJ (0181 675 2211 (H)). Fix Sec: A Elliot, 10 Birchwood Avenue, London N10 3BE (0181 444 9041). Treasurer: J Dick, 56 Selsdon Road, West Norwood,, London SE27 0PG (0181 6704143 (H) 0171 2807899 (B)). Ground: KCS Old Boys Rugby Club, Arthur Rd,Off West Barnes Lane, Motspur Park, London SW20 Tel: 0181 336 2512.

Old Birkonian - 1921 - Secretary: P Crook, The Quarry, 5 Burrell Road, Prenton, Birkenhead, Merseyside CH42 8NH (0151 608 2498 (H) 0151 236 1744 (B) 0151 236 3934 (Fax)). Fix Sec: L O Kirkham, 68 Waterpark Road, Prenton,, Birkenhead, Merseyside CH43 0RS (0151 6083023 (H) 0151 6083023 (B)). Treasurer: E A Roberts, Copley, Bryn Gwyn Lane, Northop Hall, Mold, Flintshire (01244 816243 (H) 0151 6081950 (B)). Ground: c/o Birkenhead Park FC, Park Road North, Birkenhead, Merseyside L41 0DD Tel: 0151 652 4646.

Old Dowegians - 1956 - Secretary: A Foster, Chardith, Station Road, Gomshall, Guildford, Surrey GU5 9LQ (01483 203681 (H)). Fix Sec: A Foster, Chardith, Station Road, Gomshall, Guildford, Surrey GU5 9LQ (01483 203681 (H)). Treasurer: Dr J Kerr, Simonside, 202 London Road, Wokingham, Berkshire RG11 1SN (01734 792780 (H)). Ground: Douai School, Upper Woolhampton, Reading, Berkshire RG7 5TH Tel: 01635 862735.

Old Epsomian - 1963 - Secretary: I R Edmond, Little Orchards, Prince of Wales Road, Outwood, Surrey RH1 5QU (01342 843871 (H)). Fix Sec: S T Schlaefli, 40 Broadhurst Gardens, Reigate, Surrey RG2 8AW (01737 244983 (H) 0181 542 6225 (B)). Treasurer: J Steward, 26woodcote hurst, epsom, surrey (01372722497 01714031505).

Old Malvernian - 1989 - Secretary: T Humphreys, C.F.P.L. Russell Square House, 10/12 Russell Square, London WC1B 5EH (0171 609 2086 (H) 0171 323 2828 (B) 0171 436 0304 (F)). Fix Sec: T Humphreys, C.F.P.L. Russell Square House, 10/12 Russell Square, London WC1B 5EH (0171 609 2086 (H) 0171 323 2828 (B) 0171 436 0304 (F)). Treasurer: C Collins, May Cottage, 13 Princes Road, Weybridge, Surrey KT13 9BH (0171 306 3948 (B). Grd: c/o Staines RUFC, Felthamhill Road, Feltham, Middx Tel: 0181 890 3051.

Old Newburians - 1991 - Secretary: C O Hobbs, 19 York Road, Newbury, Berkshire RG14 7NJ (01635 522546 (H)). Fix Sec: C O Hobbs, 19 York Road, Newbury, Berkshire RG14 7NJ (01635 522546 (H)). Treasurer: A Coates, 11 Sedge Grove, Dunstan Park, Thatcham, Berkshire RG18 4DY (01635 874916 (H) 01488 681005 (B) 01488 681134 (F)). Ground: St Bartholomews School, Andover Road, Newbury, Berkshire RG14 6JP Tel: 01635 521255.

Old Nottinghamians - 1922 - Secretary: I N Wood, 44 College Street, East Bridgford, Nottingham NG13 8LF (01949 20307 (H) 0115 981 1070 (B)). Treasurer: M H T Simpson, 1 Birch Lea, Redhill, Nottingham NG5 8LT (0115 926 8196 (H) 0115 960 8171 (B).

Old Persean - 1949 - Secretary: P Harvey, Rosemary Cottage, 49 Woodditton Road, Newmarket, Suffolk CB8 9BQ (01638 667615 (H) 01223 354131 (B) 01223 355301 (F)). Fix Sec: P Harvey, Rosemary Cottage, 49 Woodditton Road, Newmarket, Suffolk CB8 9BQ (01638 667615 (H) 01223 354131 (B) 01223 355301 (F)). Treasurer: P N Jaggs, September Cottage, 47 Station, Road, Dullingham,, Newmarket, Suffolk CB8 9UP (01638 507815 (H) 01638 507815 (B)). Ground: The Perse School for Boys, Hills Road, Cambridge CB2 2QF.

Old Sohamsos - 1987 - Secretary: A E Fenn, Old Forge House, High Street, Cavendish, Sudbury, Suffolk CO10 8AX (01787 281457 (H) 01440 706441 (B)). Ground: Village College Soham, Soham, Ely, Cambridgeshire CB7 5AA Tel: 01638 722569.

Old Stonehamians - 1961 - Secretary: R J Eccleston, 21 The Mount, Caversham Heights, Reading, Berkshire RG4 7RU (0118 9620264 (H) 0468 445300 (B) 0181 9475612 (F)). Fix Sec: R J Eccleston, 21 The Mount, Caversham Heights, Reading, Berkshire RG4 7RU (0118 9620264 (H) 0468 445300 (B) 0181 9475612 (F)). Treasurer: R J Eccleston, 21 The Mount, Caversham Heights, Reading, Berkshire RG4 7RU (0118 9620264 (H) 0468 445300 (B) 0181 9475612 (F)). Ground: Berkshire Sports/Social Club, Sonning Lane, Reading, Berkshire Tel: 01189 691340.

Old Standfordians - 1984 - Secretary: E T Moody, 522 Hatfield Road, St Albans, Hertfordshire AL4 0SX (01727 834413 (H) 01727 834413 (F)). Fix Sec: A Watson, 37 Downhall Ley, Buntingford, Herts SG99 9JT (01763 271139 (H)). Treasurer: G Hughes, 27 Maltings Close, Clothal Common, Baldock, Herts SG7 6RU (01462 491440 (H)). Ground: Luynes Riseane, Buntingford, Hertfordshire Tel: 01763 273062.

Old Shrewsbury - 1993 - Secretary: D Paddock, 44 Allerton Rd, Shrewsbury, Shropshire SY1 4QP (01743 360746 01743 277227 01743 277314). Fix Sec: Chris Booth, 11 Westmorland Mews, Shrewsbury SY1 2RH (01743354443). Treasurer: P E Tipton, Royal Mail, Postal Writing Room, Castle Foregate, Shrewsbury SY1 1AA (01743 242727 (H) 01743 277254 (B) 01743 277314 (F)). Ground: Sundorne Recreation Centre, Sundorne Rd, Shrewsbury, Shropshire SY1 4RQ.

Old Wellingburian - 1981 - Secretary: N J Fry, 25 St. Mary's Road, Kettering, Northants NN15 7BP (01536 390200 (H) 01203 426000 (B) 01203 426030 (F)). Fix Sec: P King, 4 The Cottons, Wellingborough,, Northants (01933 402905 (H)). Treasurer: M Thompson, Plot 2, Church Lane, Yeldon, Bedfordshire (01933 315407 (H) 01234 353221 (B) 01234 216272 (F)). Ground: Sports Ground, The Embankment, Wellingborough, Northants NN8 1LD Tel: 01933 225922.

Oldham College (Vets) - 1964 - Secretary: J K McGuire, 5 Gleneagles Avenue, Hopwood, Heywood, Lancashire OL10 2BZ (01706 622203 (H) 0836 698935 (B) 01706 622203 (F)). Fix Sec: M Garner, 21 Stansfield Street, Failsworth, Manchester M35 9FA (0161 682 6817 (H) 0161 600 6816 (B)). Treasurer: J K McGuire, 5 Gleneagles Avenue, Hopwood, Heywood, Lancashire OL10 2BZ (01706 622203 (H) 0836 698935 (B) 01706 622203 (F)). Ground: Tudor Lodge, Victoria Avenue East, Moston, Manchester M10 9SH Tel: 0161 682 9234.

Onley Park - 1972 - Secretary: N T Mapletoft, c/o Mr S L Greenhalgh, 6 Heathlands Drive, Maidenhead, Berks SL6 4NF (01788 522022 Ext 206 (B) 01788 522260 (Fax)). Fix Sec: G Husain, c/o HMY01 Onley, Rugby CV23 8AP (01788 522022 (H) 01788 522260 (B)). Ground: HMY01, Onley, Rugby CV23 8AP Tel: 01788 522022 Ext 333/332.

Orwell - 1969 - Secretary: S R J Bevan, 34 Princethorpe Rd, Ipswich, Suffolk IP3 8NX (01473 270553 (H)). Fix Sec: D Botwright, 12 Vermont Road, Ipswich, Suffolk IP4 2SR (01473 215866 (H)). Treasurer: G Chapman, 22 Whitethorn Road, Ipswich, Suffolk (01473 717775 (H)). Ground: Ransomes Reavell Sports &, Social Club, Sidegate Avenue, Ipswich IP4 4JJ Tel: 01473 726134.

Oundle School - Ground: Oundle, Peterborough PE8 4EN Tel: 01832 73536.

Oxford University - 1869 - Secretary: D J R Cole, Director of Administration, c/o University Sports Centre, Iffley Rd, Oxford OX4 1EQ (01608 678299 (H) 01865 432002 (B) 01865 432005 (F)). Fix Sec: D J R Cole, Director of Administration, c/o University Sports Centre, Iffley Rd, Oxford OX4 1EQ (01608 678299 (H) 01865 432002 (B) 01865 432005 (F)). Ground: John Radcliffe Hospital, Headington, Oxford OX3 9DU Tel: 01865 432000.

Balliol College - 1906 - Secretary: E Rees, c/o Balliol College, Oxford 0X1 3BJ. Ground: c/o Balliol college, Oxford OX1 3BJ Tel: 01865 277777.

Brasenose College - Secretary: M Forbes, Brasenose College RFC, Brasenose College, Oxford OX1 4AJ (01865 201708 (H)). Fix Sec: M Forbes, Brasenose College RFC, Brasenose College, Oxford OX1 4AJ (01865 201708 (H)). Ground: Abingdon Road, Oxford Tel: 01865 243478.

Christ Church - Secretary: B Gripaioss, The Steward's Office,, Christ Church College, Oxford 0X1 1DP. Fix Sec: J Barker, Lincoln Christs Hospital Schoo, Wragby Road, Lincoln LN2 4PN (01522 682162 (H) 01522 881144 (B) 01522 881145 (F)). Ground: Iffley Road, Oxford Tel: 01865 243992.

Corpus Christi & Somerville Colleges - 1990 - Secretary: C Barron, Corpus Christi College, Merton Street, Oxford 0X1 4JF. Fix Sec: C Barron, Somerville College, Woodstock Rd, Oxford. Ground: Corpus Christi College, Merton Street, Oxford OX1 4JF Tel: 01865 242231.

Exeter College - Secretary: P Wheaton, Exeter College, Oxford OX1 3DP. Treasurer: M Williams, Exeter College, Oxford OX1 3DQ (01865 279600 (H) 01865 279645 (B)). Ground: Exeter College Sports Ground, Edgeway Road, New Marston, Oxford Tel: 01865 243710.

Hertford College - Secretary: P Clememts, Hertford College, Catte street, Oxford OX1 3BW (01865 279400). Fix Sec: J Wilson, Hertford College, Catte Street, Oxford OX1 3BW (01865 279400). Fix Sec: P Clememts, Hertford College, Catte street, Oxford OX1 3BW (01865 279400). Ground: Catte Street, Oxford OX13BW Tel: 01865 279400.

Jesus College - 1890 - Secretary: Deri Hughes, Jesus College,, Bartlemas Ground, Cowley, Oxford 0X1 3DW. Fix Sec: J J Packer, 69 Gestridge Road, Kingsteignton, Newton Abbot, South Devon TQ12 3HJ (01626 368614 (H) 01626 362610 (F)). Treasurer: J J Packer, 69 Gestridge Road, Kingsteignton,Newton Abbot, South Devon TQ12 3HJ (01626 368614 (H) 01626 362610 (F)). Ground: Bartlemas Ground, Cowley, Oxford OX1 3DW Tel: 01865 279700.

Keble College - Secretary: S Craig, Keble College, University Parks, Oxford. Ground: University Parks, Oxford OX1 3PG Tel: 01865 272727.

Lady Margaret Hall & Trinity College - Secretary: G Samual-Gibbon, Lady Margaret Trinity, Marston Rd, Oxford. Ground: Marston Road, Oxford.

Lincoln College - Secretary: C Houston, Lincoln College, Bartlemas Close, Oxford OX4 2AA (01865 242357). Fix Sec: J Wynne, Lincoln College, Turl Street, Oxford OX1 3DR (01865 279800). Treasurer: D Smith, Lincoln College, Turl Street, Oxford OC1 3DR (01865 279800). Ground: Bartlemas Close, Oxford OX4 2AA Tel: 01865 242357.

Magdalen College - Secretary: P Reeves, Magdalen College, Marston Road, Oxford OX1 4AU (01865 276000 (H)). Fix Sec: A Campana, Magdalen College, Oxford OX1 4AU (01865 276000 01865 276103). Secretary: P Reeves, Magdalen College, Marston Road, Oxford OX1 4AU (01865 276000 (H)). Ground: Marston Road, Oxford OX1 4AU Tel: 01865 247358.

Merton and Mansfield Colleges - Secretary: J Fishley, Mansfield College, Oxford OX1 3TF (01865 270999). Ground: Manor Road, Oxford Tel: 01865 276289.

New College & Templeton - Secretary: C Houghton, New College, St Cross Rd, Holywell, Oxford OX1 3BN (01865 279555). Ground: St Cross Road, Holywell, Oxford OX1 3BN.

Oriel College - Secretary: J Rodgers, Bartlemas Farm, Cowley Rd, Oxford (01865 726440). Fix Sec: C Nelson, Oriel College, Oxford OX1 4EW. Ground: Bartlemas Farm, Cowley Road, Oxford Tel: 01865 726440.

Pembroke College - Secretary: N Shephard, Pembroke College, Oxford OX1 1DW. Ground: Oxford OX1 1DW.

Queen's College - Secretary: C Clark, Wycliffe Hall, Banbury Road OX2 6PQ (01865 274200 01865 274215). Fix Sec: C Clark, Wycliffe Hall, Banbury Road OX2 6PQ (01865 274200 01865 274215). Treasurer: L Shier, The Queens College, Oxford OX1 4AW (01865 279120 01865 790919). Ground: Abingdon Road, Oxford Tel: 01865 242129.

St Anne's and St John's Colleges - Ground: St Johns College Sports Ground, Woodstock Road, Oxford OX1 3JP Tel: 01865 515561.

St Catherine's College - Secretary: B Griffiths, St Catherine's College, The Parks, Oxford OX1 5AA. Ground: The Parks, Oxford OX1 3UJ Tel: 01865 792315.

St Edmund Hall - 1930 - Secretary: S Gough, St Edmunds Hall, Oxford OX1 4AR (01865 279000 (H)). Ground: St Edmund Hall, St Edmund Hall, Oxford OX1 4AR Tel: 01865 557106 (Groundsman).

St Hugh's College - 1987 - Secretary: A Trotter, St Hugh's College, Oxford OX2 6LE (01865 274900 (H)). Treasurer: John O Connell, St Hughes College, St Margrets Rd, Oxford OX2 6LE. Ground: St Hughes College, St Margrets Rd, Oxford OX2 6LE.

St Peter's College - Secretary: A Salvoni, St Peter's College, Southern Bypass, Oxford OX1 5AA (01865 278900 (H)). Ground: Southern Bypass, Oxford OX1 5AA Tel: 01865 727468.

University College - Secretary: C Jeffrey, University College,, Abington Road, Oxford 0X1 4BH. Ground: Abingdon Road, Oxford Tel: 01865 243490.

Wadham College - Secretary: A White, Wadham College, Parks Rd, Oxford OX1 3PN. Treasurer: J Hargraves. Ground: Marston Ferry Road, Oxford OX1 3PN Tel: 01865 53819.

Worcester College - Secretary: R Brookes, Worcester College, Oxford OX12 2HB. Ground: Worcester Street, Oxford OX1 2HB Tel: 0836 251002.

Oxfordshire Fire Service - 1980 - Secretary: A Hoar, 1 Manor Farm, Church Street, Kidlington, Oxford OX5 2BA (01865 372249 (H) 01865 855212 (B) 01865 372249 (F)). Treasurer: B Ward, 8 Meadow Way, Yarnton, Oxon OX5 1TA (01865 371665 (H) 01295 242223 (B)). Ground: Witney RFC, Witney Road, Hailey, Witney, Oxon Tel: 01993 771043.

Oxted - 1983 - Secretary: N Madgett, 69 Hurst Green Road, Oxted, Surrey RH8 9AJ (01883 717747 (H)). Fix Sec: N Madgett, 69 Hurst Green Road, Oxted, Surrey RH8 9AJ (01883 717747 (H)). Treasurer: Miles Warner, 68 Silkham Road, Oxted, Surrey (01883 715122). Ground: Holland Rd, Hurst Green, Oxted Tel: 01883 717468.

Paddington (Met Police) - 1989 - Secretary: D Morgan, Operations Office, 1 Area HQ, Whitehall Police Station, Victoria Embankment, London SW1 2JL (0171 321 9811 (B)). Fix Sec: D Morgan, Operations Office, 1 Area HQ, Whitehall Police Station, Victoria Embankment, London SW1 2JL (0171 321 9811 (B)). Treasurer: S Richards, Paddington Police Station, 2-4 Harrow Road, London W2 1XJ (0171 321 9811 (B)). Ground: Bushey Sports Club, Aldenham Road, Bushey, Watford, Hertfordshire WD2 3TR.

Pelhamians - 1969 - Secretary: J Nichols, 28 Presburg Road, New Malden, Surrey KT3 5AH (0181 9422161 (H) 0171 4364080 (B) 01716377032). Fix Sec: J Nichols, 28 Presburg Road, New Malden, Surrey KT3 5AH (0181 9422161 (H) 0171 4364080 (B) 01716377032). Treasurer: D Jacobs, 2 Norton Avenue, Berrylands, Surbiton, Surrey KT5 9DY (0181 241 5759 (H) 0181 871 2202 (B) (F)). Ground: Taunton Avenue, Raynes Park, London SW20 Tel: 0181 94683855.

Phoenix Gas - 1985 - Secretary: W K Shorter, 8 Thatchers Drive, Elmstead Market, Colchester, Essex CO7 7YE (01206 825874 (H)). Fix Sec: P Clarke, British Gas, Hertford Reporting Centre, Marshgate Drive, Hertford (01992 554521 (B)). Treasurer: D Whittle, British Gas, Cadwell Lane, Hitchin, Hertfordshire SG4 0SL (01462 450861 (B)). Ground: British Gas Eastern SSC, Whitewebbs Lane, Enfield, Middlesex Tel: 01992 760716.

Phyllosans - 1969 - Secretary: A E Walsham, The New House, Queens St, Hook Norton, Oxon OX15 5PJ (01608 730381 (H) 06908 619394 (B) 01908 619306 (F)). Fix Sec: S Samra, 7 Granton Avenue, Upminster, Essex RM14 2RX (01708 446369 (H) 01268 552022 (B)). Treasurer: R Consterdine, 37 Tindall Close, Harold Wood, Romford, Essex RM3 OPB (01708 705259 (H) 01708 475285 (B) 01708 620963 (F)).

Post Office - 1970 - Secretary: D Webb, 76 Rochelle Way, Duston, Northampton NN5 6YW (01604 581546 (H)). Fix Sec: D Webb, 76 Rochelle Way, Duston, Northampton NN5 6YW (01604 581546 (H)). Treasurer: D Webb, 76 Rochelle Way, Duston, Northampton NN5 6YW (01604 581546 (H)).

Potton - 1978 - Secretary: G G Reeve, 12 Festival Road, Potton, Bedfordshire SG19 2QN (01767 261433). Fix Sec: G Corrin, 24 Mill Lane, Potton, Bedfordshire SG19 2PG (01767 260865 (H)). Treasurer: P Wood, 149 Foster Road,, Trumpington, Cambs CB2 2JWV (01223 840301 H)). Ground: CIU Club, Station Road, Potton SG19 2PU Tel: 01767 261465.

Prep School Wanderers - 1987 - Secretary: M Farrow, Orchard Cottage, Station Road, Cookham, Berkshire SL6 9BU (01628 523229 (H)). Fix Sec: G Ruck, Dorton House School, Seal Drive, Seal, Nr Sevenoaks, Kent. Treasurer: M Farrow, Orchard Cottage, Station Road, Cookham, Berkshire SL6 9BU (01628 523229 (H)). Ground: Wellington College, Crowthorne, Berkshire RG45 7PU Tel: 01344 772262.

Prescot-Rainhill - 1949 - Secretary: K O'Keefe, 39 French St, Toll Bar, St Helens, Merseyside. Ground: Haresfinch Social Club, Haresfinch Road, St Helens, Merseyside.

Private Banks - 1983 - Secretary: M R Cordell, 94 Falstead Road, Orpington, Kent BR6 9AE (01689 834426 (H) 0171 753 1000 (B)). Ground: The Pavillion, Catford Road, London SE6 4SW Tel: 0181 690 1931.

Prudential Ibis - 1993 - Secretary: P M Chandler, 8 Ramsdell Close, Tadley, Hants RG26 6TU (01189 820150 (H) 01189 493384 (B)). Fix Sec: G McCoy, 27 Shaftesbury Road, Reading, Berkshire (01189 612530 (H) 01189 578406 (B)). Treasurer: D Fuggle, 37 Ellesmere Close, Caversham, Reading, Berkshire RG4 5HG (01189 474292 (H) 01189 578165 (B) 01189 539954 (Fax)). Ground: Prudential Ibis Club, Scours Lane, Reading, Berkshire RG3 6AY Tel: 01189 424130.

RICS - Secretary: J R Marshall, Peel Place, Moorbottom Lane, Upper Greetland, Near Halifax, West Yorkshire HX4 8PZ (01422 376100 (H) 01422 376821 (B) 01422 376216 (F)). Fix Sec: J R Marshall, Peel Place, Moorbottom Lane, Upper Greetland, Near Halifax, West Yorkshire HX4 8PZ (01422 376100 (H) 01422 376821 (B) 01422 376216 (F)). Treasurer: N Hay, 18-20 Grafton Street, London W1X 4PT (0171 663 5555 (B) 0171 491 0098 (F)). Ground: Bank of England Sports Club, Priory Lane, Roehampton, London SW15 5JH Tel: 0171 876 8417.

RNAS Culdrose - Secretary: Hon Sec RFC, RNAS Culdrose, Sports Centre, Helston, Cornwall TR12 7RH (01326 552265/552404 (B)). Fix Sec: Hon Fix Sec RFC, RNAS Culdrose, Sports Centre, Helston, Cornwall TR12 7RH (01326 552307/552404 (B)). Ground: Lizard Road, Helston, Cornwall TR12 7RH Tel: 01326 557167.

RNVR (London Division) - 1924 - Secretary: F Butler OHA, Manndin, Warrenden Road, Hughenden Valley,High Wycombe, Buckinghamshire HP14 4LX (01494 562919 (H) 00 323 240 7287 (B)). Fix Sec: P Chamberlain, 23 Elderwood Place, West Norwood, London SE27 0HJ (0181 670 1689 (H) 0181 307 4784 (B)). Treasurer: R Anderson, 57 Cressey House, Hannibal Road, London E1 3JF (0171 791 1956 (H) 0181 983 4616 (B)). Ground: HMS President, 72 St Katherines Way, London E1 9UQ Tel: 0171 480 7219.

Rags - 1983 - Secretary: W W Barrack, 15 Eastgate Close, Bramhope, Leeds LS16 9AA (0113 284 2540 (H) 0113 284 2540 (B)). Fix Sec: R Gray, 40 Summer Lane, Royston, Barnsley S71 4SE (01226 723207 (H) 01709 898697 (B)). Treasurer: A Cornwell, 8 Highfield Avenue, Pontefract Road, Pontefract WF8 2PT (01977 794095 (H) 01757 703691 (B)). Ground: c/o Pontefract RUFC, Moor Lane, Carleton, Pontefract, West Yorks WF8 3RX Tel: 01977 702650.

Ramsey IOM - 1981 - Secretary: D M Christian, Beaconsfield Cottage, Bowring Road, Ramsey, Isle Of Man IM8 3EV (01624 817580 (H) 01624 685362 (B) 01624 685351 (F)). Fix Sec: J Lord, Sunnybank, Park Road, Ramsey, Isle of Man IM8 3AR (01624 816185 (H) 01270 841487 (B)). Treasurer: P Hotchkiss, Gateways, Glen Tramman, Lezayre Road, Ramsey, IOM IM7 2AW (01624 812418 (B) 01624 676716 (F)). Ground: New Ground,, Mooragh Promenade, Ramsey, Isle of Man.

Reading School - Ground: Reading, Berkshire Tel: 01189 61406.

Reading University Old Boys - 1986 - Secretary: R G Wise, 35 Hartismere Road, London SW6 7OU (0171 385 0334 (H) 0171 499 8626 (B)). Fix Sec: T Hillier, 61A Culverden Down, Tunbridge Wells, Kent (01892 515001 (B)). Treasurer: R Spilsbury, Upper Flat, 17 Simpson Street, Battersea SW1 3HN (0171 223 4307 (H) 0171 583 5000 (B)). Ground: c/o Old Blues RFC, Arthur Road, Motspur Park.

Reading West Indians - 1975 - Secretary: K H Hinds, 243 Waverley Road, Reading, Berkshire RG30 2QH (01189 588583/0118 958 8583 (H) 01189 226524/0118 922 6524 (B) 01189 863857 (F)). Fix Sec: J R Bell, 36 Lismore Close, Woodley, Nr Reading, Berkshire RG5 3RT (0118 9618210 (H) 0118 961 8210 (B) 0118 939 9703 (F)). Treasurer: W Stewart, 115 Mays Lane, Earley, Nr Reading, Berkshire RG6 2DG (0118 926 7939 (H) 01628 34505 (B)). Ground: Redingensians Sports Ground, Old Bath Road, Sonning, Nr Reading, Berkshire RG4 0TQ Tel: 0118 969 5259.

Rugby School - 1823 - Ground: The Close, Rugby School, Rugbyckshire, Warwickshire CV22 5DP Tel: 01788 578006.

Shadwell - 1993 - Secretary: S Fryatt, 104 Hornchurch Road, Hornchurch, Essex RM11 1DL (01708 473878 (H) 0171 587 4125 (B)). Fix Sec: S Fryatt, 104 Hornchurch Road, Hornchurch, Essex RM11 1DL (01708 473878 (H) 0171 587 4125 (B)). Treasurer: A Phillips, Little Tors, School Road,, Kelvedon Hatch, Essexn (01277 373223 (H)) 0171 587 4125 (B)). Ground: Aveley Sports And Social Club, Purfleet Road, Aveley, South Ockendon, Essex RM15 4DT Tel: 01708 863611.

Shepshed - 1987 - Secretary: J S Medhurst, 20 Deanside Drive, Loughborough, Leicestershire LE11 5TH (01509 213861 (H) 01858 433376 (B)). Fix Sec: R Short, 40d Loughborough Rd, Shepshed, Leicestershire (01509 503592 (H)). Treasurer: A McPhearson, c/o The Crown Inn, Market Street, Shepshed (01509 502665 (H)). Ground: Hind Leys College, Forest Street, Shepshed, Loughborough, Leicestershire Tel: 01509 503592.

Sherborne School - 1846 - Ground: Sherborne, Dorset Tel: 01935 81891.

Shildon Town - 1986 - Secretary: Ms G Bowman, 49a Jubilee Road, Shildon, County Durham. Fix Sec: P Plews, 14 Alexandra Street, Shildon, County Durham DL4 2EY (01388 777334 (H)). Treasurer: J Higham, 28 Henry Street, Shildon DL4 1JP (01388 778564 (H)). Ground: Sunnydale Leisure Centre, Shildon, Co Durham Tel: 01388 777340.

South Devon Police - 1971 - Secretary: K Hodgins, Nutshell Cottage, Chipley, South Knighton, Newton Abbot, Devon (01626 821366 (H) 0990 777 444 (B)). Fix Sec: A Leisk, 62 Rydon Acres, Kingsteignton, Newton Abbot, Devon (01626 335946 0990 777 444). Treasurer: J Carlyon, 50 Green Park road, Windmill Green, Paignton, Devon TQ3 1AJ (01803 553821 (H) 01803 841284 (B) 01803 841291 (F)). Ground: c/o Paignton RFC, Queens Park, Queens Road, Paignton Tel: 01803 557715.

South Wigston - 1886 - Secretary: R T Green, 8 Britford Avenue, Wigston Magna, Leicester LE18 2RF (0116 2880991 (H) 0116 2522504 (B)). Fix Sec: S Wells, 5 Cherry Street, Wigston, Leicester (0116 2812306 (H)). Treasurer: D J Ross, 18 Chiltern Green, West Knighton, Leicester (0116 2812150 (H)). Ground: Leicester Road, Countesthorpe, Leicestershire Tel: 0116 277 1153.

South Yorkshire Fire Service - 1975 - Secretary: P R Shillito, 26 Westminster Close, Bramley, Rotherham S66 1WJ (0114 2692230 (B) 0114 2691899 (F)). Fix Sec: M Wordsworth, 2 Scott Walk, Maltby, Rotherham S66 8RA (01709 815949 (H) 01709 828661 (B)). Treasurer: P Best, 2 Walnut Rd, Thorne, Doncaster DN8 4HW (01405 816521 (H) 01405 812293 (B)). Ground: Thornensians RUFC, Coulman Rd, Thorne, Doncaster DN8 5BU Tel: 01405 812746.

South Yorkshire Police - 1972 - Secretary: PC 348 S W Stokes, c/o West Bar Police Station, West Bar, Sheffield S1 2DA (0114 2768522 Ext 4250 (B)). Fix Sec: John Turner, c/o Crime Prevention Dept., Woodseats Police Station, Woodseats Sheffield S8 0SL (0114 2963625). Ground: Niagra Sports Ground, Niagra Road, Sheffield S6 1LU Tel: 0114 2768522 Ext 4946.

Southampton Post Office - 1985 - Secretary: P F Evans, 68 Northlands Road, Romsey, Hants SO51 5SE (01794 500658 (H)). Fix Sec: P F Evans, 68 Northlands Road, Romsey, Hants SO51 5SE (01794 500658 (H)). Treasurer: B Duggan, 8 Hewitts Road, Freemantle, Southampton SO15 0JH (01703 315387 (H)). Ground: Test Park Playing Fields, Lower Brownhill Road, Southampton SO16 9HE Tel: 01703 737777.

Southern Nomads - 1982 - Secretary: D Welsh, 'Crink Feagh', Bradda East, Porterin, Isle of Man IM9 6QG (01624 836120 (H) 01624 688500 (B)). Fix Sec: R Hirst, Beulah, Fistard Rd, Port St Mary, I.o.M. IM9 5HE (01624 832611 (H) 01624 823360 (B)). Treasurer: G Jones, 23 Cecil Rd, Paignton, Devon TQ3 3HN (01803 527016 (H)). Ground: King Williams College, Castletown, Isle of Man.

St Bees School - 1870 - Fix Sec: H Lewis, School House, St Bees School, Cumbria CA27 0DS (01946 822374 (H) 01946 822254 (B) 01946 823657 (F)). Treasurer: H Lewis, School House, St Bees School, Cumbria CA27 0DS (01946 822374 (H) 01946 822254 (B) 01946 823657 (F)). Ground: The Foundation, St Bees, Cumbria CA27 0DS Tel: 01946 822286 / 822254.

St Helier - 1892 - Secretary: A Blaby, 8 Valley Court, Les Grands Vaux, St Helier, Jersey JE2 4NA (01534 31824 (H)). Fix Sec: M Preston, 4 Maitland Barn, Trinity Hill, St Helier, Jersey JE2 4JP (01534 607038 (H) 01534 500300 (B)). Treasurer: B Preston, 114 La Marais, St Clement, Jersey JE2 6GE (01534 23966 (H) 01534 30393 (B)). Ground: 1 Anley Street, St Helier, Jersey, Channel Islands JE2 3QE Tel: 01534 888179.

St Ives Colts - 1946 - Secretary: P Burgin, Rose Cottage, Lelant, St Ives, Cornwall TR26 3EB (01736 755542 (H)). Fix Sec: N A Simpson, Gillian Cottage, The Belyars, St Ives, Cornwall (01736 798169 (H) 01736 794424 (B)). Treasurer: B Stevens, 49 St John's Walk, St Ives, Cornwall (01736 795300 (H)). Ground: Alexandra Road, St Ives, Cornwall TR26 1ER Tel: 01736 795346.

St Jacques - 1978 - Secretary: C Moxon, The Willows, Blanche Carrier Lane, Vale, Guernsey, Channel Isles GY3 5DL (01481 45576 01481 705416). Fix Sec: R Le Prevost, Roseland, Rohais, St Peter Port, Guernsey GY1 1AB (01481 711542 (H) 04481 107548 (B)). Treasurer: Ms S Keen, 12 Lower Hauteville, St Peter Port, Guernsey, Channel Islands GY1 1LL (01481 725834 (H) 01481 710607 (B)). Ground: KGV Playing Fields, Rue Cohu, Castel, Guernsey, Channel Isles GY5 7SZ Tel: 01481 56617.

St Paul's School - Ground: Lonsdale Road, London SW13 9JT Tel: 0181 748 9162.

St Peter's School, York - 1874 - Ground: Clifton, Yorkshire YO3 6AB Tel: 01904 623213.

Staffordshire County Police - 1955 - Secretary: Det Sgt C Patten, 370 Main Rd, Glascote, Tamworth, Staffordshire B77 2BS (01827 313052 (H) 01952 290294 (B) 01952 290828 (F)). Fix Sec: A Burrows, 1 Cheadle Close, Penkridge, Staffordshire ST19 5SZ (01785 715424 (H)). Treasurer: Sgt P Fairhurst, 42 Compton Road, Baswich, Stafford ST17 0BS (01785 601137 (H) 01785 232454 (B) 10785 232315 (F)). Ground: Stafford RUFC, Newport Road, Stafford Tel: 01785 211241.

Staffordshire Fire and Rescue - 1970 - Secretary: D Hogan, 4 Sunningdale Drive, Stafford, Staffs ST16 3XL (01785 252935 01785 285102). Secretary: D Hogan, 4 Sunningdale Drive, Stafford, Staffs ST16 3XL (01785 252935 01785 285102). Treasurer: S Kenny, C/O Cannock Fire Station, Cannock, Staffordshire WS11 2LD (01543 578539 (B)).

Standard Chartered Bank - 1972 - Secretary: T F Wrafter, Standard Chartered Bank, 27-28 Clements Lane, London EC4N 7AP (01689 816843 (H) 0171 280 7448 (B)). Fix Sec: S Atkinson, Standard Chartered Bank, 37 Gracechurch Street, London EC3V 0BX (0171 280 7570 (B)). Secretary: T F Wrafter, Standard Chartered Bank, 27-28 Clements Lane, London EC4N 7AP (01689 816843 (H) 0171 280 7448 (B)). Ground: Lloyds Bank Sports Club, Copers Cope Road, Beckenham, Kent BR3 1RJ Tel: 0181 658 3818.

Standard Telephones (Greenwich) - 1936 - Secretary: R Williams, 59 High St, Bexley, Kent DA5 1AB (01322 553311(H) 01322 550742 (F)). Fix Sec: G Dorton, 698 Downham Way, Downham, Kent (0181 698 2810 (H)). Treasurer: J French, 136 Okehampton Crescent, Welling, Kent (0181 303 6050 (H)).

Sutton Bonington - Secretary: S Mistry, Guild Office, School of Agriculture, Sutton Bonington Nr L'Borough LE12 5RD (01223 835276 (H) 0115 951 5151 Ext 8648 (B) 0115 951 6350 (F)). Fix Sec: S Bishop, Guild Office, School of Agriculture, Sutton Bonington, Loughborough LE12 5RD (01462 815113 (H) 0115 951 5151 Ext 8648 (B) 0115 951 6350 (Fax)). Treasurer: S Mistry, Guild Office, School of Agriculture, Sutton Bonington Nr L'Borough LE12 5RD (01223 835276 (H) 0115 951 5151 Ext 8648 (B) 0115 951 6350 (F)). Ground: School of Agriculture, Sutton Bonington, Nr Loughborough LE12 5RD Tel: 0115 951 5151 Ext 8648.

Stansted Airport - 1991 - Secretary: J R Lester, 19 Stifford Road, Aveley, Essex RM15 4BS (01708 863072 (H) 01279 662575 (B)). Fix Sec: J R Lester, 19 Stifford Road, Aveley, Essex RM15 4BS (01708 863072 (H) 01279 662575 (B)). Treasurer: S Sage, 80 Barrells Down Road, Bishops Stortford, Hertfordshire CM23 2SX (01279 659770 (H) 01279 662020 (B)). Ground: The Sports Ground, Second Avenue, Old Terminal, Stansted Airport, Essex Tel: 01279 680243.

Stock Exchange - 1950 - Secretary: D Guild, c/o Lang & Cruikshank, 5 Appold St, London EC2A 2DA (0181 332 2271 (H) 0171 214 6141 (B) 0171 374 0066 (F)). Treasurer: D Reid, Index Investments Ltd, Paxton House, 28-30 Artillery Lane, London E1 7LS (0171 377 5207 (B) 0171 392 2032 (F)).

Stoics - 1985 - Secretary: Miss A Gallagher, 18 Waterlow Court, Heath Close, Hampstead Garden Suburbs, London NW11 7DT (0181 209 1693 (H) 0171 522 3031 (B) 0171 403 2878 (F)). Fix Sec: O Nisbett, 46 Hemstall Road, West Hampstead, London NW6 2AJ (0171 625 5884 (H) 0171 486 5888 (B) 0171 487 3686 (Fax)). Treasurer: M Billington, 93 Weir Road, Clapham, London SW12 (0181 675 5605 (H) 0171 356 7344 (B)). Ground: Cottenham Park Road, Raynes Park SW20 0TZ.

Suffolk - 1958 - Secretary: R Holloway, Galeden, North Acres, Willisham Tye, Ipswich, Suffolk IP8 4SS (01473 658360 (H) 01449 676551 (B) 01449 672954 (Fax)). Fix Sec: R Holloway, Galeden, North Acres, Willisham Tye, Ipswich, Suffolk IP8 4SS (01473 658360 (H) 01449 676551 (B) 01449 672954 (Fax)). Treasurer: R T Bouch, Sunnyside, School Road, Coddenham, Ipswich, Suffolk IP6 9PS (01449 760252 (H)).

Sutton Valence School - 1874 - Ground: Maidstone, Kent.

Swinfen Hall - 1971 - Secretary: F Watts, HM YOI Swinfen Hall, Lidchfield, Staffs WS14 9QS. Fix Sec: J Widdowson, c/o HMY01, Swinfen Hall, Lichfield, Staffordshire WS14 9QS (01283 814035 (H) 01543 481229 Ext 332 (B)). Ground: c/o HYMO1, Swinfen Hall, Lichfield, Staffordshire WS14 9QS Tel: 01543 481229 Ext 332.

Taunton Police - 1984 - Secretary: N A Holland, 39 Blackdown View, Norton Fitzwarren, Taunton, Somerset TA2 6RP (01823 333202 (H) 01823 363653 (B) 01823 363651 (F)). Fix Sec: R Tully, Police Station, Northgate, Bridgewater, Somerset (01823 363319 (B)). Treasurer: R Brown, Avon & Somerset Constabulary, Shuttern, Taunton, Somerset (01823 337911 (B)). Ground: Taunton School, Staplegrove Road, Taunton, Somerset TA2 6AD Tel: 01823 349200.

Temple Bar - 1938 - Secretary: M Gibson, Chelsfield, Hill Lane, Kingswood, Tadworth, Surrey KT20 6DZ (01737 351682 (H) 01737 370370 Ext 4838 (B) 01737 374357 (Fax)). Fix Sec: M Baker, GP/K301/CB, Legal and General House, Kingswood, Tadworth, Surrey KT20 6EU (01737 370370 Ext 4720 (B) 01737 362977 (Fax)). Ground: Legal and General House, Kingswood, Tadworth, Surrey KT20 6EU Tel: 01737 370370.

Territorial Army - 1931 - Secretary: Major P Marsland-Roberts TD, 31 Fairfax Road, Bedford Park, London W4 1EN (0181 995 3542 (H) 01189 869595 (B) 01189 876074 (Fax)). Fix Sec: Brigadier R N R P James CBE, 3 Upper Court, Old Church Road, Colwall, Malvern, Worcs WR13 6ET (01684 541121 (H) 01684 541121 (B) 01684 541121 (F)). Treasurer: Brigadier R N R P James CBE, 3 Upper Court, Old Church Road, Colwall, Malvern, Worcs WR13 6ET (01684 541121 (H) 01684 541121 (B) 01684 541121 (F)).

Tesco - 1977 - Secretary: S W Wyatt, 7 Hazeldell, Watton at Stone, Herts SG14 3SL (01920 830407 (H) 01707 325161 (B) 01920 831417 (Fax)). Fix Sec: I Bundock, 41 Telfords Yarde, 6-8 The Highway, Wapping, London E1 9BQ (0171 488 0868 (B) 0171 480 7934 (Fax)). Treasurer: C Waterfield, 38 Elmwood, Welwyn Garden City, Hertfordshire AL8 6LE (01707 339685 (H) 01707 325161 (B) 01707 320397 (Fax)). Ground: Tesco Country Club, Theobalds Lane, Cheshunt, Hertfordshire EN8 8YA Tel: 01992 625278

Thames Valley Police - 1968 - Secretary: Superintendent D R McWhirter, Crime Support Department, Police Hill, Kidlington, Oxon OX5 2NX (01865 820508 (H) 01865 855700 (B) 01865 855713 (F)). Fix Sec: R Wilks, 226 Marlow Bottom, Marlow, Bucks (01628 477992 (H)). Treasurer: Superintendent D R McWhirter, Crime Support Department, Police Hill, Kidlington, Oxon OX5 2NX (01865 820508 (H) 01865 855700 (B) 01865 855713 (F)). Ground: Oxford RFC, Southern Bypass, Oxford Tel: 01865 243984.

The Mount - 1989 - Secretary: M J Wigg, PE Instructor, HMP The Mount, Molyneaux Avenue, Bovindon, Hertfordshire HP3 0NZ (01442 834363 Ext 252 (B) 01442 834321 (Fax)). Fix Sec: I Harris, PE Instructor, HMP The Mount, Molyneaux Avenue, Bovingdon, Hertfordshire HP3 0NZ (01442 834363 Ext 252 (B) 01442 834321 (Fax)). Ground: HMP The Mount, Molyneaux Avenue HP3 0NZ Tel: 01442 834363 Ext 252.

Thirsk - 1995 - Secretary: J Pearson, 1 Bryone Court, Hutton Meadows, Guisborough, Cleveland TS14 8DX (01287 634193 (H) 01765 607452 (B)). Fix Sec: D Hewatt, 11 Victoria Avenue, Sowerby, Thirsk, North Yorks YO7 1P (01845 525676 (H) 0976 736 675 (B)). Treasurer: J Iles, 1 Danum Avenue, Sowerby, Thirsk, North Yorkshire YO7 1RU (01845 525118 (H)). Ground: Thirsk Ath. Sports & social cl, Newsham Road, Thirsk, N Yorks YO7 Tel: 01845 522910.

Tonbridge School - 1870 - Secretary: Mr G P Gales, Tonbridge School, Tonbridge, Kent TN9 1JP (01732 773231 (H) 01732 365555 (B) 01732 363424 (F)). Fix Sec: Mr G P Gales, Tonbridge School, Tonbridge, Kent TN9 1JP (01732 773231 (H) 01732 365555 (B) 01732 363424 (F)). Treasurer: Mr G P Gales, Tonbridge School, Tonbridge, Kent TN9 1JP (01732 773231 (H) 01732 365555 (B) 01732 363424 (F)). Ground: The '50', Tonbridge School, High Street, Tonbridge, Kent TN9 1JP Tel: 01732 365555.

Unicorns - 1965 - Secretary: B Hutchinson, Market Place, Easingwold, York YO6 3AG (01347 822332 (H) 01347 821645 (B) 01347 822839 (Fax)). Fix Sec: D Butler, Golden Ball, Bishop Hill, York (01904 654165 (H). Treasurer: B Hutchinson, Market Place, Easingwold, York YO6 3AG (01347 822332 (H) 01347 821645 (B) 01347 822839 (Fax)). Ground: Clifton Park, York.

United Banks - 1914 - Secretary: T Wrafter, c/o Standard Chartered Bank, 27-28 Clements Lane, London EC4N 7AP (01689 816843 (H) 0171 2807448 (B)). Fix Sec: J Jackman, 38 St Martins Drive, Walton-on-Thames, Surrey KT12 3BW (01932 222460 (H)). Treasurer: J Archer, 79 Felstead Road, Orpington, Kent BR6 9AD (01689 825804 (H)).

United Hospitals - 1875 - Secretary: David Badenock Frcs, 123 Harley Street, London W1N 1HE (0181 3415622 0171 6018391 0171 2246481). Fix Sec: Andy Platts, Dept. Radiology, The Royal Free Hospital, Pond St. Hampstead NW3 2QG (01718302013 0171 8302969). Treasurer: Martin Bircher, Fairways, The Warren, Ashtead, Surrey KT21 2SN (01372 275414 01372 271647 01372 271647). Ground: St Mary's Hospital Athletic, Ground, Udney Park Road, Teddington, Middlesex Tel: 0181 9773100.

University College School - 1882 - Ground: Frognal, London NW3 Tel: 0171 435 2215.

Uppingham School - 1889 - Ground: Uppingham, Leicestershire LE15 9QE Tel: 01572 822533.

Warwickshire Constabulary - 1947 - Secretary: G T Moreton, 118 Higham Lane, Nuneaton, Warwickshire CV11 6AX (01203 385618 (H) 01926 415000 (B)). Fix Sec: S Foster, Police Station, Vicarage St, Nuneaton, Warwickshire CV11 4DW (01203 349821 (H) 01203 643111 (B)). Treasurer: G T Moreton, 118 Higham Lane, Nuneaton, Warwickshire CV11 6AX (01203 385618 (H) 01926 415000 (B)). Ground: Police HQ-P O Box 4, Leek Wootton, Warwickshire CV35 7QB Tel: 01926 415000.

Washington - 1976 - Secretary: P Guy, 13 Beech Terrace, South Moor, Stanley, County Durham DH9 7EL (01207 237942 (H)). Fix Sec: J Watlen, 7 Bridekirk, Albany, Washington NE37 1ND (0191 4169599 (H)). Treasurer: M Wharton, 4 Baxter Road, Town End Town, Sunderland SR5 4LQ (0191 519 1315 (H)). Ground: Northern Area Playing Fields, Stephenson Industrial Estate, Washington, Tyne & Wear.

Watton - Secretary: R Watson, 4 Guarnock Terrace, King's Lynn, Norfolk PE30 5QT (01553 775144 01553 829827). Fix Sec: S Blackwood, 36 Queensway, Watton, Norfolk IP25 6BL (01953 884103Ex 249 (B)). Treasurer: M J Bayley, 7 St Georges Close, Saham Toney, Thetford, Norfolk IP25 74T (01953 884807 (H) 01379 644202 (B) 01379 652361 (F)). Ground: Dereham Road Sports Centre, Watton, Norfolk Tel: 01953 881281.

Wellcome - 1982 - Secretary: J P Watts, 16 Sunbeam Cottages, Pollards Wood Road, Oxted, Surrey RH8 0HY (01883 723084 (H) 0181 639 6595 (B) 0181 663 3526 (Fax)). Treasurer: J P Watts, 16 Sunbeam Cottages, Pollards Wood Road, Oxted, Surrey RH8 0HY (01883 723084 (H) 0181 639 6595 (B) 0181 663 3526 (Fax)). Ground: Wellcome Sports & Social Club, South Eden Park Road, Beckenham, Kent BR3 3BS Tel: 0181 658 2211.

Wellington College - 1859 - Ground: Crowthorne, Berkshire Tel: 01344 772262.

West Cornwall Police - 1947 - Secretary: M Boyling, 44 Messack Close, Falmouth, Cornwall TR11 4SH (01326 311 083(H) 01893 278 831 01326 562 289). Fix Sec: M Boyling, 44 Messack Close, Falmouth, Cornwall TR11 4SH (01326 311 083(H) 01893 278 831 01326 562 289). Ground: Truro Rugby Grounds, Truro TR4 8NG Tel: 01209 714881.

Westerham - 1983 - Secretary: A Richman, 93 Sutherland Avenue, Biggin Hill, Kent TN16 3HH (01959 575597 (H) 0410 055818 (B)). Fix Sec: S Haysom, The Oast, Hale Oak Farm, Hale Oak Lane, Weald, Sevenoaks, Kent (01732 457799 (H) 0171 620 3636 (B)). Treasurer: G Bunn, 112 Clock House Rd, Beckenham, Kent BR3 4JX (0181 402 2486 (H) 0181 460 2346 (B)). Ground: Costells Meadow, King Georges Playing Fields, Westerham, Kent Tel: 01959 561106.

West Midlands Police - 1935 - Secretary: D Ashford, c/o Crime Manager, Sutton Coldfield Police Statio, Sutton Coldfield, W Midlands B74 2NR (0121 3737604 (H) 0121 3226174 (B)). Fix Sec: J Grante, c/o CID Office, Sutton Coldfield Police Stn, Lichfield Road, West Midlands B74 2NR (0121 322 6020 (B)). Treasurer: Supt R Fowler, c/o Central Traffic Department, Park Lane, Aston, Birmingham. Ground: W Mids Police Training Centre, Tally Ho!, Pershore Road, Edgbaston, Birmingham B5 7RN Tel: 0121 472 2944.

Wheatsheaf Cabin Crew - 1992 - Secretary: Mrs L Gollop, 39a Upperwoodford, Salisbury, Wiltshire (01772 782648). Ground: Holders Rd, Amesbury, Wiltshire.

Whitgift School - 1871 - Ground: Haling Park, Nottingham Road, South Croydon CR2 6YT Tel: 0181 688 9222.

Wiltshire Police - Secretary: Det Cons A Peach, Police HQ, London Road, Devizes SN10 2DN (01380 722341 EXT582 (B)). Fix Sec: Chief Insp N J Maslen, Police Headquarters, Wiltshire Constabulary, London Road, Devizes,Wiltshire SN10 2DN (01666 824152 (H) 01380 734075 (B) 01380 734197 (F)). Treasurer: Det Sgt J Butcher, Police HQ, London Road, Devizes SN10 2DN (01380 722341 EXT582 (B)). Ground: Police Headquarters, London Road, Devizes, Wiltshire SN10 2DN Tel: 01380 734057.

Wodson Park - 1994 - Secretary: I Williams, Pond House, Back Lane, Nazeing, Essex EN9 2DD (01992 892925 (H) 0181 8865259 (B)). Fix Sec: S Langford, 97 Bury Green Road, Cheshunt, Hertfordshire EN7 5AG (01992 300540 (H) 01279 455045 (B)). Treasurer: Peter Garlick, 8E ST Catherines Rd, Broxbourne, Hertfordshire EN10 7GL (07957250038 0171 5450400). Ground: Wadesmill Rd, ware, Hertfordshire Tel: 01920 487091.

Wyvern - 1970 - Secretary: M J Howe, 11 Bluebell CLose, Taunton, Somerset TA1 3XQ (01823 334159 (H) 01823 335223 (B)). Fix Sec: J Bennett, 101 Ashbourne Crescent, Taunton, Somerset (01823 330639 (H)). Treasurer: P Summers, 3 Daws Mead, Bishops Hull, Taunton, Somerset (01823 271534 (H)). Ground: Wyvern Club, Mountfields Road, Taunton, Somerset TA1 3BJ Tel: 01823 284591.

STUDENT RUGBY FOOTBALL UNION

Edge Hill University College - 1960 - Secretary: T D McMath, 81 Childwall Valley Road, Liverpool L16 4PD (0151 722 6538 (H) 0151 722 6538 (B) 01695 579997 (Fax)). Treasurer: Tim Valentine, c/o Student Union, Edge Hill College, St Helens Rd, Ormskirk, Lancs L394QP (01695 575457 01695584255 01695 577904). Ground: St Helens Road, Ormskirk, Lancashire L39 4QP Tel: 01695 575457.

Farnborough College of Technology - 1990 - Secretary: B Burrowes, Farnborough College Of Tech., Students Union, Boundary Road, Farnborough GU14 6SB (01252 407140 (B) 01252 407141 (F)). Fix Sec: B Burrowes, Farnborough College Of Tech., Students Union, Boundary Road, Farnborough GU14 6SB (01252 407140 (B) 01252 407141 (F)). Treasurer: S Jackson, Farnborough College of Tech., Student Union, Boundary Road, Farnborough GU14 6SB (01252 407140 (B) 01252 407141 (F)). Ground: Farnborough Rugby Club, Tile Barn Close, Farnborough, Hampshire Tel: 01252 542750.

Goldsmiths College - Secretary: J Courtney, General Manager, GSCU, Dixon Road, New Cross, LONDON SE14 6NW (0181 692 1406 (B) 0181 894 9789 (B)). Fix Sec: S Henwood, Students Union Offices, Lewisham Way, New Cross, London SE14. Treasurer: J Walsh, Students Union Offices, Lewisham Way, New Cross, London SE14. Ground: Loring Hall, Water Lane, Sidcup, Kent Tel: 0181 300 8712.

Hadlow College - 1968 - Secretary: S G Hewitt, 11 Appletons, Hadlow, Tonbridge, Kent TN11 0DT (01732 851417 (H) 01732 850551 (B) 01732 851957 (Fax)). Fix Sec: S G Hewitt, 11 Appletons, Hadlow, Tonbridge, Kent TN11 0DT (01732 851417 (H) 01732 850551 (B) 01732 851957 (Fax)). Ground: Hadlow College, Hadlow, Tonbridge, Kent TN11 0AL Tel: 01732 850551.

Harper Adams Agricultural College - Secretary: I Robson, Head of Student Services, Harper Adams College, Newport, Shropshire TF10 8NB (01952 813772 (H) 01952 820280 (B) 01952 814783 (Fax)). Fix Sec: Hon Fix Sec, Harper Adams College, Newport, Shropshire TF10 8NB (01952 812307 (B) 01952 814462 (Fax)). Treasurer: Hon Treasurer, Harper Adams College, Newport, Shropshire TF10 8NB (01952 812307 (B) 01952 814462 (Fax)). Ground: Harper Adams Univ Colleg, Newport, Shropshire TF10 8NB Tel: 01952 812307.

Imperial College - Secretary: D Gol, c/o Roger Pownall Club Preside, Penthouse D, Southside, Princes Gardens, South Ken SW7 1LU (0171 594 9446 (H) 0171 594 9248 (B) 0171 594 9248 (F)). Fix Sec: A Jarvis, Imperial College Union, Prince Consort Road, London SW7 (0171 594 8066 (B) 0171 594 8065 (F)). Treasurer: T Denyer, Imperial College Union, Prince Consort Road, London SW7 (0171 594 8066 (B) 0171 594 8065 (F)). Ground: Imperial College Athletic Grd, Sipson Lane, Harlington, Middx UB3 5AQ Tel: 0181 759 9649.

Kingston University Guild of Students - 1948 - Secretary: Mrs I Holmes, Clubs/Societies Administrator, Kingston Univ Guild of Stds, Penrhyn Road, Kingston, Surrey KT1 2EE (0181 255 2222 0181 255 0032). Fix Sec: Mrs I Holmes, Clubs/Societies Administrator, Kingston Univ Guild of Stds, Penrhyn Road, Kingston, Surrey KT1 2EE (0181 255 2222 0181 255 0032). Treasurer: Mrs I Holmes, Clubs/Societies Administrator, Kingston Univ Guild of Stds, Penrhyn Road, Kingston, Surrey KT1 2EE (0181 255 2222 0181 255 0032). Ground: Tolworth Court, Old Kingston Road, Tolworth, Surrey KT4 7QH Tel: 0181 330 2865.

King's College School - 1864 - Ground: Southside, Wimbledon Common, London SW19 4TT Tel: 0181 947 9311.

Kings College - 1862 - Secretary: Ms C Down, KCLSU Strand, Macadam Building, Surrey Street, London WC2R 2NS (0171 836 7132 (B) 0171 379 9833 (Fax)). Fix Sec: K Chan, KCLSU, Macadam Building, Surrey Street, London W2CR 2NS. Treasurer: T Naito, KCLSU, Macadam Building, Surrey Street, London W2CR 2NS. Ground: KCLSU Sports Ground, Windsor Avenue, Berrylands, Surrey KT3 5HA.

Leeds Medics and Dentists - 1931 - Secretary: R Finch, 12 Norwood Terrace, Leeds LS6 1EA (0113 226 4557 (H)). Fix Sec: M Dodd, 145 Hyde Park Rd, Leeds LS6 1AJ (0113 2160632 (H)). Treasurer: A Cohen, 145 Hyde Park Rd, Leeds LS6 1AJ (0113 2160632 (H)). Ground: University Playing Fields, Weetwood, Leeds Tel: 0113 2751993.

Liverpool John Moores University - 1971 - Secretary: Miss D Jones, The Haigh Building, Maryland Street, Liverpool L1 9DE (0151 794 1928 (B) 0151 708 5334 (F)). Ground: Birkenhead Park RFC, Upper Park, Park Road North, Birkenhead, Wirral L41 8AD Tel: 0151 6524646.

Liverpool Medical School - 1960 - Secretary: M Bishton, 54 Wellington Avenue, Wavertree, Liverpool L15 0EH (0151 475 7860 (H) 0151 475 8593 (B)). Fix Sec: J Oates, Duncan Building RLUH, Daulby Street, Liverpool L69 3BX (0151 753 1704 (H) 0151 706 2000 ext4271 (B)). Treasurer: D Melling, 55 Wellington Avenue, Wavertree, Liverpool L15 0EH (0151 475 7860 (H) 0151 475 8593 (B)). Ground: Geoffrey Hughes Memorial Groun, Mather Avenue, Liverpool L18 Tel: 0151 706 2000 Ext 4271.

London School of Economics - 1992 - Fix Sec: R Sellers, LSE A V, RM E178 East BDLG, Houghton Street, London WC2A 2AE (0171 9557161 (B)). Treasurer: Sarah Breaks, LSE Athletic Union, RM E178, East Building, Houghton Street WC2 2AE (0171 955 7161 0171 955 6551). Ground: LSE Sports Ground, Windsor Avenue, New Malden, Surrey KT3 Tel: 0181 942 1229.

London Guildhall University - 1971 - Secretary: D Agyemang, Students Union, 2 Goulston Street, London E1 7TP (0171 247 1441 (B)). Fix Sec: S Murphy, Students Union, 2 Goulston Street, London E1 7TP (0171 247 1441 (B)). Treasurer: M McLeod, Students Union, 2 Goulston Street, London E1 7TP (0171 247 1441 (B)). Ground: c/o Eton Manor RFC, Eaton Park, Ruckholt Road, Leyton E10 Tel: 0181 539 7218.

Manchester Medicals - 1876 - Secretary: P Wheatley-Price, MSRC Office, Medical School, Stopford Building, Oxford Road, Manchester (01275 332488 (H) 0161 2838481/0161 2755532 (B)). Fix Sec: C Repanos, MSRC Office, Medical School, Stopford Building, Oxford Road, Manchester (01902 631971/01922 476351 (H) 0161 275 5532 (B)). Treasurer: T Wallace, MSRC Office, Medical School, Stopford Building, Oxford Road, Manchester (01494 563041 (H) 0161 2755532 (B)). Ground: University Sports Ground, Willenhall Road, Wythenshawe, Manchester Tel: 0161 998 4157.

Manchester Metropolitan University - 1957 - Secretary: G J Davison, Students Union, Manchester Polytechnic, 99 Oxford Road, Manchester M1 7EL. Ground: c/o Heaton Moor RFC, Green Lane, Stockport.**Middlesex & University College** - 1985 - Secretary: D Squires, UCL Union, 25 Gordon Street, London WC1H 0AH (0181 802 7040 (H) 0171 380 7221 (B) 0171 383 3937 (Fax)). Fix Sec: A Farmer, UCMSSU, 43-49 Huntley Street, London WC1E 6DG (01426 646411 (H) 0171 209 6497 (B) 0171 209 0650 (F)). Treasurer: L Humphreys, 81 Downhills Park Road, Tottenham, London N17 6AS (0181 8888634 (H) 0171 2096499 (B) 0171 2090650 (F)). Ground: Athletic Ground, Perry Street, Chislehurst, Kent BR7 6HA Tel: 0181 467 3859.

Middlesex University - 1972 - Ground: Worlds End Lane, Green Dragon Lane, Enfield, Middlesex Tel: 0181 326 5601.

Nene College - 1981 - Secretary: G Starmer, Student's Union, Park Campus, Boughton Green Road, Moulton Park, Northampton NN2 7AL (01604 735500/Ext2272 (B) 01604 719454 (F)). Fix Sec: D Blowers, 158 Ardington Road, Northampton NN1 5LT (01604 628870). Ground: Boughton Green Road, Northampton NN2 7AL Tel: 01604 735500.

Nottingham Trent University - 1992 - Secretary: H George, 48 Musham Sreet, The Meadows, Nottingham NG2 (07771 880613 (H)). Treasurer: H George, 48 Musham Sreet, The Meadows, Nottingham NG2 (07771 880613 (H)). Ground: Clifton Campus, Clifton Lane, Nottingham Tel: 0115 921 3316.

Nottingham Medics - 1977 - Secretary: Tim Bryant, 93 Lenton Boulevard, Lenton, Nottingham NG7 2FQ (0115 970 0499 (H)). Fix Sec: Richard Singleton, c/o 79 Lenton Boulevard, Lenton, Nottingham NG7 2FQ (0115 978 2355). Treasurer: M Hunter, c/o 73 Lenton Boulevard, Lenton, Nottingham NG7 2FQ (0115 970 2084 (H)). Ground: Grove Farm, University Sports Fields, Lenton, Nottingham NG7 Tel: 0115 951 3668.

Oxford Brookes University - 1994 - Secretary: M Dodwell, c/o Oxford Brookes Centre, Chesney Lane, Headington, Oxford OX3 0BD (01865 483158 (B) 01865 483109 (F)). Fix Sec: S Rollerson, c/o Sports Department,Oxford, Brookes University, Cheney, Lane, Headington, Oxford OX3 0BD (01865 484373 (B)). Treasurer: M Brookes, c/o Oxford Brookes Centre, Chesney Lane, Headington, Oxford OX3 OBD (01865 483151 (B) 01865 483109 (F)). Ground: Oxford Harlequins Club, Horspath Road Recreation Grnd, Cowley, Oxford Tel: 01865 775765.

Queen Mary & Westfield College - Secretary: Hon Secretary, College Students Union, 432 Bancroft Rd, London E1 4DH (0171 975 5390 (B) 0181 981 0802 (F)). Fix Sec: Hon Fix Sec RFC, Students Union, 432 Bancroft Road, London E1 4DH (0171 975 5390 (B) 0181 981 0802 (Fax)). Treasurer: Hon Treasurer, Students Union, 432 Bancroft Rd, London E1 4DH (0171 975 5390 (B) 0181 981 0802 (F)). Ground: QMW Sports Ground, Abridge Road, Theydon Bois, Essex Tel: 01992 814327.

Royal Veterinary College - Secretary: J C Dare, Royal Vetinary College, Hawksheadlane, N. Mymms, Hatfield, Herts AL9 7TA (01707 666310 01707 652090 (F)). Fix Sec: S Cooke, Royal Vetinary College, Royal College Street, London NW1 0TU (0171 468 5158 (H) 0171 387 3791 (F)). Treasurer: J Bosley, Royal Vetinary College, Hawkshead Lane, North Mymms, Hatfield, Hertfordshire AL9 7TA (01707 666310 (H) 01707 652090 (F)). Ground: Royal Vetinary College, Haweshead Lane, North Mymms, Hatfield, Hertfordshire AL9 7TA Tel: 01707 647091/655486/666310.

Royal Agricultural College - 1868 - Secretary: R Coatem, Royal Agricultural College, Stroud Rd, Cirencester, Gloucestershire GL7 6JS (01285 652531 ext.2291 (B) 01285 650219 (F)). Fix Sec: D Layon, Royal Agricultural College, Stroud Road, Cirencester, Gloucestershire GL7 6JS (01285 652187 / 652531 (B) 01285 650219 (F)). Treasurer: A Harris, Royal Agricultural College, Cirencester, Gloucestershire GL7 6JS (01285 652187 / 652531 (B) 01285 650219 (F)). Ground: Royal Agricultural College, Stroud Road, Cirencester, Gloucestershire GL7 6JS Tel: 01285 652187.

Royal Free Hospital - 1954 - Secretary: J Young, Students Union, Royal Free School of Medicine, Rowlands Hill Street, London NW3 2PF (0171 794 4110 (H) 0171 794 0500 Ext 4332 (B)). Fix Sec: R Mead, Students Union, Royal Free School of Medicine, Rowland Hill Street, London NW3 2PF (0171 267 0775 (H) 0171 794 0500 Ext 4332 (B)). Treasurer: J Young, Students Union, Royal Free School of Medicine, Rowlands Hill Street, London NW3 2PF (0171 794 4110 (H) 0171 794 0500 Ext 4332 (B)). Ground: Myddleton House, Bulls Cross, Enfield Tel: 01992 761553.

Royal School of Mines - 1929 - Secretary: M Cockayne, Royal School of Mines Union, Prince Consort Rd,, South Kensington SW7 2BP (0171 5948074 0171 594 8074). Fix Sec: Z Rehman, Royal School of Mines Union, Prince Consort Rd,, South Kensington, London SW7 2BP (0171 594 8074 0171 594 8074). Ground: Imperial Coll Athletic Ground, Sipson Lane, Harlington Tel: 0181 759 9649.

Royal Military College of Science - Secretary: Lt Col. J C S Garnet MBE, RMCS, Shrivenham, Swindon, Wilts. (01793 783592 01793 785573 01793 785577). Fix Sec: Lt Col. J C S Garnet MBE, RMCS, Shrivenham, Swindon, Wilts. (01793 783592 01793 785573 01793 785577). Ground: Shrivenham, Swindon, Wiltshire SN6 8LA.

Royal Holloway, University of London - 1985 - Hon Sec: A Purdon, Students Union, Royal Holloway, University of London, Egham, Hill, Egham, Surrey TW20 OEX (07957 460227 (B) 01784 486312). Fix Sec: M Dunster, Students Union, Royal Holloway, University of London, Egham, Hill, Egham, Surrey TW20 OEX. Treasurer: J Cummings, Students Union, Royal Holloway, University of London, Egham, Hill, Egham, Surrey RW20 OEX. Ground: Nobles Sportsground, Prune Hill, Egham TW20 0EX Tel: 01784 438702.

Seale-Hayne Agricultural College - 1929 - Secretary: Mrs P Verrall, Seale Hayne SU Administrator, Ashburton Rd, Newton Abbot, Devon TQ12 6NQ (01626 60557 (B) 01626 335181 (F)). Fix Sec: A J Cheater, Seale-Hayne College, Ashburton Road,

Newton Abbot, Devon (01626 332160 (H) 01626 60557 (B) 01626 335181 (Fax)). Treasurer: J Reed, Seale-Hayne College, Ashburton Road, Newton Abbot, Devon (01626 332160 (H) 01626 60557 (B) 01626 335181 (Fax)). Ground: Seale-Hayne, Newton Abbot, South Devon TQ12 6NQ Tel: 01626 60557/332160.

Sheffield Hallam University - 1965 - Secretary: Ms D Hallatt, Sheffield Hallam Univ A.U., Nelson Mandela Building, Pond St, Sheffield S1 2BW (0114 253 4111 0114 253 4140). Ground: Derbyshire Lane, Sheffield Tel: 0114 255 6435.

Sheffield Medicals - 1964 - Secretary: T Tipper, 14 Piscah House Rd,, Broomhill, Sheffield. Fix Sec: D Garnett, 29 Moor Oaks Rd,, Broomhill, Sheffield. Treasurer: M Ford, 335 Crookesmoor Rd, Sheffield. Ground: Norton Playing Fields, Warminster Road, Norton, Sheffield Tel: 0114 222 8524.**Anglia (Chelmsford) University** - 1969 - Secretary: S Dupree, 132 Baddow Hall Cresent, Great Baddow, Nr Chelmsford, Essex CM2 7BU (01245 474346 (H) 01245 493131 Ext 3280 (B) 01245 490835 (Fax)). Fix Sec: S Dupree, 132 Baddow Hall Cresent, Great Baddow, Nr Chelmsford, Essex CM2 7BU (01245 474346 (H) 01245 493131 Ext 3280 (B) 01245 490835 (Fax)).

Berkshire College of Agriculture - Secretary: S Alcock, Hall Place, Burchetts Green, Maidenhead SL6 6QR (01628 824444 x 244 (B) 07711 573099 (pager)). Ground: Hall Place, Burchetts Green, Nr Maidenhead, Berkshire SL6 6QR Tel: 01628 824444.

Bishop Burton College - 1968 - Secretary: R A Rank, Fieldview, Bishop Burton College, Beverley HU17 8QF (01964 553091 (H) 01964 553064 (B) 01964 553101 (Fax)). Fix Sec: S Buttle, Bishop Burton College, Beverley, East Yorkshire HU17 8QG (01964 553099 (H) 01964 553064 (B) 01964 553101 (F)). Secretary: R A Rank, Fieldview, Bishop Burton College, Beverley HU17 8QF (01964 553091 (H) 01964 553064 (B) 01964 553101 (Fax)). Ground: Bishop Burton College, Beverley, East Yorkshire HU17 8QG Tel: 01964 553064.

Bournemouth University - 1976 - Secretary: G Hawkins, Sports Department, Poole House, Talbot Campus, Fern Barrow, Poole, Dorset BH12 5BB (01202 595012 01202 595012). Fix Sec: A Eaton, Sports Department, Poole House, Talbot Campus, Fern Barrow, Poole, Dorset BH12 5BB (01202 533219 01202 595012 012023 595012). Treasurer: S Pearce, Sports Department, Poole House, Talbot Campus, Fern Barrow, Poole, Dorset BH12 5BB (01202 595012 (F)). Ground: Slades Farm, White Farm, Ensbury Park, Bournemouth, Dorset Tel: 01202 595012.

Brunel University - 1966 - Secretary: W Chapman, c/o Union of Brunel Students, Cleveland Rd,, Uxbridge UB8 3PH (01895 462200 01895 810477). Treasurer: A Rendall, c/o Union of Brunel Students, Cleveland Rd,, Uxbridge U38 3PH (01895 462200 01895 810477). Ground: University Playing Fields, Kingston Lane, Uxbridge, Middlesex UB8 3PH Tel: 01895 273214.

Brunel University College - 1891 - Secretary: J S Hunter, Dept. of Sports Sciences, Brunel University (Osterley), Borough Road, Isleworth, Middx TW7 5DU (0181 941 1985 (H) 0181 891 8255 (B) 0181 891 8269 (F)). Fix Sec: H Morgan, 52 Hitherbrook Road, Hayes, Middlesex UB3 3AD (0171 573 0557 (H) 0171 573 0557 (B)). Treasurer: M Pink, Dept of Sports Sciences, Brunel University (Osterley), Borough Road, Isleworth, Middx TW7 5DU (0181 891 8208 (H) 0181 891 0121 ext2594 (B) 0181 891 8269 (F)). Ground: Jersey Road, Osterley, Middlesex TW7 4QR Tel: 0181 891 8221.

Bucks College of Higher Education - Secretary: Mrs P Manson, Buckinghamshire College, Alexandra Road, High Wycombe, Bucks HP11 2JZ (01494 605100 (B) 01494 605046 (F)). Fix Sec: Mrs P Manson, Buckinghamshire College, Alexandra Road, High Wycombe, Bucks HP11 2JZ (01494 605100 (B) 01494 605046 (F)). Ground: Kingsmead Road, Loudwater, High Wycombe.

Cheltenham & Glos College of Higher Education - 1889 - Secretary: D L Williams, Dept of Leisure Management, Cheltenham & Glos Coll of HE, St Pauls Road, Cheltenham GL50 4BS (01242 578924 (H) 01242 532936 (B) 01242 532957 (Fax)). Fix Sec: P Hunt, c/o Francis Close Hall, Swindon Rd, Cheltenham, Glos GL51 9AZ (01242 543439). Treasurer: M Sutton, c/o Francis Close Hall, Swindon Rd, Cheltenham GL51 9AZ (01242 643439). Ground: The Folley, Swindon Road, Cheltenham, Gloucestershire GL51 9AZ Tel: 01242 543439.

City and Guilds College - Secretary: Hon Club Sec, Imperial College of Science, Technology & Medicine Level 3, Mech Eng, Exhibition Rd London SW7 2BX (0171 594 8073 (B) 0171 823 8845 (F)). Fix Sec: Hon Fix Sec, City & Guilds Students Union, Exhibition Rd, London SW7 2BX (0171 591 8073 (B) 0171 823 8845 (F)). Treasurer: Hon Treasurer, City & Guilds Student Union, Exhibition Rd, London SW7 2BX (0171 594 8073 (B) 0171 823 8845 (F)). Ground: Imperial College Athletic Gnd, Sipson Lane, Harlington, Middx Tel: 0181 759 9649.

City University - 1912 - Secretary: Hon Club Sec, City University, Students Union, Northampton Square, London EC1 0HB (0171 505 5605 (B) 0171 505 5601 (F)). Fix Sec: Hon Fix Sec, City University, Students Union, Northampton Square, London EC1 0HB (0171 505 5605 (B) 0171 505 5601 (F)). Treasurer: Hon Trea, City University, Students Union, Northampton Square, London EC1 0HB (0171 505 5605 (B) 0171 505 5601 (F)). Ground: Kings College Sports Ground, Window Avenue, New Malden, Surrey KT3 5HA Tel: 0181 942 0495.

Coventry University - 1969 - Secretary: Hon Club Sec, Coventry University,Stud Union, Priory St, Coventry CV1 5FB. Fix Sec: Hon Fix Sec, Coventry University Student Un, Priory St, Coventry CV1 5FB. Treasurer: Hon Trea, Coventry University Student Un, Priory St, Coventry CV1 5FB. Ground: Westwood Heath Playing Fields, Kirby Corner Road, Coventry Tel: 01203 465642.

Cranfield University - Secretary: The Secretary, Cranfield Univ. Rugby Club, Building 114, Cranfield Univ., Wharley End, Beds MK43 0AL. Fix Sec: M J Lewis, 4a The Crescent, Bedford MK40 2RT (01234 354305 (H) 01234 750111 Ext 5345 (B)). Ground: Bedford, Bedfordshire MK43 0AL Tel: 01234 750111 Ext 2606.

Crewe & Alsager College - 1946 - Secretary: Matt Chapman, Alsager College S.U., Hassal Rd, Alsager, Stoke-on-Trent (07887 884711 01270 882925). Fix Sec: Matt Chapman, Alsager College S.U., Hassal Rd, Alsager, Stoke-on-Trent (07887 884711 01270 882925). Ground: Alsager College, Hassall Road, Alsager, Stoke-on-Trent ST7 2HL Tel: 01270 882580.

Durham University - 1875 - Secretary: E R Wood, 62 Claypath, Durham DH1 1QS (01723 377413 (H) 0191 374 2196 (B)). Fix Sec: E R Wood, 62 Claypath, Durham DH1 1QS (01723 377413 (H) 0191 374 2196 (B)). Treasurer: R Sullivan, c/o Athletic Union, Dunelyn House, New Elvet, Durham DH1 3HP (0191 3743435 (B)). Ground: The Racecourse Ground, Green Lane, Durham DH1 Tel: 0191 374 7021.

Shuttleworth College - 1947 - Secretary: B Welti, Shuttleworth College, Old warden Park, Biggleswade, Beds SG18 9EA (01767 626214 (B) 01767 627053 (F)). Treasurer: B Welti, Shuttleworth College, Old warden Park, Biggleswade, Beds SG18 9EA (01767 626214 (B) 01767 627053 (F)). Ground: Old Warden Park, Biggleswade, Bedfordshire SG18 9DX Tel: 01525 863100.

Southampton University Hospitals - 1975 - Secretary: Mark Williams, 71 Portswood Rd, Portswood, Southampton (01703 582614). Fix Sec: Nick Harvey. Treasurer: Paddy Singh. Ground: Wellington Sports Grounds, Stoneham Lane, Eastleigh, Southampton Tel: 01703 612309.

South Bank University - 1980 - Secretary: Vice President Clubs & Society, South Bank Student Union, Keyworth Street, London SE1 6NG (0171 815 6060 0171 815 6061). Fix Sec: Vice President Clubs & Society, South Bank Student Union, Keyworth Street, London SE1 6NG (0171 815 6060 0171 815 6061). Treasurer: Vice President Clubs & Society, South Bank Student Union, Keyworth Street, London SE1 6NG (0171 815 6060 0171 815 6061). Ground: South Bank Univ Sportsground, Turney Road, London SE21 7JH Tel: 0171 737 0677.

South Devon College - 1933 - Secretary: M Herbert, South Devon College, Newton Road, Torquay, Devon TQ2 5BY (01803 812550 (H) 01803 386341 (B) 01803 386403 (Fax)). Fix Sec: A Carey, Flat 10, 54 St Marychurch Road, Torquay TQ1 3JE (01626 834444 (H)). Treasurer: S Garvey, 63 Dolphin Crescent, Paignton TQ3 1JZ (01803 529202 (H)). Ground: South Devon College, Newton Road, Torquay, Devon TQ2 5BY Tel: 01803 291212.

Sparsholt College - 1927 - Secretary: S Barlow, Sparsholt College, Sparsholt, Winchester, Hampshire SO21 2NF (0402 385839 (H) 01962 797241 (B) 01962 776587 (Fax)). Fix Sec: S Barlow, Sparsholt College, Sparsholt, Winchester, Hampshire SO21 2NF (0402 385839 (H) 01962 797241 (B) 01962 776587 (Fax)). Treasurer: S Barlow, Sparsholt College, Sparsholt, Winchester, Hampshire SO21 2NF (0402 385839 (H) 01962 797241 (B) 01962 776587 (Fax)). Ground: Sparsholt College, Sparsholt, Nr Winchester, Hampshire SO21 2NF Tel: 01962 776441.

Staffordshire University - 1992 - Secretary: I Brittain, Athletic Union, Leed Road, Stoke-on-Trent, Staffordshire ST4 2DE (01782 294117 (B) 01782 294322 (F)). Fix Sec: B Colleson, 41 Boughey Road, Shelton, Stoke-on-Trent (01782 416832 (H)). Treasurer: R White, 101 Regent Road, Hanley, Stoke-on-Trent ST1 3BL (01782 274654 (H)). Ground: Leek Road Sports Centre, Leek Road, Stoke on Trent ST4 2DE Tel: 01782 574124.

St John's College - 1885 - Secretary: J A Crooks, c/o Students Union, Univ College of Ripon and York, Lord Mayors Walk, York YO3 7EX (01904 629816 (B) 01904 620559 (F)). Fix Sec: P Sheppard, c/o Students Union, Univ College of Ripon and York, Lord Mayors Walk, York YO3 7EX (08505 80509 (H) 01904 629816 (B) 01904 620559 (F)). Treasurer: R Owen, c/o Student Union, Univ College of Ripon and York, Lord Mayors Walk, York YO3 7EX (01904 629816 (B) 01904 620559 (F)). Ground: St John's Playing Fields, Hull Road, York Tel: 01904 410180.

St Mary's College - 1913 - Secretary: T Booth, Sports Science Dept., St.Mary's U.C, Waldergrave Rd, Twickenham TW1 4SX (0181 240 4276 0181 240 4212). Fix Sec: B Shelbourne, Student's Union, St. Mary's U.C, Waldergrave Rd, Twickenham TW1 4SX (0181 891 6123 0181 744 1700). Treasurer: S Langstaff, Students' Union, St Mary's U.C, Waldegrave Rd, Twickenham TW1 4SX (0181 240 4131 0181 744 1700). Ground: Strawberry Hill, Twickenham, Middlesex TW1 4SX.

Stoke on Trent College - 1976 - Secretary: C Linsell, Stoke-on-Trent College, Stoke Road, Shelton, Stoke-on-Trent, Staffordshire ST4 2DG (01782 626206 (H) 01782 208208 Ext 3221 (B) 01782 283226 (Fax)). Treasurer: S E Sharratt, Stoke-on-Trent College, Stoke Road, Shelton, Stoke-on-Trent ST4 2DG (01782 208208 Ext 3642 (B)). Ground: Stoke Road, Shelton, Stoke on Trent, Staffordshire ST4 2DG Tel: 01782 626206.

The Royal Hospitals - 1865 - Secretary: A Goodwin, 6 Sharon Gardens, London EP 7RX (0181 525 1259 (H) 0171 377 7641 (B)). Fix Sec: Dr P Colvin, 4 Hardy Road, Blackheath, London SE3 7NR (0181 858 0373 (H) 0171 377 7793 (B)). Treasurer: M Duffy, 16 Walden Street, Whitechapel, London E1 2AN (0171 377 5322 (H) 0171 377 7641 (B)). Ground: Wadham Road, Walthamstow E17 4LT Tel: 0181 527 5724.

UMIST - 1978 - Ground: Burnage RFC, Varley Park, Battersea Road, Heaton Mersey, Stockport SK4 3EA Tel: 0161 200 3292.

University College London - Secretary: D Squires, UCL Union, 25 Gordon Street, London WC1H 0AH (0181 802 7040 (H) 0171 380 7221 (B) 0171 383 3937 (Fax)). Fix Sec: M Burdett, UCL Union, 25 Gordon Street, London WC1H OAH (0171 387 3611 (H) 0171 383 3937 (B)). Treasurer: M P C Tankel, UCL Union, 25 Gordon Street, London WC1H OAH (0171 387 3611 (B) 0171 383 3937 (F)). Ground: University College London, Sports Ground, Bell Lane, Shenley, Hertfordshire AL2 1BZ Tel: 01727 822215.

University of Birmingham - 1916 - Secretary: K Johnston, Athletic Union, Munrow Sports Centre, Edgbaston, Birmingham B15 2TU (0121 472 3686 (B) 0121 472 3686 (Fax)). Fix Sec: Z Sennett, Rowdell Cottage, The Street, Washington, West Sussex RH20 4AT (01903 743032 (H/F) 0121 472 3686 (B) 0121 472 3686 (Fax)). Treasurer: D Illingworth, Athletic Union, Munrow Sports Centre, Edgbaston, Birmingham B15 2TU (0121 472 3686 (B) 0121 472 3686 (Fax)). Ground: The Bournbrook, University of Birmingham, Birmingham B15 2TU.

University of Birmingham Medics - 1958 - Secretary: J Geoghan, 89 Reservoir Rd, Selly Oak, Birmingham B29 6SU (0121 603 9699(B)). Fix Sec: N Bosanko, 18 Poole Crescent, Harborne, Birmingham B17 0PB (0121 472 4200 (B)). Treasurer: J Lenton, 74 Gleave Rd, Selly Oak, Birmingham B29 6JN (0121 415 5108 (B)). Ground: Wast Hills, Wast Hills Road, off Redditch Road, West Heath, Birmingham Tel: 0121 458 1060.

University of Bradford - 1965 - Secretary: Chris Weatherby, Students Union, Richmond Rd, Bradford BD7 1DP (01274 233284 01274 235070). Fix Sec: Tristan Parker, Students Union, Richmond Rd, Bradford BD7 1DP (01274 233284 01274 235070). Treasurer: Rob Carr, Students Union, Richmond Rd, Bradford BD7 1DP (01274 233284 01274 235070). Ground: Woodhall Pavilion Sports Grnd, Calverly Road, Bradford BD7 1DP Tel: 01274 662406.

University of Bristol - 1876 - Secretary: R A Reeves, Dept Sport, Exercise & Health, Woodland House, 34 West Park, Bristol BS8 2LU (0117 924 9848 (H) 0117 928 8812 (B) 0117 946 7748 (Fax)). Fix Sec: Ben Lambert, Athletic Union, Student Union, Queens Road, Clifton, Bristol BS8 1LN (0117 9545875 0117 9545876). Treasurer: Simon Davies, Thletic Union, Student Union, Queens Rd, Clifton, Bristol BS8 1LN (0117 9545875 0117 9545876). Ground: Coombe Dingle Playing Fields, Coombe Dingle, Coombe Lane, (off Parry's Lane), Bristol BS9 2BJ Tel: 0117 968 1460.

University of Buckingham - 1982 - Secretary: S J Ridley, Sports Development Officer, Students Union Hunter Street, Buckingham MK18 1EG (01280 814080 Ext 2342 (B) 01280 812791 (F)).
Ground: Gawcott Sports Field, c/o University of Buckingham, Hunters Str, Buckingham MK18 1EG Tel: 01280 814080 Ext 2342.

University of Essex - 1965 - Hon Sec: G Masoud, University of Essex RFC,, Sports Federation, Wivenhoe, Park, Colchester CO4 3SQ (01206 863211). Fix Sec: D Whiteman, University of Essex RFC,, Sports Federation, Wivenhoe, Park, Colchester CO4 3SQ (01206 863211). Treasurer: S Nathan, University of Essex RFC, Sports Federation, Wivenhoe, Park, Colchester CO4 3SQ (01206 863211). Ground: Wivenhoe Park, Colchester, Essex CO4 3SQ Tel: 01206 863211.

University of Exeter - 1908 - Hon Sec: N E Beasant, Athletic Union Office,, Cornwall House, St German's, Road, Exeter EX4 6TG (01392 263505 (B) 01392 263599 (F)). Fix Sec: A J E Roberts, Athletic Union Office,, Cornwall House, St German's, Exeter EX4 6TG (01392 263505 (B) 01392 263599 (F)). Treasurer: A L Draycott, Athletic Union Office,, Cornwall House, St German's, Road, Exeter EX4 6TG (01392 263505 (B) 01392 263599 (F)). Ground: Ducks Meadow, Salmon Pool Lane, Exeter Tel: 01392 270397.

University of Hull - 1929 - Secretary: P Baker, c/o Athletic Union, University House, Cottingham Road, Hull HU6 7RX (01482 466254/6 (B) 01482 466280 (F)). Fix Sec: A Mawson, c/o Athletic Union, University House, Cottingham Road, Hull HU6 7RX (01482 466254/6 (B) 01482 466280 (F)). Treasurer: A Saro, c/o Athletic Union, University House, Cottingham Road, Hull HU6 7RX (01482 466254/6 (B) 01482 466280 (F)). Ground: Inglemere Lane, Hull HU6 7RX Tel: 01482 466234.

University of Keele - 1951 - Secretary: Ms S Alderton, Athletic Union, Leisure Centre, Keele, Staffordshire ST5 5BG (01782 583638 (B) 01782 715812 (Fax)). Fix Sec: R Gould, Athletic Union, Leisure Centre, keele Uni., Newcastle Under Lyme, Staff. ST5 5BG (01782 583638). Treasurer: A Pollard, Athletic Union,, Leisure Centre, Keele Univ., Newcastle Under Lyme, Staff. ST5 5BG (01782 583638). Ground: Keele Sports Centre, Univ of Keele, Staffs ST5 5BG Tel: 01782 583638.

University of Kent - 1965 - Secretary: B Carswell, University Sports Federation, Canterbury, Kent CT2 7NL (01227 768027 (B) 01227 768027 (Fax)). Fix Sec: G Taylor, University Sports Federation, Canterbury, Kent CT2 7NL (01227 768027 (B) 01227 768027 (Fax)). Treasurer: J Barlow, University Sports Federation, Canterbury, Kent CT2 7NL (01227 768027 (B) 01227 768027 (Fax)). Ground: University of Kent, Canterbury, Kent CT2 7NL Tel: 01227 768027.

University of Lancaster - 1965 - Secretary: Dan Wright, Student Activities, Lancaster University, Lancaster LA1 4YA (01524 593250). Fix Sec: Tom Steele, Student Activities, Lancaster University, Lancaster LA1 4YA (01524 593250). Treasurer: Andy Dodson, Student Activities, Lancaster University, Lancaster LA1 4YA (01524 593250). Ground: Student Activities, Lancaster University, Lancaster LA1 4YA Tel: 01524 593250.

University of Leeds - 1905 - Secretary: P Callow, Sports Office, PO Box 157, Leeds LS6 1UH (0113 231 4275 (B) 0113 244 8786 (F)). Fix Sec: G Simmonds, Sports Office, PO Box 157, Leeds LS6 1UH (0113 231 4275 (B) 0113 244 8786 (F)). Treasurer: P Callow, Sports Office, PO Box 157, Leeds LS6 1UH (0113 231 4275 (B) 0113 244 8786 (F)). Ground: Playing Fields, Weetwood, Leeds LS16 5AU Tel: 0113 275 1993.

University of Leicester - 1921 - Secretary: Mrs A Morgan, Sports Association, Students' Union, University Road, Leicester LE1 7RH (0116 255 3860 (B) 0116 255 4483 (Fax)). Fix Sec: Mrs A Morgan, Sports Association, Students' Union, University Road, Leicester LE1 7RH (0116 255 3860 (B) 0116 255 4483 (Fax)). Treasurer: Mrs A Morgan, Sports Association, Students' Union, University Road, Leicester LE1 7RH (0116 255 3860 (B) 0116 255 4483 (Fax)). Ground: University Sports Ground, 40 Manor Road, Oadby, Leicester LE2 2LL Tel: 0116 2719144.

University of Liverpool - 1884 - Secretary: S A Wade, Sports Administrator, Athletic Union, PO Box 187, 160 Mount Pleasant, Liverpool L69 7BR (0151 728 9938 (H) 0151 794 4126/051 708 5033 (B) 0151 794 4174 (Fax)).
Fix Sec: S A Wade, as above Treasurer: S A Wade, as above. Ground: Geoffrey Hughes Sports Ground, Wyncote Fields, Mather Avenue, Allerton, Liverpool L18 6HF Tel: 0151 724 4948.

University of Manchester - 1881 - Secretary: R Gough, Univ Manchester Athletic Union, 333 Oxford Road, Manchester M13 9PG (0161 275 6988 (H) 0161 275 6992 (F)). Fix Sec: R Gough, Univ Manchester Athletic Union, 333 Oxford Road, Manchester M13 9PG (0161 275 6988 (H) 0161 275 6992 (F)). Treasurer: M Brocklesby, Univ Manchester Athletic Union, 333 Oxford Road, Manchester M13 9PG (0161 275 6988 (H) 0161 275 6992 (F)). Ground: The Firs Athletic Ground, Moseley Road, Fallowfield, Manchester M14 6HE Tel: 0161 224 2143.

University of Newcastle - 1963 - Secretary: Dr M A A Cox, Dept Business Management, Univ of Newcastle upon Tyne, Newcastle upon Tyne NE1 7RU (0191 2226254 (B) 0191 2611192 (F)). Fix Sec: Dr M A A Cox, Dept Business Management, Univ of Newcastle upon Tyne, Newcastle upon Tyne NE1 7RU (0191 2226254 (B) 0191 2611192 (F)). Treasurer: Dr M A A Cox, Dept Business Management, Univ of Newcastle upon Tyne, Newcastle upon Tyne NE1 7RU (0191 2226254 (B) 0191 2611192 (F)). Ground: Cochrane Park, Etherstone Avenue, Heaton, Newcastle upon Tyne 6 Tel: 0191 266 1164.

University of Nottingham - Secretary: V P Williams, Director Physical Recreation, Sports Centre, University Park, University of Nottingham NG7 2RD (0115 962 4790 (H) 0115 951 5515 (B) 0115 951 5525 (F)). Fix Sec: D Ryan, Athletic Union Office, Portland Building, Univ. Of Nottingham. Notts. NG7 2RD (0115 9351104 (B)). Treasurer: R Hutchinson, Athletic Union Office, Portland Buildings, Univ.Of Notts. Nottingham NG7 2RD (0115 9351104 (B)). Ground: University Playing Fields, University Boulevard, Nottingham NG7 2RD Tel: 0115 925 6612.

University of Reading - 1926 - Secretary: M Pask, Reading University SU, PO Box 230, Whiteknights, Reading, Berks RG6 6AZ (01189 860222 (B)). Fix Sec: Constantine Lerounis, Reading Uni, Students Union, Whiteknights Campus,, Reading,Berks AG6 6AZ (01189 227489 01189 865106 01189 310869). Treasurer: Dario Castiglione, Reading Uni Students Union, Whiteknights Campus, Reading, Berks RG6 6AZ (0403 263 571 01189 865106 01189 310869). Ground: Whiteknights Park, off Queens Drive, Reading, Berkshire RG6 2AZ Tel: 01189 875123 (Students Union).

University of Salford - 1966 - Secretary: C Kirk, Students' Union, University of Salford, Salford, Lancashire M5 4WT (0161 736 7811 Ext 21 (B) 0161 737 1633 (F)). Fix Sec: D Kavanagh, Students' Union, University of Salford, Salford, Lancashire M5 4WT (0161 736 7811 Ext 21 (B) 0161 737 1633 (F)). Treasurer: C Coles, Students' Union, University of Salford, Salford, Lancashire M5 4WT (0161 736 7811 Ext 21 (B) 0161 737 1633 (F)). Ground: Castle Irwell Playing Fields, Cromwell Road, Salford M5 4WT Tel: 0161 736 7811.

University of Sheffield - Secretary: G O'Callaghan, Student Union AU Office, Western Bank, Sheffield S10 1TG (01142 724076 (B) 01142 752506 (F)). Fix Sec: R Furr, Student Union AU Office, Western Bank, Sheffield S10 1TG (01142 724076 (B) 01142 752506 (F)). Treasurer: C Hood, Student Union AU Office, Western Bank, Sheffield S10 1TG (01142 724076 (B) 01142 752506 (F)). Ground: Norton Playing Fields, Warminster Road, Sheffield Tel: 01142 554536.

University of Southampton - 1919 - Secretary: The Hon Sec, Athletic Union, University of, Southampton, Highfield, Southampton, Hants SO17 1BJ (01703 595203 (B) 01705 595234 (F)). Fix Sec: The Hon Sec, Athletic Union, University of, Southampton, Highfield, Southampton, Hants SO17 1BJ (01703 595203 (B) 01705 595234 (F)). Treasurer: The Hon Sec, Athletic Union, University of, Southampton, Highfield, Southampton, Hants SO17 1BJ (01703 595203 (B) 01705 595234 (F)). Ground: Wellington Sports Ground, North Stoneham Lane, Swaythling, Southampton Tel: 01703 612309.

University of Warwick - 1979 - Secretary: C Oxby, Warwick University Rugby Club, Students Union, Warwick Univ, Coventry CV4 7AL (01203 572777 (H) 01203 692083 (F)). Ground: Athletic Union Pitches, University of Warwick, Coventry CV4 7AL Tel: 01203 523523 Ext 2287.

University of York - 1965 - Secretary: N MacKee, SU Office, Goodricke College, University of York, Heslington, York YO1 5DD. Fix Sec: L Bostock, Athletic Union, Goodricke College, University of York, York YO1 5DD (01904 433 430 (B)). Treasurer: S Challand, Athletic Union, Goodricke College, University of York, York YO1 5DD (01904 433430 (B)). Ground: York University, Heslington, York YO1 5DD Tel: 01904 412642.

University of East Anglia - 1967 - Hon Sec: M Atkinson, Men's Rugby Club, University, of East Anglia, Norwich,, Norfolk, NR4 7TJ. Fix Sec: C Homer, 79 Winter Road, Norwich NR2 3RR (01603 627401 (H) 01603 56161 Ext 2507 (B)). Treasurer: J Scott, Sports Centre, University of East Anglia, Norwich NR4 7TJ. Ground: Sports Centre, University of East Anglia, Norwich NR4 7TJ.

University of Teesside - 1992 - Secretary: P Rathbone, Societies & Recreation Officer, University of Teeside, Borough Road, Middlesbrough TS1 3BA (0976 42 08 06(H) 01642 342234 (B) 01642 342241 (F)). Ground: Saltersgill Sports Pavillion, Saltersgill Ave, Tollesby, Saltersgill TS1 3BA Tel: 01642 326224.

University College Warrington - 1964 - Secretary: C Smith, Athletics Union, Padgate Campus, Crab Lane, Warrington, Cheshire WA2 0DB (01925 813131 (H) 01925 494226 (B) 01925 816007 (F)). Fix Sec: C Smith, Athletics Union, Padgate Campus, Crab Lane, Warrington, Cheshire WA2 0DB (01925 813131 (H) 01925 494226 (B) 01925 816007 (F)). Treasurer: N Wilkinson, c/o 113 Dundee Close, Cinnamon Brow, Warrington, Cheshire (01925 494226 (B) 01925 816077 (F)). Ground: Padgate Campus, Crab Lane, Warrington WA2 0DB Tel: 01925 821336.

University College Chester - 1890 - Formerly Chester College Secretary: T Dray, University College Chester, Cheyney Rd, Chester CH1 4BJ (01244 375444 (B)). Ground: Chester College, Cheyney Road, Chester CH1 4BJ Tel: 01244 375444(373379 Fax).

University College Of St Martins - 1968 - Formerly St Martin's College of HE Secretary: B Cutts, Univ Coll of St Martin, Students Union, Bowerham Rd, Lancaster LA1 3JD (01524 65827 (B)). Ground: Univ College of St Martin, Bowerham Rd, Lancaster LA1 3JD Tel: 01524 35827.

University Of East England - 1990 - Formerly Anglia Polytechnic University Secretary: D Cosnett, 30 King Edgar Close, Ely, Cambridge CB6 1DP (01353 665170 (H) 01223 63271 EXt 2199 (B) 01223 352973 (F)). Fix Sec: D Cosnett, 30 King Edgar Close, Ely, Cambridge CB6 1DP (01353 665170 (H) 01223 63271 EXt 2199 (B) 01223 352973 (F)). Treasurer: D Cosnett, 30 King Edgar Close, Ely, Cambridge CB6 1DP (01353 665170 (H) 01223 63271 EXt 2199 (B) 01223 352973 (F)). Ground: c/o The Gymnasium, University of East England, East Road, Cambridge CB1 1PT.

University of Aston - 1992 - Secretary: Gareth Davies, 37 Gadwell Croft, Erdington, Birmingham B23 7RN (0121 3563574 0121 3334218). Fix Sec: William Wilson, Athletic Union, Aston Students Guild, Aston University B4 7ET (0121 3596531). Treasurer: Miles Raithby-Veill, Athletic Union, Aston Students Guild, Aston University B4 7ET (0121 359 6531). Ground: Recreation Ground, Birmingham Road, Walsall Tel: 0121 357 3675.

University of Brighton - 1992 - Secretary: T Kelly, c/o UBSU Sport, Steam House, Lewes Rd,Brighton BN2 4AF (01273 628277 01273 642871 01273 694060). Fix Sec: C Johnson, UBSU Sport, Steam House, Lewes Rd, Brighton BN2 4AF (01273 642871). Treasurer: B Griffiths, UBSU Sport, Steam House, Lewes Rd, Brighton BN2 4AF (01273 642871). Ground: Falmer Site, Brighton, Sussex BN1 9HP Tel: 01273 643547.

University of Central England - 1967 - Secretary: C McArdle, Students' Union, Franchise Street, Perry Barr, Birmingham B42 2SU (0121 356 8164 (B)). Fix Sec: E Bentley, c/o Students Union, Franchise Street, Perry Barr, Birmingham B42 2SU (0121 356 8164 (H) 0121 356 8164 (B)). Ground: Moor Lane, Witton, Birmingham B6 7AA Tel: 0121 356 2142.

University of Central Lancashire - 1969 - Secretary: J Brown, Students Union, University of, Central Lancashire, Fylde Rd, Preston PR1 2TQ (01772 258382 (B)). Fix Sec: Ms B Woodruff, c/o The Students Union, UCLSU, Fylde Road, Preston PR1 2TQ (01772 258382 Ext 206 (B) 01772 882689 (F)). Treasurer: Miss S Roundell, c/o Office 7, Students' Union, Fylde Road, Preston, Lancashire PR1 2TQ (01772 885527 (H) 01772 258382 Ext 256 (B) 01772 882689 (F)). Ground: c/o Fylde RUFC, The Woodlands Memorial Ground, Blackpool Rd, Lytham St Annes Tel: 01253 734733.

University of East London - 1972 - Secretary: M Yates, 12 Hawksway, Basildon, Essex SS16 5JQ (01268 452792 (H) 01268 42792 (F)). Fix Sec: M J Grant, RASSU, Univ of East London, Longbridge Road, Dagenham, Essex RM8 2AS (0181 989 7565 (H) 0181 590 7000 Ext 2463 (B)). Treasurer: M J Grant, RASSU, Univ of East London, Longbridge Road, Dagenham, Essex RM8 2AS (0181 989 7565 (H) 0181 590 7000 Ext 2463 (B)). Ground: Longbridge Road, Dagenham, Essex RM8 2AS Tel: 0181 590 7722 Ext 2475/2463.

University of Greenwich - 1992 - Secretary: Miss R Hanshaw, Student Union, Univ Greenwich, Avery Hill Campus,, Southwood Site, Eltham, London SE9 1UG (0181 331 9403 (B) 0181 331 9639 (F)). Fix Sec: Miss R Hanshaw, Student Union, Univ Greenwich, Avery Hill Campus,, Southwood Site, Eltham, London SE9 1UG (0181 331 9403 (B) 0181 331 9639 (F)). Treasurer: Miss R Hanshaw, Student Union, Univ Greenwich, Avery Hill Campus,, Southwood Site, Eltham, London SE9 1UG (0181 331 9403 (B) 0181 331 9639 (F)). Ground: Sparrows Farm Centre, Sparrows Lane, New Eltham, London SE9 2BU Tel: 0181 859 2921.

University of Hertfordshire - 1956 - Secretary: A Colvin, University of Hertfordshire SU, College Lane, Hatfield, Hertfordshire AL10 9AB (0966 409402 (H) 01707 285997 (B) 01707 251118 (F)). Fix Sec: A Colvin, University of Hertfordshire SU, College Lane, Hatfield, Hertfordshire AL10 9AB (0966 409402 (H) 01707 285997 (B) 01707 251118 (F)). Treasurer: Marty Dedman, University of Hertfordshire SU, College Lane, Hatfield AL10 9AB. Ground: Angerland Common, Bishops Rise, Hatfield, Hertfordshire AL10 9AB Tel: 01707 284461.

University of Huddersfield - 1969 - Secretary: P Wood, Sport Officer Univ Huddersfiel, Student Union, Queensgate, Huddersfield HD1 3DH (01484 538156 (B) 01484 432333 (F)). Ground: Salendine Nook Playing Fields, New Hey Road, Huddersfield Tel: 01484 657880.

University of Luton - 1952 - Secretary: J Harris, University of Luton,, Students Union, Europa House,, Vicarage Street, Luton, Beds. LU1 3HZ (01582 743271 (B) 01582 487157 (F)). Fix Sec: N Butler, 82 Reginald Street, Luton, Beds (01582 418351 (H) 01582 743271 (B) 01582 487157 (F)). Ground: Luton RFC, Newlands Road, Bedfordshire LU1 4BQ Tel: 01582 20355.

University of North London - 1939 - Secretary: I Jennings, Sports & Recreation Officer, 166-220 Holloway Road, London N7 8DB (0171 753 5147 (B) 0171 753 5154 (Fax)). Fix Sec: J Morris, 166,220 Holloway Rd, University of North London N7 8DB (0171 753 5147 0171 757 5154). Ground: Hackney Rugby Club, Spring Hill, London E5 Tel: 0181 519 0017.

University of Northumbria - 1969 - Secretary: I Smith, University Athletic Union, Wynne Jones Centre, Northumbr., University, Newcastle-on-Tyne NE1 8ST (0191 422 4339 (H) 0191 227 3534 (B) 0191 227 4561 (F)). Fix Sec: I Smith, University Athletic Union, Wynne Jones Centre, Northumbr., University, Newcastle-on-Tyne NE1 8ST (0191 422 4339 (H) 0191 227 3534 (B) 0191 227 4561 (F)). Treasurer: G Taylor, University Athletic Union, Wynne-Jones Centre, Newcastle Upon Tyne NE1 8ST (0191 414 0907 (H) 0191 227 3217 (B) 0191 227 3217 (F)). Ground: Bullockstead Sports Ground, off Ponteland Road, Kingston, Park, Newcastle-upon-Tyne NE13 8AH Tel: 0191 286 0088.

University of Sunderland - 1959 - Secretary: Hon Secretary, Men's RUFC, USSU,, Wearmouth Hall, Chester Rd, Sunderland, Tyne & Wear SR1 3SD. Fix Sec: M R K Clayton, 2 South Hill Crescent, Durham Road, Sunderland. Ground: South Bents Avenue, Seaburn.

University of Westminster - 1992 - Secretary: G Richards, Recreation Office, University of Westminster, 309 Regent Street, London W1R 8AL (0171 9115000 Ext 2033 (B) 0171 9115892 (Fax)). Fix Sec: G Richards, Recreation Office, University of Westminster, 309 Regent Street, London W1R 8AL (0171 9115000 Ext 2033 (B) 0171 9115892 (Fax)). Treasurer: G Richards, Recreation Office, University of Westminster, 309 Regent Street, London W1R 8AL (0171 9115000 Ext 2033 (B) 0171 9115892 (Fax)). Ground: Cavendish Road, off Hartington Road, Chiswick, London W4 3UH Tel: 0181 994 0467/0664.

University of Wolverhampton - 1935 - Secretary: A Mann, Athletic Union, University of Wolverhampton, Wulfruna Street, Wolverhampton WV1 1LY (01902 322022 (B) 01902 322020 (F)). Ground: Walsall RFC, Delves Road, Walsall W51 3JY Tel: 01922 26818.

West Hertfordshire College - 1968 - Secretary: T Hunt, 14 Trowley Rise, Abbots Langley, Hertfordshire WD5 0LW (01923 269840 (H) 01923 812672 (B) 01923 812523 (F)). Fix Sec: T Hunt, 14 Trowley Rise, Abbots Langley, Hertfordshire WD5 0LW (01923 269840 (H) 01923 812672 (B) 01923 812523 (F)). Ground: Watford Fullerians, Newfield, Conningesby Drive, Watford WD5 0ZW Tel: 01923 224483.

Writtle College - 1967 - Secretary: M Rawlinson, 27 Melba Court, Writtle, Chelmsford, Essex CM1 3EW (01245 422816 (H) 01245 424235 (B) 01245 420456 (F)). Fix Sec: M Rawlinson, 27 Melba Court, Writtle, Chelmsford, Essex CM1 3EW (01245 422816 (H) 01245 424235 (B) 01245 420456 (F)). Ground: Lordship Road, Writtle, Chelmsford CM1 3RR Tel: 01245 424200.

Wye College - 1937 - Fix Sec: D Wells, c/o JCR, Wye College, Nr Ashford, Kent TN25 5AH. Ground: Wye, Nr Ashford, Kent TN25 5AH Tel: 01233 812401.

ASSOCIATE MEMBERS

Anti-Assassins - 1950 - Secretary: A T Higgin, 50 Barton Road, Lancaster LA1 4EP (01524 64580 (H) 01254 52023 (B) 01524 64580 (F)). Fix Sec: P E Hughes, Height Top Smithy, Higham, Burnley, Lancashire BB12 9BU (01282 771129 (H) 01282 779529 (F)). Treasurer: John K G Aikman, 29 Cartmel Drive, Burnley, Lancashire BB12 8UX (01282 459437 (H) 01282 770044 (B) 01282 777207 (F)).

Barbarian - 1890 - Secretary: G Windsor-Lewis, Wilcote Place, Ramsden, Oxfordshire OX7 3BA (01993 868370 (H) 01993 868858 (B) 01993 868882 (F)). Fix Sec: G Windsor-Lewis, Wilcote Place, Ramsden, Oxfordshire OX7 3BA (01993 868370 (H) 01993 868858 (B) 01993 868882 (F)). Treasurer: G A Ferguson, 63 Robin Hood Lane, Kingston Vale, London SW15 3PX (0181 546 3709 (H) 0181 546 3709 0181 974 8218 (F)).

Bristol and District Combination - 1901 - Secretary: N A Mitchell, 48 Rockside Drive, Henleaze, Bristol BS9 4NX (0117 962 4149 (H) 0117 928 9727 (B) 0117 925 1154 (F)). Fix Sec: T Webb, 50 Monks Park Avenue, Filton, Bristol BS7 0UH (0117 983 0273 (H)). Treasurer: B C Jordan, 17 Royal Close, Henbury, Bristol BS10 7XF (0117 950 4723 (H)). Ground: Headquarters, Bristol FC, Memorial Ground, Filton Avenue, Bristol BS7 0AG Tel: 0117 908 5500.

Cheltenham and District Combination - 1963 - Secretary: B F Didlick, 15 Stoneville Street, Cheltenham, Gloucestershire GL51 8PH (01242 519285 (H)). Fix Sec: M Kedward, 35 Bishops Cleeve, Cheltenham, Glos. GL52 4NU (01242 675424 (H) 01242 238866 (B)). Treasurer: P Shortell, 81 Hales Road, Cheltenham GL52 6SR (01242 510849).

Combined Birmingham Old Boys - 1951 - Secretary: C W Hayward, 6 Princethorpe Close, Shirley, Solihull, West Midlands B90 2LP (0121 744 7746 (H) 0121 733 8060 (Fax)). Fix Sec: C W Hayward, 6 Princethorpe Close, Shirley, Solihull, West Midlands B90 2LP (0121 744 7746 (H) 0121 733 8060 (Fax)). Treasurer: D Wemyss, 7 Pinfold Hill, Shenstone, Lichfield, Staffordshire WS14 0JN (01543 480614 (H) 01543 481949 (B)).

Derbyshire County Union - 1922 - Secretary: D N Robinson, 42 Eccles Road, Chapel-en-le-Frith, High Peak, Derbyshire SK23 9RG (01298 814113 (H)). Fix Sec: G Morgan, 55 Lower Market Street,, Broadbottom, Hyde SK14 6AA (01457 762180 (H) 0161 2752318 (B)). Treasurer: M A Hadfield JP FCA, The Warren, 404 Old Road, Chesterfield, Derbyshire S40 3QF (01246 566655 (H) 01246 566667 (B) 01246 566918 (F)).

Forest of Dean Combination - 1923 - Secretary: G Ward, Willow Brae, Gorsley, Ross-on-Wye, Herefordshire HR9 7SH. Fix Sec: Cyril Edwards, Windbourne, High Beech Road, Bream, Nr Lydney, Gloucestershire GL15 6JG (01594 562237 (H) 01594 824396 (B)). Treasurer: Cyril Edwards, Windbourne, High Beech Road, Bream, Nr Lydney, Gloucestershire GL15 6JG (01594 562237 (H) 01594 824396 (B)).

Greater Birmingham - 1936 - Secretary: C Humphreys, 75 Loxley Avenue, Shirley, Solihull, West Midlands B90 2QL (0121 745 2688 (H) 01905 793309 (B) 01905 795193 (Fax)). Fix Sec: K Jordan, 74 William Road, Warley, West Midlands B67 6LW (0121 429 1921 (H) 0802 443237 (B)). Treasurer: M Goode, 9/34 Sherbourne Road, Acocks Green, Birmingham B27 6AE (0121 707 9656 (H)).

Leicester Thursday - 1888 - Secretary: J Coulthurst, 39 Kirby Lane, Kirby Muxloe, Leicester LE3 3JG (0116 239 5121 (H) 01555 387206 (B) 0116 238 7206 (F)). Fix Sec: M Higgins, 36 Beechwood Avenue, Leicester Forest East, Leicester LE3 3PL (0116 238 63343 (H) 0116 2511 7749 (B)). Treasurer: P T Pugh, 37 Herrick Way, Wigston Harcourt, Leicester (0116 281 3215 (H)).

Lincolnshire County Union - 1947 - Secretary: M A Ross, Blacksmith's House, 26 Lincoln Road, Branston, Lincoln LN4 1PA (01522 822618 (H) 01522 881403 (B) 01522 822619 (F)). Fix Sec: C Moon, 5 Manor Close, Welton, Lincoln LN2 3TQ (01673 861873 (H) 01522 532222 (B)). Treasurer: S Powell, 99 Wetherby Crescent, North Hykeham, Lincoln LN6 8TE (01522 801528 (H)).

London - 1911 - Secretary: D S Straw, 161 High Street, Hampton Hill, Middlesex TW12 1NL (0181 977 9653 (H) 0181 941 7610 (B) 0181 941 7630 (Fax)).

North Gloucester Combination - 1912 - Secretary: M S Slatter, 135 Grange Road, Tuffley, Gloucester GL4 0PR (310907 (H) 396520 (B)). Fix Sec: D L Howell, 255c Stroud Road, Gloucester GL1 5JZ (01452 414010 (H) 01452 425611 (B)). Treasurer: S Green, 27 Winsley Road, Matson, Gloucester GL4 9NE (527486 (H) 425820 (B)).

Nottinghamshire County Union - 1920 - Hon Sec: D Sutton, 22 Vernon Avenue,, Wilford Village,, Nottingham HG11 7AE (0115 9818621 (H) 0115 9728637 (B)). Fix Sec: V P Williams, 1 Carisbrooke Drive, Mapperley Park, Nottingham NG3 5DS (0115 9624790 (H) 0115 9515516 (B) 0115 9515525 (Fax)). Treasurer: R Swain, Disablement Services Centre, Nottingham City Hospital, Hucknall Road, Nottingham NG5 1PJ (0115 9691169 ext 47567 (B) 0115 9826052 (F)). Ground: Ireland Avenue, Dovecote Lane, Beeston, Nottingham NG9 1JD Tel: 0115 9254238/9224920.

Penguin International - 1959 - Secretary: A G L Wright, 11 Little St James's Street, London SW1A 1DP (0171 629 1852 (H) 0171 629 1854 (F)). Fix Sec: I M Bullerwell, Bullerwell and Co., 13 Goldington Road, Bedford MK40 3JY (01234 771419 01234 268818 (B) 01234 301511 (F)). Treasurer: D Hearn, Bishops Platt, Norlands Lane, Thorpe, Surrey TW20 8SS (01932 560 376 (H) 01932 567 008 (F)).

Plymouth & District Rugby Combination - 1901 - Secretary: S Reeves, 129 York Road, Weston Mill, Plymouth PL5 1AU (01752 363036 (H) 07887 552413 (B) 01752 363036). Treasurer: P Rendle, 37 North Down Road, Beacon Park, Plymouth (01752 568234 (H) 01752 568234 (F)).

Shropshire - 1959 - Secretary: B Roberts, 2 Mount Cottages, Knighton, Adbaston, Stafford ST20 0QQ (01785 280330 (H) 01785 258669 (B) 01785 252086 (F)). Fix Sec: S Rossiter Stead, 8 Lower Forge, Eardington,, Bridgnorth, Shropshire WV16 5LQ (01746 764286(H) 01746 764286(F)). Treasurer: G S Jackson, 99 Highfields, Shrewsbury, Shropshire SY2 5PJ (01743 361802 (H)). Ground: c/o Shrewsbury RUFC, Sundorne Castle, Uffington, Shrewsbury SY4 4RR Tel: 01743 353380.

Stroud and District Combination - 1974 - Secretary: B J Darlaston, Windrush, Field Lane, Dursley, Gloucestershire GL11 6JF (01453 543135 (H) 0171 304 6863(B) 01453 543135 (Fax)). Fix Sec: B J Darlaston, Windrush, Field Lane, Dursley, Gloucestershire GL11 6JF (01453 543135 (H) 0171 304 6863(B) 01453 543135 (Fax)). Treasurer: P Winterbottom, Quarry Farmhouse, The Quarry, Dursley, Glostershire GL11 (01453 542106 (H)). Ground: Fromehall Park, Stroud, Gloucestershire GL5 3HS Tel: 01453 763019.

The Wanderers (PSW) - 1940 - Secretary: Mrs J G Lowe, 46 Kingston Lane, Shoreham by Sea, West Sussex BN43 6YB (01273 592039 (H) 01273 592039 (F)). Fix Sec: Brigadier R N R P James CBE, 3 Upper Court, Old Church Road, Colwall, Malvern, Worcs WR13 6ET (01684 541121 (H) 01684 541121 (B) 01684 541121 (F)). Treasurer: Mrs J G Lowe, 46 Kingston Lane, Shoreham by Sea, West Sussex BN43 6YB (01273 592039 (H) 01273 592039 (F)).

Worcestershire and Herefordshire - 1923 - Secretary: J P Hartley, Nightingate House, Bishampton, Worcs WR10 2NH (01386 462325 (H) 01527 873457 (B) 01527 872022 (F)). Fix Sec: D S Price, Uplands Farm, Wellington Heath, Ledbury HR8 1NF (0151 633752 (H)). Treasurer: C E Hemmings, 37 Oaklands, Worcester WR5 1SL (01905 763724 (H)).

Blood, Sweat & Free Gear

The New Business Manager for your area would enjoy spending some time with you to explain how you could take advantage of our Rugby portfolio.

If you would like more information on the services and promotions Carlsberg Tetley can offer you, then please contact our Customer Service Centre on

0345 820820.

Could you have the following details available:-

- **Club Name**
- **Contact Name**
- **Current Brewer**
- **Post Code**
- **Phone number**

Let's all pull together for the club!

Bryn Locke wins good line-out ball for Bakewell Mannerians in thei Notts., Lincs & Derbys. 1 league match against Worksop last season, against a very pleasant background.

Rob Andrew, now Director of Rugby at Newcastle Falcons was the man responsible for that most wonderful moment in the last World Cup, in South Africa, when he dropped a goal in the very last minute of the Quarter Final to gain victory for England over Australia.

INTERNATIONAL RUGBY SECTION

RUGBY WORLD CUP

QUALIFYING ROUNDS 706
RWC FINALS SCHEDULE 711
COUNTRY BY COUNTRY RECORDS 712
STATISTICS 716

THE 1998-99 INTERNATIONAL SEASON

AUSTRALIA 718
ENGLAND 719
FRANCE 720
IRELAND 721
NEW ZEALAND 723
SCOTLAND 724
SOUTH AFRICA 725
WALES 726

THE FIVE NATIONS 727

GENERAL FIXTURE LIST 733

RUGBY WORLD CUP 1999

QUALIFYING ROUNDS

Qualifying for the 1999 Rugby World Cup started way back in 1996. Although some of the following match results may seem rather old it was felt that including them gave the best idea of the breadth that the rugby orld cup now has.

EUROPEAN ZONE

ROUND A

Pool One

5th October 1996
Ukraine 60 Yugoslavia 0 (Kiev)
26th October 1996
Austria w/o Yugoslavia
2nd November 1996
Switzerland 0 Ukriane 30 (Nyon)
23rd November 1996
Israel 15 Austria 3 (Tel Aviv)
30th November 1996
Israel 9 Switzerland 9 (Tel Aviv)
1st March 1997
Yugoslavia 8 Switzerland 0 (Belgrade)
26th April 1997
Austria 6 Ukraine 36 (Vienna)
10th May 1997
Yugoslavia 10 Israel 7 (Belgrade)
17th May 1997
Ukraine 51 Israel 15 (Odessa)
24th May 1997
Switzerland 31 Austria 3 (Basel)

FINAL TABLE

	P	W	D	L	F	A	Pts
Ukraine	4	4	0	0	177	21	12
Yugoslavia	4	2	0	2	18	70	8
Israel	4	1	1	2	46	73	7
Switzerland	4	1	1	2	40	50	7
Austria	4	1	0	3	12	51	6

Ukraine win Round A Pool 1 and go through to Round B

Pool Two

28th September 1996
Latvia 44 Norway 6 (in Riga)
12th October 1996
Bulgaria 6 Moldova 14 (Sofia)
Norway 7 Croatia 43 (Oslo)
19th October 1996
Moldova 3 Latvia 8 (Chisinau)
26th October 1996
Bulgaria 31 Croatia 46 (Sofia)
3rd May 1997
Moldova 31 Norway 7 (Chisinau)
10th May 1997
Latvia 89 Bulgaria 0 (Riga)
Croatia 60 Moldova 5 (Split)
17th May 1997
Croatia 43 Latvia 24 (Makarska)
24th May 1997
Norway 22 Bulgaria 7 (Oslo)

FINAL TABLE

	P	W	D	L	F	A	Pts
Croatia	4	4	0	0	192	93	12
Latvia	4	3	0	1	165	52	10
Moldova	4	2	0	2	53	81	8
Norway	4	1	0	3	42	125	6
Bulgaria	4	0	0	4	59	171	4

Croatia win Round A Pool 2 and go through to Round B

Pool Three

5th October 1996
Lithuania 26 Luxembourg 3 (Vilnius)
Luxembourg 16 Andorra 30 (in Luxemb
19th October 1996
Andorra 54 Lithuania 24 (Andorra La Vella)
Sweden 39 Hungary 17 (Vanersborg)
2nd November 1996
Luxembourg 3 Hungary 12 (Cessange)
Andorra 21 Sweden 20 (Andorra La Vella)
15th March 1997
Luxembourg 16 Andorra 30 (in Luxembourg)
19th April 1997
Sweden 48 Luxembourg 5 (Kariskrona)
3rd May 1997
Lithuania 17 Sweden 84 (Plunge)
31st May 1997
Hungary 16 Lithuania 3 (Budapest)
14th June 1997
Hungary 5 Andorra 34 (Budapest)

FINAL TABLE

	P	W	D	L	F	A	Pts
Andorra	4	4	0	0	139	65	12
Sweden	4	3	0	1	191	60	10
Hungary	4	2	0	2	50	79	8
Lithuania	4	1	0	3	70	157	6
Luxembourg	4	0	0	4	27	116	4

Andorra win Round A Pool 3 and go through to Round B

ROUND B

Pool One

12th October 1997
Georgia 29 Croatia 15 (Tibilisi)
18th October 1997
Denmark 8 Georgia 19 (Frederiksberg)
19th October 1997
Croatia 23 Russia 16 (Makarska)
1st November 1997
Italy 102 Denmark 3 (Brescia)
11th April 1998
Italy 31 Georgia 14 (L'Aquila)
18th April 1998
Russia 18 Italy 48 (Krasnoiarsk)
2nd May 1998
Russia 45 Denmark 9 (Penza)
16th May 1998
Denmark 6 Croatia 40 (Aalborg)
20th May 1998
Georgia 12 Russia 6 (Tbilisi)
6th June 1998
Croatia 27 Italy 39 (Zagreb)

FINAL TABLE

	P	W	L	F	A	Pts
Italy	4	4	0	220	62	12
Georgia	4	3	1	74	60	10
Croatia	4	2	2	105	90	8
Russia	4	1	3	85	92	8
Denmark	4	0	4	26	206	4

Pool 2

5th October 1997
Belgium 13 Romania 83 (Brussels)
18th October 1997
Ukraine 48 Belgium 5 (Kiev)
26th October 1997
The Netherlands 49 Poland 7 (Amsterdam)
1st November 1997
The Netherlands 35 Ukraine 13 (Amsterdam)
4th April 1998
Poland 30 Belgium 10 (Gdansk)
18th April 1998
Belgium 16 The Netherlands 19 (Brussels)
25th April 1998
Romania 42 The Netherlands 3 (Bucharest)
2nd May 1998
Romania 74 Poland 13 (Bucharest)
16th May 1998
Poland 8 Ukraine 19 (Gdansk)
30th May 1998
Ukraine 17 Romania 39 (Odessa)

FINAL TABLE	P	W	L	F	A	Pts
Romania	4	4	0	238	46	12
The Netherlands	4	3	1	106	78	10
Ukraine	4	2	2	96	87	8
Poland	4	1	3	58	151	6
Belgium	4	0	4	44	180	4

Pool 3

13th September 1997
Czech Republic 45 Andorra 20 (Prague)
4th October 1997
Andorra 11 Germany 56 (Andorra La Vella)
19th October 1997
Germany 31 Czech Republic 17 (Hanover)
??th November 1997
Andorra 3 Spain 62 (Andorra La Vella)
30th November 1997
Spain 39 Czech Republic 8 (Santander)
4th April 1998
Portugal 30 Germany 6 (Lisbon)
18th April 1998
Czech Republic 10 Portugal 15 (Prague)
26th April 1998
Germany 9 Spain 24 (Heidelberg)
10th May 1998
Spain 33 Portugal 22 (Madrid)
30th May 1998
Portugal 53 Andorra 11 (Andorra la Vella)

FINAL TABLE

	P	W	L	F	A	Pts
Spain	4	4	0	158	42	12
Portugal	4	3	1	120	60	10
Germany	4	2	2	102	82	8
Czech Republic	4	1	3	80	105	6
Andorra	4	0	4	45	216	4

ROUND C (EUROPEAN QUALIFYING ZONE)

POOL ONE - IRELAND
(at Lansdowne Road, Dublin)

Saturday, 14th November 1998
Ireland 70 Georgia 0
Wednesday, 18th November 1998
Georgia 23 Romania 27
Saturday, 21st November 1998
Ireland 53 Romania 35

FINAL TABLE	P	W	L	F	A	Pts
Ireland	2	2	0	123	35	6
Romania	2	1	1	62	78	4
Georgia	2	0	2	23	97	2

Ireland &Romania qualify for the Finals.
Georgia go through to the repechage.

POOL TWO - ENGLAND

(at McAlpine Stadium, Huddersfield)

Saturday, 14th November 1998
England 110 The Netherlands
Wednesday, 18th November 1998
Italy 67 The Netherlands 7
Sunday, 22nd November 1998
England 23 Italy 15 >>>

FINAL TABLE	P	W	L	F	A	Pts
England	2	2	0	133	15	6
Italy	2	1	1	82	30	4
The Netherlands	2	0	2	7	177	2

England & Italy qualify for the Finals.
The Netherlands go through to the repechage,

POOL THREE - SCOTLAND

(at Murrayfield, Edinburgh)

Saturday, 28th November 1998
Scotland 85 Portugal 11
Wednesday, 2nd December 1998
Portugal 17 Spain 21
Saturday, 5th December 1998
Scotland 85 Spain 0

FINAL TABLE	P	W	D	L	F	A	Pts
Scotland	2	2	0	0	170	14	6
Spain	2	1	0	1	24	102	4
Portugal	2	0	0	2	28	106	0

Scotland & Spain qualify for Finals.
Portugal go through to the repechage.

AFRICA ZONE

ROUND A
18th April 1997
Arabian Gulf 52 Botswana 13 (Bahrain)
25th April 1997
Zambia 30 Arabian Gulf 44 (Ndola)
17th May 1997
Botswana 13 Zambia 20 (Jwaneng)

FINAL TABLE	P	W	D	L	F	A	Pts
Arabian Gulf	2	2	0	0	97	43	6
Zambia	2	1	0	1	50	57	4
Botswana	2	0	0	1	26	73	2

Arabian Gulf win Round A and proceed to Round B

ROUND B
13th June 1997
Arabian Gulf 12 Tunisia 11 (Bahrain)
6th September 1997
Kenya 37 Arabian Gulf 18 (Nairobi)
20th September 1997
Tunisia 52 Kenya 5 (Tunis)

FINAL TABLE	P	W	D	L	F	A	Pts
Tunisia	2	1	0	1	63	17	4
Arabian Gulf	2	1	0	1	30	48	4
Kenya	2	1	0	1	42	70	4

Tunisia win Round B and proceed to Round C

ROUND C
4th April 1998
Zimbabwe 43 Tunisia 9 (Bulawayo)
18th April 1998
Tunisia 20 Namibia 17 (Tunis)
9th May 1998
Namibia 32 Zimbabwe 26 (Windhoek)

FINAL TABLE	P	W	D	L	F	A	Pts
Zimbabwe	2	1	0	1	69	41	3
Namibia	2	1	0	1	49	46	3
Tunisia	2	1	0	1	29	60	3

Zimbabwe and Namibia proceed to Round D

ROUND D (Casablanca)
12th September 1998
Morocco 15 Zimbabwe 9
Cote d'Ivoire 10 Namibia 22
16th September 1998
Morocco 8 Namibia 17
Cote d'Ivoire 0 Zimbabwe 32
19th September 1998
Morocco 6 Cote d'Ivoire 3
Namibia 39 Zimbabwe 14

FINAL TABLE	P	W	L	F	A	Pts
Namibia	3	3	0	78	32	9
Morocco	3	2	1	29	29	7
Zimbabwe	3	1	2	55	54	5
Cote d'Ivoire	3	0	3	13	60	3

Namibia qualify for the Finals (for the first time).
Morocco go through to the repechage.

RUGBY WORLD CUP 1999

QUALIFYING ROUNDS CONTINUED

ASIA ZONE

ROUND A

1st February 1997
Singapore 11 Thailand 16 (Singapore)
15th February 1997
Thailand 15 Sri Lanka 30 (Bangkok)
30th March 1997
Sri Lanka 18 Singapore 15 (Kuala Lumpur)
Sri Lanka win Round A and go through to Round B

FINAL TABLE

	P	W	D	L	F	A	Pts
Sri Lanka	2	2	0	0	48	30	6
Thailand	2	1	0	1	31	41	4
Singapore	2	0	0	2	26	34	2

ROUND 'B'

29th November 1997
Malaysia 15 Sri Lanka 37 (Kuala Lumpur)
20th December 1997
Chinese Taipeh 51 Malaysia 13 (Taipeh)
10th January 1998
Sri Lanka 29 Chinese Taipeh 34 (Bangkok)
Chinese Taipeh win Round B and join Japan, Korea and Hong
Kong in Round C in Singapore

ROUND C
(Singapore)

24th October 1998
Japan 40 South Korea 12
Hong Kong 12 Chinese Taipeh 30
27th October 1998
Japan 134 Chinese Taipeh 6
Hong Kong 20 South Korea 11
31st October 1998
South Korea 81 Chinese Taipeh 21
Japan 47 Hong Kong 7

FINAL TABLE

	P	W	D	L	F	A	Pts
Japan	3	3	0	0	221	25	12
South Korea	3	1	0	2	104	81	6
Hong Kong	3	1	0	2	39	88	6
Chinese Taipeh	3	1	0	2	57	227	2

Japan qualify for the Finals.
South Korea go through to the repechage.

PACIFIC ZONE

ROUND A
22nd November 1996
Cook Islands 22 Papua New Guinea 18 (Raratonga)
8th February 1997
Papua New Guinea 82 Tahiti 8
20th February 1997
Tahiti 0 Cook Islands 40

FINAL TABLE	P	W	D	L	F	A	Pts
Cook Islands	2	2	0	0	62	19	6
Papua New Guinea	2	1	0	1	111	28	4
Tahiti	2	0	0	2	6	132	2

ROUND B
21st June 1997
Fiji 20 Tonga 10 (Suva)
27th June 1997
Cook Islands 7 Fiji 58 (Rarotonga)
5th July 1997
Tonga 68 Cook Islands 12 (Nuku-Alofa)

FINAL TABLE	P	W	D	L	F	A	Pts
Fiji	2	2	0	0	78	17	6
Tonga	2	1	0	1	78	32	4
Cook Islands	2	0	0	2	19	126	2

ROUND C (SOUTH PACIFIC ZONE) (Australia)

Friday, 18th September 1998 (Sydney)
Australia 66 Fiji 20
Western Samoa 28 Tonga 20
Tuesday, 22nd September 1998 (Canberra)
Australia 74 Tonga 0
Fiji 26 Western Samoa 18
Saturday, 26th September 1998 (Brisbane)
Australia 25 Western Samoa 13
Fiji 32 Tonga 13

FINAL TABLE	P	W	L	F	A	Pts
Australia	3	3	0	165	33	9
Fiji	3	2	1	78	97	7
Western Samoa	3	1	2	59	71	5
Tonga	3	0	3	33	134	3

Australia, Fiji & Western Samoa qualify for the Finals.
Tonga go through to the repechage.

AMERICAS ZONE

ROUND A

Pool 1
11th November 1996
Trinidad & Tobago 41 Brazil 0 (Port of Spain)

FINAL TABLE	P	W	L	F	A	Pts
Trinidad & Tobago	1	0	0	41	0	3
Brazil	1	0	1	0	41	1

Guyana withdrew. Trinidad & Tobago go to Round B
Pool 2
22nd March 1997
Bahamas 3 Bermuda 24 (Nassau)
5th April 1997
Barbados 23 Bahamas 37 (Bridgetown)
19th April 1997
Bermuda 52 Barbados 3 (Hamilton)

FINAL TABLE	P	W	D	L	F	A	Pts
Bermuda	2	2	0	0	76	6	6
Bahamas	2	1	0	1	40	47	4
Barbados	2	0	0	2	26	89	2

Bermuda win pool and go through to Round B

ROUND B

20th September 1997
Trinidad & Tobago 6 Chile 35 (Port of Spain)
5th October 1997
Bermuda 52 Trinidad & Tobago 6 (Nassau)
Sunday, 19th October 1997
Chile 65 Bermuda 8 (Santiago)

FINAL TABLE	P	W	L	F	A	Pts
Chile	2	2	0	100	14	6
Bermuda	2	1	0	60	71	4
Trinidad & Tobago	2	0	2	12	87	2

Chile win Round B and go through to Round C

ROUND C

21st March 1998
Chile 54 Paraguay 6 (Santiago)
28th March 1998
Paraguay 3 Uruguay 43 (Asuncion)
4th April 1998
Uruguay 20 Chile 14 (Montevideo)

FINAL TABLE	P	W	L	F	A	Pts
Uruguay	2	2	0	63	17	6
Chile	2	1	1	68	26	4
Paraguay	2	0	2	9	97	2

Uruguay win group and qualify for Round D

ROUND D (in Buenos Aires)

15th August 1998
Argentina 52 United States 24
Uruguay 15 Canada 38
19th August 1998
Argentina 55 Uruguay 0
Canada 31 United States 14
22nd August 1998
Argentina 54 Canada 28
United States 21 Uruguay 16

FINAL TABLES

	P	W	L	F	A	Pts
Argentina	3	3	0	161	52	9
Canada	3	2	1	97	83	7
United States	3	1	2	59	99	5
Uruguay	3	0	3	31	114	3

Argentina, Canada & United States qualify for the Finals
Uruguay go through to the repechage.

REPECHAGE

Match A

Saturday, 13th March 1999 (1st leg- Montevideo)
Uruguay 46 Portugal 9
Saturday, 3rd April 1999 (2nd leg - Lisbon)
Portugal 24 Uruguay 33
Uruguay win 79-33 on aggregate

Match B

Sunday, 14th March 1999 (1st leg - Amsterdam)
The Netherlands 31 South Korea 30
Sunday, 4th April 1999 (2nd leg - Seoul)
South Korea 78 The Netherlands 14
South Korea win 108-45 on aggregate

Match C

Saturday, 6th March 1999(1st leg - Nuku-alofa)
Tonga 37 Georgia 6
Sunday, 28th March 1999 (2nd leg - Tbilisi)
Georgia 28 Tonga 27
Tonga win 64-34 on aggregate

Bye - Morocco

* * * * *

Match 1

Sunday, 25th April 1999 (1st Leg - Montevideo)
Uruguay 18 Morocco 3
Sunday, 2nd May 1999 (2nd Leg - Casablanca)
Morocco 21 Uruguay 18

Uruguay win 36-24 on aggregate, and qualify for the Finals

Match 2

Friday, 16th April 1999 (1st leg - Naku'alofa)
Tonga 58 South Korea 26
Saturday, 24th April 1999 (2nd Leg - Seoul)
South Korea 15 Tonga 82

Tonga win 140-41 on aggregate, and qualify for the Finals

RUGBY WORLD CUP 1999

SCHEDULE OF MATCHES

POOL A (Murrayfield, Hampden Park)
Scotland, South Africa, Spain, Uruguay.
POOL B (Twickenham, Leicester, Bristol, Huddersfield)
England, New Zealand, Italy, Tonga (Ikale Tahi).
POOL C (Paris, Bordeaux, Toulouse, Beziers, Lens)
France, Fiji, Canada, Namibia.
POOL D (Cardiff, Llanelli, Wrexham)
Wales, Argentina, Western Samoa, Japan.
POOL E (Dublin, Belfast, Limerick)
Ireland, Australia, United States, Romania.

POOL A

Saturday, 4th October 1999 (Match No 4)
Spain v Uruguay (Galashiels)
Sunday, 3rd October 1999 (Match No 9)
Scotland v South Africa (Murrayfield - 5.00 pm)
Friday, 8th October 1999 (Match No 11)
Scotland v Uruguay (Murrayfield - 4.00 pm)
Sunday, 10th October 1999 (Match No 19)
South Africa v Spain (Murrayfield - 5.00 pm)
Friday, 15th October 1999 (Match No 26)
South Africa v Uruguay (Hampden Park - 5.00 pm)
Saturday, 16th October 1999 (Match No 29)
Scotland v Spain (Murrayfield - 3.00 pm)

POOL B

Saturday, 2nd October 1999 (Match No 5)
England v Italy (Twickenham - 5.00 pm)
Sunday, 3rd October 1999) (Match No 8)
New Zealand v Tonga (Bristol - 3.00 pm)
Saturday, 9th October 1999 (Match No 15)
England v New Zealand (Twickenham - 4.30 pm)
Sunday, 10th October 1999 (Match No 20)
Italy v Tonga (Leicester - 7.00 pm)
Thursday, 14th October 1999 (Match No 21)
New Zealand v Italy (Huddersfield - 1.00 pm)
Friday, 15th October 1999 (Match No 25)
England v Tonga (Twickenham - 1.00 pm)

POOL C

Friday, 1st October 1999 (Match No 2)
Fiji v Namibia (Beziers - 9.00 pm)
Saturday, 2nd October 1999 (Match No 3)
France v Canada (Beziers - 2.00 pm)
Friday, 8th October 1999 (Match No 12)
France v Namibia (Bordeaux - 9.00 pm)
Saturday, 9th October 1999 (Match No 13)
Fiji v Canada (Bordeaux - 1.30 pm)
Thursday, 14th October 1999 (Match No 24)
Canada v Namibia (Toulouse - 8.30 pm)
Saturday, 16th October 1999 (Match No 28)
France v Fiji (Toulouse - 2.00 pm)

POOL D

Friday, 1st October 1999 (Match No 1)
Wales v Argentina (Cardiff - 3.00 pm)
Sunday, 3rd October 1999 (Match No 7)
Western Samoa v Japan (Wrexham - 1.00 pm)
Saturday, 9th October 1999 (Match No 14)
Wales v Japan (Cardiff - 2.30 pm)
Sunday, 10th October 1999 (Match No 17)
Argentina v Western Samoa (Llanelli - 1.00 pm)
Thursday, 14th October 1999 (Match No 22)
Wales v Western Samoa (Cardiff - 3.00 pm)
Saturday, 16th October 1999 (Match No 30)
Argentina v Japan (Cardiff - 7.00 pm)

POOL E

Saturday, 2nd October 1999 (Match No 6)
Ireland v United States (Dublin - 7.00 pm)
Sunday, 3rd October 1999 (Match No 10)
Australia v Romania (Belfast - 7.00 pm)
Saturday, 9th October 1999 (Match No 16)
United States v Romania (Dublin - 7.00 pm)
Sunday, 10th October 1999 (Match No 18)
Ireland v Australia (Dublin - 3.00 pm)
Thursday, 14th October 1999 (Match No 23)
Australia v United States (Limerick- 5.00 pm)
Friday, 15th October 1999 (Match No 27)
Ireland v Romania (Dublin - 7.00 pm)

QUARTER-FINAL PLAY-OFFS

Wednesday, 20th October 1999 (Match Nos 31)
Runner-up B v Runner-up C
(Twickenham - 1.00 pm)(H)

Wednesday, 20th October 1999 (Match No 32)
Runner-up A v Runner-up D
(Murrayfield - 3.30 pm)(G)

Wednesday, 20th October 1999 (Match No 33)
Runner-up E v Third best
(Lens - 8.30 pm)(F)

QUARTER-FINALS

Saturday, 23rd October 1999 (Match No 34)
Winner D v Winner E
(Cardiff - 3.00 pm)(M)

Sunday, 24th October 1999 (Match No 35)
Winner A v Winner H
(Paris - 2.00 pm)(J)

Sunday, 24th October 1999 (Match No 36)
Winner C v Winner F
(Dublin - 3.30 pm)(L)

Sunday, 24th October 1999 (Match No 37)
Winner B v Winner G
(Murrayfield - 6.00 pm)(K)

SEMI-FINALS

Saturday, 30th October 1999 (Match No 38)
Winner J v Winner M
(Twickenham - 3.00 pm)

Sunday, 31st October 1999 (Match No 39)
Winner K v Winner L
(Twickenham - 3.00 pm)

PLAY-OFF

Thursday, 4th November 1999 (Match No 40)
Play-off between losing semi-finalists
(Cardiff - 8.00 pm)

FINAL

Saturday, 6th November 1999 (Match No 41)
(Cardiff - 3.00 pm)

WORLD CUP FINALS RECORD

(Each team's complete record)

AUSTRALIA

1987:

Coach: A Jones. Captain: A Slack.

Gp:	Won	19-6	v England	Sydney
Gp:	Won	47-12	v United States	Brisbane
Gp:	Won	42-23	v Japan	Sydney
QF:	Won	33-15	v Ireland	Sydney
SF:	Lost	24-30	v France	Sydney
3rd	Lost	21-22	v Wales	Roturua

1991

Coach: R Dwyer. Captain: N Farr Jones.

Gp:	Won	32-19	v Argentina	Llanelli
Gp:	Won	9-3	v Western Samoa	Pontypool
Gp:	Won	38-3	v Wales	Cardiff
QF:	Won	19-18	v Ireland	Dublin
SF:	Won	16-6	v New Zealand	Dublin
Fin	Won	12-6	v England	Twickenham

1995:

Coach: R Dwyer. Captain: M Lynagh.

Gp:	Lost	18-27	v South Africa	Cape Town
Gp:	Won	27-11	v Canada	Port Elizabeth
Gp:	Won	42-3	v Romania	Stellenbosch
QF:	Lost	22-25	v England	Cape Town

ARGENTINA

1987:

Coach: H Silva. Captain: H Porta.

Gp:	Lost	9-28	v Fiji	Hamilton
Gp:	Won	25-16	v Italy	Christchurch
Gp:	Lost	15-46	v New Zealand	Wellington

1991

Coach: L Gradin. Captain: P Garreton.

Gp:	Lost	19-32	v Australia	Llanelli
Gp:	Lost	7-16	v Wales	Cardiff
Gp:	Lost	12-35	v Western Samoa	Pontypridd

1995

Coach: A Petra & R Paganini. Captain: S Salvat

Gp:	Lost	18-24	v England	Durban
Gp:	Lost	26-32	v Western Samoa	E London
Gp:	Lost	25-31	v Italy	E London

CANADA

1987:

Coach: G Johnston. Captain: H de Goede.

Gp:	Won	37-4	v Tonga	Napier
Gp:	Lost	19-46	v Ireland	Dunedin
Gp:	Lost	9-40	v Wales	Invercargill

1991

Coach: I Birtwell. Captain: M Wyatt.

Gp:	Won	13-3	v Fiji	Bayonne
Gp:	Won	19-11	v Romania	Toulouse
Gp:	Lost	13-19	v France	Agen
QF:	Lost	13-29	v New Zealand	Lille

1995

Coach: I Birtwell. Captain: G Rees.

Gp:	Won	34-3	v Romania	Port Elizabeth
Gp:	Lost	11-27	v Australia	Port Elizabeth
Gp:	Lost	0-20	v South Africa	Port Elizabeth

ENGLAND

1987:

Coach: M Weston. Captain: M Harrison.

Gp:	Lost	6-19	v Australia	Sydney
Gp:	Won	60-7	v Japan	Sydney
Gp:	Won	34-6	v United States	Sydney
QF:	Lost	3-16	v Wales	Brisbane

1991

Coach: G Cooke. Captain: W Carling.

Gp:	Lost	12-18	v New Zealand	Twickenham
Gp:	Won	36-6	v Italy	Twickenham
Gp:	Won	37-9	v United States	Twickenham
QF:	Won	19-10	v France	Paris
SF:	Won	9-6	v Scotland	Murrayfield
Fin:	Lost	6-12	v Australia	Twickenham

1995

Coach: J Rowell. Captain: W Carling

Gp:	Won	24-18	v Argentina	Durban
Gp:	Won	27-20	v Italy	Durban
Gp:	Won	44-22	v Western Samoa	Durban
QF:	Won	25-22	v Australia	Cape Town
SF:	Lost	29-45	v New Zealand	Cape Town
3rd	Lost	9-19	v France	Pretoria

FIJI

1987:
Coach: J Savau. Captain: K Rakoroi.

Gp:	Won	28-9	v Argentina	Hamilton
Gp:	Lost	13-74	v New Zealand	Christchurch
Gp:	Lost	15-18	v Italy	Dunedin
QF:	Lost	16-31	v France	Sydney

1991
Coach: S Viriviri. Captain: M Taga.

Gp:	Lost	3-13	v Canada	Bayonne
Gp:	Lost	9-33	v France	Grenoble
Gp:	Lost	15-17	v Romania	Brive

1995: Did not qualify

FRANCE

1987:
Coach: J Fouroux. Captain: D Dubroca.

Gp:	Drew	20-20	v Scotland	Christchurch
Gp:	Won	55-12	v Romania	Wellington
Gp:	Won	70-12	v Zimbabwe	Auckland
QF:	Won	31-16	v Fiji	Sydney
SF:	Won	30-24	v Australia	Sydney
Fin	Lost	9-29	v France	Auckland

1991
Coach: D Dubroca. Captain: S Blanco.

Gp:	Won	30-3	v Romania	Beziers
Gp:	Won	33-9	v Fiji	Grenoble
Gp:	Won	19-13	v Canada	Agen
QF:	Lost	10-19	v England	Paris

1995
Coach: P Berbizier. Captain: P Saint Andre.

Gp:	Won	38-10	v Tonga	Pretoria
Gp:	Won	54-18	v Ivory Coast	Rustenburg
Gp:	Won	22-19	v Scotland	Pretoria
QF:	Won	36-12	v Ireland	Durban
SF:	Lost	15-19	v South Africa	Durban
3rd	Won	19-9	v England	Pretoria

ITALY

1987:
Coach: M Bollesan. Captain: M Innocenti.

Gp:	Lost	6-70	v New Zealand	Auckland
Gp:	Lost	16-25	v Argentina	Christchurch
Gp:	Won	18-15	v Fiji	Dunedin

1991
Coach: B Fourcade. Captain: G Zanon.

Gp:	Won	30-9	v United States	Otley
Gp:	Lost	6-36	v England	Twickenham
Gp:	Lost	21-31	v New Zealand	Leicester

1995
Coach: G Coste. Captain: Massimo Cuttita

Gp:	Lost	18-42	v Western Samoa	E London
Gp:	Lost	20-27	v England	Durban
Gp:	Won	31-25	v Argentina	E London

IRELAND

1987:
Coach: M Doyle. Captain: D Lenihan.

Gp:	Lost	6-13	v Wales	Wellington
Gp:	Won	46-19	v Canada	Dunedin
Gp:	Won	32-9	v Tonga	Brisbane
QF:	Lost	15-33	v Australia	Sydney

1991
Coach: C Fitzgerald. Captain: P Matthews.

Gp:	Won	55-11	v Zimbabwe	Dublin
Gp:	Won	32-16	v Japan	Dublin
Gp:	Lost	15-24	v Scotland	Murrayfield
QF:	Lost	18-19	v Australia	Dublin

1995
Coach: G Murphy. Captain: T Kingston.

Gp:	Lost	19-43	v New Zealand	Johannesburg
Gp:	Won	50-28	v Japan	Bloemfontein
Gp:	Won	24-23	v Wales	Johannesburg
QF:	Lost	12-36	v France	Durban

IVORY COAST

1987 & 1991: Did not qualify

1995

Coach: D Davanier, C Ezoua. Captain: A Dahli

Gp: Lost 0-89 v Scotland Rustenburg
Gp: Lost 18-54 v France Rustenburg
Gp: Lost 11-29 v Tonga Rustenburg

JAPAN

1987:

Coach: K Moyaji. Captain: T Hayashi.

Gp: Lost 18-21 v United States Brisbane
Gp: Lost 7-60 v England Sydney
Gp: Lost 23-42 v Australia Sydney

1991

Coach: H Shukuzawa. Captain: S Hirao.

Gp: Lost 9-47 v Scotland Murrayfield
Gp: Lost 16-32 v Ireland Dublin
Gp: Won 52-8 v Zimbabwe Belfast

1995 Coach: O Koyabu. Captain: M Kunda

Gp: Lost 10-57 v Wales Bloemfontein
Gp: Lost 28-50 v Ireland Bloemfontein
Gp: Lost 17-145 v New Zealand Bloemfontein

NEW ZEALAND

1987:

Coach: B Lochore. Captain: A Dalton.

Gp: Won 70-6 v Italy Auckland
Gp: Won 74-13 v Fiji Christchurch
Gp: Won 46-15 v Argentina Wellington
QF: Won 30-3 v Scotland Christchurch
SF: Won 49-6 v Wales Brisbane
Fin Won 29-9 v France Auckland

1991

Coach: A Wyllie. Captain: G Whetton.

Gp: Won 18-12 v England Twickenham
Gp: Won 46-6 v United States Gloucester
Gp: Won 31-21 v Italy Leicester
QF: Won 29-13 v Canada Lille
SF: Lost 6-16 v Australia Dublin
3rd Won 13-6 v Scotland Cardiff

1995

Coach: L Mains. Captain: S Fitzpatrick

Gp: Won 43-19 v Ireland Johannesburg
Gp: Won 34-9 v Wales Johannesburg
Gp: Won 145-17 v Japan Bloemfontein
QF: Won 48-30 v Scotland Pretoria
SF: Won 45-29 v England Cape Town
Fin Lost 12-15 v South Africa Johannesburg

ROMANIA

1987:

Coach: M Naca. Captain: M Paraschiv.

Gp: Won 21-20 v Zimbabwe Auckland
Gp: Lost 12-55 v France Wellington
Gp: Lost 28-55 v Scotland Dunedin

1991

Coach: P Ianusevic. Captain: H Dumitras.

Gp: Lost 3-30 v France Beziers
Gp: Lost 11-19 v Canada Toulouse
Gp: Won 17-15 v Fiji Brive

1995

Coach: C Fuigig & M Paraschiv. Captain: T Brinza.

Gp: Lost 3-34 v Canada Port Elizabeth
Gp: Lost 8-21 v South Africa Cape Town
Gp: Lost 3-42 v Australia Stellenbosch

SCOTLAND

1987:

Coach: D Munro. C Deans.

Gp: Drew 20-20 v France Christchurch
Gp: Won 60-21 v Zimbabwe Wellington
Gp: Won 55-28 v Romania Dunedin
QF: Lost 3-30 v New Zealand Christchurch

1991

Coach: I McGeechan. Captain: D Sole.

Gp: Won 47-9 v Japan Murrayfield
Gp: Won 51-12 v Zimbabwe Murrayfield
Gp: Won 24-15 v Ireland Murrayfield
QF: Won 28-6 v Western Samoa Murrayfield
SF: Lost 6-9 v England Murrayfield
3rd Lost 6-13 v New Zealand Cardiff

1995

Coach: D Morgan. Captain: G Hastings.

Gp: Won 89-0 v Ivory Coast Rustenburg
Gp: Won 41-5 v Tonga Pretoria
Gp: Lost 19-22 v France Pretoria
QF: Lost 30-48 v New Zealand Pretoria

SOUTH AFRICA

1987 & 1991: Did not enter

1995
Coach: K Christie. Captain: F Pienaar

Gp:	Won	27-18	v Australia	Cape Town
Gp:	Won	21-8	v Romania	Cape Town
Gp:	Won	20-0	v Canada	Port Elizabeth
QF:	Won	42-14	v W Samoa	Johannesburg
SF:	Won	19-15	v France	Durban
Fin	Won	15-12	v New Zealand	Johannesburg

TONGA

1987:
Coach: M Tuku'aho. Captain: F Valu.

Gp:	Lost	4-37	v Canada	Napier
Gp:	Lost	16-29	v Wales	Palmerston North
Gp:	Lost	9-32	v Ireland	Brisbane

1991: Did not qualify

1995
Coach: F Valu. Captain: M 'Otai.

Gp:	Lost	10-38	v France	Pretoria
Gp:	Lost	5-41	v Scotland	Pretoria
Gp:	Won	29-12	v Ivory Coast	Rustenburg

UNITED STATES

1987:
Coach: R Mayes. Captain: E Burlingham.

Gp:	Won	21-18	v Japan	Brisbane
Gp:	Lost	12-47	v Australia	Brisbane
Gp:	Lost	6-34	v England	Sydney

1991
Coach: J Perkins. Captain: B Vizard.

Gp:	Lost	9-30	v Italy	Otley
Gp:	Lost	6-46	v New Zealand	Gloucester
Gp:	Lost	9-37	v England	Twickenham

1995: Did not qualify

WALES

1987:
Coach: A Gary. Captain: R Moriarty.

Gp:	Won	13-6	v Ireland	Wellington
Gp:	Won	29-16	v Tonga	Palmerston North
Gp:	Won	40-9	v Canada	Invercargill
QF:	Won	16-3	v England	Brisbane
SF:	Lost	6-49	v New Zealand	Brisbane
3rd	Won	22-21	v Australia	Roturua

1991
Coach: A Davies. Captain: I Evans.

Gp:	Lost	13-16	v Western Samoa	Cardiff
Gp:	Won	16-7	v Argentina	Cardiff
Gp:	Lost	3-38	v Australia	Cardiff

1995
Coach: A Evans. Captain: M Hall.

Gp:	Won	57-10	v Japan	Bloemfontein
Gp:	Lost	9-34	v New Zealand	Johannesburg
Gp:	Lost	23-24	v Ireland	Johannesburg

WESTERN SAMOA

1987: Did not qualify

1991
Coach: P Schuster. Captain: P Fatialofa.

Gp:	Won	16-13	v Wales	Cardiff
Gp:	Lost	3-9	v Australia	Pontypool
Gp:	Won	35-12	v Argentina	Pontypridd
QF:	Lost	6-28	v Scotland	Murrayfield

1995
Coach: P Schuster. Captain: P Fatialofa.

Gp:	Won	42-18	v Italy	E London
Gp:	Won	32-26	v Argentina	E London
Gp:	Lost	22-44	v England	Durban
QF:	Lost	14-42	v South Africa	Johannesburg

ZIMBABWE

1987:
Coach: B Murphy. Captain: M Jellicoe.

Gp:	Lost	20-21	v Romania	Auckland
Gp:	Lost	21-60	v Scotland	Wellington
Gp:	Lost	12-70	v France	Auckland

1991
Coach: I Buchanan. Captain: B Currin.

Gp:	Lost	11-55	v Ireland	Dublin
Gp:	Lost	12-51	v Scot;and	Murrayfield
Gp:	Lost	8-52	v Japan	Belfast

1995: Did not qualify

WORLD CUP FINALS' STATISTICS

PREVIOUS FINALS

1987	New Zealand	29	9	France
1991	Australia	12	6	England
1995	South Africa	15	12	New Zealand

Most points in a competition

126	Grant Fox (NZ)	1987
112	Thierry Lacroix (Fra)	1995
104	Gavin Hastings (Scot)	1995
84	Andrew Mehrtens (NZ)	1995
82	Michael Lynagh (Aust)	1991

Most points in a Match

45	SD Cullane NZ v Jpn	1995
44	AG Hastings Scot v ICoast	1995
31	AG Hastings Scot v Tonga	1995
30	MCG Ellis NZ v Jpn	1995
30	D Camberabero Frav Zimb	1987

Most points in a World Cup career

227	Gavin Hastings (Scot)	1987-95
195	Michael Lynagh (Aust)	1987-95
170	Grant Fox (NZ)	1987-91

Most penalties in a competition

26	Thierry Lacroix (Fra)	1995
21	Grant Fox (NZ)	1987
20	Rob Andrew (Eng)	1995

Most penalties in a match

8	Gavin Hastings Scot v Tonga	1995
8	Thierry Lacroix Fra v Ire	1995

Most tries in a competition

7	Mark Ellis (NZ)	1995
7	Jonah Lomu (NZ)	1995

Most tries in a match

6	Mark Ellis NZ v Jpn	1995
4	John Gallagher NZ v Fiji	1987
4	Craig Green NZ v Fiji	1987
4	Ieuan Evans Wal v Can	1987
4	Brian Robinson Ire v Zimb	1991
4	Jonah Lomu NZ v Eng	1995
4	Chester Williams SA v W S	1995
4	Gavin Hastings Scot v IC	1995

Most tries in a World Cup career

11	Rory Underwood (Eng)	1987-95
10	David Campese (Aust)	1987-95

Most conversions in a competition

30	Grant Fox (NZ)	1987
20	Simon Culhane (NZ)	1995
20	Michael Lynagh (Aust)	1987

Most conversions in a match

20	SD Cullane NZ v Jpn	1995
10	Grant Fox NZ v Fiji	1987
9	Gavin Hastings Scot v IC	1995
9	Didier Camberabero Fra v Z	1987

Most drop goals in a competition

3	J Davies (Wales)	1987
3	R Andrew (Eng)	1995
3	A Mehrtens (NZ)	1995
3	J Stransky (SA)	1995

Most drop goals in a match

2	Jonathan Davies Wal v Ire	1987
2	L Arbizu Arg v Aust	1991
2	T Rabaka Fij v Rom	1991
2	Rob Andrew Eng v Arg	1995
2	Joel Stransky SA v NZ	1995

Highest Score

145-17	New Zealand v Japan	1995
89-0	Scotland v Ivory Coast	1995
74-13	New Zealand v Fiji	1987
70-6	New Zealand v Itlay	1987
70-12	France v Zimbabwe	1987
60-7	England v Japan	1987

Lowest Score

0-89	Ivory Coast v Scotland	1995
0-20	Canada v South Africa	1995
3-42	Romania v Australia	1995
3-38	Wales v Australia	1991
3-34	Romania v Canada	1995
3-30	Scotland v New Zealand	1987
3-30	Romania v France	1991
3-16	England v Wales	1987
3-13	Fiji v Canada	1991
3-9	Australia v W Samoa	1991

Players Sent Off

H Richards	Wales v New Zealand	1987
D Codey	Australia v Wales	1987
P Sporleder	Argentina v W Samoa	1991
M Keenan	W Samoa v Argentina	1991
R Snow	Canada v South Africa	1995
G Rees	Canada v South Africa	1995
J Dalton	South Africa v Canada	1995
F Mahoni	Tonga v France	1995

Most Used Venue

7	Sydney (Concord Oval)
5	Brisbane (Ballymore Oval)
5	Durban
5	Murrayfield
5	Pretoria

The Concord Oval in Sydney has staged the most World Cup matches with seven. In 1987 it staged four group matches, two quarter finals and a semi final.

Overall Playing Record

Pts		Pd	W	D	L
32	New Zealand	18	16	0	2
25	France	16	12	1	3
24	Australia	16	12	0	4
20	England	16	10	0	6
17	Scotland	14	8	1	5
14	Wales	12	7	0	5
12	South Africa	6	6	0	0
12	Ireland	12	6	0	6
8	W Samoa	8	4	0	4
8	Canada	10	4	0	6
6	Italy	9	3	0	6
4	Romania	9	2	0	7
2	Japan	9	1	0	8
2	Argentina	9	1	0	8
2	Fiji	7	1	0	6
2	Tonga	6	1	0	5
2	United States	6	1	0	5
0	Zimbabwe	6	0	0	6
0	Ivory Coast	3	0	0	3

New Zealand,
France and
South Africa
are the only sides never to have lost a group match.

Italy
have won three matches but have never managed to reach the Quarter finals.

France and
Scotland
are the only sides to have drawn a match. In 1987 they drew their group match 20 all.

New Zealand
are the only side which has reached the semi final in all three World Cups, winning two and losing one. Australia, England and France have all reached the semi finals twice.

AUSTRALIA'S INTERNATIONAL RECORD - 98-99

	1	2	3	4	5	6	7	8	9	10
Joe Roff	15	15	15	11	11	11	11	11	11	11
Jason Little	14	14	14	14	14	r14	14			
Daniel Herbert	13	13	13	13	13	13	13	13	13	13
Tim Horan	12	12	12			12	12	10	10	10
Damian Smith	11									
Stephen Larkham	10	tr14	10	10	10					
George Gregan	9		9	9	9	9	9	9	9	9
Richard Harry	1									
Phil Kearns	2		2	2	2		r7		r2	
Andrew Blades	3		3	3	3	r1				
Tim Bowman	4		4	4	4	4	4			
John Eales	5	5	5	5	5					
Matt Cockbain	6	r5	6	6	6	6	6	6	6	6
David Wilson	7		7	7	7	7	7	7	7	7
Willie Ofahengaue	8		8							
Nathan Grey	r12	r12		12	12	r13	r10	12	12	12
Chris Whitaker	r9	9								
Glen Panocho	r3	3	r3				1	1	r1	1
Toutai Kefu	r4	8	r8	8	8	8	8	8	8	r8
Jeremy Paul	r2	2				2	2	2	2	2
Mitch Hardy		11	11							
Manuel Edmonds		10								
Brett Robinson		7								
Owen Finegan		6	r4		r6					
Jon Welborn		4						4	4	4
Dan Crowley		1	1		r2	1	r1	r1	1	r1
Michael Foley		r2								
Patricio Noriega				1	1	3	3	3	3	3
Chris Latham				15	15	15	15	15		
Ben Tune						14		14	14	14
Nathan Spooner						10	10			
David Giffin						5	5	5	5	5
Tiaan Strauss						r8	r8	r8	r8	8
Jim Wiliams						r6	r6	r6		
Matt Burke							r15	r14	15	15
Mark Connors									r6	r4

Match 1 18.09.98 H v Fiji Won 66-20 HT: 24-6 Att: 17,242 Sydney
(T: Larkham 2, Smith 2, Little, Finegan, Roff, Grey,Paul. C: Eales 9. P: Eales.)

Match 2 22.09.98 H v Tonga Won 74-0 HT: 41-0 Att: 14,176 Canberra
(T: Little 4, Edmonds 2, Paul, WhitakerHoran, Robinson, Finegan, Roff. C: Eales 2, Edmonds 5.)

Match 3 26.09.98 H v Western Samoa Won 25-13 HT: 15-5 Att: 9,239 Brisbane
(T: Ofahengaue, Crowley, Herbert. C: Eales 2. P: Eales 2)

Match 4 21.11.98 A v France Won 32-21 HT: 20-21 Att: 80,000 Stade de France
(T: Wilson, Bowman, Kefu. C: Eales. P: Eales 5)

Match 5 28.11.98 A v England Won 12-11 HT: 3-3 Att: 75,000 Twickneham
(P: Eales 4)

Match 6 12.06.99 H v Ireland Won 46-10 HT: 13-3 Att: 24,177 Brisbane
(T: Strauss 3,Tune, Herbert, Wilson.. C; Spooner 5. P: Spooner 5.)

Match 7 19.06.99 H v Ireland Won32-26 HT: 9-11 Att: 26,267 Perth
(T: Latham, Horan. C: Roff 2.P: Roff 3, Spooner 3)

Match 8 26.06.99 H v England Won 22-15 HT: 10-7 Att: 81,006 Sydney
(T: Tune 2, Roff, Wilson. C: Roff.)

Match 9 17.07.99 H v South Africa Won 32-6 HT: 20-6 Att: 40,000 Brisbane
(T: Roff 2, Burke, Horan. C: Burke 3. P: Burke 2.)

Match 9 24.07.99 A v New Zealand Lost 15-34 HT: 3-22 Att: 47,000 Auckland
(T: Gregan, Herbert. C: Burke. P: Burke.)

IRELANDS INTERNATIONAL RECORD - 1998-99

	1	2	3	4	5	6	7	8	9	10
Conor O'Shea	15	15	15	15	15	15	15	15	15	
Justin Bishop	14	14	14	14	14	14	14	14	14	14
Pat Duignan	13	13								
Jonathan Bell	12	12	13	12	12		12	r12		11
Kevin Maggs	11	r13	12	13	13	13	13	12	12	12
Eric Elwood	10	10	10					10		
Conor McGuinness	9	r9	9	9	9	9	9			
Peter Clohessy	1	1	3	1	1	1	1	3	1	1
Ross Nesdale	2		r2		-		-	2	-	r2
Paul Wallace	3	3	3	3	3	3	3	r3	3	3
Paddy Johns	4	4	4	4	4	4	4	4	4	4
Malcolm O'Kelly	5	5	5						r5	5
Eric Miller	6	6		8	8	r8	8			
Andy Ward	7	7	7		7	7	7	r8	7	7
Victor Costello	8	8	8	7	r8	8	r8	8	8	
Girvan Dempsey	r15		11	11		11	11	11		15
Ciaran Scally	r9	9					r9	9		
Justin Fitzpatrick	r1	r3	1	r1	r1	r1		1		
Alan Clarke	r2	2								
Jeremy Davidson	r5	r4	r5	5	5	5	5	5	5	r4
Dion O'Cuinneagain	r8	r6	6	6	6	6	6	7	6	8
Darragh O'Mahony		11								
David Humphreys		r10		10	10	10	10		10	10
Keith Wood		r2	2	2	2	2	2	r2	2	2
Reggie Corrigan			r1						r1	r1
Rob Henderson				r12		12	r12	13		
Niall Woods					11					
Mick Galway					r4					
Trevor Brennan								6		6
Brian O'Driscoll									13	13
Matt Mostyn									11	
Tom Tierney									9	9
David Corkery									r8	r6

Match 1 14.11.98 H v Georgia Won 70-0 HT: 28-0 Att: 11,648 Dublin
(T: Dempsey 2, Wallace, Johns, Maggs, O'Shea, Costollo, Duignan, Bell, Scally. C: Elwood 10)

Match 2 21.11.98 H v Romania Won 53-35 HT: 19-13 Att: 13,100 Dublin
(T: Bell, 2, Pen tries 2, O'Shea, Scally, Ward. C: Elwood 3, Humphrtys 3. P: Elwood 2)

Match 3 28.11.99 H v South Africa Lost 13-27 HT: 6-7 Att: 49,000 Dublin
(T: Wood. C: Elwood. P: Wood 2)

Match 4 06.02.99 H v France Lost 9-10 HT:6-0 Att: 49,000 Dublin
(P: Humphreys 3)

Match 5 20.02.99 A v Wales Won 29-23 HT: 16-6 Att: 76,000 Wembley
(T: Maggs, Wood. C: Humphreys. P: Humphreys 2. DG: Humphreys 2)

Match 6 06.03.99 H v England Lost 15-27 HT: 18-16 Att: 49,000 Dublin
(P: Humphreys 5)

Match 7 20.03.99 A v Scotland Lost 13-30 HT: 10-15 Att: 67,500 Murrayfield
(T: Pen try. C: Humphreys. P: Humphreys 2)

Match 8 10.04.99 H v Itlay Won 39-30 HT: 11-23 Att: 25,000 Dublin
(T: O'Shea 2, Bishop, Dempsey, Johns. C: Elwood. P: Elwood 4.)

Match 9 12.06.99 A v Australia Lost 10-41 HT: 3-13 Att: 24,177 Brisbane
(T: Maggs. C: Humphreys. P: Humphreys.)

Match 10 19.06.99 A v Australia Lost 26-32 HT: 11-9 Att: 26,267 Perth
(T: Clohessy, Maggs, Bishop. C: Humphreys. P: Humphreys 3.)

Keith Wood, the Irish & Quins hooker, proving that front row forwards can be mobile, as he takes on Matt Allen of Northampton Saints.
Photo: Joe McCabe

NEW ZEALAND'S INTERNATIONAL RECORD - 98-99

	1	2	3	4	5	6	7	8	9	10	11
Christian Cullen	15	15	15	15	15	15	15	14	14	14	14
Jeff Wilson	14	14	14	14	14	14	14	15	15	15	15
Mark Mayerhofler	13	12		13	13	12	12				
Walter Little	12		12	12	12						
Jonah Lomu	11	11	r11	11	11	11	11	r14		r11	r11
Andrew Mehrtens	10	10	10	r10	10	10	10		10	10	10
Ofisa Tonu'u	9	9		r9							
Olo Brown	3	3	3	3	3	3					
Anton Oliver	2	2	2	2	2	2	2	2	2	2	2
Craig Dowd	1	1	1	1	1		r1				
Ian Jones	4	4	4	4	4				r4		
Robin Brooke	5	5	5	5	5	5	5	5	5	5	5
Michael Jones	6		6	6	6						
Josh Kronfeld	7	7	7	7		7	7	7	7	7	7
Taine Randell	8	8	8	8	8	6	6	8	8	8	8
Todd Blackadder	r6	6									
Mark Robinson	r9										
Caleb Ralph		13									
Carl Hoeft		r3			r1	1	1	1	1	1	1
Carlos Spencer		r12	r13	10			r10				
Mark Carter		r6			7						
Norm Hewitt		tr2									
Joeli Vidiri		r11	11								
Isitola Maka		r4	r6	r6		8					
Scott McLeod			13	r13							
Justin Marshall			9	9	9	9	9	9	9	9	9
Scott Robertson					r7	r8	r7				
Royce Willis						4	4			r5	r5
Eroni Clarke						13	13				
Norm Berryman						r13					
Xavier Rush							8				
Kees Meeuws							3	3	3	3	3
Daryl Gibson								12	12	12	12
Alama Ieremia								13	13	13	13
Tane Umaga								11	11	11	11
Tony Brown								10	r10	r10	r10
Norm Maxwell								4	4	4	4
Dylan Mika								6	6	r6	6
Andrew Blowers									r6	6	r6
Greg Feek								r1			r1
Pita Alatini									r13		
Byron Kelleher								r9		r12	
Mark Hammett									r7		

Match 1 29.06.98 H v England Won 64-22 HT: 26-8 Att: 40,000 Dunedin
(T: Cullen 2, Wilson 2, Randell, Mayerhofler, Lomu, Kronfeld. C: Mehrtens 5. P: Mehrtens 3.)

Match 2 27.06.98 H v England Won 40-10 HT: 14-7 Att: 43,000 Auckland
(T: Wilson 2, Mayerhofler, Vidiri,Maka, Randell. C: Mehrtens 3 Spencer 2.)

Match 3 11.07.98 A v Australia Lost 16-24 HT: 13-15 Att: 75,147
(T: Kronfeld, Jones. P: Spencer, Mehrtens.)

Match 4 25.07.98 H v South Africa Lost 3-13 HT:0-3 Att: 35,000 Wellington
(P: Mehrtens.)

Match 5 01.08.98 H v Australia Lost 23-27 HT: 3-10 Att: 36,800 Christchurch
(T: Cullen, Lomu. C: Mehrtens 2. P: Mehrtens 3.)

Match 6 15.08.98 A v South Africa Lost 23-24 HT: 17-5 Att: 42,000 Durban
(T: Marshall, Randell. C; Mehrtens 2. P: Mehrtens 3.)

Match 7 29.08.98 A v Australia Lost 14-19 HT: 11-0 Att: 40,501 Sydney
(T: Cullen. P: Mehrtens 2. DG: Mehrtens.)

Match 8 18.06.99 H v W Samoa Won 71-13 HT: 31-3 Att: 25,000 Albany
(T: Wilson 4, Umaga 2, Maxwell, Randell,Lomu. C: Brown 7. P: Brown 4.)

Match 9 26.06.99 H v France Won 54-7 HT: 30-0 Att: 35,000 Wellington
(T:Umaga3, Cullen 2, Marshall 2. C: Mehrtens 5. P: Mehrtens 3.)

Match 10 10.07.99 H v South Africa Won 28-0 HT: 6-0 Att: 40,000 Dunedin
(T: Cullen , Marshall, Wilson . C: Mehrtens, Brown. P: Mehrtens 3.)

Match 11 24.07.99 H v Australia Won 34-15 HT: 22-3 Att: 47,000 Auckland
(T: Marshall . C: Mehrtens. P: Mehrten9.)

SOUTH AFRICA INTERNATIONAL RECORD - 1998-99

	1	2	3	4	5	6	7	8	9
Percy Montgomery	15	15	15	15	15	15	15	15	15
Stefan Terblanche	14	14	14	14	r11	11	14		14
Andre Snyman	13	13	13	13					
Franco Smith	12								
Pieter Roussouw	11	11	11	11	11		11	11	
Henry Honiball	10	10	10	10					
Joost van der Westhuizen	9	9	9	9					
Russell Kempson	1	1	1	1	1	1	1		
James Dalton	2	2	2	2					
Andrew Garvey	3	3	3	3					
Krynauw Otto	4	4	4	4	5		5	4	5
Mark Andrews	5	5	5	5					
Johan Erasmus	6	6	6	6	6	7	7		6
Andre Venter	7	r4	r5	r4	7	r8	r4	7	7
Gary Teichmann	8	8	8	8	8		8	8	
Christian Stewart		12	12	12					
Bobby Skinstad	r5	7	7	7					
Ollie Le Roux	r3	r3	r1	r3	r1	r1	r1		r1
Naka Drotske			r2		2	2	2	2	2
Werner Swanepoel				r9	9	r9	9		
Breyton Paulse					14	14		14	11
Robbie Fleck					13	13		r13	13
Pieter Muller					12				12
Gaffie du Toit					10	10	r10	10	
Cobus Visagie					3		3	3	3
Selborne Boone					4	4	4	r5	4
Japie Muller					r12	12	12	12	
David von Hoesslin					r9	9	r9	9	r9
Charl Marais					r2	r2			
Albert van den Burgh					r5	5			
Deon Kayser						r14			r12
Andre Vos					r7	8		r6	
Willie Meyer						3		r1	rr1
Corne Krige						6	6	6	
Braam van Straaten						r10	10	r15	10
Os du Randt								1	1
Anton Leonard									8

Match 1 14.11.98 A v Wales Won 28-20 HT: 14-14 Att: 55,000 Wembley
(T: Pentry, Venter, Westhuizen. C: Smith 2 P: Smith 3)

Match 2 21.11.98 A v Scotland Won 35-10 HT: 11-7 Att: 35,000 Murrayfield
(T: Snyman, Terblanche, Roussouw, Skinstad, Westhuizen. C: Montgomery 2. P: Montgomery 2)

Match 3 28.11.98 A v Ireland Won 27-13 HT: 7-6 Att: 49,000 Dublin
(T: Westhuizen, Erasmus, Skinstad. C: Montgomery 3. P: Montgomery 2)

Match 4 05.12.98 A v England Lost 7-13 HT: 7-7 Att: 76,000 Twickenham
(T: Roussouw. C: Montgomery.)

Match 5 12.06.99 H v Italy Won 74-3 HT: 22-3 Att: 35,000 Port Elizabeth
(T: Paulse 3, du Toit 2, Pentry, Fleck, Terblanche, Montgomery, Boone. C: du Toit 8. P: du Toit.)

Match 6 19.06.99 H v Italy Won 101-0 HT: 40-0 Att: 20,000 Durban
(T: Terblanche 5, Kayser 3, van Hoesslin 2, Marais, Vos, Fleck, Montgomery, Drotske. C; du Toit 8, van Straaten 5.)

Match 7 26.06.99 A v Wales Lost 19-29 HT: 6-19 Att: 27,000 Cardiff
(T: Montgomery, Swanepoel. P: van Straaten 2, du Toit.)

Match 8 10.07.99 A v New Zealand Lost 0-28 HT: 0-6 Att: 40,000 Dunedin
()

Match 9 17.07.99 A v Australia Lost 6-32 HT: 6-20 Att: 40,000 Brisbane
(P: van Straaten 2)

SCOTLAND'S INTERNATIONAL RECORD - 1998-99

	1*	2	3*	4*	5	6	7	8	9
Derrick Lee	15	15							
Tony Stanger	14								
Jamie Mayer	13	13	13	13					
R Shepherd	12								
Cameron Murray	11	11	11	11	14	14	14	14	14
Gregor Townsend	10	r15	15	15	13	10	10	10	10
Bryan Redpath	9	9	9	9					
Tom Smith	1	1	1	1	1	1	1	1	
Graham Bulloch	2	2	2	2	2	2	2	2	2
Paul Burnell	3	3	r3		3	3	3	3	3
Scot Murray	4	4	4	4	5	4	4	4	4
Stuart Grimes	5		r5	r4	r4	5	5	5	5
Rob Wainwright	6		r8						
Budge Pountney	7	7	7		r6	r6	r8	r6	6
Eric Peters	8	8	8	8	8	8	8	8	
Alan Tait	r12	14	r12		r10	13	13	13	13
Duncan Hodge	r10	10	10	10	10				
David Hilton	r3	r3	3	r3	r3	r3	r1	r1	1
Dodie Weir	r5	5	5	5	4				
Martin Leslie	r6	r6	6	7	7	7	7	7	7
John Leslie		12	12	12	12	12	12	12	12
Kenny Logan		r14	14	14	11	11	11	11	11
Peter Walton		6			6	6	6	6	r6
Gary Armstrong		r9	r9		9	9		9	9
Shaun Longstaff			r11	r14			r13	r14	
Steve Brotherstone			r2					r2	
C Mather				6					
W Anderson				3					
Glen Metcalfe					15	15	15	15	15
Ian Fairley							9	r9	
Graeme Burns							r9		
George Graham									r1
Andy Reed									r4
Stuart Reid									8

Scotland did not award caps for the matches marked * but did put out first choice sides.

Match	Date	H/A	Opponent	Result	HT	Att	Venue
Match 1	14.11.99	H	v NZ Maoris*	Lost 8-24	HT: 3-9	Att: 19,200	Murrayfield
							(T: Lee. P: Lee)
Match 2	21.11.98	H	v South Africa	Lost 10-35	HT: 7-11	Att: 35,000	Murrayfield
							(T: Hodge. C: Hodge. P: Hodge)
Match 3	28.11.98	H	v Portugal*	Won 85-11	HT: 52-0	Att: 6,000	Murrayfield
							(T:Mayer 3,Townsend 2, Logan 2, C Murray, Bulloch, Peters, Pountney. C: Hodge10)
Match 4	05.12.98	H	v Spain*	Won 85-3	HT: 40-3	Att: 6,524	Murrayfield
							(T: Logan 5, J Leslie, M Leslie, Longstaff, C Murray, Redpath, T Smith, Townsend, Weir. C: Hodge 10.)
Match 5	06.02.99	H	v Wales	Won 33-20	HT: 8-13	Att: 67,500	Murrayfield
							(T: J Leslie, Townsend,Tait,S Murray. C: Logan 2. P: Logan 2, Hodge)
Match 6	20.02.99	A	v England	Lost 21-24	HT: 17-7	Att: 75,000	Twickenham
							(T: Tait 2, Townsend. C; Logan 3.)
Match 7	06.03.99	H	v Italy	Won 32-31	HT: 20-12	Att: 25,000	Murrayfield
							(T: Howarth, Gibbs. C: Jenkins 2. P: Jenkins 6)
Match 8	20.03.99	H	v Ireland	Won 30-13	HT: 15-10	Att: 67,500	Murrayfield
							(T: C Murray, Townsend, Grimes. C: Logan 2. P: Logan 2.)
Match 9	10.04.99	A	v France	Won 36-22	HT: 33-22	Att: 80,000	Stade de France
							(T: M Leslie 2, Tait 2, Townsend. C: Logan 4. P: Logan.)

* Non cap internationls

WALES INTERNATIONAL RECORD - 1998-99

	1	2	3	4	5	6	7	8	9	10
Shane Howarth	15	15	15	15	15	15	15	15	15	15
Gareth Thomas	14	14	-	-	r14	14	14	-	14	14
Mark Taylor	13	13	13	13	13	13	13	13	13	13
Scott Gibbs	12	12	12	12	12	12	12			
Dafydd James	11	11	11	11	11	11	11	11	11	11
Neil Jenkins	10	10	10	10	10	10	10	10	10	10
Rob Howley	9	9	9	9	9	9	9	9	9	9
Andrew Lewis	1	1			r1		r1	r1	r1	r1
Jonathan Humphreys	2	2	2						r2	r2
Chris Anthony	3	3	3	r3						
Craig Quinnell	4	4	-	4	4	4	4	4	4	4
Chris Wyatt	5	5	4	5	5	5	5	5	5	5
Colin Charvis	6	6	6	6	6	6	6	6		6
Martyn Williams	7	7	7	7						
Scott Quinnell	8	8	8	8	8	8	8	8	8	8
Ben Evans	r3				3	3	3	3	3	
Barry Williams		r7	r2	2		r2				
Mike Voyle		r8	r6	tr7		r4				r4
Matthew Robinson			14	14	14			14		
Allan Bateman			13					12	12	12
Darren Morris			1	1		r1				
Ian Gough			5							
Garin Jenkins				r2	2	2	2	2	2	2
David Young				1			r3	r3	r3	3
David Llewellyn					r9	r9				
Peter Rogers					1	1	1	1	1	1
Brett Sinkinson					7	7	7	7	7	7
Nick Walne						r11	r14			
Nigel Boobyer							r13			
Geraint Lewis							r6		6	

Match 1	14.11.98	H	v South Africa	Lost 20-28	HT: 14-14	Att: 55,000	(T:G Thomas. P: Jenkins 5)
Match 2	21.11.98	H	v Argentina	Won 43-30	HT: 26-25	Att: 10,500	(T: Charvis 2, James, M Taylor. C: Jenkins 4. P: Jenkins 5)
Match 3	06.02.99	A	v Scotland	Lost 20-33	HT: 13-8	Att: 67,500	(T: Gibbs, James. C: Jenkins 2. P: Jenkins 2)
Match 4	20.02.99	H	v Ireland	Lost 23-29	HT: 6-16	Att: 76,000	(T: C Quinnell, Howarth. C: Jenkins 2. P: Jenkins 3)
Match 5	06.03.99	A	v France	Won 34-33	HT: 27-9	Att: 49,000	(T: James, Charvis, C Quinnell. C: Jenkins 2. P: Jenkins 5)
Match 6	20.03.99	A	v Italy	Won 60-21	HT: 18-16	Att: 20,000	(T: Thomas 4, C Quinnell, Howley, Jenkins. C; Jenkins 5. P: Jenkins 5)
Match 7	11.04.99	H	v England	Won 32-31	HT: 18-25	Att: 76,000	(T: Howarth, Gibbs. C: Jenkins 2. P: Jenkins 6)
Match 8	05.06.99	A	v Argentina	Won 36-26	HT: 10-23	Att: 22,000	(T: James, Sinkinson, Howarth. C: Jenkins 3. P: Jenkins 4. DG : Howarth)
Match 9	12.06.99	A	v Argentina	Won 23-16	HT: 9-11	Att: 29,000	(T:Jenkins. P: Jenkins 5. DG: Jenkins)
Match 10	26.06.99	H	v South Africa	Won 29-19	HT:19-6	Att: 27,000	(T:Thomas, Taylor. C: Jenkins 2P: Jenkins 5.)

FIVE NATIONS CHAMPIONSHIP 1998-99

Saturday, 6th February 1999

At Lansdowne Road, Dublin.

IRELAND 9-10 FRANCE

Attendance: 49,000.

Half-time: 6-0

Referee: P Marshall, Australia.

IRELAND: C O'Shea (London Irish); J Bishop (London Irish), K Maggs (Bath), J Bell (Dungannon), G Dempsey (Terenure College); D Humphreys (Dungannon), C McGuinness (St Mary's College); P Clohessy (Young Munster), K Wood (Harlequins), P Wallace (Saracens), E Miller (Terenure College), P Johns (Saracens)(captain), J Davidson (Castres), D O'Cuinneagain (Sale), V Costello (St Mary's College).
Replacements: R Henderson (Wasps) for Bell 15 mins., T Brennan (St Mary's College) for Costello 51 mins.. J Fitzpatrick (Dungannon) for Clohessy 63 mins.. Temporary replacement: Fitzpatrick for Wallace 45-47 mins.. New cap: Brennan. Yellow card: Brennan.
SCORER: Pens: Humphreys (3).

FRANCE: E Ntamack (Toulouse); P Bernat-Salles (Biarritz), R Dourthe (Stade Francais), P Comba (Stade Francais), T Lombard (Stade Francais); T Castaignede (Castres), P Carbonneau (Brive); C Califano (Toulouse), R Ibanez (Perpignan)(captain), F Tournaire (Toulouse), P Benetton (Agen), O Brouzet (Begles-Bordeaux), F Pelous (Toulouse), O Magne (Brive), T Lievremont (Perpignan).
Replacements: S Marconnet (Stade Francais) for Califano 40 mins., T Cleda (Pau) for Pelous 60 mins.. A Gomes (Stade Francais) for Comba 80 mins.. No new caps. Yellow card: Bernat-Salles.
SCORERS: Try: Dourthe. Con: Castaignede. Pen: Castaognede.

At Murrayfield.

SCOTLAND 33-20 WALES

Attendance: 68,500.

Half-time: 8-13

Referee: E Morrison, England

SCOTLAND: G Metcalfe (Glasgow Caledonians); C Murray (Edinburgh Reivers), G Townsend (Brive), J Leslie (Glasgow Caledonians), K Logan (Wasps); D Hodge (Edinburgh Reivers), B Redpath (Edinburgh Reivers), G Armstrong (Newcastle Falcons)(captain); T Smith (Glasgow Caledonians), G Bulloch (Glasgow Caledonians), P Burnell (London Scottish), P Walton (Newcastle Falcons), S Murray (Bedford), G Weir (Newcastle Falcons), M Leslie (Edinburgh Reivers), E Peters (Bath).
Replacements: S Grimes (Glasgow Caledonians) for Weir 41 mins., A Tait (Edinburgh Reivers) for Hodge 44 mins., B Pountney (Northampton) for Walton 67 mins., D Hilton (Bath) for Burnell 73 mins.. Temporary replacement: Pountney for M Leslie 20-26 mins..
SCORERS: Tries: J Leslie (1), Townsend (1), Tait (1), S Murray (1). Pens: Logan (2), Hodge (1). Cons: Logan (2).

WALES: S Howarth (Sale); M Robinson (Swansea), A Bateman (Richmond), S Gibbs (Swansea), D James (Pontypridd); N Jenkins (Pontypridd), R Howley (Cardiff); D Morris (Swansea), J Humphreys (Cardiff), C Anthony (Swansea), C Charvis (Swansra), I Gough (Pontypridd), C Wyatt (Llanelli), M Williams (Pontypridd), S Quinnell (Llanelli). Replacements: B Williams (Richmond) for Humphreys 56 mins.. M Voyle (Llanelli) for Gough 66 mins.. New cap: Robinson.
SCORERS: Tries: James (1), Gibbs (1). Pens: Jenkins (2). Cons: Jenkins (2)
Man of the Match: S Murray (Scotland)

Saturday, 20th February 1999.

At Twickenham.

ENGLAND 24-21 SCOTLAND

Attendance: 75,000.

Half-time: 17-7

Referee: D McHugh, Ireland.

ENGLAND: N Beal (Northampton); D Rees (Sale), J Wilkinson (Newcastle Falcons), J Guscott (Bath), D Luger (Harlequins); M Catt (Bath), M Dawson (Northampton); J Leonard (Harlequins), R Cockerill (Leicester), D Garforth (Leicester), L Dallaglio (Wasps)(captain), M Johnson (Leicester), T Rodber (Northampton/Army), N Back (Leicester), R Hill (Saracens).
Replacements: D Grewcock (Saracens) for Johnson 67 mins., K Bracken (Saracens) for Dawson 69 mins.. No new caps. Yellow card: Johnson.
SCORERS: Tries: Rodber (1), Luger (1), Beal (1). Pen: Wilkinson. Cons: Wilkinson (3).

SCOTLAND: G Metcalfe (Glasgow Caledonians); C Murray (Edinburgh Reivers), A Tait (Edinburgh Reivers), J Leslie (Glasgow Caledonians), K Logan (Wasps); G Townsend (Brive), G Armstrong (Newcastle)(capt.); T Smith (Glasgow Caledonians), G Bulloch (Glasgow Caledonians), P Burnell (London Scottish), P Walton (Newcastle Falcons), S Murray (Bedford), S Grimes (Glasgow Caledonians), M Leslie (Edinburgh Reivers), E Peters (Bath). Replacements: B Pountney (Northampton) for Walton 53 mins., D Hilton (Bath) for Burnell 67 mins..
SCORERS: Tries: Tait (2), Townsend (1); Cons: Logan (3).
Man of the Match: S Murray (Scotland).

At Wembley.

WALES 23-29 IRELAND

Half-time: 6-16

Referee: S Young, Australia.

WALES: S Howarth (Sale); M Robinson (Swansea), M Taylor (Swansea), S Gibbs (Swansea), D James (Pontypridd); N Jenkins (Pontypridd), R Howley (Cardiff)(captain); D Morris (Swansea), B Williams (Richmond), D Young (Cardiff), C Charvis (Swansea), C Quinnell (Richmond), C Wyatt (Llanelli), M Williams (Pontypridd), S Quinnell (Llanelli).
Replacements: G Jenkins (Swansea) for B Williams 52 mins., C Anthony (Swansea) for Young 67 mins.. Temporary replacement: M Voyle (Llanelli) for M Williams 27-33 mins.. No new caps. Yellow cards: Young, C Quinnell.
SCORERS: Tries: C Quinnell (1), Howarth (1). Pens: N Jenkins (3). Cons: N Jenkins (2).

IRELAND: C O'Shea (London Irish); J Bishop (London Irish), K Maggs (Bath), J Bell (Dungannon), N Woods (London Irish); D Humphreys (Dungannon), C McGuinness (St Mary's College); P Clohessy (Young Munster), K Wood (Harlequins), P Wallace (Saracens), D O'Cuinneagain (Sale), P Johns (Saracens)(captain) J Davidson (Castres), A Ward (Ballynahinch), E Miller (Terenure College).
Replacements: J Fitzpatrick (Dungannon) for Clohessy 66 mins., V Costello (St Mary's College) for Miller 66 mins., M Galwey (Shannon) for Johns 80 mins.. No new caps.
SCORERS: Tries: Maggs (1), Wood (1). DG: Humphreys (2). Pens: Humphreys (3). Cons: Humphreys (2)
Man of the Match: D Humphreys (Ireland).

Saturday, 6th March 1999

At Stade de France, Paris.

FRANCE 33-34 WALES

Attendance: 80,000.

Half-time: 18-28

Referee: J Fleming, Scotland

FRANCE: E Ntamack (Toulouse); P Bernat-Salles (Pau), R Dourthe (Stade Francais), F Comba (Stade Francais), T Lombard (Stade Francais); T Castaignede (Castres), P Carbonneau (Brive); C Califano (Toulouse), R Ibanez (Perpignan)(captain), F Tournaire (Toulouse), P Benetton (Agen), O Brouzet (Begles-Bordeaux), F Pelous (Toulouse), M Raynaud (Narbonne), T Lievremont (Perpignan).
Replacements: D Aucagne (Pau) for Dourthe 5 mins., X Garbajosa (Toulouse) for Bernat-Salles 41 mins., S Marconnet (Stade Francais) for Tournaire 41 mins., R Castel (Beziers) for Benetton 64 mins. New cap: Raynaud.
SCORERS: Tries: Ntamack (3), Castaignede (1). Pens: Castaignede (3). Cons: Castaignede (2).

WALES: S Howarth (Sale); M Robinson (Swansea), M Taylor (Swansea), S Gibbs (Swansea), D James (Pontypridd); N Jenkins (Pontypridd), R Howley (Cardiff)(captain); P Rogers (London Irish), G Jenkins (Swansea), B Evans (Swansea), C Charvis (Swansea), C Quinnell (Richmond), C Wyatt (Llanelli), B Sinkinson (Neath), S Quinnell (Llanelli). Replacements: G Thomas (Cardiff) for Robinson 52 mins., A Lewis (Cardiff) for Rogers 66 mins., D Llewellyn (Ebbw Vale) for Howley 69 mins.. New caps: Rogers, Evans, Sinkinson.
SCORERS: Tries: Charvis (1), James (1), C Quinnell (1). Pens: Jenkins (5). Cons: Jenkins (2)
Man of the Match: N Jenkins (Wales). NB: This was Jim Fleming's 32nd International refereeing appointment.

At Lansdowne Road, Dublin.

IRELAND 15-27 ENGLAND

Attendance: 49,000.

Half-time: 9-11

Referee: P O'Brien, New Zealand

IRELAND: C O'Shea (London Irish); J Bishop (London Irish), K Maggs (Bristol), R Henderson (Wasps), G Dempsey (Terenure College); D Humphreys (Dungannon), C McGuinness (St Mary's College); P Clohessy (Young Munster), K Wood (Harlequins), P Wallace (Saracens), D O'Cuinneagain (Sale), P Johns (Saracens)(captain), J Davidson (Castres), A Ward (Ballynahinch), V Costello (St Mary's College).
Replacements: E Miller (Terenure College) for Costello 63 mins., J Fitzpatrick (Dungannon) for Clohessy 66 mins.. No new caps.
SCORER: Pens: Humphreys (5).

ENGLAND: M Perry (Bath); D Rees (Sale), J Wilkinson (Newcastle), J Guscott (Bath), D Luger (Harlequins); P Grayson (Northampton), K Bracken (Saracens); J Leonard (Harlequins), R Cockerill (Leicester), D Garforth (Leicester), R Hill (Saracens), M Johnson (Leicester), T Rodber (Northampton/Army), N Back (Leicester), L Dallaglio (Wasps)(captain).
Temporary replacement: N McCarthy (Gloucester) for Cockerill 66-68 mins.. New cap: McCarthy. Yellow card: Johnson.
SCORERS: Tries: Perry (1), Rodber (1). DG: Grayson. Pens: Wilkinson (4)
Man of the Match: L Dallaglio (England).

Saturday, 20th March 1999 At Twickenham

ENGLAND 21-10 FRANCE

Half-time: 9-0

Referees: C Hawke, New Zealand, replaced by J Fleming, Scotland, second half.

ENGLAND: M Perry (Bath); D Rees (Sale), J Wilkinson (Newcastle), J Guscott (Bath), D Luger (Harlequins); M Catt (Bath), K Bracken (Saracens); J Leonard (Harlequins), R Cockerill (Leicester), D Garforth (Leicester), R Hill (Saracens), M Johnson (Leicester), T Rodber (Northampton/Army), N Back (Leicester), L Dallaglio (Wasps)(captain).
Replacements: M Dawson (Northampton) for Bracken 34 mins., M Corry (Leicester) for Hill 49 mins., N Beal (Northampton) for Rees 64 mins., V Ubogu (Bath) for Garforth 78 mins.. No new caps.
SCORER: Pens: Wilkinson (7).

FRANCE: E Ntamack (Toulouse); X Garbajosa (Toulouse), P Giordani (Dax), F Comba (Stade Francais), C Dominici (Stade Francais); T Castaignede (Castres), P Carbonneau (Brive); S Marconnet (Stade Francais), R Ibanez (Perpignan)(captain), F Tournaire (Toulouse), T Lievremont (Perpignan), F Brouzet (Begles-Bordeaux), F Pelous (Toulouse), R Castel (Beziers), C Juillet (Stade Francais).
Replacements: C Califano (Toulouse) for Marconnet 47 mins., M Raynaud (Narbonne) for Lievremont 65 mins., D Auradou (Stade Francais) for Pelous 65 mins. New caps: Giordani, Juillet, Auradou.
SCORERS: Try: Comba. Pen: Castaigne. Con: Castaignede.

At Murrayfield

SCOTLAND 30-13 IRELAND

Half-time: 15-10

Referee: D Bevan, Wales.

SCOTLAND: G Metcalfe (Glasgow Caledonians); C Murray (Edinburgh Reivers), A Tait (Edinburgh Reivers), J Leslie (Glasgow Caledonians), K Logan (Wasps); G Townsend (Brive), G Armstrong (Newcastle)(captain); T Smith (Glasgow Caledonians), G Bulloch (Glasgow Caledonians), P Burnell (London Scottish), P Walton (Newcastle), S Murray (Bedford), S Grimes (Glasgow Caledonians), M Leslie (Edinburgh Reivers), E Peters (Bath). Replacements: D Hilton (Bath) for Smith 39 mins., B Pountney (Northampton) for Walton 67 mins., S Longstaff (Glasgow Caledonians) for C Murray 76 mins., S Brotherstone (Edinburgh Reivers) for Bulloch 77 mins., I Fairley (Edinburgh Reivers) for Armstrong 80 mins.. New cap: Brotherstone.
SCORERS: Tries: C Murray (2), Townsend (1), Grimes (1). Pens: Logan (2). Cons: Logan (2).

IRELAND: C O'Shea (London Irish); J Bishop (London Irish), K Maggs (Bristol), J Bell (Dungannon), G Dempsey (Terenure College); D Humphreys (Dungannon), C McGuinness (St Mary's College); P Clohessy (Young Munster), K Wood (Harlequins), P Wallace (Saracens), D O'Cuinneagain (Sale), P Johns (Saracens)(captain), J Davidson (Castres), A Ward (Ballynahinch), E Miller (Terenure College).
Replacements: V Costello (St Mary's College) for Miller 16 mins., T Brennan (St Mary's College) for Ward 64 mins., R Henderson (Wasps) for Bell 64 mins., C Scally (University College Dublin) for McGuinness 76 mins..
SCORERS: Try: Penalty-try. Pens: Humphreys (2). Con: Humphreys
Man of the Match: G Townsend (Scotland).
NB: This was Johns' 50th cap for Ireland, while Brotherstone gained his first cap during his 16th appearance on the bench for Scotland.

Saturday, 10th April 1999 At Stade de France, Paris

FRANCE 22-36 SCOTLAND

Attendance: 80,000.

Half-time: 22-33

Referee: C Thomas, Wales.

FRANCE: E Ntamack (Toulouse); X Garbajosa (Toulouse), P Giordani (Dax), F Comba (Stade Francais), C Dominici (Stade Francais); T Castaignede (Castres), P Carbonneau (Brive); C Califano (Toulouse), R Ibanez (Perpignan)(captain), F Tournaire (Toulouse), R Castel (Beziers), T Cleda (Pau), O Brouzet (Begles-Bordeaux), C Labit (Tolouse), C Juillet (Stade Francais). Replacements: D Aucagne (Pau) for Castaignede 2 mins., C Laussucq (Stade Francais) for Carbonneau 39 mins., S Marconnet (Stade Francais) for Califano 56 mins., D Auradou (Stade Francais) for Cleda 56 mins., P Benetton (Agen) for Castel 56 mins., T Lombard (Stade Francais) for Giordani 62 mins.. New caps: Labit, Auradou.
SCORERS: Tries: Ntamack (1), Juillet (1), Dominici (1). Pen: Aucagne. Cons: Aucagne (2).

SCOTLAND: G Metcalfe (Glasgow Caledonians); C Murray (Edinburgh Reivers), A Tait (Edinburgh Reivers), J Leslie (Glasgow Caledonians), K Logan (Wasps); G Townsend (Brive), G Armstrong (Newcastle)(captain); D Hilton (Bath), G Bulloch (Glasgow Caledonians), P Burnell (London Scottish), B Pountney (Northampton), S Murray (Bedford), S Grimes (Glasgow Caledonians), M Leslie (Edinburgh Reivers), S Reid (Leeds). Replacements: G Graham (Newcastle) for Hilton 66 mins., P walton (Newcastle) for Pountney 73 mins., A Reed (Wasps) for S Murray 80 mins.. No new caps.
SCORERS: Tries: M Leslie (2), Tait (2), Townsend (1). Pen: Logan. Cons: Logan (4) Man of the Match: G Metcalfe (Scotland).

Sunday, 11th April 1999

At Wembley Stadium

WALES 32-31 ENGLAND

Attendance: 78,000

Half-time: 18-25

Referee: A Watson, South Africa

WALES: S Howarth (Sale); G Thomas (Cardiff), M Taylor (Swansea), S Gibbs (Swansea), D James (Pontypridd); N Jenkins (Pontypridd), R Howley (Cardiff)(captain); P Rogers (London Irish), G Jenkins (Swansea), B Evans (Swansea), C Charvis (Swansea), C Quinnell (Richmond), C Wyatt (Llanelli), B Sinkinson (Neath), S Quinnell (Llanelli).
Replacements: N Walne (Richmond) for Thomas A Lewis (Cardiff) for Rogers 68 mins., D Young (Cardiff) for Evans 68 mins.
No new caps.
SCORERS: Tries: Howarth (1), Gibbs (1). Pens: N Jenkins (6). Cons: N Jenkins (2).

ENGLAND: M Perry (Bath); D Luger(Harlequins), J Wilkinson (Newcastle), B-J Mather (Sale), S Hanley (Sale); M Catt (Bath), M Dawson (Northampton); J Leonard (Harlequins), R Cockerill (Leicester), D Garforth (Leicester), R Hill (Saracens), M Johnson (Leicester), T Rodber (Northampton/Army), N Back (Leicester), L Dallaglio (Wasps)(captain).
Replacement: V Ubogu (Bath) for Garforth 68 mins.. New caps: Mather, Hanley. Yellow cards: Leonard, Rodber.
SCORERS: Tries: Luger (1), Hanley (1), Hill (1). Pens: Wilkinson (4). Cons: Wilkinson (2).
Man of the Match: N Jenkins (Wales).
NB: The yellow cards to Leonard and Rodber meant that England had been so cautioned four times during the Championship - Johnson (twice), Leonard (once) and Rodber (once).

Gregor Townsend scored a try in each of the four Five Nations games that Scotland played.
He joins an elite band of four other players who have managed to do this.

FIVE NATIONS ROUND UP

Final Table

	Pd	W	D	L	F	A	Tries	Pens	Pts
Scotland	4	3	0	1	120	79	16	6	6
England	4	3	0	1	103	78	8	16	6
Wales	4	2	0	2	109	126	9	16	4
Ireland	4	1	0	3	66	90	3	16	2
France	4	1	0	3	75	100	9	6	2

Most Points

Pts	Player	T	C	P	DG	
64	Neil Jenkins (Wales)		-	8	16	-
60	Jonny Wilkinson (Eng)		-	6	16	-
51	David Humphreys (Ire)		-	3	13	2
37	Kenny Logan (Scot)	-	11	5	-	
28	Thomas Castaignede (Fra)	1	4	5	-	
25	Alan Tait (Scot)	5	-	-	-	

Most Tries

5: Alan Tait (Sco.)

4: Emile N'Tamack (Fra.)
Gregor Townsend (Sco.)

2: Tim Rodber (Eng.), Craig Quinnell (Wal.), Cameron Murray (Sco.), Dafydd James (Wal.), Martin Leslie (Sco.), Scott Gibbs (Wal.), Dan Luger (Eng.)

HOT SHOTS

%	Player	Attempts	Succcessful
91.67	Jonny Wilkinson (Eng)	24	22
82.76	Neil Jenkins (Wal)	29	24
69.56	David Humphreys (Ire)	23	16
61.54	Kenny Logan (Scot)	26	16
57.14	Thomas Castaignede (Fra)	14	8

Fair Play - Discipline

The first two columns show penalties conceded in the team's own half and opposition half. One point has been awarded for a penalty conceded in the opposition half and two for a penalty in their own half. Five points are added for each yellow card received by the team.

Penalties conceded	Own	Opposition	YC	Pts
Scotland	20	23	-	63
Ireland	26	23	-	75
Wales	29	23	2	91
France	36	22	1	99
England	29	27	4	105

Part of Scotland's success was their discipline, which is illustrated above with our Fair Play table. They conceded just 43 penalties during their campaign, which was six less than the next best by Ireland. More importantly they conceded fewer in their own half than in the opposition half, as opposed to each of the other nations.

Who scores the tries?

T=Total, B=Backs, F=Forwards.

	For			Against		
	T	B	F	T	B	F
England	8	5	3	6	6	-
France	9	8	1	8	4	4
Ireland	3	1	2	9	6	3
Scotland	16	12	4	9	6	3
Wales	9	6	3	13	10	3
Total	45	32	13	45	32	13

When the tries are scored

	1/4	2/4	3/4	4/4	Tot
England	3	3	-	2	8
France	3	2	1	3	9
Ireland	1	1	1	-	3
Scotland	5	4	3	4	16
Wales	1	3	2	3	9
Total	13	13	7	12	45

When the tries are conceded

	1/4	2/4	3/4	4/4	Tot
England	-	1	2	3	6
France	4	4	-	-	8
Ireland	1	2	2	4	9
Scotland	5	2	-	2	9
Wales	3	4	3	3	13
Total	13	13	7	12	45

FIXTURES 1999-2000

Pools for European Competitions:

EUROPEAN CUP:
POOL 1: Glasgow Caledonians, Leicester, Leinster, Stade Francais.
POOL 2: Bath, Padova, Swansea, Toulouse.
POOL 3: Bourgoin, Llanelli, Ulster, Wasps.
POOL 4: Colomiers, Munster, Pontypridd, Saracens.
POOL 5: Cardiff, Harlequins, Montferrand, Treviso/
POOL 6: Edinburgh Reivers, Grenoble, Neath, Northampton.

EUROPEAN SHIELD:
POOL 1: Begles-Bordeaux, Bristol, Calvisano, Dax.
POOL 2: Bedford, Castres, Italy 3, Newport.
POOL 3: Caerphilly, Pau, Perpignan, Sale.
POOL 4: Connacht, Ebbw Vale, Romania 1, Toulon.
POOL 5: Biarritz, Bridgend, Gloucester, Spain.
POOL 6: Dunvant, Nargonne, Newcastle, Portugal.
POOL 7: Agen, Brive, London Irish, Roma.

All teams will meet each other home and away in Pool matches.

AUGUST 1999

Sat, 14th	Wales Domestic Week-end 1	
Tue, 17th	Scotland 'A' v Argentina 'A'	Perth
Sat, 21st	ENGLAND v UNITED STATES (7 p.m.)	Twickenham
	SCOTLAND v ARGENTINA	Murrayfield
	WALES v ROMANIA	Cardiff
	Wales Dometsic Week-end 2	
Sat, 28th	ENGLAND v CANADA (7 p.m.)	Twickenham
	IRELAND v ARGENTINA	Dublin
	SCOTLAND v ROMANIA	Hampden Park (Glasgow)
	WALES v FRANCE	Cardiff
	Jewson National Leagues (Divs 1 & 2)(1)	
	Tetley's Bitter Cup (Preliminary Round	
	Scottish Premier Leagues (1)	
	Wales Domestic Week-end 3	

SEPTEMBER 1999

Sat, 4th	Jewson National Leagues (Divs 1 & 2)(2)	
	Scottish Premier Leagues (2)	
	Scottish National Leagues (all divs)(1)	
	Wales Domestic Week-end 4	
Tue, 7th	ENGLAND XV v EFDR	Anfield, Liverpool
	Allied Dunbar Premiership Two (1)	
Sat, 11th	Allied Dunbar Premiership One (1)	
	Allied Dunbar Premiership Two (2)	
	Jewson National Leagues (Divs 1 & 2)(3)	
	National Leagues (various)	
	Scottish National Cup (1st Round)	
	Scottish Premier Leagues (3)	
	Scottish National Leagues (Divs 1/3)(2)	
	Wales Domestic Week-end 5	
Sat, 18th	ENGLAND XV v EFDR	Twickenham
	Allied Dunbar Premiership Two (3)	
	Jewson National Leagues (Div 1)(4)	
	Tetley's Bitter Cup (First Round)	
	NPI Cup (1st Round)	
	Tetley's Bitter Vase (1st Round)	
	Scottish Premier Leagues (4)	
	Scottish National Leagues (1/3 -3)(4/5 -2)	
	Wales Domestic Week-end 6	
Sat, 25th	Allied Dunbar Premiership One (2)	
	Allied Dunbar Premiership Two (4)	
	Jewson National Leagues (Divs 1 & 2)(5/4)	
	National Leagues (various)	
	Scottish Premier Leagues (5)	
	Scottish National Leagues (1/3 -4)(4/5 -3)	
	Wales Domestic Week-end 7	

OCTOBER 1999

Fri, 1st	Scottish Premier Leagues (6)
Sat, 2nd	Allied Dunbar Premiership One (3)
	Allied Dunbar Premiership Two (5)
	Jewson National Leagues (Divs 1 & 2)(6/5)
	National Leagues (various)
	Scottish Premier Leagues (6)(Other Dists)
Sat, 9th	Allied Dunbar Premiership One (4)
	Allied Dunbar Premiership Two (6)
	Jewson National Leagues (Divs 1 & 2)(7/6)
	National Leagues (various)
	Scottish Premier Leagues (7)
	Scottish National Leagues (1/3 -5)(4/5 -4)
Sat, 16th	Allied Dunbar Premiership One (5)
	Allied Dunbar Premiership Two (7)
	Tetley's Bitter Cup (2nd Round)
	NPI Cup (2nd Round)
	Tetley's Bitter Vase (2nd Round)
Sun, 17th	Scottish National Cup (2nd Round)
	Scottish Premier Leagues (8)
Sat, 23rd	Allied Dunbar Premiership Two (8)
	Jewson National Leagues (Divs 1 & 2)(8/7)
	Scottish Premier Leagues (9)
	Scottish National Leagues (1/3 -6)(4/5 - 5)
Sat, 30th	Allied Dunbar Premiership One (6)
	Jewson National Leagues (Divs 1 & 2)(9/8)
Sun, 31st	Scottish National Leagues (1/3 -7)(4/5 -6)
	(subject to Scotland's World Cup progress)

NOVEMBER 1999

Sat, 6th	Allied Dunbar Premiership One (7)	
	Jewson National Leagues (Divs 1 & 2)(10/9)	

NB: Matches on Sat., 6th Nov. in England may be re-arranged and played by 2nd January 2000 according to World Cup results)

Sun, 7th	Scottish National Leagues (1/3 -8)(4/5 -7)	
Tue, 9th	Combined Services v Barbarians	Gloucester
Sat, 13th	Allied Dunbar Premiership One (8)	
	National Leagues (various)	
	Scottish National Cup (3rd Round)	
	Wales Domestic Week-end 8	
Sat, 20th	European Matches (1)	
	Allied Dunbar Premiership Two (9)	
	Jewson National Leagues (Divs 1 & 2)(11/10)	
	National Leagues (various)	
	Scottish National Leagues (all divs)(9)	
Sat, 27th	European Matches (2)	
	Jewson National Leagues (Divs 1 & 2)(12/10)	
	Scottish Premier Leagues (10)	
	Scottish National Leagues (1/3-9)(4/5-8)	
Sat, 27th	Allied Dunbar Premiership Two (10)	
	Scottish Premier Leagues (11)	
	Scottish National Leagues (1/3-10)(4/5-9)	
	AIB League Divisions 2,3 & 4 (1)	
Mon, 29th	Scottish U21 XV v New Zealand U21	TBA

DECEMBER 1999

Wed, 1st Scotland U21 XV v New Zealand U21 TBA
Sat, 4th Allied Dunbar Premiership One (9)
Allied Dunbar Premiership Two (11)
Jewson National Leagues (Divs 1 & 2)(13/12)
National Leagues (various)
Scottish Premier Leagues (12)
Scottish National Leagues (1/3-12)(4/5-11)
Wales Domestic Week-end 9
Dubai Sevens
AIB League Division 1 (1)
AIB League Divisions 2, 3 & 4 (2)
Tue, 7th OXFORD v CAMBRIDGE (Bowring Bowl) Twickenham
Oxford v Cambridge (Bowring Plate - U21s) Twickenham
Sat, 11th European Matches (3)
Allied Dunbar Premiership Two (12)
Jewson National Leagues (Divs 1 & 2)(14/13)
NPI Cup (4th Round)
Tetley's Bitter Vase (4th Round)
Scottish Premier Leagues (13)
Scottish National Leagues (1/3-12)(4/5-11)
AIB League Divisions 2,3 & 4 (3)
Sat, 18th European Matches (4)
Allied Dunbar Premiership Two (13)
Jewson National Leagues (Divs 1 & 2)(15/14)
National Leagues (various)
Scottish National Cup (4th Round)
AIB League Division 2, 3 & 4 (4)
Sun, 26th Allied Dunbar Premiership One (10)
Tue, 28th Wales Domestic Week-end 10
Leicester v Barbarians (provisional) Leicester
AIB League Division 1 (2)
Malone v Blackrock (AIB Division 2)
Old Wesley v Skerries (AIB Division 3) Dublin
Wed, 29th Allied Dunbar Premiership One (11)

JANUARY 2000

Sat, 1st Wales Domestic Week-end 11
Sun, 2nd Tetley's Bitter Cup (4th Round)
Sat, 8th European Matches (5)
Allied Dunbar Premiership Two (14)
Jewson National Leagues (Divs 1 & 2)(16/15)
National Leagues (various)
Scottish National Cup (5th Round)
AIB League Divisions 2, 3 & 4 (5)
Sat, 15th European Matches (6)
Allied Dunbar Premiership Two (15)
Jewson National Leagues (Divs 1 & 2)(17/16)
NPI Cup (5th Round)
Tetley's Bitter Vase (5th Round)
Scottish Premier Leagues (14)
Scottish National Leagues (1/3-13)(4/5-12)
AIB Divisions 2, 3 & 4 (6)
Sat, 22nd Allied Dunbar Premiership One (12)
Allied Dunbar Premiership two (16)
Jewson National Leagues (Divs 1 & 2)(18/17)
National Leagues (12 team divisions)
Scottish Premier Leagues (15)
Scottish National Leagues (1/3-14)(4/5-13)
Wales Domestic Week-end 12
AIB League Division 1 (3)
AIB League Division 2, 3 & 4 (7)
Tue, 25th Allied Dunbar Premiership One (13)
Sat, 29th Tetley's Bitter Cup (5th Round)
NPI Cup (6th Round)
Tetley's Vase (6th Round)
Jewson National Leagues (Div 2)(18)
Scottish Premier Leagues (16)
Scottish National Leagues (all divs)(15)
Wales Domestic Week-end 13
AIB League Division 1 (4)
AIB League Division 2 (8)
Ards v Queens Univ Belfast (AIB Lge Div 4)
Dublin University v Bangor (AIB Lge Div 4) Dublin

FEBRUARY 2000

Fri, 4th England 'A' v Ireland 'A'
England U21 v Ireland U21
England Students v Ireland Students
Italy 'A' v Scotland 'A'
Italy U21 v Scotland U21
Wales 'A' v France 'A'
Wales U21 v France U21
Sat, 5th ENGLAND v IRELAND (2.30 p.m.) Twickenham
ITALY v SCOTLAND (2 p.m) Rome
WALES v FRANCE (4 p.m) Cardiff
Scottish Premier Leagues (stand-by)
Scottish National Leagues (1/3 -stand-by)
Scottish National Leagues (4/5 - 15)
Wed, 9th Lansdowne v St Mary's (AIB League Div 1) Dublin
Sat, 12th Allied Dunbar Premiership One (14)
Allied Dunbar Premiership Two (17)
Jewson National Leagues (Divs 1 & 2)(19)
National Leagues (various)
Scottish National Cups (Quarter-finals)
Wales Domestic Week-end 14
AIB League Division 1 (5)
AIB League Division 2 (9)
AIB Leagues Divisions 3 & 4 (8)
Sun, 13th Dolphin v UC Cork (AIB Division 2) Ireland
Fri, 18th France 'A' v England 'A' TBA
France U21 v England U21 TBA
France Students v England Students TBA
Ireland 'A' v Scotland 'A' TBA
Ireland U21 v Scotland U21 TBA
Wales 'A' v Italy 'A' TBA
Wales U21 v Italy U21 TBA
Sat, 19th FRANCE v ENGLAND Paris
IRELAND v SCOTLAND (4 p.m.) Dublin
WALES v ITALY (2 p.m.) Cardiff
Sat, 26th Tetley's Bitter Cup (quarter-finals)
NPI Cup (quarter-finals)
Tetley's Bitter Vase (quarter-finals)
Allied Dunbar Premiership Two (18)
Jewson National Leagues (Divs 1 & 2)(20)
National Leagues (various)
Scottish Premier Leagues (17)
Scottish National Leagues (all divs)(16)
Wales Domestic Week-end 15
AIB League Division 1 (6)
AIB League Division 2 (10)
AIB League Divisions 3 & 4 (9)
Sun, 27th Bohemians v Monkstown (AIB League Div 3)

MARCH 2000

Fri, 3rd	England 'A' v Wales 'A'	
	England U21 v Wales U21	
	England Students v Wales Students	
	Scotland 'A' v France 'A'	
	Scotland U21 v France U21	
	Italy 'A' v Ireland 'A'	
	Ireland U21 v Italy U21	
Sat, 4th	ENGLAND v WALES (2.30 p.m.)	Twickenham
	SCOTLAND v FRANCE (2 p.m.)	Murrayfield
	IRELAND v ITALY (4 p.m.)	Dublin
	Scottish Premier & National Leagues (s-by)	
Wed, 8th	East Midlands v Barbarians (prov)	Northampton
Sat, 11th	Allied Dunbar Premiership One (16)	
	Allied Dunbar Premiership Two (19)	
	Jewson National Leagues (Divs 1 & 2)(21)	
	National Leagues (various)	
	Scottish Premier Leagues (18)	
	Scottish National Leagues (all divs)(17)	
	Wales Domestic Week-end 16	
	AIB League Division 1 (7)	
	AIB League Division 2 (11)	
	AIB League Divisions 3 & 4 (10)	
Fri, 17th	France 'A' v Ireland 'A'	
	France U"! v Ireland U21	
	Italy 'A' v England 'A'	
	Italy U21 v England U21	
	Italy Students v England Students	
	Wales 'A' v Scotland 'A'	
	Wales U21 v Scotland U21	
Sat, 18th	ITALY v ENGLAND (2 p.m.)	Rome
	WALES v SCOTLAND (4 p.m.)	Cardiff
	NPI Cup (semi-finals)	
	Tetley's Bitter Vase (semi-finals)	
	Jewson National Leagues (Divs 1 & 2)(22)	
	National Leagues (12 team divisions)	
Wed, 22nd	BUSA Championships Finals	Twickenham
Sun, 19th	FRANCE v IRELAND	Paris
Sat, 25th	Hong Kong Sevens (to Sun, 26th)	
	Allied Dunbar Premiership One (16)	
	Allied Dunbar Premiership Two (20)	
	Jewson National Leagues (Divs 1 & 2)(23)	
	National Leagues (various)	
	Scottish National Leagues (all divs)(18)	
	Wales Domestic Week-end 17	
	AIB League Division 1 (8)	
	AIB League Division 2 (12)	
Wed, 29th	Army v Royal Air Force	Gloucester
Fri, 31st	France 'A' v Italy 'A'	
	France U21 v Italy U21	
	Ireland 'A' v Wales 'A'	
	Ireland U21 v Wales U21	
	Scotland 'A' v England 'A'	
	Scotland U21 v England U21	
	Scotland Students v England Students	

APRIL 2000

Sat, 1st	FRANCE v ITALY	Paris
	IRELAND v WALES	Dublin
Sun, 2nd	SCOTLAND v ENGLAND	Murrayfield
	Scottish National Cup (Semi-finals)	
	Scottish Premier & National Leagues (s-by)	
Wed, 5th	Wanderers v Blackrock College (AIB Div 2)	Ireland
Sat, 8th	Tetley's Bitter Cup (semi-finals)	
	Allied Dunbar Premiership One (17)	
	Allied Dunbar Premiership Two (21)	
	Jewson National Leagues (Divs 1 & 2)(24)	
	National Leagues (various)	
	Melrose Sevens	
	Wales Domestic Week-end 18	
	AIB League Division 1 (9)	
	AIB League Division 2 (13)	
	AIB League Divisions 3 & 4 (11)	
Wed, 12th	Scottish Premier Leagues (stand-by)	
Sat, 15th	European Cup & Shield quarter-finals	
	Allied Dunbar Premiership Two (22)	
	NPI Cup Final	Twickenham
	Tetley's Bitter Vase	Twickenham
	Jewson National Leagues (Divs 1 & 2)(25)	
	National Leagues (various last rounds)	
	FIRA Under 19 Championships	
	Lansdowne v Garryowen (AIB League Div 1)	
Tue, 18th	Allied Dunbar Premiership One (18)	
Wed, 19th	Royal Navy v Royal Air Force	
Sat, 22nd	Scottish Cup Finals Day	Murrayfield
	Allied Dunbar Premiership One (19)	
	Allied Dunbar Premiership Two (23)	
	Jewson National Leagues (Divs 1 & 2)(26)	
	County Championship area matches	
	Wales Domestic Week-end 19	
	AIB League Division 1 (10)	
	AIB League Division 2 (14)	
	FIRA Under 19 Championships	
	Home Unions Under 18 Championships begin	
Sat, 29th	Allied Dunbar Premiership One (2))	
	Allied Dunbar Premiership Two (24)	
	County Championship area matches	
	Wales Domestic Week-end 20	
	Rugby League Challenge Cup Final	Murrayfield
	AIB League Division 1 (11)	
	AIB League Division 2 (15)	

MAY 2000

Sat, 6th	European Cup & Shield semi-finals	
	Allied Dunbar Premiership One (21)	
	Allied Dunbar Premiership Two (25)	
	County Championship area matches	
	Royal Navy v Army	Twickenham
Sat, 13th	Allied Dunbar Premiership Two (26)	
	County Championship quarter-finals	
	Wales Domestic Week-end 21	
Sat, 20th	Tetley's Bitter Cup Final	Twickenham
	Allied Dunbar Premiership One (22)	
	SWALEC Cup Final (Wales)	Cardiff
	County Championship semi-finals	
	Wales Domestic Week-end 22	
Sat, 27th	European Cup & Shield Finals	TBA

JUNE 2000

Sat, 3rd	County Championship Final	Twickenham

SPORT SUPPORTS ST. JOHN

To commemorate the 900th anniversary of the Order of St. John in 1999,
St. John Ambulance is launching its biggest ever public appeal.

It is aiming to raise £10 million,

over the next three years, through the Sports Industry.

The money will be spent on three specific projects.

* **First Aid for School Children** - putting a lifesaver in every family.
* **Automated External Defibrillators** - providing vital `heartstart' machines into community locations such as sports centres.
* **Crusader 900 Ambulances** - replacing St. John's existing fleet with new variable-purpose vehicles to service the community.

The appeal was officially launched on May 12th 1999,
by the Rt. Hon. Frank Dobson, Secretary of State for Health.